Ursa Major

Coma Berenices

Leo

Cancer   M44

Castor   **Gemini**

Pollux

Regulus

M67

Canis Minor

Procyon

Virgo

Hydra

Monoceros

Crater   M50

Spica   Sirius

Corvus   **Canis Major**   M41

Hydra

Understanding the Universe

Understanding the Universe

Phillip Flower

CLEMSON UNIVERSITY

WEST PUBLISHING COMPANY

St. Paul   New York   Los Angeles   San Francisco

To Alice, my love

Production Credits

Copyediting and Indexing: Patricia Lewis
Interior Design: Kristen M. Weber
Artwork: Alexander Teshin Associates and John and Judy Waller
Composition: The Clarinda Company
Page Layout: David J. Farr/Imagesmythe, Inc.
Cover Design: David J. Farr/Imagesmythe, Inc.
Cover Image: Vincent van Gogh, *The Starry Night* (1889).
  Oil on canvas, 29 × 36¼″. Collection, The Museum of Modern Art, New York.
  Acquired through the Lillie P. Bliss Bequest. Photograph © 1990 The Museum of
  Modern Art, New York. Background photograph of the Pleiades copyright © Royal
  Observatory Edinburgh/Anglo-Australian Telescope Board 1985. Photograph by
  David Malin.
Frontispiece: *Empyrean Diorama* by Geoffrey Chandler.
AstroProbe photo bars: IRAS map of the central portion of the Milky Way Galaxy
  courtesy NASA.
For Contents photo credits, see corresponding chapter-opening pages.

Copyright ©1990 By WEST PUBLISHING COMPANY
                50 W. Kellogg Boulevard
                P.O. Box 64526
                St. Paul, MN 55164–1003

Library of Congress Cataloging-in-Publication Data

Flower, Phillip J.
   Understanding the universe / Phillip Flower.
       p.   cm.
       1. Astronomy.   I. Title.
QB45.F784   1990
520—dc20

   ISBN 0–314–57880–3
   ISBN 0–314–04091–9 (with *Observer's Handbook*)

89–36019
CIP

Contents

Preface   xi

INTRODUCTION
How to Read a Science Textbook   xvi

Reading   I-2
Inspectional Reading   I-2
Analytical Reading   I-3
Chapter Capsule   I-6
Review Questions   I-6
For Further Reading   I-6

CHAPTER 1
Astronomy and Astronomers   1

Astronomers   2
The Universe: A Brief History   5
A Sense of Scale   8
The Real Motions of the Earth   11
Clocks and Calendars   13
    Stellar and Solar Clocks   13
    Time Zones   15
    Calendars   18
Summary   20
Chapter Capsule   20
Review Questions   21
For Further Reading   21
    ▬▬▬ ASTROPROBE 1: MathTools 1   22

CHAPTER 2
The Naked Eye Universe   36

The Apparent Celestial Motions of the Stars   37
    At the Poles and the Equator   37
    At Intermediate Latitudes   39

The Apparent Celestial Motions of the Sun   41
    Spring and Fall   42
    Summer and Winter   43
    The Rest of the Year   44
Lunar Phases   47
Eclipses   53
    Solar Eclipses   54
    Lunar Eclipses   57
    Eclipse Seasons   60
The Apparent Celestial Motions of the Planets   62
    Inferior Planets   63
    Superior Planets   63
    Retrograde Motion   66
Summary   68
Chapter Capsule   68
Review Questions   69
For Further Reading   69
    ▬▬▬ ASTROPROBE 2: Archaeoastronomy   70

CHAPTER 3
The Process of Scientific Discovery   82

The Scientific Approach   83
Competing Models   85
    The Greek Geocentric Model   86
    The Copernican Heliocentric Model   89
Tycho Brahe   93
Johannes Kepler   98
Galileo Galilei   102
    Observational Astronomer   103
    Experimental Physicist   106
Isaac Newton   108
    Force   109
    Mass   110
    Universal Gravitation   111
Summary   113
Chapter Capsule   114
Review Questions   114
For Further Reading   115
    ▬▬▬ ASTROPROBE 3: Interplanetary Travel:
        Satellites and Space Probes   116

CHAPTER 4
Light and Matter 127

Electricity and Magnetism 128
Electromagnetic Spectrum 130
Radiation Laws 133
Chemical Elements 137
Atomic Spectra 140
Radioactivity 144
Summary 147
Chapter Capsule 148
Review Questions 148
For Further Reading 149
ASTROPROBE 4: The Forces of Nature 150

CHAPTER 5
Earth 157

Habitat for Life 158
The Size, Shape, and Mass of the Earth 159
The State of the Earth's Interior 161
The Earth's Surface 162
Studying the Earth's Interior 163
Seismology 163
Heat Flow 165
A Model of the Earth's Interior 165
Formation of a Layered Earth 166
Plate Tectonics 167
The Age of the Earth 171
The Atmosphere of the Earth 174
Composition 174
The Earth's Primitive Atmosphere 174
The Atmosphere's Role as a Shield 175
The Atmosphere's Role as a Blanket 177
Atmospheric Pressure 178
Winds: Global Circulation 179
The Earth's Magnetic Field 181
Geomagnetism 181
Magnetosphere 183
Summary 187
Chapter Capsule 188
Review Questions 188
For Further Reading 189
ASTROPROBE 5: Ice Ages:
The Astronomical Connection 190

CHAPTER 6
The Moon and Mercury 198

The Planets and Moons in the Solar System: An
Introduction 199
The Moon 201
Tides 201
Exploration of the Moon 204
The Moon's Surface Features 207
Craters 207
Maria 212
Volcanism 213
Ages of Surface Rocks 214
The Interior and History of the Moon 216
Surface Rocks 216
Interior 218
Mercury 219
The Orbit and Rotation of Mercury 219
Exploration of Mercury 221
The Surface of Mercury 223
Craters 223
Plains 225
Scarps 226
Ages 226
The Interior of Mercury 227
Summary 228
Chapter Capsule 229
Review Questions 230
For Further Reading 230
ASTROPROBE 6: Craters:
Scars on the Earth's Surface 231

CHAPTER 7
Venus and Mars 240

Venus 241
The Orbit and Rotation of Venus 241
Exploration of Venus 243
Venusian Surface Features:
Cratering and Tectonism 245
The Atmosphere of Venus 249
Atmospheric Composition, Structure,
and Evolution 249
Atmospheric Dynamics 251
The Venusian Magnetosphere 252

Mars   253
  Exploration of Mars   253
    Earth-based Observations   254
    Spacecraft Observations   257
  Martian Surface Features   258
    Craters   259
    Canyons and Channels   261
    Volcanism   262
    The Nature of the Martian Surface:
      The Viking Landers   263
    The Geological History of Mars   264
  The Atmosphere of Mars   265
    Global Circulation   266
    Water   267
  The Moons of Mars   269
Summary   271
Chapter Capsule   272
Review Questions   272
For Further Reading   273
  ASTROPROBE 7: Terraforming   274

CHAPTER 8
The Outer Planets   283

Jovian Planets: Characteristics   284
  Chemical Composition and Internal Structure   285
  Internal Energy Sources   287
  Rotations and Orientations   287
Jupiter and Saturn   291
  Exploration of Jupiter and Saturn   291
  Jupiter and Saturn: Features and Observations   293
Uranus and Neptune   298
  Discovery and Exploration   298
  Uranus   301
  Neptune   302
Pluto   304
  Discovery   304
  Pluto and Its Satellite   306
  The Origin of Pluto   310
Summary   311
Chapter Capsule   312
Review Questions   313
For Further Reading   313
  ASTROPROBE 8: Remote Sensing
    of the Planets   314

CHAPTER 9
Satellites and Rings   321

Discovery   322
Satellites of the Jovian Planets   326
  The Moons of Jupiter   326
    Galilean Satellites   326
    Small Jovian Satellites   329
  The Moons of Saturn   330
    The Classical Moons   330
    Co-orbitals and Lagrangians   333
  The Moons of Uranus and Neptune   335
Planetary Rings   341
  The Rings of Saturn   341
  The Rings of Jupiter, Uranus, and Neptune   345
Summary   349
Chapter Capsule   350
Review Questions   351
For Further Reading   351
  ASTROPROBE 9: Planetary Pedigree   352

CHAPTER 10
Asteroids, Meteorites,
and Comets   356

Asteroids and Meteorites   357
  The Discovery of Asteroids   357
  Physical Nature of Asteroids   359
  Meteors and Meteorites   361
  Asteroid Orbits   365
Comets   368
  Early Observations   368
  Comets and Halley   370
  The Modern View   373
  The Origin of Comets   378
Summary   381
Chapter Capsule   382
Review Questions   383
For Further Reading   383
  ASTROPROBE 10: Extinctions:
    Dinosaurs and Comets   384

CHAPTER 11
Origin of the Solar System   391

Characteristics of the Solar System   392
The Formation of Planets and Moons   397
  The Distribution of Elements in the Solar Nebula   397
Planetary Accretion   399
The Formation of Planetary Satellites   403
  Subsequent Development of the Planets   406
  Summary   408
  Chapter Capsule   409
  Review Questions   410
  For Further Reading   410
  ▬ ASTROPROBE 11: The Solar System:
    Resources for the Future   411

CHAPTER 12
The Sun   418

Physical Characteristics of the Sun   419
Nuclear Reactions in the Sun   421
The Chemical Composition of the Sun   425
The Sun's Interior   426
The Sun's Outer Layers   428
  The Photosphere and Sunspots   428
  The Chromosphere   435
  The Corona   436
  Prominences and Flares   439
Summary   441
Chapter Capsule   442
Review Questions   443
For Further Reading   443
  ▬ ASTROPROBE 12: Sun-Earth Connections   444

CHAPTER 13
Observing the Stars   452

Classification of Stars   453
  Stellar Temperatures   454
  Spectral Classes   456
  The Chemical Composition of Stars   458
Magnitudes   460
Colors   461
Distances to Nearby Stars   465

Motions of Stars   468
  Doppler Shifts   468
  Proper Motions   471
Summary   473
Chapter Capsule   474
Review Questions   474
For Further Reading   475
  ▬ ASTROPROBE 13: Observatories and
    Observing   476

CHAPTER 14
Characteristics of Stars   483

Absolute Magnitudes and Stellar Luminosities   484
The HR Diagram   487
The Masses of Stars   490
  Binary Stars   490
  The Mass-Luminosity Relationship   499
The Sizes of Stars   500
Summary   503
Chapter Capsule   505
Review Questions   506
For Further Reading   506
  ▬ ASTROPROBE 14: Pixels and Stars:
    Stellar Imaging   507

CHAPTER 15
The Birth of the
Main Sequence   515

Star Formation   516
  Dark Clouds: Sites of Star Formation   517
  Contraction and Protostars   520
  Observations   525
  Star Formation Triggers   531
  Distant Planetary Systems   535
The Main Sequence   536
  Main-Sequence Lifetimes   536
  Ages of Star Clusters   538
Summary   541
Chapter Capsule   543
Review Questions   543
For Further Reading   543
  ▬ ASTROPROBE 15: How to Build a Star   544

**CHAPTER 16
Stellar Evolution and
End States**   550

Interior Developments: The Burning of the Ashes   551
 A 15 $\mathfrak{M}_\odot$ star   551
 The Iron Core   554
Surface Developments: The Changing
  Appearance of Stars   556
 Red Giants and Supergiants   557
 Planetary Nebulae and White Dwarfs   561
 Supernovae   565
 Nucleosynthesis   571
 Neutron Stars   573
 Black Holes   576
Summary   581
Chapter Capsule   583
Review Questions   583
For Further Reading   584
 ═══ ASTROPROBE 16: Relativity   585

**CHAPTER 17
The Milky Way Galaxy**   592

Galactic Dimensions   593
The Rotating Disk   597
 Stellar Populations   597
 Rotation and Structure of the Disk   599
 The Nature of Spiral Arms   604
 Mass of the Milky Way Galaxy   607
The Distribution and Evolution of
  Stellar Populations   609
The Galactic Center   613
Summary   616
Chapter Capsule   617
Review Questions   617
For Further Reading   618
 ═══ ASTROPROBE 17: $N \geq 1$:
  Extraterrestrial Civilizations   619

**CHAPTER 18
Galaxies**   628

Island Universes   629
Appearances of Galaxies   632
 Content and Classification of Galaxies   632
 Beyond the Hubble Classification   640

Distances to Galaxies   644
Quasars   647
Clusters of Galaxies   650
 The Local Group   650
 Larger Clusters of Galaxies   654
 Superclusters   657
Summary   658
Chapter Capsule   659
Review Questions   660
For Further Reading   660
 ═══ ASTROPROBE 18: Quasars: Far or Near?   661

**CHAPTER 19
The Expanding Universe**   666

The Big Bang   667
Expansion of the Universe   673
3 K Microwave Background Radiation   677
Age of the Universe   679
Future of the Universe   682
Summary   689
Chapter Capsule   690
Review Questions   690
For Further Reading   691
 ═══ ASTROPROBE 19: Origins   692

**MODULE 1
MathTools 2**   M1-1

Proportions   M1-1
Percentages and Fractions   M1-4
Error and Uncertainty   M1-4
Units   M1-6
Powers and Roots   M1-6
Angular Measurement   M1-8
 Angles   M1-8
 Triangles   M1-10
Cubes, Circles, and Spheres   M1-11
Temperature   M1-12

MODULE 2
Astronomical Instruments and Telescopes   M2-1

Before the Telescope   M2-1
Optical Telescopes   M2-2
  The First Telescopes   M2-2
  The Long Telescopes   M2-6
  Shorter Telescopes   M2-8
  Larger Reflectors   M2-10
  The Great Refractors and Reflectors   M2-16
  New Technology Optical Reflectors   M2-19
Radio Telescopes   M2-23
Space Astronomy   M2-29
Astronomical Detectors   M2-34
  Imaging   M2-34
  Spectroscopy   M2-35
  Photometry   M2-37

APPENDIX A Asteroids and Comets   A-1

APPENDIX B Astronomical and Physical Constants   A-3

APPENDIX C Abundances of the Major Elements   A-4

APPENDIX D Eclipses   A-6

APPENDIX E The Greek Alphabet   A-8

APPENDIX F The Brightest and Nearest Stars   A-9

APPENDIX G Nuclear Reactions in Stars   A-12

APPENDIX H Planets and Satellites   A-15

Glossary   G-1
Index   IX-1

Preface

Humans are naturally curious and are attracted to the beauty of the heavens. Walk outside on a clear, dark night and fill your eyes with the splendors of the night sky. We want to know what those lights in the sky are. Amateurs peer toward these tiny pinpoints of light with an impressive array of binoculars and telescopes and sense the wonder of the universe. Professional astronomers observe with large telescopes at major observatories to obtain unprecedented views of the sky, yet they take great pleasure in using small scopes to view or photograph a planet, a star cluster, or a galaxy. Amateur and professional astronomers share an enthusiasm for the beauty of the celestial universe.

If you ever attended a public observing session sponsored by an amateur astronomy club and listened to the observers explain the objects they are viewing, you would certainly feel that astronomy is comprehensible. Indeed, astronomy is understandable, yet much of its subject matter is conceptually and literally far removed from our everyday experiences. This book describes the objects and concepts that belong to the realm of astronomy. It was written for nonscientists, whether they are college students fulfilling a science elective or intelligent laypersons curious about the universe around them. At the same time, *Understanding the Universe* describes astronomy without apology. I have kept the terminology of astronomy intact, opting to help the reader develop the appropriate vocabulary needed to understand the descriptions of the observations, models, and theories required to comprehend the subject. Difficult topics are addressed directly, rather than oversimplified as is often done in popularizations for the public and even in some texts. This book will not read like a novel; it is not meant to. It will challenge the reader, not with detail after detail, but by carefully describing both easy and difficult concepts and observations.

The emphasis of this book is on the logical development of ideas and discoveries within the framework of the approach used by scientists, usually called the scientific method. Science is a world view that does not distinguish between human beings and nature. It is a strict and rigorous discipline of thought and action applied toward the goal of understanding the physical universe around us. It will become clear as you read that the discoveries of science are not accomplished through a rigid 1, 2, 3 process. Discovery in science is a continuous and challenging quest based on experiments and observations; it is a story of reasoning, creativity, and much hard work. And the results are both fascinating and provocative.

Organization

The discoveries of astronomy are presented in an Earth to stars sequence following our development in understanding the universe. The first section of the book, Chapters 1–3, describes the celestial motions visible to the unaided eye and our progress toward an understanding of these motions. The descriptions and concepts introduced here are fundamental and should be understood by all students of astronomy.

Chapters 5–11 describe the solar system and its origin. The Earth-Moon system is used as the basis for comparing the planets and moons in the solar system. The last section, Chapters 12–19, describes the universe beyond the solar system. This section includes a detailed account of the Sun, which provides an important basis for the study of other stars; a study of the fundamental properties of stars; and a description of the evolution and "deaths" of stars. The last three chapters describe our Galaxy, nearby galaxies, and the study of the birth and evolution of the universe.

An important theme that runs throughout the book, particularly in the last section, is the scale of the universe. How big is the solar system, the Galaxy, and the universe? Astronomers have worked painstakingly to determine the distances between planets, stars, and galaxies. The ultimate goal of these distance studies is knowledge of the age of the universe.

Learning Features

To help the reader rise to the challenge of this book and the science of astronomy, I have included an introductory chapter entitled *How to Read a Science Textbook.* It is a short introduction to the art of reading for understanding. It provides tips on how to identify and highlight important concepts in a book; rewrite important discussions; summarize a chapter; make margin notes; and outline. This information will help you understand astronomy as well as help you prepare for quizzes and exams.

It is important that readers realize science is mathematical. At the same time, many students enrolled in introductory science courses suffer from "math anxiety" and some readers may not have been exposed to mathematical concepts for many years. Mathematics is treated as a tool in this book. The endpiece to Chapter 1, called MathTools 1, reviews powers of ten and scientific notation and introduces graph reading and plotting. MathTools 2, called Module 1 and located just before the appendices, reviews several other mathematical concepts. Math-Tools 1 and MathTools 2 are reference manuals to be used by the reader whenever a review is needed. I will sometimes refer to one of the MathTools in the text as a reminder to the reader that the information is readily available. The idea behind MathTools is to give the reader a handy reference that lists and explains high-school-level mathematical principles.

Technical vocabulary is printed in **boldface** in the text and explained in general terms. The formal definition will often be given in the margin near where the term is first introduced. A comprehensive glossary is placed at the end of the book. Several terms that are new but not used beyond the immediate discussion will be presented in *italics*, and their definition should be clear from the text.

Each chapter concludes with a short endpiece called an AstroProbe. The subjects covered are sometimes a logical extension of the chapter material such as "Relativity" and "Interplanetary Travel: Satellites and Space Probes." Others present controversial topics such as "Quasars: Far or Near?" Several are descriptions of what astronomers do and how they do it, such as "Observatories and Observing," "Remote Sensing of the Planets," and "Pixels and Stars: Stellar Imaging." Some are concerned with issues of the day: "Extinctions: Dinosaurs and Comets," "Sun-Earth Connections," and "Solar System: Resources of the Future." The last AstroProbe, "Origins," deals with the controversy over teaching creationism as a science.

Observer's Handbook

Available with this book is a separate small booklet called the *Observer's Handbook*. This is designed for the beginning observer. No equipment is necessary to observe and appreciate the nighttime sky. The *Observer's Handbook* gives the locations of the major constellations and a description of each, including interesting objects you can see with the naked eye and binoculars. The front and back inside covers of the text also include Figure 3 of the *Observer's Handbook*, which shows the major constellations visible to northern hemisphere observers. Use the *Observer's Handbook* as a guide to many hours of observing pleasure.

Acknowledgments

The reviewers of the manuscript, listed below, provided numerous comments and criticisms ranging from scientific content to the philosophy of teaching. I have tried to incorporate the relevant comments into the text. I appreciate the effort of these reviewers in helping the astronomical community produce a textbook that tries to faithfully describe the nature of astronomy at this level. When writers think about it, they realize that even as they write the words on paper, the words describe the collection of the work and philosophy of the entire astronomical community, past and present.

Lee Bonneau
Foothills College

John Burns
Mount San Antonio College

Joseph Carr
University of South Florida

Roger Culver
Colorado State University

Richard Dittman
University of Wisconsin—Milwaukee

John Evans
University of Wisconsin—Oshkosh

Alexander Hall
Kean College

Ronald Haybron
Cleveland State University

Richard Herr
University of Delaware

Bill Hiscock
Montana State University

Sara Hoffman
Santa Fe Community College

Hollis Johnson
Indiana University

Burton Jones
University of California—Santa Cruz

Devon Shawley
Cypress College

Lyle Joyce
Central Connecticut State University

Paul Sipiera
William Rainey Harper College

John Kennedy
Bradley University

Mark Slovak
University of Wisconsin—Madison

Norman Markworth
Stephen F. Austin State University

Billy Smith
Chabot College

James Peters
San Francisco State University

Lewis Smith
Hofstra University

James Regas
California State University—Chico

Jack Sulentic
University of Alabama

Thomas Robertson
Ball State University

Charles Tolbert
University of Virginia

John Safko
University of South Carolina

Allen Wasserman
Oregon State University

Robert Schmidt
University of Nebraska—Lincoln

Kenneth Yoss
University of Illinois

John Schopp
San Diego State University

Lois Zimring
Michigan State University

I would like to thank Miguel Larsen, Carl Ulbrich, and John Ray for reading several AstroProbes and providing many helpful comments and criticisms and John Wagner for reading and making extensive comments on a lengthy version of Chapter 5. I am especially grateful to Anthony Aveni for critically reading an early draft of AstroProbe 2 and giving me a better appreciation of ancient observatories. Tom Collins has been a great help in reading the entire manuscript at different stages, for providing the review questions at the end of the chapter, and for general discussions of teaching astronomy.

I would like to thank Will Graben, Fred Keller, Ed Gettys, and Tom Collins for their support; they understood the situation that led to the writing of this book, accepted the decision to do so, and gave encouragement during the writing. I would also like to thank Gary Woodruff for launching this project and Phyllis Mueller for summarizing the initial reviewer reports.

For the last few years I have had the pleasure of working with Peter Marshall and Jane Bacon at West's Atlanta office. Pete has been the untiring editor always asking the appropriate questions (the ones I never asked!) and offering suggestions in the most persuasive manner. Jane Bacon had the difficult job of reading and summarizing all of the reviewer analyses. Her reports have helped this project immensely.

During the last year of this project, I was under the direction of a most capable and organized production editor, Barbara Fuller. She had the demanding job of obtaining the photographs and managing the large art program as well as the impossible job of keeping me on schedule. The art program benefited greatly from the artistic skill and dedication to this project from John and Judy Waller.

It gives me great pleasure to acknowledge the assistance of Chester R. Flower. He took the role of an intelligent layperson and read two versions of the original manuscript, looking intently for ways to make the text more understandable to everyone. His comments proved invaluable. Appreciation goes farther back in time for it was my father who gave me my first book on astronomy, *The Book of the Universe*, in 1964, and who has quietly encouraged my interest in the subject over the years.

I would like to thank my son, Evan Flower, for spending a considerable amount of time producing several critical photographs and finding several errors in the galleys.

The person that has spent nearly as much time on this project as I have is Alice Flower. She has read *all* versions of the manuscript and the galleys. Her word-by-word editing significantly reduced the number of errors in type and greatly improved the readability of the text. She has supported this project with her patience and understanding as well as her untiring reading.

Writing a book of this magnitude demands a great deal of time from the writer's family. I appreciate the patience and support of Alice and Evan Flower.

How to Read a Science Textbook

OUTLINE

Reading

Inspectional Reading

Analytical Reading

Chapter Capsule

Review Questions

For Further Reading

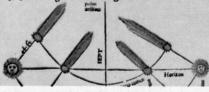

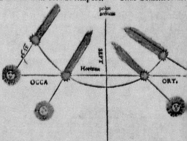

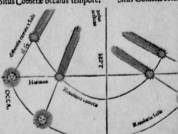

Page from Peter Apian's *Astronomicum Caesarem* (1540).

SOURCE: Donald K. Yeomans.

INTELLIGENT AND WELL-READ PEOPLE today are expected to read books and articles on scientific subjects such as AIDS, environmental problems, space exploration, emerging technologies, and new discoveries in science and engineering. Science has many specialties, each of which has its own vocabulary and technical background. Specialized and technical language helps scientists because it enables them to communicate efficiently, but it has the disadvantage of being difficult for you, the nonspecialist. Nevertheless, you are not completely left out. Many magazines such as *Sky & Telescope, Astronomy,* and *Scientific American* contain popularizations of recent advances in science, particularly in astronomy. Books on astronomy are also plentiful. During the late 1980s, a new book on astronomy was published every 28 hours (Figure I.1)!

Popularizations generally avoid two main difficulties that confront readers of more technical literature. First, popularizations generally leave out the details of experiments and report only the results and interpretations. Second, they contain little or no mathematics. Despite these two simplifications, scientific articles are not as easy to read as fiction because they describe circumstances and places with which the reader is not very familiar—no one has stood on the plains of Mars or orbited a black hole in a spaceship, for example.

This textbook is a bit more complex than a popularization of astronomy in that it describes many experiments and explains how astronomical discoveries came to be made. Consequently, careful reading will be required. This short chapter describes some techniques you can use to improve your reading skills and understanding of the subject.

First, however, a note on mathematics is necessary. This text does contain some mathematics, but that should not be a cause for concern. Mathematics is a language with its own vocabulary, symbols, and syn-

■■■ FIGURE I.1

The Reader Today Can Choose from a Wide Selection of Books and Magazines on Scientific Topics

SOURCE: Evan Flower.

MathTools 1:

■ Powers of Ten
■ Graphs and Plots
■ Approximation Signs

MathTools 2:

■ Proportions
■ Percentages and Fractions
■ Error and Uncertainty
■ Units
■ Powers and Roots
■ Angular Measurement
■ Cubes, Circles, and Spheres
■ Temperature

Three levels of reading:

■ Elementary reading
■ Inspectional reading
■ Analytical reading

tax. In fact, you have already learned enough of that language to make your way through this book. To help you refresh your memory, Math-Tools 1, located after Chapter 1, and MathTools 2, located just before the appendixes, provide quick reviews of the mathematical procedures, operations, and symbols you will encounter in this text. Reading Math-Tools 1 as soon as possible will help relieve any "math anxiety " you may have. Another way to relieve anxiety is to work out with pencil and paper any mathematical example you come across as you read. Use MathTools 1 and MathTools 2 if necessary. Each time you work out an example you will gain confidence in your mathematical abilities. Remember that your purpose in reading this text is not to become a mathematician but to understand the problem under consideration.

▄▄▄READING

The purpose of reading is to increase your understanding of a subject, not to accumulate information that you may not fully comprehend. Just as scientists learn about phenomena they do not fully comprehend by conducting experiments, you learn by reading material you do not fully understand at first. As you develop your reading skills, your level of understanding will increase. This chapter describes some reading techniques that will help you in this process.

Reading can be done on three levels. All literate people have reached the first level, *elementary reading*. This simply involves the basic reading skills taught in elementary school, such as recognizing words and their meanings in paragraphs. The next level—*inspectional reading*—is a technique for learning as much as possible about a book in a short amount of time. Just as you look at a roadmap when you travel into an area for the first time, you should engage in inspectional reading when you sit down with a new book. Inspectional reading involves determining the structure of the book—how it is laid out, what features it has that are useful to the reader, and basically what the book is about.

The third level of reading is *analytical reading*. Its goal is understanding. Unlike elementary and inspectional reading, which are essentially passive processes, analytical reading is active. It requires readers to ask many questions as they read. Since everyone reading this book has reached the level of elementary reading, the following sections will concentrate on inspectional and analytical reading.

▄▄▄INSPECTIONAL READING

During inspectional reading, the reader becomes familiar with the broad outline of the book by pre-reading, or skimming, the book. Study the table of contents to gain an overall view of the topics covered and their order. Ask yourself if there is a reason for the particular order of the chapters. You will notice that, besides chapters, this book has end-pieces called *AstroProbes* as well as two chapter-sized modules called *MathTools 2* and *Astronomical Instruments and Telescopes*. It also has several appendixes and an *Observer's Handbook*. A dictionary called the *Glossary* is also provided. Take a look at these features and ask yourself how they are related to the material in the chapters and how they will be of help to you. This sort of skimming will give you an overview of the book's contents and will allow you to make efficient use of the special features when you begin reading.

Each chapter has an introduction and a summary. Read them now. While you are at it, read a few pages in several chapters—not too many pages yet. After doing this you will have a good idea of what the text is about and the kind of reading expected of you.

Now read the entire book. Because this textbook is divided into units containing several chapters arranged by topic, you can simplify your task by reading one unit at a time. The units are

- *Chapters 1 through 3:* Naked eye observations and the scientific method
- *Chapters 5 through 11:* The solar system and its origin
- *Chapters 12 through 16:* Stars
- *Chapters 17 through 19:* Galaxies and cosmology

Also Chapter 4, combined with the module *Astronomical Instruments and Telescopes*, provides a thorough description of how astronomers observed the universe. During this reading, concentrate on the big points made by the author. Don't stop to ponder what you do not understand. If you stop now to master the fine points, you will miss the big points and will not obtain the overview of the subject that is the purpose of inspectional reading. Note that this is not the kind of reading that you do when you study for a test. That comes in the next stage—analytical reading—but the knowledge of the book's structure and content that you have obtained through inspectional reading will help you when you move to that level.

ANALYTICAL READING

Your obligation as a reader is to ask questions while you read. Whether you are reading a section, a chapter, or the whole book, you must continuously ask four questions:

- *What is the book about?* You already know that this is a book about astronomy but, there is more to astronomy than descriptions of planets and stars. This book is trying to tell you something. What is it? Try to locate the leading themes and determine how they are developed.
- *What is being said in detail?* Try to discover the main ideas and assertions in each chapter or section of a chapter.
- *Is what is being said true?* You have to make up your own mind. This requires answering the first two questions and understanding what the author has said. Are the information and examples sufficient to convince you? If not, perhaps your instructor or another more technical book can provide you with additional information.
- *So what?* Is anything you read significant? Why is it important? Is there more to learn?

Some useful features in the book that will help the reader:

- Table of Contents
- AstroProbes
- Modules
- Observer's Handbook
- Glossary
- Index
- Chapter Topic Outlines
- Chapter Summaries
- Chapter Capsules

Questions a reader must ask during inspectional reading:

- What are the major parts of the book?
- How are they organized?

A science textbook presents the reader with information but does not tell the reader what to do with it. It describes facts—how things happen, why they happen, and what the consequences are—and deals mainly with things that lie outside the scope of your normal, everyday experiences. Answering the four questions that are the essence of analytical reading helps you decide what to do with this information.

The best way to answer these questions is with pencil in hand. Writing in and marking the text and figures helps you keep awake! It also keeps your mind active: writing something in your own words, helps you remember your thoughts when you wrote them down. Various types of markings are at your disposal:

■ *Underlining:* Draw lines under the main points of a section or chapter. Do not underline the whole paragraph! Choosing the important points to underline is an important part of analytical reading because it forces you to think as you read.

■ || *Vertical lines in the margin:* These are useful for emphasizing underlined statements in a paragraph or pointing out long but important passages.

■ * # *Doodles in the margin:* Use these markers sparingly to point out the most important passages or sentences in a chapter or book. You may want to fold the corners of the pages these are on so that you can refer to them later or label them with letters such as A, B, C to indicate a logical sequence. Transparent tape makes good tabs on which you can write a letter or number describing what is marked. Do this with MathTools, for instance, so that you can locate them quickly when needed.

■ 1 2 3 *Numbers in the margin:* Use these to mark a sequence of points. A long paragraph or part of a section may be a list of observations supporting a theory or of facts pertinent to the topic under discussion.

■ Cf 23 *Refer to page number:* Use the abbreviation "Cf" to mean compare to, or refer to, page 23 or whatever for related material. When you read analytically, you will begin to notice connections across the whole book. Sometimes the same point is made more than once but, when it is made later in the book, you may have learned enough additional knowledge to see it in a new context and gain further insight.

■ (Circle) or [box] *key words or phrases:* This is partially done for you with boldfaced terms, but the words are used later on many times. Again, this will help your mind stay awake by "physically" noticing important words and phrases.

Writing in the margins is an important means of writing questions or reducing complicated arguments to single phrases. It is especially important for you to rewrite important points *in your own words.* If you read a section and do not understand it completely, mark it and come back to it later. All of the marks you make in a chapter will help you review the important aspects of the chapter without reading it all over again.

Once you have superficially read the book or appropriate sections and have begun the analytical stage of reading, you should outline each chapter. Use the topic outline at the beginning of each chapter as a starting point. Each section describes some aspect of astronomy; summarize this in an outline. You can write, for instance, that section 1 of Chapter 2 is about the apparent motions of stars; section 2 is about the apparent motions of the Sun; section 3 is about the phases of the Moon and so on. Next you can subdivide your outline by noting that section 1 describes the apparent motions of the stars as viewed from the equator and geographic poles and then as viewed from other locations on Earth. You can then list the important points in each subsection.

Since the paragraph is the basic unit of writing in each section, concentrate on these. Each paragraph has a topic. Search for the topic and mark it accordingly. Many times the first or the last sentence of a paragraph is the topic sentence, summarizing the subject discussed. Sometimes a paragraph will be a list of observations, assumptions, or examples pertinent to the topic. Each paragraph is also related to the preceding and following paragraphs. Find these connections. When you finish, you should have an outline describing the topics and subtopics in each section in your own words.

This text will introduce many new terms. Some of these terms are technical and are defined in the margins and the glossary. Others are familiar from everyday language but are used here in unfamiliar ways. Find these important terms and mark them, by circling them, for instance. For example, in the descriptions of the motions of the stars, and Sun in Chapter 2, an important term is "apparent." As a way of mastering the important words, write the meaning of each new term in your own words. When a term is defined either in the text or in the margin, make sure you understand the terms used in the definition. As you delve deeper into the book, you will find that definitions of new terms incorporate the technical vocabulary developed in earlier chapters. In this way, as your understanding of the terms increases, so will your understanding of the subject.

Finally, analytical reading involves understanding the interpretations put forth by the author. For example, the first section of Chapter 17 puts forth an argument for the huge dimensions of our Galaxy. This argument is based on a series of observations made by various astronomers over several centuries. To understand an argument or interpretation, which will usually be presented over several paragraphs, first ask yourself what is the author trying to show here? The introduction to the chapter, the introduction to the section, the section title, and the topic sentences of the paragraphs will all provide clues to the author's purpose. Next locate the important sentences in each paragraph; these will present observations, established theory, or logic supporting the interpretation. How do you recognize an important sentence? First of all, it will probably be a difficult sentence. When you read one, stop and ask yourself what you just read. Secondly, important sentences will usually contain important terms. Since you have already identified the important terms, you should have little difficulty finding the important sentences. Once you have identified the important sentences, ask yourself how these sentences spread over several paragraphs fit together to support the author's interpretation. When you have accomplished this, you will be well on your way to understanding the subject.

The point being made here is that reading is active and that the more active it is, the more you will benefit. The activity of reading fundamentally is asking questions. The techniques for answering these questions range from marking your book with a variety of symbols to identifying arguments made by the author. Even if you follow all the suggestions in this chapter, you will not be an expert astronomer after reading this book, but you will have some understanding of the great problems astronomers and scientists have tried to solve, how they solved some of them, and how they are still trying to solve others.

▰CHAPTER CAPSULE

Topics and Terms	Review and Remarks
Levels of reading	Elementary Inspectional Analytical
Inspectional reading	The reader becomes familiar with the book without worrying about details. Read the entire book without stopping at difficult places. Concentrate on the overall picture, on the big points being made.
Analytical reading	Ask questions while you read. Mark important words, main points, and arguments. Outline each chapter. Rewrite in your own words.

▰REVIEW QUESTIONS

1. Review your book. Thumb through the pages and make notes on the broad areas covered by each section. Write a brief paragraph about the general character of the book and of astronomy. Look for the main theme of the book. What ties everything together?

2. What particular value is there in outlining a chapter of a book? Read the paragraph you wrote for question 1 above. Does it recall for you some of the things you noticed while thumbing through the text?

3. Outline this chapter using the "formula" given in the text. Outline each chapter in the text as you begin to study it.

4. Each discipline (astronomy, physics, philosophy, language, and so forth) has its own jargon or terminology. In this text words that are likely to be unfamiliar to the reader appear boldfaced and are defined in the glossary. In your opinion, why does a terminology (that must be defined for nonspecialists) develop in a field or discipline like astronomy? Other than having to learn definitions so you will understand the material, what value should you derive from learning the terminology of a field that is new to you?

5. List the key words (that is, the words you think are important) in this chapter. Can you give their definitions in your own words? You should do this for each chapter as you read it.

6. What is the difference between inspectional reading and analytical reading? Define these terms in your own words. Which of these do you do while preparing for a test?

▰FOR FURTHER READING

Adler, M. J., and C. Van Doren. 1972. How to read a book. New York: Simon & Schuster, Inc.

YOU ARE HERE ➤

Astronomy and Astronomers

OUTLINE

Astronomers

The Universe: A Brief History

A Sense of Scale

The Real Motions of the Earth

Clocks and Calendars
Stellar and Solar Clocks
Time Zones
Calendars

Summary

Chapter Capsule

Review Questions

For Further Reading

███████ **ASTROPROBE 1:**
  MathTools 1

You Are Here.
ARTIST: Anne Norcia.

I N THE DAYS WHEN CITY AND COUNTRY SKIES were dark, a young child's curiosity about the sky could easily have been aroused by mom or dad pointing out the Big Dipper and the North Star. Today, this interest is more likely to be sparked by televised accounts of the space program. Thanks to numerous newspaper articles about the latest discoveries in astronomy and televised pictures of the outer most reaches of the solar system taken by space probes, astronomical topics have become part of everyday conversations. Students talk about black holes or the extinction of the dinosaurs, and nations consider future space stations and flights to Mars.

The earliest observations, which began centuries before the invention of the telescope, were concerned with the positions and motions of celestial objects. The first observers discovered some significant facts that proved to be of great practical importance to early humans. These early astronomers used the apparent celestial motions of the Sun, Moon, planets, and stars to construct clocks and calendars. Only later did scientists realize that these motions were intimately connected with the motions of the Earth.

ASTRONOMERS

The stars, planets, and the Moon, all easily seen on a dark night, are part of the realm of **astronomy,** the science that studies the material universe beyond the Earth's atmosphere. Astronomy encompasses several broad disciplines: planetary, solar, stellar, galactic, extragalactic, and cosmology. *Planetary astronomy* is the study of the planets, the moons, and the numerous small bodies that orbit the Sun. It tries to answer practical questions—What mineral resources are to be found on other planets and moons?—and theoretical questions—How did the solar system form and evolve to its present state? *Solar astronomy* concentrates on the Sun and its interaction with planetary atmospheres and magnetic fields. A very practical part of solar astronomy is the study of solar-terrestrial relations and how solar activity affects life on Earth. *Stellar astronomy* is a broad subject that includes the study of the atmospheres of stars, their interior structure and chemical composition, and their formation and evolution. Systems of billions of stars called galaxies are the major structural unit of the universe. The study of our Galaxy, the Milky Way Galaxy, is called *galactic astronomy*. In *extragalactic astronomy*, astronomers apply their knowledge of galactic astronomy to galaxies that lie beyond the Milky Way. Much work in extragalactic astronomy bears directly on *cosmology*, the study of the formation, structure, and evolution of the universe. It tries to answer the questions, How did the universe begin? How has it evolved, or changed, since its creation?

Each of these disciplines contains many specialized areas and requires special techniques and instruments, from telescopes to space probes (Figure 1.1), for different observing conditions and purposes. Furthermore, many new fields of study with close ties to astronomy have recently developed:

(a)

(b)

- *Archaeoastronomy:* The study of the astronomy of ancient peoples.
- *Astrobiology (also exobiology):* The study of life in the universe.
- *Astrochemistry:* The study of the composition and evolution of planets, stars, interstellar matter, and galaxies.
- *Astrodynamics:* The study of the paths of space vehicles.
- *Astrogeology:* The study of the geology and composition of other planets and moons.

Many of these new fields successfully apply what we have learned from centuries of studying the Earth to the study of alien worlds and distant stars and galaxies. Astronomy itself took on a new emphasis about a hundred years ago when astronomers began to apply the principles and laws of physics, then a relatively new science, to the study of the structure and content of individual stellar objects. This new approach was called *astrophysics.* Today, astronomy and astrophysics are synonymous.

An **astronomer,** or astrophysicist, is a scientist trained to study the heavens. The basic tool of the *observational* astronomer is, of course, the telescope, which can be either Earth-based or spaceborne. When astronomers collect their data, they hope that they will discover something really new. This is part of the excitement of being a scientist. There is much work involved in making a new discovery. Astronomers try to interpret their observations by comparing them with known physical laws or by using detailed descriptions generated by *theoreticians.* Theoreticians apply the laws of physics to observed phenomena. They are excellent mathematicians who apply powerful computers and analytical techniques to complex and often perplexing problems.

■ FIGURE 1.1

Two Instruments Used by Astronomers

(a) Optical telescopes, such as the Anglo-Australian Telescope shown here, collect light from distant stars that are much too faint to see with our eyes. *(b)* Space probes, such as this *Viking* lander, allow astronomers to sample the soil and atmosphere of other planets in the solar system.

SOURCES: Part (a) copyright Anglo-Australian Telescope Board 1977. Photograph by David Malin. Part (b) courtesy NASA.

■■■ FIGURE 1.2

Amateur Observers

Amateur astronomers, who come from all
walks of life, spend many nights observing; some spend many hours building telescopes.

SOURCE: John Sanford/Science Photo Library,
Photo Researchers.

Training to become an astronomer requires four years of undergrad-
uate study, usually with a major in physics or mathematics, and another three to six years of graduate work or more. Colleges and universities, national laboratories, government agencies such as the National
Aeronautics and Space Administration (NASA), and private industry
employ astronomers. Most of them work in universities and national
laboratories such as the National Optical Astronomy Observatories in
Tucson, Arizona. Astronomers in academia divide their time between
teaching and research, often traveling several times a year to national
facilities to make observations or perform calculations on supercomputers.

Astronomy, however, is accessible to everyone. For only a modest investment, anyone can purchase or build a telescope and begin viewing
the sky (Figure 1.2). Magazines such as *Sky & Telescope* and *Astronomy*
are written for amateurs and help them keep up with the latest research
results. In addition, many books for the nonscientists have been written
on a variety of astronomical subjects, from the origin of the solar system to the future of the universe. If you are also a computer enthusiast,
computer programs are available that show the sky at any hour of any
day in the year and for any year in the past or future. Hundreds of
amateur astronomy clubs exist throughout the United States and the
world. These clubs sponsor many activities, and several times a year
amateurs meet for national conventions and star parties.

Both professional and amateur astronomers enjoy studying and looking at the universe. Their telescopes reveal the diversity of planets, the
history of the stars, and the mystery of galaxies. All of these objects are
the result of the long, complex evolution of the universe. A brief version
of this rich history is presented next.

THE UNIVERSE: A BRIEF HISTORY

Astronomers have been accumulating information about the universe for thousands of years. The development of spacecraft and sophisticated instrumentation in the last few decades has greatly accelerated this information gathering. Even greater strides are expected with the building of larger telescopes and the launching of new spaceborne telescopes. With the data on hand, astronomers can construct a plausible history of the universe, from its violent beginning to the present.

Current thinking with the aid of observations traces the beginning of the universe to an explosion we call the _big bang_ that occurred about 15 billion years ago. The universe literally exploded into existence. All of the matter seen in the universe today was created in that explosion. This visible matter is composed mainly of hydrogen and helium thought to have been produced during _nuclear reactions_ in the first few minutes of the big bang. In fact, hydrogen and helium atoms were nearly all that were produced in the early universe, according to our present understanding.

As the universe aged, it expanded and cooled. After about a million years, it cooled sufficiently to allow matter to begin to collect in clumps. In a billion years or so, these became the organized matter we call _galaxies_, huge systems of billions of stars (Figure 1.3). Huge, stringy structures composed of many millions of galaxies span vast distances across space. These immense aggregates of galaxies, called _superclusters_, are the largest structures seen in the universe today. Each super-

FIGURE 1.3

A Cluster of Galaxies

The spiral- and elliptical-shaped objects in this picture are individual galaxies consisting of billions of stars.

SOURCE: Palomar Observatory, California Institute of Technology.

■■■ **FIGURE 1.4**

A Galaxy near the Milky Way Galaxy

Nearby galaxies such as this one allow us to study in detail the contents of galaxies.

SOURCE: National Optical Astronomy Observatories.

cluster contains many clusters of galaxies as well as individual galaxies. Our Galaxy, the Milky Way, is a member of a small cluster of about 20 galaxies (Figure 1.4). The largest clusters can contain thousands of members. At the centers of these are often found immense "cannibal" galaxies, whose large size is the result of engulfing smaller members of the clusters.

Galaxies are composed of stars, dust, and gas. The gas, of course, is mainly hydrogen and helium atoms produced in the big bang. The dust is composed of solid particles of heavy elements and is the remains of stars that have destroyed themselves in fiery explosions. The Milky Way Galaxy is the result of the accumulated history of all of the stars that exist and have existed from its formation, just as the present state of the world is the accumulated history of individual nations, past and present. The oldest stars are about 15 billion years old by current estimates. The youngest stars are still forming today. Our Sun, for instance, is about 4.6 billion years old. It is a part of a recent generation of stars but not the most recent by far. An important goal of astronomers is to trace the "lives" of past generations of stars so that the entire history of the Milky Way Galaxy can eventually be reconstructed, from its formation to the present.

The Milky Way Galaxy exhibits a rich variety of stellar activity; stars are born, mature, and die. Stars have finite lifetimes because they have a finite amount of the fuel needed to generate the fantastic amounts of energy that we see mainly as light. Once they use up all of their fuel, some literally blow themselves apart in a violent explosion called a *supernova* (Figure 1.5). In fact, supernovae are an important source of new dust and gas in the Galaxy because much of the debris of these stellar

■■■ **FIGURE 1.5**

The Crab Nebula

The gaseous looking matter in this photograph of a remnant of a supernova is the remains of a star that blew itself up about 900 years ago.

SOURCE: Lick Observatory, University of California, Santa Cruz.

explosions consists of elements manufactured deep inside the star by nuclear reactions. New generations of stars are born out of this increasingly enriched debris.

Current theory suggests that in some cases several stars form at once, but in other cases a star and attendant planets result when new stars form. This idea is bolstered by observations, such as rings of dust around young stars and possible large planets orbiting other stars. Planetary formation is thought to result from an accumulation of the leftover dust and gas surrounding a newly formed star. The observed moons of planets are also thought to form by accumulation, either together with the planet or at a different location, in which case they are later captured by the planet. The final stage of the accumulation process can be seen as craters on planets with solid surfaces, such as Mercury, Mars, and most moons (Figure 1.6).

Our solar system contains the only example of planets available for study in the universe. Consequently, astronomers spend considerable time investigating these objects. The Earth forms a reference point from which astronomers try to make sense out of what they observe on other planets (Figure 1.7). Geologists, oceanographers, atmospheric scientists, and other scientists have gathered a tremendous amount of information about the Earth. Planetary astronomers apply this knowledge to understanding how surfaces of planets change, how their atmospheres evolve, and how their climates vary over the eons. This, in turn, adds to our understanding of Earth as a planet, and that knowledge will hopefully help us survive in our own environment.

This brief history of the universe has recounted the major events that have occurred in the universe since the beginning of time and intro-

■■■ FIGURE 1.6

The Moon

A close-up view of the Moon's surface.

SOURCE: Lick Observatory, University of California, Santa Cruz.

■■■ FIGURE 1.7

The Planet Earth

SOURCE: NASA.

duced the kinds of objects found in the universe today. It did not, however, address the question, How far is it between planets, stars, and galaxies? This brings up yet another aspect of the universe—its size.

A SENSE OF SCALE

The universe is mainly empty. To illustrate this, let's look at the size of the Earth-Moon system and the solar system as a whole. The dimensions involved in the Earth-Moon system are the diameter of the Earth (12,765 km = 7934 mi), the diameter of the Moon (3,476 km = 2160 mi), and the distance to the Moon (384,401 km = 238,910 mi). Panel a in Figure 1.8 shows the Earth-Moon system to scale; that is, it shows the relative sizes of the Earth and the Moon. In this case the Earth's diameter is almost four times that of the Moon and the distance between the Earth and the Moon is about 30 Earth diameters. The *Voyager* photograph (Figure 1.9) of the Earth and the Moon also gives you an idea of the relative sizes of the two bodies. Comprehending the scale of the Earth-Moon system just by looking at a scale drawing is difficult. You can get a better sense of the distance from travel times. Many of us have traveled across the United States by automobile, taking four or five days traveling at an average speed of 55 MPH for most of each day. Driving constantly at that speed, it would take 180 days to travel the distance to the Moon! Another way to get a sense of scale in the solar system is to compare the size of the Earth-Moon system with the diameter of the Sun. The Sun is by far the largest object in the solar system; it has a diameter of 1,390,000 km (866,000 mi). The large size

■■■■ ■ FIGURE 1.8

Earth and Moon System

(a) The Earth, Moon, and their average separation are drawn to scale. *(b)* The orbit of the Moon about the Earth will easily fit within the diameter of the Sun.

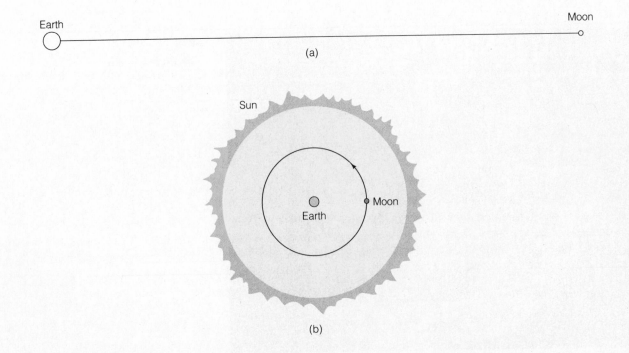

(a)

(b)

■ FIGURE 1.9

The Earth and Moon from the
***Voyager* Spacecraft**
SOURCE: NASA.

of the Sun is illustrated by the fact that the entire orbit of the Moon around the Earth would fit inside the Sun (Panel b of Figure 1.8).

Let's extend our analysis to the size of the solar system. Imagine that the Sun is located in Boston, Massachusetts, and the most distant planet in the solar system, Pluto, is located in San Francisco. On this scale the Sun would be a sphere about a kilometer (⅔ of a mile) across, the same size as the Boston Common. Mercury, the closest planet to the Sun would lie just outside the city limits of Boston, almost in Gloucester, Massachusetts, and would be a small sphere with a diameter equal to the length of an automobile. The orbit of Venus reaches Providence, Rhode Island, and Earth's orbit would pass through Cape Cod. Both Venus and the Earth would have diameters about the length of a large travel trailer. Mars' orbit reaches to Springfield, Massachusetts, and Mars would be half the size of the Earth and Venus, about 5 meters (15 ft) across. Figure 1.10 shows these orbits superimposed on a map of the United States. The radii of the orbits of Mercury, Venus, Earth, and Mars are less than the width of Massachusetts on this scale.

The next planet out from the Sun, Jupiter, would have an orbit that takes it to Baltimore and almost to Washington, D.C., over 5 times farther from the Sun than the Earth. The orbit of Saturn would lie as far west as Toledo and Columbus, Ohio, almost 10 times farther away from the Sun as the Earth. The diameters of Jupiter and Saturn would be about the length of a football field. Uranus's orbit would pass through Miami, Florida, and Kansas City, Kansas. Neptune's and Pluto's orbits are out west. Neptune's orbit would pass through El Paso, Texas, and Glacier National Park in northern Montana. Uranus and Neptune would have diameters equal to that of the length of an Olympic-sized swimming pool, while Pluto would be represented by a sphere only 1.5 meters (5 ft) across.

Those of you who have traveled across the United States realize that it is a long way from coast to coast. While traveling, you can appreciate the distances between cities. At the same time, there are mountains,

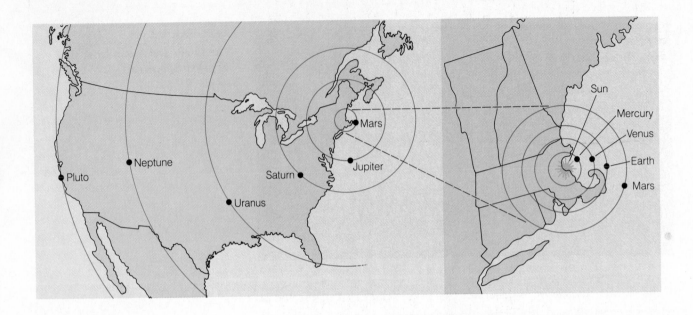

FIGURE 1.10

A Sense of Scale

The solar system has been scaled down to fit on a map of the United States.

rivers, and forests between major cities. When you think of the solar system, you must eliminate all of the "mountains, rivers, and forests," as well as small towns and replace them with nothing. Instead of a map with symbols for roads and cities, picture a vast sheet of black paper representing the solar system with the planets as small spheres in this vast emptiness. The solar system is mainly empty space.

To reinforce this view of a vast emptiness, consider communicating across the solar system. Radio communications travel at the speed of light (3×10^5 km/s, or 186,000 mi/s). A message sent to a distant outpost on Pluto from Earth would take over 5 hours! Radio communications with the *Voyager* spacecraft as it passed Uranus took 4 hours and 6 minutes. The instructions to the spacecraft's computer must be sent hours before the spacecraft is to make its maneuvers. Even with the speeds our rockets are able to attain, travel to Mars and Venus, the nearest planets to the Earth, takes months.

What about the stars? How far away are they? The nearest star is over 200,000 times farther from the Sun than the Earth and over 5,000 times farther away than Pluto. Radio signals to the nearest star, Alpha Centauri, would take over 4 years to reach the star. If humans one day find a planet in this star system on which to build a colony, a reply to a communications from Earth would take over 8 years. Much can happen in 8 years.

The emptiness between neighboring stars and in the solar system is hard for humans to comprehend. We are on more familiar ground on the Earth, where we will begin our study of the universe with a look at the Earth's own motions and how they relate to our ways of keeping track of the time and the days of the year. Some knowledge of the Earth's motions is necessary for understanding the description of the celestial motions of the stars, Sun, Moon, and planets in Chapter 2. Although ancient humans for the most part accepted an Earth-centered view of the universe whereby all celestial bodies moved around the Earth, they were able to predict the motions of the stars, Sun, Moon, and planets accurately because, unknown to them, these celestial motions reflect the motion of the Earth.

THE REAL MOTIONS OF THE EARTH

The most conspicuous object in the solar system is the brilliant star we call the Sun, although it has had a variety of names in other cultures (Table 1.1). The third planet from the Sun, the Earth, completes one *revolution*, or orbit, around the Sun in one year. The planets closer to the Sun than the Earth revolve in less than a year, while those farther away take longer. It is useful to describe a planet's orbit as lying on a flat, imaginary surface in space. For instance, if the Earth's orbit were drawn on a sheet of paper, the paper would represent the **plane** of the Earth's orbit (Figure 1.11). The Sun would lie very near the center of the Earth's orbit.

Besides revolving around the Sun, the Earth spins. The spinning Earth is like a spinning bicycle wheel in that both spin, or rotate, about an *axis*. For the wheel, the axis of rotation is a real, physical object, the

■ TABLE 1.1 **Some Names of the Sun in Earth Mythologies**

Name	Mythology
Sol	Roman
Apollo	Greek
Ra or Amon Ra	Egyptian
Shamash	Semitic
Savitar	Hindu

Plane: Any flat, level, or even surface.

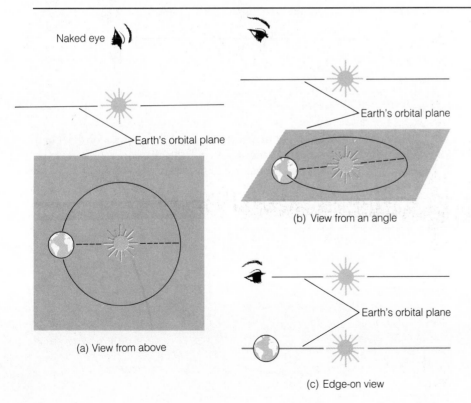

(a) View from above

(b) View from an angle

(c) Edge-on view

■ FIGURE 1.11

The Earth's Orbital Plane from Three Different Perspectives

The Earth is not drawn to scale.

■■■ FIGURE 1.12

The Spinning Earth and a Spinning Wheel

The Earth turns on its axis of rotation as a wheel spins on its axle.

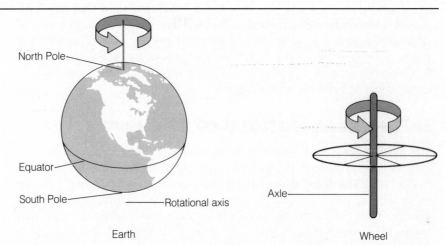

North Pole

Equator

South Pole

Rotational axis

Axle

Earth

Wheel

axle; for the Earth, it is an imaginary line, passing through the Earth (Figure 1.12). The Earth's North and South Poles mark the locations where the axis of rotation of the Earth projects through the surface. Midway between the poles lies the equator. It is an imaginary circle around the Earth dividing the Earth into the *Northern Hemisphere*, the area north of the equator in which the United States and Europe are located, and the *Southern Hemisphere*, the area south of the equator in which Australia and most of South America are located. Careful observation shows that the rotational axis of the Earth is *tilted 23½°* away from being perpendicular to the orbital plane of the Earth (Figure 1.13). Because the Earth's axis of rotation keeps this orientation while the Earth orbits the Sun, the tilt of the Earth's rotational axis causes the seasons (see Chapter 2 for more on the seasons.).

Humans took thousands of years to deduce that the Earth orbited the Sun and rotated about its axis. It took so long partly because our ancestors were not able to view the solar system from outside. They could only see the solar system from the surface of the Earth and lacked knowledge of the Earth's movement around the Sun or about its axis. Nevertheless, they accurately measured the length of the year and the day.

■■■ FIGURE 1.13

The Earth's Axis of Rotation and the Orbital Plane

The Earth's axis of rotation is tilted 23½° with respect to the Earth's orbital plane. The Earth maintains this tilt as it orbits the Sun.

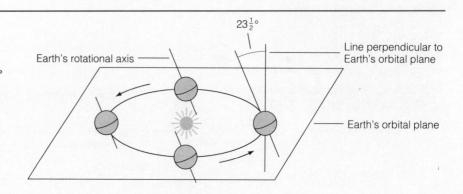

$23\frac{1}{2}°$

Earth's rotational axis

Line perpendicular to Earth's orbital plane

Earth's orbital plane

■■■CLOCKS AND CALENDARS

How long does the Earth take to turn exactly once on its axis? How long does the Earth take to revolve exactly once around the Sun? If you go by your wristwatch and the calendar on the wall, you would answer 24 hours for the Earth's rotation and 365 days for the Earth's revolution. Recalling that an extra day is added to our calendar every 4 years, you might answer that the length of the year is 365 days and 6 hours. All of these answers are wrong.

Stellar and Solar Clocks

Looking at the sky at night, you can easily imagine you are on the inside of a huge, hollow sphere dotted with twinkling lights. Only half of this **celestial sphere** can be seen at any moment because the Earth hides the other half (Figure 1.14). Any object on the celestial sphere that is due south or north is on the observer's **meridian,** an imaginary arc on the sky that passes exactly overhead, or at the **zenith,** and crosses the horizon due south and north. The line 90° from the zenith cutting the celestial sphere in half is the *celestial horizon*. The actual visible horizon is defined by the objects, such as trees, mountains, and buildings, in the distance.

Consider doing an experiment. Point a telescope at a star that is on the meridian at midnight and leave the telescope undisturbed throughout the night and the next day. If the Earth rotated once on its axis every 24 hours, the star should again be visible through the telescope at midnight on the next night, exactly 24 hours later. If this experiment is done carefully, however, the star will not be visible. Do the experiment again but, instead of looking for the star 24 hours later, time how long it takes for the star to return into the center of the field of view of the telescope. If the timing is precise, the star will be visible through the

Celestial sphere: An imaginary sphere of the heavens to which celestial objects like the Sun, Moon, and stars are considered to be attached.

Meridian: An imaginary arc on the celestial sphere passing through the poles and zenith and crossing the horizon due south at a right angle.

Zenith: The point on the celestial sphere directly above the observer.

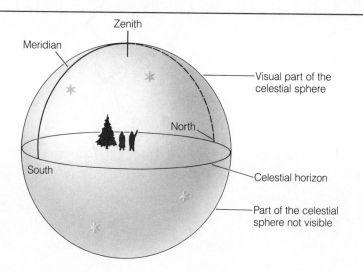

■■■ FIGURE 1.14

The Celestial Sphere, Zenith, and Meridian

A convenient way to write hours, minutes, and seconds is to use superscripts, **h** for hours, **m** for minutes, and **s** for seconds: $23^h56^m4^s$.

telescope exactly $23^h56^m4^s$ later. This is how long it takes for the Earth to turn exactly once on its axis. We refer to this period as the **sidereal day** from the Latin *sidereus* meaning "star." The sidereal period is the Earth's rotational period measured *with respect to the stars.*

If the Earth turns exactly once in $23^h56^m4^s$, why do clocks and watches keep 24-hour time? Isn't the period from noon to noon one day? Do we just ignore this 4-minute difference because it seems so small? From noon to noon is indeed 24 hours; it is one **solar day.** Daily activities are governed by the solar day, the interval of time between meridian crossings of the Sun. In fact, the term "meridian" is derived from the Latin *meridianus* meaning "of noon" or "midday." *Post meridiem,* or P.M., refers to the hours after midday and *ante meridiem,* or A.M., to the hours before midday.

The solar day differs from the sidereal day because, while the Earth is turning on its axis of rotation, it is also traveling around the Sun. The Earth travels about 3.2 million kilometers (2 million miles) in its orbit around the Sun for every revolution about its axis of rotation. This causes the Sun to appear to move a little on the celestial sphere, as a nearby telephone pole would appear to move against the distant horizon to passengers in a passing car (Figure 1.15). Consequently, the Sun will not be at the same place on the celestial sphere after exactly one Earth rotation. The Earth's orbital motion requires that the Earth spin around a little bit more for the Sun to return to the same place in the sky. This extra spinning of the Earth takes, on the average, an extra 4 minutes.

The 4-minute difference between the motions of the Sun and stars adds up. Imagine seeing the Sun and a star on the meridian at noon. Both steadily move toward the western horizon as the Earth rotates west to east. Which one will reach the meridian first the next day? After one sidereal day, $23^h56^m4^s$, the star is back on the meridian, but the Sun needs 24 hours to reach the meridian again. The star is ahead by 4 minutes. After two days, the same star is 8 minutes ahead since at the beginning of the second day the star had a 4-minute lead; that is, the

---

■ FIGURE 1.15

Solar Days and Sidereal Days

The solar day is longer than the sidereal day. The Earth turns exactly once on its axis every $23^h56^m4^s$. At the same time, the Earth moves about 3 million kilometers in its orbit around the Sun. Consequently, if the Sun is directly above a marker on one day, it will *not* be directly overhead $23^h56^m4^s$ later. The Earth needs to make up for its orbital motion by turning a little bit more.

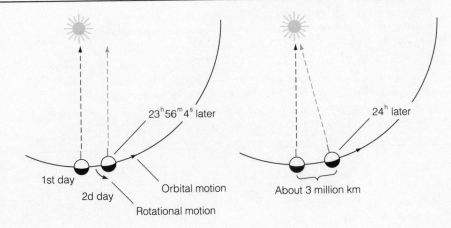

Earth has moved another 3.2 million kilometers in its orbit the second day. After 3 days, the star is ahead by 12 minutes. Each day the star "gains" 4 minutes on the Sun. After a year the star "leads" the Sun by just 24 hours; that is, the star has gained 360° on the Sun and both are together again.

The same relative motion can be seen at sunrise and sunset. Since clocks keep track of solar time, stars rise and set 4 minutes earlier each day than the day before. As a result, the Sun appears to move eastward on the celestial sphere with respect to the stars. After one month, a star that rose with the Sun at the beginning of the month will rise 120 minutes (4 minutes per day times 30 days), or 2 hours, before the Sun. The same star will, of course, set 2 hours before the Sun. Furthermore, the star will also cross the meridian 2 hours before it did at the beginning of the month. For example, if the star crossed the meridian at midnight at the beginning of the month, it will cross it at 10:00 P.M. at the end of the month. Consequently, we see different stars in the evening at different times of the year.

Clearly, it would be difficult to keep time with sidereal watches and clocks. Even using the solar day can lead to problems if it is done without care.

Time Zones

In everyday affairs time differences of hours are of practical interest. For instance, if you make a telephone call to Seattle from New York at noon, it is only 9:00 A.M. in Seattle. Why the time difference? Noon is roughly the time of day when the Sun is on the meridian. Because New York is farther east than Seattle, the Sun is on the meridian at New York first. The rotation of the Earth will eventually bring the Sun across Seattle's meridian. Locations on the Earth eastward or westward are described by **longitudes** (Figure 1.16). These are angular distances measured east or west along the equator. The line of zero longitude is arbitrary; by international convention, longitudes are measured from Greenwich, England. Greenwich, therefore, has a longitude of 0°. The Sun is on the meridian of cities of different longitudes at different times.

Before the twentieth century, major cities in the United States kept local time, and cities to the east experienced noon before cities to the west. In fact, about 56 irregularly shaped time zones covered the United States. Each group of cities in one of these time zones kept the same time. Noon, for instance, was the same for all of the cities in a time zone. The existence of many time zones led to much confusion for travelers in the nineteenth century when travel by trains and communication by telegraph increased dramatically. Travelers had to adjust their watches constantly. They had to calculate the difference in time between their city, or local time, and the time standard used by the railroads. For example, if travelers in Baltimore needed to catch the 9:10 to Washington, D.C., they would have to arrive at the train station by 9:00 local time because the railroad schedules were based on New York

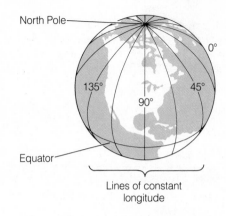

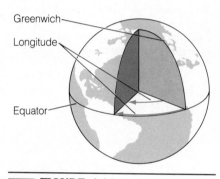

■ **FIGURE 1.16**
Longitude

Longitude: An angle measured east or west from Greenwich, England.

time, which was 10 minutes ahead of Baltimore time. The 9:10 written on the train schedule referred to New York time.

Congress simplified matters by dividing the continental United States into just 4 standard time zones on November 18, 1883 (Figure 1.17). All cities in a given time zone kept the same time. The jagged boundaries of the time zones conform to local geographical regions and are a matter of convenience for the localities near the boundaries. Communities, for instance, that are economically linked through the local labor force try to be on the same time. Each time zone is approximately 15° of longitude wide. Because the Earth's apparent motion relative to the Sun is 360° in 24 hours, every hour of time corresponds to 15° of longitude: 15° per hour times 24 hours equals 360°. (Table 1.2 illustrates the relationship between time units and angular units of a circle.) Since the Sun rises in the east, the eastern time zones are ahead in time of the western time zones. Whenever travelers cross a time zone boundary, they have to change their watches. Traveling west they move their clocks back and gain an hour, traveling east they move them forward and lose an hour.

■■■ FIGURE 1.17

Time Zones in the United States and Canada

Whenever a time zone is crossed, we must change our clocks by one hour. Because 4 time zones span the continental United States, 3 hours separate the East and West coasts.

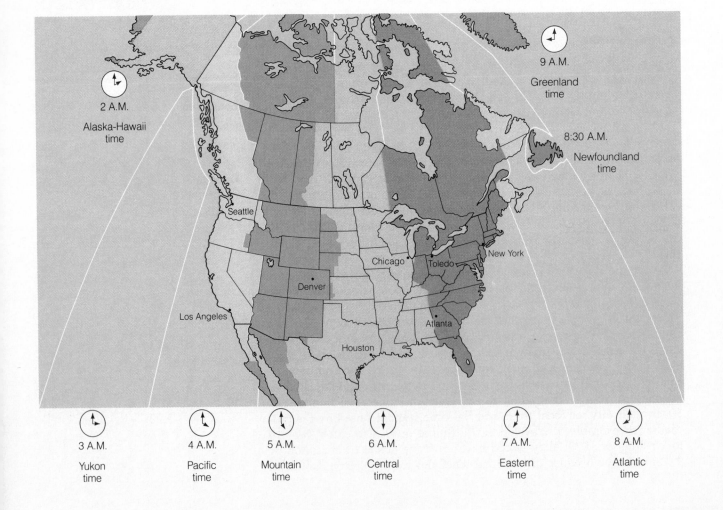

Not all cities changed to standard time immediately. Bangor, Maine, did not approve the change until 1887, and Cincinnati waited until 1890. Detroit found itself on the border between the eastern and central time zones. At first the city decided to keep local time, then in 1900 half of the city chose eastern time and the other half central time. After switching back to local time for a while and then adopting central time, the city finally adopted eastern standard time in August 1916.

A variation of standard time occurs during the summer. Most states take advantage of the long summer days by keeping *daylight saving time.* By moving the clocks ahead one hour in the spring, people are able to enjoy sunlight late in the evening. For example, if it is still daylight at 9:00 P.M. on standard time, it will be daylight at 10:00 P.M. on daylight saving time. Daylight saving time usually begins at 2 A.M. on the first Sunday in April and ends at 2 A.M. on the last Sunday in October.

The entire world is also divided into time zones (Figure 1.18). Starting at Greenwich, England, approximately every 15° of longitude defines a time zone, each one hour apart in time. London, for instance, is five hours ahead of Atlanta. To call someone in London at noon London time, you would have to place your call in Atlanta at 7 A.M. The jagged appearance of the zones is just a matter of convenience; small countries, for instance, prefer to keep the entire country on the same time.

Those of us living on the West Coast realize that New Yorkers get to celebrate New Year's Eve first. Similarly, Londoners celebrate the New Year before New Yorkers. Where is the first New Year's Eve party of the year?

Consider an amateur radio operator in Chicago listening to radio stations around the world on a Tuesday at noon. A station in New York, 1 time zone east, would be broadcasting at 1:00 P.M., a station in Halifax, Nova Scotia, 2 time zones east, would be broadcasting at 2:00 P.M., while a station in Moscow, 8 time zones east, would be broadcasting at 8:00 P.M. Furthermore, a station in Denver, 1 time zone west, would be broadcasting at 11:00 A.M., and a station in Los Angeles, 2 time zones west, would be broadcasting at 10:00 A.M., and so forth for time zones to the west. A problem arises on the other side of the world. Consider listening to a station in Bombay, 11 time zones east of Chicago. An amateur radio operator in Chicago might think that the Bombay station is broadcasting at 11:00 P.M. Tuesday. Bombay, however, is also 13 time zones west of Chicago and, because clocks are moved back one hour for each time zone to the west, 13 hours earlier than noon Tuesday is 11:00 P.M. on Monday! Which is it: 11:00 P.M. Tuesday or 11:00 P.M. Monday?

The solution to this dilemma is a rule, which dictates that a new day begins on the **International Date Line,** which is located in the middle of the Pacific Ocean at a longitude of 180°, 12 time zones from Greenwich, England. This imaginary line is drawn to avoid cutting over land so that the same island does not have two different dates simultaneously. The date is changed such that a ship or plane crossing the line from the east loses one day; that is, if the line is crossed on a Tuesday, it becomes Wednesday (Table 1.3). Crossing from west to east gains a day.

▬▬ TABLE 1.2
Time and Angular Units of a Circle

Time Units	Arc Units
24^h	$360°$
1^h	$15°$
4^m	$1°$
1^m	$15'$
4^s	$1'$
1^s	$15''$

To help you remember which way to turn your clock to adjust for daylight saving time, *spring* ahead, *fall* back.

▬▬ TABLE 1.3
Crossing the International Date Line

Japan Airlines Flight #3:
Leave San Francisco 9:30 A.M. Dec. 31
Arrive Tokyo   1:10 P.M. Jan. 1
Flight time = 10^h40^m

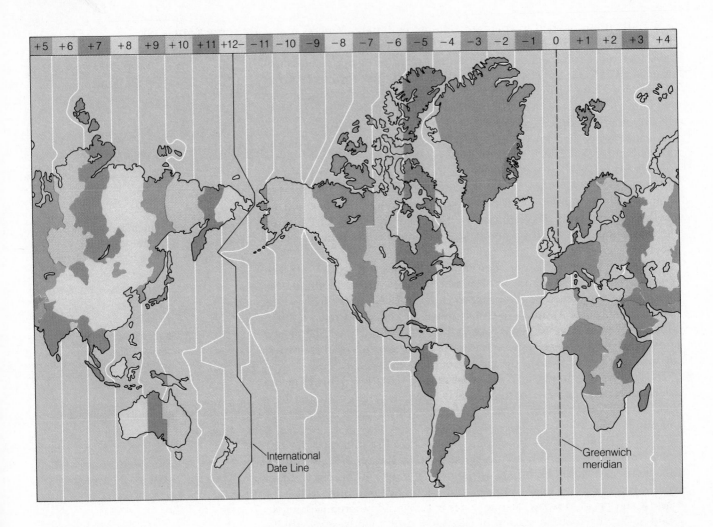

| +5 | +6 | +7 | +8 | +9 | +10 | +11 | +12− | −11 | −10 | −9 | −8 | −7 | −6 | −5 | −4 | −3 | −2 | −1 | 0 | +1 | +2 | +3 | +4 |

International
Date Line

Greenwich
meridian

■ FIGURE 1.18

Time Zones of the World

Now the location of the first New Year's Eve party can be established. It is held first in the time zone just west of the International Date Line. Consequently, the Fiji Islands celebrate the New Year first (Figure 1.19). The last to welcome in the New Year is West Samoa, which lies just to the east of the International Date Line.

Calendars

This section started by asking how long the Earth takes to orbit the Sun; that is, how long is the year? The 365-day calendar is not quite right. The length of time the Sun takes to travel around the celestial sphere, the *tropical year*, is 365.24220 days. The fraction 0.24220 of a day corresponds to $5^h48^m46^s$ and has been a constant source of problems for calendar makers. For instance, if a 365-day calendar is used, after 4 calendar years, the first day of winter, called the winter solstice, will occur one calendar day later than the calendar predicts because 4

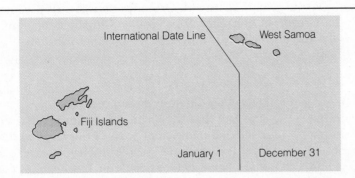

The International Date Line

The first New Year's Eve party is celebrated in the Fiji Islands and the last in West Samoa.

times $5^h48^m46^s$ is about 24 hours. After a century, the error would be almost a month; after several centuries, the winter solstice would occur in the calendar summertime! One way to adjust the calendar is to add a day occasionally. This has been the practice throughout history. Our current calendar had its origins in 45 B.C. when Julius Caesar implemented a 365-day calendar, the **Julian calendar,** with an extra day, a *leap day*, added every four years.

It would appear that the calendar was in good shape after the changes made by Caesar. With the addition of the leap year, a 366-day year every fourth year, over 4 years the Julian year averaged 365.25 days exactly. But the tropical year is not so nice and even; it is 11^m14^s shorter than the Julian year. This 11-minute difference adds up over the centuries. After 128 years the Julian calendar was 1 day ahead of the Sun. "What is one day?" you may ask. Roman Catholic church officials realized if this went on long enough, Christmas would eventually be celebrated in the spring at Easter. In A.D. 1582 when the difference reached 10 days, the church corrected the Julian calendar; Pope Gregory XIII introduced a new 365-day calendar, the **Gregorian calendar.**

The difference between the Julian and Gregorian calendars is in the leap year rule. The Gregorian calendar does not allow leap years in century years that are not evenly divisible by 400, such as 1700, 1800, 1900, and 2100. Century years such as 1600 and 2000, however, are divisible by 400: 1600/400 = 4 and 2000/400 = 5; they are leap years. The average length of the Gregorian calendar year, 365.2425 days, is still 25 seconds longer than the tropical year but results in a calendar that loses only 1 day every 3,300 years.

Several amusing effects of these changes have caused certain problems throughout history. For example, Catholic nations adopted the Gregorian calendar on October 15, 1582, but England did so only on September 14, 1752, 170 years later! Consequently, England was 10 days out of step with the Continent until 1700, and, because England observed 1700 as a leap year, it was 11 days out of step from 1701 until 1752. Historians who need to correlate events between England and the Continent between 1582 and 1752 must be aware of this calendar difference. Although many nations changed quickly, China only adopted the Gregorian calendar in 1911 and most other countries did not change until after World War I. The Greek Orthodox church still does not recognize the Gregorian calendar! It celebrates Christmas on January 7 because the Julian calendar is now 13 days ahead of the Sun.

▰SUMMARY

Astronomy is an old science with its roots in celestial observations begun thousands of years ago. Astronomers today continue the tradition of celestial observations with sophisticated telescopes, satellites, and instrumentation. These observations, together with known physical laws, allow astronomers to construct a plausible history of the universe. The universe began as a gigantic explosion in which all the matter in the universe was created. During the first few minutes of this expansion, hydrogen and helium were produced in tremendous quantities, and after one or two billion years this matter condensed into immense systems of stars called galaxies. In many of these galaxies stars are still forming.

The Earth turns exactly once on its axis in $23^h56^m4^s$; this is, on the average, about 4 minutes faster than the time from noon to noon, or 24 hours. The revolution of the Earth around the Sun causes this difference between the sidereal day and the solar day and results in the Sun moving on the celestial sphere relative to the stars. Since the solar day regulates our clocks, we see different stars in the evening sky on different days of the year.

The fact that the Earth rotates means that the Sun is overhead in different parts of the world at different times. For example, people in New York experience noon 3 hours before people in Los Angeles. For convenience, the entire world is divided into 24 time zones, each one hour wide. Every time travelers cross a time zone, they must change their watches; one hour back if traveling west or one hour ahead if traveling east. Furthermore, travelers crossing the International Date Line must change their calendar days; going from east to west adds a day and going west to east subtracts a day.

The regularities exhibited by celestial objects due to the Earth's revolution are the basis of the calendar. Thousands of years ago humans recognized these regularities and were motivated to make careful observations of the sky. The present-day calendar takes into account the observation that the Earth does not revolve around in an even number of days. Hence leap years and leap days in the proper proportion are needed to ensure accurate calendars.

▰CHAPTER CAPSULE

Topics and Terms	Review and Remarks
Evolution of the universe	The major events in the history of the universe: The big bang marks the explosive beginning of the universe. Hydrogen and helium were created within the first few minutes. The first galaxies formed within 1 to 2 billion years. The Sun formed after 10 billion years.
Sidereal day = $23^h56^m4^s$ Solar day = 24^h	The difference is due to the revolution of the Earth around the Sun.
Time zones	Corrections to clocks and calendars due to the rotation of the Earth: Traveling west across a time zone—subtract one hour. Traveling east across a time zone—add one hour. Traveling west across the International Date Line—add one day. Traveling east across the International Date Line—subtract one day.
Calendar	Adjustments to the 365-day calendar are needed because the length of the orbital period of the Earth is not an integral number of days: 1 leap year every 4 years No leap years in certain centuries

REVIEW QUESTIONS

1. Scientists are often referred to as theorists (theoreticians), experimenters (experimentalists), or a combination of the two. Astronomers, however, are generally referred to as theorists, *observers*, or a combination of the two. Can you explain the difference? Why does this difference make Chapter 4 very important?

2. Astronomy is the oldest of the natural sciences. Why do you think scientific curiosity developed for astronomy earlier than, for example, chemistry?

3. Review the section "The Universe: A Brief History." For each paragraph write a single sentence describing its main points.

4. Briefly describe the motions of the Earth. On what evidence does your knowledge of each part of the Earth's motion depend?

5. Is civil time (the time system our clocks keep) based on the sidereal day or the solar day? What difference should this make?

6. Time zones are ideally 15° wide in the east-west direction. If it is noon at Greenwich, England, what time is it in New York City? (New York is at about 73°59′ west longitude and 40°45′ north latitude.) Should Atlanta, Georgia (84°23′ west longitude and 33°45′ north latitude) be in the same time zone as New York City? What time would it be where you are?

7. There is about 4 minutes difference between a sidereal day and a solar day. Can you explain this difference? Which is longer? Through what angle does the Earth turn in 4 minutes? Through what angle does the Earth revolve, in its orbit, in one day?

8. By about how much would the Julian and Gregorian calendars be different now?

9. We refer to a particular time as 9:00 A.M. or 1:00 P.M. To what do the A.M. and P.M. refer? Why doesn't it make sense to refer to noon or midnight as 12:00 A.M. or 12:00 P.M.?

FOR FURTHER READING

Bartky, I. R. 1987. The bygone era of time balls. *Sky & Telescope*, Jan., 32.

Kippenhahn, R. 1987. Light from the depths of time. *Sky & Telescope*, Feb., 140.

Kluepfel, C. 1982. How accurate *is* the Gregorian calendar? *Sky & Telescope*, Nov., 417.

Parker, B. 1985. Celestial pinwheels: The spiral galaxies. *Astronomy*, May, 14.

Stott, A. 1984. Greenwich: Where east meets west. *Sky & Telescope*, Oct., 300.

Wahr, J. 1986. The Earth's inconstant rotation. *Sky & Telescope*, June, 545.

ASTROPROBE 1

MathTools 1

Science uses mathematics to express the phenomena of nature, the relationships between physical quantities, and scientific laws. Virtually all of the information in astronomy, for example, is expressed in numbers. Even photographs of planets and distant star systems can be reduced to numbers (see AstroProbe 14). Scientists express their hypotheses and theories with numbers; they present observations as numbers. The advantage of using numbers is that we can manipulate them—we can add, subtract, multiply, and divide numbers. And computers do this millions of times faster than we can. Thus science depends on numbers.

You also depend on numbers. A tremendous amount of information in our society is transmitted with numbers. Sporting events are scored by numbers; the team with the largest score is the winner. Team averages and baseball batting averages are expressed with numbers as fractions. Interest rates on auto loans and home mortgages, presidential popularity polls, and humidity are expressed with numbers as percentages. Distances are expressed with numbers as miles or kilometers; temperatures are expressed with numbers as degrees Fahrenheit or Celsius. You may not be able to calculate batting averages or compute your monthly loan premium, but you do have an understanding of what these numbers mean. You realize that a batting average of .295 is better than one of .125 or that a 3.9% loan is better than one at 10%. Numbers are a necessary part of our information society.

Mathematics is the *tool* we use to manipulate numbers. A carpenter, for example, uses hammer, nails, and saw to construct a house. The framework of the house is complex, but the tools are simple. Similarly, scientists over the millennia have constructed a complex of "houses" called science. The tool used to construct the "framework" of these houses is mathematics. In this book we will investigate one of these houses—astronomy. We will explore many of its rooms and study its framework. To do this properly we must use numbers.

Just as carpenters have toolboxes to organize their tools so they are ready when needed, this text provides you with a "toolbox." It has two major compartments called **MathTools 1** and **MathTools 2**. You are reading MathTools 1; MathTools 2 is a module placed just before the appendixes. MathTools 1 and MathTools 2 are reference manuals. If you encounter a number manipulation that is unfamiliar to you or that you recall only vaguely, you can refer to MathTools 1 or MathTools 2 for an explanation and brief review. For instance, if you are reading the section of the text discussing the temperature at the center of the Earth but you are unfamiliar with temperatures given in degrees Celsius or Kelvins, you can turn to the section on temperatures in MathTools 2. In cases where you are likely to have

TABLE 1A.1 **MathTools Topics and Symbols**

MathTools 1		MathTools 2	
Topic	*Symbol*	*Topic*	*Symbol*
Powers of Ten	10^a	Proportions	a/b
Graphs and Plots		Percentages and Fractions	%
Approximation Signs	$=, \approx, \sim$	Error and Uncertainty	$\triangle$
		Units	
		Powers and Roots	$\sqrt{}$
		Angular Measurement	
		Cubes, Circles, and Squares	
		Temperature	°F/°C/K

difficulties, you will find a reference to the appropriate section in MathTools 1 or MathTools 2 in the margin. The margin notes will be in the form of MathTools 1 or 2, the section name, and the symbol; for example, "MathTools 2: Percentages and Fractions %" refers to the section called "Percentages and Fractions" in MathTools 2. The entire list of MathTools topics and symbols appears in Table 1A.1.

You will not be expected to become as proficient in mathematics as a good carpenter is with hammer and nails. MathTools 1 and 2 are to facilitate your comprehension of astronomy by providing explanations and examples of number manipulations found in the text. Use MathTools 1 and 2 as a toolbox; rummage around in them until you find the right tool. MathTools 1 covers topics that you will need right away. The first tool described is standard, or scientific, notation. It is a shorthand method for writing very large or very tiny numbers. Everywhere in the text you will encounter graphs of data. In the section called "Graphs and Plots," you will be introduced to several different kinds of graphs and shown how they are constructed. Graphs contain much information, and you will need to spend time with each one analyzing this information. When you are finished with MathTools 1, it would be a good idea to glance through MathTools 2 just to familiarize yourself with its contents.

POWERS OF TEN 10^a

Distances to planets and stars are huge numbers and the masses of atoms and electrons are tiny numbers when expressed in ordinary units such as kilometers and grams. For instance, the distance to the Sun and the mass of an electron, respectively, are written in the ordinary manner as

150,000,000 kilometers and
0.000000000000000000000000000911 grams

Normally, we express numbers as simple decimals, 1.5 inches or 9.11 pounds. This is acceptable for the kinds of numbers we encounter in everyday life, but it is extremely clumsy when very large or very tiny numbers must be manipulated. Instead, scientists reduce these large and tiny numbers to a standard form: 150,000,000 kilometers becomes 1.5×10^8 kilometers, and the mass of the electron becomes 9.11×10^{-28} grams. This standard form is also referred to as *powers-of-ten notation*.

To see how we change large or tiny numbers to standard form, let's convert the weight of 1 cubic inch of water, 0.036 pounds, to standard form. First, multiplying 0.036 by 10 gives 0.36; multiplying it by 10 again gives 3.6. That is, $0.036 \times 10 \times 10 = 3.6$. The product 10×10 is written in a special way: $10 \times 10 = 10^2$. The **exponent** "2" tells us to multiply the number 10 by itself twice—the power of ten is 2. Now if $0.036 \times 10 \times 10$ is 3.6, then 0.036 is $3.6/10^2$. In other words, to recover 0.036 we must divide 3.6 by 10^2. "Divided by 10^2" is written "multiplied by 10^{-2}," or 0.036 pounds $= 3.6 \times 10^{-2}$ pounds in standard form. Similarly, $0.2 = 2/10 = 2 \times 10^{-1}$ and $0.04 = 4/100 = 4/10^2 = 4 \times 10^{-2}$. Standard form consists of a decimal number multiplied by 10 raised to a power.

The mass of an electron can now be put into powers-of-ten notation by dividing 9.11 by 10^{28}. Since multiplying 0.000000000000000000000000000911 by 10^{28} gives 9.11, the mass of the electron is written as 9.11×10^{-28} grams in standard notation. The exponent "-28" in this case also means to move the decimal place in 9.11 to the left 28 places. The distance to the Sun, 150,000,000 kilometers, is written in standard form as 1.5×10^8 kilometers. The term 10^8 means multiplying by 10 eight times—the power of ten is 8.

In this book you will be mainly concerned with interpreting numbers in standard form. From time to time numbers will be expressed and manipulated in standard form to show how we arrive at a certain result. To ensure that you fully understand the manipulations, study the following examples of multiplication and division in standard form. To *multiply* numbers in standard notation, multiply their decimal numbers and *add* their exponents to get a new power of ten. To *divide* numbers in standard notation, divide the decimal numbers as usual but *subtract* their exponents.

TABLE 1A.2 Common Prefixes		
Factor	**Prefix**	**Symbol**
10^{12} = 1,000,000,000,000	Tera	T (trillion)
10^9 = 1,000,000,000	Giga	G (billion)
10^6 = 1,000,000	Mega	M (million)
10^3 = 1,000	Kilo	k (thousand)
10^{-2} = 0.01	Centi	c (hundredths)
10^{-3} = 0.001	Milli	m (thousandths)
10^{-6} = 0.000 001	Micro	μ (millionths)

(a) $(2 \times 10^2) \times (3 \times 10^6) = 6 \times 10^{2+6} = 6 \times 10^8$ (600,000,000)

(b) $(4 \times 10^2) \times (2 \times 10^{-6}) = 8 \times 10^{2-6} = 8 \times 10^{-4}$ (0.0008)

(c) $\dfrac{3.2 \times 10^4}{2.0 \times 10^3} = 1.6 \times 10^{4-3} = 1.6 \times 10^1$ (16)

(d) $\dfrac{6.4 \times 10^{-4}}{4.0 \times 10^3} = 1.6 \times 10^{-4-3} = 1.6 \times 10^{-7}$ (0.00000016)

Try to work out these examples to get the answer indicated:

(e) $\dfrac{5 \times 10^{-4}}{2.5 \times 10^{-3}} = 2 \times 10^{-1}$ (0.2)

(f) $\dfrac{(3.2 \times 10^{-4}) \times (5.0 \times 10^6)}{(2.0 \times 10^{-3}) \times (4.0 \times 10^2)} = 2.0 \times 10^3$ (2,000)

The standard form is simply a shorthand way of writing very large or very small numbers. We have also given names to some of the powers of ten. Table 1A.2 lists the more common names you will encounter in this text and other science textbooks. You may be familiar with the prefix "centi" in centimeter and with "kilo" in kilometer. You read about our national debt passing the "trillion" dollar mark, budget items of "billions" of dollars, and budget cuts in the "millions" of dollars. Sometimes we combine names and speak of "a thousand million" dollars instead of a billion. We can refer to very large numbers, such as $10^{21} (= 10^{3+9+9})$, as "a thousand billion billion." Of course, the standard form allows us to refer to these numbers simply as "ten to the ninth" for 10^9 and "ten to the twenty-first" for 10^{21}.

GRAPHS AND PLOTS

If you flip through the pages of this book, you will see many illustrations. Some are photographs, some are drawings, but many are

TABLE 1A.3 **World Series Winners, 1903–1989**

Year	Winner	Year	Winner	Year	Winner	Year	Winner
1903	Boston (AL)	1925	Pittsburgh (NL)	1947	New York (AL)	1969	New York (NL)
1904	No series	1926	St. Louis (NL)	1948	Cleveland (AL)	1970	Baltimore (AL)
1905	New York (NL)	1927	New York (AL)	1949	New York (AL)	1971	Pittsburgh (NL)
1906	Chicago (AL)	1928	New York (AL)	1950	New York (AL)	1972	Oakland (AL)
1907	Chicago (NL)	1929	Philadelphia (AL)	1951	New York (AL)	1973	Oakland (AL)
1908	Chicago (NL)	1930	Philadelphia (AL)	1952	New York (AL)	1974	Oakland (AL)
1909	Pittsburgh (NL)	1931	St. Louis (NL)	1953	New York (AL)	1975	Cincinnati (NL)
1910	Philadelphia (AL)	1932	New York (AL)	1954	New York (NL)	1976	Cincinnati (NL)
1911	Philadelphia (AL)	1933	New York (NL)	1955	Brooklyn (NL)	1977	New York (AL)
1912	Boston (AL)	1934	St. Louis (NL)	1956	New York (AL)	1978	New York (AL)
1913	Philadelphia (AL)	1935	Detroit (AL)	1957	Milwaukee (NL)	1979	Pittsburgh (NL)
1914	Boston (NL)	1936	New York (AL)	1958	New York (AL)	1980	Philadelphia (NL)
1915	Boston (AL)	1937	New York (AL)	1959	Los Angeles (NL)	1981	Los Angeles (NL)
1916	Boston (AL)	1938	New York (AL)	1960	Pittsburgh (NL)	1982	St. Louis (NL)
1917	Chicago (AL)	1939	New York (AL)	1961	New York (AL)	1983	Baltimore (AL)
1918	Boston (AL)	1940	Cincinnati (NL)	1962	New York (AL)	1984	Detroit (AL)
1919	Cincinnati (NL)	1941	New York (AL)	1963	Los Angeles (NL)	1985	Kansas City (AL)
1920	Cleveland (AL)	1942	St. Louis (NL)	1964	St. Louis (NL)	1986	New York (NL)
1921	New York (NL)	1943	New York (AL)	1965	Los Angeles (NL)	1987	Minnesota (AL)
1922	New York (NL)	1944	St. Louis (NL)	1966	Baltimore (AL)	1988	Los Angeles (NL)
1923	New York (AL)	1945	Detroit (AL)	1967	St. Louis (NL)	1989	Oakland (AL)
1924	Washington (AL)	1946	St. Louis (NL)	1968	Detroit (AL)		

AL represents American League; NL signifies National League.

graphs. You also see many examples of graphs in everyday life. Newsmagazines, newspapers, and television news programs use graphs to show the increase in the national debt over the years, changes in popularity polls of presidents, and the weekly rise and fall of the stock market. Graphs are used because they present a lot of information in a small space. They also help us interpret and analyze the information by allowing our eyes to compare different pieces of data. It is easier for us to comprehend collections of numbers if we see them in graphical form. For example, Table 1A.3 lists the winners of the World Series between 1903 and 1989. If you analyze the table carefully, you could answer a question such as "Which team won the most World Series?", but it might take you a while to sort through the data. Figure 1A.1 presents the same information in the form of a graph. Just a glance at Figure 1A.1 allows you to answer the question—the New York Yankees. A **graph** is a compressed format for displaying information. It is an illustration, or drawing, showing a set of data or how two or more sets of data are related to one another. Graphs that use a column, or a bar, to represent the values of a data set are called *bar charts* or *histograms*. A graph is as indispensable to a scientist as a brush is to a painter.

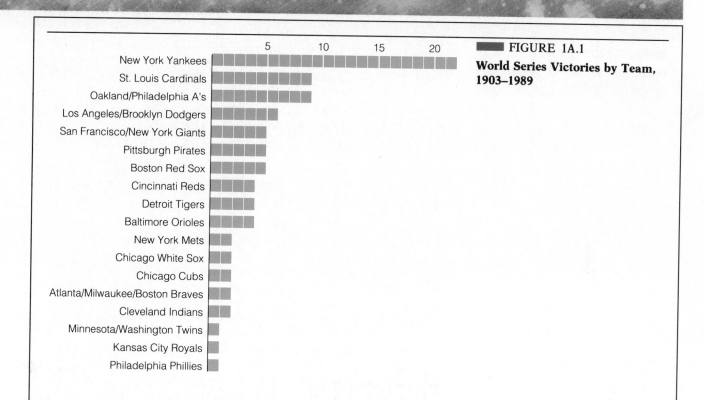

FIGURE 1A.1

World Series Victories by Team, 1903–1989

Sometimes the relationship between data sets is slight in the sense that once the data are plotted, we cannot use the graph to predict anything. For example, the World Series graph clearly shows that the New York Yankees have won more World Series than any other team. But we cannot predict from the bar chart that the Yankees or the Red Sox or the Dodgers or any other team will win the World Series next year. Another example of a graphic that cannot be used to predict is a graph of the number of moons for different planets in the solar system (Figure 1A.2). This graph can certainly help us remember which planets have the most moons and may also lead us to investigate further the relationship between the data. For instance, you will learn later that the planets Jupiter, Saturn, Uranus, and Neptune are huge planets. The graph suggests that planetary size may influence the number of moons orbiting a planet. We might next try plotting the number of moons versus planetary size. In other words, graphs can show or hint at important physical connections between data.

Let's see how we would draw a two-**variable,** or two-parameter, graph. We plot variables along *axes;* these are lines used as fixed references to determine position. One variable is plotted along a hori-

Variable: A quantity that may assume any given value or set of values.

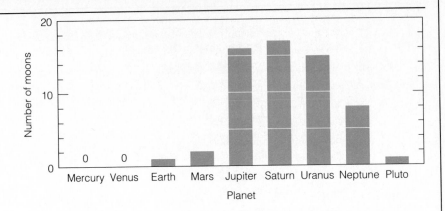

FIGURE 1A.2

Number of Moons for Planets in Our Solar System

zontal axis and the other variable along a vertical axis. We call the intersection of the two axes the *origin*. Panel a of Figure 1A.3 shows a graph of the *number of children* at summer camp on three different weekends and the *number of hot dogs* needed to feed them at the Saturday dinner. The variables are the "number of children" and the "number of hot dogs." Each point on the graph corresponds to a pair of values of the variables. The point closest to the origin, for instance, represents the pair (10 children, 20 hot dogs). To locate this point on the graph, we move along the horizontal axis (labeled "Number of hot dogs") to 20 and up to a value 10 on the vertical axis (labeled "Number of children"). The same is done for the other pairs of numbers and a point is placed at each position. In Panel b of Figure 1A.3, a line is drawn connecting the points. We can use this line to predict the number of hot dogs needed for numbers of children not represented in the table in Panel a. For example, if 50 children attend a future summer camp, we predict, using the line in Panel b, that 100 hot dogs will be needed. In this example, a close relationship exists between the number of children attending summer camp and the number of hot dogs needed to feed them.

It is sometimes useful to connect the points representing data pairs even if the line will not be used to predict something. Panel a in Figure 1A.4 shows a graph of the average speed of the winners of the Indianapolis 500 auto race for each year from 1949 to 1988. Here a line is drawn through the points for each data pair although the points themselves are not shown on the graph. We did the same for the one-mile land speed records in Panel b. Both graphs show a variable, speed, as a function of the year, another variable. In neither case can we use the graph to predict the speed of the next year's winner or a future record. The Indy 500 data show a general trend of increasing speed of the winning cars. The trend is not definite be-

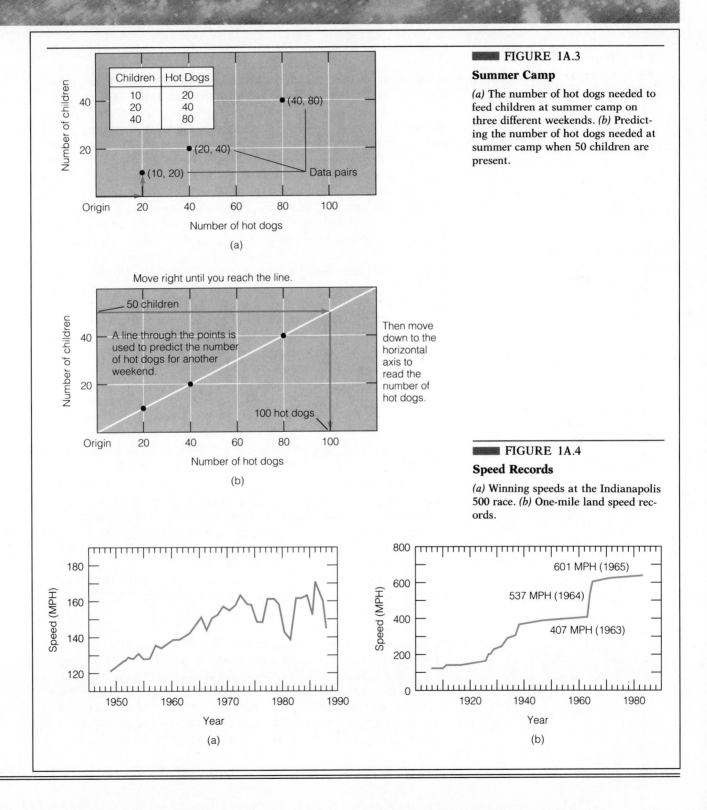

FIGURE 1A.3

Summer Camp

(a) The number of hot dogs needed to feed children at summer camp on three different weekends. *(b)* Predicting the number of hot dogs needed at summer camp when 50 children are present.

FIGURE 1A.4

Speed Records

(a) Winning speeds at the Indianapolis 500 race. *(b)* One-mile land speed records.

cause the average speed of a particular race depends on the conditions of the track, the weather, and the number of crashes. The graph of the speed records is also not predictive. On the other hand, these data are interesting in that they show definite jumps in speed. Between about 1925 and 1938 speeds increased from 175 MPH to about 400 MPH. Then in the early 1960s speeds made another jump, this time to about 600 MPH. Although we cannot predict the next record, we can probably guess that it will not rise much above 600 MPH until some technological breakthrough occurs. Graphs can be useful even when they are not predictive.

Sometimes data can be represented by an **equation,** a mathematical expression signifying the equality between two quantities. Physical laws describing phenomena, such as gravity, expansion of gases, or molecular binding, can be represented by equations. Let's consider a simple equation: $Y = \frac{1}{2}X$. Can you "visualize" this equation? You can if you make a graph of it. This can be done by constructing a table of X and Y values. The insert in Panel a in Figure 1A.5 shows such a table; it was constructed by choosing values of X and then calculating the corresponding Y values. For example, when $X = 0$, Y also equals 0; when $X = 1$, $Y = \frac{1}{2} \times 1$, or $\frac{1}{2}$; when $X = 2$, $Y = \frac{1}{2} \times 2$, or 1. The arrows in Panel a show how you would plot the data pairs in the table: move to the X value from the origin and up a distance equal to the Y value, just as we did with children and hot dogs. You can place as many points on the graph as you wish. You would soon notice, however, that these data can be represented by a straight line. Once you notice this, you could just plot enough points to allow you to draw a straight line with a ruler. The graph shown

■■■ FIGURE 1A.5

Graphing an Equation

(a) Graphing the equation $Y = \frac{1}{2}X$.
(b) Graphing the equation Distance = 50 MPH × time.

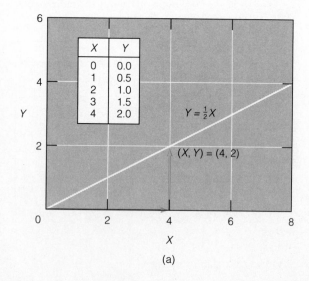

(a)

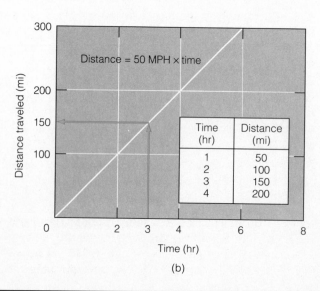

(b)

in Panel b is an example familiar to those who take vacations by car. It is a plot of the function "distance = 50 MPH × time." It shows how far you will travel in a given time interval at an average speed of 50 MPH. As with the data in Panel a, the relationship is a straight line, or *linear*. We can now use this line to estimate the distance traveled for any length of time on the road. In 3 hours, for example, you would travel 150 miles. When the variables are closely related, such as time, distance, and speed or hot dogs and children, we are able to see a clear relationship between the variables in a graph.

We sometimes have to deal with variables that cover a huge range of values. For example, the temperature at the surface of the Sun is several thousands of degrees, but the temperature at the center is tens of millions of degrees—an increase of a factor of several thousand. If we tried to plot the inward increase in temperature of the Sun in equal temperature intervals, we would need a huge piece of paper for a graph, as Panel a in Figure 1A.6 suggests. If we let 10,000° correspond to 0.64 cm (0.25 in), we would need a sheet of graph paper 34 feet long. We can reduce our paper needs by plotting the temperature axis in powers of ten; that is, let every major division mark on the axis be ten times the previous mark (Panel b). Instead of the axis increasing as 20,000, 40,000, 60,000, it increases as 10^4, 10^5, 10^6, 10^7. Such a scale is called a **logarithmic** scale. The vertical axis in Panel b starts at a temperature of 1,000° and increases to 100 million degrees. Although the logarithmic scale is useful for plotting, it is not as easy to read the axis. If you look closely at Panel b, you will notice that the short marks between the major divisions are unevenly spaced. Between 1,000° and 10,000° they represent 2,000°, 3,000°, 4,000°, 5,000°, 6,000°, 7,000°, 8,000°, and 9,000°; between 10^4 and 10^5 they represent 2×10^4, 3×10^4, 4×10^4, 5×10^4, 6×10^4, 7×10^4, 8×10^4, and 9×10^4. We can represent a large range of a variable by using a logarithmic scale. When two parameters cover a large range, both axes are drawn logarithmically.

Many times in science we plot data that appear to be related but the relationship is not clear. For instance, Panel a in Figure 1A.7 shows a graph of the heights and weights of students who have studied astronomy at Clemson University. This is what we might call a *scatter* diagram; the data seem to be scattered all over the graph. With this kind of data, we try to find the relationship between the variables. Careful inspection of Panel a does show trends, however. Tall students are generally heavier than short students. The trend is from the lower right corner of the graph to the upper left corner. The scatter, in this case, simply reflects the variation in the heights and weights of humans. For any height we see a range of weights; for example, students 5'8" tall weigh from 115 pounds to 210 pounds. We can try to define a typical or average height-weight curve by drawing

■ FIGURE 1A.6

Logarithmic Graphs

(a) Temperature distribution in the Sun plotted with a linear scale along the vertical temperature axis.
(b) Temperature distribution in the Sun plotted logarithmically.

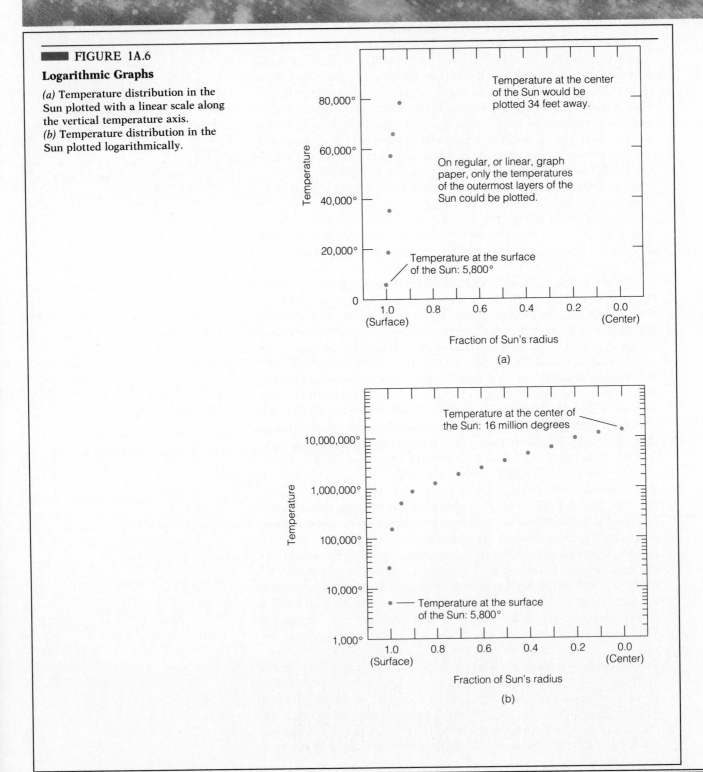

(a)

(b)

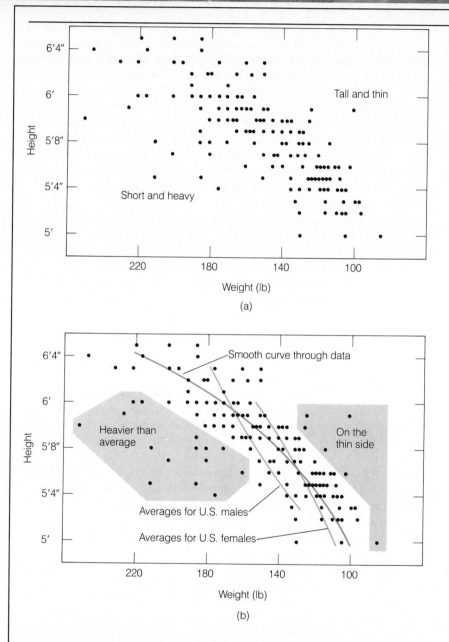

FIGURE 1A.7

Height-Weight Diagram for Students

(a) Distribution of heights and weights of Clemson University students.
(b) Distribution of heights and weights of Clemson students with a curve drawn through the data; also shown are the average distributions for U.S. males and females.

a *smooth curve* through all of the data points. One such curve is shown in Panel b. We see a greater range in weights toward the left of the average line, indicating that most of the students who do not lie near the "average" curve are heavier than average. Also shown are the average heights and weights of men and women as tabulated by the American Medical Association. You see immediately that the student average curve is clearly different from the male and female average curves. You can explore this graph further, possibly discovering more trends or reasons for the differences in the three average curves. The point is that graphs can reveal relationships and trends in data that we might never notice by looking at tables of data.

Graphs reveal data and relationships between data. A graph can show a large quantity of data clearly, such as the bar chart of World Series winners. A graph can be a scatter plot from which we have to work hard to find any relationships between the data, such as the student height-weight diagram. Some data sets are very closely related, and a graph allows us to make predictions, such as the number of hot dogs eaten by children. Even when data sets are not closely related enough to allow definite predictions, trends may still be discovered, such as the increase over time of Indy 500 winning speeds. Trends and relationships, whether simple or complex, are most easily discovered through graphs.

APPROXIMATION SIGNS: =, ≈, ~

When you see the expression "$\pi = 3.142$," you have a pretty good idea that the quantity π (the Greek letter pi) equals 3.142. The symbol "$=$", read "equals" or "equals to," is your clue. In science, the last digit of a number, in this case 2, is understood to be unreliable. All we denote here is that the last digit of π we have written is closer to 2 than to either 1 or 3. The quantity π is the geometrical constant that gives the ratio between the circumference of a circle and its diameter. It is a very accurately determined number; calculations in 1989 using a Cray-2 supercomputer determined π's decimal expansion to over a billion digits. If we satisfy ourselves with just five or six digits, we will be able to see why the "2" in 3.142 is uncertain. To five decimal places, $\pi = 3.14159$. Look at the last three digits, 159. Since 159 is closer to 200 than 100, we *rounded* it to 200 and ignored the zeros, giving us 3.142. If we kept the zeros, we would imply that π equals 3.14200 with only the last zero uncertain.

Many times in science, as well as in everyday life, we make approximations. We might try to estimate the cost of groceries as we wait in the checkout line to make sure we have enough money or how long a certain trip will take so we can plan when to leave. In these cases we are not looking for an exact value of a quantity. We only need an approximate number, such as the nearest dollar for the groceries or the nearest half-day for a cross-country trip. To indicate such an approximation, we use the symbol "$\approx$" to mean "approxi-

MathTools 2: Angular Measurement

mately equals." We would write our estimate of groceries or the length of a trip as

$$\text{Groceries} \approx \$5.00$$

and

$$\text{Length of trip} \approx 3\tfrac{1}{2} \text{ days}$$

Sometimes we just need a very rough estimate and may write $Y \sim 1,000$, meaning Y is closer to 1,000 than to 10,000 or to 100. The symbol "$\sim$" means an "order of magnitude," or within a factor of 10. Order of magnitude estimates are often sufficient; the temperature is warm enough to paint the house; the rock is heavy enough to hold down the paper; the wind is strong enough to fly a kite. When numbers are expressed in standard notation, such as $X = 2.62 \times 10^3$ or $Y = 7.5 \times 10^6$, we can write approximations as

X approximately equals 3×10^3 and X is on the order of 10^3
Y approximately equals 7×10^6 and Y is on the order of 10^7

You have completed your first inspection of one compartment of your "toolbox." You may rummage around in the second compartment, MathTools 2, now or continue on in the text. Do not hesitate to use these tools; refer to them often. Review the tools inside them whenever a mathematical operation or a graph confuses you. The less confused you are about numbers, the better you will understand the concepts presented in the text.

CHAPTER 2

The Naked Eye Universe

OUTLINE

The Apparent Celestial Motions of the Stars
At the Poles and the Equator
At Intermediate Latitudes

The Apparent Celestial Motions of the Sun
Spring and Fall
Summer and Winter
The Rest of the Year

Lunar Phases

Eclipses
Solar Eclipses
Lunar Eclipses
Eclipse Seasons

The Apparent Celestial Motions of the Planets
Inferior Planets
Superior Planets
Retrograde Motion

Summary

Chapter Capsule

Review Questions

For Further Reading

███████ **ASTROPROBE 2:**
Archaeoastronomy

Navajo Stargazer.
ARTIST: Trudy Griffin-Pierce.

THE SUN, MOON, STARS, AND PLANETS appear to move in the sky. Their motions can be tracked without sophisticated instruments and traced back to the spin of the Earth and its revolution around the Sun. From most places on Earth a viewer can observe the stars rising and setting, but at two locations the stars neither rise nor set. The Sun's motions are slightly more complex than those of the stars. Sometimes the Sun is high in the sky, at other times it stays low in the sky throughout the day. At certain locations on the Earth the Sun stays above the horizon for six months at a time and remains below the horizon the other six months.

The Moon also changes its position in the sky during the day and night. In addition, it changes its appearance from a thin sliver of light to a full disk. Under the right celestial conditions, the Moon may cover the Sun or be engulfed by the shadow of the Earth, causing eclipses in both cases. Planets exhibit their own brand of celestial acrobatics by making "loops" on the celestial sphere as both they and the Earth race around the Sun. The reasons for all these apparent motions are the subject of this chapter.

THE APPARENT CELESTIAL MOTIONS OF THE STARS

The Sun appears to rise each morning, move slowly across the sky during the day, and then set. Stars exhibit similar motions in the night sky. Stars appear to rise in the east and move slowly across the sky toward the west, tracing out an arc on the celestial sphere. In fact, if an observer remains at a fixed place on Earth, the stars always rise and set at the same places on the horizon. These apparent motions are caused by the Earth's turning on its axis of rotation. As the Earth turns from west to east, the celestial sphere and all the stars appear to turn in the opposite direction. The particular paths that stars follow across the sky during the night depend on the viewer's exact location on Earth.

At the Poles and the Equator

Imagine the Earth's axis of rotation as a long line that passes through the Earth and extends outward at both poles to the celestial sphere above the Earth's poles. The places where this imaginary line meets the celestial sphere mark the *celestial north and south poles* (Figure 2.1). The celestial sphere appears to turn about an axis passing through the celestial poles, but this apparent rotation of the celestial sphere is just a reflection of the Earth's rotation.

The celestial north pole is relatively easy to locate from the Northern Hemisphere because it lies within 1° of the direction of Polaris, the North Star. No bright star lies in the direction of the south celestial pole, so we do not have a "South Star." Midway between the north and south celestial poles lies the *celestial equator*, the projection of the Earth's equator onto the celestial sphere. It is conceptually important to realize that although the celestial sphere is described as the inside of a globe for convenience, in reality no spherical "surface" exists in space.

See the "Observer's Handbook" for instructions on how to find the Big Dipper and Polaris.

FIGURE 2.1

The Celestial Poles and Equator

The celestial poles and equator are projections of the Earth's poles and equator onto the celestial sphere.

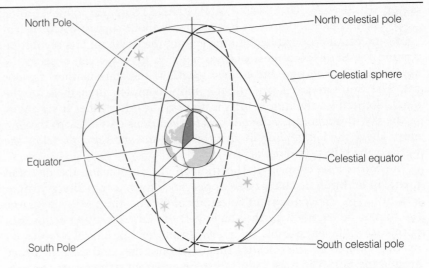

Now suppose you are standing at the Earth's North Pole. The north celestial pole is directly overhead at your zenith, and the sky appears to spin around that point as the Earth turns. A time exposure photograph shows a portion of the circular paths that stars follow around the north celestial pole (Figure 2.2). Since the exposure time for this photograph was just over 10 hours, only part of the stars' paths were recorded. At both the North and South Poles, the stars appear to move in circles, parallel to the horizon, never rising or setting (Figure 2.3). They always

FIGURE 2.2

Stars at the South Pole

This time exposure photograph shows the circular arcs made by stars around the south celestial pole in 10½ hours.

SOURCE: Copyright Anglo-Australian Telescope Board 1980. Photograph by David Malin.

remain above the horizon and, if it is dark, as it is in winter, are visible for 24 hours.

Now imagine that you are standing at the equator. The sky appears to rotate around the celestial poles, both of which are now on the celestial horizon, one directly north and one directly south. The stars appear to move straight up in the east and straight down in the west (Figure 2.4). Furthermore, at the equator the stars are visible for only 12 hours instead of for 24 hours as at the poles.

Where should you stand on Earth to see all of the stars on the celestial sphere that are visible to the naked eye? At the equator! Although you can see only half of both celestial hemispheres at any moment at the equator, the turning of the Earth causes more stars to come into view as the night progresses. After the Earth turns halfway around, you will have seen all the stars in both hemispheres except, of course, those rising and setting in the glare of the Sun.

At Intermediate Latitudes

Before we describe the motions of stars seen from places other than the poles or the equator, we need to consider how the view of the celestial sphere is affected by the observer's position on the Earth's surface. Positions on Earth between the equator and the poles are called **latitudes** (Figure 2.5). Latitude is an angular distance and is measured north or south from the equator to either pole. The latitude is 0° at the equator and 90° at the poles.

Now place yourself at the equator again and imagine walking toward the North Pole. You would notice that Polaris, which starts out on the northern celestial horizon, moves higher and higher in the sky as you move farther and farther north and would be overhead when you reached the North Pole. Moving through 90° of latitude from the equator to the North Pole shifts Polaris 90° in **altitude** from the horizon to the zenith (Figure 2.6). For every degree of latitude moved toward the pole, Polaris shifted one degree above the horizon. Therefore, the altitude of Polaris above the horizon equals the observer's latitude in the Northern Hemisphere. For example, in Atlanta, 34° north of the equator, the altitude of Polaris is 34°. This relation between Polaris and latitude is very useful for navigation because a navigator can easily deter-

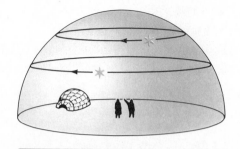

■■■ FIGURE 2.3

Stars at the North and South Poles

At the Earth's poles the stars appear to circle around the celestial poles, never rising or setting, and are visible for 24 hours.

Latitude: An angle measured from the center of the Earth either north or south of the equator.

Altitude: The angular distance of a star, a planet, the Moon, or the Sun above the horizon measured along a line running from a point on the horizon exactly below the object toward the observer's zenith.

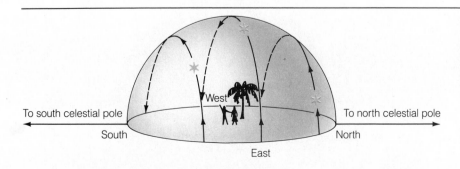

■■■ FIGURE 2.4

Stars at the Equator

At the equator stars appear to rise straight up and set straight down at the horizon and are visible for 12 hours.

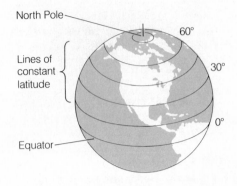

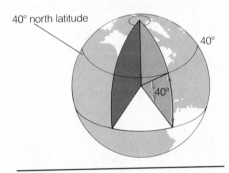

FIGURE 2.5

Latitude

mine a ship's latitude in the Northern Hemisphere by measuring the altitude of Polaris.

While you watched Polaris rise above the horizon as you moved north, stars that were on the southern horizon when you started disappeared from view. For example, by the time you reach Atlanta, stars within 34° of the celestial south pole are not visible; they lie *below* the southern horizon. In addition, stars within 34° of the celestial north pole always circle *above* the horizon; they never set. Stars that are always visible at night or stars that are never visible from a given latitude on Earth are called **circumpolar stars.** For New York at a latitude of 41°, circumpolar stars are those within 41° of the celestial poles; for Thule, Greenland, at a latitude of 75°, circumpolar stars are those within 75° of the celestial poles. At the equator, no stars are circumpolar, while at either pole, all stars are circumpolar. Thus the latitude of the observer determines which stars are circumpolar.

Whereas circumpolar stars either stay above or below the horizon, stars between the northern and southern circumpolar stars rise and set. The apparent path of a star on the sky during a complete rotation of the Earth is called its **diurnal circle.** Part of a noncircumpolar star's diurnal circle is above the horizon and part is below the horizon. The portion of the diurnal circle above the horizon as seen from a given latitude on Earth determines how long a star is visible at night.

From a vantage point in the Northern Hemisphere, more than half of the diurnal circle of a star north of the celestial equator lies above the horizon (Figure 2.7). Accordingly, these stars spend more than 12 hours above the horizon. Their paths are long arcs across the sky, starting north of east and ending north of west. Exactly half of the diurnal circle of stars with positions that coincide with the celestial equator lies above the horizon. These stars spend exactly 12 hours above the horizon; that is, they rise due east and, 12 hours later, set due west. For stars south of the celestial equator, less than half of their diurnal circle lies above the horizon. These stars spend most of their time below the horizon, invisible to us, and their celestial paths are very short arcs across the sky. These stars rise south of east, set south of west, and spend less than 12 hours above the horizon.

FIGURE 2.6

Altitude

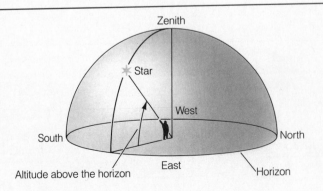

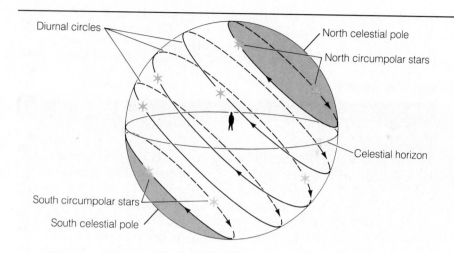

FIGURE 2.7

The Celestial Sphere from a Latitude of 45° in the Northern Hemisphere

Stars with diurnal circles that are either completely above or below the celestial horizon are circumpolar stars. The length of time other stars stay above the horizon depends on how much of their diurnal circle is above the celestial horizon.

THE APPARENT CELESTIAL MOTIONS OF THE SUN

The celestial motion of the Sun is more complex than that of the stars. First, the Sun moves across the sky from the eastern horizon to the western horizon each day. Like the apparent motion of the stars, this is due to the Earth's rotation. Secondly, the Sun's noontime altitude changes from day to day. In the Northern Hemisphere summer, for example, the noontime Sun is high in the sky; in the winter it is low in the sky. This is caused by the constant tilt of the Earth's axis of rotation relative to its orbital plane. The third apparent motion of the Sun is its yearly drift eastward on the celestial sphere relative to the stars; this is due to the Earth's revolution around the Sun.

This section describes these apparent motions of the Sun, starting with its motion on four well-known days of the year: the first day of spring, summer, fall, and winter. Figure 2.8 shows the orientation of the

The Sun's apparent motions:

1. *Daily:* Across the sky from east to west.
2. *Yearly:* North and south shift.
3. *Yearly:* Eastward on the celestial sphere.

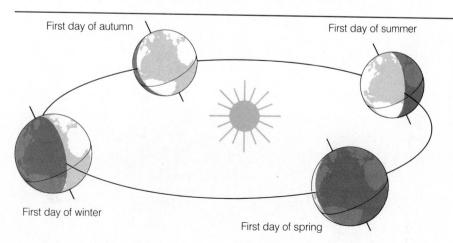

FIGURE 2.8

Solstices and Equinoxes

The orientation of the Earth and Sun on the first day of summer, autumn, winter, and spring in the Northern Hemisphere.

Earth's axis of rotation for these four days. Once the motion of the Sun on these days is understood, it will be much easier to visualize how the Sun appears to move during the rest of the year.

Spring and Fall

The first day of spring, the **spring,** or **vernal, equinox,** occurs on March 20 or 21, and the first day of fall, the **autumnal equinox,** occurs on September 22 or 23. The dates of the equinoxes vary slightly because the length of the year is slightly longer, by nearly 6 hours, than the 365-day calendar year. Every year the time of the equinox moves up by about 6 hours, but during a leap year, the equinox dates are moved back one day as an extra day is added to the calendar. The term *equinox* comes from the Latin *aequus* meaning "equal," combined with the Latin *nox*, meaning "night"; thus an equinox is a time when night and day are of equal length. At the equinoxes, the Sun is above the celestial horizon for 12 hours.

The Sun rises *directly* east and sets *directly* west on these dates. People realize, of course, that the Sun always rises in the east, but it rises directly, or due, east only on the equinoxes. The directions *due east* and *due west* refer specifically to the points where the celestial equator crosses the celestial horizon. At the North or South Pole, for instance, the celestial equator coincides with the celestial horizon. Now imagine walking toward the equator from the North Pole. The celestial equator directly ahead of you will appear higher and higher in the sky until it is directly overhead at the equator. At the same time, the horizon behind you blocks the celestial equator from view as you head south. Consequently, only half of the celestial equator is above the horizon and visible during your trip south. The celestial equator appears to pivot on the horizon to your left and right (Figure 2.9). The "pivot" points where the celestial equator crosses the horizon are the east and west points, defining due east and due west.

At the time of the spring and autumnal equinoxes, the Sun's diurnal circle coincides with the celestial equator. This means that the path of the Sun on the sky is exactly along the celestial equator. Consequently, the Sun must rise due east and set due west. Furthermore, since only half of the celestial equator is above the horizon on any day, only half of the Sun's diurnal circle is above the horizon on these two days. As a

▬▬ FIGURE 2.9

The Noontime Sun at the Equinoxes at a Latitude of about 45°

The daily path of the Sun across the sky coincides with the celestial equator. The celestial equator intersects the horizons in the east and west at due east and due west, respectively.

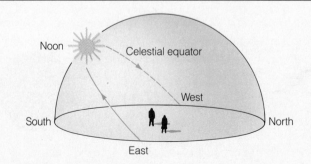

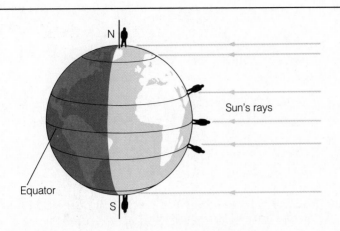

FIGURE 2.10

The Earth at the Equinoxes, March 20 or 21 and September 22 or 23

The Sun is directly over the Earth's equator and shines on both poles.

result, the Sun spends only 12 hours above the horizon (Figure 2.10). In addition, the Sun is directly overhead at noon for people on the equator. At either pole, the Sun will be right on the celestial horizon and will therefore be visible for 24 hours.

Summer and Winter

The first day of summer occurs on June 21 or 22 in the Northern Hemisphere. We refer to this day as the **summer solstice.** On this day the Sun is as high, or as far north, as it gets in the sky all year. The daily path of the Sun on the first day of summer lies north of the celestial equator (Figure 2.11). The Sun's position in the sky will be 23½° north of the position it had at either equinox because the Northern Hemisphere is tilted 23½° toward the Sun at the solstice relative to the equinoxes. Consequently, the noontime Sun will be directly overhead places on Earth with latitudes of 23½°. This latitude is given a special name, the **Tropic of Cancer.** Furthermore, since more than half of the diurnal circle of the Sun is above the horizon, the Northern Hemisphere receives more than 12 hours of sunshine.

The first day of winter occurs on December 21 or 22 in the Northern Hemisphere and is called the **winter solstice.** The conditions at winter solstice are opposite those at summer solstice. The Sun is as low, or as far south, as it gets during the year. At this time the Southern Hemi-

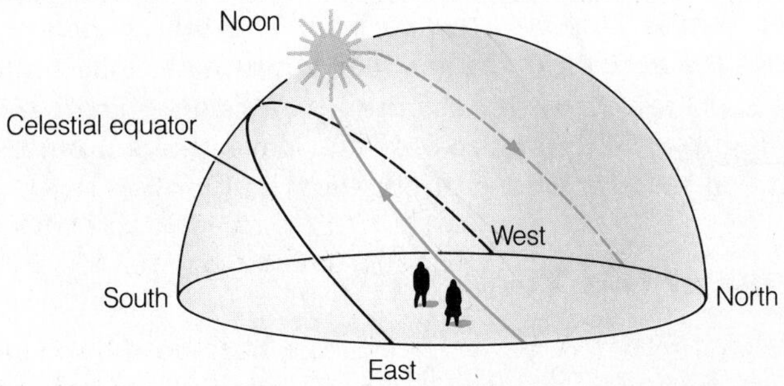

FIGURE 2.11

The Noontime Sun at the Northern Hemisphere Summer Solstice

The long summer days occur because most of the Sun's diurnal circle is above the horizon.

■ FIGURE 2.12

The Noontime Sun at the Northern Hemisphere Winter Solstice

The short days occur because only the small portion of the Sun's diurnal circle is above the horizon.

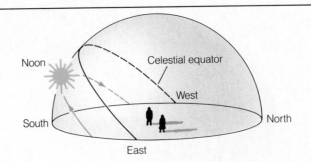

sphere is tilted toward the Sun. The daily path of the Sun on the first day of winter lies 23½° south of the celestial equator (Figure 2.12). This means that the noontime Sun will be directly overhead places on Earth with southern latitudes of 23½°. This latitude is called the **Tropic of Capricorn.** Furthermore, the Southern Hemisphere will now receive more than 12 hours of sunshine each day while the Northern Hemisphere receives less than 12 hours. As viewed from the Northern Hemisphere, less than half of the Sun's diurnal circle is above the horizon.

At summer solstice the Northern Hemisphere is tilted toward the Sun, and daylight at the North Pole on the first day of summer lasts 24 hours. The complete diurnal circle of the Sun is 23½° above the horizon. The Sun does not rise *or* set at the North Pole on the summer solstice. In fact, for all of the region north of latitude 66½° in the Northern Hemisphere, the Sun does not rise or set on the summer solstice. This latitude is called the **Arctic Circle** (Figure 2.13). When the Sun is visible for 24 hours, including midnight, it is called the *midnight sun*. Farther south, where part of the Sun's diurnal circle dips below the horizon, fewer hours of sunshine result. Furthermore, in the Southern Hemisphere at this time, the length of the day decreases for latitudes approaching the South Pole. In fact, at a southern latitude of 66½° the Sun does not rise! This latitude is called the **Antarctic Circle.** During the Northern Hemisphere summer solstice, areas of the Earth south of the Antarctic Circle experience no sunrise, and the South Pole is dark all day long.

Figure 2.14 summarizes the apparent path of the Sun at the equinoxes and solstices for the Northern Hemisphere. Both the noontime altitude of the Sun and the amount of time it spends above the horizon differ on these dates. The summer Sun is high in the sky at noon while the winter Sun is closer to the horizon. The Sun spends most of 24 hours above the horizon in the summer, resulting in long summer days. The Sun's short arc across the sky in the winter gives short winter days. Although Figure 2.14 applies to only four days, the Sun moves continuously between these positions throughout the year.

The Rest of the Year

The Sun's eastward motion relative to the stars on the celestial sphere defines a path called the **ecliptic.** On the equinox dates the Sun is di-

Ecliptic: The apparent annual path of the Sun projected onto the celestial sphere; it defines the orbital plane of Earth's orbit.

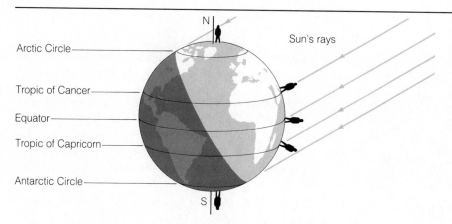

Arctic Circle
Tropic of Cancer
Equator
Tropic of Capricorn
Antarctic Circle

Sun's rays

(a) Summer solstice (June 21–22)

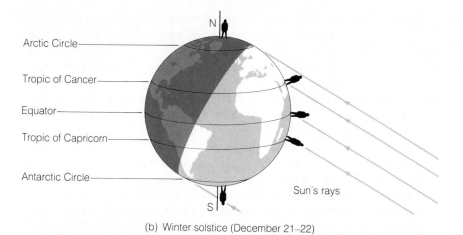

Arctic Circle
Tropic of Cancer
Equator
Tropic of Capricorn
Antarctic Circle

Sun's rays

(b) Winter solstice (December 21–22)

■■■■ FIGURE 2.13

The Earth at Summer and Winter Solstice

(a) At summer solstice all regions north of the Arctic Circle receive 24 hours of sunshine. *(b)* At winter solstice all regions south of the Antarctic Circle receive 24 hours of sunshine.

rectly on the celestial equator. Actually, the Sun is crossing the celestial equator. We know it is crossing because at the solstices the Sun is either north or south of the celestial equator. At the spring equinox, for instance, the Sun is crossing the celestial equator from south to north. In other words, not only do the equinoxes and solstices refer to certain dates in the year, they also represent specific locations on the celestial sphere (Panel a of Figure 2.15). The solstices, for instance, mark the extremes in the position of the Sun relative to the celestial equator. To better visualize the Sun's path between these extremes, the celestial sphere can be drawn on a flat surface just as Earth's globe is drawn on a flat map.

Panel b of Figure 2.15 shows the region of the sky near the celestial equator. Imagine cutting the strip shown in Panel b at the autumnal equinox and then unfolding it (Panel c). The unfolded strip (Panel d) shows the ecliptic and the celestial equator. From September 23 to December 22, the Sun reaches lower and lower noontime altitudes and then moves north toward the celestial equator between December 22 and March 21. At the spring equinox the Sun is crossing the celestial

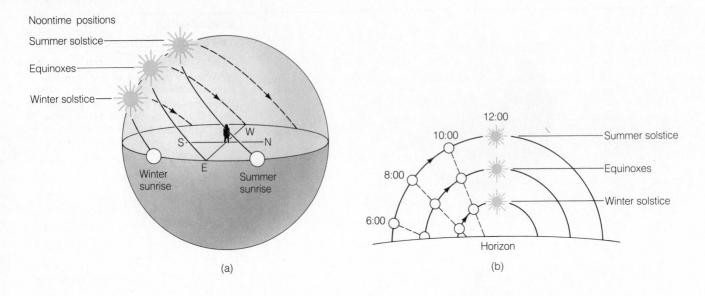

Noontime positions

Summer solstice

Equinoxes

Winter solstice

S   W   N

E

Winter sunrise

Summer sunrise

(a)

12:00

10:00   Summer solstice

8:00   Equinoxes

6:00   Winter solstice

Horizon

(b)

███ **FIGURE 2.14**

The Position and Path of the Sun for the Summer and Winter Solstices and Both Equinoxes for Latitude of about 45°

Twilight: Interval of time preceding sunrise and following sunset during which the Earth's surface is partially illuminated by sky brightness; the Sun is below the horizon during twilight.

equator from south to north and continues moving north until the summer solstice. Following the summer solstice, the Sun moves south on the celestial sphere once again and completes its movement around the ecliptic as it crosses the ecliptic going from north to south at the autumnal equinox.

Now that we have described the motion of the Sun for the whole year, we can ask how long is the day at the North Pole? Certainly at the summer solstice the North Pole enjoys 24 hours of sunshine. What about June 20 or June 23? How many hours of sunshine are there on those days? The answer is also 24 hours. The Earth's poles do not have normal days and nights; they have "light seasons" and "dark seasons." These terms refer to the times when the Sun is above or below the horizon for more than 24 hours. For instance, sunrise at the North Pole occurs on the vernal equinox and sunset on the autumnal equinox; the light season at the North Pole is 6 months long. During this 6-month period the Earth is tilted in such a way that the North Pole is always facing the Sun. Of course, the dark season at the North Pole, from the autumnal equinox to the vernal equinox, is also 6 months long. The light and dark seasons at the South Pole are of the same duration but reversed in time (Figure 2.16).

At latitudes between the Arctic and Antarctic Circles and the poles, the population experiences one light season that lasts less than 6 months, one dark season that also lasts less than 6 months, and periods in between of normal 24-hour cycles of day and night. For example, the dark season at Thule, Greenland, at a latitude of about 75° north, lasts 3 months from early November to early February. This means that the Sun sets in November and does not rise again until February. Although the Sun does not rise during the dark season, Thule receives between 7 and 9 hours of **twilight** during each 24 hours.

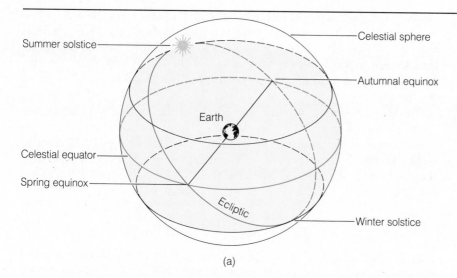

(a)

■■■ **FIGURE 2.15**

Visualization of the Ecliptic

(a) The celestial sphere with the ecliptic.
(b) The section of the celestial sphere
within about 30° of the celestial equator.
(c) Unfolding the section near the celestial
equator shown in Panel b. *(d)* The unfolded, or flat, map of the region near the
celestial equator showing the ecliptic.
MathTools 1: Graphs and Plots

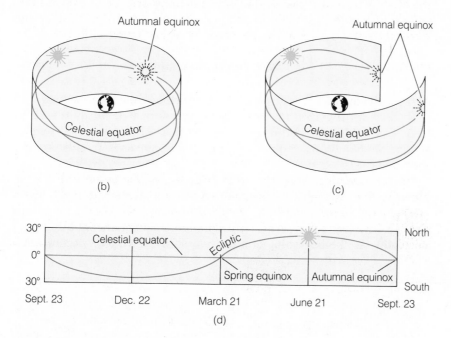

(b)   (c)

(d)

■■LUNAR PHASES

Although the Moon is not as bright as the Sun, it has nevertheless attracted much attention throughout history. The Moon not only changes
its position on the celestial sphere during the day or night, the month,
and the year, it changes its appearance as well. Throughout the month,
the Moon appears in different shapes, from the round face of a full
moon to the silver curve of a thin crescent moon. These shapes, or

■ FIGURE 2.16

The Christmas Tree at Thule Air Base, Greenland

The Christmas tree is erected in November to kick off the dark season and stays up until the return of the Sun in February.

SOURCE: Department of the Air Force.

phases, are part of a continuous light and shadow act played by the Sun and Moon. The Sun provides the illumination; the Moon reflects the light toward us. The portion of the illuminated side of the Moon that we see depends on the orientation of the Earth and Moon relative to the Sun. This depends on the position of the Moon in its orbit about the Earth.

The Moon revolves around the Earth in the same direction as the Earth rotates (Figure 2.17). The Moon's orbital motion can be detected with careful observations in an evening. The Moon takes 27.32 days to circle the Earth once relative to the stars, moving from west to east in the sky. This is the sidereal period of the Moon. Consequently, the Moon appears to move eastward on the sky by about 13° each day:

$$\frac{360°}{27.32 \text{ days}} \approx 13° \text{ per day}$$

This 13° daily motion of the Moon means that if the Moon is on the meridian next to a star one evening, at the same time the next evening the Moon will be 13° east of that star. Furthermore, for the Moon to be on the meridian again, the Earth must turn eastward 13°. Since the Earth turns 15° per hour, the extra 13° takes just under an hour:

$$\frac{13°}{15°} \times 60 \text{ minutes} \approx 52 \text{ minutes}$$

As a result, the Moon will rise and set about an hour later each day.

Throughout its orbit, the Moon keeps the same side facing the Earth because the Moon's orbital period is identical to its rotational period; that is, the Moon turns on its axis at the same rate as it revolves around the Earth.

Lunar phases are changes in the fraction of the sunlit side of the Moon visible to observers on Earth. When the sunlit half of the Moon faces away from the Earth, the Moon cannot be seen. Astronomers call this phase **new moon** because ancient lunar calendars usually designated this as the beginning of a lunar month. New moon occurs when

■ FIGURE 2.17

Revolution of the Moon

The Moon revolves around the Earth in the same direction as the Earth turns, west to east.

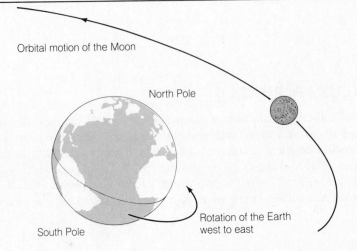

the Moon lies between the Earth and the Sun. Consequently, the Moon is positioned on the celestial sphere near the Sun and rises and sets with the Sun even though we are unable to see it.

Imagine yourself as a lunar colonist in a settlement in the lunar Alps, which are located about 60° north of the lunar equator facing the Earth (see the map of the Moon in the Observer's Handbook). At new moon, colonists would experience nighttime because the colony is on the dark side of the Moon. At the same time they are in the dark, they view the side of the Earth that faces the Sun. The Earth is fully illuminated; colonists will surely refer to this phase of Earth as "full Earth." As the Earth slowly turns, new areas of the planet are brought into view on the sunlit side—it is morning (Figure 2.18). At the same time, areas on the opposite side of the Earth are rotated out of the sunlit side—the Sun is setting there.

As the Moon moves around the Earth, the orientation of the Earth and Moon relative to the Sun changes. The Moon moves out of alignment between the Earth and the Sun and, little by little, begins to show us more of its sunlit hemisphere. At first only a very thin crescent is visible near the western horizon at sunset. Because the crescent moon is very close to the brilliant Sun in the sky, it is sometimes very difficult to find. A crescent moon in the western sky is usually seen at sunset when it is at least 2 days old; that is, 2 days past new moon. As the days pass, more and more of the lighted hemisphere of the Moon becomes visible as the Moon sets later and later each day. The crescent phases last for about a week and are called **waxing crescents.**

Remember: Half of the Moon is always lighted by the Sun; the other half is shaded.

Waxing: Derives from the Old English *weaxan* meaning "to grow" and is used to designate times when the Moon's visible lighted portion increases in size.

■■■ FIGURE 2.18

Imaginary View of the Full Earth from the Lunar Alps

The Earth is turning from left to right. People on the left are just waking up to dawn; those on the right are viewing sunset. Since the Moon is at new moon, no one on Earth will see it.

Earth-Moon-Sun Geometry

The top panels shows the orientation of the Earth, Moon, and Sun for three phases of the Moon. The view from the Earth shows the Moon as it would look to an observer standing on the Earth. In this figure and similar ones in this section, only the portion of the Moon on the Earth side of the line drawn through the Moon can be seen by an observer on Earth. The lower panels show the appearance of the sky for the two observers shown in the top panels.

A 4-day old waxing crescent moon, for instance, rises about 4 hours after the Sun. At noon, it is about halfway between the meridian and the eastern horizon (Panel b in Figure 2.19). The Moon and Sun maintain roughly this orientation in the sky throughout the day, changing slightly because the Moon is moving eastward relative to the stars faster than the Sun. As a result, a 4-day old moon sets about 4 hours after the Sun and is visible in the evening sky (Panel c).

About a week after new moon, half of the side of the Moon facing the Earth is sunlit. This is **first-quarter moon.** The Moon has traversed one quarter of its orbit, sets about 6 to 7 hours after the Sun, and is due south at sunset (Panel f in Figure 2.19). The Sun and the Moon are 90° apart in the sky; this orientation remains roughly the same throughout the day. For instance, at sunrise the first-quarter moon is on the other side of the Earth and cannot be seen. Similarly, at noon, the first-quarter moon is just rising (Panel e).

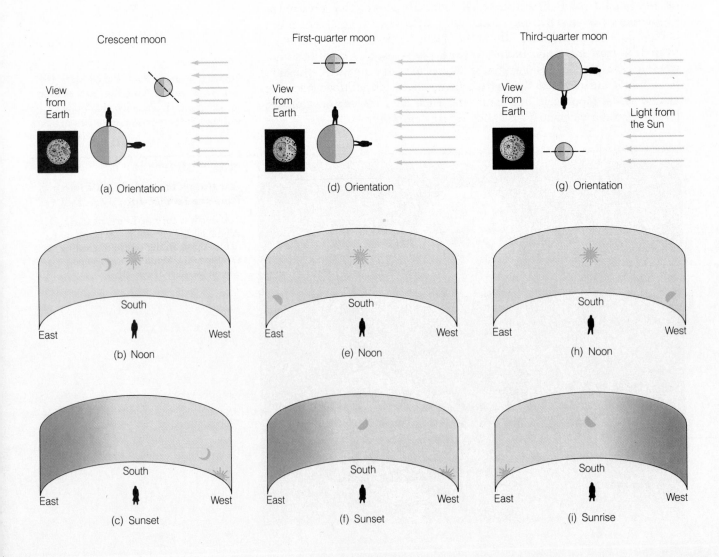

(a) Orientation

(d) Orientation

(g) Orientation

(b) Noon

(e) Noon

(h) Noon

(c) Sunset

(f) Sunset

(i) Sunrise

The Moon takes another week to pass from first quarter to full. At **full moon** the entire lighted hemisphere of the Moon faces Earth. We call it "full" moon although only half of the total lunar surface area is sunlit. During this second week, the fraction of the sunlit face visible from Earth grows from half illuminated at first quarter to fully illuminated at full moon. We call these phases, between first quarter and full, **waxing gibbous** (Figure 2.20). The term *gibbous* refers to a shape that is convex at both edges. When the Moon is full, the Earth lies between the Moon and the Sun. Consequently, the full moon rises when the Sun sets and sets when the Sun rises. At midnight, the full moon is due south.

From the lunar Alps at the time of full moon, colonists will probably call the appearance of the Earth "new Earth" because its sunlit side faces away from the Moon. It was noted earlier that at the time of new moon the Earth is full. In other words, as viewed from the Moon, the Earth also cycles through phases, but their order is opposite that of the Moon's. In between full and new Earth, the Earth passes through gibbous, quarter, and crescent phases. At first-quarter moon, the Sun rises in the lunar Alps while the Earth is at quarter phase. As the Earth hangs immobile in the lunar sky and the Sun slowly rises higher and higher, the phase of the Earth changes from quarter to new.

The second half of the Moon's orbit is the reverse of the first half. About two weeks after full moon, the Moon is again at new moon ready to start its cycle over. The term **waning,** from Old English *wanian*

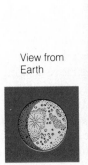

View from Earth

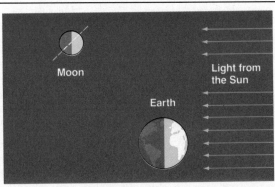

Moon

Light from the Sun

Earth

(a) Waxing gibbous

View from Earth

Moon

Earth

Light from the Sun

(b) Full moon

■■■ FIGURE 2.20

Orientation of the Earth, Moon, and Sun at Waxing Gibbous and Full Moon

■ FIGURE 2.21

Orientation of the Earth, Moon, and Sun at Waning Gibbous and Waning Crescent

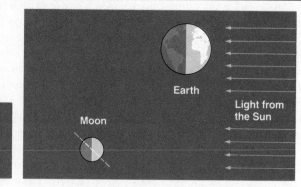

View from Earth

Earth

Moon

Light from the Sun

(a) Waning gibbous

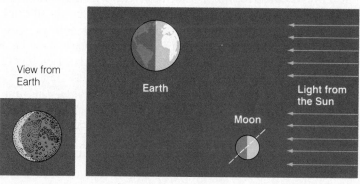

View from Earth

Earth

Light from the Sun

Moon

(b) Waning crescent

■ TABLE 2.1

Moonrise and Moonset

Phase	Moonrise	Moonset
New moon	Sunrise	Sunset
First-quarter	Noon	Midnight
Full moon	Sunset	Sunrise
Third-quarter	Midnight	Noon

meaning "to decrease," is used to describe the continuous decrease in the fraction of the illuminated side of the Moon visible from Earth during these last two weeks of the lunar month. We then have waning gibbous and waning crescent (Figure 2.21).

Third-quarter moon occurs about three weeks after new moon and marks the end of the waning gibbous phase. At this time the Moon has traversed three quarters of its orbit, hence the name third quarter. Because the Moon at third quarter is on the opposite side of its orbit than it was at first quarter, the half of the facing lunar hemisphere illuminated at first quarter is now dark, and the half that was dark at first quarter is now illuminated. Because the Earth turns toward sunrise, the third-quarter moon is in the dawn sky before the Sun (Panel i in Figure 2.19). At sunrise the third-quarter moon is due south on the meridian and will set at noon (Panel h). Table 2.1 summarizes the times of moonrise and moonset at the various phases.

During the last week of the Moon's orbit, the **waning crescent** phase, the crescent becomes narrower and narrower until the Moon cannot be seen. This is new moon where our description of lunar phases began.

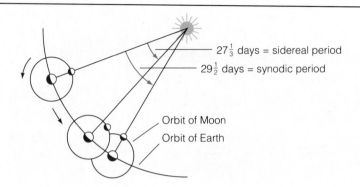

27⅓ days = sidereal period

29½ days = synodic period

Orbit of Moon
Orbit of Earth

■■■ FIGURE 2.22
Synodic Period

Because the Earth-Moon system has moved partly around the Sun during one sidereal period, the Moon needs 2 more days to reach conjunction again.

Although the Moon needs about 27.32 days to orbit the Earth, it takes longer to complete its cycle of phases. As the Moon orbits the Earth, the Earth-Moon system also orbits the Sun. At new moon, the Earth, Moon, and Sun are lined up with the Moon between the Earth and the Sun (Figure 2.22). After 27.32 days the Moon has gone around the Earth exactly once but, because the Earth-Moon system has also moved around the Sun by about 27°, the Moon will not lie between the Earth and the Sun. The Moon needs to move farther around in its orbit to be lined up between the Earth and the Sun again. Since the Moon moves 13° each day, it needs another 2 days and 5 hours. The period from new moon to new moon is called the **synodic period** of the Moon: 29.53 days.

The phases of the Moon represent different viewing orientations in the Sun-Earth-Moon system in which observers on Earth see different fractions of the Moon illuminated. More dramatic variations in the Moon's appearance occur when the Sun, the Earth, and the Moon lie in a straight line. In these orientations, the Moon can block the light from the Sun or hide in the shadow of the Earth. These events are called eclipses.

■■■ ECLIPSES

Eclipses are the result of the Moon or Earth entering the other's shadow. Two types of eclipses can occur: solar eclipses and lunar eclipses. During a **solar eclipse** the Moon's shadow sweeps across parts of the surface of the Earth. During a **lunar eclipse** the Moon passes through the Earth's shadow. Thus eclipses are ways by which we can detect the shadows of the Earth and the Moon. During a solar eclipse, we detect the shadow of the Moon; during a lunar eclipse, we detect the shadow of the Earth.

The Moon and the Earth create cone-shaped shadows that have definite lengths because the light source—the Sun—is larger than either the Earth or the Moon. Celestial shadows produced by the Sun are structured into two parts. The inner region, called the **umbra,** is dark. For viewers within the umbra, the Sun is completely blotted out during a

Eclipse: Derived from the Greek *ekleipsis* meaning "abandonment"; the Sun or Moon abandons us during an eclipse.

Length of the Earth's shadow: 1,384,860 km (860,000 mi)

Length of the Moon's shadow: 375,080 km (232,920 mi)

■■■■ FIGURE 2.23

Eclipse Shadows

The shadow of a planet or the Moon caused by the Sun has two parts: an *umbra* that has no illumination and a *penumbra* that has only partial illumination. The cross sections of the shadows are circular as shown on a flat surface inserted into the shadows.

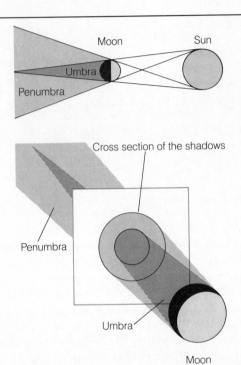

total solar eclipse. Outside the umbra, where only part of the Sun can be seen, the illumination or brightness is reduced. This partially lighted area surrounding the umbra is called the **penumbra,** from the Latin *paene* meaning "almost" and *umbra* meaning "shade or shadow" (Figure 2.23).

Solar Eclipses

Solar eclipses are dramatic, out-of-the-ordinary events. In the past when a solar eclipse plunged them into darkness, our ancestors cowered in fear, afraid that something had gone wrong with the universe and that the sunlight had disappeared forever. Today solar eclipses are not frightening because we understand their causes, but they are still one of nature's extraordinary occurrences.

Solar eclipses occur because the Moon's shadow is longer than the distance between the Moon and the Earth at the Moon's closest approach to the Earth during its orbit (Figure 2.24). As it happens, the Sun's diameter is about 400 times larger than that of the Moon, but the Sun is 400 times farther away from the Earth than the Moon. As viewed from the Earth, the Moon and Sun have the same apparent, or *angular*, diameter. Consequently, the Moon can completely cover the Sun. This does not happen at every eclipse, however. Figure 2.24 shows that, although the Moon's umbral shadow is long enough when the Moon is closest to the Earth, it does not reach the Earth's surface when the Moon is farthest from the Earth.

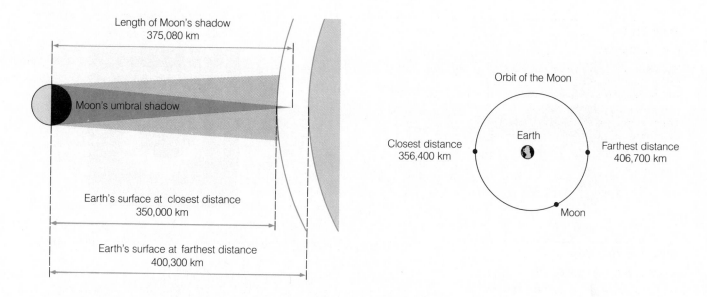

Length of Moon's shadow
375,080 km

Moon's umbral shadow

Earth's surface at closest distance
350,000 km

Earth's surface at farthest distance
400,300 km

Orbit of the Moon

Earth

Closest distance
356,400 km

Farthest distance
406,700 km

Moon

If the shadow of the Moon reaches the Earth's surface, observers within the shadow's umbra will experience a **total solar eclipse** (Figure 2.25). A solar eclipse begins when the Moon just starts to cover the Sun. As the Moon covers more and more of the Sun, the Sun appears as a thinner and thinner crescent (Figure 2.26). During this time the amount of sunlight reaching observers in the penumbral shadow is steadily decreasing, resulting in an eerie "twilight." Plants and animals are fooled into behaving as if it were dusk. Fifteen to 30 minutes before the Sun is completely covered, animals begin their "bedtime behavior," and even automated streetlights turn on.

Totality is the climax of a total solar eclipse. In the darkness birds stop singing, and stars and planets are visible. The Sun, which was slowly being transformed into a thin sliver of light by the Moon, is suddenly aglow from the light of its corona, or outer atmosphere (Figure 2.25), which is otherwise too faint to be seen in the bright daylight sky (see Chapter 12 for more on the corona). The duration of totality is the time it takes for the Moon's umbral shadow to move across a spot on the Earth. This in turn depends on the width and speed of the umbral shadow as it sweeps across the Earth's surface. Totality typically lasts a few minutes, but may last up to 7½ minutes or come and go in a matter of seconds.

The speed of the Moon's shadow across the Earth is the difference between the Moon's orbital speed around the Earth and the rotation-caused speed of a point on the Earth's surface that the shadow passes over. The Moon's average orbital speed is its orbital circumference divided by its orbital period:

$$\textbf{Moon's orbital speed} = \frac{2\pi \times 384{,}401 \text{ km}}{27.32 \text{ days}} = 3690 \text{ km/h}$$

Because the Earth turns once in 24 hours as one solid body, the speed of a given location on Earth depends on latitude. At the equator, a per-

■ **FIGURE 2.24**

The Moon's Orbit and Shadow

The Moon's orbit is not circular. Because the distance between the Moon and the Earth varies, the Moon's shadow sometimes does not reach the Earth's surface. The distances shown in the orbital diagram refer to distances measured between the centers of the Earth and the Moon. In the shadow diagram, distances are measured from the center of the Moon to the Earth's surface. Moon and its shadow not drawn to scale.

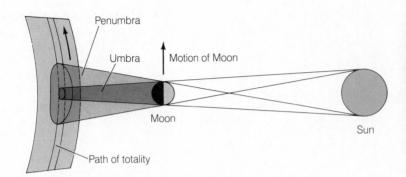

Eclipse watcher's view
during a total solar eclipse

■ FIGURE 2.25

A Total Solar Eclipse

During a total solar eclipse the observer
on Earth is in the umbral shadow of the
Moon.

SOURCE: Photo insert J. M. Pasachoff/Visuals
Unlimited.

son turns through the 40,075 km circumference of the Earth in 24 hours.
This corresponds to a

$$\text{Speed at the equator} = \frac{\text{circumference}}{24 \text{ hours}} = \frac{40,075 \text{ km}}{24 \text{ hours}} = 1670 \text{ km/h}$$

Therefore, the Moon's shadow travels across the Earth's equator at an
average speed of 3690 km/h − 1670 km/h = 2020 km/h. Because the
Moon's orbital speed is faster than that of the Earth's rotation, the narrow umbral shadow travels west to east across Earth's surface. The
maximum width of the Moon's umbral shadow is 270 km, so that the
length of time for totality is 270 km divided by 2020 km/h, approximately 8 minutes. Detailed calculations that consider the faster speed
of the Moon when it is closest to the Earth and its shadow is largest
give the maximum possible duration for a total eclipse of 7½ minutes.
At 40° latitude, where the circumference is only 30,760 km, the speed is

■ FIGURE 2.26

**The Crescent Sun during a Total
Solar Eclipse**

As the Moon moves eastward in its orbit,
it covers more and more of the Sun's visible disk.

SOURCE: J. M. Pasachoff/Visuals Unlimited.

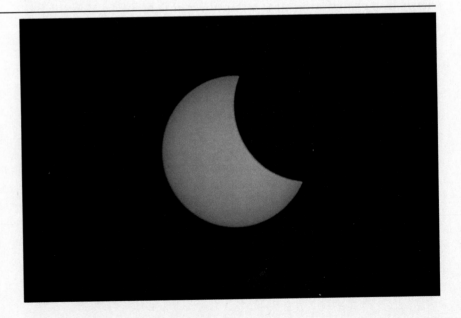

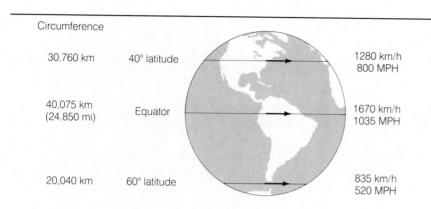

Circumference

30,760 km	40° latitude	1280 km/h 800 MPH
40,075 km (24,850 mi)	Equator	1670 km/h 1035 MPH
20,040 km	60° latitude	835 km/h 520 MPH

■■■■ ■ FIGURE 2.27

Latitude and Rotational Speed

The rotational speed of any location on Earth depends on its latitude.

only 1280 km/h (Figure 2.27). The Moon's shadow crosses the Earth's surface 20% faster than at the equator so that the maximum length of totality is only 6 minutes.

The path of the lunar umbral shadow across the surface of the Earth is called the *path of totality*. The maximum width of the umbra is less than 270 km, but the penumbra can blanket a vast area with a diameter of 6000 km centered on the umbral path (Figure 2.28). Those in the penumbra see the Sun only partially covered by the Moon. The further they are from the path of totality, the smaller the fraction of the Sun they see covered. An eclipse viewed from the penumbra is called a *partial eclipse*.

Often the Moon is too far away for the umbra to reach the Earth's surface, in which case observers at the shadow's center do not see the Moon completely cover the Sun (Figure 2.29). Instead, the Moon covers all but a ring, or *annulus*, of sunlight when it is directly in front of the Sun. For this reason these occurrences are called "annular" eclipses. The thin circle of sunlight seen during an annular eclipse is generally bright enough to prevent us from seeing the pale corona. Nevertheless, it still becomes noticeably dark and cool. Animals and plants react as if it were evening, and streetlights may turn on.

For a solar eclipse to occur, the Moon must always be between the Earth and the Sun. Solar eclipses occur, therefore, only at new moon.

Lunar Eclipses

Whereas the Earth enters the Moon's shadow to produce a solar eclipse, the Moon enters the Earth's shadow to produce a lunar eclipse. The Earth's shadow is, of course, directly opposite the Sun. Accordingly, lunar eclipses can take place only when the Moon is opposite the Earth from the Sun, or at full moon.

Whereas the very tip of the Moon's shadow cone sweeps across a small portion of the Earth's surface during a solar eclipse, the entire Moon can be engulfed in the Earth's shadow during a lunar eclipse. The Earth's umbral shadow is about 4 times longer than that of the Moon, and the diameter of the Earth's shadow at the average distance of the Moon is about 9000 km. The penumbral shadow is about 16,000 km

■ FIGURE 2.28

Two Views of the Solar Eclipse of June 30, 1973

(a) The small dark area was the size of the umbral shadow, and the larger shaded area was the size of the penumbral shadow. The penumbral shadow becomes darker as the umbral shadow is approached. The double line shows the actual path of the umbral shadow; in this path the eclipse was total. *(b)* This figure shows the Earth, Moon, and the Moon's shadows as viewed from north of the Moon's orbit. Starting from the bottom, it shows the movement of the lunar shadows across the Earth.

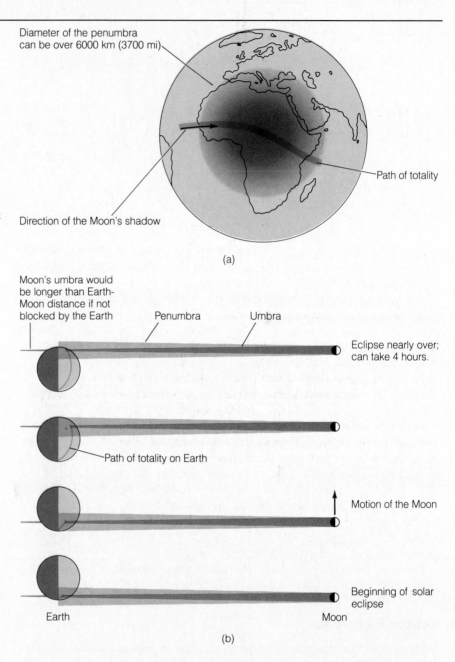

Diameter of the penumbra can be over 6000 km (3700 mi)

Path of totality

Direction of the Moon's shadow

(a)

Moon's umbra would be longer than Earth-Moon distance if not blocked by the Earth

Penumbra   Umbra

Eclipse nearly over; can take 4 hours.

Path of totality on Earth

Motion of the Moon

Beginning of solar eclipse

Earth   Moon

(b)

wide (Table 2.2). If the Moon passes through the center of the shadow, it takes 1¾ hours to go from one end of the umbra to the other. It can take as long as 6 hours to pass through both the umbral and penumbral shadows. The passage takes less time if the geometry of the eclipse is such that the Moon passes either above or below the center of the umbra (Figure 2.30).

The Moon does not *completely* disappear from view while in the Earth's umbral shadow. Most of the time the Moon is a faint, coppery-

■ TABLE 2.2 **Shadow Diameters**

	Moon's Shadow	Earth's Shadow
Umbra	270 km	9,000 km
Penumbra	6,000 km	16,000 km

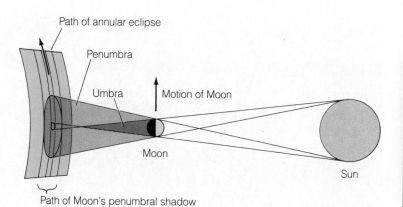

Eclipse watcher's view during an annular solar eclipse

red sphere inside the umbra. The visibility and color of the Moon in the umbra depend on the conditions in the Earth's atmosphere. Some light from the daytime side of the Earth is always scattered into the umbral shadow. Minute dust particles and gas in the atmosphere are responsible for this scattering. The Moon has a reddish hue while it is in the umbral shadow for the same reason sunsets are red—red light, more than any other color, can pass through a thick layer of an atmosphere.

To lunar colonists, a lunar eclipse viewed from the Moon will be much more spectacular than a solar eclipse viewed from the Earth. It will be a solar eclipse! The entire Moon is plunged into darkness as the Sun passes behind the Earth. Every colonist on the lunar hemisphere facing the Earth will experience a total solar eclipse (if the entire Moon passes through the umbral shadow). Furthermore, such a solar eclipse would last much longer, up to 1¾ hours, than one viewed on Earth. The reason, of course, is that the angular diameter of the Earth as viewed from the Moon is almost 4 times that of the Sun (Figure 2.31). On the other hand, since the Earth would appear so much larger than the Sun,

■■■ **FIGURE 2.29**

An Annular Eclipse

During an annular eclipse the observer on Earth may be directly below the Moon, but the umbral shadow of the Moon does not reach the surface of the Earth.

SOURCE: Photo insert official U.S. Naval Observatory photograph.

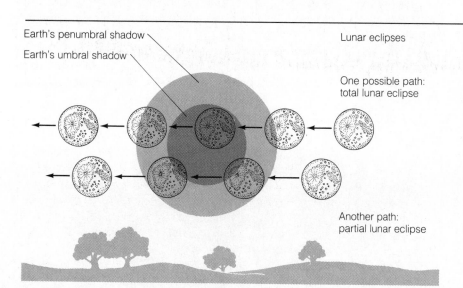

■■■ **FIGURE 2.30**

Lunar Eclipses

The Moon passes through the Earth's shadow during a lunar eclipse. The upper sequence results in an umbral or total lunar eclipse because the entire Moon enters the Earth's umbra. The lower sequence results in a penumbral or partial eclipse of the Moon since only part of the Moon enters the Earth's umbra.

■■■ FIGURE 2.31

Relative Sizes of the Sun and the Earth from the Moon

From the surface of the Moon, the angular diameter of the Earth is almost 4 times larger than that of the Sun.

the solar corona would not be visible. Since the Earth's atmosphere is able to pass on light from the sunlit side to its dark side, lunar observers would see a ring of light surrounding the Earth.

Eclipse Seasons

Eclipses can only occur at either new or full moon. If the Moon's orbit were in the same plane in space as that of the Earth, the Moon would trace out a monthly path on the celestial sphere identical to the ecliptic and an eclipse would occur at every new and full moon. The Moon's orbit, however, is tilted just over 5° relative to the ecliptic. As a result, only two places in the Moon's orbit, called the *nodes*, coincide with the ecliptic.

The tilt of the Moon's orbit relative to the plane of Earth's orbit is shown in Figure 2.32. The two points, N and N', where the Moon's orbit crosses the plane of the Earth's orbit are the nodes. The line connecting

■■■ FIGURE 2.32

The Line of Nodes

Positions N and N' are the nodes of the Moon's orbit. The line of nodes, line NN', passes through the center of the Earth and lies on the Earth's orbital plane.

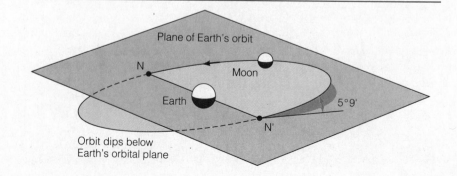

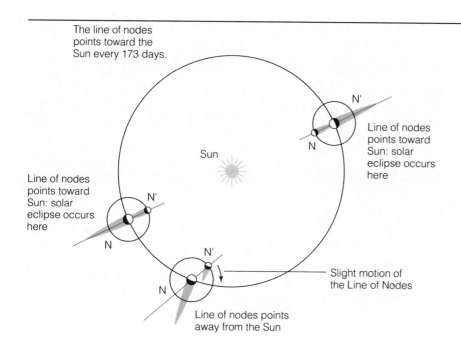

The line of nodes points toward the Sun every 173 days.

Line of nodes points toward Sun: solar eclipse occurs here

Sun

Line of nodes points toward Sun: solar eclipse occurs here

Slight motion of the Line of Nodes

Line of nodes points away from the Sun

■■■ FIGURE 2.33

Shifts in the Line of Nodes

The motion of the Earth-Moon system around the Sun causes the line of nodes, line NN′, to point away from the Sun. The line of nodes actually has a slight motion so that eclipses can occur less than a half a year apart.

them that passes through the Earth is called the **line of nodes.** When the line of nodes points toward the Sun, eclipses can occur if the Moon happens to be at N or N′ at the time.

Eclipses do not occur each month because the line of nodes keeps a relatively fixed orientation in space. As the Earth-Moon system orbits the Sun, the line of nodes points in about the same direction relative to the stars but away from the Sun. The gravitational interaction between the Sun, the Moon, and the Earth does cause the line of nodes to shift slowly westward in the sky relative to the stars (Figure 2.33). In one year the line of nodes moves about 19° on the sky but in the opposite direction as the Sun moves relative to the stars. Consequently, the line of nodes points to the Sun every 173.3 days, just a little less than half a year. Eclipses can only occur during those periods, called *eclipse seasons*, in which the line of nodes points at the Sun.

An eclipse occurs if the line of nodes points directly at the Sun *and* if the Moon is near a node. This happens at last twice a year (Table 2.3). In addition, because the time between three eclipse seasons, 346.6 days, is less than the tropical year of 365.24 days, it is possible to have three eclipse seasons in a year if the first eclipse season starts in early January. The second eclipse season would then start in late June or early July leaving time for part of an eclipse season in late December. This is the case in 1991 and 1992 shown in Table 2.3.

Table 2.3 illustrates several of the time scales associated with eclipses. The successive solar and lunar eclipses are all nearly half of an eclipse year apart. They are not exactly 173.3 days apart because, although the line of nodes points directly at the Sun every 173.3 days, the Moon and Sun only need to be near the line of nodes for an eclipse to

■■■ TABLE 2.3 Visible Solar and Lunar Eclipses: 1985–1992

Year	Solar Eclipse	Lunar Eclipse
1985	May 19 Nov. 12	May 4 Oct. 28
1986	Apr. 9 Oct. 3	Apr. 24 Oct. 17
1987	Mar. 18 Sept. 11	— Oct. 7
1988	Mar. 29 Sept. 23	— Aug. 27
1989	Mar. 7 Aug. 31	Feb. 20 Aug. 17
1990	Jan. 26 Jul. 22	Feb. 9 Aug. 6
1991	Jan. 15 Jul. 11 —	— — Dec. 21
1992	Jan. 4 Jun. 30 —	— Jun. 15 Dec. 10

■■■ TABLE 2.4
Known Planets of the Solar System

Mercury
Venus
Earth
Mars
Jupiter
Saturn
Uranus
Neptune
Pluto

take place. Moreover, the solar and lunar eclipses that take place in the same eclipse season do so within two weeks of each other. For example, in 1986, the October 17 lunar eclipse occurred 176 days after the April 24 lunar eclipse and 14 days after the October 3 solar eclipse. Furthermore, successive yearly eclipses occur about 11 days earlier each year. The lunar eclipse on February 9, 1990, occurs 11 days earlier than the lunar eclipse on February 20, 1989. The same occurs with the solar eclipses on January 26, 1990, and January 15, 1991.

■■■THE APPARENT CELESTIAL MOTIONS OF THE PLANETS

The Sun and the Moon are the brightest celestial objects, and astronomers in antiquity paid much attention to them. Their diligent observations allowed them to construct accurate calendars and even to predict eclipses. The much fainter objects called planets were also studied in ancient times. In particular, early astronomers noticed that their motions were not nearly as predictable as those of the Sun, Moon, and stars.

Nine planets are known to orbit the Sun, but only five, Mercury, Venus, Mars, Jupiter, and Saturn, are readily visible to the unaided eye (Table 2.4). Over the course of a night, the apparent motion of any one of these planets is a steady, slow westward drift across the sky similar to the daily motions of the Sun and stars; this motion is the result of the Earth's rotation. If you carefully watch these planets from night to night, however, you will notice that they move relative to the stars and the Sun. The name **planet** is based on this apparent motion; it is derived from the Greek *planetes* meaning "wanderer."

Astronomers refer to the planets with orbits closer to the Sun than the Earth as **inferior planets;** these are Mercury and Venus. They are seen in the evening or morning skies. Astronomers call those planets that are more distant from the Sun than the Earth the **superior planets;** they are Mars, Jupiter, Saturn, Uranus, Neptune, and Pluto. Only the first three of these were visible to astronomers before the invention of the telescope (Figure 2.34). The relative motions of the Earth and these

■■■ FIGURE 2.34

Inferior and Superior Planets Visible to Early Astronomers

The names of the superior planets are shown in bold type.

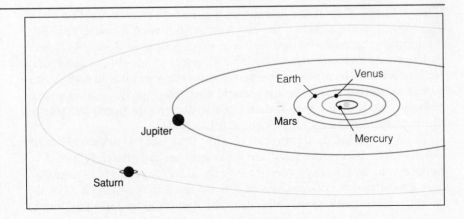

planets cause the apparent complexity of the celestial motions of the planets. Here we discuss each group of planets separately.

Inferior Planets

Figure 2.35 shows the orbits of Venus and the Earth for four configurations as seen from the direction of the north celestial pole. From this vantage point the planets orbit the Sun in a counterclockwise direction with the inner planet, Venus, traveling faster than the Earth.

Venus is closest to the Earth at **inferior conjunction** (Panel a of Figure 2.35) when it lines up between the Earth and the Sun. Most of the time the orbit of Venus, as well as that of Mercury, takes it either above or below the Sun as seen from the Earth. Although the overwhelming brightness of the Sun makes viewing Venus or Mercury at inferior conjunction very difficult, astronomers occasionally can see them transit in front of the Sun.

As Venus swings around the Sun, its apparent motion in the morning sky from day to day is away from the Sun. The angular separation between Venus and the Sun is called **elongation** (Figure 2.36). It starts at

Elongation: The angular distance between a planet and the Sun.

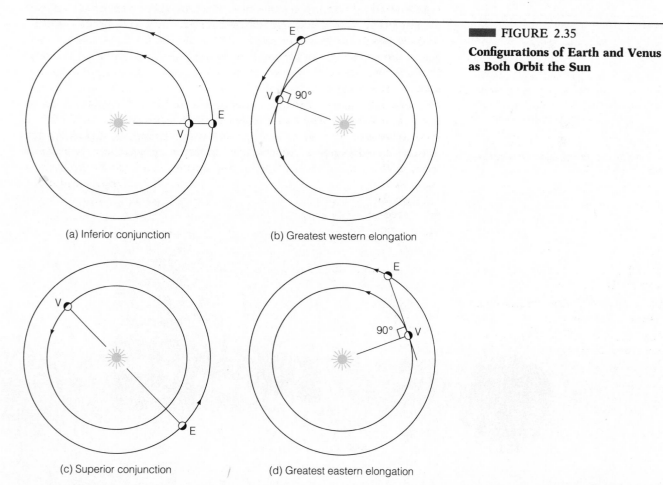

(a) Inferior conjunction

(b) Greatest western elongation

(c) Superior conjunction

(d) Greatest eastern elongation

■■■■ ■ FIGURE 2.35

Configurations of Earth and Venus as Both Orbit the Sun

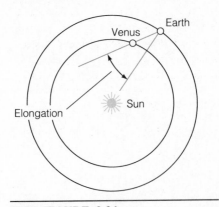

■ **FIGURE 2.36**

Elongation

0° at inferior conjunction when the Sun and Venus line up and increases to a maximum at its *greatest western elongation* (Panel b of Figure 2.35). We use the term "western" elongation because Venus is then west of the Sun in the morning sky (Figure 2.37). The greatest western elongation of Venus is about 46°. Consequently, Venus can rise about 3 hours before the Sun. Mercury's greatest western elongation varies between 18° and 28°. This variation is due to Mercury's orbit not being very circular. At greatest western elongation Mercury can rise from 1 to 2 hours before the Sun. Because Mercury is always very close to the Sun, it is only visible in evening or morning twilight and, as a result, is very difficult to view. Venus and Mercury seen before sunrise are called "morning stars."

As both Earth and Venus continue to circle the Sun, Venus reaches **superior conjunction** when it is on the opposite side of the Sun from the Earth (Panel c of Figure 2.35). Venus, as well as Mercury, is very difficult to observe at superior conjunction because of its visual proximity to the Sun. Eventually, Venus comes out of the glare of the Sun and reaches its *greatest eastern elongation* as an "evening star" (Panel d of Figure 2.35). At this time Venus is east of the Sun and sets after the Sun.

At one time ancient astronomers thought there were four inferior planets because they did not realize that Mercury and Venus could be both evening and morning stars. They called Mercury *Apollo* when it was a morning star and *Mercury* when it was an evening star. Venus also had two names: as a morning star Venus was called *Phosphorus* and as an evening star *Hesperus*.

Figure 2.38 summarizes the annual paths of both Mercury and Venus relative to the Sun. The figure shows them at greatest elongation at the same time, but they do not go through the different configurations in unison. As each planet moves from inferior conjunction to greatest western elongation, it rises earlier and earlier each day. From greatest

■ **FIGURE 2.37**

Venus as a Morning Star

Because Venus is west of the Sun in the sky and because the Earth turns toward the east, we see Venus at greatest western elongation before we see the Sun in the morning. *(a)* The observer sees Venus but not the Sun yet. *(b)* The observer sees Venus in the morning sky as a "morning star" while the Sun is just about to rise above the horizon.

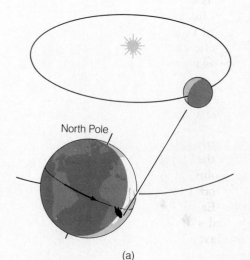

(a)

(b)

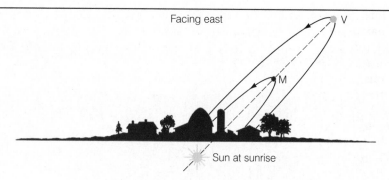

Facing east

Sun at sunrise

(a) Mercury and Venus at greatest western elongation

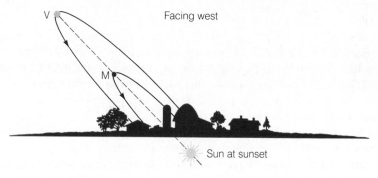

Facing west

Sun at sunset

(b) Mercury and Venus at greatest eastern elongation

■ FIGURE 2.38
Annual Paths of Mercury and Venus

Both planets are always found close to the Sun in the sky and are therefore always seen near sunrise or sunset. Both planets are shown at their greatest elongations; this does not often happen at the same time for both planets and is shown for convenience.

western elongation to superior conjunction, it gets closer to the Sun on the celestial sphere and therefore rises nearer to the Sun. At superior conjunction, of course, both Mercury or Venus are difficult to see since they are in the Sun's glare. As each planet orbits around the Sun, it reappears as an evening star, setting later and later each day until it reaches greatest eastern elongation. Mercury or Venus then sets closer and closer to the Sun and eventually disappears from view at inferior conjunction. Consequently, the apparent motions of Mercury and Venus relative to the Sun from inferior conjunction to inferior conjunction are relatively simple—they move either away or toward the Sun as morning or evening stars (Table 2.5).

Superior Planets

Since superior planets orbit farther from the Sun than the Earth, they can be seen on the opposite side of the celestial sphere from the Sun; that is, at any time after sunset or before sunrise and at any point near the ecliptic. Figure 2.39 illustrates two configurations of the orbits of superior planet, Mars, and the Earth. Mars is nearest to the Earth at **opposition** when it is directly opposite the Sun on the celestial sphere (Panel a). Mars is then on the meridian at midnight and most favorably placed for viewing.

■ TABLE 2.5
Morning and Evening Stars

Greatest western elongation: Morning star
Greatest eastern elongation: Evening star

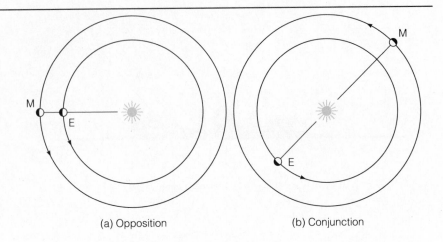

■■■■ FIGURE 2.39

Configurations of the Earth and Mars as They Orbit the Sun

(a) Opposition   (b) Conjunction

Because the Earth will swing around the Sun faster than Mars, Mars eventually will be positioned on the opposite side of the Sun from the Earth. This configuration is called **conjunction,** and Mars is then at its farthest distance from the Earth (Panel b of Figure 2.39). Because of its relatively small size as viewed from Earth and its proximity to the Sun, Mars is very difficult to observe at conjunction. Just before and after conjunction when Mars is near the Sun but not yet directly behind it, Mars can be seen in the morning or evening sky together with Mercury and Venus.

The cycle is completed when opposition is reached again. Figure 2.39, of course, applies to all of the superior planets, not just to Mars. The only difference will be the times between the different configurations. Because Jupiter and Saturn are farther away from the Sun, they move more slowly in their orbits and the Earth passes them often, so that they pass from opposition to opposition *faster* than Mars does.

Occasionally, the apparent motions of two or more planets bring them in close proximity to each other on the celestial sphere. Such a meeting is also called a *conjunction* but should not be confused with the configuration of a superior planet with respect to the Earth. The exact date of a conjunction is when both planets have the same elongation as seen from the Earth. Many conjunctions occur each year. Dates of conjunctions are given in *The Astronomical Almanac* prepared jointly by the United States Naval Observatory and the Royal Greenwich Observatory. Because the planets are generally very bright, conjunctions are visually very pleasing and provide an opportunity to detect the relative motions of the planets on a night-to-night basis.

Retrograde Motion

Planets normally appear farther and farther eastward on the celestial sphere from night to night. Occasionally, however, they seem to move westward in a very peculiar manner. Such westward motion of a planet is called **retrograde motion.** Early astronomers found retrograde motion

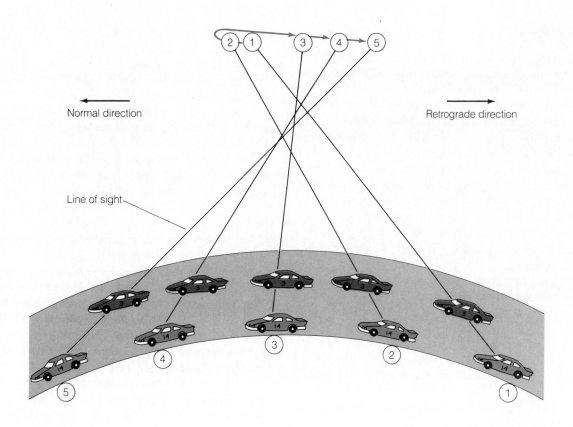

Normal direction

Retrograde direction

Line of sight

to be the most difficult apparent celestial movement to understand. Retrograde motion of a superior planet occurs when the Earth "overtakes" it as both orbit the Sun. The situation is similar to two cars racing on a circular track with one car on the inner part of the track and the other on the outer part. If the inner car moves faster than the outer car, the outer car will seem to move backward to the driver of the inner car. That is how it works when the Earth passes a slower outer planet. Figure 2.40 shows the relative positions of the two cars after a series of equal time intervals, say, 10 seconds apart. As the inner car passes the outer car, the line of sight between the two cars appears to move backward along any background on the outside of the track.

Similarly, whenever Earth overtakes a planet, Mars, for instance, Mars will appear to move backward or westward, on the celestial sphere. Once the Earth moves far enough ahead, Mars will again move eastward on the celestial sphere as normal.

Although retrograde motion is essentially a back-and-forth movement in the sky, the observed path of a planet may be a line, a loop, or even a figure S. The shape of the retrograde maneuver depends on the tilt of the planet's orbit relative to the Earth's orbit and on the position of the planet in its orbit. An example of the retrograde motion of Mars, which takes about 3 months, is shown in Figure 2.41. The inferior planets also perform retrograde motion with respect to the stars. They change their directions, of course, near their greatest elongations.

■■■ FIGURE 2.40

Racing Cars

Because the inner car moves faster than the outer car, the line of sight between the two cars appears to move backward, positions 2 through 5, on the background.

■■■ FIGURE 2.41

Retrograde Motion of Mars

Tick marks are shown for 10-day intervals and are numbered for intervals of 50 days.

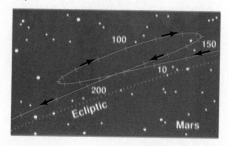

▰SUMMARY

The Earth's rotation about its axis and its revolution about the Sun causes the observed celestial motions of the Sun, Moon, stars, and planets.

The Earth's rotation makes the celestial sphere appear to rotate around the Earth. The celestial north and south poles as well as the celestial equator are projections of the Earth's poles and equator onto the celestial sphere. Stars rise and set, but their time above the horizon depends on the latitude of the observer. At the poles the visible stars stay above the horizon for 24 hours while at the equator they stay above for 12 hours. In the Northern Hemisphere at intermediate latitudes, we see stars whose diurnal circles are north of the celestial equator for more than 12 hours and those with diurnal circles south of the celestial equator for less than 12 hours.

Whereas the stars have one apparent motion—rising, moving across the sky, and setting—the Sun has three apparent motions. It rises and sets each day; it moves north or south during the year; and it drifts eastward relative to the stars. We associate four special days with the Sun's celestial motions: the first day of summer and winter, called the summer and winter solstices, and the first day of spring and fall, called the vernal and autumnal equinoxes. The solstices coincide with the maximum distance of the Sun from the celestial equator; the equinoxes coincide with the Sun's crossing of the celestial equator.

Although the Moon appears to rise and set like the Sun and stars, it is actually moving eastward on the sky about 13° per day. The Moon's sidereal period is 27⅓ days, but because of the motion of the Earth-Moon system around the Sun, the Moon has a synodic period of 29½ days. At the same time, the Moon's sidereal period is identical with its rotational period and keeps the same face directed at the Earth. The visible face of the Moon changes as it passes through different phases. These are the result of the changing relative positions of the Earth, Moon, and Sun during the lunar synodic period.

Eclipses occur when the line of nodes points toward the Sun. The line of nodes is drawn between the points where the orbital planes of the Earth and Moon intersect. When the line of nodes points toward the Sun, solar eclipses occur when the Moon is at new moon, and lunar eclipses occur at full moon. Shadows are responsible for eclipses. The shadows of the Earth and Moon have two parts: the umbra, within which light is completely blocked, and the penumbra, a region of partial illumination. Because the diameter of the Moon's umbral shadow is so small, less than 270 km, total solar eclipses only last a few minutes at any location on Earth and are visible from only a narrow path on the Earth's surface. Since the Earth's shadow is much larger, lunar eclipses can last almost 2 hours and are visible from half the surface of the Earth.

Of all the celestial motions visible to the unaided eye, the retrograde motion of the planets was the most peculiar and puzzling. Planets normally drift slowly eastward on the celestial sphere relative to the stars during the year. They do spend a little time moving westward relative to the stars, however. This retrograde motion is the result of both the planet and the Earth revolving around the Sun in the same direction but at different speeds.

Planets closer to the Sun than the Earth are only visible in the morning or evening skies. Sometimes they are referred to as morning and evening stars. The other planets in the solar system can be seen at anytime at night, depending on their position relative to the Earth and the Sun.

▰CHAPTER CAPSULE

Topics and Terms	Review and Remarks
Apparent celestial motions	The rotation of the Earth causes risings and settings of celestial objects.
	The constant tilt of the Earth's axis causes the north and south movement of the Sun.
	The orbital motion of the Earth causes the eastward drift of the Sun relative to the stars.
	The Moon's orbital motion causes the eastward drift of the Moon relative to the stars.
Summer solstice	June 21 or 22—first day of summer
	Sun is 23½° north of the celestial equator. *(continued)*

CHAPTER CAPSULE (continued)

Topics and Terms	Review and Remarks
Winter solstice	December 22 or 23—first day of winter Sun is 23½° south of the celestial equator.
Spring equinox	March 20 or 21—first day of spring Sun is on the celestial equator—moving south to north.
Autumnal equinox	September 22 or 23—first day of fall Sun is on the celestial equator—moving north to south.

Eclipses	The Earth or the Moon enters the other's shadow:
	    Solar eclipses occur at new moon.
	    Lunar eclipses occur at full moon.

Eclipse seasons	The time of year when the line of nodes points toward the Sun; this occurs at least twice a year.
Retrograde motion of the planets	Caused by the relative motion of the Earth and other planets as they orbit the Sun.

REVIEW QUESTIONS

1. Consider a star that rises directly in the east as viewed from your latitude. As it moves away from the horizon, how does its apparent motion differ from that of a circumpolar star?

2. The word solstice comes from a combination of *sol*, meaning Sun, and *sistere*, meaning to stand still. Explain why the term *winter solstice* (or *summer solstice*) is appropriate when referring to the beginning of winter (or summer).

3. Using Figures 2.11 and 2.12, explain why the daylight period is longest at the time of summer solstice.

4. Except at the equator, a star that rises in the east does *not* appear to move upward along a vertical path as the Earth rotates. Relate the apparent motion of such a star to the observer's latitude for several different latitudes.

5. Using your local latitude, estimate the maximum altitude, in degrees, of the Sun (a) at the time of the summer solstice and (b) at the time of the winter solstice.

6. How are the apparent direction of the Sun and Moon related at the time of full moon? Repeat the question for the directions of the Sun and Moon at times of new and first-quarter moon.

7. At approximately what time does a first-quarter moon rise? Set? (Assume the Sun sets at 6:00 P.M.)

8. Suppose one evening you notice the time at which a thin crescent moon sets. Describe the apparent position and appearance of the Moon *at the same time* the next evening.

9. What is the phase of the Moon at the time of a solar eclipse? Why do we not have a solar eclipse each time the Moon is in that phase?

10. What is an annular eclipse and why do they occur?

11. Solar eclipses are more numerous than lunar eclipses. Why then do more people see lunar eclipses?

12. Describe the apparent daily motion of the Sun and Moon relative to the local horizon. How does this apparent motion differ from their apparent motion relative to the distant stars?

13. How is the retrograde motion of a superior planet related to its apparent direction relative to the Sun? A planet's apparent brightness depends on its distance from the observer and from the Sun. Would a planet be near its maximum or minimum brightness when it is in retrograde motion?

FOR FURTHER READING

Aveni, A. F. 1986. Archaeoastronomy: Past, present, and future. *Sky & Telescope*, Nov., 456.

Deitmer, S. 1985. The observatories of Jai Singh. *Astronomy*, Jan., 18.

Gibbons, C. 1986. Some reflections on Earthshine. *Astronomy*, Aug., 83.

Loudon, J. 1986. Learning the sky by degrees. *Astronomy*, Dec., 54.

McClure, B. 1987. Watching the Earth move with the shadow clock. *Astronomy*, Aug., 32.

O'Fee, B. 1986. Sundials. *Astronomy*, Jan., 47.

Piini, E. W. 1986. Ulugh Beg's forgotten observatory. *Sky & Telescope*, June, 542.

Shawcross, W. E. 1985. Venus and the Maya. *Sky & Telescope*, Aug., 111.

Walter, R. C. 1987. What time is it? *Astronomy*, Feb., 38.

ASTROPROBE 2

Archaeo-astronomy

Evidence from ancient monuments and classical literature indicates that humans throughout history have paid careful attention to the sky. The Sun rises and sets every day; the Moon cycles through its phases every month; and the seasons come and go every year. This dependable repetition of celestial events enabled many ancient peoples to construct **calendars.**

▅▅ SOLAR CALENDARS

A calendar arranges the year into time intervals, such as our days, weeks, and months. Calendars are important tools for organizing human activities. We use calendars to orient ourselves within the year and to plan ahead. We can plan our Christmas shopping because we know that Christmas Day falls on the twenty-fifth day of the twelfth month every year. We make long-range plans for events such as school openings and closings, athletic events, weddings, and summit meetings.

Ancients also made long-range plans for important events. In many ancient cultures, solstices were times of celebration. The winter solstice, for example, represented the completion of a celestial cycle; the Sun now would start rising earlier and earlier and the days would become longer. People needed time to prepare for these celebrations. For instance, ancient Peruvian purification rites of fasting began exactly three days before the winter solstice. Similarly, the ancient Pueblos of Southwest America planned and practiced for two weeks before their summer solstice celebration.

Today we simply look at a wall or desk calendar to locate ourselves in the year. The ancients looked to the tapestry of the sky for their calendar; they used the regularities exhibited by celestial objects to locate themselves in the year.

Since the Sun changes its position in the sky throughout the year, it is the most obvious celestial object to observe for the purpose of keeping track of the year. At summer solstice, for example, the Sun rises as far north of east as it does all year; at winter solstice it rises as far south of east as it does all year. Consequently, from summer to winter, the Sun shifts its rising and setting positions on the horizon southward. A natural observation to make is to note the horizon position of the Sun each day.

If the horizon is irregular, such as the mountain range shown in Figure 2A.1, it is easy to keep track of the year by using the various peaks and valleys of the range as calendrical markers. After the end of November, however, the horizon has no natural markers. Moreover, as the Sun gets closer to the solstice position, it changes its day-to-day setting position on the horizon more slowly. Consequently, an-

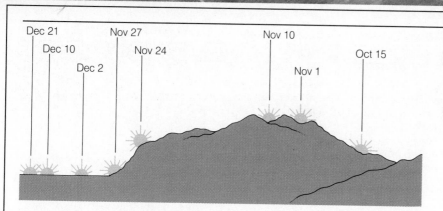

Dec 21 Nov 27 Nov 10
Dec 10 Nov 24 Oct 15
Dec 2 Nov 1

Fictitious Horizon with Setting Sun

The mountain range provides a natural marker for the dates of the year. The flat horizon, however, is a poor marker.

cient peoples needed observatories if they were to predict when the solstice would occur.

Some observatories in the American Southwest, for instance, were buildings with windows or small openings that allowed sunlight to strike an inside wall. Markings were placed on the wall so that an observer could follow the progress of the Sun near the solstices very accurately. In ancient cultures, ritual and astronomy went hand in hand because ancient peoples often believed that nature and the divine were very much connected. Consequently, the markings in these building observatories could indicate when to begin preparations for a celebration or to start a ritual fast. Observatories were an integral part of some ancient cultures, and the study of these observatories provides us with insights into their culture as well as with information about the extent of their knowledge of the sky.

Archaeoastronomy, the study of the astronomy of ancient people, relies on the study of ancient observatories and, when possible, on written records. In excavating a ruin, however, we often do not know for sure that it was an observatory, especially when we have no written records that describe the nature of the site. Furthermore, since we generally do not fully comprehend an ancient culture, it is very difficult to understand the purpose of a suspected observatory. The first question we must ask is, "does the geometry of a site correspond to astronomical events, such as sunrises or sunsets at particular times of the year?" The "geometry of a site" in most cases is one or more **alignments.** For example, a person standing at a marked spot on a certain day would see the Sun rise between two mountain peaks in the distance or set behind a specifically placed rock. To determine whether an ancient site was used as an observatory, we must carefully survey the site and compare the survey results with calculated positions of the Sun, Moon, stars, and planets for all of the seasons at the latitude of the site. In doing this, astronomers have discovered

Alignment: An arrangement in a straight line between an observer, a marker or markers, and a celestial object.

■■■ TABLE 2A.1 **Ancient Observatories**

Name	Location	Date	Marker	Circle	Temple
Newgrange	Ireland	3200 B.C.	X		X
Stonehenge	England	2800 B.C.		X	X
Pyramid of Khufu	Egypt	2600 B.C.			X
Majorville Cairn*	Canada	2500 B.C.		X	
Kintraw	Scotland	1700 B.C.	X		
Megalithic sites	Scotland, Wales	1600 B.C.		X	
Amon-Ra	Egypt	1400 B.C.			X
Namoratugna II*	Kenya	300 B.C.	X		
Teotihuacán	Mexico	A.D. 150			X
Alta Vista	Mexico	A.D. 400			X
Uaxactún	Guatemala	A.D. 800			X
Caracol at Chichén Itzá	Mexico	A.D. 1000			X
Cahokia Sun Circle	Illinois	A.D. 1000		X	
Bighorn Medicine Wheel*	Wyoming	A.D. 1050		X	
Angkor Wat	Cambodia	A.D. 1100			X
Measuring Tower	China	A.D. 1270	X		
Casa Grande*	Arizona	A.D. 1350			X
St. Peter's	Rome	A.D. 1500			X
Cuzco	Peru	A.D. 1500			X
Sun dagger	New Mexico	?	X		
Machu Picchu	Peru	?			X
Desert markings*	Peru	?	X		

*Highly controversial sites.

hundreds of sites throughout the world that appear to show astronomical alignments.

Structures found at various sites around the world can be conveniently grouped into three categories:

■ *Simple markers* appear to exhibit one alignment.

■ *Circles* usually appear to exhibit many alignments produced with markers on a perimeter and viewed from near the center.

■ *Temples and tombs* are stone or earthern monuments exhibiting one or more alignments.

Several ancient observatories are described in the next section. A more extensive, but not exhaustive, list is given in Table 2A.1. Some of the sites discussed here and listed in the table are controversial in that not all archaeoastronomers agree that the possible alignments are significant. Archaeoastronomers must always be cautious when trying to interpret a site and must not analyze it in terms of their own way of looking at the sky. Ancients had their own perception of the universe and their own purposes for their observations.

ANCIENT OBSERVATORIES

Some of the ancient sites described here were clearly used to keep track of the seasons and to determine the length of the year; they were true observatories. Many times these observations were associated with rituals of religious significance. On the other hand, some of the alignments attributed to the sites are probably accidental, and others may have no real meaning. We sometimes have difficulty discovering the purposes the original builders of ancient sites had in mind when they built the structures. Consequently, the study of the astronomy of our ancestors is easily open to speculation and inappropriate interpretations of site surveys and alignment calculations.

There is no question that ancient people knew the sky, however. From their knowledge of celestial motions, ancient astronomers were able to define the cardinal points. They then could erect structures with almost perfect north-south and east-west orientation. They also constructed solar and lunar calendars from which to plan their activities. Many ancient civilizations knew the length of the year to within a few hours.

Stonehenge

Although approximately 900 **megalithic** circles are known to have existed in the British Isles, Stonehenge is probably the most famous (Figure 2A.2). Located west of the town of Amesbury, England, Stonehenge is actually several concentric circles erected in three different periods of history. Ancient Britons built the first and most astronomical circle in about 2800 B.C. This circle shows numerous astronomical alignments, the most famous of which is the rising of the Sun behind a large stone, called the heel stone, as viewed from the center of the circle near the time of the summer solstice. The builders of Stonehenge were careful and skillful celestial observers, who clearly believed celestial phenomena were of great importance.

Newgrange

Neolithic farmers in Ireland built the world's oldest known prehistoric passage graves in about 3200 B.C. Newgrange lies about 42 kilometers (26 miles) northwest of Dublin and is a heart-shaped mound with a 21-meter (70-foot) passageway leading to a stone chamber (Figure 2A.3). This passage points directly to the location on the horizon of the rising Sun on winter solstice. Just above the tomb's sealed entrance is a special window that allows sunlight to enter the tomb at sunrise on the first day of winter. The passage slopes upward

FIGURE 2A.2

Stonehenge, England

Stonehenge is actually three monuments, each of which was built at a different time. Pictured here is the third monument built in about 1700 B.C. Alignments are made between the stones.

SOURCE: J. Ferner/Visuals Unlimited.

Megalith: Prehistoric monuments constructed with huge stones.

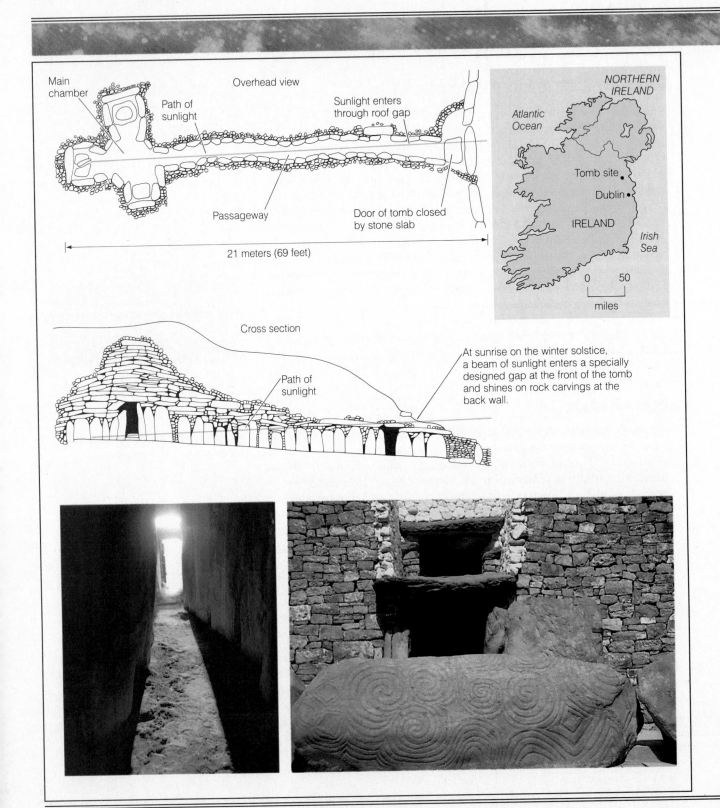

Overhead view

Main chamber

Path of sunlight

Sunlight enters through roof gap

Passageway

Door of tomb closed by stone slab

21 meters (69 feet)

NORTHERN IRELAND

Atlantic Ocean

Tomb site

Dublin

IRELAND

Irish Sea

0   50

miles

Cross section

Path of sunlight

At sunrise on the winter solstice, a beam of sunlight enters a specially designed gap at the front of the tomb and shines on rock carvings at the back wall.

toward the chamber such that sunlight that does enter the window cannot reach the central chamber on any other day.

Pyramid of Khufu

The Great Pyramid at Giza, built as a tomb for the Pharaoh Khufu, appears to exhibit two stellar alignments that reflect traditional myths of the Egyptians pertaining to their pharaohs. Two narrow ventilating shafts emerge from the king's chamber deep inside the pyramid (Figure 2A.4). One points to the position the north celestial pole had 5,000 years ago and the other to the ancient wintertime position of the belt in the constellation Orion. These alignments may be significant because Egyptians believed that the dead pharaoh makes two celestial trips: one to Orion where he maintains the calendar and governs the seasons and one to join the circumpolar stars as a symbol of his eternal life among the stars that never set. This pyramid, like most of the other 80 pyramids in Egypt, also exhibits almost perfect north-south and east-west alignment.

Caracol

The Maya constructed the Caracol tower at Chichén Itza in Yucatán in about A.D. 1000. Several archaeologists in the first half of the twentieth century commented on its lack of aesthetic beauty and its confusing ground plan and symmetries (Figure 2A.5). The lower platforms and upper windows appear to show some solar equinox and solstice alignments and possible stellar alignments. More interesting are the apparent alignments with the planet Venus, which the Maya believed was the celestial manifestation of the god Kukulchan. This interpretation of the site receives some support from ancient Mayan

FIGURE 2A.3 (preceding page)

The Tomb at Newgrange, Ireland

In this prehistoric Irish tomb, the passage to the central chamber allows light to reach the chamber only at the winter solstice sunrise. The photograph at left shows light entering the passage at winter solstice. The photograph at right shows the window above the tomb's entrance.

SOURCE: Photo at left courtesy Commissioners of Public Works, Ireland. Photo at right courtesy Owen Gingerich, Harvard-Smithsonian Center for Astrophysics.

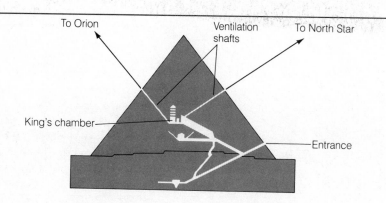

FIGURE 2A.4

Pyramid of the Pharaoh Khufu, Egypt

The ventilation shafts appear to align with astronomical objects that play an important role in ancient Egyptian myths.

FIGURE 2A.5

Caracol Tower at Chichén Itzá in Yucatán

SOURCE: John D. Cunningham/Visuals Unlimited.

tables that appear to have been written at about the same time the Caracol tower was built. These tablets list the times when Venus was first visible in the dawn sky before sunrise and other dates of ritual significance. Thus the Caracol tower is an example of astronomical alignments that make sense in light of the written record of the people who built the observatory.

Uaxactún Group E

In Guatemala, three Mayan temples align with the summer solstice sunrise, the equinox sunrise, and the winter solstice sunrise when viewed from a fourth temple (Figure 2A.6). These alignments, however, do not appear precise enough to measure the length of the year accurately or to predict the exact day of the equinox or the solstices. Perhaps these temples were used more as ceremonial symbols than as observatories.

Chinese Tower

Another way to determine the length of the year is to observe the changes in the length of the noontime shadow cast by a stick. As the noontime Sun rises higher and higher in the sky as the summer solstice nears, the shadow becomes shorter and shorter. The Chinese "Tower for the Measurement of the Sun's Shadow," built in A.D. 1270, is 12 meters (40 feet) high and has a 37-meter (120-foot) long horizontal measuring wall extending from its base (Figure 2A.7). This long wall allowed a very accurate measurement of the length of the year.

FIGURE 2A.6

Uaxactún Temples, Guatemala

Viewed from a pyramid just to their west, these three temples align with the equinox and solstice sunrises, though not entirely accurately.

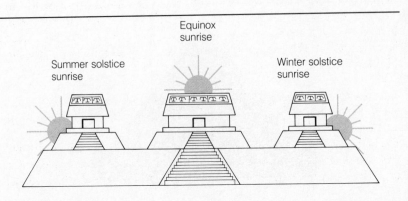

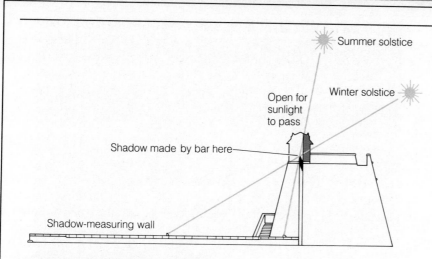

Summer solstice

Winter solstice

Open for sunlight to pass

Shadow made by bar here

Shadow-measuring wall

FIGURE 2A.7

Ancient Chinese Observatory

The Chinese astronomer Guo Shou Jing used this tower and its measuring wall to estimate the length of the year.

Bighorn Medicine Wheel

Great Plain Indians built the circle, known as the Bighorn Medicine Wheel, near present-day Sheridan, Wyoming, in about A.D. 1050. The circle looks like a giant bicycle wheel with 28 spokes and a diameter of almost 27 meters (90 feet) (Figure 2A.8). Using piles of rocks as markers, it appears to exhibit at least five astronomical alignments: the summer solstice sunrise and sunset and the rising of at least three stars and possibly four of the brightest stars visible from the Northern Hemisphere. The Great Plain Indians of the United States and Canada built about 50 of these circles. The oldest appears to be the Majorville Cairn in Alberta, Canada, built in about 2500 B.C., about the same time the Egyptians built the pyramids at Giza.

The stellar alignments at the Bighorn Medicine Wheel are controversial. As it happens, the three known stellar alignments are the number we would expect to occur by chance; that is, there are so many bright stars visible in the night sky and so many possible alignments from the many piles of rocks that some alignments will happen just by chance. Of course, this does not mean that the alignments have no significance. We simply do not have other evidence, such as a written record, indicating the importance of such stars in the Great Plain Indian culture.

LUNAR CALENDARS AND ECLIPSE PREDICTION

Early calendars were undoubtedly lunar calendars. They followed the phases of the Moon instead of the cyclic variations of the Sun, and the natural calendar unit was the lunar synodic period, the

■■ FIGURE 2A.8

Bighorn Medicine Wheel, Wyoming

Alignments are made between the center pile of rocks and the outside piles. This is one of about 50 known wheels in the United States and Canada.

SOURCE: Photo by John A. Eddy/Visuals Unlimited.

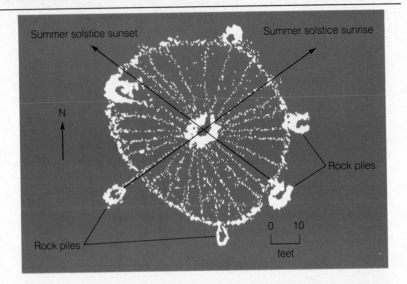

month. It is easy to keep lunar months synchronized with lunar phases. The lunar synodic period is 29½ days. Since half days are awkward to tally, the length of a lunar calendar month alternates between 29 and 30 days. The first month of a lunar calendar lasts 29 days, the second month 30 days, the third 29 days, and so on. Accordingly, the average month is 29½ days and keeps pace with the Moon's cycle with the new moon occurring at the beginning and the full moon halfway through the month.

At the same time, lunar calendars are inconvenient. The length of the lunar year, 12 lunar months, is 354 days, 11 days short of the tropical year. This 11-day difference builds up over time. After 3 lunar years, the lunar calendar is over a month behind a solar calendar. Consequently, the seasons, which are a solar phenomena, cycle through all the lunar calendar months in about 33 years. The Hebrew calendar, for instance, is a lunar calendar that uses lunar months of 29 and 30 days but catches up with the Sun by inserting "leap months" or **intercalary months.** Lunar years are arranged in groups of 19. In each group intercalary months are added in year 3, 6, 8, 11, 14, 17, and 19.

Although the seasons can be associated with a month in lunar calendars as with solar calendars, lunar calendars seem unnecessarily complicated. Lunar calendars continue to be used in our modern society, however, as a consequence of centuries of tradition that even affects our present-day solar calendar. Many Christian religious holidays, for instance, are tied to the Moon. Early Christians were, of course, of Jewish origin and therefore used a lunar calendar. Easter, for example, always falls on the first Sunday after the first full moon after the spring equinox. Other religious holidays are then determined relative to Easter. Ash Wednesday falls on the seventh Wednesday before Easter while Pentecost is the seventh Sunday after Easter. The fact that successive months in our calendar do not have an equal number of days but alternate mainly between 30 and 31 days is a relic of lunar calendar tradition. Thus our solar calendar still contains reference to the Moon even though our months no longer necessarily coincide with its phases.

It is clear that humans took notice of the Moon from the very earliest times in history. In doing so, they certainly must have witnessed eclipses. Eclipses, of course, occur at new and full moons. The new moon, watched by calendar makers, marked the beginning of the lunar month, and the full moon is a most conspicuous sight. We know that many ancient cultures were able to track the motions of the Sun, planets, and stars, and that they sometimes built observatories for both astronomical and ceremonial purposes. Could they predict eclipses? It appears that, if they were able to keep records, the 173-day eclipse half-year would have been discovered. This cycle could then be used to predict eclipses.

Humans have kept records of celestial events in various forms for the last 20,000 to 30,000 years. The earliest records of lunar observations appear to be markings on ancient bone fragments apparently used to keep track of the Moon's phases. The continuous viewing of the Moon necessary for depicting lunar phases on bones guaranteed eclipse observations thousands of years ago. For any single locality on Earth, lunar eclipses can be viewed by more people than can solar eclipses, and two lunar eclipses, partial or total, are typical in a year.

Intercalary month: From Latin *intercalare* meaning "to insert"; a month periodically inserted into a calendar to keep it in phase with the seasons or the solar calendar.

These Mayan eclipse tables were named after the German city, Dresden, where they were found 300 years after the Maya were conquered, apparently having been brought there sometime in the intervening period.

If a lunar calendar were used, ancients would have found that eclipses coincided with the beginning and middle of lunar months. Thus, in all likelihood, eclipse cycles were known.

We know, for example, that Mayan astronomers predicted eclipses. Several fragments of Mayan manuscripts exist that contain information on religion, history, mythology, calendars, and astronomy. In particular, the Mayan Dresden eclipse tables, dating from the twelfth century A.D., clearly indicate that the Maya knew the 173-day eclipse half-year and realized that this was very close to the 177 days in 6 lunar calendar months. Therefore Mayan astronomers knew that eclipses might take place every sixth moon.

The Dresden eclipse tables cover nearly 33 years: 11,960 days or 405 lunar months. Dividing the total number of days by the number of lunar months in the tables, we calculate a lunar month equal to 29.53086 days—less than a half a minute longer than our modern value of 29.53059 days. Such accuracy is only achieved by a long series of lunar observations. With these tables, the Maya did not need to build observatories to predict eclipses; they could do it numerically.

We find more evidence of eclipse predictions from further back in history in the first century B.C. At the beginning of this century, sponge divers in the Mediterranean discovered fragments of a geared mechanism that scientists have identified as a Sun and Moon computing machine. The gears are such that it could keep track of the line of nodes and the positions of the Sun and Moon. The builders of this machine fully understood the celestial cycles of the Sun and Moon. Their celestial knowledge, probably in written form originally, must have been used to construct the machine.

Extensive written records are probably not necessary for eclipse prediction. Many experts believe that many stone circles in Scotland and Wales as well as those at Stonehenge were in part lunar observatories (Figure 2A.9). Stonehenge is particularly interesting in that observers may have kept track of the position of the line of nodes, the Moon, and the Sun by moving rocks through a series of holes, called Aubrey holes. Although solar eclipses occur several times a year, they do not occur at the same place on Earth in that year. The lines of nodes, however, rotates exactly once relative to the stars about every 18 years. As a result the alignment between the Earth, Moon, and Sun is nearly identical every 18 years. A solar eclipse visible from Stonehenge, for instance, at a given time would again be visible from Stonehenge 18 years later.

Ancient artifacts, monuments, and manuscripts reveal that humans carefully kept track of the Sun and the Moon and used both as calendars for thousands of years. Ancients were also aware of eclipse

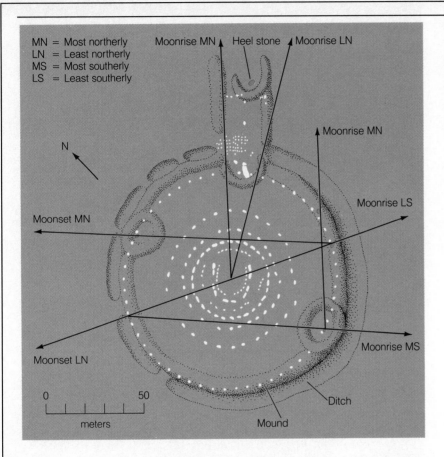

MN = Most northerly
LN = Least northerly
MS = Most southerly
LS = Least southerly

Moonrise MN   Heel stone   Moonrise LN

N

Moonrise MN

Moonset MN

Moonrise LS

Moonrise MS

Moonset LN

0   50
meters

Moonrise MS

Ditch

Mound

■■■■ **FIGURE 2A.9**

Lunar Alignments at Stonehenge

The Moon can rise and set between 18½° and 28½° north or south of the celestial equator. Stonehenge alignments mark the most northerly (28½° north of the celestial equator), most southerly (28½° south of the celestial equator), least northerly (18½° north of the celestial equator), and least southerly (18½° south of the celestial equator) rising and setting positions of the Moon.

seasons and were capable of predicting eclipses. This knowledge was based on generations of exacting observations of the Sun and Moon and was incorporated into the design and construction of observatories such as Stonehenge.

The Process of Scientific Discovery

OUTLINE

The Scientific Approach

Competing Models
The Greek Geocentric Model
The Copernican Heliocentric
Model

Tycho Brahe

Johannes Kepler

Galileo Galilei
Observational Astronomer
Experimental Physicist

Isaac Newton
Force
Mass
Universal Gravitation

Summary

Chapter Capsule

Review Questions

For Further Reading

████████ASTROPROBE 3:
**Interplanetary Travel: Satellites
and Space Probes**

Reflections of Future Past.
ARTIST: Kurt C. Burmann.

AFTER SERIOUSLY STUDYING THE HEAVENS for several thousand years, humans finally established that the Earth revolves around the Sun and spins on its axis. In the sixteenth and seventeenth centuries, western civilization struggled through a period of intense inquiry into the nature of the universe. This 200-year period of scientific discovery began with a conflict between two opposing views of the universe—the Earth-centered view versus the Sun-centered view. Through the precise, naked eye observations of the Danish astronomer Tycho Brahe and their analysis by the German mathematician Johannes Kepler, astronomers learned to describe the motions of the planets around the Sun accurately. At the same time, the telescope observations by the Italian scientist Galileo Galilei gave strong support for the Sun-centered view. While Kepler and Galileo summarized experimental and observational data into precise mathematical form, the British physicist Isaac Newton discovered the explanation of planetary motion in his formulation of universal gravitation.

■■■THE SCIENTIFIC APPROACH

Historians refer to the two centuries of intellectual advancement following the Renaissance as the *scientific revolution*. The Renaissance itself was the great revival of literature, art, and learning that took place in Northern and Central Italy between about A.D. 1275 and 1475. The subsequent scientific revolution played an important part in the transition from the medieval world to our modern world.

The term **science** derives from the Latin *scientia* meaning "to know." Science is a consistent body of knowledge, strongly tied to experiment, and expressed in as few laws as possible. This concise definition contains two very important concepts: experiment and laws. Science relies on experimental and observational *facts of nature*. For instance, statements such as the following are examples of scientific facts; that is, they are descriptions of nature.

- The orbital period of Mars is 687 days.
- Lead is 11.3 times more dense than water.
- The sidereal day is $23^h56^m4^s$ long.

We obtain such facts through experiments or observations, which are repeatable by scientists the world over. **Scientific laws** or rules are statements or mathematical relations formulated from facts of nature—they are generalizations of nature.

We formulate general rules by more or less following a sequence of steps commonly called the *scientific method*. First, the facts of nature relevant to the problem being studied are gathered. This can be done through experimenting, observing, collecting, and cataloging. In the seventeenth century, scientists measured the time it took for objects to roll down inclines or fall to the ground and determined their speeds at different times. These measurements were relevant to the study of gravity. Second, scientists then search through a huge collection of experimental data, observations, measurements, collections of life-forms or rocks for a common thread, for a possible unifying principle, or *hypoth-*

The scientific approach involves the following steps:

1. Obtain facts of nature.
2. Summarize facts as hypotheses.
3. Deduce consequences of the hypothesis and test them.

esis. The hypothesis is formulated as a statement or a mathematical relation. The experimental data on the motions of objects near the Earth's surface led to a mathematical description of these motions. Finally, a scientific hypothesis must be verifiable; that is, scientists must be able to deduce and test consequences from a hypothesis. The mathematical description of gravity formulated by the British physicist Isaac Newton described the motions observed for objects on Earth. Newton's formulation predicted how fast a ball will fall or how far a projectile will travel before striking the ground. Using Newton's description of gravity, astronomers and mathematicians successfully predicted the existence and location of Neptune, the eighth planet in the solar system. These were successful tests of Newton's mathematical description of gravity. As more and more consequences of this description were verified and the scientific community became more and more confident of its accuracy, the hypothesis was recognized as the "law of universal gravitation."

The term *theory* often refers to a hypothesis that has considerable experimental support; Newton's description of gravity is often referred to as Newton's theory of gravity. Within this theory are equations describing the gravitationally caused motions of objects. Even though many consequences of a theory are verified, a theory cannot be proved, only disproved. For example, Newton's theory of gravity fails when it is used to describe motions very near massive bodies. This deficiency was overcome by a more general theory of gravity in the form of Einstein's theory of general relativity. This does not mean that the theory of general relativity was proved. Someday physicists may find that Einstein's theory has its limits and will eventually replace it with a more general theory.

To win acceptance in the scientific community, a scientific law or theory must be based on experimental or observational results and must be able to make testable predictions. Science permits new ideas and new theories, but they must be verifiable.

The conduct of scientific research depends on the individual investigator, the subject being studied, the development of the field at the time, and the techniques available for measurement and analysis. At times scientists mainly gather data looking for the unexpected. They may detour from one line of investigation to a completely different line because of a chance discovery. For example, astronomers observing a star for a specific reason or with a new instrument may make a completely unexpected discovery. This could lead to more observations on the same star or other stars, or it might open up a whole new field of research, as did the development of the radio telescope. More frequently, scientific research is very ordered in that a series of experiments or observations is planned. The results of each experiment or observation guide the investigator to the next one. Sometimes a mathematical model is constructed describing observed phenomena, and experiments are conducted to verify it. No matter how the research is conducted, however, the final test of a hypothesis is experiment.

Of course, sometimes astronomers simply point their telescopes at an interesting object, wondering what they will see. You have probably heard the expression that mountaineers climb mountains because mountains are there; similarly, astronomers observe stars because stars are there. This chapter describes the effect on astronomical thought when the Italian scientist Galileo did just that. He built a telescope and pointed it at the heavens to see what was visible.

COMPETING MODELS

In the mid-sixteenth century, near the beginning of the scientific revolution, scientists had two opposing models that described the structure of the universe. One was Earth-centered, or **geocentric.** Ptolemy (c. A.D. 100–200), a Greek philosopher who studied in Alexandria, Egypt, summarized this model in the *Almagest,* a title derived from the Greek *al magiste,* meaning "the greatest" (Figure 3.1). The geocentric model asserted that the Earth was the center of the universe with the Sun, Moon, planets, and stars moving around it. Copernicus (A.D. 1473–1543), a Polish astronomer, presented a Sun-centered, or **heliocentric,** model in his *De revolutionibus orbium coelestrium,* "On the Revolutions of the Heavenly Spheres." He placed the Sun at the center with the Earth and planets in motion around it.

These two models offered explanations for the observed motions of celestial bodies as viewed from the Earth. Today scientists realize that the Copernican model is closer to the truth. Why did the sixteenth-century astronomers not know this? Why did some choose the geocentric model and others the heliocentric model? The answer lies in the criteria used to judge a model and in the ability of the Renaissance mind to accept certain consequences of the models.

The first criterion for any successful model is that it must account for the entire body of knowledge applicable to the subject being studied. Any astronomical model of the universe must account for all known observations of the present and past positions of the Sun, Moon, planets, and stars. It must be able to work in reverse; that is, given the present positions of the planets, the model must predict where the planets were 10 years, 100 years, and 1,000 years ago. Both the geocentric and heliocentric models could do this. In this sense, both were good models.

A model must also be verifiable. The test for astronomical models was the ability to predict future positions of the Sun, Moon, and planets; both did equally well. Although they were not perfect, both were imperfect by about the same amount. Therefore, to the sixteenth-century astronomers, both were equally good models.

Another criterion is the ability to explain other observable behavior. The Copernican model did explain phenomena that the Greek system could not; in this sense it was a better model. For instance, the Copernican model explains why superior planets are much brighter at opposition than at conjunction. Many Renaissance astronomers, however, were not ready for the "revolutionary" ideas, such as a spinning Earth, that these explanations required. In the end, a deep prejudice against the Copernican model hindered progress toward a rational choice of models.

Geo-: From the Greek *gē* meaning "the Earth."

Helio-: From the Greek *helios* meaning "the Sun."

The terms *model* and *hypothesis* are used interchangeably. The geocentric and heliocentric models were hypotheses to be verified. The terms *theory* and *law* are much stronger descriptions and imply that considerable evidence supports an explanation.

FIGURE 3.1

Ptolemy

SOURCE: The Granger Collection.

A good model

1. Accounts for all data
2. Is verifiable
3. Explains other experiments or observations
4. Is simple

Today scientists recognize yet another criterion for models—simplicity. We expect the best models and theories to explain and predict observations and experimental results correctly with as few assumptions and rules as possible. The simple and economical are preferred to the complex and cumbersome. A model's success lies in its ability to relate observed behavior to other bodies of general knowledge also derived from experiment. A prediction from a model cannot contradict evidence from another set of experiments. A good model gives us a sense of satisfaction; the more knowledge that is linked through a model, the more satisfied we feel. In the case at hand, both the Ptolemaic geocentric and the Copernican heliocentric models were complex and cumbersome rather than simple and economical.

The geocentric and heliocentric models are important to study because the Copernican system initiated the scientific revolution and because debate centered on the conflict between the two. An understanding of both models is needed to appreciate the depth of the struggle that eventually led to our present-day view of the universe. In addition, they illustrate that an explanation by a model or theory is not the final "reason why" something is so. Many of our present ideas, models, and theories, for instance, are probably wrong to some degree, but they appear to describe nature correctly. In fact, a model can be based on an incorrect physical description but still give a reasonable description of the observable universe. Both the Ptolemaic and Copernican models were guilty of this.

The Greek Geocentric Model

The Greeks convinced themselves through reasoning based on the visually observed motion of celestial objects that the Earth was at the center of the universe and that the Earth was motionless. They then tried to account for celestial motions by assuming that celestial bodies moved at a uniform speed and in circular motion. Uniform circular motion derives from the Greek idea that celestial bodies were composed of a perfect, unchanging substance that was completely different from anything on Earth. They believed that such ideal objects could properly move only in a perfect circle at an unchanging, or uniform, speed. When celestial bodies were observed not to move uniformly or in circles, the Greek's ingeniously combined circular motions in ways that duplicated the observed motion.

The first Greek geocentric models were simple. They described the stars as set in a rotating sphere that turned from east to west once a day. The planets, Moon, and Sun were also set in spheres, but these spun slower than the stellar sphere, resulting in the observed eastward motions of these objects relative to the stars. Successive Greek geocentric models grew more complicated as more detailed observations of planetary motion were gathered. By about 300 B.C., schemes with dozens of spheres were needed to reproduce the observed motions.

Not all Greek models were geocentric. Aristarchus of Samos (c. 310–230 B.C.) taught a heliocentric model of the universe. He suggested that the motions of the planets could be explained more simply if the Sun were at the center of the universe with the planets revolving around it. This model was to be revived by Copernicus 17 centuries later.

Although the Greek geocentric models were masterpieces of geometry, Greek astronomers found it conceptually and mathematically difficult to manipulate the great number of concentric spinning spheres. In time, they replaced the spheres with circles. The simplified Greek circular "orbit" used two geometric constructs, the *epicycle* and the *deferent*. The deferent was a circle centered on the Earth while the epicycle was a circle whose center moved along the circumference of the deferent (Figure 3.2). The planet moved on the epicycle. Accordingly, the planet's motion was a combination of two circular motions; the result was that a planet did not move around the Earth in a circle.

This noncircular planetary motion can be reproduced by observing the motion of a reflector on the rim of a bicycle wheel. The reflector's motion is a series of half circles (Figure 3.3). This pattern is called a *cycloid* and is the result of the combined circular motion of the reflector on the rim of the wheel and the horizontal motion of the wheel. Attaching a ruler to the wheel and extending the reflector beyond the rim produces a cycloid pattern that is a series of *loops* instead of half circles. Moreover, if it were possible to roll the wheel around another larger wheel, the resulting pattern of the reflector's motion would be an *epicycloid* (Panel a of Figure 3.4). This is the pattern a planet would make in the Greek system if viewed from above the solar system. The circular motion of the reflector corresponds to the planet's motion on the epicycle, and the motion of the small wheel around the larger wheel corresponds to the circular motion of the center of the epicycle along the deferent.

The purpose of the Greek epicyclic geometry is to mimic retrograde motion. To see that this works, let's view a planet moving according to the Greek epicyclic plan from two orientations. First, imagine yourself in space with a view of the entire epicyclic orbit of a planet (Panel b of Figure 3.4). The numbers in Panel b indicate the planet's position at weekly intervals for 6 weeks. When the planet is making the innermost

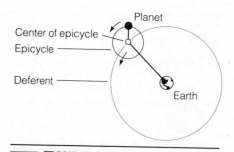

FIGURE 3.2
Epicycle and Deferent

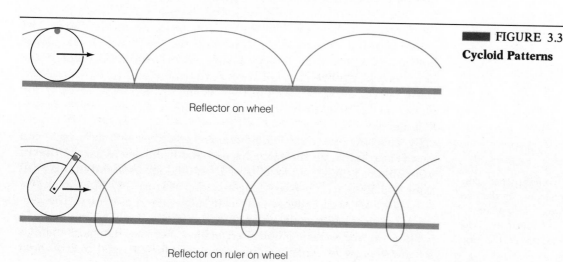

FIGURE 3.3
Cycloid Patterns

Reflector on wheel

Reflector on ruler on wheel

88

■■ FIGURE 3.4

Epicyclic and Retrograde Motion

(a) Two circular motions, one along the epicycle and one along the deferent, produce the epicycloid pattern of a planet in the Greek system. The number of loops depends on the relative speeds of the planet on the epicycle and the deferent.
(b) The motion on the deferent is in the direction from point 1 to point 7, but from point 3 to point 5 the planet appears to move in the opposite direction.
(c) When the epicycloid motion is viewed from the Earth at weekly intervals, the planet moves westward in the sky between points 3 and 5 before resuming its normal eastward motion at point 5.

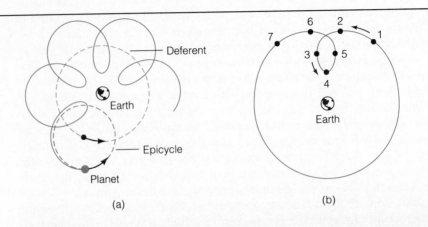

(a)   (b)

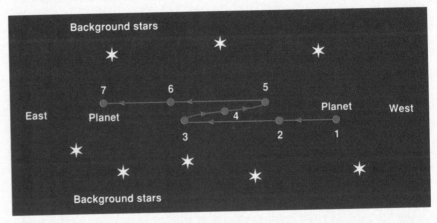

(c)

part of the small loop, weeks 3 and 4, it is actually moving opposite to the motion of the epicycle along the deferent. A planet's retrograde motion on the celestial sphere corresponds to this "backward" motion in the Greek model. Now mentally ignore the planet's distance from the Earth and only view its sideways motion as seen from the Earth. The planet appears to move back-and-forth in the sky (Panel c). The planet first moves eastward on the sky during weeks 1 and 2. As it enters the inner loop at the beginning of week 3, the planet begins to move backward for two weeks, but then renews its forward motion at week 5. The planet moves east, then retrogrades moving west, and finally moves east again.

By choosing the right diameters for epicycles and deferents and speeds of rotation on the epicycles and about the deferents, the Greeks were able to produce a model that accounted for past and future positions of planets with century-long accuracy (Figure 3.5). The Greek system, however, was unnecessarily complicated and arbitrary. The geometric devices, such as the deferent and epicycle, were invented to help explain the seemingly complicated behavior of the planets. Ptolemy's scheme was an *ad hoc* model, one concocted for a special case without

"If the Lord God Almighty had consulted me before embarking on the Creation, I would have recommended something simpler"—Alfonso the Wise on the Ptolemaic system in the thirteenth century.

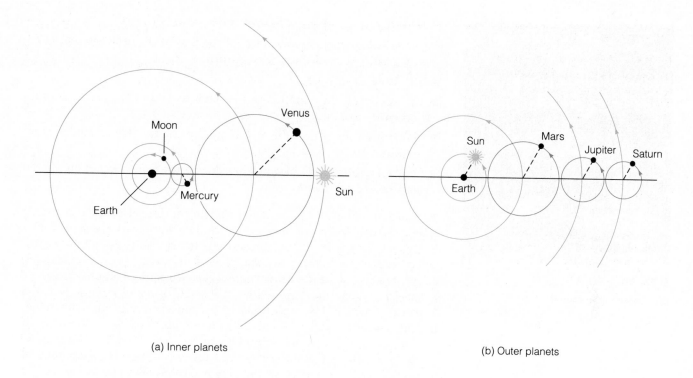

(a) Inner planets

(b) Outer planets

general application. Since no physical reason existed for epicycles, they could be introduced whenever needed. For instance, whenever more data became available and retrograde motions were better defined, more epicycles were added. Nevertheless, despite its complexity, astronomers accepted this system for more than 14 centuries.

The Copernican Heliocentric Model

Nicolaus Copernicus wrote only two astronomical treatises in his life: *Commentariolus*, "Brief Outline," written between 1510 and 1514, is a short summary of his heliocentric model; *De revolutionibus orbium coelestrium* contained the details of his model and was published in 1543, the year he died (Figure 3.6). These writings show that he was dissatisfied with the arrangement of circles in the Ptolemaic system in which the planets actually did not move with uniform speed in perfect circles. He kept the ideas of uniform speed and circular orbits and simply looked for an arrangement of circles in which the planets would move uniformly about a proper center. Copernicus adopted the heliocentric scheme of Aristarchus, using the Sun as a proper center for planetary motion. Furthermore, because he knew of no other mathematical machinery besides epicycles, Copernicus used them in his heliocentric model.

The principal elements of the Copernican heliocentric model were as follows:

■ The universe occupies the space bounded by motionless stars with the Sun at the center.

■ FIGURE 3.5

Configurations of Inner and Outer Planets in the Ptolemaic System

The relative sizes of the deferents and epicycles are shown.

- Both the Sun and the sphere of stars are at rest.
- The visible planets revolve around the Sun in the order Mercury, Venus, Earth, Mars, Jupiter, and Saturn.
- The Moon revolves around the Earth.
- The apparent daily motion of the heavens is due to the Earth's motion on its axis.
- The annual motion of the Sun is due to the Earth's motion around the Sun.
- Planetary retrograde motions are due to the relative motions of the planets and the Earth.

Although this appears very modern on the surface, Copernicus needed epicycles to position the planets accurately because he assumed perfectly circular orbits about the Sun. Planetary orbits are slightly oval, however. Putting the Sun at the center of the solar system and keeping circular orbits did not eliminate epicycles, it required smaller ones.

The Copernican model relied heavily on the same observations as the geocentric model. Although Copernicus himself was a mathematician, not an observer, *De revolutionibus orbium coelestium* did contain about 30 new observations, many from his observatory at Frombork in northern Poland. These few observations, however, were not new empirical facts that could in themselves persuade astronomers to give up the old system for the new.

Regardless of the shortcomings of his heliocentric system, Copernicus was the first to determine the *relative* distances of the planets from the Sun correctly. The term *relative* is important here. Copernicus was able to say that Mars was one and a half times farther from the Sun than the Earth and that Jupiter was about five times farther from the Sun than the Earth (Table 3.1). He simply assigned a value of 1.0 to the distance between the Earth and the Sun. This distance is called the **astronomical unit** and is abbreviated as AU. The absolute size, or *scale*, of the solar system can be obtained by using Copernicus's relative distances and an absolute measure of the astronomical unit. For example, if Mars is 1.5 AU from the Sun, then the distance to Mars is 1.52 × 150,000,000 km, or 228,000,000 km. Copernicus used an accepted value of the astronomical unit that was 20 times smaller than today's. This estimate was made about 250 B.C. and remained unchallenged until the seventeenth century. But the fact that Copernicus did not know the correct, or absolute, value of the astronomical unit makes no difference to the correctness of his scale model where only relative distances are needed.

How could an astronomer without modern instruments, such as telescopes and computers, determine that Mars was one and a half times farther from the Sun than the Earth? All he could see were mere specks of light in the sky, and only five out of the thousands were planets. First, Copernicus's assumption that the Sun was the center of the solar system was absolutely critical. Without it relative distances could not be determined. It is important to realize that the order and sizes of planetary orbits are natural consequences of the heliocentric model. In the

■ FIGURE 3.6
Nicolaus Copernicus
SOURCE: The Granger Collection.

Astronomical unit: The mean distance from the Earth to the Sun; it is equal to 149,598,000 km, or 92,956,000 miles. The modern value for the astronomical unit is obtained from radar observations of objects in the solar system and is accurate to about 1 kilometer (see Chapter 5).

■ TABLE 3.1
Relative Scale of the Solar System

Planet	Distance from the Sun	
	Copernicus	*Modern Value*
Mercury	0.38 AU	0.39 AU
Venus	0.72	0.72
Earth	1.00	1.00
Mars	1.52	1.52
Jupiter	5.2	5.20
Saturn	9.2	9.54

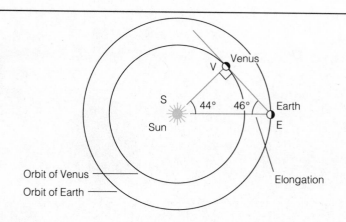

FIGURE 3.7

Geometry of the Earth, Venus, and the Sun at Greatest Western Elongation

Copernicus used this geometry to determine the *relative* distance to Venus. The 46° angle is measured on Earth as the greatest distance Venus is from the Sun.

Ptolemaic system, the ordering although correct, except for the Sun and Earth, was arbitrary. Secondly, Copernicus was an excellent mathematician and a master of geometry. The observational data available to Copernicus were angular positions of the planets on the celestial sphere. Mars was so many degrees south of such and such a star on a certain date, or Jupiter moved so many degrees in a week. Copernicus was able to convert these data into geometric pictures and diagrams to which he was able to apply the axioms of geometry to determine planetary distances from the Sun.

The scaling of the solar system by Copernicus was the first meaningful step in determining the size of the solar system. The method he used for the inferior planets, for instance, requires observations at either of their greatest elongations. Figure 3.7 shows such an orbital geometry for Venus and Earth as viewed from space. The line from Earth to Venus, EV, is tangent to the orbital path of Venus. From the geometry of circles, this line forms a 90° angle with the radius of the orbit of Venus, line SV. Therefore, the triangle EVS has a 90° angle at V and an angle at E that can be measured from Earth. Measuring angle E is not difficult; it is just the greatest elongation of Venus, 46°. Since the sum of the three angles of triangle EVS is 180°, the angle at the Sun, is 180° − 90° − 46° = 44°. Once the three angles, 44°, 46°, and 90°, are known, a triangle can be drawn on paper. Try it! Draw the line SE, the astronomical unit, 10 cm long. Draw another line from E at an angle of 46° to line SE and another from S at an angle of 44° to line SE. Measure the angles with a protractor. The point on the paper where the last two lines meet is the position of Venus relative to the Earth at greatest western elongation. Line SV, the radius of Venus's orbit, will be 7.2 cm long. Since 1 AU was 10 cm, 7.2 cm corresponds to 0.72 AU; that is, the relative distance of Venus from the Sun is 0.72 astronomical units.

The Copernican heliocentric model accounts for the observed retrograde motions of the planets by the relative motions of the Earth and the other planets. Even though Copernicus used epicycles, they were very small compared to the orbits of the planets and could not in themselves generate the observed retrograde motions. In addition, the heliocentric model predicts that both Venus and Mercury will exhibit

MathTools 2: Angular Measurement

██████ FIGURE 3.8

Phases of Venus

The views from Earth show how the fraction of the sunlit portion and the size of Venus vary with its position relative to the Earth. Only the portion of Venus on the side of the line drawn through the planet facing Earth can be seen by observers on Earth (see also Figure 3.23).

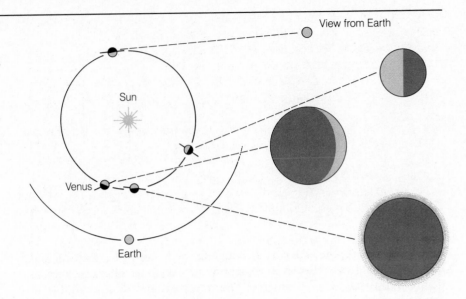

phases, from crescent to whole. As they orbit the Sun, different fractions of their lighted surfaces are seen (Figure 3.8). We see only a sliver of the lighted surface of Venus when it is very close to inferior conjunction because the dark side is facing us. Near superior conjunction when the lighted side is facing us, we see nearly the whole disk lit up. The Ptolemaic system predicts only crescent phases, never a gibbous or full phase for Mercury or Venus. Although these phases are not visible with the naked eye, Galileo later verified this prediction in the early 1600s with telescopic observations of Venus, providing strong support for the heliocentric model.

Finally, the Copernican model predicted something different. If the Earth is moving around the Sun, then it may be possible to see this motion reflected in the distant stars. Try the following experiment. Extend one arm in front of you with your thumb up. Now look at your thumb first with your right eye, then with your left eye; alternate closing and opening your eyes. Your thumb appears to move back and forth relative to the background. This motion is called *parallax*. Now imagine observing a star from Earth in January and again in July. The Earth's position in January corresponds to your right eye and its position in July corresponds to your left eye; the star corresponds to your thumb. Copernicus thought that astronomers should not see stellar parallax as the Earth orbits the Sun because the universe was too large and the stars too far away. He was right, parallax motion is so small that it could not be detected in his time. Astronomers had to wait until the middle of the nineteenth century before detecting parallax.

Although Copernicus was not able to sever himself completely from ancient tradition and produce a physically plausible model of the solar system acceptable to all, he did provide a new framework through which humans could view the universe. The Copernican view challenged traditional thought and opened the way for us to think differently about the universe. For instance, the Earth no longer had to be a motionless, stable foundation; it could have many motions, such as orbiting the Sun or turning on its axis. Perhaps the Moon and planets were like the Earth and harbored other life. Furthermore, stars would not have to be at the same distance; some could be close while others could be very far away.

Only a handful of astronomers took much interest in the Copernican model, which provoked very little controversy for nearly 70 years. The Catholic church was also largely indifferent to Copernicus's texts. It placed *De revolutionibus* on the index of prohibited books only in 1616, 73 years after publication, and Galileo's famous trial took place in 1633, 90 years after *De revolutionibus*. Even during his lifetime, Copernicus was publicly criticized only twice, once in a carnival play in 1541 and once by Martin Luther in 1553. Nevertheless, although it was virtually unnoticed for three quarters of a century, the Copernican heliocentric model initiated a complete upheaval in the way people looked at the world around them.

TYCHO BRAHE

In the mid-sixteenth century, the Ptolemaic system was taught in practically all universities. On the whole, the astronomical community had no compelling reason to adopt the Copernican view. Nevertheless, this was to change. A conjunction between Jupiter and Saturn in 1563, observed by a young Danish nobleman Tycho Brahe (1546–1601), was very poorly predicted (Figure 3.9). The Ptolemaic predictions were a month in error, the Copernican predictions were several days in error. Tycho was greatly disappointed with these predictions. He reasoned correctly that the problem with the predictions lay with the crudeness of existing instruments; that is, if more accurate observations were available, better refinements to the models would be possible, leading to better predictions. In fact, Tycho believed that better observations would allow him to choose between the geocentric and heliocentric models. He resolved to correct the problem by making more accurate measurements.

In 1572 a significant celestial event occurred: a new star appeared in the constellation Cassiopeia (Figure 3.10). The new star was visible from early November 1572 to February 1574; during that time it gradually became fainter and fainter until it disappeared from sight. Tycho observed the position and brightness of the star all through those 16 months. He published his results in *De Nova Stella* in 1573 where he concluded that the new star

is located neither in the region of the Element [Earth's atmosphere], below the Moon, nor in the orbits of the seven wandering stars but in the eighth sphere, among the other fixed stars.

This statement was backed by 27 pages of scientific facts. Even though many other astronomers published work indicating that the new star

"People gave ear to an upstart astrologer, who strove to show that the earth revolves, not the heavens or the firmament, the sun and the moon . . . . This fool wishes to reverse the entire science of astronomy. But sacred scripture tells us that Joshua commanded the sun to stand still, not the earth"—Martin Luther on the Copernican heliocentric model of the universe.

FIGURE 3.9
Tycho Brahe
SOURCE: The Granger Collection.

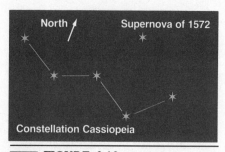

■■■■ FIGURE 3.10

Cassiopeia and the Supernova

Tycho's new star, now called Supernova 1572, was seen very near the constellation Cassiopeia; see the "Observer's Handbook" for more on constellations.

No one has discovered any mistake due to carelessness in any of Tycho's observations.

had moved and therefore was closer, Tycho's observational techniques and instruments far surpassed the others. He also observed the comet of 1577 and showed that it was in the realm of the planets. Furthermore, after observing the comet's motion and being unable to reconcile it with a circular orbit, Tycho suggested that the orbit was an oval. This was the first suggestion of a noncircular orbit for a heavenly body.

Given that Tycho had no telescope and could only sight along peepholes arranged in a fashion similar to rifle sights how was he able to make observations of unequaled precision? Tycho's success was due to his unsurpassed zeal for exact measurement; he improved existing instrumentation and observing techniques in three basic ways:

- He calibrated his instruments.
- He built bigger and bigger instruments.
- He developed new techniques to sight on stars and to measure angles more accurately.

These improvements enabled Tycho to design and build the most advanced astronomical instruments in the sixteenth century for naked eye observing. Although Tycho's instruments were more like a surveyor's sextant than a modern telescope, the data he obtained with them eventually proved good enough to solve the problem of the motions in the sky.

Tycho's idea of calibrating instruments was new. He realized that instruments are not perfectly accurate and understood that if he knew how inaccurate an instrument was, he could correct his observations to take this into account. For example, suppose you bake with an oven that always heats to a temperature 25 degrees less than the oven temperature dial indicates. If you set the dial to 400°, the oven will only heat up to 375°. You could correct for this by either cooking longer or dialing a higher temperature. You would essentially construct a "table of errors" like that in Table 3.2 and refer to it every time you baked. The same principle applies to scientific instruments. They are designed to be sensitive, not perfect. Good experimentalists will construct a table of errors for their instrument and use the table to correct their results. The best experimentalists today always follow this procedure; Tycho was the first to do so.

In the sixteenth century, the observational facts of astronomy were *positions* on the celestial sphere given in angles between two stars, a star and a planet, or a star and the horizon. Tycho's first instrument was a pair of sticks joined together like a drawing compass. He would point one leg to a planet and the other to a star. Locking the legs so that they would not move, he would place the sticks on a graduated circle drawn on paper from which he could measure the angle formed by the two legs. The angle between the two legs of his joined sticks is the angular separation between the star and the planet. Two such observations using two different stars as a reference would allow the planet's position to be located on a map showing the two stars. This is a two-step process. First, the joined sticks are used to measure the angular separation of a planet from two stars (Panel a in Figure 3.11). Sec-

■■■■ TABLE 3.2

Table of Errors for an Oven

Baking Temperature	Dial Setting
300°	325°
325°	350°
350°	375°
375°	400°
400°	425°

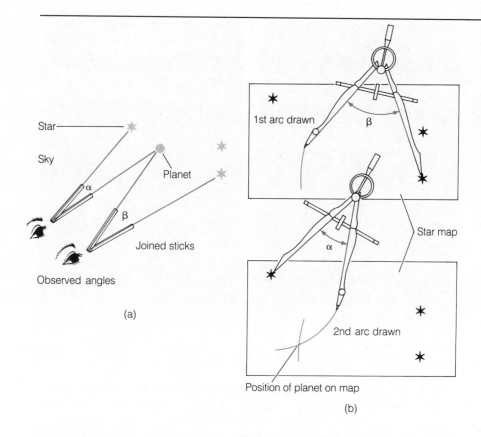

■■ FIGURE 3.11

Position Measurements

(a) Angular distances, α and β, of a planet from two stars are measured. *(b)* Using a star map and a drawing compass set once for angle α and once for angle β, the position of the planet is marked. Several such observations made over many nights allow the path of a planet to be plotted on a star map.

ondly, the stars are located on a star map. A drawing compass is set for one of the angles, and an arc is drawn on the map (Panel b). The same is done for the other angle. The position of the planet is the point where the two arcs cross. A series of such observations over many nights would allow Tycho to follow the celestial motions of any planet, comet, or new star.

Simple instruments, such as the joined sticks or a simple cross-staff, were portable, but two other commonly used instruments, the sextant and the quadrant, generally were not. Sextants, constructed of two arms, one fixed and one movable, were used to measure angles between objects, and quadrants, graduated arcs of 90° with one movable sight, were used mainly for measuring altitudes above the horizon (Figure 3.12). Both instruments, however, could be made very large, and could therefore attain very high accuracy. The reason large size brings high accuracy is that for a given angle, say, that formed at the tip of a triangle, the longer the sides forming the angle, the more divisions a ruler can have at the base of the triangle (Figure 3.13). This means that the angle can be divided into smaller parts, allowing the observer to perceive smaller increments of the angle.

Tycho also improved his sighting devices. The problem with just using two peepholes was that an observer's eye would not always be in the exact center of the nearest peephole. This causes an error in the measured angle since the instrument would not be pointing directly at

■ FIGURE 3.12

Sextants and Quadrants

(a) Tycho's observatory showing an observer using a sextant. *(b)* Tycho's Great Mural Quadrant; the observer at the middle of the far right is sighting through the window at the upper left.

SOURCES: Part (a) painting by Blaeuw. Copyright © G. Tomsich/Photo Researchers. Part (b) from The Granger Collection.

(a)   (b)

the star or planet. Tycho replaced the peephole nearest the eye with a metal plate in which two horizontal slits were cut. The slits were separated by a distance equal to the thickness of a cylindrical peg placed between the sights and the slits. If the observer looked alternately from one slit to the other and saw equal parts of the star projected above and below the peg, the star was exactly centered and the sights pointed directly at the star (Figure 3.14).

■ FIGURE 3.13

Angular Measurements with Large Instruments

Bigger is better. Angle α can be measured more accurately at the base of the triangle than near the apex because more divisions fit between the sides of the triangle at its base, 55 versus 18 in this example.

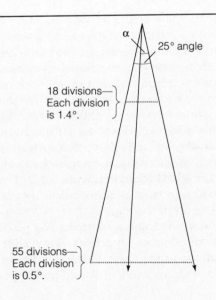

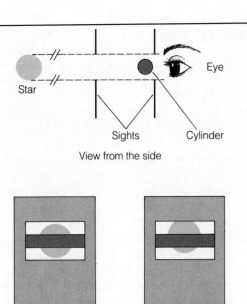

View from the side

Correctly
centered

Offcenter

View from the back

FIGURE 3.14

Tycho's Sighting Device

The cylinder helped Tycho place his eye
in line with the far sight. A correctly centered eye will see equal parts of the star
in both slits.

Tycho's reputation as a methodical observer eventually paid off. He
was given a grant by the king of Denmark to build an observatory,
called Uraniborg, on the island of Hveen just northeast of Copenhagen.
Here he built his finest instruments and made accurate and continuous
observations of the stars, planets, Sun, and Moon for 20 years. He determined the paths of several comets, established the exact orbit of the
Moon, produced an accurate map of the sky of 777 stars, and measured
the length of the year to within just one second of our modern value.
His most important direct contribution to astronomy, however, was his
accurate and continuous observations of the planets. This provided the
data needed to prove that planets orbited the Sun.

Tycho was not able to do this himself, however. He began his astronomical career with the idea that sufficiently accurate observations
would allow him to decide between the geocentric and heliocentric
views of the universe. To this end he became the greatest naked eye
observer the world has ever known. Yet he was not able to choose one
model over the other. Although Tycho saw the advantages of the heliocentric model, he was not able to detect any parallax motions of stars.
Seeing problems with both systems, he derived his own. His model of
the universe placed the Earth at the center with the Sun and the Moon
orbiting the Earth as in the geocentric model. The planets, however,
orbited the Sun as in the heliocentric model. Tycho never worked out
the mathematical details of his model so it never gained acceptance in
the astronomical community. In any event, his model would not have
survived long. A German astronomer, using Tycho's data, refuted the
geocentric model.

Uraniborg or *Uraniburg* translates as
the "castle of the heavens." Besides
being an extraordinary observatory,
Uraniborg was also a magnificent pal-
ace.

FIGURE 3.15

Johannes Kepler

SOURCE: The Granger Collection.

JOHANNES KEPLER

At the end of the sixteenth century, three individuals, Tycho Brahe, Johannes Kepler (1571–1630), and Galileo Galilei (1564–1642), were involved in solving the mystery of planetary motion. Tycho provided the observational data; Kepler revealed the true motions of the planets; and Galileo detected these motions through telescopes, providing strong observational support for the heliocentric model. Let's now examine Kepler's pivotal contribution to the understanding of planetary motion.

Kepler was interested in the answers to two questions: (1) Why were there only six planets? (2) How were orbital periods related to distances from the Sun? The apparent answer to the first question is found in Kepler's first published scientific work, *Mysterium Cosmographicum*, "The Cosmic Mystery," which was printed in 1596 (Figure 3.15). In this book he introduced two new and important concepts that were to motivate him for the rest of his life. Kepler imagined that the spheres supporting the planets might be separated by invisible **regular solids.** A regular solid is a three-dimensional figure in which (1) all edges are of equal lengths; (2) all facing sides have equal areas; and (3) all corners and angles between corners are the same. Only five regular solids are possible. For example, a cube is a regular solid. All of its edges are the same length, all corners have 90° angles, and all six surfaces have the same area. The four other regular solids are shown in Figure 3.16 along with the cube. Because the six planets would have five spaces between their orbital spheres, Kepler's idea was to nest the five regular solids, like nested wooden dolls, so that they would fill the spaces between the planetary spheres (Figure 3.17). Of course, the existence of only five regular solids had nothing to do with the fact that only six planets were known in the sixteenth century. Nevertheless, this hypothesis seems to have been responsible for much of Kepler's work.

The second concept was that a *physical force* moved the planets. Astronomers knew that the outer planets not only took longer to orbit the Sun, but also moved slower in their orbits. Kepler hypothesized that a force that *diminished with distance* would account for the orbital behavior of the planets. A planet close to the Sun, for instance, would feel a stronger force than a distant planet and would therefore move faster. The concept of a physical force in itself was a monumental step in our cultural development. Kepler was on the verge of assigning real physical causes to celestial motions. This would force him to construct an entirely new concept of the universe. The idea of a physical force would not allow him to simply add more epicycles, spheres, or whatever to his system.

Kepler and Tycho met for the first time on February 4, 1600, when Kepler began working as Tycho's assistant. Tycho knew that the motions of Mars were the most difficult to decipher. Neither the Ptolemaic nor the Copernican model could predict the positions of Mars as accurately as Tycho could measure them. Tycho immediately put Kepler to work on the problem, but Kepler found it very difficult to work with Tycho mainly because Tycho did not supply Kepler with enough data to permit significant progress. Only after Tycho's death in 1601 was Kepler able to obtain all of Tycho's data. Kepler then spent eight years analyzing these data. Kepler's study of the orbit of Mars is described step by step in his *Astronomia Nova*, "The New Astronomy," published in 1609.

The analysis of Tycho's Mars data was a mathematical nightmare; the solution could only be obtained by trial and error. Kepler approached the problem of Mars with the geometry of epicycles and deferents, circular motion, and uniform speed. Over four years Kepler made 70 attempts, which cover 900 pages of folio in small writing, to find an orbit for Mars that agreed with Tycho's measurements. His final orbit, which included combinations of uniform motion and circles, agreed with 10 of Tycho's opposition measurements of Mars to within 2′ of arc.

At first Kepler was overjoyed; but, when he compared his new orbit with two more observations by Tycho, he found that the difference between his orbit and the data was 8′ of arc. He then took a bold step—he declared his cherished orbit of Mars to be wrong! All that work, all those years, he threw away. Why? Why didn't he just brush aside 8′ of arc and say that the predictions from his orbit were good enough? They were certainly better than those based on any other model. In the past with both the Copernican and Ptolemaic systems, any differences were either ignored or another epicycle was added. Not Kepler—he had Tycho's data! The uncertainties in Tycho's data were much less than 8′ of arc. That meant if an orbit did not predict the position measured by Tycho within 1′ or 2′ of arc, the orbit was *wrong*. That is, Kepler had developed a hypothesis of the orbit of Mars, and it failed the test predicting the position of Mars for all observations. Being well aware of Tycho's abilities, Kepler realized he had to start over from the beginning.

Where was the beginning now? The idea was to obtain the orbit of Mars; that is, to be able to draw it on paper. Tycho's observations were only positions on the sky that resulted from a combination of the Earth's motion and that of Mars. If Kepler knew the orbit of either the Earth or Mars, he could easily compute the orbit of the other. Kepler devised an ingenious method using Tycho's observations of Mars to obtain the Earth's orbit and discovered that the Earth's orbit was *not* circular. The orbital shape he found after plotting the orbit on paper was some sort of oval, but he could not give its mathematical form. He eventually discarded the circles of Ptolemy and Copernicus.

Kepler also discarded the idea of uniform motion. He found that Earth's orbital speed varied at different times of the year such that it moved fastest when it was closest to the Sun and slowest when it was farthest from the Sun. He showed that an imaginary line connecting the Sun and the Earth sweeps out equal areas during equal time intervals. As Figure 3.18 shows, the area swept out in a two-month interval by a planet near its closest point to the Sun, its *perihelion* (position 2), was equal to the area swept out near its farthest point from the Sun, its *aphelion* (position 5), in the same interval of time. When the Earth is

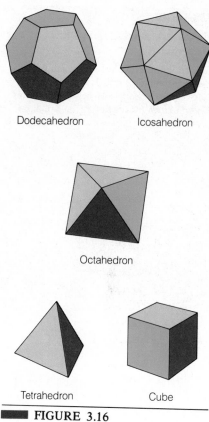

Dodecahedron   Icosahedron

Octahedron

Tetrahedron   Cube

■ FIGURE 3.16

Five Regular Solids

■ FIGURE 3.17

Nested Regular Solids in Two Dimensions

Kepler envisioned that the five spaces between the six planetary spheres were filled with the five regular solids. Here four spheres are shown with three nested regular solids.

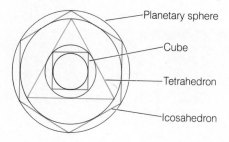

Planetary sphere

Cube

Tetrahedron

Icosahedron

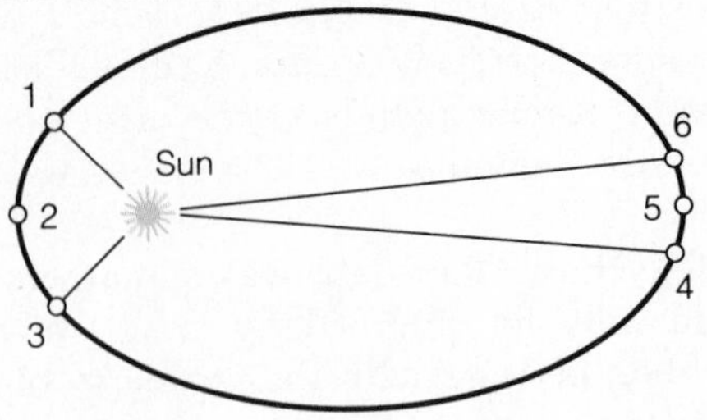

FIGURE 3.18

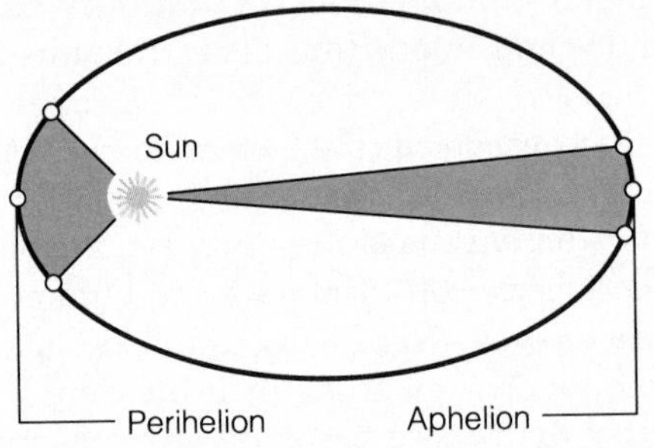

Equal Areas and Equal Time Intervals

The time intervals between each set of points, 1 and 2, 2 and 3, 4 and 5, and 5 and 6, are the same. At perihelion, point 2, the planet moves fastest; at aphelion, point 5, it moves slowest. The areas of the shaded regions are the same.

What we now call Kepler's second law of planetary motion was actually discovered before what we call his first law of planetary motion. Kepler discovered how the orbital speed of a planet varied before he could mathematically describe the orbit.

TABLE 3.3 Eccentricities

Venus	0.007
Neptune	0.010
Earth	0.017
Uranus	0.046
Jupiter	0.048
Saturn	0.056
Mars	0.093
Mercury	0.206
Pluto	0.248
Halley's comet	0.967

far from the Sun and traveling slower, the imaginary line makes long skinny triangles; when the Earth is close the Sun and traveling faster, the triangles are fatter. Both triangles cover the same area. We call this simple relation Kepler's **second law of planetary motion.** It implies that the closer a planet is to the Sun in its orbit, the faster it moves. When Kepler reversed the process in order to obtain Mars' orbit, he was able to test his second law—it worked for Mars as well.

The true orbit of Mars was even less of a circle than the Earth's. It took almost two years for Kepler to realize that its orbital shape is that of an **ellipse.** An ellipse is the shape of a circle when viewed at an angle. Hold a dinner plate in front of you face on; the edge of the plate forms a circle. Now tilt the plate; the edge seen forms an ellipse. Since a circle can be tilted at many angles, ellipses have many shapes (Figure 3.19). The property of an ellipse that describes its shape is its **eccentricity.** Figure 3.20 shows the various parameters that mathematically define eccentricity. The two points F_1 and F_2 are called the *foci* of the ellipse. If we call F the distance between F_1 and F_2 and A the length of the long diameter, or major axis, the eccentricity, e, is defined as $e = F/A$. A circle is a special case of an ellipse with $e = 0$; when the two foci are placed exactly at the center, F equals zero. The largest eccentricity is $e = 1.0$, when F approaches the length of A. Table 3.3 lists the eccentricities of the orbits of the planets and Halley's comet.

The statement that planets move in elliptical orbits with the Sun at one focus is Kepler's **first law of planetary motion.** Note that this law

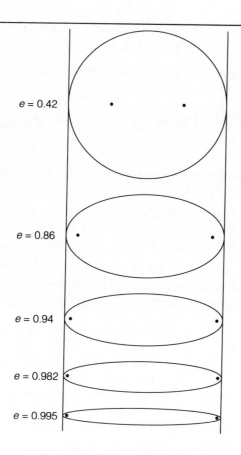

Ellipses with Different Eccentricities

The two points within each ellipse are the foci.

not only give the shape of planetary orbits but states that the Sun is located at one of the foci of the ellipse—*the Sun is not located at the center of the orbit*. Furthermore, because an ellipse can be described by a mathematical equation and because the speed of a planet at any position can also be described mathematically, the statements that an orbit is an ellipse and that it sweeps out equal areas in equal time intervals are precise mathematical statements; they are scientific laws.

Kepler discovered one more law and tucked it away in his book *Harmonice Mundi* (1619), "Harmony of the Worlds." This book was a continuation of his quest to discover why there are only six planets. He finally found the mathematical relation, which he set out to obtain in 1596, between the size of a planetary orbit and its orbital period, P. Since the distance from the Sun varies in an elliptical orbit, we define the orbital size as equal to half of the major axis and call this distance the *semimajor axis*, a; $a = \frac{1}{2}A$. Kepler's **third law of planetary motion** states that the fraction a^3/P^2 is the same for all of the planets.

The constancy of this ratio implies that, if the period of a planet is known in Earth years, its semimajor axis in astronomical units is the cube root of P^2. For instance, if a planet has a period of 8 Earth years, then it semimajor axis is the cube root of 8^2: $(8^2)^{1/3} = (8 \times 8)^{1/3} = (64)^{1/3} = (4 \times 4 \times 4)^{1/3} = 4$, or $a = 4$ astronomical units. The ratio a^3/P^2

MathTools 2: Powers and Roots $\sqrt{}$

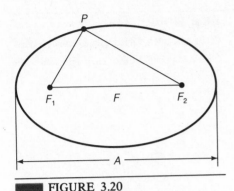

FIGURE 3.20

Geometrical Parameters of the Ellipse

For a planet P orbiting the Sun, F_1 and F_2 are the foci of the ellipse and the semimajor axis is ½ A. The Sun is located at one of the foci. F is the distance between F_1 and F_2, and the eccentricity, e, is F/A.

P^2 for the Earth always equals 1 if P and a are given in years and astronomical units, respectively. That is, since a^3/P^2 is the same for all planets, then

$$\frac{(a_{planet})^3}{(P_{planet})^2} = \frac{(a_{Earth})^3}{(P_{Earth})^2} = 1$$

so that $a^3 = P^2$, or $a = (P^2)^{1/3}$. Kepler's third law applies to any object orbiting the Sun; its distance can be determined from its observed orbital period.

Kepler's Three Laws of Planetary Motion can be summarized as follows:

■ *First law:* Planets orbit the Sun in elliptical orbits with the Sun at one focus.

■ *Second law:* The imaginary line from the Sun to an orbiting planet sweeps over equal areas in equal time intervals.

■ *Third law:* The squares of the orbital periods of planets are proportional to the cubes of their semimajor axes.

These three laws are based on facts; they are generalizations of accurate data. Kepler replaced the cumbersome epicyclic machinery with three mathematical laws that allowed the past and future positions of the planets to be predicted with accuracies more than 10 times better than was previously possible with either the Ptolemaic or the Copernican model. Kepler started with traditional concepts, such as circular motion and epicycles, but threw them away when they did not work. Little by little, he dumped the ballast of antiquity until he was left with the first physical laws of nature and the beginnings of a new science. He replaced the universe of spheres, circles, and epicycles with real planets orbiting the Sun, controlled by hitherto unthought of forces.

GALILEO GALILEI

Galileo Galilei (1564–1642) was born in Pisa to parents of moderate wealth (Figure 3.21). Although he began to study medicine at the university, his natural abilities led him to mathematics. His brilliance in mathematics earned him a position as professor of mathematics and astronomy at Pisa in 1589 and later at the University of Padua. Galileo was a contemporary of Kepler but, although they exchanged correspondence, it was usually one way; Galileo responded only twice to Kepler's many letters. Galileo's failure to correspond was due not to a lack of high regard for Kepler but to his belief that Kepler's work was only a small part of the study of motion. Galileo considered his own work more fundamental in that he was seeking the more general principles that underlie all motion, celestial and terrestrial. Like Tycho Brahe, Galileo collected data that proved to be critical for the development of science. Galileo made important observations with telescopes that provided very strong support for a heliocentric view of the universe, and he laid the foundations for experimental physics.

■■■ FIGURE 3.21
Galileo Galilei Demonstrating His Telescope in Venice
SOURCE: The Granger Collection.

Observational Astronomer

In 1609 Galileo heard of the invention of the telescope and commenced to build several for himself. All of them were refractors; that is, light from distant sources was brought to a focus by being bent, or refracted, by glass lenses. Because a larger image is produced by lenses with long focuses, Galileo made his instruments quite long; the last had a length of 4 feet. The primitive design he used was capable of very limited magnification; his telescopes ranged from about 3 power for the first to a magnification of 33 times for his last. These were clearly not "powerful" telescopes by today's standards, but their optical quality was good enough for Galileo to make significant observations.

See Module 2, "Astronomical Instruments and Telescopes," for more on refraction and telescopes.

Galileo pointed his telescopes to the heavens—and changed our view of the universe. He was the first to report telescopic observations of the heavens and did so in a small book *Sidereus Nuncius*, "Sidereal Messenger," in which he reported observations of new stars, mountains on the Moon, moons of Jupiter, phases of Venus, and spots on the Sun. These observations were significant because they cast doubt on the view of the perfection of the heavens promoted by Aristotle and Plato and because they illuminated the deficiencies in the Ptolemaic model of the universe.

In Galileo's time, the study of nature was essentially the study of the works of Aristotle and Plato. Both these early Greek philosophers promoted the idea that the heavens were perfect and unchanging. They regarded distortions of the Earth, such as mountains and valleys, as the products of the corrupt processes of change. The assumption of uniform circular motion of celestial objects, for instance, reflected the idea of the perfection of the heavens. Galileo, however, found the heavens far

■ FIGURE 3.22

The Moon As Sketched by Galileo

SOURCE: Reproduced by permission of the Trustees of the Science Museum.

from perfect. His observations of the Moon revealed lunar mountains, valleys, and vast flat dark areas (Figure 3.22). Clearly, the Moon was not a perfect sphere. The Sun was also blemished; Galileo found dark spots on its surface. Furthermore, these spots appeared to travel around the Sun about once a month. Galileo took this as evidence of the rotation of the Sun. If the Sun could rotate, perhaps the Earth could also!

Galileo's observations of the planets revealed that they were disks, not pinpoints of light. This indicated that they were closer to the Earth than the stars. The planets also exhibited regular change. Venus, for instance, cycled through phases, from crescent to gibbous, as did the Moon. Phases for Venus implied that it shone by reflected light and revolved around the Sun (Figure 3.23). The Ptolemaic system predicted that Venus would never be viewed at gibbous or full phase. The inability of the geocentric model to account for the new data from telescopic observations clearly indicated that the geocentric model was not a good

■ FIGURE 3.23

Relative Size of Venus Correlates with Its Phase

Shown are the phases of Venus from inferior conjunction (top left) to superior conjunction (lower right).

SOURCE: New Mexico State University Observatory.

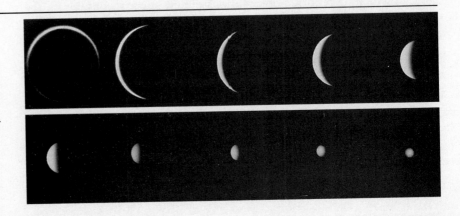

model. On the other hand, the phases of Venus are a natural consequence of a heliocentric model.

A further blow to the geocentric view came from observations of Jupiter. Galileo discovered four moons that revolved around Jupiter (Figure 3.24). Except for comets, these moons were the first new planetary bodies discovered in recorded history and bear Galileo's name, the Galilean moons. This discovery showed that centers of motion other than the Earth existed. Thereafter it was not possible to believe in a purely geocentric universe unless, of course, Galileo's observations were ignored.

The observations Galileo made of the rings of Saturn were the most puzzling. Galileo's telescopic optics were so poor that when he looked at Saturn he could only see a planetary disk with two appendages on each side; they looked like handles (Figure 3.25). Galileo thought that

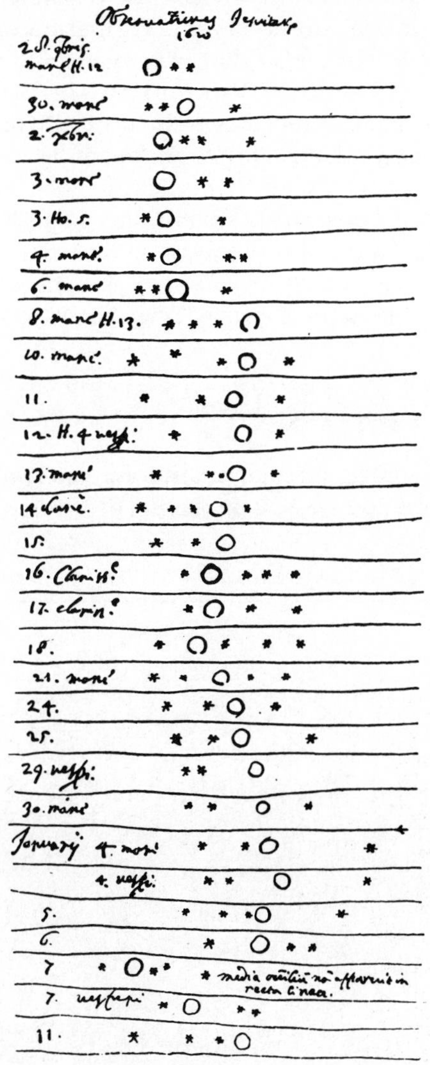

FIGURE 3.24

Sketches of the Positions of the Moons of Jupiter by Galileo

The circle represents Jupiter and the asterisks represent the locations of Jupiter's moons. The moons are seen to move back and forth.

SOURCE: Yerkes Observatory.

Drawings of Saturn by Galileo

Sketches of what Galileo called the "triple nature" of Saturn from a letter he wrote in December 1612 to his friend Marcus Welser.

SOURCE: Ann Ronan Picture Library.

Saturn had two bright moons. About 50 years later astronomers deduced that these appendages were rings, not moons. Finally, Galileo discovered many more stars than were visible with the unaided eye. In the hazy streak on the celestial sphere we call the Milky Way, Galileo saw hundreds more stars, much fainter than those he could see without a telescope. These observations cast doubt on Greek natural philosophy because it showed that Greek knowledge was limited.

Galileo clearly spelled out his support for the Copernican heliocentric model in his book *Dialogo dei Due Massimi Sistemi*, "Dialogue on the Two Great World Systems." This book reached a wide audience because it was published in Italian, not Latin. Furthermore, Galileo had the ability to popularize science so that everyone could understand intricate and complicated results. Unfortunately, he presented his arguments supporting the Copernican view so forcefully that he came under fire from the Roman Catholic church. Although he was tried for political and religious reasons rather than scientific, he was forced to give a public denial of the Copernican system and was placed under house arrest for the last decade of his life. But the investigation of nature cannot be halted by house arrest or censorship. Although science in Italy was dealt a severe blow, the center of scientific investigation moved to northern Europe.

In 1983 after the Roman Catholic church reexamined the evidence against Galileo, the church admitted that it had erred and cleared Galileo's name.

Experimental Physicist

Galileo accepted uniform circular motion for celestial objects, but determined for himself how objects on the Earth moved (Figure 3.26). Gal-

Galileo's Heliocentric Model of the Universe

Galileo drew planetary orbits as circles, not ellipses.

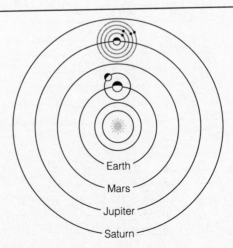

Earth

Mars

Jupiter

Saturn

ileo was responsible for introducing precise measurement to *mechanics*, the study of the motions of material bodies. Before Galileo, scientists studied the universe using philosophical arguments and discussions rather than performing experiments. Galileo changed all that.

Galileo's interest in mechanics grew out of his study of pendulums. He showed that the period of the swing of a pendulum depended only on its length, not on the size of its swing. The study of pendulums eventually led to the development of pendulum clocks. Galileo also studied the motion of projectiles by separating it into horizontal motion and vertical motion. He used inclines to approximate vertical motion because motions down inclined planes were slower than those of falling objects, enabling him to make more accurate measurements (Figure 3.27). Galileo predicted, and then verified, that the distance a ball falls or rolls down an incline is proportional to the square of the length of time it has fallen or rolled (Figure 3.28); that is, distance $\propto$ (time)^2. For instance, if a ball rolled 1 meter in 1 second, then it would travel 4 meters in 2 seconds, and 9 meters at the end of 3 seconds. He also found that its speed increased uniformly. The same ball rolling down the incline would be traveling at 2 meters per second after the first second. At the end of 2 seconds, it would be moving at 4 meters per second, and at the end of 3 seconds, it would be moving at 6 meters per second Galileo expressed this also in mathematical terms: velocity $\propto$ time.

Galileo discovered that, in both aspects of vertical motion, the motion does not depend on the weight of the rolling ball or of a falling object. Consider the famous experiment attributed to Galileo in which two objects of different weights are dropped from a height. Galileo's equations imply that both objects will hit the ground at the same time. This is true if air resistance does not influence the motion. For example, on Earth if a feather and a lead ball are dropped at the same time, the lead ball will reach the ground first. Astronauts did a similar experiment on the Moon, which has no air, and found that a hammer and a feather fell at exactly the same rate, reaching the ground at the same time.

When Galileo studied horizontal motion, he discovered that every object resisted *change* in its motion. For example, you must push a box

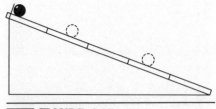

■ FIGURE 3.27

Incline Planes

Galileo did experiments in mechanics by rolling objects down incline planes. This allowed him to slow the "fall" of an object so that he could make accurate time and velocity measurements.

MathTools 2: Proportions a/b

■ FIGURE 3.28

Plots of Galileo's Experimental Results

(a) The distance a ball rolls down an incline as a function of time. *(b)* The velocity of the ball after an interval of time.

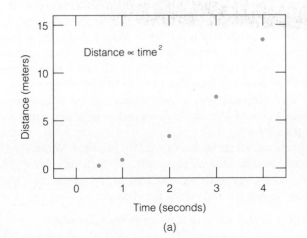

(a)

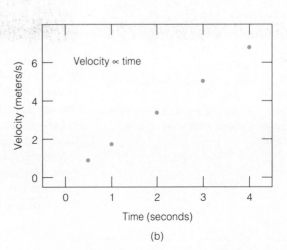

(b)

FIGURE 3.29

Isaac Newton Experimenting with Prisms

SOURCE: The Granger Collection.

"If I have been able to see farther, it was because I stood on the shoulders of giants"—Newton referring to the works of Kepler, Galileo, Descartes, and others before him.

that is at rest to get it moving. Once the box is moving, Galileo realized that it would continue to move unless something slowed it down. This property of a body that resists changes in motion is called *inertia*. Aristotle supposed that the natural state of matter was at rest; that is, a rolling ball came to rest because it is natural. Galileo's experiments showed that a rolling ball came to rest because it was *forced* to stop moving. A hockey puck can slide a long way on ice but only a short distance on a wooden floor because there is less friction between the puck and the ice than between the puck and the floor. Friction represents a *force* that acts to slow the motion of the puck. Galileo saw that if all friction were removed, an object would continue to move at a constant speed. The concept of inertia and force was to be very important for the further development of science.

ISAAC NEWTON

The English physicist Isaac Newton (1642–1727) lived in a scientific community vastly different from that of Copernicus, Tycho, Kepler, and Galileo (Figure 3.29). Those scientists lived in relative isolation, corresponding with other scientists by letter, a very slow process, or publishing their results in books, a very costly enterprise. As a result, scientific knowledge was not widespread. But, by the mid-seventeenth century, Europe was teeming with scientific activities; researchers were making remarkable progress in experimental physics and chemistry, mathematics, and biology and medical science. New scientific societies, such as the Royal Society of London (1660) and the French Académie des Sciences (1666), encouraged scientific activities by supporting experiments and circulating knowledge. Scientific journals and international cooperation resulted in a wide interchange of knowledge among scientists in Europe. Consequently, results of scientific work became easily available for others to test, add to, or use as inspiration for further experiments.

When Newton entered Cambridge University in 1661, the scientific world had accepted the heliocentric model. Kepler had produced a mathematical theory that agreed with the observed planetary motion, and Galileo had supplied supporting observational evidence with his telescopic observations of Venus and Jupiter. Although both Kepler and Galileo had cast considerable doubt on the ancient beliefs, the scientific revolution was not yet over. Many unanswered questions remained. What force explains planetary motion? Why do the planets move around the Sun? Why does the Moon not fall to the Earth as does a ball thrown into the air? Newton was a great interrogator of nature. He gathered the information of the scientific world and found answers to these and other questions.

Newton's answers are given in his book *Philosophiae Naturalis Principia Mathematica*, "Mathematical Principles of Natural Philosophy," published in 1687 and commonly referred to as *Principia*. The key to the *Principia* is the concept of universal gravitation:

Every object in the universe attracts every other object.

This principle is based on the concepts of force and mass, which Newton clarified for seventeenth-century scientists in his three laws of motion.

■ *First law:* Every object remains at rest or moves at a constant speed in a straight line unless an unbalanced external force acts on it.

■ *Second law:* The acceleration a produced by an applied force F on an object of mass m is $a = F/m$.

■ *Third law:* If an object exerts a force on another object, the second object exerts an equal and opposite force on the first; action = reaction.

Although these three laws are simple to state, they have far-reaching consequences; entire physics and engineering courses are devoted to studying these laws. In this chapter, our goal will be to explain these laws as they apply to astronomy. The first step is to examine the concepts of force and mass and discover how they, together with the principle of universal gravitation, helped Newton decipher celestial motions.

Force

You already have a pretty good idea what is meant by **force.** Any push or pull is a force, and a force can be accompanied by motion if it is unbalanced. "Unbalanced" simply means that the forces acting on an object are greater in one direction than another. If two opposite but equal forces are applied, no movement occurs. Every time you open a door or pull open a drawer, you apply an unbalanced force. Notice, however, that these motions are really *changes* in motion. The door and the drawer were intially at rest but began to move after a sufficient force was applied. *Force and changes in motion are inseparable; you cannot have a change in motion without a force.*

What happens when no force is applied? Of course, the door and the drawer will remain shut—no force, no change in motion. If an object is already moving and a force is applied, what happens? A force will slow an object down if directed against the direction of travel. Brakes in a car do just this. On the other hand, a force directed along the direction of travel speeds an object up. The gas pedal of a car causes the engine to push the car forward increasing its speed. A push in the direction of motion increases the speed, while one in the opposite direction decreases the speed.

What about applying a sideways force to a moving object? From experience you probably know that if you twirl a ball tied to a string over your head and let go of the string, the ball will fly off. The ball actually flies off in a straight line tangent to its circular path, that is to say, in whichever direction it was going at the moment of release. When you hold the string, however, it applies a sideways force to the ball, causing it to continuously change its direction of travel. Scientists generalize

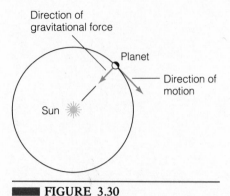

Direction of
gravitational force

Planet

Direction of
motion

Sun

■ FIGURE 3.30

Gravitational Force

The gravitational force of the Sun pulls
the planet sideways. The planet tries to
move in a straight line but is forced into
a curved path.

this and say that a force, if not directed along the path of motion, will
result in a *change of direction*. Consequently, forces, depending on their
direction of application, can result in changes in speed, direction, or
both. We give a name to these changes in motion: **acceleration.**

What happens to an object that is moving but with no unbalanced
forces acting on it? It continues to move—but in a straight line. This is
basically Galileo's concept of inertia. It is experimentally difficult to
show because it is impossible to isolate an object from all forces. However, we can perform experiments that show us what would happen
under the ideal situation of no force. In the last section we used the
example of a hockey puck sliding on a floor and on ice to illustrate the
idea of inertia. The point is that if no unbalanced force is applied to the
puck, it is not compelled to change its motion *or* direction. Its acceleration is zero. Newton summarized all of these ideas in his **first law of
motion:** If no unbalanced forces are applied, then

■ an object at rest will remain at rest, and

■ an object in motion will remain in motion with constant speed and
travel in a straight line.

This law implies two things. First, no changes in motion occur unless
they are accompanied by an unbalanced force. Second, the natural path
of anything moving is a straight line.

Armed with his first law of motion and Kepler's second law of planetary motion, Newton took his first step in deciphering the mystery of
celestial motions. First, because planets orbit the Sun in curved paths,
Newton deduced from his first law that a force was acting on the planets. If no force were acting on them, the planets would travel in straight
lines and would be long gone by now. Secondly, from a precise mathematical description of Kepler's second law of planetary motion, Newton
showed that this force was directed toward the Sun at the focus of a
planetary orbit; that is, planets are prevented from moving in a straight
line by a force acting sideways to their motion (Figure 3.30). Newton
showed mathematically that a force directed toward the Sun satisfies
Kepler's law of equal areas.

Mass

A force acts on the planets. How strong is this force? What is its magnitude? Do all planets feel the same force? In order to begin to answer
these questions, Newton had to clarify the concept of **mass.** Mass is a
measure of a quantity of matter; in general terms, you know that the
greater the mass of an object, the more difficult it is to move. It is precisely this experience that scientists use to define mass quantitatively—
a definition that involves the concepts of force and acceleration.

Sports cars can accelerate, for instance, from 0 MPH to 60 MPH in
less than 10 seconds. How long do you think a sports car towing a 30-
foot travel trailer would take to accelerate from 0 MPH to 60 MPH? It
takes longer, of course. Why? The engine of the car is pulling a greater
load; more precisely, with the trailer attached, the engine is trying to

move more mass. Intuitively, you realize that more force is needed to give the same acceleration to a more massive object. This is expressed mathematically in Newton's **second law of motion:** force = mass × acceleration. Using the letter F for force, m for mass, and a for acceleration, gives

$$F = m \times a$$

For example, let's say that to move a box of mass m with acceleration a, you must push with a force F. To produce the same acceleration pushing 2 boxes, each with mass m, so that the total mass is $2m$, Newton's second law implies that you must push with a force twice as great. Twice the mass requires twice the force to produce the same acceleration. Similarly, if you are limited to pushing with the same force, F, as above, the acceleration of 1 box of mass m is, of course, still a. The acceleration produced by pushing with a force F against 2 boxes, with a combined mass equal to $2m$, is only half of a. Twice the mass with the same force produces half the acceleration.

Newton knew that since a force was acting on the planets, the mass of the planets must be considered in any attempt to calculate the magnitude of the force. He used his third law of motion to deduce how the masses are involved in such a calculation.

Universal Gravitation

Newton's **third law of motion** states that every action is accompanied by an opposite and equal reaction. It implies that, when sitting in a chair, you exert a force on it and, at the same time, the chair exerts an equal and opposite force on you. You do not accelerate because the forces are balanced. If the chair were not capable of pushing back, say, its legs were broken, the gravitational force exerted by the Earth would pull you to the floor (Figure 3.31).

On the other hand, if you dive off a small rowboat, you and the boat will accelerate in opposite directions. In this case, while you exert a force on the boat and the boat exerts an equal force on you, unbalanced forces are acting on both you and the boat. The boat's force on you will propel you out over the water, and your force on the boat will push it away. Although you and the boat experience unbalanced forces with the same magnitude, the individual accelerations are different because your mass and the boat's are different. Similarly, if you jump off an ocean liner, the ocean liner does not perceptibly change its motion. Since the ocean liner's mass is much greater than yours and since the force on it is the same as the force on you, except in the opposite direction, the ocean liner's acceleration is much less than yours.

Considering the force between a planet and the Sun, Newton deduced from his third law that both felt equal but opposite forces. Since the Sun is so much more massive than the planets, the planets experience the greater acceleration. Indeed, it is the Sun's great mass that ensures that it is located near the center of the solar system. He also surmised a remarkable property of the gravitational force between a planet and

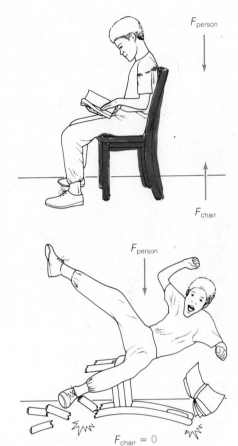

F_{person}

F_{chair}

F_{person}

$F_{\text{chair}} = 0$

■ FIGURE 3.31
Balanced and Unbalanced Forces

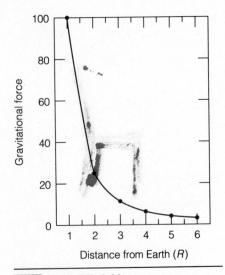

FIGURE 3.32

Gravitational Force versus Distance

The gravitational force decreases with the square of the distance. At 5 Earth radii the gravitational force on an object would be ½₅ that felt at the Earth's surface.

FIGURE 3.33

Equating the Mass of a Planet to a Point

Standing at the Earth's poles is gravitationally equivalent to being 6357 km away from a point with the same mass as the Earth.

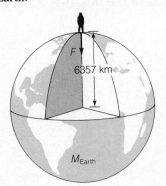

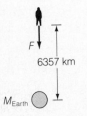

the Sun; this force is directly proportional to the product of the masses of the planet and Sun:

$$F_{\text{gravity}} \propto m_{\text{Sun}} \times m_{\text{planet}}$$

Years before Newton was born, Kepler had laid the groundwork for Newton's next step. Kepler's third law of planetary motion is a precise mathematical statement of the fact that the outer planets take longer to orbit the Sun and move more slowly. Kepler attributed this to a force that diminished with distance; Newton stated mathematically exactly how it diminished. The force exerted on the planets is inversely proportional to the square of the planet's distance, R, from the Sun:

$$F_{\text{gravity}} \propto \frac{1}{R^2}$$

This proportionality implies that if the Earth were twice as far from the Sun, the gravitational force between it and the Sun would be one-fourth of what it now experiences (Figure 3.32). On the other hand, if the Earth were twice as close to the Sun, it would experience a gravitational force four times as great as it experiences at its present distance. Venus is about three-quarters of the Earth's distance from the Sun and has about the same mass as the Earth. Consequently, it feels a gravitational force about twice what the Earth does. Since the gravitational force is greater, the path, or orbit, of Venus is more curved than the Earth's orbit. As a result, Venus has a smaller orbital radius than the Earth, and it moves faster.

Newton further showed that the force due to a large spherically symmetric mass distribution, like a planet or the Sun, was mathematically equivalent to having all of the mass of the planet and the Sun concentrated at their centers. That is, standing on the Earth's North Pole is gravitationally the same as standing 6357 km from a tiny ball that has the same mass as the Earth (Figure 3.33). Therefore, when calculating forces between objects, R equals the distance between the *centers* of the objects.

As a result of his investigation into the forces involved in celestial motions, Newton was able to formulate a mathematical expression for the force acting between the planets and the Sun:

$$F_{\text{gravity}} = G\,\frac{m_{\text{Sun}} \times m_{\text{planet}}}{R^2}$$

Here G is a proportionality constant and is called the *gravitation constant* (its value is given in Appendix B).

Newton's triumph was identifying this force with what is commonly called gravity on Earth. If we apply Newton's law of universal gravitation to objects on Earth, we replace m_{Sun} with the mass of the Earth and m_{planet} with the mass of an object on the Earth. We can measure the acceleration of objects on Earth caused by Earth's gravity by simply dropping them or rolling them down inclined planes as Galileo did. Newton went one step further. He calculated the gravitational acceleration at the distance of the Moon using his gravitational force law and compared it to the Moon's actual orbital acceleration. Because the

Moon is about 60 times farther from the center of the Earth than an object, such as an apple, on the Earth's surface, the Moon's acceleration should be $1/60^2 = 1/3600$ times the apple's acceleration. He found that the actual measured acceleration and that predicted by his law were equal! The force that maintains the Moon in its orbit is the same that causes an apple to fall on Earth; the force is gravity (Figure 3.34).

Thus the force of gravity accounts for the motions of the planets. This force is described by a simple mathematical formula—no crystalline spheres, no epicycles, no uniform speed in circles. The Sun's gravitational force prevents the planets from moving in straight lines.

■ SUMMARY

Ancient Greek observers and philosophers constructed a geocentric, or Earth-centered, model of the universe to predict the positions of planets. Their system used epicycles and deferents to account for the apparent motions of the planets, in particular, their retrograde motions. The heliocentric system also had its roots in ancient Greek science, but it was not until the sixteenth century that Copernicus developed the heliocentric system—with the Earth and all of the planets orbiting the Sun—into a comprehensive model. A Sun-centered system greatly simplifies the description of planetary motion. Retrograde motion, for instance, is an apparent motion caused by the relative speeds of the planets in their orbits about the Sun.

Johannes Kepler gave us the precise description of planetary movement in his three laws of planetary motion. Kepler's formulation was only possible because of the accumulation of accurate data on planetary positions by Tycho Brahe. Galileo, a contemporary of Kepler, is credited with developing experimental physics. His precise measurements of the motions of objects on the Earth's surface later helped Newton formulate his laws of motion. Galileo

also constructed telescopes and observed the heavens, finding strong evidence to support the Copernican heliocentric model of the universe. In particular, the observed phases of Venus highlighted the difficulties of a geocentric system.

Isaac Newton synthesized Galileo's measurements and Kepler's laws into three laws of motion and the law of universal gravitation. With these laws astronomers can predict the positions of planets and the Moon very accurately. We can do this so well that we have sent spacecraft to planets to which the travel time is measured in years. The paths taken by these spacecrafts were calculated using Newton's law of universal gravitation.

The intense period of study of the universe from the time of Copernicus to Newton is called the scientific revolution and resulted ultimately in the development of the scientific method. Scientists, such as Tycho and Galileo, conducted experiments, made observations, and recorded their results. Their techniques defined the first step in the scientific process—collecting accurate data.

Kepler, Galileo, and Newton summarized these data into mathematically precise hypotheses—the second step. They then deduced consequences from them. Kepler predicted the positions of planets, and Galileo and Newton predicted velocities and accelerations of objects moving near the Earth's surface and of planets moving around the Sun. This last step is critical to science; all hypotheses must be verifia-

ble, they must pass the tests imposed by experiment and observation. In the case of planetary motion, velocities and accelerations of planets must be correctly predicted so that their positions can be determined at any time in the future, present, and past.

CHAPTER CAPSULE

Topics and Terms	Review and Remarks
Geocentric model	The Sun, Moon, and planets move around the Earth. The apparent motions of the planets are determined by epicycles and deferents.
Heliocentric model	The Earth and planets revolve around the Sun. Orbital paths are ellipses.
Scientific revolution	It arose from the conflict between the geocentric and heliocentric models. The key figures in the revolution were: Tycho Brahe—provided observations to help choose between the two models. Kepler—derived the first scientific laws: the three laws of planetary motion. Galileo—his telescope observations supported the heliocentric model. Newton—synthesized previous work in his laws of motion and universal gravity.
Scientific approach	Obtain the facts of nature. Summarize the facts as hypotheses. Deduce consequences of the hypotheses and test them.
Criteria for a good model	It accounts for all data. It is verifiable. It explains other experiments or observations. It is simple.

REVIEW QUESTIONS

1. Describe how the details of construction of the Ptolemaic system accounted for the apparent motions and changes in brightness of a superior planet. Can you see any difficulty with this version of the motion of inferior planets?

2. From direct observation of the apparent motions of the Sun, Moon, and planets, which seems more logical, a heliocentric system or a geocentric system? Which would be more simple to model? How would this change if you could view the solar system from a nearby star?

3. Why were epicycles required by ancient solar system models? Why were these models so complex?

4. Even though the Copernican system was heliocentric, it still used epicycles. Why was this necessary?

5. Why did astronomers in the time of Copernicus use the astronomical unit for planetary distances? Could they have used miles or kilometers?

6. We know the planets are illuminated by the Sun. How does the Copernican system do a better job than the Ptolemaic system in explaining the variations in the brightness of an inferior planet? (See question 1 above.)

7. Tycho Brahe's mural quadrant was constructed on a wall and oriented in the north-south direction. As a star or planet passed through that plane, its altitude and azimuth (east-west direction) could be measured. Why were good clocks essential for accurate measurements?

8. Why did Tycho put Kepler to work on predicting the positions of Mars rather than one of the other planets? It has been said that if Kepler had studied Venus he would never have discovered the nature of the motion of the planets. How could this be? (*Hint:* From Table 3.3, find the eccentricities of the orbits of Mars and Venus.)

9. What are the relative times of occurrence of the following: Tycho's observations of Mars, the publication of Kepler's *Astronomia Nova*, the publication of Newton's *Principia* (and the law of universal gravitation), and the first use of the telescope by Galileo?

10. State Kepler's laws of planetary motion *in your own words*. What does the second law imply about the speed of a planet, in its orbit, as it gets closer to the Sun?

11. The formulation of Kepler's laws was primarily a geometric problem for each individual planet. Which of the three laws actually links the motions of all the planets?

12. Review the telescopic observations of Galileo. Which of these do you believe to be most scientifically significant? Which is most interesting to you? Which did Galileo find most confusing?

13. It has been said that had *Dialogue* been written in Latin (rather than Italian), Galileo would not have gotten into difficulty with the Roman Catholic church. Why would that have made a difference?

▰▰▰FOR FURTHER READING

Chapman, A. 1987. Gauging angles in the 17th century. *Sky & Telescope*, Apr., 362.

Gingerich, O. 1986. Islamic astronomy. *Scientific American*, Apr., 74.

King-Hele, D., and R. Eberst. 1986. Observing artificial satellites. *Sky & Telescope*, May, 457.

Lerner, L. S., and E. A. Gosselin. 1986. Galileo and the specter of Bruno. *Scientific American*, Nov., 126.

Maley, P. D. 1986. Photographing Earth satellites. *Sky & Telescope*, June, 563.

Taylor, G. E. 1986. Geostationary satellites. *Sky & Telescope*, June, 557.

ASTROPROBE 3

Inter-planetary Travel: Satellites and Space Probes

Today we often read in the newspaper of a launch of a new satellite. In fact, the most common kind of space vehicle is the Earth satellite. We have found many uses for orbiting electronic equipment. Satellites are used for search and rescue operations, military surveillance, navigation, and communications. Most satellites are scientific research satellites used for experiments and data collecting in astronomy, geophysics, meteorology, oceanography, and physics (Figure 3A.1). We have also launched space probes to Mercury, Venus, the Moon, Mars, Jupiter, Saturn, Uranus, Neptune, and two comets. Future missions include probes to Jupiter, comets, and asteroids as well as manned flights to the Moon and Mars. All of these missions have one thing in common: spacecrafts must overcome the gravitational force that keeps us on the surface of the Earth.

ORBITS

How can a satellite circle the Earth without firing its rockets? Why doesn't it fall back to Earth after launch? Why must a manned vehicle fire its rockets to break out of orbit before landing? Isaac Newton was the first to understand how a satellite, man-made or natural, can orbit the Earth. Although Newton did not have the means to launch a satellite physically, he could "launch" one mathematically, using his laws of motion and universal gravity. Accordingly, he devised a "thought" experiment to explain why satellites stay in orbit.

Galileo and Newton both realized that if air resistance is negligible, the only force on a projectile fired *horizontally* is the gravitational force acting downward. As a result, the projectile's horizontal velocity is unchanged—gravity does not hinder or help the horizontal motion. The projectile drops but does not slow down.

Furthermore, two projectiles fired horizontally from the same height at different velocities will strike the ground at the *same* time. This is the same length of time needed for an object without any horizontal motion to fall from the same height. Although this is hard to believe at first, you can build a simple apparatus to prove it (Figure 3A.2). Again, the reason the fall times are the same is that the only force acting on all three objects is the force of gravity, and it acts downward.

Newton extended these ideas by considering what will happen if the horizontal velocity of a projectile is increased more and more. Figure 3A.3 suggests that a critical velocity is reached at which the projectile never strikes the ground; it is therefore in orbit. Actually, any horizontal velocity produces an orbit. It is just that the projectiles strike the Earth's surface before completing one orbit (Figure 3A.4). The reason for a critical velocity is that the Earth has a curved surface. Because the gravitational force acts sideways to the motion

FIGURE 3A.1

Photograph of the Earth from a Weather Satellite

Local television stations use similar photographs during their weather reports.

SOURCE: NASA.

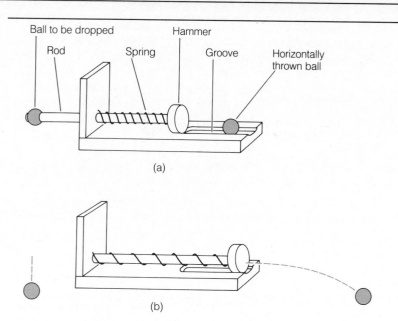

Ball to be dropped

Rod   Spring   Hammer   Groove   Horizontally
                                                              thrown ball

(a)

(b)

of a projectile, its path is also a curve. Accordingly, if the path of the projectile has the same curvature as the Earth, the projectile will never strike the Earth.

Objects near the surface of the Earth fall about 5 meters in one second. The Earth's surface is such that it "falls" about 5 meters from the horizontal every 8000 meters; that is, if you could walk in a straight line that does not curve with the Earth, you would be 5 meters off the ground after walking 8 km, or about 5 miles. If we could fire a projectile at a velocity of 8 km/s, or about 28,800 km/h (18,000 MPH), as it fell 5 meters in the first second of flight, the Earth would curve away 5 meters. The projectile would not strike the Earth—it would be in orbit. Therefore a spacecraft in orbit is falling around the Earth. Similarly, a planet is falling around the Sun. In

True horizontal

Falls 5 meters
in 1 second

Rifle bullet

Artillery shell

Satellite orbit

FIGURE 3A.3

An Increase in Horizontal Velocity

The curvature of a satellite's orbit is the same as the curvature of the surface of the Earth. Its velocity is high enough that it falls at the same rate as the Earth's surface curves.

■ FIGURE 3A.4

Horizontal Velocity Produces an Orbit

Two orbits are shown here. A "low" horizontal velocity produces an orbit about the center of the Earth that intersects the Earth's surface. A useful orbit, of course, is one that does not strike the Earth's surface; that is, if the horizontal velocity is large enough, a circular orbit is attained.

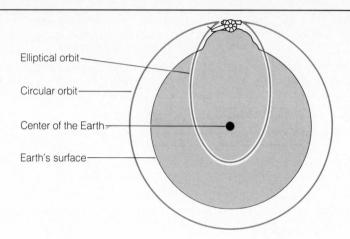

Elliptical orbit
Circular orbit
Center of the Earth
Earth's surface

both cases the gravitational force is acting sideways relative to the direction of motion.

If it were not for the imperfections of the Earth's surface, a rocket fired horizontally at the Earth's surface would travel in a circular orbit around the Earth. Since the circumference of the Earth is 40,075 km, the orbital period of such a rocket would be

$$\frac{40{,}075 \text{ km}}{28{,}800 \text{ km/h}} = 1.4 \text{ hours} = 84 \text{ minutes}$$

This orbital period does not change much with altitude close to the Earth's surface (Table 3A.1). Satellite orbits of a few hundred kilometers above the Earth have periods of about 90 minutes. An orbital period that is of interest in communication is the $23^h56^m4^s$ period. If a satellite orbited the Earth over the equator at the same rate that the Earth turns on its axis, the satellite would remain above one lo-

■ TABLE 3A.1 Orbital Velocities

Altitude	Period	Velocity km/s	Velocity MPH	
0 km	1^h24^m	7.91	17,690	Earth's surface
100 km	1^h26^m	7.85	17,560	
500 km	1^h34^m	7.62	17,050	
1000 km	1^h45^m	7.36	16,460	
2000 km	2^h07^m	6.91	15,470	
10,000 km	5^h48^m	4.94	11,050	
35,790 km	$23^h56^m4^s$	3.07	6,870	Geosynchronous orbit
378,000 km	$27^d7^h44^m$	1.02	2,282	Lunar orbit

cation on Earth. Such an orbit is called a **geosynchronous** orbit and lies 35,790 km above the Earth's surface. Communication satellites are often placed at this altitude. Satellite television antennae that you see at homes and motels are pointed to such satellites. Let's go through the steps necessary to place a satellite in a geosynchronous orbit.

Geosynchronous Orbits

Placing a satellite 35,790 km above the Earth in a circular orbit generally requires three separate rocket firings, or impulses. First comes the launch. The orbit of a spacecraft after launch is an ellipse with the center of the Earth at one focus (Figure 3A.5). If no more impulses are given, the spacecraft will fall back to Earth. This simple up and down is the kind of orbit a ballistic missile is programmed to follow. Most of this elliptical orbit is within the Earth. The *perigee*, or closest point to the focus (at the Earth's center), is near the center of the Earth, and the *apogee*, or farthest point from the focus, is the highest point above the Earth. It is here, at the apogee, that a horizontal rocket thrust must be executed to place the spacecraft into a second orbit. Low-altitude satellites and the space shuttle attain circular orbits by firing their rockets long enough to attain the correct orbital velocity for a circular orbit at the desired altitude.

To reach a geosynchronous orbit, however, the spacecraft must attain a higher velocity than that required for a circular orbit. Consequently, the thrust must propel the spacecraft beyond the circular orbit. Changing the velocity from that required for a circular orbit results in an elliptical orbit. The apogee of the launch orbit now be-

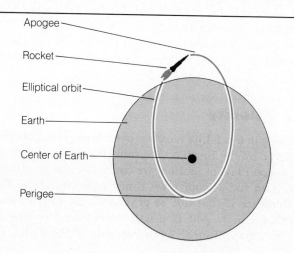

Apogee

Rocket

Elliptical orbit

Earth

Center of Earth

Perigee

■ FIGURE 3A.5

Launch Orbit

After launch the orbit of a rocket is an ellipse with the center of the Earth at one focus.

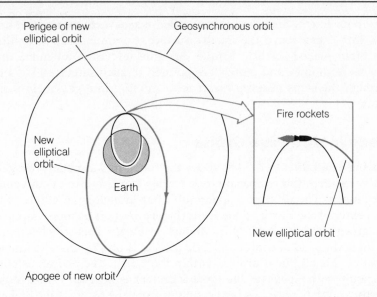

FIGURE 3A.6

A New Elliptical Orbit

The second step in acquiring a geosynchronous orbit is to fire rockets at the aphelion of the launch orbit to place the satellite into a large elliptical orbit.

comes the perigee of an elliptical orbit that has an apogee of 35,790 km above the Earth (Figure 3A.6).

A final rocket thrust must be applied when the spacecraft reaches the apogee of the new elliptical orbit. Kepler's second law of planetary motion also applies to satellites; at apogee, the velocity is lower than it was at perigee. That is, the velocity of the satellite is too low to keep it in a geosynchronous circular orbit. The final thrust increases the velocity of the spacecraft enough to maintain a circular orbit with an orbital period of $23^h56^m4^s$ (Figure 3A.7).

The technique used to maneuver a spacecraft into a geosynchronous orbit is to execute at least two horizontal rocket thrusts. The thrusts increase the velocity of the spacecraft, changing its orbit. The amount of thrust determines the final orbit, be it circular or elliptical. If the thrust is great enough, the satellite can escape from the Earth.

Escape Velocity

The launching of a satellite requires overcoming the continuous gravitational force by the Earth on the launch vehicle. Recall that, using Newton's second law of motion, we can write the gravitational force of the Earth on you as your mass times an acceleration. The acceleration in this case is that due to gravity at the Earth's surface; it is called *surface gravity* and is usually designated by the letter "g." Therefore the gravitational force exerted by the Earth on you is

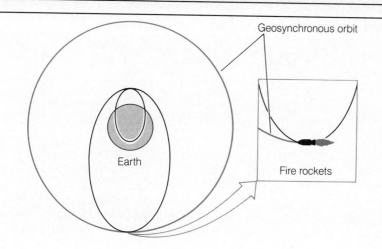

Geosynchronous orbit

Earth

Fire rockets

■ FIGURE 3A.7

Geosynchronous Orbit

Rockets must again be fired to attain final geosynchronous orbit.

$m_{you} \times g$. We give the name "weight" to this force. Your weight is just the Earth's gravitational force on you:

$$\text{Weight} = m_{you} \times g$$

Since we know the value of g at the Earth's surface, we can convert your weight to mass. The unit of weight in the United States is the pound, abbreviated lb, and the metric unit of mass is the kilogram, abbreviated kg. At the Earth's surface 1 kg corresponds to 2.2 lb; an object that weighs 2.2 lb has a mass of 1 kg. To convert your weight to mass, just divide by 2.2. For instance, a person weighing 140 lb has a mass of 64 kg.

At the surface of the Earth, the gravitational force on you can also be written in the form of Newton's law of universal gravity using the mass and radius of the Earth. Comparing this with the equation for weight, we conclude that the Earth's surface gravity is

$$g = G \frac{m_{Earth}}{(R_{Earth})^2}$$

We can generalize this result for any planet by replacing the mass and radius of the Earth with those of the planet. Your weight on any planet, therefore, depends on two factors: the mass of the planet and the radius of the planet. Since masses and radii of the planets in the solar system differ, your weight will be different on each one. Table 3A.2 shows how much a person weighing 140 lb would weigh on different planets. As is common in astronomy, all parameters in Table 3A.2 are given in terms of the Earth. For instance, Jupiter is 11.2 times larger than the Earth, Venus is 0.82 times as massive as the Earth, and the surface gravity of Saturn is 1.07 times the Earth's.

■ TABLE 3A.2 Surface Gravity

Planet	Radius (Earth = 1)	Mass (Earth = 1)	Surface Gravity (Earth = 1)	Weight (lb)
Mercury	0.38	0.055	0.38	53
Venus	0.95	0.82	0.91	127
Earth	1.00	1.00	1.00	140
Moon	0.27	0.012	0.17	23
Mars	0.53	0.107	0.38	53
Jupiter	11.2	317.8	2.53	355
Saturn	9.41	94.3	1.07	150
Uranus	4.11	14.6	0.92	130
Neptune	3.81	17.2	1.18	165
Pluto	0.2	0.002	0.1	14

$$\text{Circular velocity} = \sqrt{\frac{G \times M_{\text{planet}}}{R_{\text{planet}}}}$$

$$\text{Escape velocity} = \sqrt{\frac{2 \times G \times M_{\text{planet}}}{R_{\text{planet}}}}$$

$$= \sqrt{2} \times \text{circular velocity}$$

Since the force of gravity on a person or a satellite varies from planet to planet, so does the velocity needed to maintain an orbit. The greater the gravitational force, the greater the velocity needed to keep from striking the surface of the planet. Furthermore, the greater the gravitational force, the harder it is to escape from a planet. A satellite in a circular orbit around the Earth is still trapped by Earth's gravitational field. To travel to another planet, we must overcome Earth's gravitational field. The velocity needed to accomplish this is called the **escape velocity.**

The escape velocity, of course, is greater than that needed to attain a circular orbit. The escape velocity for the Earth is 11.2 km/s (25,100 MPH). Note that the escape velocity for the Earth is just 3 km/s greater than the velocity needed for a circular orbit. This means that most of the energy expended by the launch vehicle is used to attain a circular orbit; it does not take much more energy to escape. Once a satellite or space vehicle escapes the Earth, it is an interplanetary probe or spacecraft with an orbit around the Sun.

Interplanetary Orbits

The simplest path taken by a spacecraft launched from the Earth and traveling between planets is an elliptical orbit around the Sun that is tangent to the orbit of the Earth and to the orbit of the destination planet. We use the term *interplanetary* to refer to the regions within the solar system outside the atmosphere of any planet. Interplanetary orbits that take spacecraft from one planet to another are called **Hohmann orbits.** For instance, the perihelion of the interplanetary orbit for a trip from Earth to Mars is the position of the Earth in its

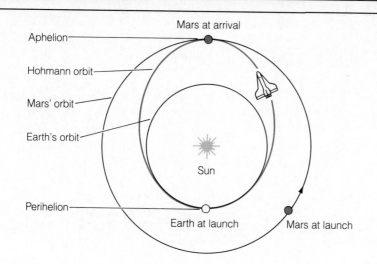

■■■■ ■ FIGURE 3A.8
Interplanetary Orbit

The ellipse drawn in a heavier line is the Hohmann orbit between Earth and Mars.

orbit at the time of launch (Figure 3A.8). The position of Mars at the time of the arrival of the spacecraft is the aphelion of the interplanetary orbit.

Hohmann orbits are fuel efficient. The spacecraft requires an acceleration at the beginning and a deceleration at the end of the trip. Once the spacecraft leaves the Earth with the correct velocity, it is just another planet orbiting the Sun. As a result, it does not require constant rocket thrusts to maintain its orbit. Let's consider interplanetary trips to Mars and Venus.

Interplanetary Mission to Mars. A Hohmann orbit to Mars is shown in Figure 3A.9. The launch to Mars must be carefully timed. Mars and the Earth must be in just the right position at launch so that when the spacecraft reaches its aphelion, Mars also arrives. These configurations of the Earth and Mars occur at intervals of about 780 days. For an interval of a few weeks, called a launch window, fuel-efficient orbits can be achieved if the spacecraft is launched during this short interval.

The time for a one-way trip to Mars is easily calculated from the Hohmann orbital parameters. The semimajor axis of the Hohmann orbit to Mars (Figure 3A.9) is

$$a = \tfrac{1}{2}(a_{Earth} + a_{Mars}) = \tfrac{1}{2}(1.00 \text{ AU} + 1.52 \text{ AU}) = 1.26 \text{ AU}$$

Kepler's third law of planetary motion gives the round-trip flight time:

$$P = a^{3/2} = (1.26 \text{ AU})^{3/2} = 1.41 \text{ years}$$

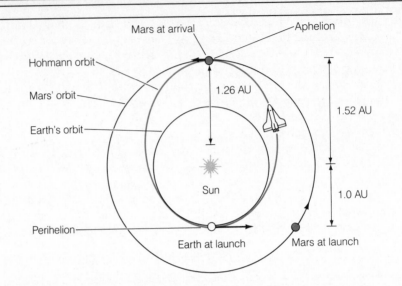

Interplanetary Trip to Mars

The semimajor axis of the spacecraft orbit to Mars is 1.26 AU. A spacecraft needs 8½ months to travel between Earth and Mars. Arrows indicate the velocities of the spacecraft at Earth and Mars.

Accordingly, a one-way trip to Mars will take 0.71 years or about 8½ months.

When a spacecraft is launched from Earth it already has the Earth's orbital velocity of about 30 km/s. Since this velocity is necessary for a circular orbit around the Sun and since the needed Hohmann orbit to Mars is outside the Earth's orbit, the spacecraft will need an increase in velocity to attain the new orbit. Therefore, once in orbit around the Earth, a rocket thrust is executed that allows the spacecraft to move away from the Earth and attain a Hohmann orbit to Mars.

An 8½-month trip requires accurate navigation. Space navigation, like sea navigation, requires a map, a travel plan, a means of determining the ship's location, and a means of correcting the route of the ship if it drifts off course. For an interplanetary spacecraft, the map is the configuration of all objects in the solar system. Unlike a map of the world, the solar system map changes continuously during the journey. The port of call, Mars in this case, is moving, as are other objects that can gravitationally affect the flight of the spacecraft. The gravitational attraction of the Sun on the spacecraft is responsible for most of the accelerations of the spacecraft during its flight. These accelerations determine the actual trajectory of the spacecraft. Furthermore, since these accelerations depend on the distance from the Sun, the spacecraft's distance from the Sun must be continuously monitored. This is done by range measurements from tracking stations on Earth. Once the exact position of the spacecraft relative to everything else in the solar system is known, the exact orbit is determined using Newton's laws of motion and gravity. If the spacecraft is not following its preplanned trajectory, its flight path is changed by firing on-board thrusters. The first trajectory-correction maneuver is usually done a few days after launch and removes most of the velocity errors introduced at launch.

Because the spacecraft is in an elliptical orbit that takes it farther from the Sun than the Earth, the spacecraft's velocity at its apogee (at Mars) will be less than it was at the Earth. In fact, when the spacecraft encounters Mars it will be traveling slower than Mars; that is, it will not have a velocity high enough to be in a circular interplanetary orbit at the distance from the Sun to Mars. The spacecraft must arrive at its apogee "before" Mars so that Mars catches up with it. Since the spacecraft is moving about ten times faster than that needed for a circular satellite orbit about Mars, it must slow down once it is close to Mars to achieve an orbit around the planet.

Interplanetary Mission to Venus. The Hohmann orbit to Venus is similar to that for Mars except that Venus is closer to the Sun than the Earth (Figure 3A.10). The Hohmann orbit has a semimajor axis of 0.86 AU with a period of 0.80 years. Therefore the one-way trip to Venus takes 0.40 years or 4¾ months. Because the Hohmann orbit to Venus lies inside the Earth's orbit, the velocity required of the spacecraft at the Hohmann orbit's aphelion, that is, at Earth, is less than the Earth's orbital velocity. Consequently, after the spacecraft is launched away from the Earth, its velocity must be reduced so that it falls toward the inner solar system. At Venus the spacecraft will have a velocity greater than that of Venus and will catch up with Venus. It will, of course, need to slow down once it nears Venus to place itself into orbit.

Sometimes the upper stage of a launch vehicle trails the spacecraft after launch. The trajectory-correction maneuver is made in part to separate the two vehicles. Velocity errors are intentionally introduced at launch to ensure that the launch vehicle will not follow the spacecraft to Mars or any other planet.

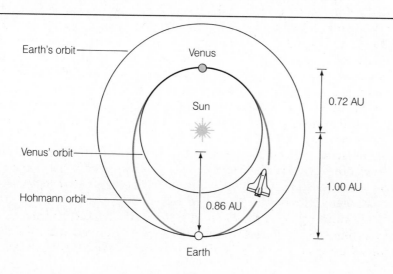

■ FIGURE 3A.10

Interplanetary Trip to Venus

The semimajor axis of an interplanetary orbit to Venus is 0.86 AU, and the trip to Venus takes a spacecraft 4¾ months.

■■■■ TABLE 3A.3 **Interplanetary Flight Times from Earth**

Planet	Flight Time (years)
Mercury	0.29
Venus	0.40
Mars	0.71
Jupiter	2.73
Saturn	6.05
Uranus	16.1
Neptune	30.6
Pluto	45.5

Hohmann orbit flight times are long. Table 3A.3 lists the one-way trip times from Earth to the planets in the solar system. These are the kinds of flight times you can expect to hear about during the next couple of decades of space exploration. If you are in a hurry, however, you must be willing to use more fuel. If you apply continuous or long-lasting thrusts during the flight, the velocity of the spacecraft can be increased. At the same time, your velocity at the destination will be greater and require more energy to decelerate the spacecraft if it is to orbit or land at its destination.

In its exploration of the outer planets of the solar system, the United States used another technique to alter spacecraft orbits. Several spacecraft were launched to fly by Jupiter, Saturn, Uranus, and Neptune. In the 1970s these planets were concentrated in one quadrant of the solar system and would remain so for a decade. The interplanetary orbits were such that as a spacecraft flew by Jupiter, for instance, it used Jupiter's gravitational field to change its direction of travel so that it headed toward the next planet, in this case Saturn. The gravitational field of Jupiter would also increase the velocity of the spacecraft. The velocities attained are much greater than could ever be attained by a direct launch from Earth. This is referred to as a "slingshot" maneuver. It allows one spacecraft to explore the four outer planets, an ambitious but economical mission.

Light and Matter

OUTLINE

Electricity and Magnetism

Electromagnetic Spectrum

Radiation Laws

Chemical Elements

Atomic Spectra

Radioactivity

Summary

Chapter Capsule

Review Questions

For Further Reading

ASTROPROBE 4:
The Forces of Nature

Stellar Spectrum.
ARTIST: Geoffrey Chandler.

128

THE DEVELOPMENT OF THE SCIENCE OF ELECTRICITY and magnetism was as monumental a step for humans as the development of the science of mechanics and gravity. The investigation of electricity and magnetism led to the discovery of the wavelike nature of light and to the realization that all radiations, including X-rays, radio, ultraviolet, and infrared, are also wave phenomena. The most remarkable aspect of radiation is that it exhibits properties of waves and of particles. Light, for instance, can be described as a beam of particles in which the more particles in the beam the brighter the light. Light can also be described in terms of the characteristics of waves, such as length and frequency.

Although much of the light that enters our eyes is reflected off objects, light can interact with matter in more complex ways. The basic unit of matter, the atom, consists of a tiny positively charged nucleus surrounded by a cloud of negatively charged particles. Radiation can cause these particles to move away from the nucleus for short distances or to escape the atom altogether. Such interactions can produce changes in the intensity of light from stars. Astronomers soon realized that by analyzing the light from stars, they could identify the elements making up distant objects and determine their temperatures.

Finally, some atoms are unstable and naturally transform into other atoms. These radioactive elements help geologists determine the ages of the Earth and the Moon and to estimate the age of the solar system.

ELECTRICITY AND MAGNETISM

Copernicus, Tycho, Kepler, and Galileo accumulated experimental and observational data in the study of mechanics, and Newton synthesized their work in his laws of motion and gravity. In the study of electricity and magnetism, called electromagnetism, a similar process occurred: Coulomb, Oersted, and Ampère accumulated a mass of data that were later synthesized by Maxwell. Progress in understanding electricity and magnetism was rapid once scientists began to study these phenomena because major developments in this area came in the nineteenth century after the method of scientific inquiry had been established.

Since Greek times, humans have been familiar with electricity in the form of "static," the kind usually associated today with clingy clothes from drying in a mechanical dryer or sparks generated by walking across a carpet in dry weather. Humans have also long been familiar with the magnetic properties of lodestone, a naturally occurring iron deposit. The Chinese, for instance, invented the first crude compass about 3,000 years ago by suspending a piece of lodestone by a string.

By the eighteenth century, experiments with static electricity showed that it involved two kinds of "charges," which were named negative and positive. Objects with similar charges repelled each other whereas those with opposite charges attracted each other. Americans know the story of Benjamin Franklin (1706–1790) flying a kite in a thunderstorm, but he showed in other experiments that electricity was actually the flow of electrical charges. Today scientists realize that the flow is that of the subatomic particles of negative charges called *electrons*. Any electrical charge has an *electric field* surrounding it as a mass has a gravitational field surrounding it. Other charges in the electric field feel the repulsive or attractive force of the charge, as other masses within the gravitational field feel the force of gravity. In the late 1700s, the French physicist Charles A. de Coulomb (1736–1806) discovered that the form of the mathematical equation describing the attractive and repulsive forces between two charges was the same as that for gravity. That is, the force between two charges, q and Q, a distance R apart is proportional to the product of the charges, $q \times Q$, and inversely proportional to the distance separating them squared, R^2.

Magnets can also repel or attract each other. They also attract certain metal objects. Like gravity and electricity, magnetism's ability to influence distance objects can be described in terms of a field. Iron filings, for instance, outline the pattern of a magnetic field when placed near a magnet (Figure 4.1). The filings experience a magnetic force and align themselves along lines scientists refer to as magnetic field lines. The magnetic field pattern of a bar magnet is known as a *dipole;* it has two poles, north and south, where the field lines appear to emerge.

In 1820 Hans Christian Oersted (1777–1851), a Danish scientist, made a landmark discovery showing for the first time a connection between electricity and magnetism. During a lecture demonstration in which an electric current flowed through a wire, he noticed that a compass needle was deflected when placed near the wire. Since an electric current is composed of electric charges moving through a wire, Oersted's discovery meant that a *moving* electric charge, which has its own electric field, also produces a magnetic field.

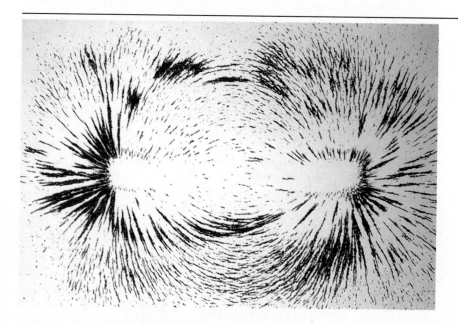

■ FIGURE 4.1

A Bar Magnet and Its Field

Iron filings line up along magnetic field lines.

SOURCE: Rich Treptow/Visuals Unlimited.

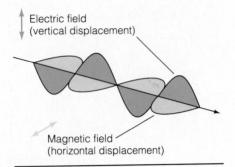

Electric field
(vertical displacement)

Magnetic field
(horizontal displacement)

FIGURE 4.2

Electromagnetic Radiation

Electromagnetic radiation, such as light, is depicted here as two waves perpendicular to each other. One wave represents a changing electric field while the other represents a changing magnetic field.

Wavelength: The distance between successive maxima or minima of a wave; usually designated by the Greek letter *lambda*, λ.

Although scientists such as Oersted in the late eighteenth and early nineteenth centuries realized that electricity and magnetism were intimately connected, this relationship was not expressed in mathematical form until 1873 when the British mathematician James Clerk Maxwell (1831–1879) summarized all the earlier discoveries and experiments in four equations. We call these *Maxwell's equations*, and they form the foundation of the theory of *electromagnetism*. Maxwell's equations play the same role in electromagnetism that Newton's laws play in mechanics—they represent a synthesis.

The modern description of radiation combines both electric and magnetic fields. The radiation emitted by hot objects will be described in the next section in terms of the wavelike nature of light while the interaction of radiation will be described later in terms of the particlelike nature of light.

ELECTROMAGNETIC SPECTRUM

Throwing a stone into a pond generates water waves. If a fishing float is nearby, it will bob up and down as the waves pass. The waves produced by the stone carry information across the pond about the disturbance the stone produced as it struck the water. Light can also be described in terms of waves, which carry information. The human eye, for instance, translates this information into colors and intensities. Light is one aspect of a more general phenomenon called *electromagnetic radiation*.

As the last section showed, nineteenth-century physicists discovered that every changing electric field, such as that produced by a moving charge, generates a magnetic field. James Clerk Maxwell showed further that electromagnetic radiation is really the propagation of changing electric *and* magnetic fields. Figure 4.2 illustrates the inseparability of electric and magnetic fields by depicting electromagnetic radiation as two *electromagnetic waves* perpendicular to each other and traveling in the same direction. A fundamental characteristic of each wave is its **wavelength** (Figure 4.3). With water waves, the wavelength is easily visualized; for it is just the distance between successive wave crests or troughs. Ocean waves, for instance, can have longer wavelengths than waves produced in a small pond by a thrown stone. Similarly, electromagnetic waves have different wavelengths. The colors of a rainbow

FIGURE 4.3
Wavelength

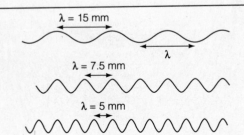

λ = 15 mm

λ

λ = 7.5 mm

λ = 5 mm

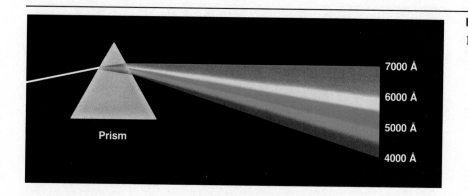

FIGURE 4.4
Refraction

FIGURE 4.4
Refraction

represent different wavelengths of the electromagnetic radiation called visible light. If sunlight is passed through a prism, a rainbow of color is seen. This fanning out, or dispersion, of colors is caused by **refraction** of light by the glass of the prism (Figure 4.4). The difference between red and blue light is their wavelengths. The eye perceives radiation with wavelengths in a band from about 6.5×10^{-5}cm to about 7.0×10^{-5} cm as red light and radiation with wavelengths from about 4.2×10^{-5} cm to about 4.9×10^{-5} cm as blue light.

That such electromagnetic waves exist is readily proved by any working radio. All around us are invisible radio waves, crisscrossing this way and that. They can be detected by the antenna of a radio, which is designed to detect the oscillating electric fields of radio waves. The radio waves cause the electrons in the antenna to move back and forth, producing an oscillating electric current. This current can be amplified and changed to sound by the electronic circuitry in the radio. Our eyes, of course, can detect visible electromagnetic radiation, and instruments have been designed to detect other electromagnetic radiation.

Radio waves and light are both forms of electromagnetic radiation. They have different names for convenience. The nomenclature that scientists use to describe different kinds of radiation reflects the grouping of radiation into wavelength regions that we call collectively the **electromagnetic spectrum** (Figure 4.5). Wavelengths of electromagnetic radiation range from less than a billionth of a meter to millions of meters. Wavelengths of visible light are so short that scientists sometimes express them in micrometers; a micrometer is one-millionth of a meter and is abbreviated as 1 μm. Visible electromagnetic radiation ranges in wavelength from about 0.4 μm for violet light to about 0.7 μm for red light. Astronomers often use a unit of length equal to 10^{-8} centimeters called the Ångström (abbreviated Å), after the Swedish physicist Anders J. Ångström: 1 Å = 10^{-8} cm. Blue light has a wavelength of 4200 Å to 4900 Å and red light 6500 Å to 7000 Å (Table 4.1). Infrared wavelengths extend from red wavelengths to about 100 μm. Although infrared cannot be seen, it can be felt as heat from hot objects, such as ovens and fires. Microwaves are still longer wavelength radiation; they are familar from microwave ovens, which use microwaves to cook food. Television, AM and FM radio, and shortwave radio are longer wavelength radiation and are grouped together as radio waves. On the short wavelength side

Refraction: The bending of electromagnetic radiation as it passes from one transparent medium to another. A prism disperses sunlight into the colors of the rainbow by refracting different wavelengths by different amounts.

TABLE 4.1
Wavelengths of Visible Light

Color	Wavelength, λ
Red	≈6500–7000 Å
Orange	≈5900–6500 Å
Yellow	≈5800–5900 Å
Green	≈4900–5800 Å
Blue	≈4200–4900 Å
Violet	≈4000–4200 Å

■■■ FIGURE 4.5

Wavelength Regions of the *Electromagnetic Spectrum* and Their Nomenclature

Units: 1 mm = 10^{-3} meters; 1 μm = 10^{-6} meters; 1Å = 10^{-10} meters.

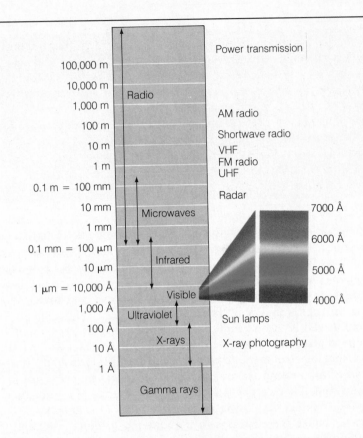

of visible light is ultraviolet radiation from about 0.01 μm to 0.4 μm. This is the radiation that gives us suntans (and sunburns!). The shortest wavelength radiations are the X-rays and gamma rays.

How fast does electromagnetic radiation transmit information? First, it is important to realize that electromagnetic information does not need a medium through which to pass. Water waves, of course, need water to propagate through. Less obvious perhaps is the fact that sound, also a wave phenomenon, requires a medium through which to travel. For sound the medium can be air, liquid, or even a solid. Sound cannot be transmitted in space because space is a near perfect vacuum. Imagine the ignition of the space shuttle engines observed from another shuttle. Silence! No thundering blast would be heard even right next to the engines. Science fiction movies show spaceships firing their rockets in space or blowing up or colliding—all with explosive sound! Of course, the scene might seem a little dull without sound. Electromagnetic radiation, on the other hand, can travel in a vacuum. This is why astronauts on the Moon could communicate with mission control on Earth. Radio transmissions do not rely on a material medium. This is a fundamental difference between electromagnetic waves and other waves, such as water waves or sound waves. In fact, the reason we can see stars is because light is a form of electromagnetic radiation and can therefore travel through the vacuum of space.

Transmitting information through nothing is possible because the electric and magnetic *fields* are what is changing. For instance, a charged particle at rest is surrounded by its electric field. If the particle begins to move up and down, its electric field will also move. At some distance away, another charged particle would experience the changing field since it is within the electric field of the moving particle. In this manner information can be transmitted through space by the changing fields. To put it another way, an electric or magnetic field or a gravitational field is a property of space itself rather than a characteristic of the medium through which the field passes.

How long does it take one charged particle to feel a change in the electric field of another? That is, how fast does the disturbance travel? Experiments and theory both show that electromagnetic waves travel at the **velocity of light.** Modern experiments measure this as 299,792.458 km/s (186,282 mi/s) with an uncertainty of about 0.004 km/s. The velocity of light is also the velocity of all electromagnetic radiation traveling in a vacuum. This is a high velocity. Radio waves take less than 2 seconds to travel from the Moon to the Earth and light only about 8 minutes to reach the Earth from the Sun. Furthermore, if current theories of physics are correct, the speed of light is the fastest speed attainable by anything in the universe (see AstroProbe 16 for more on the speed of light and Einstein's special theory of relativity).

Since all electromagnetic radiation travels at the same speed, the **frequency,** or the number of waves passing any given point in a second, depends on the wavelength of the light. If the wavelength is large, fewer wave crests pass each second and the frequency is low. If the wavelength is small, many wave crests pass each second and the frequency is high. For any wave, therefore, the wavelength multiplied times the frequency equals the velocity of the wave:

$$\text{Wavelength} \times \text{frequency} = \text{velocity of the wave}$$

For electromagnetic waves the wave velocity is the velocity of light. Frequency is described in terms of cycles per second, referring to the number of complete cycles or crests passing each second; one cycle per second is abbreviated as one *hertz*. Short wavelength gamma rays have frequencies as high as 10^{23} hertz while long wavelength radio waves have frequencies of a few thousand hertz. FM radio frequencies are about a hundred million hertz, and AM radio frequencies are between 540 to 1650 thousand hertz. Frequency and wavelength are two equivalent ways to identify electromagnetic radiation.

Electromagnetic waves transmit more information than just their wavelengths or frequencies. They also provide information about the object that emitted the radiation; the radiation laws enable scientists to interpret this information.

RADIATION LAWS

As you read this book, you are emitting electromagnetic radiation. So are all of the objects around you; the reading lamp, the chair, the table or desk, and the floor. In fact, any object with a temperature above absolute zero emits electromagnetic radiation. Most of the objects around us are emitting mainly infrared radiation, which cannot be detected by the human eye although it can be detected by special instruments. Naturalists, for example, use night-vision cameras to locate animals in the dark by their infrared glow, and a sensitive radiation detector would be able to detect infrared and ultraviolet radiation coming from your desk. Most objects are usually not hot enough to *emit* visible radiation. We recognize their color because they *reflect* visible light. A red-hot iron, however, appears red to us, because it *emits* more red light than any other color, although it, like most other objects, radiates mainly infrared radiation. The relative amounts of visible radiation and infrared radiation emitted by an object are controlled by its temperature. The relationship between the distribution of radiation emitted at different wavelengths and temperature is described by *radiation laws.*

Studying the radiation emitted by objects of different temperatures requires measuring only emitted radiation without interference from reflected radiation. Special furnaces can be constructed that have an internal cavity kept at a uniform temperature and connected to the outside by a small hole. Scientists can then change the temperature of the furnace and measure only emitted radiation. These radiators are called **black bodies.** The radiation from a black body is referred to as *black body radiation* because, if the black body temperature were absolute zero, it would be black—no radiation at any wavelength is emitted by an object at 0 K. Figure 4.6 compares the intensity of the radiation at each wavelength by black bodies at different temperatures. The curves rise steeply at short wavelengths, reach a peak in intensity, and gradually decrease at long wavelengths. Note also that the intensity of a hot black body is greater *at every wavelength* than that of a cooler black body. These curves are called **Planck curves** after Max Planck (1858–

Black body: A perfect radiator that absorbs and re-emits all radiation incident upon it; the distribution of radiation from the black body depends only on its temperature.

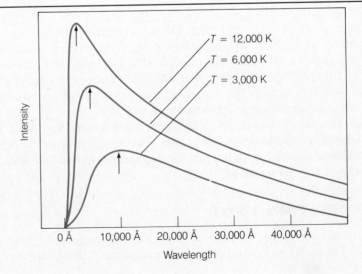

■ FIGURE 4.6

Planck Curves

The Planck curve of the hottest object lies completely above the Planck curves of both cooler objects. This means that at all wavelengths the hotter object is brighter. The arrows point to the location of maximum intensity; this shifts to longer wavelengths as temperature decreases.

1947), who discovered their mathematical form. Black bodies are important to astronomers because stars come close to being ideal radiators.

The intensity of radiation is a measure of the amount of **energy** radiated by a black body. Let's take a moment to define energy. Suppose someone is lifting a 1-kilogram (2.2 lb) box a distance of 1 meter. Physicists describe the energy expended, or work done, by that person as the product of the force applied to lift the box and the distance the box is moved: work = force × distance. The basic unit of force in physics is the newton: 1 newton is the force needed to change the velocity of a mass of 1 kilogram at a rate of 1 meter/second each second. The work done by a person moving the 1-kilogram box a distance of 1 meter while applying a force of 1 newton is defined as 1 *joule* of energy. A joule is roughly the amount of energy a shopper expends placing a pound of beans in a grocery cart. On the atomic scale, energies can be so much smaller than a joule that astronomers often use the *erg*, a unit of energy that is one ten-millionth of a joule.

The amount of energy radiated from a unit area, such as 1 square centimeter (cm^2), of the surface of a black body each second corresponds to the amount of energy in the electromagnetic waves emitted by the black body. The ability of waves to use energy to do work is readily apparent in water waves where objects on the surface are moved up and down by the waves; think of a ship being "tossed around" in a stormy sea. Electromagnetic waves also can do work. The light that enters the eye, for instance, causes chemical reactions that send electrical impulses along nerves to the brain.

The amount of energy in the radiation from a black body or a star is controlled by its temperature. The hotter the star, the more intense the radiation is at *every* wavelength. Two Austrian physicists, Josef Stefan in 1879 and Ludwig Boltzmann in 1884, independently showed that the total energy emitted through each cm^2 of the surface of a black body every second is proportional to its temperature raised to the fourth power:

$$\text{Total energy} = \sigma \times T^4$$

This relation is called the **Stefan-Boltzmann law,** and the proportionality constant, σ, is called the Stefan-Boltzmann constant; its exact value is given in Appendix B. The Stefan-Boltzmann law gives astronomers a way to measure the temperature of a star. The area under a Planck curve, shown as the shaded area in Figure 4.7, for a given temperature is mathematically equal to the total emitted energy per unit surface area per second. This means that, if observers can measure the intensity of the radiation from a star at nearly all wavelengths, they can determine the area under the observed Planck curve of a star. For instance, when astronomers measure the total energy emitted by the Sun through each cm^2 of its surface each second, they determine that the Sun's surface must be at a temperature of 5800 K.

The Planck curves in Figure 4.6 show that the peak in the intensity distribution shifts toward shorter wavelengths for hotter objects. A sim-

Energy: Capacity to do work. This is a qualitative definition. Quantitatively, work is the product of a force and a distance over which it acts. A person expends energy pushing a box across the floor. Forms of energy include elastic (spring), chemical, heat, kinetic (motion), gravitational, and nuclear.

MathTools 2: Proportion a/b

■ FIGURE 4.7

Total Energy under a Planck Curve

The area under a Planck curve is a measure of the energy emitted by a black body or a star summed up over all wavelengths.

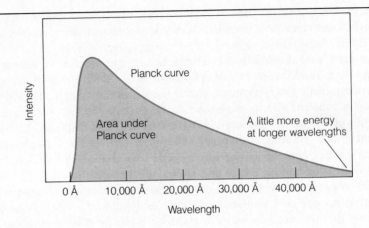

ple experiment with visible light demonstrates what this means. Place a clear glass light bulb into a light socket controlled by a dimmer. When the dimmer is set to allow only a small amount of current to pass through the filament of the bulb, the filament is a reddish orange color. As the dimmer is turned to let more current flow, the filament becomes brighter (because it is hotter), and its color changes to orange, to yellow, and eventually to white. The color change is caused by the peak in the emitted radiation shifting to shorter wavelengths as the current heats the filament. It eventually turns white because, although it emits its greatest intensity in wavelengths between green and blue, the filament is emitting strongly at all colors, which mix together to produce white light.

In 1893 the German physicist Wilhelm Wien (1864–1928) discovered the mathematical relationship, called **Wien's displacement law,** between the wavelength of maximum intensity, λ_{max} (in centimeters), of a Planck curve and the temperature (in Kelvins) of the emitting black body:

$$T = \frac{0.29}{\lambda_{max}}$$

Wien's law allows astronomers to estimate the temperatures of stars. The peak in the Sun's Planck curve, for instance, is at a wavelength of about 5000 Å, or 5×10^{-5} cm. Using this as λ_{max} in Wien's law gives a temperature of 5800 K for the surface of the Sun:

$$T = \frac{0.29}{5 \times 10^{-5}} = 5800 \text{ K}$$

Wien's displacement law is very useful for determining temperatures of stars because the intensity of radiation in only a small spectral region is required.

Determining the temperatures of planets presents a slightly different problem, however. The visible light received from the planets is a combination of emitted radiation from the planet and reflected sunlight. The observed peak in a planet's energy distribution in the visible part of the spectrum indicates solar temperatures! Clearly planets are not

5800 K. The observed peak in the visible radiation is due to reflected sunlight. Analyses of the radiation from planets show that they emit mainly in the infrared and that their surface temperatures range from just under 100 K for the most distant planets from the Sun to over 700 K for the inner planets. Consequently, the peak in a Planck curve of *emitted* radiation for a planet lies in the infrared. For Mars' surface temperature of about 260 K, the peak is at about 11 μm; for Pluto's surface temperature of about 50 K, the peak is at about 50 μm.

▬CHEMICAL ELEMENTS

As we have seen, the radiation laws describe emitted radiation in terms of the wavelike nature of radiation. Certain phenomena associated with radiation, however, are more conveniently explained in terms of the particlelike nature of radiation. These phenomena involve the interaction of radiation and atoms. Before we examine these phenomena, however, it is necessary to look at atoms.

Atoms are the smallest particles that retain the properties of an **element.** We speak of an atom of iron or copper or aluminum. Individual atoms consist of a nucleus, with a diameter of about 10^{-13} cm, containing two kinds of subatomic particles, *protons* and *neutrons*. The protons are positively charged while the neutrons are electrically neutral. Each atom of a particular element contains the same number of protons; all iron atoms have 26 protons and all gold atoms have 79 protons. The number of neutrons in an element can vary, however. Iron, for instance, can have between 26 and 35 neutrons; the most common form of iron found in nature has 30 neutrons. Atoms of a given element that have different numbers of neutrons are called *isotopes* of that element. Scientists designate a particular isotope of an element by writing its *atomic weight*, the number of protons plus the number of neutrons in the nucleus, after the name of the element, such as iron-56, or by writing the atomic weight in superscript to the left of the chemical symbol of the element, as in ^{56}Fe for iron-56.

Surrounding the nucleus are the negatively charged *electrons*. Each neutral atom has exactly the same number of electrons as protons; the positive charges of the protons are balanced by the negative charges of the electrons. When an atom loses one or more electrons, it has an excess of positive charge and we call it a positive *ion*. Electrons surround the nucleus at distances of up to 10^{-8} cm, or more than 100,000 nuclear diameters, from the protons and neutrons at the center (Figure 4.8). Electrons "orbit" the nucleus at certain distances in *orbitals* that only a limited number of electrons can occupy. These two restrictions, fixed orbitals and limited number of electrons per orbital, indicate that orbitals are not orbits in the normal sense of the word as applied, for instance, to orbits of satellites around the Earth. Satellites can be placed at any distance from the Earth, and hundreds of satellites can be placed in the same orbit.

Most substances, such as water, alcohol, plastic, or marble, are not pure elements but compounds of two or more elements. The smallest units of compounds are *molecules*. The water molecule, for instance,

Element: A substance that cannot be separated into a combination of other substances by normal chemical methods; iron, for example, cannot be broken down into simpler elements—iron is iron. Salt, on the other hand, is composed of two elements, sodium (Na) and chlorine (Cl): NaCl.

FIGURE 4.8

Schematic Illustration of an Atom

Can you guess which element?

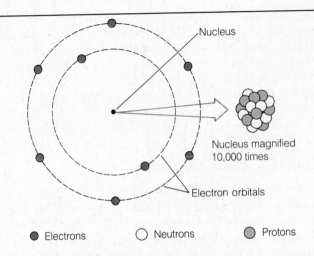

Nucleus

Nucleus magnified
10,000 times

Electron orbitals

● Electrons   ○ Neutrons   ● Protons

Properties of Atomic Particles

Particle	Charge	Mass	Location	Symbol
Proton	Positive	1.673×10^{-24}g	Nucleus	p
Neutron	Neutral	1.675×10^{-24}g	Nucleus	n
Electron	Negative	9.110×10^{-28}g	Orbitals	e

consists of two hydrogen atoms and an oxygen atom. The properties of different compounds, as well as of individual elements, depend in part on the distribution of electrons in their outermost orbitals. The bonding of elements, such as hydrogen and oxygen to form water, involves the "sharing" of these outer electrons (Figure 4.9). For example, oxygen has an outer orbital that can accommodate two more electrons. The two hydrogen atoms, each with only one electron, fill oxygen's outer orbital by sharing the orbital. On the other hand, an element such as neon, which has an outer orbital completely filled with electrons, does not easily bond with other elements since it does not have a vacancy in its outermost orbital. These examples are not intended to provide a detailed account of the bonding of elements, but only to indicate where electrons come into play.

Two properties of elements, their number of protons and their chemical similarity are conveniently displayed in the **periodic table** (Figure 4.10). The number of protons is called the *atomic number* of an atom and is displayed in the periodic table just above the chemical symbol of the element. The atomic number of hydrogen (H) is one because its nucleus contains only one proton while the atomic number of iron is 26 because its nucleus contains 26 protons. The periodic table is arranged in order of increasing atomic number reading from left to right. Although elements in the same columns have different atomic numbers, they have similar chemical properties. As mentioned above, chemical properties are dictated primarily by the number of electrons in the outermost orbitals, which in turn depends on the number of protons in the nucleus. Elements to the far left, such as hydrogen and sodium (Na)

FIGURE 4.9

Schematic Representation of a Water Molecule

Hydrogen bonds to oxygen in such a way that the two hydrogen electrons share the outer orbital of the oxygen atom.

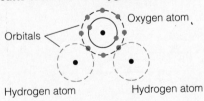

Oxygen atom

Orbitals

Hydrogen atom   Hydrogen atom

● Nucleus
● Electron
● Shared electron

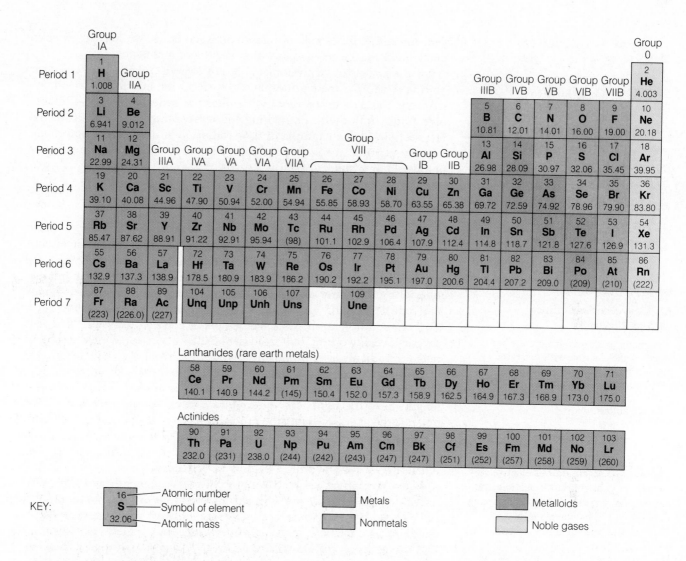

KEY:

16	
S	— Atomic number
32.06	— Symbol of element
	— Atomic mass

▢ Metals

▢ Nonmetals

▢ Metalloids

▢ Noble gases

have one electron in their outer orbitals while those to the far right, such as helium (He) and neon (Ne), have full orbitals.

Compounds and elements can be in a gaseous, liquid, or solid state. Water when cooled becomes ice, a solid, and when heated becomes water vapor, a gas. Astronomers encounter all states of matter in their study of the universe. Among the most important solids in the solar system are rocks, which are composed of one or more *minerals*, each of which has a definite composition, or combination of elements. For instance, most rocks found on the Earth's surface are made largely of minerals called silicates, combinations of silicon and oxygen. An example of a silicate-rich Earth mineral is feldspar ($NaAlSi_3O_8$), which is a sodium (Na) atom bonded to an aluminum (Al) silicate consisting of 1 aluminum atom, 3 silicon atoms, and 8 oxygen atoms. A typical rock found in a field probably contains several different types of silicates. In contrast to solid, rocky planets such as the Earth and Mars, the stars are gaseous mixtures of elements, the most abundant of which is hydro-

■ **FIGURE 4.10**

Periodic Table of the Elements

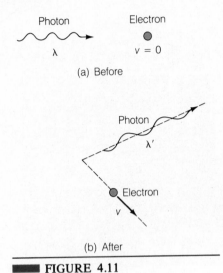

Photon

λ

Electron

v = 0

(a) Before

Photon

λ'

Electron

v

(b) After

■■■ FIGURE 4.11
An X-ray Photon Collides with an Electron

The photon with wavelength λ is scattered off the electron with increased wavelength λ'. After the collision, the electron moves off with velocity v. The recoil of the electron shows the particle nature of photons.

Photon: A discrete unit of electromagnetic energy having both particle and wave behavior; the energy of a photon, ε, is related to its wavelength, λ, through the relationship $\epsilon = hc/\lambda$.

Spectral line: A radiative feature in a spectrum of a star or planet representing an excess of radiation (emission line) or a deficiency of radiation (absorption line).

gen. In dark, cold clouds of matter between stars, we find small solid particles of matter as well as a rich variety of molecules.

For the most part, astronomers are not able to travel to these distant objects to sample their atmospheres, surfaces, or interiors. Instead, astronomers must use the radiation emitted or reflected by these remote objects to study them. Estimating the temperature of a star, as in the last section, is one example of how radiation is used. The electromagnetic spectrum can also be used to determine the chemical composition of a world or a star.

ATOMIC SPECTRA

Planck's discovery of the mathematical formula for the energy distribution of the radiation from black bodies led to a reexamination of classical physics and resulted in the development of *quantum mechanics*, a mathematical theory describing subatomic particles and their interaction with each other and with electromagnetic radiation. After Planck derived the formula for a Planck curve, he could not explain the emission of radiation from black bodies using classical physics. He spent several weeks working out a physical explanation, for which he had to make a radical assumption: atoms can emit energy only in *discrete* quantities. Planck found that the discrete quantities of energy, ε (the Greek letter *epsilon*), had to be inversely proportional to the wavelength, λ, of the light: $\epsilon = hc/\lambda$. Here h is called the Planck constant and c is the speed of light (the product $h \times c = 1.99 \times 10^{-16}$ ergs cm). Einstein provided the next insight into the development of quantum theory. He suggested that light, or radiation, exists in discrete bundles of energy, or quanta, which we now call **photons.**

Planck's relationship between energy and wavelength and Einstein's quanta of energy illustrate the particle-wave nature of subatomic particles. Scientists can describe a photon as a wave with a certain wavelength or as a particle, a sort of electromagnetic "bullet." For instance, if X-ray photons collide with electrons, physicists can detect the electrons recoiling from the collision (Figure 4.11). When physicists describe a photon or an electron as a wave or as a particle, they are just emphasizing one attribute over the other. When we measure the intensity of radiation at different wavelengths, it is convenient to describe photons as waves; when we knock electrons out of atoms with high-energy photons, it is convenient to describe photons as particles. In fact, photons, electrons, and protons are neither waves nor particles. When it comes to describing subatomic particles, our intuitive notions, based on everyday experiences, are inadequate. Moreover, it is not easy to explain to the nonspecialist why subatomic particles behave in a different way from macroscopic objects. Nevertheless, although quantum mechanics may not be intuitive, it works; it correctly predicts and describes observations.

The wavelike nature of light is used to describe the colors of the rainbow as wavelength groups that we call red, orange, yellow, green, blue and violet. Raindrops in the atmosphere act like little prisms, spreading sunlight into wavelength groups that the eye translates as the colors of the rainbow. The spectrum of white light, from an incandescent bulb, for instance, also shows the colors of the rainbow. It is called a *continuous spectrum* because the colors blend smoothly from one to the next. In 1814 the German physicist Joseph von Fraunhofer (1787–1826) passed sunlight through a prism and subjected it to intense magnification. He saw more than just the colors of the rainbow. Fraunhofer saw hundreds of dark, vertical lines across the solar spectrum. Atoms in the solar atmosphere, as well as in the Earth's atmosphere, absorb light at some of the wavelengths emitted by the Sun. Light at these wavelengths is diminished relative to light at the surrounding wavelengths, producing dark lines in the spectrum called *absorption lines*. Experiments in the middle of the nineteenth century by the German physicist Gustav Kirchhoff (1824–1887) and chemist Robert Bunsen (the inventor of the Bunsen burner) revealed that light from artificial sources also produced dark lines if the light passed through a gas before being dispersed by a prism. Furthermore, the spectra of hot, glowing gases showed bright lines without the full range of colors of the rainbow. The bright lines in the spectrum of glowing gases represent light that has been emitted by the atoms of the gas; they are called *emission lines*. Both the dark absorption lines and the bright emission lines are known as **spectral lines** (Figure 4.12).

Kirchhoff summarized his experiments with light and prisms and identified three types of spectra:

■ *Continuous spectrum:*   The spectrum emitted by a luminous solid is a continuous sequence of wavelengths, uninterrupted by dark or bright spectral lines.

■ *Emission spectrum:*   The spectrum of a rarified heated gas is a series of bright, colored lines in an otherwise dark spectrum.

■ *Absorption spectrum:*   The spectrum of a luminous object, the light of which is passed through a cool gas, will show dark lines, representing the absence of light.

The particlelike nature of light, describing light as composed of photons with certain energies, suggests that absorption or emission lines must correspond to the absorption or emission of individual photons by atoms. The diminished intensity of light is interpreted as a reduction in the number of photons of certain energies. When a photon is absorbed or emitted, electrons change their distance from the nucleus. If an atom absorbs a photon, an electron can move away from the nucleus to another orbital. The energy of the photon, hc/λ, is used to partially overcome the attractive electromagnetic force between the orbiting electron and the protons in the nucleus. The discrete nature of the absorptions implies that atoms cannot absorb just any photon. They can absorb only photons with particular energies and, therefore, certain wavelengths because only particular orbitals are available to the electrons. The hydrogen atom, for instance, under the conditions in the Sun's atmosphere can absorb visible photons with wavelengths of 6562 Å,

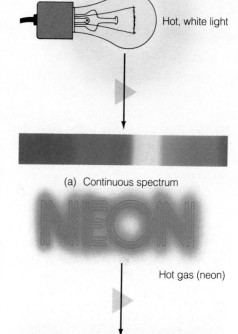

(a) Continuous spectrum

(b) Emission line spectrum

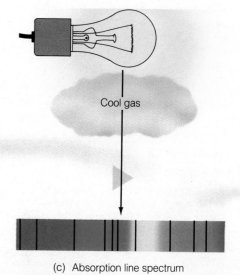

(c) Absorption line spectrum

■ FIGURE 4.12

Spectral Lines

Passing light from the sources shown through a prism results in the spectrum shown below each source.

4861 Å, 4340 Å, 4101 Å, and 3970 Å, but not photons with wavelengths in between these. Similarly, if hydrogen gas is heated to the same temperature as the Sun's surface, it will produce an emission line spectrum by emitting light at those same wavelengths but not at wavelengths in between.

An electron can jump from orbital to orbital if the atom absorbs the right photon. Consider an atom with an electron in the orbital closest to the nucleus. The atom absorbs a photon with just the right amount of energy for the electron to move from the lowest orbital to a more distant orbital (Figure 4.13). The atom is now in an **excited** state. Excited atoms do not stay excited. Within a hundred-millionth of a second or so, the electron drops back down to a lower orbital. If it returns directly to the original orbital, it emits a photon with the same wavelength as the one the atom first absorbed. On the other hand, if the absorbed photon had enough energy to boost the electron several orbitals away from the nucleus, the electron may emit more than one photon as it cascades down to its original distance from the nucleus.

A convenient way to represent electron transitions is to plot the amount of energy needed to change distances from the nucleus in an *energy level diagram*. Figure 4.14 shows the energy level diagram for hydrogen. The closest orbital to the nucleus is represented by the line labeled $n = 1$, and the energies (relative to the $n = 1$ orbital) needed to move from the $n = 1$ orbital to the other orbitals are shown to the right of each orbital line. The energy required for a transition between the $n = 2$ orbital and the $n = 3$ orbital is simply the difference in the energy of the two levels:

$$(1.937 - 1.634) \times 10^{-11} \text{ erg} = 3.03 \times 10^{-12} \text{ ergs}$$

The corresponding wavelength of a photon causing this transition is

$$\lambda = \frac{hc}{\epsilon} = \frac{1.99 \times 10^{-16} \text{ ergs cm}}{3.03 \times 10^{-12} \text{ ergs}} \approx 6.6 \times 10^{-5} \text{ cm} \approx 6600 \text{ Å}$$

A more exact calculation gives 6562 Å. Because the hydrogen atom is the simplest atom to study, the possible transitions for the hydrogen

Excited state (of an atom): The state of an atom in which an electron has been moved to an orbital farther away from the nucleus.

■■■ FIGURE 4.13

Absorption

An atom with an electron, pictured here in the $n = 3$ orbital, absorbs a photon with exactly the right energy to boost the electron farther from the nucleus to the $n = 4$ orbital.

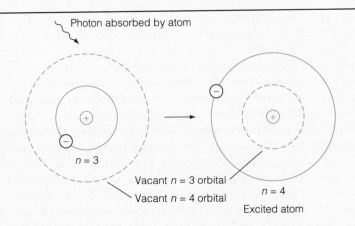

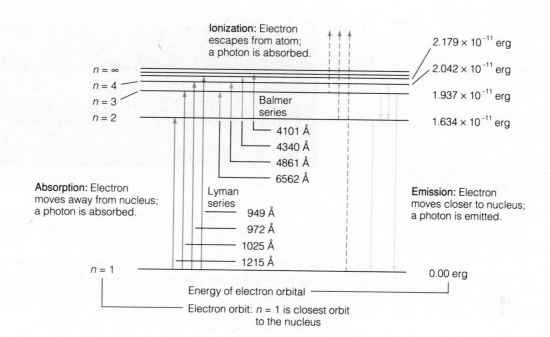

atom have been given names. Those from the ground level represent the Lyman series; those from $n = 2$ represent the Balmer series; and those from $n = 3$ represent the Paschen series. The Balmer series is important in the study of stars because it produces spectral lines in the visible part of stellar spectra.

Electrons in an atom can also change orbitals by collisions with other atoms. Atoms in a gas are moving at high speeds and are continuously colliding with other atoms. The energy imparted to an atom during a collision can excite the atom if the energy corresponds to that needed for a transition between orbitals. A hot gas, therefore, produces emission lines because the collisionally excited atoms emit photons as their electrons return to the lowest permitted orbital. It is important to realize that the lowest permitted orbital may not be the ground state. In a hot gas, so many collisions can occur that an atom is re-excited before its electron can reach the ground state. For instance, hydrogen gas at a temperature of 10,000 K has many atoms whose electrons can only drop to the $n = 2$ orbital and, therefore, emit the Balmer series of emission lines.

If the photons in the environment of the atom have short wavelengths and are therefore very energetic, they can remove an electron completely from an atom. When this happens, we call the atom **ionized**. Any photon with an energy greater than 2.18×10^{-11} ergs (see Figure 4.14) or a wavelength shorter than 912 Å will ionize hydrogen if the photon is absorbed. If a hydrogen atom is ionized, it will not have any electrons orbiting the nucleus. Consequently, an ionized hydrogen atom cannot absorb photons. Elements with more than one electron, of course, must be ionized more than once before they lose their electrons. Helium with two electrons, for example, must be ionized twice before it is unable to

■ FIGURE 4.14

Energy Level Diagram

Electron transitions are shown as movements from one orbital to another. The distances between orbitals are scaled to reflect the energy needed to reach an orbital from the lowest, or ground, level.

Ionized state (of an atom): The state of an atom in which an electron has been lost.

FIGURE 4.15

Spectral Line Series for Several Different Elements

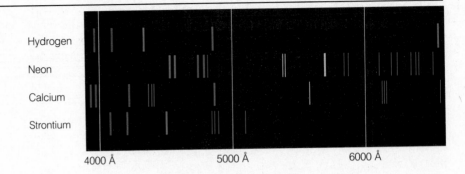

absorb photons. We say that helium is once ionized if one electron escapes or twice ionized if both are gone.

Because different elements have different numbers of protons in their nuclei, they have different numbers of electrons and correspondingly different electron orbital radii. Elements with many protons in their nuclei exert a stronger hold on the innermost electrons. This leads to different energy differences between orbitals and, therefore, to different sets of photons they are able to absorb and emit. Consequently, each element has its own spectral signature; that is, each element produces a different set of spectral lines (Figure 4.15). We can identify elements by their spectral lines just as we can identify humans by their fingerprints.

RADIOACTIVITY

Changes in the orbitals of electrons produce spectral lines, but changes in the nucleus itself can produce different elements. Some atoms of one element can change naturally into atoms of another element by emitting fragments from their nuclei. These **radioactive** elements emit helium nuclei (called alpha particles), electrons (called beta rays), and gamma rays, which are high energy photons. The loss of particles from the nuclei produces different elements. For instance, carbon-14 decays into nitrogen-14 when a neutron transforms into a proton and an electron, and the electron is ejected from the nucleus. Uranium-238 decays into lead-206 after emitting eight alpha particles and six electrons in a chain of transformations. In each case, the resulting **daughter** nucleus has a different mixture of protons and neutrons than the original, or **parent** nucleus (Figure 4.16). Because of the change in proton number, the daughter nucleus is a different element.

Radioactive decay occurs randomly. Scientists have no way of telling when it will happen to a particular nucleus. Although we cannot predict when a given atom will radioactively change, we can measure how long it takes for a quantity of a radioactive element to transform into another element. For example, let's start with 1,000,000 radioactive atoms of radon-222 in a laboratory. (In this example, the atoms are too few and their decay too exact for authentic measurements, but they illustrate the concept.) After 4 days 500,000 radioactive atoms of radon are

Radioactivity: Spontaneous disintegration of unstable atomic nuclei, resulting in the ejection of a helium nucleus, an electron, or a gamma ray.

Daughter nucleus: The nucleus of the new element produced by spontaneous radioactive decay; the daughter nucleus may also be radioactive.

Parent nucleus: The nucleus of the original radioactive element.

left, after 8 days 250,000 radon atoms remain, and after 12 days only 125,000 radon atoms are left (Figure 4.17). At the same time, the measurements would show an increase in the number of daughter atoms, an isotope of lead. Measurements after 4 days would show 500,000 lead atoms, after 8 days the number would be 750,000, and after 12 days the number of lead atoms would be 875,000. Every 4 days half of the *remaining* radon atoms transform into lead.

The time after which half of a quantity of a radioactive element has transformed itself into another element is called its **half-life.** After one half-life, half of the radioactive atoms remain; after two half-lives, one-fourth of the original radioactive atoms remain (Figure 4.18). Each atom has a 50:50 chance to decay within the next half-life.

Short half-lives, such as 4 days for radon-222 or 25 minutes for radioactive iodine-128, are directly measurable with devices called *Geiger counters.* Geiger counters electrically measure the number of ions produced in the detector tube by any radioactive source. These pulses can be added up by counting circuitry or fed into an audio amplifier to produce a sound, the clicking of a Geiger counter. For short half-life radioactive elements, the number of decays per second measured by a Geiger counter decreases significantly in a short time.

For radioactive elements with long half-lives, such as 1.3 billion years for potassium-40 or even the relatively short 5,570 years for carbon-14, it is not possible to wait long enough to detect a measurable *change* in the Geiger counter readings. Since scientists can measure how many radioactive atoms are present in a sample and, by the Geiger counter measurements, how fast the radioactive element is decaying, they can calculate how long it will take for the number of radioactive elements to halve. Table 4.2 lists some radioactive elements and their measured half-lives.

Geologists use radioactive decay as a method of dating rock formations. The procedure is to measure the amount of both parent and

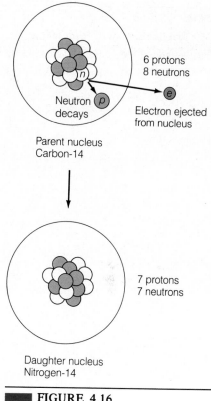

6 protons
8 neutrons

Neutron decays

Electron ejected from nucleus

Parent nucleus
Carbon-14

7 protons
7 neutrons

Daughter nucleus
Nitrogen-14

■■■ FIGURE 4.16

Radioactive Decay

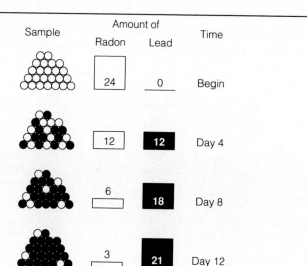

■■■ FIGURE 4.17

Radioactive Decay of Radon Gas with a Half-Life of 4 Days

As radon radioactively decays, its atoms decrease in number while those of its final daughter element, lead, increase. This small sample shows only 24 "atoms," but in reality billions of atoms are involved.

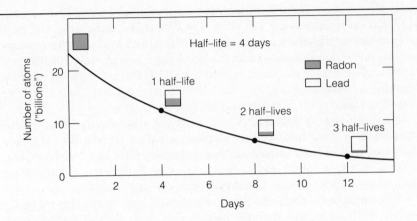

FIGURE 4.18

Radioactive Decay of Radon Gas

The amount of radon gas is halved during *each* 4-day half-life.

daughter elements because their ratio is a measure of the time it has taken for the parent to decay. A molten rock will reach the surface of a planet through a volcanic fissure and then solidify. Before it solidifies, any daughter nuclei are free to migrate away, either by flowing in the melt, for instance, or escaping as a gas, such as argon-40, the product of the decay of potassium-40. Most of the rock formations on Earth consist of rocks that have been melted many times in the past. For instance, the oldest rocks in the Atlantic Ocean are no more than 200 million years old. These ocean rocks are new rock that formed the seafloor as it welled up in the form of lava. Once the lava cooled and solidified, any radioactive decay left new daughter nuclei in the rock. Consequently, the age of a rock is usually the time since the rock *solidified;* the age is calculated by a process called *radiometric dating*, which involves analysis of the rock's radioactive parent and daughter atoms. For example, a rock that contains equal amounts of potassium-40 and argon-40 gas is about 1.3 billion years old since the half-life of the decay of potassium to argon is 1.3 billion years. If the ratio was 1 potassium to 3 argon atoms, then the rock would be about 2.6 billion years old, or two half-lives.

Radiometric dating using potassium-40, for instance, assumes that no argon gas was trapped in the rock when it solidified. This is a reason-

TABLE 4.2 Important Radioactive Elements

Parent	Daughter*	Half-Life (years)
Carbon-14	Nitrogen-14	5,570
Plutonium-241	Bismuth-209	2.4 million
Uranium-235	Lead-207	713 million
Potassium-40	Argon-40	1.3 billion
Uranium-238	Lead-206	4.5 billion
Thorium-232	Lead-208	14.1 billion
Rubidium-87	Strontium-87	50 billion

*Daughter product may result after several steps with intermediate daughter nuclei.

able assumption since argon gas in a melt, such as a lava flow, can bubble up through the lava before solidification. Other daughter isotopes, however, are not necessarily gases. In such cases, geologists must determine the amount of the daughter nuclei initially present in their rock sample. This can be done by using a stable isotope of the daughter element as a reference.

Not all rocks are suitable for radiometric dating. Geologists can recognize, for instance, rocks that have been reheated but not completely melted and may have had some daughter nuclei or parent nuclei driven out. Certain rocks are exposed to atmospheric gases and water and may lose some material to erosional processes. Most Moon rocks, however, have solidified from lava and therefore have trapped daughter nuclei. Some of these rocks have also been pulverized by meteoritic impacts that have allowed daughter nuclei to escape. In that case, the ages of the rocks record the time of the impacts rather than the time of solidification. On both the Earth and the Moon, geologists find many rocks suitable for radiometric dating.

When geologists apply radiometric dating techniques to the Earth, they find that the oldest rocks are in Greenland and are about 3.9 billion years old. Scientists interpret this to mean that the Earth is at least 3.9 billion years old. While most Earth rocks are younger than about 3 billion years, most lunar rocks are older than 3 billion years. Chapters 6 and 11 present additional information from lunar rocks and the formation of the solar system that fixes Earth's age at about 4.6 billion years.

SUMMARY

Physicists describe the ability of electric charges and magnets to generate a force at a distance in terms of electric and magnetic fields just as the force due to masses is described in terms of gravitational fields. Moving electric charges generate a magnetic field, illustrating the intimate relationship between electricity and magnetism. This relationship is inherent in the description of the propagation of electric and magnetic fields in terms of electromagnetic waves of characteristic wavelengths that travel at the velocity of light. Electromagnetic radiation of different wavelengths comprises the electromagnetic spectrum. Any object with a temperature above absolute zero emits a spectrum of electromagnetic radiation. Planck curves describe the intensity of the radiation emitted at various wavelengths.

Two radiation laws related to the Planck curve can be used to determine the temperatures of planets and stars. Wien's law relates the temperature of a black body to the wavelength of the peak of its energy distribution: the peak shifts toward shorter wavelengths for hotter objects. The Stefan-Boltzmann law relates the total energy emitted at all wavelengths to the temperature of the black body: the total energy emitted is proportional to the fourth power of the temperature.

All electromagnetic radiation, including light, can be described as consisting of small particles, called photons, each with a definite energy, hc/λ, related to its wavelength. Photons act like particles in many interactions and like waves in others. The photons comprising bright and dim light are identical; the differences in intensity are due to differences in the number of photons.

Photons can interact with atoms by moving electrons between orbitals. Electrons are restricted to certain orbitals at various distances from the nucleus. The interaction between photons and atoms can produce three types of spectra: (1) hot, luminous objects emit a continuous spectrum of wavelengths; (2) hot, rarified gases emit a pattern of bright spectral lines; and (3) light passed through a gas produces dark, spectral lines in the same pattern the gas would emit if it were hot.

Electron transitions generate absorption lines in a continuous distribution of wavelengths when photons are absorbed. Absorption causes an electron to move farther away from the nucleus to another allowed orbital; the atom is said to be excited. Transitions in which the electron moves closer to the nucleus generate emission lines because a photon is emitted, adding to the intensity of light at a particular wavelength. Interactions in which electrons escape from atoms are said to ionize the atom. Each element can absorb and emit only certain photons (except when the photons have enough energy to ionize the atoms). These photons must have exactly the right amount of energy and, therefore, the right wavelength to cause a transition. Furthermore, each

element has a different arrangement of electron orbitals and therefore produces a unique spectral pattern of absorption and emission lines.

Some elements are radioactive and spontaneously transform into other elements with the ejection of helium nuclei, electrons, or high-energy gamma rays. Although the decay is random in the sense that any atom of a radioactive element can decay anytime, half of a quantity of the element decays in one half-life. Half-lives range from fractions of seconds to billions of years. The measured half-lives of radioactive elements found in minerals allow geologists to use them for estimating the ages of rock formations, both on the Earth and on the Moon.

CHAPTER CAPSULE

Topics and Terms	Review and Remarks
Forces at a distance	These are described by fields: Magnetic and electric fields are generated by moving electric charges. Gravitational fields are generated by masses.
Electromagnetic spectrum	This is a convenient representation of electromagnetic waves, describing radiation in terms of wavelengths: gamma rays, X-rays, ultraviolet, visual, infrared, radio.
Photon energy	The energy of a photon is proportional to $1/\lambda$; λ represents wavelength: Short wavelength—high energy Long wavelength—low energy
Radiation laws	Wien's law: temperature $= 0.29/\lambda$. Stefan-Boltzmann law: total energy emitted $\propto T^4$.
Spectra	Continuous Emission Absorption
Spectral lines	Emission lines are produced when electrons move closer to the nucleus. Absorption lines are produced when electrons move farther from the nucleus.
Radioactive decay	Spontaneous Half-life is the time it takes for half of the remaining radioactive element to decay.

REVIEW QUESTIONS

1. Why is an understanding of the properties of electromagnetic radiation of such great importance in the study of astronomy? (See question 1, Chapter 1.)

2. Explain what is meant by the term *spectrum*. Does a rainbow fit this definition?

3. What allows us to see most of the objects we see in everyday life is light that has been reflected by the object. We usually don't notice a difference in the color of objects due to the source of light, but if you look at your hand under a mercury vapor lamp it has a lifeless blue-gray color. Why?

4. How are each of the following "detected" by our bodies: (a) ultraviolet radiation, (b) visible light, and (c) infrared light?

5. If you could travel as fast as electromagnetic radiation travels, how long would it take you to travel

around the Earth? How long to go to the Moon? The Sun?

6. Why does the Earth usually get cooler at night? Why does the temperature usually drop less at night if it is cloudy than if it is clear? Explain using the Stefan-Boltzmann law.

7. According to Wien's displacement law, the color of a radiating body depends on its temperature. What "color" would you expect a normal human body to be?

8. What kind of spectrum would you expect the Earth to radiate? Would the Earth radiate energy at a greater rate in summer or winter (in a given hemisphere)?

9. What causes all atoms of hydrogen to produce exactly the same emission spectrum? Why is the emission spectrum of hydrogen (or any element or molecule) different from that of other elements (or molecules)?

10. The visible limits of the spectrum are about 4000 to 7000 Å. Which of these is at the red "end" of the spectrum? What are these wavelengths in meters and in feet? At which of these wavelengths are the photons more energetic?

11. All of the visible hydrogen spectral lines (Balmer series) originate as the result of transitions of the electron between the $n = 2$ orbital and those of higher number. How could hydrogen produce a spectrum with no visible lines?

12. If a Balmer series line is produced by an electron transition to the $n = 2$ orbital, is it an emission line or an absorption line?

13. Part of the Earth's heat source is that of natural internal radioactivity. Would you expect this to be due to elements of short or long half-life? How do you think this contribution to the surface temperature of the Earth compares to that from the Sun?

14. Suppose element x has a half-life of 1 hour and the decay product is element y. If you start with 10,000 atoms of element x, how many atoms of each element will you have in 4 hours?

15. The Earth is believed to be about 4.6 billion years old. Most of the rocks found on Earth are less than 3 billion years old and none are older than 3.9 billion years. Can you account for this?

FOR FURTHER READING

Davies, P. 1985. Relics of creation. *Sky & Telescope*, Feb., 112.

———. 1987. Particle physics for everyone. *Sky & Telescope*, Dec., 582.

Goldman, T., R. J. Hughes, and M. M. Nieto, 1988. Gravity and antimatter. *Scientific American*, Mar., 48.

Shimony, A. 1988. The reality of the quantum world. *Scientific American*, Jan., 46.

Washburn, M. 1985. Maxwell's last frontier. *Sky & Telescope*, Mar., 212.

Williams, E. R. 1988. The electrification of thunderstorms. *Scientific American*, Nov., 88.

Williams, L. P. 1989. André-Marie Ampère. *Scientific American*, Jan., 90.

ASTROPROBE 4

The Forces of Nature

Over the millennia, humans have slowly learned to harness the forces of nature. First, fire warmed our ancestors, cooked their food, and helped them produce everything from metal alloys to medicines. All of these uses involve reactions between atoms and molecules that are bonded together through the **electromagnetic force.** We then began to take advantage of the **gravitational force** by producing mechanical energy from flowing water and then electricity from falling water (Figure 4A.1). More recently, we have harnessed the power within the atom, the **nuclear force,** to generate electrical power to supply our increasing appetite for energy. Further progress can be made only with a deeper understanding of the forces of nature. The tool modern science uses to investigate these forces is quantum physics. The goal of this AstroProbe is to introduce you to the quantum view of force.

FOUR FORCES

Gravity, of course, "glues" us to our planet, raises ocean tides, guides the Earth in its orbit, and holds the Galaxy together. Although gravity has not been completely harnessed, we have learned to defy it through air travel and even to escape the Earth's gravitational pull and travel to other worlds. The gravitational force exists between all pairs of particles in the universe from atoms to galaxies, but it is a relatively weak force.

Lightning during a thunderstorm and the movement of a compass needle are common examples of the electromagnetic force (Figure 4A.2). With more understanding of the electromagnetic force, we have developed radio and television, a planetwide communication system, computers and much more. Like gravity, the electromagnetic force is a long-range force, affecting particles infinitely far away. On the other hand, it only affects particles with electrical charge or magnetic polarity. It is, however, a very strong force, much stronger than the gravitational force. The electromagnetic force between two protons 10^{-13} cm apart (the size of a nucleus) is about 10^{40} times greater than the gravitational force between them.

The gravitational and electromagnetic forces were the only forces known before the 1940s. Then experiments on the structure of the atom and theoretical work on energy sources in stars revealed the existence of the two nuclear forces—the *weak* and *strong* nuclear forces. Both forces operate only over very short distances, only within the atom itself. The strong force binds the nucleus of the atom. Without the strong force holding protons and neutrons together, atomic nuclei would fly apart because of the repulsive electromagnetic force between the positively charged protons. The weak force governs the slow disintegration of atomic nuclei as observed in radioactive decay and in the cataclysmic supernova explosions of

■ FIGURE 4A.1

A Dam at a Hydroelectric Plant

We use the gravitational force to produce electricity from falling water.

SOURCE: David L. Pearson/Visuals Unlimited.

stars. As their names imply, the strong nuclear force is the stronger of the two. In fact, the strong force is the strongest force known in nature. It must be stronger than the electromagnetic force just to hold nuclei together. Table 4A.1 compares the relative strengths of the four forces of nature. This ranking holds for temperatures and energies typical of the universe today; in the past, when the universe was hotter and particles more energetic (see Chapter 19), these forces were more nearly equal.

ELEMENTARY PARTICLES

In the first quarter of the twentieth century, we knew that two forces of nature and four subatomic particles, the neutron, the proton, the photon, and the electron, existed. Now we know of four forces and hundreds of subatomic particles, and physicists are still searching for and finding new particles. These searches use *accelerators*, instruments designed to shoot beams of particles, such as protons and electrons, at atomic targets at tremendous speeds (Figure 4A.3). Collisions can produce new particles that survive briefly. This occurs because energy and mass are equivalent as described by Einstein's important and famous equation $E = mc^2$. That is, if a particle of mass "m" were completely destroyed, it would provide an amount of energy equal to the product of that mass and the speed of light squared. Accelerators create new particles by producing energy through very violent collisions. The energy made available by a collision, if it is great enough, is converted into particles. These newly created particles come flying out of the collision area into detectors that record their brief appearance.

Physicists call particles that appear inseparable, with no internal structure, *elementary* particles. The electron, for instance, appears to

FIGURE 4A.2

Lightning

Lightning is a common example of the electromagnetic force.

SOURCE: Dr. Vic Bradbury/Science Photo Library, Photo Researchers.

TABLE 4A.1 **Forces of Nature**

Force	Range	Relative Strength
Strong	$< 10^{-13}$cm	1
Weak	$< 10^{-16}$cm	10^{-13}
Electromagnetic	Infinite	10^{-2}
Gravity	Infinite	10^{-42}

■ FIGURE 4A.3

The CERN Accelerator

Scientists use accelerators, such as the one operated by CERN (Conseil Européen pour la Recherche Nucléaire) near Geneva, Switzerland, to accelerate subatomic particles to high speeds so that they collide with atomic targets and other subatomic particles. The CERN accelerator is a ring more than 2 km in diameter (drawn as a white circle in the photograph) that is contained in a tunnel about 40 meters below the surface.

SOURCE: CERN/Visuals Unlimited.

Quark: A fundamental constituent of matter with a fractional electric charge but not observable as an isolated particle. The name comes from the phrase "three quarks for Muster Mark" from James Joyce's *Finnegans Wake*.

Antiparticle: A particle with the same mass and spin (spin describes the rotational state of a subatomic particle) as a normal particle, but all other attributes, such as electric charge, are the opposite.

be one of these subdivisions of matter. The neutrino (Italian for "little neutral one") is another important elementary particle. It is generally thought to be massless and to move at the speed of light, as does a photon; recent experiments, however, indicate that it may, in fact, have a very small mass. This particle is important in nuclear reactions and may play an important role in the cosmological theories of the universe to be discussed in Chapter 19. In contrast, protons and neutrons, do not appear to be elementary particles. Each is thought to be composed of elementary particles called **quarks.** At least six different kinds of quarks have been postulated. Their designations are somewhat peculiar: there are "up" and "down" quarks, "strange" and "charmed" quarks, and "truth" and "beauty" quarks, which are sometimes referred to as "top" and "bottom" quarks. The individual properties of the different quarks give the proton, the neutron, and other particles their particular properties (Figure 4A.4). For instance, a proton is composed of 3 quarks, 2 "up" quarks and 1 "down" quark (uud); a neutron is composed of 2 "down" quarks and 1 "up" quark (udd). An "up" quark has a charge of $+\frac{2}{3}$ and a "down" quark has a charge of $-\frac{1}{3}$. A proton, therefore, has a charge of $+1$ ($= \frac{2}{3} + \frac{2}{3} - \frac{1}{3}$) while a neutron has a charge of zero ($= \frac{2}{3} - \frac{1}{3} - \frac{1}{3}$).

Moreover, all subatomic particles have corresponding **antiparticles.** Antiparticles have the same mass as their particle counterparts, but their other properties, such as charge, are the opposite (Table

4A.2). The antiparticle of the electron is called the positron and is designated by "e^+." It is an electron with a positive charge. Antiparticles normally are designated by placing a bar over the symbol of the particle; an antiproton is designated as $\bar{p}$. An important property of particles and antiparticles is that when a particle and antiparticle come together, they annihilate themselves, converting all of their mass into energy. In principle, it is possible to build "antiatoms," or what we call *antimatter*. A hydrogen antiatom would have a positron orbiting an antiproton. Although accelerator experiments have generated antiparticles, no one has been able to manufacture antiatoms.

Elementary particles, other particles, and macroscopic objects interact with each other through the forces of nature. How do these forces arise? How does a proton in a nucleus of an atom "know" that a neutron or another proton is nearby? The everyday macroscopic concept of force as a push or a pull does not work in the microscopic world. It even fails in the macroscopic world in the concept of gravity; that is, how does the Moon "feel" the Earth's gravitational force? If you push me, I would feel your push as a physical sensation. But if you try to push me without touching me, you would look rather silly. The Moon, on the other hand, is obviously influenced by the Earth's gravity without any apparent physical contact. Thus the physicist's modern concept of "force" is very different from our intuitive notions of force. Let's further explore how physicists describe "forces" by introducing a very fundamental principle of modern quantum physics.

UNCERTAINTY

At the beginning of the twentieth century, Lord Rutherford (1871–1937) and his colleagues at the Cavendish Laboratory at Cambridge University in England designed experiments in which they bombarded gold-foil targets with helium nuclei produced from radioactive elements. They discovered that the helium nuclei that did not pass through the foil targets were deflected from their original path; some even bounced backward. These experiments showed that most of the mass and all of the positive charge of an atom are located in a tiny nucleus at the center, and the helium nuclei collided with and bounced off the tiny nucleus. This implied that the negatively charged electrons must lie outside the nucleus. Furthermore, spectroscopic studies of atoms showed that the electrons could only orbit at certain discrete distances from the nucleus. Classical physics, on the other hand, taught that the electrons could orbit the atom at any distance. In fact, classical physics also indicated that electrons should spiral into the nucleus. On the contrary, atoms are stable;

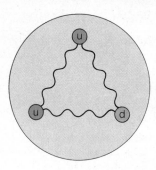

(a) Proton

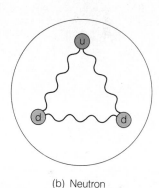

(b) Neutron

FIGURE 4A.4

Quark Model of the Proton and Neutron

The sinuous line between the quarks represents the strong nuclear force between them.

TABLE 4A.2
Particles and Antiparticles

Particles		Antiparticles	
Electron	e^-	Positron	e^+
Proton	p	Antiproton	$\bar{p}$
Neutron	n	Antineutron	$\bar{n}$
Neutrino	ν	Antineutrion	$\bar{\nu}$

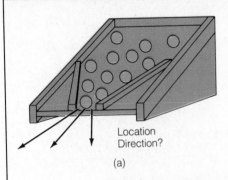

Location
Direction?

(a)

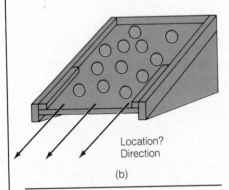

Location?
Direction

(b)

■ **FIGURE 4A.5**

Heisenberg Uncertainty Principle

Imagine rolling marbles down two
ramps that are covered so that you
cannot see the marbles inside. (The
ramps are shown uncovered here for
clarity.) (*a*) When marbles exit the
ramp with the narrow opening, they
can come out in many directions; we
cannot predict their direction after
they pass through the opening, but we
can predict where they will exit.
(*b*) When the opening is large, the
marbles will roll straight out; we can
predict their direction after they pass
through the opening, but because the
opening is wide, we cannot predict
where an individual marble will exit.

electrons do not plunge into the nucleus. Clearly, something was
wrong with classical physics. Indeed, classical physics, although successful in the macroscopic world, breaks down when it tries to explain the behavior of microscopic bodies such as atoms or electrons.
Newton's laws do not apply in the realm of atoms. The twentieth
century invention of *quantum mechanics* successfully describes the
behavior of the microscopic world. This behavior, however, is so unusual, so unnatural, that it is difficult to visualize. We have no direct
experience in our macroscopic world that we can apply to the microscopic world.

In the everyday world, for instance, the exact position of an object
and its exact velocity can easily be measured. Radar, for example,
gives the altitude, distance, and velocity of an incoming airplane. In
the microscopic world, this cannot be done; we cannot know exactly
where a particle is and exactly how fast it is moving. We do not have
"microscopic radar." Before stating this in more scientific terms, an
example from the macroscopic world will illustrate this uncertainty
in position and velocity.

Imagine rolling marbles down a covered inclined plane under two
different conditions. First roll them so that they must pass through a
narrow gate (Figure 4A.5). Then roll them with the gate opened as
wide as the width of the inclined plane. In both cases, the ramp is
covered and the marbles inside cannot be seen. Now try to predict
the position of a marble and its velocity (direction and speed) as it
passes through the gate in the two different situations.

In the first case, since the gate through which the marbles pass is
narrow, the exact location of a marble is known as it passes through
the gate. But the marbles bunch up as they are funneled together and
bump each other. The collisions can send the marbles passing
through the gate at different angles and speeds. We cannot predict
exactly the speed or the direction a marble will have coming out of
a narrow gate; its position at the gate is known but not its velocity
coming out. In the second case, the gate is so wide that the marbles
do not collide. They all move more or less straight through the gate.
But, since the gate is wide, we cannot predict exactly where an individual marble will pass through. It could be anywhere along the
width of the inclined plane; thus the marble's direction coming out
is known but not its position.

In quantum mechanics, the statement that we cannot know exactly
where a particle is and, at the same time, how fast and in what direction it is moving is known as the **Heisenberg uncertainty principle.** One or the other can be accurately measured but not both. The
measure of the uncertainty is *Planck's constant, h.* Numerically,
Planck's constant is very small, about 10^{-28}. The Heisenberg uncer-

tainty principle is generally expressed in terms of momentum (mass times velocity) instead of simply velocity. If Δx represents the uncertainty in position and Δp the uncertainty in momentum, then the Heisenberg uncertainty principle is written as

$$\Delta x \Delta p \geq h$$

If, for instance, the uncertainty in position is very small, then the uncertainty in momentum must be correspondingly large. For example, we can measure the position of billiard ball with an accuracy of a millionth of a cm. This implies that the uncertainty in its velocity is about 10^{-23} cm per second. This is a very precise measurement. On the other hand, if we tried to locate an electron to a precision of 10^{-10} cm, the size of an atom, the uncertainty in its velocity would be a third of the velocity of light. What happens is that when we try to "see" the electron by bouncing a photon off of it, the electron recoils at being struck by the photon and moves away at an unknown speed in some unknown direction (Figure 4A.6). The very measurement of its position disturbs the electron's motion. Subatomic particles behave in peculiar ways!

The Heisenberg uncertainty principle plays a very important role in the quantum description of force. It allows the brief existence of particles, an existence so brief that we cannot detect them, but atoms and other particles are aware of them.

FORCES AND EXCHANGE PARTICLES

Quantum mechanics describes forces as the result of the exchange of particles. For example, protons and neutrons are bound together in the nucleus of an atom because they exchange subatomic quantalike particles. This is the quantum mechanical way of treating communications of a force over a distance. The binding between protons and neutrons is like the "binding effect" of a tennis ball on two tennis players. As long as the ball is bouncing back and forth, the players stay on the court.

Each force is conveyed by a different exchange particle. The strong force is transmitted by *gluons;* the weak force by *weakons;* the electromagnetic force by *photons;* and the gravitational force by *gravitons.* Gluons operate between the quarks that make up particles, such as protons and neutrons, and allow the strong force to extend between the individual protons and neutrons in the form of massive particles called *pions.* Both gluons and photons have zero mass, but weakons are very massive particles, much more massive than the proton or neutron. Although gluons, photons, and weakons have been observed experimentally, gravitons have yet to be confirmed. Theory

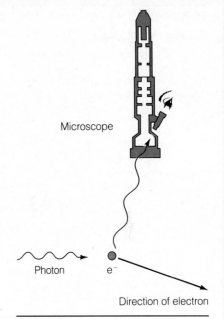

Microscope

Photon   e⁻

Direction of electron

■■ FIGURE 4A.6

Measuring the Position and Velocity of an Electron

Because the electron recoils after being struck by a photon, it will move away at an unknown speed and direction. We will see the scattered photon indicting the position of the electron before it recoiled.

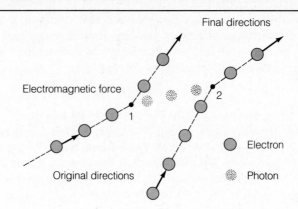

■ FIGURE 4A.7

Electron Scattering

By exchanging a photon, the two electrons detect each other's presence. Each electron recoils and changes its direction of motion.

indicates that they are massless particles that travel at the speed of light as do photons.

Figure 4A.7 schematically shows the interaction between two electrons. As the electron on the left emits an exchange photon at position one, it recoils and changes its direction of motion. When the second electron receives the exchange photon at position 2, it recoils and changes its direction of motion. The interaction between electrons is repulsive so that both particles move away from each other.

You may feel a bit uncomfortable with this description of forces. Part of the reason it may appear strange is that it is new to you. In addition, this quantum mechanical description may appear strange because this kind of behavior is not seen in the macroscopic world. Remember that quantum mechanics is our mathematical model for describing the microscopic world. The Greeks used circles as the basis for their mathematical model that described the universe. Certainly, it was very difficult for a Greek student studying the geocentric model to visualize and understand huge crystalline spheres rotating in the heavens. The Greeks did realize, however, that their mathematical model properly described the motions they were trying to predict. Modern science has replaced that model, first with the mathematics of Newton and now with quantum mechanics. As with all scientific descriptions and models, the true test of the validity of quantum mechanics is its predictive powers. Physicists are able to use quantum mechanics to predict the existence and properties of particles hitherto unknown. Thus quantum mechanics works.

Another aspect of the forces of nature appears in the study of the evolution and structure of the universe (Chapter 19); at the very earliest moments of the universe, conditions existed that united all four forces into a single force.

Earth

OUTLINE

Habitat for Life

The Size, Shape, and Mass of the Earth

The State of the Earth's Interior
The Earth's Surface
Studying the Earth's Interior
Seismology
Heat Flow
A Model of the Earth's Interior
Formation of a Layered Earth

Plate Tectonics

The Age of the Earth

The Atmosphere of the Earth
Composition
The Earth's Primitive Atmosphere
The Atmosphere's Role as a Shield
The Atmosphere's Role as a Blanket
Atmospheric Pressure
Winds: Global Circulation

The Earth's Magnetic Field
Geomagnetism
Magnetosphere

Summary

Chapter Capsule

Review Questions

For Further Reading

ASTROPROBE 5:
Ice Ages: The Astronomical
Connection

Spatium Lux (Space Light).
ARTIST: Dennis Davidson.

THE STUDY OF THE EARTH BEGINS by asking what humans, as part of the evolved life on this planet, need from Earth to survive. Earth's geological, atmospheric, and magnetic environments ensure Earth's habitability, yet they can also threaten life. All three environments are dynamic. Scientists construct a picture of the Earth's interior using clues obtained from seismic waves, from violent geological processes, such as earthquakes and volcanoes, and from measurements of the Earth's temperature. The Earth's surface reflects its interior activity as the collisions and separations of the huge crustal plates that cover our planet generate high mountain ranges and deep oceanic trenches. Our atmosphere is also dynamic and evolved to its present chemical composition as gases were driven out of the Earth's interior and interacted with the emerging life. The atmosphere shields us from harmful ultraviolet radiation and warms the Earth's surface through the greenhouse effect. Earth's magnetic field helps protect life on the Earth's surface and is generated by motions of a fluid metallic core deep in the interior.

▬HABITAT FOR LIFE

Earth is the habitat for over 3 million species of living organisms. It also appears to be the only inhabited planet in the solar system. What makes life possible on Earth? What do you, the reader, require from this planet to survive? You certainly require warmth. Nearly all humans live in regions where the average annual temperatures are between freezing and about 30°C (86°F). This range is also optimum for agricultural crops and domesticated animals. Of course, some of us, such as the Eskimos in Greenland and northern Canada or the aborigines in the deserts of Australia, manage to survive in harsher climates.

You obviously need air containing oxygen to breathe. The density of air is highest near the surface of the Earth and thins with altitude. Mountain climbers maintain that they can live and be active indefinitely at altitudes of 7000 m (23,000 ft), although the number of oxygen atoms in each breath at this elevation is less than half that at sea level (Figure 5.1). Although mountaineers have not taken up residency on mountain tops, inhabitants of mining communities in the Peruvian Andes live and work permanently at altitudes above 5300 m (17,500 ft). They have adapted to these conditions by developing unusually large lung capacities to make up for the reduced number of oxygen atoms in the air they breathe.

The Earth's atmosphere also contains carbon dioxide and nitrogen, both of which are necessary for plant and animal life. Carbon dioxide is needed for *photosynthesis*, the process by which plants synthesize complex organic materials from the energy they receive from sunlight. An important by-product of photosynthesis is oxygen. The Earth's atmosphere contains an ever-increasing amount of carbon dioxide, too much of which can adversely influence our climate and produce conditions inhospitable to life. Nitrogen is needed as part of the nitrogen compounds used by plants and animals. Fertilizers contain nitrogen for just this reason.

▬ FIGURE 5.1

Air Becomes Thinner at High Altitudes

Mountain climbers find it difficult to breathe at high altitudes because of the lack of oxygen.

SOURCE: Didier Givois/Photo Researchers.

You also need plenty of liquid water, sunlight, and protection from ultraviolet radiation. The large bodies of water on the Earth are necessary for the extensive precipitation that produces the quantities of fresh water upon which the entire ecology of this planet depends (Figure 5.2). Ocean organisms also carry out large amounts of oxygen-producing photosynthesis, which requires energy from sunlight. Finally, the atmosphere allows only a very small fraction of the Sun's harmful ultraviolet radiation to reach the surface of the Earth.

Life and the inanimate but dynamic Earth are constantly interacting. The answers to questions such as "How does the Earth maintain the conditions necessary for life?" or "What caused the conditions on Earth conducive for the origin and development of life?" are not simple. The environment of the Earth represents a complex interaction between the energy received from the Sun, the Earth's atmosphere and surface, its deep interior, and life on the surface. This chapter investigates this interaction by looking at each aspect individually, starting with a description of the global characteristics of the Earth and then a study of its interior.

THE SIZE, SHAPE, AND MASS OF THE EARTH

The size of the Earth was reasonably well determined more than 2,000 years ago. (See Table 5.1 for the size of the Earth and other data.) The Greek astronomer Eratosthenes (c. 276–195 B.C.) observed that at the summer solstice at Syene, Egypt (present-day Aswan), the Sun's image was reflected in the water at the base of a vertical well. On the same day of the year, the Sun produced shadows with angles of 7°15′ at Al-

FIGURE 5.2

Earth's Oceans

Oceans cover 71% of the Earth's surface area.

SOURCE: Phillip Flower.

TABLE 5.1 Earth Data

Orbital semimajor axis	1.000 AU (150 million km)
Perihelion distance	0.983 AU (147 million km)
Aphelion distance	1.017 AU (152 million km)
Eccentricity	0.0167
Orbital period (sidereal)	365.2564 days
Rotational period	$23^h56^m4^s$
Inclination	23°27′
Diameter	12,756 km
Mass	5.98×10^{24} kg
Mean density	5.5 g/cm^3
Escape velocity	11.2 km/s
Surface temperature (mean)	293 K (20°C = 70°F)
Maximum	333 K (60°C = 140°F)
Minimum	183 K (−90°C = −130°F)

exandria, Egypt, about 800 km north of Syene. Eratosthenes realized that when the Sun was directly overhead at Syene at noon, it was 7°15′ south of the zenith at Alexandria. He reasoned, therefore, that Syene must be 7°15′ of latitude south of Alexandria.

This reasoning is correct if the Earth's surface is curved (Figure 5.3). Not only do differences in the shadow angles suggest that the Earth's surface is curved, they also provide the means for estimating its size. Since 7°15′ is about 1/50 of the circumference of a circle, the 800 kilometers between Syene and Alexandria must be about 1/50 of the circumference of the Earth. The circumference of the Earth is then 800 km times 50, or about 40,000 km, and the diameter is just the circumference divided by π. We do not know how accurately Eratosthenes knew the distance between Syene and Alexandria, but his estimate of Earth's diameter was probably within 10 to 20% of today's value of 12,756 km.

Modern measurements of the Earth's size show that the Earth is flatter at the poles than at the equator. The difference between the polar and equatorial radii is only 21 km. This slight equatorial bulge together with the tilt of the Earth's rotational axis causes the Earth to move like a spinning top. As a top spins, it continuously feels the gravitational force of the Earth trying to topple it. The top, however, does not topple but swings, or **precesses,** around in a circle as it spins (Figure 5.4). The Earth feels the gravitational forces of the Sun and the Moon trying to pull its equatorial bulge into the plane of the ecliptic. Because the Earth is rotating, these forces cause the Earth to precess about the perpendicular to its orbital plane. As a result, Earth's rotational axis will trace out a circle on the celestial sphere, taking 25,725 years (Figure 5.5). Although slow, precession can be detected over hundreds of years by naked eye observations and over a few nights with modern instrumentation. The Greeks detected the precession of the Earth more than 2,000 years ago.

The Greeks, however, could not conceive of the mass of the Earth. In fact, physicists were only able to determine its mass at the end of the eighteenth century after they learned how to measure the value of the gravitational constant, G, in Newton's law of universal gravity. This required measuring the small attraction between two known masses. The Earth has a mass of 5.98×10^{27} grams, or about 6×10^{21} tons. Taken alone, this number is incomprehensible, but we can get a sense of its size by expressing it in terms of more familiar objects. For example, the mass of a large mountain such as Mt. Everest might be on the order of 10^{15} grams. This means that the mass of the Earth is equivalent to several trillion (10^{12}) Mt. Everests. Although several trillion is also a staggering number, it does emphasize the incredible mass of the Earth.

The average **density** of the Earth, or how much Earth material, on the average, occupies 1 cubic centimeter of volume, can be calculated by dividing the total mass of the Earth by its volume:

$$\text{Average density of the Earth} = \frac{\text{total mass of the Earth}}{\text{volume of the Earth}}$$

$$= \frac{5.98 \times 10^{27} \text{ g}}{1.08 \times 10^{27} \text{ cm}^3} = 5.5 \text{ g/cm}^3$$

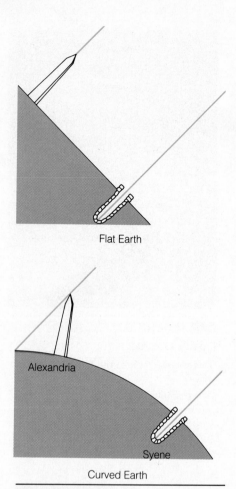

Flat Earth

Curved Earth

■■■■ FIGURE 5.3

Shadows on a Flat and Curved Earth

Eratosthenes reasoned that if the Earth were flat, the noontime Sun would produce shadows with the same angle everywhere on the Earth. Noontime shadows on a curved Earth produce different shadow lengths depending on the latitude.

Precession: A slow, conical motion of the rotational axis of a spinning body.

Density: A measure of the compactness of matter; the ratio of the mass of an object to its volume. Density is expressed in this text as grams per cubic centimeter, or g/cm³.

The density of water is 1 g/cm³. Therefore the Earth has a mass 5.5 times that of a globe of water of equal size.

Density is a measure of how closely individual atoms of matter are packed and of the masses of the individual atoms making up the material. The greater the density, the greater the mass of a given volume of some object. For instance, at room temperature and pressure, a volume of 3.8 liters (1 gallon) of water has a mass of 3.8 kg (a little more than 8 lb), but 3.8 liters of mercury has a mass of 52 kg, or more than 100 lb! Mercury is 13.6 times denser than water because individual mercury atoms are more massive and because they are packed closer together. Table 5.2 lists the densities of several common substances. Granite and basalt are typical rocks found on the Earth's surface. Since their densities are less than the average density of the Earth, the Earth cannot be made up completely of the kinds of rocks found on the surface. At the same time, elements such as iron or nickel cannot make up the whole interior of the Earth because they are too dense. Therefore the composition of the Earth must be a combination of materials of different densities, with the surface being less dense than the center.

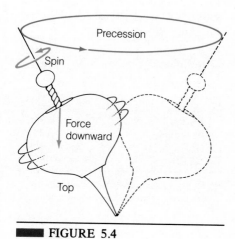

■■ FIGURE 5.4

Precession

■■■THE STATE OF THE EARTH'S INTERIOR

The last sentence of the preceding section hinted that the interior of the Earth is composed of materials that are different from those on the surface. In fact, the Earth can be divided into three major divisions—crust, mantle, and core—based on differences in composition and physical properties (Figure 5.6). The **crust** is the outermost layer, the skin of the Earth. It is 30–50 km thick under the continents and 5–10 km under

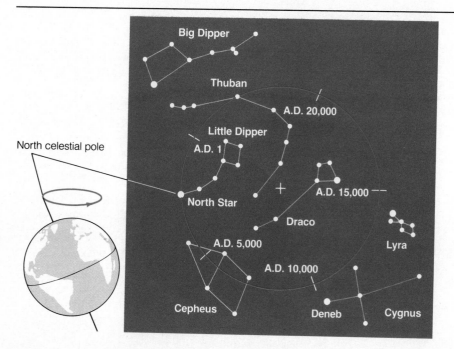

■■ FIGURE 5.5

The Path of the North Celestial Pole

The precession of the Earth causes the north celestial pole to change. Over about 260 centuries it traces out a circle on the celestial sphere. Currently, the north celestial pole is located near the present North Star, Polaris. About 10,000 years from now, it will be near the star Deneb in the constellation Cygnus.

■■■ TABLE 5.2 **Densities of Some Common Substances**

Substance	Density (g/cm³)
Water	1.0
Granite*	2.6
Basalt**	2.9
Iron oxide	5.2
Iron	7.9
Nickel	8.9

*Molten rock that cooled below ground.
**Molten rock that cooled above ground.

Silicate: Any of a large class of minerals containing silicon and oxygen mixed with calcium, aluminum, and other elements; the chemical symbols, or abbreviations, for silicon and oxygen are "Si" and "O," respectively. The chemical symbol for silica, a silicate with 1 silicon atom and 2 oxygen atoms is SiO_2. The "2" slightly below the "O" represents 2 oxygen atoms.

the oceans. The **mantle** is a thick layer of denser rock extending 2900 km below the crust. Under the mantle is 3450 km of the metallic **core,** consisting of an outer fluid region and an inner solid region.

The Earth's Surface

The Earth's crust consists mainly of the element oxygen (Figure 5.7). The oxygen readily combines chemically with the other abundant elements in the crust so that free oxygen gas is generally not found in the interior. The *minerals* forming the rocks in the crust are mainly oxygen chemically bonded to other elements. Since oxygen and silicon represent 74% of the crust, most of the minerals are **silicates.** The simplest form of silicate is *silica*, SiO_2, known as quartz. Most crustal minerals are combinations of sodium, calcium, potassium, and aluminum with silicates.

Rocks in the crust are divided into three major categories based on their origin. *Igneous* rocks form from the cooling and solidification of a hot, molten rock, called "magma" when it is underground and "lava" when it reaches the surface. From the standpoint of planetary studies, igneous rocks are the most important because surface rocks are generally formed by cooling of interior magma, which is expected to contain most of the elements in a planet. *Sedimentary* rock is an accumulation of fragments of rocks either by mechanical means, such as the transport of fragments by wind, as in the formation of sand dunes, or by hydraulic means such as moving grains down a river to a delta or settling on the ocean floor. Fossils are often found in sedimentary rocks. *Metamorphic* rock is any igneous or sedimentary rock that has been transformed by being subjected to high temperatures, high pressures, impact, or all three. Metamorphic rocks are usually found deep in the crust.

■■■ FIGURE 5.6

Major Divisions of the Earth's Structure

The Earth's crust varies in thickness from 10 km below the oceans to as much as 50 km under the continents.

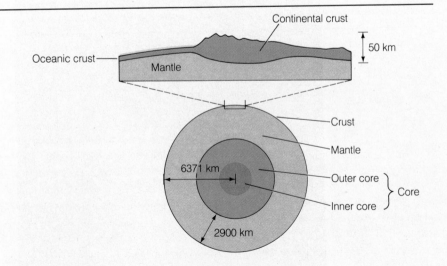

Studying the Earth's Interior

Information about the interior of the Earth generally comes from indirect sources. Geologists cannot inspect a shovel of mantle material originating 1000 km below the crust or look at it under a microscope. They must rely on less direct means of identifying the minerals in the Earth's interior. This information comes mainly from two sources: seismic studies and surface heat flow measurements.

Seismology. Seismology (derived from the Greek *seismos* meaning "the shaking of the Earth") is the investigation of earthquakes and the related propagation of **seismic waves** through the Earth and along its surface. Earthquakes are caused by sudden movements of the Earth along a crack, or fracture, in the Earth's crust. These abrupt movements generate the seismic waves, and the subsequent motions of seismic waves within the Earth provide clues to the physical nature of the Earth's interior.

Waves are a common feature in nature. We have all experienced and generated water waves. Sound is also transmitted by waves. Water and sound waves are mechanical waves in that they cause part of a deformable medium to oscillate about its normal, undisturbed position. A fishing float in a lake, for instance, moves up and down in roughly the same place as wave after wave of water sweeps by it. The molecules of water near the float are oscillating near their undisturbed positions. A wave is transmitted by energy being passed from one molecule to the next. Similarly, seismic waves propagate through the Earth because the different parts of the Earth are connected together; any movement of one part of the Earth is transmitted to a nearby part.

Earthquakes generate waves that travel through the Earth in the form of both *transverse waves* called **S waves,** in which particle motion is perpendicular to the direction of propagation, and *compressional waves,* or **P waves,** in which the particles move back and forth along the direction of travel (Figure 5.8). The S and P waves start from the focus, or origin, of the earthquake and propagate through the Earth. Both can pass through solid rock but S waves cannot pass through liquid or molten material. Liquids do not resist changes in shape caused by the S waves, so the oscillations are attenuated, or damped out. Solids and liquids resist compression and spring back, allowing compressional waves to propagate through.

The movement of the Earth caused by seismic waves is detected and recorded by instruments called *seismographs.* Seismograph stations are located all around the world, and the time between an earthquake and its arrival at a station is proportional to the distance between the station and the focus of the earthquake. The seismic waves detected at stations located near an earthquake have only traveled through shallow parts of the Earth's mantle (Figure 5.9). Faraway stations detect seismic waves that have traveled through deeper parts of the Earth; some have even traveled through the center of the Earth. Geologists can calculate

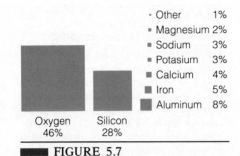

• Other	1%
▪ Magnesium	2%
▪ Sodium	3%
▪ Potassium	3%
▪ Calcium	4%
▪ Iron	5%
▪ Aluminum	8%

Oxygen 46%   Silicon 28%

■ FIGURE 5.7

Chemical Mixture of the Earth's Crust by Atomic Mass

About 74% of the crust is oxygen and silicon by mass.

Seismic waves: Vibrations produced by earthquakes and explosions that propagate through the Earth's interior and across its surface as a result of an elastic response of the Earth.

Transverse and Compressional Waves

(a) Transverse wave motion: If you tie a Ping-Pong ball to a rope and send a wave down the rope, the ball will move up and down as the wave propagates horizontally through the ball's position. *(b)* Compressional wave motion: A Ping-Pong ball tied to a spring, such as a Slinky, will move back and forth as a wave propagates horizontally.

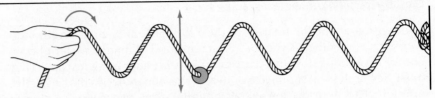

Motion perpendicular to direction of travel

(a) Transverse wave

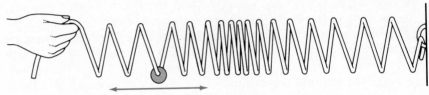

Motion back and forth along direction of motion

(b) Compressional wave

the velocity of the waves by measuring the different travel times and distances to the various stations. Since seismic waves move faster in denser rock, velocities indicate the density of the medium through which the waves traveled.

When geologists analyze the data from all seismic stations around the globe, they obtain a density profile, or map, of the Earth's interior. The crust is mainly low-density rock ($\approx$3 g/cm^3), the mantle slightly higher density ($\approx$4.5 g/cm^3), and the core very dense ($\approx$12 g/cm^3). Furthermore, the density of rock does not change smoothly all the way to the center of the Earth—sharp jumps occur because the interior of the Earth is layered. Finally, seismic waves from a strong earthquake can be detected on the opposite side of the Earth from the focus of an earthquake.

Seismic Waves through the Earth

Seismic waves from an earthquake take different lengths of time to reach seismic stations at different points on the Earth's surface. The travel times are a function of distance traveled and the characteristics of the material the waves pass through. Notice that only P waves are detected on the opposite side of the Earth from an earthquake.

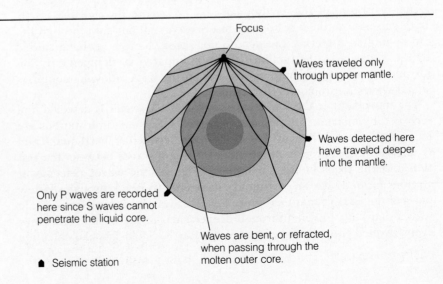

Focus

Waves traveled only through upper mantle.

Waves detected here have traveled deeper into the mantle.

Only P waves are recorded here since S waves cannot penetrate the liquid core.

Waves are bent, or refracted, when passing through the molten outer core.

♠ Seismic station

The observation that the S waves do not travel directly through the Earth is the critical evidence suggesting that part of the Earth's center is liquid.

Heat Flow. The Earth is hot inside. Hot springs, volcanoes, and the higher temperatures found in mines are clear evidence of a hot Earth. Temperatures inside the Earth *increase* inward at an average rate of about 25°C per kilometer (75°F per mile). For instance, the temperatures in the diamond mines in South Africa reach the boiling point of water at depths of about 3 km so the mines must be air-conditioned for the miners to survive. The heat flow measured at the surface comes from the decay of radioactive elements in crustal rocks and heat transported from the hot center of the Earth.

MathTools 2: Temperature °F/°C/K

How much hotter is the inside of the Earth than its surface? What is the temperature 1000 km, 2000 km, or 6000 km inside the Earth? It would be tempting to *estimate* the temperature at the center by simply increasing the temperature 25°C for every kilometer of depth. Starting with the Earth's average surface temperature of about 15°C, such a calculation gives a temperature of about 40°C at 1 km, 65°C at 2 km, and 90°C at 3 km. At a depth of 75 km, the estimated temperature is 1900°C, already higher than the melting point of most minerals. At the base of the mantle, temperatures based on this estimate would be greater than 25,000°C, implying that most of the Earth's interior must be a sea of magma. Yet we know that this cannot be true—the temperature cannot increase deep inside the Earth as fast as it does near the crust because most of the Earth's interior is not liquid.

To determine how much more slowly the temperature increases, geologists combine all of the seismic data and heat flow measurements with measurements of mineral properties, such as their melting temperatures, how fluid they are under different conditions, and how their structure changes with temperature, chemical composition, and pressure. Figure 5.10 shows the predictions of how the temperature changes with depth in the Earth. The temperature rises rapidly near the surface, but at depths below a few hundred kilometers, the temperature increase per kilometer is less steep and eventually almost levels off. Central temperatures reach over 4000°C. Furthermore, at a depth of 2900 km, iron-rich material will melt while at greater depths it can resolidify because increased pressure, due to the tremendous compression of the core by the overlaying mass of the Earth, raises the melting temperatures. As a result, the Earth has a solid inner core.

A Model of the Earth's Interior

The mantle begins as shallow as 5 km under the oceanic crust and extends downward another 2900 km. The boundaries between the crust and the mantle, as well as between the mantle and the core, correspond to major discontinuities in the density of the Earth's interior. The mantle is richer in iron- and magnesium-bearing silicates than is the crust, which accounts for the mantle's higher density. Although very dense,

■ FIGURE 5.10

How the Earth's Interior Temperature Changes with Depth

The magenta line is the melting temperature of iron at each depth inside the Earth. The temperature of magma from volcanoes constrains predictions at low temperatures. The point where the predicted temperature curve crosses the melting curve of iron defines the extent of the liquid outer core; that is, at a depth of 2900 km, the predicted temperature of the Earth is above the melting temperature of iron.

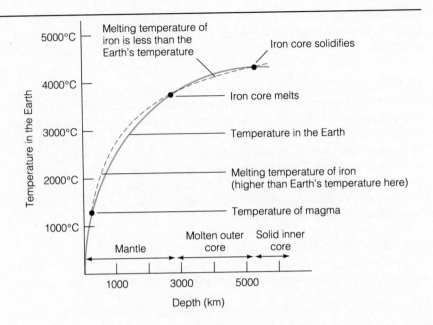

the mantle is not entirely solid. Under conditions of high temperature and pressure, rock can behave more like a viscous fluid than a brittle solid. For instance, at room temperature, iron is very solid, but near its melting point it can be shaped. Under great pressure, what would normally be solid rock can be made to flow slowly. Of course, at temperatures above its melting temperature, metal can flow as a liquid. Geologists use the ability of the rocks to flow as a criterion for dividing the upper mantle into two regions. The upper 100 km of the Earth is solid in the usual sense of the word. This region is called the *lithosphere* and includes the upper mantle and the crust (Figure 5.11). The mantle below the brittle rock of the lithosphere is a semifluid, or plastic, region called the *asthenosphere*.

The outer core, from 2900 km to 5100 km, is fluid. The sharp increase in the velocity of P waves at 5100 km implies that the inner core is solid. It is generally thought that the core is mainly composed of an iron-nickel alloy with a small fraction of a lighter element, such as sulfur, silicon, or oxygen. The evidence for a high-density core is indirect. First, a high core density averaged with a low crust density gives the calculated average density of 5.5 g/cm³ for the Earth. Secondly, the Earth has a strong magnetic field (see the last section in this chapter) that is thought to be generated by the movement of the metallic core. Finally, meteorites (see Chapter 10), which are mainly an iron-nickel alloy, are believed to originate in larger bodies that also formed high-density cores.

Formation of a Layered Earth

How did the Earth become layered? Studies of magma show that, as the molten rock cools, it passes through different phases in which min-

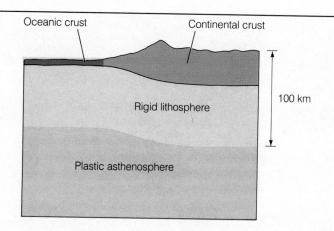

Oceanic crust   Continental crust

Rigid lithosphere

100 km

Plastic asthenosphere

■■■ FIGURE 5.11

The Lithosphere and Asthenosphere

The lithosphere includes the crust and the solid part of the upper mantle. Just below the lithosphere is a fluid layer called the asthenosphere.

eral structures become unstable and are replaced by other minerals. As heavy minerals form in the magma, they tend to sink while light minerals tend to rise. We call this process *differentiation*. If the Earth were molten in its past, a layered structure would be the natural result of planetwide differentiation. Although the study of the Earth itself offers no evidence that it was in a molten state in the past, meteorites and Moon rocks do provide evidence of melting in the early solar system. Both show signs of having undergone melting within the first few hundred million years of the formation of the solar system. If these small bodies were hot enough to be molten, Earth was probably hot enough to be totally molten at least in the upper few hundred kilometers and partially molten the rest of the way to the center. Consequently, the Earth as a whole would differentiate. The dense iron would sink toward the center forming the core. Light silicates would naturally float to the surface and form the crust. As the Earth cooled and magma moved toward the surface, moderately dense minerals would crystallize and form the mantle.

Other evidence for a hot, molten interior for the Earth comes from continental and oceanic features indicative of a slow, plastic motion of the mantle. This motion causes the lithosphere of the Earth to break into separate segments called plates.

■■■PLATE TECTONICS

The topic of global **plate tectonics,** the study of rigid lithospheric **plates** floating on the upper mantle, represents a transition from the study of the Earth's interior to its surface. The forces that move these plates and form Earth's mountain ranges and volcanoes stem from deep within the Earth.

Before the 1960s, most geologists believed the continents and ocean basins were stationary and that geological features, such as mountains, were the result of gradual upward shifts in the crust. An alternate view, involving the movement of continents, had been around since the seventeenth century when naturalists noticed that the continents facing each other across the Atlantic Ocean appeared to fit together, much like

Plate tectonics: The theory and study of plate formation, movement, interaction, and destruction; the attempt to explain the formation and deformation of large-scale structural features on the Earth in terms of plate motions.

Plates: Rigid segments of the lithosphere that move independently of each other.

■■■ FIGURE 5.12

An Ancient Continent 200 Million Years Ago

South America and Africa appear to fit together. Several mountain ranges at the edges of each continent are very similar and form continuous ranges when the continents are placed side by side. The parts of the continents under the ocean, the continental shelves, are shown extending beyond the visible landmasses.

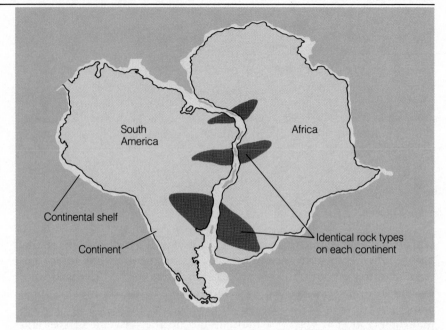

Convection: Movement of a fluid or gas because of differences in density caused by localized heating; in a boiling liquid convection causes the liquid to rise and sink.

■■■ FIGURE 5.13

Convection

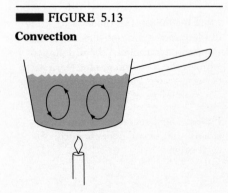

pieces in a jigsaw puzzle (Figure 5.12). In the early part of this century, Alfred Wegener (1880–1930), a German meteorologist, pointed out that rocks, geological structures, and fossils on opposite sides of the Atlantic were very similar. Wegener and others constructed a case for "continental drift" in which they proposed that the continents retained the outline of the pieces that broke off a single "supercontinent" they called *Pangaea*. However, since they were not able to devise a plausible driving mechanism for the drifting of these pieces and since their evidence did not appear convincing at the time, most geologists did not accept the theory.

In 1928, the British geologist Arthur Holmes suggested a mechanism to drive continental drift that involved motions in the mantle. If rock is fluid, it can transport heat by *moving* from a hot region to a cooler region. We call this motion and heat transport mechanism **convection** (Figure 5.13). An example of convection can be seen when hot cereal is boiled in a pan. When the cereal at the bottom becomes hot enough, it rises to the top, moves horizontally to the edge of the pan, and then sinks back down. When it is heated again at the bottom, it rises and repeats its circular motion. Convective motion in the Earth is also a circulation—from a deep, hot region to a higher, cool region and back again. One such loop is called a convective cell. Holmes's idea was that the slow convective motion of a partially molten upper mantle could move continents. Evidence in support of these ideas began to emerge only after World War II when extensive exploration of the seafloor began. Scientists soon discovered an underwater mountain range, now called the mid-Atlantic Ridge, along the length of the Atlantic Ocean (Figure 5.14). Further studies showed that the ocean floor along the ridge was spreading apart, moving east and west away from the ridge, and that the rock on either side was recently solidified magma. In the

1960s, as more evidence accumulated supporting continental drift and seafloor spreading, geologists began to look at the old data in a new light and soon developed the present theory of plate tectonics.

Even with supporting evidence, the theory of plate tectonics developed slowly. Geologists simply had difficulty imagining the huge landmasses of the continents moving. Recall the controversy over the spinning Earth required by the Copernican heliocentric model. Moving continents were just as unimaginable at first. Such roadblocks to a theory are removed in time as data constantly accumulate until they eventually become overwhelming. Then the flow of scientific inquiry will resume with a greater understanding of nature.

The theory of plate tectonics describes the surface of the Earth as a mosaic of plates that move relative to each other (Figure 5.15). The speed and direction of each plate can be measured to determine how the plates interact with each other. Plates can move away from, collide with, or slide past each other. These plates are lithospheric slabs sitting on top of the plastic mantle below. Geologists contend, as Holmes proposed, that plate movement involves the transport of heat from the Earth's interior to the surface as giant convective cells, moving about as fast as a fingernail grows, circulate mantle rock (Figure 5.16). Plate movement occurs over the upper part of a convective cell where the motion is horizontal.

As a result of huge continent-sized pieces of land and ocean bumping, sliding past, and moving away from each other, the boundaries of plates are locations of intense geological activity. For example, the surface of the Earth separates just above the position where two convective cells rise. This is occurring right now all along the Mid-Atlantic Ridge. The plates on either side of the Mid-Atlantic Ridge are moving away from

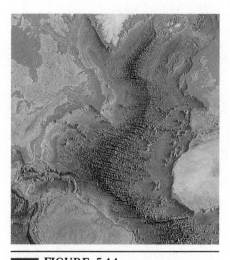

■ FIGURE 5.14

Mid-Atlantic Ridge

This mountain range was created by magma from the mantle pushing up to the surface.

SOURCE: Portion of world ocean floor map by Bruce C. Heezen and Marie Tharp, 1977. Copyright © 1977 by Marie Tharp. Reproduced by permission of Marie Tharp, 1 Washington Ave., South Nyack, NY 10960.

■ FIGURE 5.15

Major Lithospheric Plates on Earth

Arrows indicate direction of plate motion.

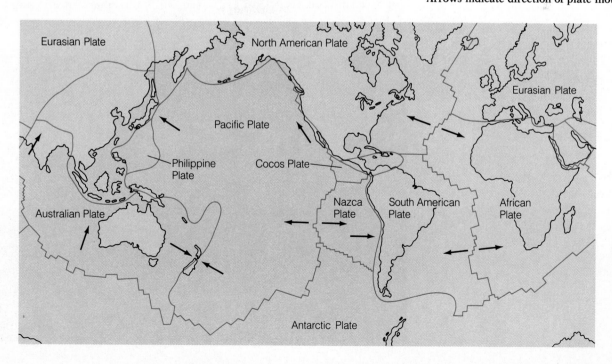

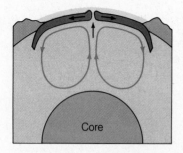

(a) Deep mantle convection

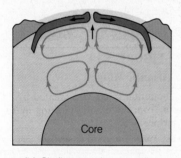

(b) Shallow mantle convection

■ FIGURE 5.16

Mantle Convection

Two possible orientations for convective cells in the Earth's mantle below an oceanic ridge.

each other at measured rates of 2–4 centimeters per year, generating earthquakes and volcanism all along the ridge. Most earthquakes are caused by the shifting of plates while volcanoes arise from magma transported upward to the surface by the convective cells below. Iceland, for instance, is an exposed section of the Mid-Atlantic Ridge that is subject to both earthquakes and volcanism. Iceland is being slowly pulled apart, with one section moving eastward and the other westward, as the North American and Eurasian plates spread apart. At the same time, magma surfaces and adds to the landmass; Iceland is a volcanic island, built upon many layers of lava. Volcanism is still producing new Icelandic islands. In 1963, volcanic eruptions produced the island Surtsey about 40 km southwest of the main island (Figure 5.17). Under the ocean all along the Mid-Atlantic Ridge, magma is swelling upward through the fissures, or long linear cracks, produced by the separating plates, thereby adding new rock to the spreading plates. Furthermore, when geologists followed the motions of the plates on either side of the Mid-Atlantic Ridge backward in time, they discovered that approximately 200 million years ago North America, South America, Africa, and Europe were merged into one continent—Wegener's Pangaea. The rising convective currents in the Earth's mantle broke up this supercontinent, allowing the pieces to drift apart and form today's continents.

Where plates slide past each other, intensive earthquake activity occurs. Californians, for example, are plagued by an extensive network of cracks in the Earth extending southward across western California to the Gulf of California. The San Andreas Fault is part of this network separating the Pacific Plate and the North American Plate. Los Angeles is part of the Pacific Plate and is moving toward San Francisco. In about 25 million years San Francisco will be a suburb of Los Angeles

■ FIGURE 5.17

An Icelandic Volcano

The new island of Surtsey lies on the Mid-Atlantic Ridge near Iceland and was formed by lava flowing up through the ridge and solidifying.

SOURCE: Sólarfilma.

or vice versa. It was the rupture of the San Andreas Fault that generated the 1989 earthquake near San Francisco (Figure 5.18) and the 1906 earthquake that destroyed most of San Francisco. Earthquakes are generated when the tension between two plates, which builds up over time as the two blocks of crust try to move, is suddenly released. The tension in the San Andreas fault has been building since 1906 and was partially relieved in 1989. Californians are not the only victims of plate slippage. On October 10, 1980, two plates slipped, causing a devastating earthquake in San Salvador in which 1500 people died. About 10,000 people were injured and a quarter of a million were left homeless.

Plates also collide with other plates. In a head-on collision, one plate can buckle, forming high mountains, while the other plate can slide underneath. For instance, India is part of a plate that is crashing into the Eurasian Plate. The result is the Himalayas. Similarly where the Nazca Plate collides with the South American Plate, the Andes formed. Deep trenches, or valleys, on the ocean floor are formed when an oceanic plate dives below a continental plate. Along the western coast of South America lies the deep Peru-Chile Trench. The deepest trench is the Marianas Trench, in the western Pacific Ocean, which reaches depths of 11 km below sea level. Trenches are intense earthquake zones as one plate slides deep into the mantle. The 1985 earthquake centered 360 miles southwest of Mexico City was caused by such plate subduction. Nearly 5000 people were killed as several hundred buildings in Mexico City were destroyed. Volcanism is also prevalent along trenches because the rock that dives under one plate is melted, providing magma for surface volcanoes, such as those along the western coasts of North and South America (Figure 5.19). In fact, the distribution of earthquakes and volcanoes around the world shows high concentrations near all plate boundaries.

When they study the worlds in the solar system, astronomers and geologists are particularly interested in what can be seen on the surface of planets and moons. It is clear that plate tectonics produces very visible surface features on the Earth. Plate collisions form mountain ranges, plate boundaries are sites of active volcanoes, and active spreading produces giant rift valleys. It is also clear that the theory of plate tectonics cannot account for all geological features on the Earth, such as erosional features and the formation of sediment. Nevertheless, it is a unifying model in geology that explains the origin of many geological features. The surfaces of other planets and the Moon are similar to the surface of the Earth in that some features are definitely tectonic in origin while others are not.

■■■THE AGE OF THE EARTH

The creation and destruction of geological formations take time. How long have these processes been going on? How old is the Earth? And how can such questions be answered since they involve events that occurred far back in the past? Just as historians must turn to historical records to learn about events that occurred beyond the reaches of hu-

FIGURE 5.18

Damage Caused by the 1989 Earthquake in San Francisco

SOURCE: Jeff Reinking/Picture Group.

FIGURE 5.19

Mt. St. Helens Erupting

SOURCE: John H. Meehan/Science Source, Photo Researchers.

Relative age: Age meaningful only in relation to another; one object is older than another. Old is a relative term.

Absolute age: Definite or certain age in the sense that a number is assigned to the age of an object; a rock is 400 million years old (not necessarily a correct age).

Stratification: Arranged in layers or strata. The walls of the Grand Canyon exhibit the stratification of rocks that the Colorado River cut through to form the canyon. Each layer accumulated over another layer; the highest layers are the most recent.

Fossils: Mineralized remains (impressions, outlines, tracks, or body parts) of plants and animals of some previous geological period preserved in a rock formation on the Earth's crust after the original organic material is transformed or removed; the original bone, shell, stem, and so forth is seldom preserved because it has usually been dissolved by groundwater. Hard minerals precipitate in their place and produce a cast of the original.

man memory, astronomers and geologists must rely upon historical records to learn about events that occurred long ago. In astronomy historical records are found in the light from stars, in geology they are found in the rocks of the Earth.

Two aspects of time are important for determining the age of the Earth. The first is **relative** age. The statement "an elderly person is older than a child" is an example of the relative ages of people. The second is **absolute** age. The elderly person is 72 years old and the child is 12 years old—here age is given as a number. The same two aspects of time apply to the Earth. One rock formation can be identified as being older than another just by considering their appearances and relative positions in the layering of rocks. Sometimes absolute ages can be assigned; formation "A" may be 200 million years old while formation "B" is only 100 million years old. Geological relative ages come from observing the layering in rock formations; absolute ages result from nuclear properties of certain elements.

A superb example of relative dating by observing layering, or **stratification,** can be seen in the walls of the Grand Canyon (Figure 5.20). Over a dozen layers of geologically identifiable rock formations form the walls. The obvious deduction is that one layer was placed on top of another in sequence, with the highest layers being the most recent. The strata in the Grand Canyon are layers of sediment deposited by ancient lakes and oceans that once covered the area.

These layers of sediment also contain **fossils**. Fossils are the remains of ancient organisms, usually animal shells but also plants. Some of the fossil shells are very similar to shells found on beaches today. These familiar fossils lie in the highest layers of sediment (Figure 5.21). Below these are fossils that are somewhat similar but distinctly different from

FIGURE 5.20

Strata in the Walls of the Grand Canyon

SOURCE: John Gerlach/Visuals Unlimited.

the seashells found today. In the deepest layers are fossil shells that are unlike anything found today. Obviously, these deep fossils represent earlier life-forms since the deepest layers were deposited first. Unless the rock formations have been overturned, the vertical layers in which fossils are found *always* show the same sequence of fossils. Familiar shells lie on top and dissimilar ones lie in the deeper formations. Consequently, rocks record a succession of both animal and plant fossils from which rock formations all over the world are ordered. This stratigraphic time scale is shown Table 5.3. The stratigraphic time scale is a relative time scale, from young rock formations to old rock formations.

The absolute age of the stratigraphic time scale is established by radiometric dating (see Chapter 4) of embedded and crosscutting igneous rock within the sedimentary layers containing fossils. The ages of igneous rocks in the sedimentary layers represent the time since the rocks in each formation solidified. If rocks are heated, daughter nuclei are free to migrate away, either by flowing in a melt or escaping as a gas. Most of the rock formations on Earth consist of reprocessed rocks. For instance, the oldest rocks in the Atlantic Ocean are no more than 200 million years old. They represent relatively new rock that formed the seafloor as it welled up in the form of magma. The magma cooled and solidified upon reaching the seafloor, and new daughter nuclei remained trapped in the rock.

The oldest rocks on Earth are found in Greenland and are 3.9 billion years old. This means that the Earth is at least 3.9 billion years old. Additional information from lunar rocks and meteorites (see Chapters 6 and 10) fixes the Earth's age at 4.6 billion years.

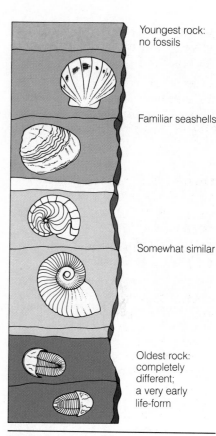

Youngest rock:
no fossils

Familiar seashells

Somewhat similar

Oldest rock:
completely
different;
a very early
life-form

■■ FIGURE 5.21

Fossils

The youngest rocks exhibit fossils most similar to today's life-forms; the oldest, deepest rocks exhibit the most dissimilar fossils.

■■ TABLE 5.3 Geologic Time Scale

Era	Period	Epoch	Time before Present (in millions of years)
	Relative Age Sequence		*Absolute Age Sequence*
Cenosoic	Quaternary	Holocene	Now–0.1
		Pleistocene	0.1–2
	Tertiary	Pliocene	2–8
		Miocene	8–25
		Oligocene	25–39
		Eocene	39–60
		Paleocene	60–65
Mesozoic	Cretaceous		65–135
	Jurassic		135–190
	Triassic		190–225
Paleozoic	Permian		225–280
	Pennsylvanian		280–320
	Mississippian		320–345
	Devonian		345–395
	Silurian		395–440
	Ordovician		440–500
	Cambrian		500–570
	Precambrian		570–4,600

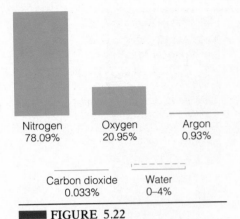

Chemical Composition of the Earth's Atmosphere

Gaseous components in trace amounts include neon, carbon monoxide, ozone, helium, sulfur dioxide, methane, krypton, and hydrogen.

■■■THE ATMOSPHERE OF THE EARTH

The Earth's atmosphere plays a major role in our daily lives. We watch weather reports; we feel the wind, rain, and snow; we enjoy cool summer breezes and crisp winter nights; we protect ourselves from storms; we expose ourselves to the Sun. The Earth's atmosphere is ever-changing. Yet it constantly acts as a shield blocking harmful solar radiation from reaching the surface. It also acts as a blanket trapping heat deposited by the Sun's radiation. The shielding and blanketing characteristics of the atmosphere arise mainly from the ability of individual atoms and molecules to interact with electromagnetic radiation emitted from the Sun and the Earth's surface.

Composition

The atmosphere is composed of particles and gases, but the mixture is not entirely fixed. Considering only "dry air," that is, ignoring for the moment the variable water vapor content, 99% of the atmosphere is composed of nitrogen and oxygen, and most of the remaining 1% is the inert gas argon (Figure 5.22). Certain other gases, such as carbon dioxide and methane, and suspended particles vary from day to day, place to place, and even year to year. In addition, the amount of water vapor in the atmosphere is quite variable. In tropical jungles it can reach concentrations of 3–4% by volume; in cold regions or deserts it can be less than 1%. After water vapor, carbon dioxide is the most abundant of the "other" components of the atmosphere. The amount of carbon dioxide in the atmosphere has been rising since humans began burning fossil fuels (coal, oil, and natural gas) in large quantities. In the last 80 years the carbon dioxide content has increased by almost 20%.

Besides gases, the atmosphere also contains solid particles. While the largest particles reside for only a few weeks in the atmosphere, small particles can stay aloft for a couple of years. These particles are fine soils blown into the air, smoke and soot from fires, pollen and microorganisms, and volcanic ash and dust.

The Earth's Primitive Atmosphere

The atmosphere has not always been rich in the nitrogen and oxygen we breath today. Although the initial mixture of gases in the Earth's atmosphere is unknown, the Earth's early atmosphere probably had very little free oxygen. The small amount of inert gases, such as neon, in the atmosphere today indicates either that the Earth's primitive atmosphere was about 100 times less dense than it is now or that the Earth somehow lost most of its early atmosphere. In either case, much of the present atmosphere came from within the Earth.

Billions of years ago, dynamic processes of the Earth generated an atmosphere by ejecting trapped gases from the Earth's interior. Today's volcanoes, for instance, eject mainly water vapor, carbon dioxide, nitrogen, and sulfur-bearing compounds (Figure 5.23). The Earth's second atmosphere probably was made up of these same gases released

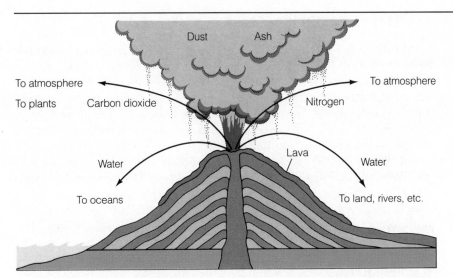

FIGURE 5.23
Volcanic Eruptions and the Atmosphere

Volcanoes contibute enormous amounts of water, carbon dioxide and other gases, dust, and ash to the atmosphere as well as lava to the crust. Some of the carbon dioxide is washed out of the atmosphere by rain and forms carbonate rock.

through ancient volcanic eruptions. For hundreds of millions of years, water vapor, carbon dioxide, and nitrogen were spewed out from the molten rocks within the Earth. During this time the Earth cooled, allowing water to condense out of the atmosphere, forming lakes, rivers, and oceans. Most of the carbon dioxide dissolved in the oceans and now resides in carbonate rocks in the Earth's crust while the nitrogen abundance gradually increased. About 2.5 billion years ago, primitive plant life that relied on **photosynthesis** appeared on land and in the seas. The process of photosynthesis by plants releases oxygen into the atmosphere. Oxygen was then added to the atmosphere in large quantities, becoming an abundant and permanent gas used to support higher forms of life. The presence of life and water, therefore, modified the atmosphere by adding oxygen and removing carbon dioxide, leaving the atmosphere we now breathe.

Photosynthesis: The production of organic molecules, mainly carbohydrates, and atmospheric oxygen from carbon dioxide and water by green, or chlorophyll-bearing, plants.

The Atmosphere's Role as a Shield

Both water vapor and carbon dioxide absorb some of the energy the Earth receives from the Sun in the form of electromagnetic radiation and, therefore, influence the transfer of this energy through the atmosphere. Some materials and gases are *opaque* to certain radiation; they either absorb it or reflect it. Some are *transparent;* they let radiation pass through. Glass, for instance, is transparent to visible radiation but rock is not. Water vapor and carbon dioxide are also transparent to visible radiation and to short wavelength infrared radiation but opaque to long wavelength infrared radiation. Consequently, not all of the radiation from the Sun reaches the Earth's surface.

A very important absorber of ultraviolet radiation in the atmosphere is ozone, the triatomic form of oxygen. A little ultraviolet radiation gives a nice tan, a bit too much gives a sunburn, and a lot can kill. Over the last decade, the world has become increasingly alarmed because the average ozone concentration in the atmosphere has dropped about

2.5%. The decrease has been particularly obvious over the South Pole in what is called the ozone hole. For a 1% decrease in ozone abundance, health officials expect a 5% increase in the incidence of skin cancer—about 25,000 additional cases each year. A major cause of ozone reduction appears to be gases called chlorofluorocarbons, which are used in air conditioners, plastic foam, and as solvents. Fortunately, in 1988 world governments, concerned about the effects of the depletion of ozone in the upper atmosphere, signed an international treaty to cut the use of the chemicals in half by 1999.

The absorption of solar radiation by ozone and also by oxygen and nitrogen molecules produces an intricate vertical temperature structure in the atmosphere (Figure 5.24). Near the Earth's surface the temperature decreases with altitude, as any mountain climber can attest. This bottommost layer of the atmosphere is known as the *troposphere*. The temperature, however, does not continue to decrease all the way to the edge of the atmosphere. Between 10 and 20 km above the surface, the temperature remains constant and then increases with height to approximately 50 km; this layer of the atmosphere is called the *strato-*

■■■ FIGURE 5.24

Distribution of Temperature with Height in the Earth's Atmosphere

On the right is the approximate penetration depth of solar radiation of different wavelengths into the Earth's atmosphere. Visible and infrared radiation reach the surface of the Earth while most of the ultraviolet radiation is absorbed before it reaches the surface.

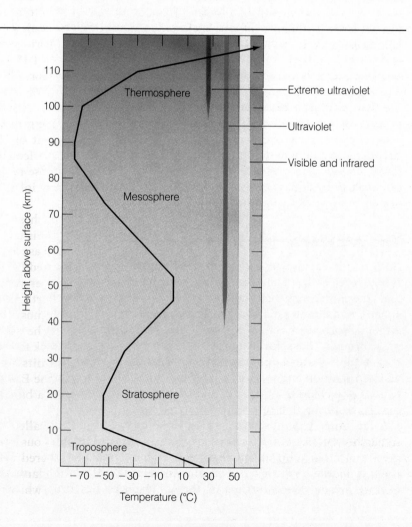

sphere. The temperature increases in the stratosphere because ozone absorbs ultraviolet radiation. A common example of heating by absorbing radiation is the heating of a cup of water in a microwave oven; the water comes to a boil by absorbing microwave radiation. The ozone at the upper reaches of the stratosphere is hotter because it absorbs ultraviolet radiation first, leaving less to heat the ozone in the lower levels. In fact, ozone and oxygen molecules begin to absorb ultraviolet radiation above the stratosphere at about 85 km, causing temperatures to rise gradually and to reach a maximum at about 50 km where concentrations of these molecules become significant. The highest temperatures in the atmosphere are found in the *thermosphere* where oxygen and nitrogen molecules absorb very short wavelength ultraviolet radiation.

The Atmosphere's Role as a Blanket

Although the rise in temperature in the troposphere is due to absorption of solar radiation, the mechanism is slightly more complicated than that at higher elevations. A delicate balance exists between the amount of incoming solar radiation and the amount radiated back into space by the Earth. The Earth reflects back into space about 35% of all solar radiation incident on it. Of this, clouds reflect 25%, atmospheric gases and particles reflect 6%, and the land and sea reflect 4%. About 15% of the incoming solar radiation is absorbed by clouds, water vapor, nitrogen, oxygen, ozone, and dust in the atmosphere. The other 50% is absorbed by the ground.

The solar radiation that is absorbed by the ground heats the ground. Most of us have experienced this when walking on pavement or the beach on a hot day. You may also have noticed that you can feel the heat of the pavement or sand by placing your hands or feet close to but not touching the surface. The pavement and sand are emitting infrared radiation.

Reradiation of solar energy is not limited to roads and beaches. The entire Earth is emitting infrared radiation. What happens to this radiation? Is it all emitted back into space? This would be the case if no atmosphere were present. Most of the infrared radiation emitted by the Earth's surface is absorbed in the atmosphere by clouds, water vapor, and carbon dioxide. As a result, the atmosphere above the Earth's surface heats up (Figure 5.25). This means, of course, that the atmosphere now, because it is warm, also emits infrared radiation. But the atmosphere emits this radiation in all directions, into space *and* back toward the ground. Consequently, the ground heats even more and emits more infrared radiation, thereby further heating the atmosphere. The Earth's surface temperature stays the same, on the average, because a balance exists between all of these sources of radiation.

The insulating effect of the atmosphere just described is called the **greenhouse effect** because the glass walls and roof of a greenhouse produce similar results. The visible and short wavelength infrared solar radiation passes through the glass and is absorbed by the plants and ground inside. This absorption heats the plants and ground, which, in

Greenhouse effect: The increase in temperature at and near the Earth's surface due to the absorption and emission of infrared radiation by water vapor and carbon dioxide in the atmosphere.

FIGURE 5.25

Temperature of the Earth's Surface with and without an Atmosphere

The Earth wears its atmosphere as we wear a coat—to keep warm.

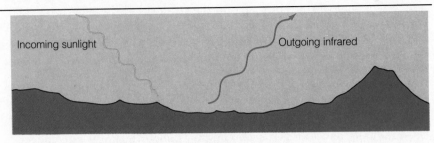

(a) No atmosphere: −19°C

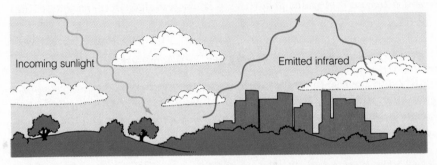

(b) With atmosphere: +20°C

turn, emit long wavelength infrared radiation. The properties of glass, however, impede the flow of long wavelength infrared radiation. Because the greenhouse cannot pass these infrared wavelengths to the outside, the interior heats up.

Atmospheric Pressure

Atoms and molecules in our atmosphere obey a simple relation between temperature, density, and **pressure** called the *perfect gas law:*

$$\text{Pressure} \propto \text{density} \times \text{temperature}$$

Pressure is the result of collisions between atoms and molecules. Colliding particles exert forces on each other in the same way you exert a force on something that you strike. Although a single collision lasts for only a short time, millions of collisions occur continuously between particles. An individual atom in the troposphere, for instance, is bombarded by an unending stream of other particles. Atmospheric pressure is the continuous pushing by the moving atoms and molecules.

The perfect gas law implies that pressure increases with increases in density and temperature. The speeds of molecules in a gas are directly related to the temperature of gas—the higher the temperature, the faster the molecules move. Faster moving molecules impart a greater force during collisions and collide more frequently. Consequently, they collectively exert a greater pressure. On the other hand, if particles are squeezed closer together, they travel a shorter distance between collisions. This means that an individual particle will be subjected to colli-

Pressure: The force per unit area exerted by a fluid (gas or liquid) against a surface within itself or bounding it.

sions more often and will therefore feel a greater pressure. The increase in pressure due to an increase in density is a result of more collisions per second while the increase in pressure due to an increase in temperature is the result of collisions that are more violent as well as more frequent.

The average atmospheric pressure at sea level is 1.033 kg/cm² (14.7 lb/in²) and is defined as 1 atmosphere (atm). Both atmospheric pressure and density decrease with height in the atmosphere. The lower layers of the atmosphere must support the weight of the upper layers and are therefore more compressed than the upper layers. Of course, it is the gravitational attraction between individual particles and the Earth that causes atoms and molecules to concentrate near the surface. In fact, more than half of all atmospheric particles lie below 5.5 km. Mountain climbers, as well as astronomers who observe at high elevations, feel the effects of a thinning atmosphere. The thin atmosphere is also the reason the air in passenger jet aircraft is pressurized. Moreover, 98% of atmospheric molecules and atoms lie below 33 km, or about three times the height of Mt. Everest. The atmosphere is clearly a very thin cover to our globe. The total mass of this thin covering is only one-millionth of the mass of the Earth.

The lowest level of our atmosphere, the troposphere, contains about 75% of the atmosphere. Nearly all of the weather on Earth takes place within the troposphere. In particular, the movement of air called wind occurs in this lowest level.

Winds: Global Circulation

"Chinook winds screamed out of the Rockies causing heavy damage along the foothills; high winds are expected today over much of the Midwest; winds will be out of the northwest with gusts up to 30 MPH." What generates **wind?** Is the wind you feel today blowing randomly, or is it part of a well-defined circulation pattern? To answer these questions we must determine what causes air to move.

The underlying cause of wind is the unequal heating of the Earth's surface. At either equinox, for instance, the Earth's equatorial regions receive a greater amount of solar radiation per square kilometer than do more northern or southern latitudes. Consequently, the air over the equatorial regions heats more than at other latitudes. This heated air expands and rises while, at the surface, air from higher latitudes flows toward the equator to replace the rising air. Thus winds are generated.

The movement of air just described is convective motion. The circulation is such that heat is transported from the equator toward higher latitudes. At the same time, the rotation of the Earth imposes an east-west or west-east flow on the general north-south circulation pattern. Figure 5.26 shows the overall global atmospheric circulation. Near the equator the winds are dominated by the "easterly trade winds" while higher latitudes are characterized by the "prevailing westerlies." Most of the weather in the United States, for instance, is from the west because of the prevailing westerlies.

Wind: Horizontal motion of air due to horizontal differences in air pressure.

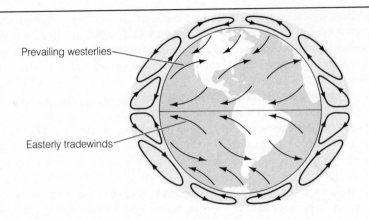

FIGURE 5.26

Global Circulation

Global wind patterns at the Earth's surface are shown as arrows. Atmospheric circulation cells are shown as ellipses and represent both surface and aloft winds. During the summer and winter as few as four circulation cells can exist worldwide.

Coriolis effect: The apparent motion of projectiles or air relative to the Earth's surface caused by the Earth's rotation; the motion is a deflection, toward the right in the Northern Hemisphere and left in the Southern Hemisphere, of the direction of motion.

FIGURE 5.27

Trajectory of a Rocket

Because the Earth turns on its rotational axis, the rocket will miss its target if no course correction is applied.

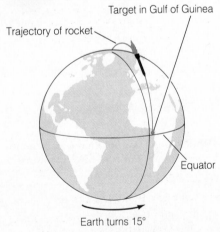

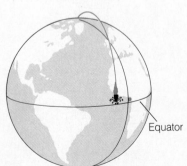

The **Coriolis effect,** named after G. G. de Coriolis (1792–1843), a French mathematician, is the name used to describe the Earth's rotational effects on movement in the atmosphere. The effect is mathematically complicated, but it can be illustrated by imagining the path of a rocket launched from the North Pole toward testing grounds on the equator (Figure 5.27). If the rocket's flight time is 1 hour, then during its flight the Earth will turn 15° on its axis. Consequently, the rocket will miss its target because the target moved about 15°. To an observer on Earth, the rocket's path appears to be deflected to the rocket's *right.* If the launch is repeated from the South Pole, the apparent deflection will be toward the rocket's left. This deflection applies to wind as well as to rockets. In the Northern Hemisphere, winds moving toward the south will be deflected to the right, or westward; winds moving toward the north will be deflected to the right, or eastward. The opposite occurs in the Southern Hemisphere.

The Coriolis effect on air flow caused by the Earth's rotation produces rotating weather systems such as hurricanes and tornadoes. Weather maps shown on television or in the newspaper usually indicate high and low pressure regions. Air flow is from high to low pressure regions because high pressure "pushes" air toward low pressure. Air flow into a low pressure region produces a counterclockwise, or cyclonic, rotation as individual air parcels are deflected to their right as they approach the low pressure region. In the Southern Hemisphere the flow will be clockwise.

The Earth's rotation through the Coriolis effect helps hinder the general north-south atmospheric circulation produced by uneven solar heating. As a result, both hemispheres are divided into several circulation cells (Figure 5.26). These cells are convective cells with air rising over the equator and falling near 30° latitude. The increase in air temperature in the stratosphere prevents the rising air currents in the troposphere from spreading into the stratosphere. Instead the air moves laterally toward the poles, and as it cools and becomes more dense, it descends. The winds aloft from the equator will also be deflected to the east in the Northern Hemisphere, reaching maximum velocity at about 30° latitude. High-velocity winds, called *jet streams,* occur at both 30° and 60° latitude. The jet streams tend to meander in latitude and have velocitiesoften exceeding 160 km per hour and sometimes as high as 400 km per hour. Jet streams can be thousands of kilometers long, hundreds of kilometers wide, and a few kilometers thick.

Atmospheric winds are caused by pressure differences within the atmosphere. Wind is a phenomenon with obvious visible and physical effects. A less physical but sometimes visible phenomenon is the movement of charged particles. These particles interact with the Earth's magnetic field and move along magnetic field lines.

▬▬THE EARTH'S MAGNETIC FIELD

The Earth has two North Poles and two South Poles. The north and south geographic poles by definition are oriented along Earth's rotational axis. The Earth also has a magnetic axis and corresponding magnetic poles (Figure 5.28). Currently, the North Magnetic Pole is located near Bathurst Island in northern Canada at a longitude of 101° west, and the South Magnetic Pole is located just off Wilkes Land in Antarctica at a longitude of 140° east. A compass points to the North or South Magnetic Pole, not to the geographic poles. Compasses involve an aspect of the Earth's magnetism called **geomagnetism,** which is very much related to the interior structure of the Earth. Another aspect of the Earth's magnetism is the **magnetosphere.** In this region surrounding the Earth, Earth's magnetism interacts with the environment of space. Besides protecting life from harmful radiation, this interaction produces the aurorae and two radiation-intensive regions surrounding the Earth.

Geomagnetism

The Earth's magnetic field pattern is similar to that of a dipole (Figure 5.29). It has a north and a south magnetic pole and a similar pattern of

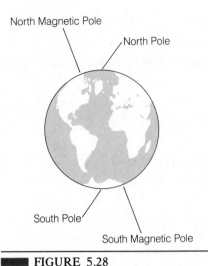

■ FIGURE 5.28

Earth's Geographic and Magnetic Poles

Geomagnetism: The description of the Earth's magnetic field in terms of a bar magnet with north and south poles.

Magnetosphere: The region of space surrounding the Earth in which the Earth's magnetic field controls the motion of charged particles.

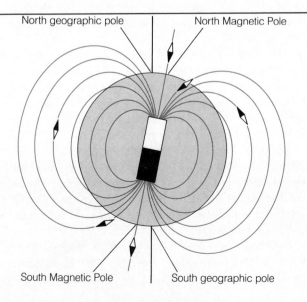

■ FIGURE 5.29

Earth as a Magnetic Dipole

The Earth's magnetic field resembles a dipole field surrounding a bar magnet.

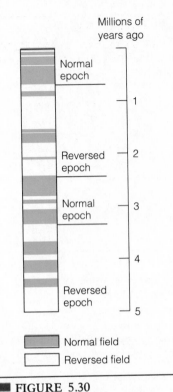

Millions of
years ago

Normal
epoch

Reversed
epoch

Normal
epoch

Reversed
epoch

Normal field
Reversed field

■■ **FIGURE 5.30**

**Record of Past Magnetic Pole
Reversals on Earth**

Paleomagnetism: Remnant magnetization in ancient rocks; also the study of
such "fossil" magnetism.

magnetic field lines, at least close to the Earth's surface. Whereas the magnetic field pattern surrounding a bar magnet is stable, the magnetic pattern around the Earth varies. First, the Earth's magnetic poles wander. During the last 135 years of detailed investigation, the dipole field has moved about 1° every 5 years. Secondly, the Earth's magnetic field has reversed itself many times in the past. That is, the North Magnetic Pole was not always a north pole; it has been a South Magnetic Pole.

Geologists can trace the reversals of the Earth's magnetic field by studying magnetized rocks. Inside a magnet most of the various magnetically susceptible mineral grains act as individual magnets and line up in the same direction. In unmagnetized material, however, the grains are randomly oriented, resulting in no overall magnetic field. A characteristic of magnetic material is that if heated beyond a critical temperature, the *Curie temperature*, it loses its magnetic properties. At its Curie temperature a rock's magnetic minerals assume a random order and are free to align themselves with any external magnetic field as do the iron filings near a bar magnet. Subsequent cooling of the rock can preserve the mineral alignment. Any rock that has magnetic mineral grains embedded in it can be magnetized if it is heated enough and allowed to cool in a magnetic field. The last magnetic field reversal, which occurred about 30,000 years ago, was discovered in rocks that were used by Australian aborigines to contain a camp fire. The rocks cooled and preserved the orientation of the Earth's magnetic field of 30,000 years ago—it was opposite to the present orientation.

This impressed magnetic field is a very important tool in **paleomagnetism,** the study of the Earth's ancient magnetic fields. In the past three decades, scientists have collected rocks from all over the world and have been able to reconstruct the history of the Earth's variable geomagnetic field. The results have been startling. The Earth has reversed its magnetic field polarity at irregular intervals, on average every half million years (Figure 5.30). Magnetic north becomes south and south becomes north. Superimposed on these major epochs are short-lived flips of the field lasting from several thousand years to 200,000 years. The time it takes for a reversal appears to be only a few thousand years.

How can the Earth's magnetic field just flip? At present geophysicists do not have a complete and verifiable model describing the generation of the Earth's magnetic field nor of its reversals. Not enough is known about the detailed structure and behavior of the Earth's interior. Today's models, however, are consistent with the available data. The Earth's magnetic field could be a remnant of an earlier time, perhaps an original magnetic field developed at the time of the Earth's formation, or it could be generated by some process operating today. It is not likely, however, to be left over from some previous age because the temperatures in the Earth's interior become higher than the Curie temperature very near the surface. Therefore, any static magnetic field in the interior could not last long.

On the other hand, it is possible to generate magnetic fields by accelerating an electrically conducting material. Metals, in general, are good conductors. Recall that the Earth's core is mainly iron. Note also that

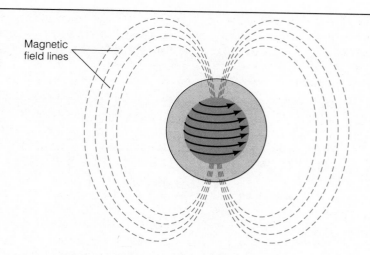

Magnetic
field lines

■■■ FIGURE 5.31

The Generation of the Earth's Magnetic Field by Its Rotating Metallic Core

the core rotates and therefore accelerates along with the Earth. The core's conductivity and motion combined appear to be necessary ingredients for the generation of a planetwide magnetic field. A moving iron core generates a magnetic field because heated iron supplies many electrons. Since the rotation of the Earth moves the iron, an electric current is produced, and therefore a magnetic field is generated (Figure 5.31). The magnetic poles will be near the Earth's rotational poles because the motion of the core follows the rotation of the Earth itself. The essence of models, called *dynamo models*, that try to explain Earth's dipole magnetic field is the motion of metallic iron producing electric currents that generate magnetic fields.

The motions of the matter in the fluid outer core are influenced by the rotation of the Earth, convective motions, and the existence of a solid inner core. As this core material is being flung around by the Earth's rotation, it is also trying to move up and down in a convective cell. The resulting motion is a cyclonic swirling oriented mainly north-south. The swirling action may induce slight changes in the orientation of the magnetic field, causing the magnetic poles to wander. Although the overall magnetic field at the surface resembles a dipole, at the center it is a twisted, chaotic entanglement of magnetic field lines. This tangled mess of magnetic field lines in the outer core can, in time, become more and more twisted and contorted. Dynamo models predict that chaos in the core will eventually lead to a collapse of the dipole field and to a reversal of the Earth's polarity. These models do not, however, predict when a reversal will occur next.

Magnetosphere

Although the Earth's magnetic field is similar to a dipole near its surface, beyond the atmosphere the Earth's magnetic field is severely distorted. The reason for this is that the Earth's magnetic field interacts with the **solar wind.** At the Earth's distance from the Sun, the solar wind consists of charged particles, such as electrons, protons, and he-

Solar wind: A continuous stream of ionized gas, mostly protons and electrons, escaping from the Sun; see Chapter 12 for more on the solar wind.

■■■ FIGURE 5.32

**Motion of Charged Particles around
Magnetic Field Lines**

The general motion of a charged particle
when not moving at exactly a right angle
to a magnetic field line is a spiral.

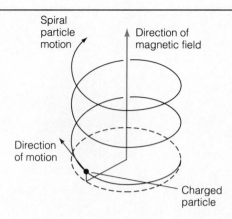

lium nuclei, streaming past the Earth at speeds in excess of 1.4 million
km/hr. This interaction deforms the Earth's magnetic field, flattening
and compressing it on the sunward side and stretching it on the side of
the Earth away from the Sun.

The magnetosphere shields humans from the biologically damaging
effects of the solar wind by forcing charged particles to change their
direction of motion. A charged particle moving in a magnetic field will
feel an electromagnetic force perpendicular to both its direction of motion and the direction of the magnetic field lines (Figure 5.32). The magnitude of this force is greatest when the motion of the particle is at right
angles to the magnetic field lines and zero when the motion of the particle is parallel to the field lines. Consequently, an electron or proton
moving exactly at right angles to a magnetic field line will be forced to
move in a circle around the field line. More likely, the electron or proton
moves at an angle other than a right angle and is therefore forced to
move in a spiral along the magnetic field line. Charged particles in the
solar wind encounter the outermost regions of the Earth's magnetic
field and begin spiraling along the magnetic field lines. Since the field
lines are oriented nearly north-south, the particles of the solar wind
will be deflected north or south along the field lines instead of traveling
directly toward the Earth.

The region is turbulent where the impinging particles change their
direction of motion as they are forced to follow the magnetic field lines.
This change in direction also means that the incoming solar wind particles will crash into the particles now moving along the magnetic lines.
These collisions produce a discontinuity in the flow of solar particles,
called a *bow shock*, and compress the sunward side of Earth's magnetic
field (Figure 5.33). The region inside the bow shock, called the *magnetosheath*, is a very turbulent area of disordered magnetic fields and variable particle densities and is about 20,000 km thick directly toward the
Sun. The inner boundary of the magnetosheath, 70,000 to 80,000 km
from the Earth's surface, is the beginning of the Earth's magnetosphere
and is characterized by an abrupt increase in magnetic field strength.

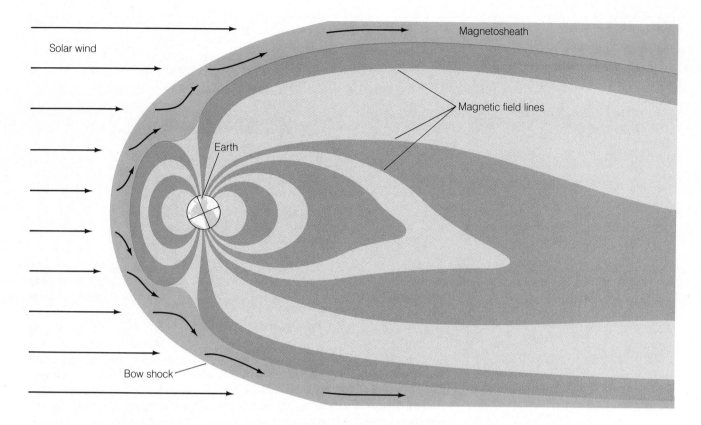

Solar wind

Magnetosheath

Magnetic field lines

Earth

Bow shock

Trapped solar wind particles form two radiation zones, the **Van Allen belts,** which surround the Earth (Figure 5.34). They were discovered in the late 1950s by J. A. Van Allen with satellite-based instruments. When a satellite passes through these belts, the on-board Geiger counters are saturated by the bombardment of energetic particles. These two belts surround the Earth in concentric, doughnutlike shells, concentrated over the equator. The Van Allen belts are not a threat to people on Earth, but pose a potential hazard to space travelers. Charged particles colliding at their characteristic high speeds with a human could cause severe heat damage to biological tissues. The *Apollo* spacecraft, which took astronauts to the Moon, had to use shielding to protect the occupants through the radiation belts on the way to the Moon.

Trapped solar wind particles spiraling around the Earth's magnetic field lines are responsible for the aurora displays seen at high latitudes (Figure 5.35). In the Northern Hemisphere the aurorae are called *aurorae borealis,* and in the Southern Hemisphere they are called *aurorae australis.* These are seen at high latitudes because the charged particles follow the Earth's magnetic field lines toward the magnetic poles. At the Earth's polar regions, these particles collide with atmospheric molecules and atoms. These collisions cause the atmospheric molecules and atoms to emit visible radiation, causing the sky to glow like a neon light. In the very northern reaches of the continental United States, au-

▬▬ FIGURE 5.33

Earth's Magnetosphere

The shading between the magnetic field lines is used to give you a better picture of the distortion in the magnetic field lines.

Van Allen radiation belts: Two dough-nut-shaped regions above the Earth's magnetic equator where electrons and protons oscillate in a north-south direction in the Earth's magnetic field; peak intensity of charged particles occurs at a height of about 3000 km and is a hazard to living organisms and sensitive instruments.

■■■■■ FIGURE 5.34

Van Allen Radiation Belts

Regions of intense radiation surround the Earth in concentric, doughnutlike shells.

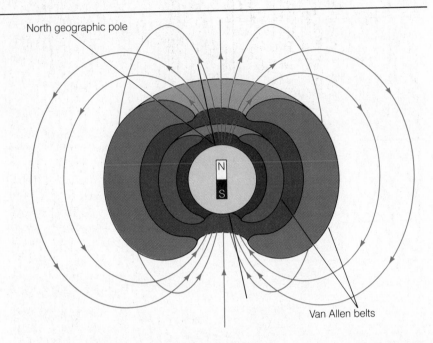

North geographic pole

Van Allen belts

■■■■■ FIGURE 5.35

Aurora Displays

(a) Aurora australis (the southern lights) seen above the British Antarctic Survey's Halley Station, Antarctica. *(b)* Aurora as seen by *Spacelab 3* orbiting the Earth.

SOURCE: Part (a) by Doug Allan/Science Photo Library, Photo Researchers. Part (b) by NASA/ Science Source, Photo Researchers.

rorae can typically be seen about 25 times a year while in northern Alaska and Canada aurorae can be seen more than 200 nights a year.

Aurorae are the visible signs that the Earth's magnetic field shields life on its surface from harmful particles. The Earth's magnetic field is part of a complicated environment that protects life on the surface of the Earth.

(a)

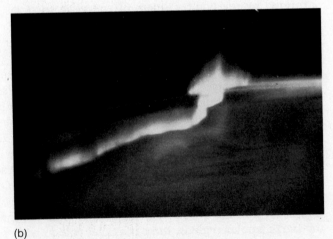

(b)

SUMMARY

The Greek scientist Eratosthenes measured the size of the Earth 2,000 years ago by observing differences in shadow lengths at different locations on the Earth's surface. Detailed studies of the shape of the Earth reveal that the Earth bulges at the equator. The gravitational forces of the Moon and the Sun operating on our nonspherical planet cause it to precess with a period of nearly 26,000 years.

The Earth is chemically and physically differentiated into three distinct regions: crust, mantle, and core. The crust contains mainly oxygen and silicon bonded into silicates; the mantle consists of iron- and magnesium-rich silicates; and the core is mainly iron and nickel. This layered structure of the Earth is the result of differentiation that occurred early in Earth's history. While the crust and lithosphere are rigid, both the outer part of the core and the asthenosphere are fluid; material in these regions flows, albeit slowly. Heat transfer in these plastic regions is accomplished by convection. The resulting convective motions in the mantle are responsible for lithospheric plate movement and those in the outer core are partially responsible for Earth's variable magnetic field.

Mass and size measurements of the Earth give an average density of 5.5 g/cm^3. Since crustal rock has a smaller density, 3 g/cm^3, the Earth's interior must be composed of rock denser than that found in the crust. Geologists obtain most of their knowledge of the Earth's interior from seismic data and heat flow measurements. With these data, they predict temperatures over 4000°C and densities between 12 and 14 g/cm^3 at the center of the Earth. Pressures, densities, and temperatures increase with depth inside the Earth. The tremendous heat reservoir of the Earth drives the processes that move lithospheric plates and provides molten mantle material for the building of volcanoes. Plate tectonics produce surface features, such as volcanoes, deep ocean trenches, and mountains.

The processes that shape the Earth's surface have been operating for billions of years. Rock formations all over the world can be arranged into a relative age sequence using the observed stratigraphic sequence. Radiometric dating of the rock formations in this sequence gives their absolute ages. The oldest rock formations on the Earth's surface are nearly 4 billion years old; the oldest rocks in the solar system appear to be 4.6 billion years old. This presumably is also the age of the Earth.

The Earth's atmosphere is principally responsible for maintaining surface temperatures comfortable for life. The atmosphere consists mainly of nitrogen (78%) and oxygen (21%); the nitrogen has been built up over the eons by volcanic activity while oxygen is mainly the result of plant photosynthesis.

Atmospheric carbon dioxide and water vapor trap heat in the troposphere, producing the greenhouse effect. The Earth's surface temperature is nearly 40°C higher than it would be without the insulating effect of its atmosphere. The atmosphere also shields life from harmful ultraviolet solar radiation by absorbing most of it before it can reach the surface. The Earth's complex global wind circulation is a result of uneven solar heating between the equatorial and polar regions and the Earth's rotation.

The Earth's magnetic field, or magnetosphere, also acts as a shield. It prevents solar wind particles, which are biologically damaging, from reaching the surface. The magnetic field deflects these particles, mainly protons and electrons, around the Earth. Far from the Earth's surface, the magnetosphere is distorted by its interaction with the solar wind. Some solar wind particles, however, are trapped in the two doughnut-shaped Van Allen radiation belts.

The Earth's magnetic field is generated by the movement of its metallic core. The overall magnetic field resembles that of an ordinary bar magnet. The field, however, is variable and the polarity of the Earth's magnetic field reverses from time to time. This flip in the magnetic field appears to be associated with the complicated motion of the molten material in the fluid outer core.

CHAPTER CAPSULE

Topics and Terms	Review and Remarks
Structure of the Earth	The interior of the Earth is divided into three physically distinct layers: Crust—the continental and oceanic crusts are mainly silicates; the average density of the crust is about 3g/cm³. Mantle—the rigid lithosphere and plastic asthenosphere are mainly iron- and magnesium-rich silicates; the average density of the mantle is about 5 g/cm³. Core—the fluid outer and solid inner core are mainly iron and nickel; the density at the center of the Earth is about 12 to 14 g/cm³.
Ages of rock formations	Relative ages are based on the stratigraphic sequence seen in rock formations. Absolute ages are based on radiometric dating of rock formations.
Age of the Earth	Radiometric dating of Earth rocks gives an age of about 4 billion years. Radiometric dating of lunar rocks and meteorites gives an age of 4.6 billion years for the solar system.
Atmosphere of the Earth	Its composition is 78% nitrogen, 21% oxygen, and traces of other gases. It prevents harmful electromagnetic radiation from reaching the surface. It traps heat in the lower atmosphere via the greenhouse effect.
Greenhouse effect	Earth's atmosphere is transparent to visible radiation but partly opaque to infrared. Solar radiation heats the Earth's surface, which then radiates infrared radiation. The atmosphere absorbs the infrared radiation, heating the lower atmosphere.
Magnetic field of the Earth	It is generated by motions of the metallic core. Its north-south polarity reverses in an unpredictable way. The two Van Allen belts trap solar wind particles.

REVIEW QUESTIONS

1. What properties of a planet and its orbit affect its ability to support life as we know it?

2. During your life you have learned enough about the Earth that you could probably give a visiting alien a pretty good general description of it. How would this be different if you had only *your own direct experience* from which to formulate a description?

3. The Earth's crust is composed mostly of silicate materials. The core is thought to be composed mainly of an iron-nickel alloy. What evidence points to this composition for the core?

4. What evidence do we have for the existence of a liquid outer core?

5. That the Earth's interior has undergone differentiation implies what about its history?

6. How are the motion of the Earth's surface plates and earthquakes related?

7. Briefly discuss the chemical composition of the Earth's atmosphere. Would you expect the atmosphere to be differentiated near the surface? How about differentiation at high altitudes?

8. What is the primary mechanism for heating the Earth's atmosphere (a) near the surface and (b) at higher altitudes?

9. The atmospheres of the Sun and Jupiter are mostly hydrogen. Why do you think the Earth's atmosphere is so different?

10. Suppose the circulation of the atmosphere could be stopped. What affect would you expect on atmospheric temperature extremes (a) near the equator, (b) at mid-latitudes, and (c) near the poles?

11. How can radiometric dating tell us the condition of the Earth's magnetic field in the past? Why is radiometric dating important in the study of plate tectonics?

12. Our possible influence on global temperatures through an enhanced greenhouse effect has been given much time and space by the media in recent

years. What is the greenhouse effect and how is it possible for humans to influence it?

13. Can you imagine circumstances such that humans could, through pollution, cause the Earth to cool?

14. The average atmospheric pressure, at sea level, is 14.7 lb/in^2. From this value, determine the weight of the Earth's atmosphere.

▬ FOR FURTHER READING

Akasofu, S. 1989. The dynamic aurora. *Scientific American*, May, 90.

Badash, L. 1989. The age-of-the-Earth debate. *Scientific American*, Aug., 90.

Gillett, S. L. 1985. The rise and fall of the early reducing atmosphere. *Astronomy*, July, 66.

Hartmann, W. K. 1989. Piecing together Earth's history. *Astronomy*, June, 24.

Hoffman, K. A. 1988. Ancient magnetic reversals: Clues to the geodynamo. *Scientific American*, May, 76.

Houghton, R. A., and G. M. Woodwell. 1989. Global climate change. *Scientific American*, Apr., 36.

Lanzerotti, L. J. 1988. Earth's magnetic environment. *Sky & Telescope*, Oct., 360.

Maslowski, A. 1986. Eyes on the Earth. *Astronomy*, Aug., 6.

Nance, R. D., T. W. Worsley, and J. B. Moody. 1988. The supercontinent cycle. *Scientific American*, July, 72.

ASTROPROBE 5

Ice Ages: The Astronomical Connection

Ice age: Any period of geological time when large parts of the Earth are covered with glaciers; the beginning of an ice age is signaled by the disappearance of forests.

On a time scale of a day, the temperature at a given location on the Earth can change very much. It can be almost shirtsleeve weather on a sunny winter afternoon lunch break but below freezing for a cup of evening tea. Of course, large temperature changes also occur from season to season. Averaged over a year or a few years, however, the temperature of the Earth does not change very much. For many of us, cold winters always follow hot summers.

To sustain a more or less constant average temperature, the Earth maintains an energy, or heat, balance. The warming of the Earth by incoming solar radiation is balanced by a cooling of the Earth due to the outgoing radiation from the Earth itself. It is a delicate balance between emission and absorption of radiation. If changes occur in either the amount of solar radiation reaching the Earth's surface or in the ability of the surface or atmosphere to absorb radiation, the balance will be tipped and could lead to long-term changes in climate. Historical studies of the Earth's climate clearly show that periods of significant changes in the Earth's surface temperature occur; the Earth experiences **ice ages.**

About 20,000 years ago the Earth was very cold. Ice expanded over continental masses, and the continents themselves bent under the great weight of massive ice sheets covering the land. So much water from the oceans was used to form the ice sheets that ocean levels dropped about 85 m (280 ft). In North America, a glacial ice sheet a kilometer thick buried all of Canada, the New England states, most of the Midwest, and portions of the American Northwest. A European ice sheet covered Scandinavia, Scotland, most of England and Denmark, and much of northern Germany, Poland, and the Soviet Union. Switzerland was completely covered by a small ice sheet. In the Southern Hemisphere parts of South America, Australia, New Zealand, and Africa and all of Antarctica were covered by a giant ice sheet.

This was not the only time the world was cold. The Earth has experienced at least three periods of global glaciation: 600 million years ago, 300 million years ago, and, most recently, 2 million years ago. This last period, called the *Pleistocene Glacial Cycle*, lasted until about 10,000 years ago. The Pleistocene Glacial Cycle developed slowly. About 65 million years ago the Earth was so warm that it did not have polar ice caps. Starting about 55 million years ago, however, a cooling trend began, and by 10 million years ago a thick ice sheet covered the Antarctic. Further cooling generated continental-sized glaciers in the Northern Hemisphere and plunged the Earth into an ice age. The most recent maximum extent in glaciation occurred, as mentioned above, about 20,000 years ago. A few thousand years later, the continental ice sheets retreated until today only alpine glaciation and thick polar ice sheets remain.

During the latter part of the Pleistocene Glacial Cycle, extremes in coldness appear to have occurred regularly about every 100,000 years. Figure 5A.1 illustrates this 100,000-year cycle for nearly the last half million years. The pattern is one of a global cooling of the Earth and a build-up of ice for nearly 100,000 years followed by a rapid increase in surface temperatures, a decrease in the volume of ice on the Earth, and a relatively warm *interglacial age*. The 100,000-year cycle then starts over again. This cycle is punctuated by periods of warmings; that is, superimposed on the general cooling trends are ice-free ages in which ice build-up is reversed temporarily. These ice-free ages appear to occur cyclically with periods of approximately 43,000 years and 22,000 years.

This, of course, is the big picture, which is the concern of many researchers. They are also interested in the immediate future; that is, when is the next ice age? Will the continents soon be buried in ice again? Figure 5A.1 indicates that the world has been warming for approximately the last 20,000 years and is now experiencing an interglacial age. The current interglacial age may last on the order of thousands of years, perhaps even tens of thousands of years.

The Earth, however, has experienced global cooling on an even shorter time scale. The most recent global cooling ended less than 200 years ago when the "Little Ice Age," between A.D. 1450 and 1850, came to an end. During those 400 years mountain glaciers all over the world advanced considerably beyond their present limits. The Thames River froze solid at times, and Londoners celebrated "frost fairs" on the frozen water (Figure 5A.2). Even George Washington

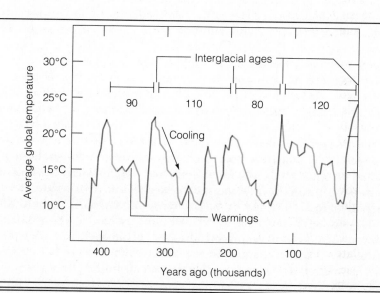

FIGURE 5A.1

Pleistocene Ice Age Cycles

The curves show a rapid heating of the Earth (upward in graph) followed by a gradual (approximately 100,000-year) decline in surface temperatures. The declines (blue) are occasionally interrupted by warming trends (magenta).

■ FIGURE 5A.2

Frost Fairs on the Thames River in 1683–84

SOURCE: The Granger Collection.

Insolation: The amount of solar radiation falling on the Earth's surface.

and his men at Valley Forge were victims of this recent global cooling, but apparently the winter of 1777–78 was notably mild. The year 1816, however, is known as "the year without summer" because of the extreme cold spells in Canada, North America, and Europe, which caused poor crop yields and famine.

What causes ice ages? The whole climatic system of the Earth depends on the growth or decay of ice sheets. If an ice sheet is developing, it will tend to reflect more solar radiation. This, in turn, will reduce global temperatures and add more ice to the ice sheet. The opposite happens if an ice sheet is shrinking. What then causes ice sheets to grow and shrink? Possible factors promoting ice ages involve both the reduction in the amount of solar energy received by the Earth, called **insolation,** and the interconnection between the Earth's global climatic elements of ice sheets, oceans, and atmosphere.

The atmosphere plays a very important role in climate control, and changes in its constituents can change the amount of sunlight absorbed or reflected by the Earth's surface. For instance, the amount of carbon dioxide in the atmosphere has been increasing due to the burning of fossil fuel and to the deforestation of tropical rain forests, which are being replaced by less efficient users of carbon dioxide. Carbon dioxide is a very good absorber of infrared radiation and, therefore, enhances the greenhouse effect in the troposphere. Scientists estimate that the carbon dioxide content in the atmosphere will double in less than a hundred years, which means an increase in surface temperatures of 2° to 4°C. Higher temperatures could result in rising ocean levels due to melting polar caps and reduced precipitation for middle latitudes caused by a shifting of the jet stream. Particles in the atmosphere can cause similar changes. If particles are dark in color, they can absorb sunlight, causing heating of the atmosphere; light particles, on the other hand, can cause atmospheric cooling by reflecting solar energy. One source of these particles is the pollutants from industrial complexes (Figure 5A.3).

Another source of pollutants is the fine particles of ash and dust from volcanic eruptions (Figure 5A.4). Volcanic dust, for instance, can reduce insolation by reflecting incoming solar radiation back into space. The haze layer produced from outgassed sulfur that interacts with water vapor to form sulfuric acid can stay in the stratosphere for years. Evidence of acidic ices found in Greenland and Antarctica, corresponding to the time of the Little Ice Age, suggests that it was triggered by sulfuric-rich volcanic eruptions. The ultimate pollutants, moreover, may be generated by our ability to destroy the world in a nuclear holocaust. The extensive burning caused by nuclear detonation would send hundreds of thousands of tons of fine soot into the stratosphere. The soot readily absorbs sunlight, and studies indicate that the world would be very dark for several weeks and that daytime temperatures could drop below freezing even during the summer. This scenario of fire and gloom is called the *nuclear winter*. Nuclear winter models are indeed gloomy. Cold and dark conditions may last several years, causing worldwide food shortages. Intricate chemical reactions in the atmosphere may generate very acidic rains and even destroy 50% of the atmospheric ozone. Admittedly, researchers do not completely understand the impact of a nuclear war, but all agree that an unprecedented degree of destruction would occur to the atmosphere and to life itself.

In addition, ocean currents play a part in global climate by transporting heat between hemispheres. Atmospheric winds drive these currents. Changes in global wind patterns, therefore, could drastically change the heat transport between hemispheres, perhaps cooling one hemisphere. Or winds may transport more moisture than usual and deposit it in cold, snowy regions encouraging more snow and ice. In fact, the Pleistocene Glacial Cycle may have been caused by global changes in atmospheric circulation generated by the formation of the Tibetan plateau and the high country of western North America. Both rose within the last 10 million years and could have caused profound changes in weather patterns.

The distribution of landmass is also critical in determining the insolation at different latitudes. Large landmasses near the poles, for example, will receive less solar radiation than they would at lower

■ FIGURE 5A.3

Industrial Pollution Is Common in the United States

SOURCE: John D. Cunningham/Visuals Unlimited.

■ FIGURE 5A.4

Volcanic Dust

Volcanic eruptions can eject tons of
fine dust into the atmosphere; sulfuric
compounds can cause long-term climatic changes.

SOURCE: Krafft-Explorer/Science Source,
Photo Researchers.

latitudes, encouraging glaciation. Plate tectonics, of course, play a
critical role in the distribution of landmasses. The positioning of
landmasses can affect ocean currents while the location of mountain
ranges can disturb the overall atmospheric circulation pattern. For
instance, 300 million years ago the landmasses on Earth were
grouped into a single giant continent. Parts of this continent that
later became South America, Africa, Australia, and all of Antarctica
were located very near the Earth's rotational South Pole and were
covered with a large ice sheet about twice the size of the present-day
Antarctic ice sheet.

The problem of explaining the onset of an ice age is extremely complex. An ice age is probably the result of a combination of many factors operating under favorable conditions. Scientists cannot say with
certainty yet what triggered the ice ages 600 million, 300 million,
and 2 million years ago. Progress has been made, however, in understanding the periodicities in the temperature variations during the
last half million years (see Figure 5A.2). Terrestrial factors, such as
volcanism or continental drift, are not periodic within relatively
short time scales; that is, they do not repeat over and over in a systematic manner. For instance, scientists have no indication that periods of extensive global volcanism occur every 22,000 years or
43,000 years or 100,000 years or that global ocean currents change
periodically on these time scales. These observed Pleistocene cycles
are like mechanical, spring-wound clocks, they must be wound periodically. The 100,000-year cycle, for instance, needs a winding every

100,000 years. Since terrestrial factors are not periodic, it appears that this winding is controlled by an outside forcing mechanism, an extraterrestrial influence.

In 1938 Milutin Milankovitch, a Yugoslavian geophysicist and astronomer, presented an astronomical theory that attempted to explain ice age periodicities in terms of *periodic* changes in the Earth's orbit and orbital tilt. The forcing mechanisms that he proposed controlled insolation. The amount of solar radiation falling at a given latitude can change as a result of a change in the Earth's distance from the Sun or in the angle at which solar radiation strikes the surface of the Earth. Milankovitch identified three processes that cause periodic variations in the Earth's orbital parameters and result in insolation changes:

- Precession of the equinoxes
- Variation in the Earth's tilt
- Variation in the Earth's orbital eccentricity

A subtle effect of precession is to change the position of the solstices and equinoxes relative to the aphelion and perihelion positions in the Earth's orbit. This is shown in Figure 5A.5 for the winter solstice in the Northern Hemisphere. This would occur nearly every 13,000 years, or half of the precessional period, except for the fact that the Earth's orbit itself rotates with respect to the stars every 111,270 years. First, this means that the positions of aphelion and perihelion will be on opposite sides of the Sun 55,635 years from now

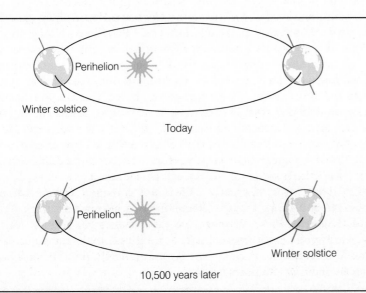

Today

10,500 years later

■■■■ ▪ FIGURE 5A.5

**Changing Orbital Position
of the Winter Solstice**

Today winter solstice occurs near perihelion, but 10,500 years from now winter solstice will occur near aphelion; then the Earth will be at its greatest distance from the Sun, and more severe Northern Hemisphere winters will be likely.

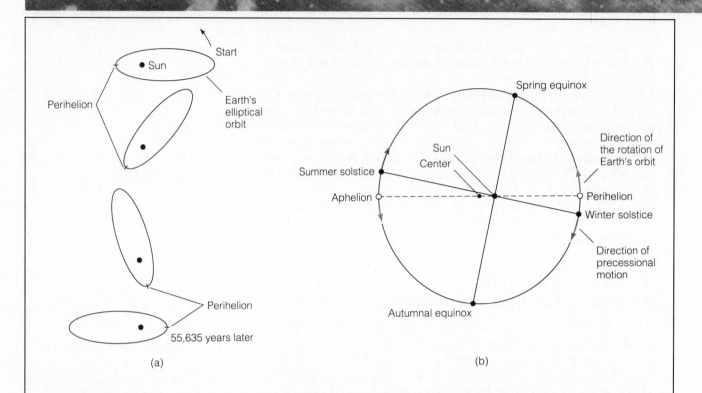

(a)   (b)

▓▓ FIGURE 5A.6

Precessional Changes in the Earth's Orbital Parameters

(a) The Earth's orbit rotates about the Sun once every 111,270 years. Here the Earth's orbital eccentricity has been exaggerated to show clearly the difference between aphelion and perihelion positions. *(b)* As the position of the perihelion moves counterclockwise in this figure, the position of the winter and summer solstices moves clockwise; winter solstice occurs at perihelion after 21,000 years (precession takes the winter solstice position around once every 25,725 years). Note that the time between the spring and autumnal equinoxes changes as their position relative to the Earth's perihelion and aphelion changes.

(Panel a in Figure 5A.6). Secondly, the rotation of the Earth's orbit is in the opposite direction to the precessional changes in the equinox and solstice positions. That is, when viewed from the north celestial pole, the Earth's elliptical orbit rotates counterclockwise whereas the positions of the equinoxes and solstices move clockwise (Panel b). The combined motions result in the Northern Hemisphere experiencing a winter solstice at aphelion every 21,000 years. Notice in Panel b that if winter solstice occurs near aphelion, the winter "season," from autumnal to spring equinox, will be longer and, since the Earth is far from the Sun, it will be cooler. The long winters and corresponding short summers encourage ice to accumulate. Furthermore, since most of the world's landmass has been in the Northern Hemisphere during the last 2 million years, glaciers and ice sheets would develop over much of the Earth's landmass and, consequently, lead to a global ice age. Scientists, therefore, identify the 21,000-year time scale with the shortest of the ice age periodicities.

The Earth's tilt, currently 23°5 is not constant. Over a period of about 44,000 years the tilt of the Earth's axis varies from 21°8 to 24°4. This, of course, changes the insolation at any given latitude, especially the poles (Figure 5A.7). If the tilt is small, the poles receive a smaller amount of radiation (yes, smaller!); this encourages ice ages by making the poles cooler.

Finally, the eccentricity of the Earth's orbit also varies in time. Its variation is on an even longer time scale. Earth's orbital eccentricity varies from nearly zero, a perfect circular orbit, to about 0.05 over periods that range between 90,000 years to 100,000 years and average about 96,000 years. At large eccentricities, the variations in the distance from perihelion to aphelion are much larger than at small eccentricities and exaggerate the differences in the lengths of winters relative to summers. The variation in eccentricities results in 30% variations in the amount of solar energy reaching the Earth's surface between aphelion and perihelion.

It appears that the 100,000-year variation in Earth's orbital eccentricity has dominated the world's long-term climatic pattern over the last half million years. The precession of the equinoxes and the variations in the Earth's tilt produce warm periods superimposed on the 100,000-year global cooling trend. The important aspect of these astronomical periods that gives the Milankovitch theory credibility is that they are very close to the observed cycles of the Pleistocene Ice Age.

Although obviously a link exists between ice ages and orbital variations, scientists do not have the answer to what triggered the Pleistocene Ice Age or the earlier ice ages. Clearly, predictions of future climatic change are extremely difficult, but given the uncertainties, a general forecast given today might sound like this: 1,000 years of warming, mixed with short cooling periods, and followed by 100,000 years of general cooling, ending in a major global ice age.

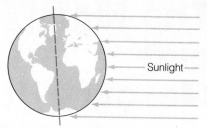

Small tilt — South Pole receives little light

(a)

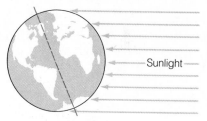

Large tilt — South Pole receives more light

(b)

■ FIGURE 5A.7

Insolation and Tilt

The poles receive less light the smaller the tilt of the Earth's rotational axis.

The Moon and Mercury

OUTLINE

The Planets and Moons in the Solar System: An Introduction

The Moon
Tides
Exploration of the Moon
The Moon's Surface Features
    Craters
    Maria
    Volcanism
    Ages of Surface Rocks

The Interior and History of the Moon
    Surface Rocks
    Interior

Mercury
The Orbit and Rotation of Mercury
Exploration of Mercury
The Surface of Mercury
    Craters
    Plains
    Scarps
    Ages
The Interior of Mercury

Summary

Chapter Capsule

Review Questions

For Further Reading

ASTROPROBE 6:
Craters: Scars on the Earth's Surface

Discovery Rupes.
ARTIST: Michael Carroll.

SURVEY OF THE MAJOR CHARACTERISTICS of the planets reveals that some planets are similar in size, structure, and chemical composition. In fact, most planets belong to one of only two distinct classes. At the same time, each planet is a distinct and unique world. The moons of the planets are also unique worlds. Our Moon has never been considered a "planet," although we know now that its surface is very similar to Mercury's. The closeness of the Moon to the Earth has allowed astronomers to scrutinize the lunar surface, and, because astronauts have been to the Moon and returned with lunar rocks, scientists know more about the Moon than any other world beside the Earth. These visits have helped scientists begin the science of lunar geology, understand the origin of some visible lunar surface features, and improve the methods used to determine relative and absolute ages of the lunar surface. In particular, the ages of the oldest known lunar rocks are greater than the oldest known terrestrial rocks. The oldest lunar rocks probably date the origin of the solar system. The study of the small planet Mercury, the innermost planet of the solar system, is combined with lunar studies in this chapter because these two worlds have a number of similar features. Both have intensely cratered surfaces; both are small airless worlds; and both have been geologically inactive for billions of years. No volcanoes or plate motions give rise to surface features, and no wind or water erodes their cratered, ancient surfaces.

THE PLANETS AND MOONS IN THE SOLAR SYSTEM: AN INTRODUCTION

An overview of the planetary bodies in the solar system is appropriate before we begin our studies of individual planets and will provide some reference points for comparing the planets. Chapter 11 presents a more detailed comparison of planetary characteristics and their relationship to the origin and evolution of the solar system.

The Sun is the center of the solar system because of its great mass, which is almost a thousand times that of all the planets combined. The planets orbit the Sun in a counterclockwise direction as viewed from the north celestial pole, and nearly all of them, as well as the Sun, rotate in this same direction. Planetary orbits also define a flat plane with orbits in nearly the same plane as the Earth's orbit. The "flatness" of the system of planets is the reason why observers on Earth always see the planets near the ecliptic. There are exceptions to these orbital and rotational characteristics, which provide important clues to understanding the processes that led to the formation of the solar system (see Chapter 11).

A careful study of planetary data reveals two broad classes of planets based on compositional and size differences: (1) the Earth-like, or **Terrestrial,** planets, which consist of Mercury, Venus, Earth, and Mars; and (2) the Jupiter-like, or **Jovian,** planets, which include Jupiter, Saturn, Uranus, and Neptune (Table 6.1 and Figure 6.1). Pluto, the most recently discovered planet, is more similar to the large, icy moons found orbiting the Jovian planets than to any of the other eight planets.

■ TABLE 6.1 **Major Characteristics of the Planets in the Solar System**

Planet	Symbol	Distance	Diameter		Mass	Density	Composition
		AU	km	Earth = 1	Earth = 1	g/cm³	
		⟨·⟩	⊖	●	⬜		
Terrestrial planets							
Mercury	☿	0.39	4,878	0.38	0.06	5.4	Oxygen, silicon, iron
Venus	♀	0.72	12,104	0.95	0.82	5.2	Oxygen, silicon, iron
Earth	⊕	1.00	12,756	1.00	1.00	5.5	Oxygen, silicon, iron
Mars	♂	1.52	6,787	0.53	0.11	3.9	Oxygen, silicon, iron
Jovian planets							
Jupiter	♃	5.20	142,796	11.23	317.83	1.3	Hydrogen, helium
Saturn	♄	9.54	120,000	9.41	95.16	0.7	Hydrogen, helium
Uranus	♅	19.19	51,200	4.01	14.50	1.2	Hydrogen, helium
Neptune	♆	30.06	48,600	3.81	17.20	1.8	Hydrogen, helium
Pluto	♇	39.43	≈2,300	≈0.2	≈0.002	≈2	Ice, dirt (?)

Terrestrial planets are "rocky" worlds. Their crusts and mantles are mainly silicates, and their cores are probably metallic iron. Their surfaces show the scars of impacts with nonplanetary material as well as features, such as volcanoes and rift valleys, generated from processes originating in their dynamic interiors. Venus, Earth, and Mars have gaseous atmospheres. Those of Venus and Mars are mainly carbon dioxide and nitrogen while the Earth's is mostly nitrogen and oxygen. These atmospheres provide very thin coverings for the Terrestrial planets and are an insignificant fraction of their masses. Furthermore, very little of their planetary material is composed of hydrogen or helium. The Jovian planets, especially Jupiter, are mainly hydrogen and helium and are more similar in composition to the Sun than the Terrestrial planets (Table 6.1). The Jovian planets are actually mixtures of gas and rock with their hydrogen- and helium-rich atmospheres representing a large fraction of their radii. Methane and ammonia are also significant constituents of the Jovian planets. The Jovian planets probably have rocky cores, but these cores are much larger than the Earth itself!

■ FIGURE 6.1

Planetary Sizes

The Terrestrial planets are small compared to the Jovian planets and lie closer to the Sun. Pluto is an exception in that it is small and lies far from the Sun, but it does not appear to have the characteristics of the Terrestrial planets. (See MathTools 1: Graphs and Plots ⬓ for a description of the logarithmic scale used in this graph.)

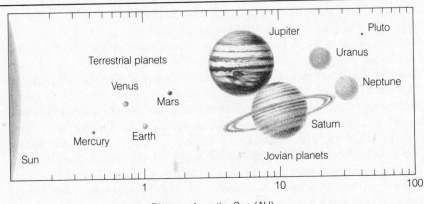

Distance from the Sun (AU)

Jovian planets are also distinguished by their extensive satellite systems. These resemble miniature solar systems, with large and small moons orbiting their parent planet as planets orbit the Sun. Some Jovian moons are larger than Mercury and several are larger than Pluto. The Jovian planets are also surrounded by rings, systems of ice-coated particles ranging in size from specks of dust to large boulders (Figure 6.2).

No two planets are exactly alike. Venus has sulfuric acid clouds; Earth has life; Mars has planetwide dust storms; Jupiter has a peculiar cloud pattern that has been visible for over three hundred years; Uranus has rotational axes that lie in its orbital plane; and Neptune has high white frozen methane clouds. This chapter and the three that follow are devoted to a description of the planets and moons in the solar system. Our study of the unique worlds of the solar system begins with Mercury and the Moon.

THE MOON

Scientists know more about the Moon than any other extraterrestrial object because it is so close; astronomers on Earth have observed its surface features in detail while astronauts have brought back pieces of the Moon for direct study. The Moon is also an exceptional satellite in that it is so large compared to the planet it orbits. The Moon is twice as large as Pluto and about half the size of Mercury.

Tides

The Moon is kept near the Earth by the force of gravity. One aspect of the gravitational interaction between two large masses, of course, is orbital motion; another aspect involves the gravitational forces felt across an entire planet or moon. Those who live near the coast or take seaside vacations have experienced one effect of these forces in ocean **tides.** Along the coasts, the water level difference between high tide and low tide is typically a meter or two. Differences caused by the shapes of coastal contours can be as great as 6 m (20 ft) at Eastpoint, Maine, or even 17 m (56 ft) in the narrow channel of the Bay of Fundy, Canada, the world's largest. Figure 6.3 dramatically illustrates the daily changes tides bring to the small fishing port of Halls Harbour, Nova Scotia.

Tides rise and fall nearly twice a day. The interval between two high tides or two low tides is 12^h25^m on the average. As a result, high tide will be about 50 minutes later each day. For instance, if high tide occurred today at 12:00 P.M., tomorrow it would occur at about 12:50 P.M. The 50-minute delay in high or low tide from day to day is related, of course, to the 50-minute delay in the rising of the Moon from day to day. It is the Moon that causes the Earth's ocean tides.

More precisely, Earth's tides are the result of gravitational forces by the Moon acting across the Earth. The side of the Earth facing the Moon feels a greater gravitational force due to the Moon than the far side of the Earth simply because the near side is closer to the Moon. Across the diameter of the Earth, therefore, a *differential gravitational force* exists.

FIGURE 6.2

Saturn

Beautiful rings made up of thousands of small ice-coated pebbles surround this gaseous giant.

SOURCE: Hale Observatories.

Tides: The gravitational distortion of one celestial object by another; normally refers to the alternate rise and fall of the surface of oceans.

■ FIGURE 6.3

Halls Harbour, Nova Scotia

Boats can only sail at high tide, and they must be docked carefully so they do not dangle from the dock at low tide.

SOURCE: Courtesy of Nova Scotia Information Service.

Panel a in Figure 6.4 shows the direction and strength of the gravitational forces across the Earth due to the Moon. In a similar manner, we can illustrate *tide-generating forces* as *differences* between the Moon's gravitational force on the Earth's center minus that on the near and far sides (Panel b). A complete explanation of the tide-generating forces requires mathematical techniques beyond the scope of this text, but calculations, which consider forces on every point on the Earth's surface, show that tides are a result of forces directed *along* the Earth's surface. The point is that although Earth's gravity ensures that the tide-generating forces will not lift ocean water off the Earth, flow occurs along the Earth's surface toward the point where the Moon lies directly overhead and toward the point just opposite this on the far side of the Earth. It is this flow along the Earth's surface that causes water to pile up on opposite sides of the Earth.

■ FIGURE 6.4

Tidal Forces

(a) The gravitational force on the Earth due to the Moon is strongest on the near side (long arrow) simply because it is closer to the Moon. The distance between the Earth and the Moon is not drawn to scale. *(b)* Tide-generating forces are shown as the difference between the gravitational force due to the Moon at the Earth's center and that at other locations on the Earth.

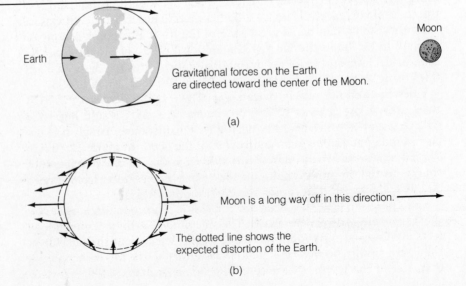

Earth

Gravitational forces on the Earth
are directed toward the center of the Moon.

Moon

(a)

Moon is a long way off in this direction. ⟶

The dotted line shows the
expected distortion of the Earth.

(b)

The differential tidal forces on the Earth caused by the Sun are about half that due to the Moon. Even though the Sun is more massive and can exert stronger gravitational forces, it is much farther away from the Earth than the Moon. Casual observations on a beach, where rocks or shoals are completely covered one day and laid bare another day, reveal that high tides differ in height. Careful observations reveal that the highest tides occur when the Sun and Moon line up with the Earth at new moon and full moon; these are called *spring tides* (even though they occur every month and not just in the spring). On the other hand, when the Moon is at first or third quarter, the tidal effects of the Moon and Sun partially cancel. We then have *neap tides* where the difference between high and low tide is the smallest.

Besides generating the daily rise and fall of ocean levels, the Moon is also indirectly slowing the rotation of the Earth and, at the same time, is slowly spiraling away from the Earth. Earth's rotation is slowed by the friction between the water and the seafloor as the water moves toward the Earth's tidal bulges. Currently, the Earth's rotation is slowing by about 1.5 seconds every 100,000 years. Since these forces have operated throughout Earth's history, the Earth must have rotated faster in the past. By simple extrapolation, astronomers calculate that 4.6 billion years ago the Earth rotated in about 5 hours:

$$\text{Increase in Earth's rotation rate} = \frac{1.5 \text{ seconds}}{\text{every } 100,000 \text{ yrs}} \times 4.6 \times 10^9 \text{ yrs}$$
$$= 69,000 \text{ seconds or } 19 \text{ hours}$$

Astronomers are not sure that they are justified in making this extrapolation over such a long period of time. Nevertheless, more detailed calculations, which take into account that in the past the Moon was closer, the Earth's equatorial bulge was larger, the angle between the tidal bulge and the Moon was different, and the Moon's orbit was more elliptical, also indicate that the Earth's day was 5 hours long billions of years ago. Confidence in such extrapolations has been bolstered by recent research in the yearly and daily growth patterns of fossil coral. From counts of the daily growth ridges within yearly growth bands, scientists estimate that the number of days in a year was nearly 400 during the Devonian period some 380 million years ago. At that time, the day was 22 hours long and the Moon was 12,000 km closer to the Earth. Older fossils hint at a 17-hour day about 3 billion years ago.

At the same time that the Earth's rotation is slowing, the Moon must be spiraling away from the Earth. Because the Earth rotates faster than the Moon orbits the Earth, it carries its ocean tidal bulge in the direction of rotation so that high tide occurs before the Moon is directly overhead. The forces acting on the Moon are shown in Figure 6.5. The tidal bulge raised by the Moon on the Earth tends to pull the Moon forward in its orbit and therefore accelerates the Moon in the direction of its motion, causing it to spiral slowly away from the Earth. As the Moon's orbit becomes larger, the Moon's orbital period increases. The Moon will continue to spiral away from the Earth until the length of the month becomes about 47 days. At that time, the Earth's rotation period will also be 47 days, and the tidal bulge on the Earth will line

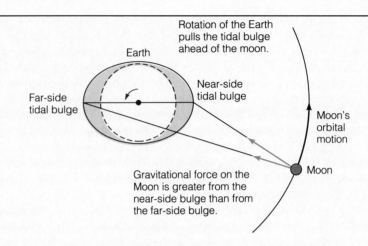

FIGURE 6.5

Earth's Tidal Bulges and the Moon's Orbit

Ocean tides on the Earth pull the Moon ahead in its orbit. The blue ellipse suggests the shape of the Earth's tidal bulges caused by the Moon. The near-side bulge tends to speed the Moon along in its orbit while the far-side bulge tends to slow the Moon down. Since the gravitational force due to the near-side bulge is greater than that due to the far side (magenta arrows), the net force tends to hurry the Moon onward in its orbit. Earth's tidal bulge is exaggerated. Sizes of Earth and Moon and distance between them are not to scale.

up with the Moon. Since the Moon is moving away from the Earth at about 3–4 cm per year, the Moon will reach its greatest distance from the Earth in an enormous length of time, about 50 billion years—long after the Sun, Earth, and Moon have perished!

Exploration of the Moon

The Moon is easily observed with the naked eye. It looks spherical and exhibits bright and dark regions that always face the Earth. Telescope observations reveal round bowl-shaped holes of all sizes, vast solidified lava pools, and high mountains. From Galileo's first telescopic look at the Moon until 1959, astronomers were limited to viewing the Moon from a distance. Between 1959 and 1976, spacecraft photographed the Moon from orbit and from its surface, and astronauts retrieved rocks for close-up study and explored the lunar landscape. Table 6.2 summarizes some of the lunar data that has been compiled from these studies.

The Soviet Union began successful lunar exploration in 1959 with *Luna 1*, which flew within 3000 km of the surface of the Moon (Table 6.3). The Soviet Luna spacecrafts were very successful probes that carried out a variety of missions from flybys and orbiters to soft landings and returns. Although the Soviets never landed a cosmonaut on the Moon, their spacecraft brought back lunar samples and deployed roving vehicles that traversed the lunar surface. In fact, the first vehicle to reach the lunar surface was *Luna 2* in 1959, and *Luna 3* gave us the first glimpse of the far side of the Moon. The *Luna 9* spacecraft in 1966 performed the first soft landing and took the first close-up pictures of the lunar surface.

The American lunar effort began slowly but culminated with manned exploration of the Moon. Before landing astronauts on the Moon, however, spacecraft engineers needed to know if the lunar surface could support the weight of a manned spacecraft. Was the surface rough and littered with boulders or did a 10-meter layer of soft dust cover the surface? The American Ranger, Surveyor, and Lunar Orbiter programs

■ TABLE 6.2 **Lunar Data**

Orbital semimajor axis	384,401 km
Perigee distance	356,400 km
Apogee distance	406,700 km
Eccentricity	0.055
Orbital period (sidereal)	27.32 days
Rotational period	27.32 days
Inclination	5° 09′
Diameter	3476 km
Mass	7.35×10^{22} kg (0.0123 Earth masses)
Mean density	3.34 g/cm³
Escape velocity	2.4 km/s (5370 MPH)
Surface temperature (mean)	250 K (-23°C $= -10$°F)
Maximum	400 K (125°C $=$ 260°F)
Minimum	100 K (-170°C $= -280$°F)

were designed to photograph the entire Moon and ascertain the nature of the lunar surface. The Ranger spacecrafts were designed as kamikaze vehicles that would crash into the lunar surface but transmit close-up pictures during their descent. The pictures transmitted by the Rangers showed details as small as 1 m across.

Five Surveyor spacecraft soft-landed on the Moon, took pictures of the lunar surface, and analyzed the lunar surface soil. The Surveyor program clearly showed that the lunar surface was strong enough to support spacecrafts and astronauts (Figure 6.6). The Moon is covered with a loose layer of rock fragments called **regolith.** The thickness of the regolith ranges from a few meters to a few tens of meters. During the Surveyor program the United States initiated another program designed to photograph the entire lunar surface in preparation for an eventual manned landing. This was the mission of the Lunar Orbiter program. The Orbiters obtained pictures 1000 times clearer than any Earth-based photography could achieve.

The preliminary work for a manned landing on the Moon was done in America's Mercury Project (6 single-man flights) and Gemini Series (10 two-man flights) between May 1961 and November 1966. The Apollo program followed with the first landing on the Moon on July 20, 1969, and five other successful manned landings and explorations of the lunar surface (Figure 6.7). The Apollo astronauts brought back 382 kg of lunar rock samples for analysis on Earth. Together with the Soviet core samples and the data obtained from experiments, such as seismograph measurements, heat flow measurements, and the laser reflector array left by the Apollo astronauts, these rocks form the experimental basis for our present understanding of the Moon.

Regolith: Crushed rock fragments weathered by meteorite bombardment lying on the surface of the Moon and other bodies.

■ FIGURE 6.6

Footpad of *Surveyor 3* Spacecraft on the Moon Photographed by *Apollo 12* Astronauts

SOURCE: NASA.

TABLE 6.3 Lunar Exploratory Missions

Spacecraft	Launch Date	Accomplishment
Luna 2 (USSR)	9–59	Crashed on moon; 1st spacecraft on the Moon.
Luna 3 (USSR)	10–59	Flyby; 1st photos of far side; 1st detection of solar wind.
Ranger 4 (USA)	4–62	Crashed on Moon's far side; 1st American spacecraft on the Moon.
Ranger 6 (USA)	1–64	Crashed on Moon.
Ranger 7 (USA)	7–64	Hard landing; took 4308 pictures of the lunar surface.
Ranger 8 (USA)	2–65	Hard landing; took 7137 pictures of the lunar surface.
Ranger 9 (USA)	3–65	Hard landing; took 5814 pictures of the lunar surface.
Luna 9 (USSR)	1–66	1st soft landing; televised pictures to Earth.
Surveyor 1 (USA)	5–66	Soft landing; 1st surface soil analysis; televised pictures to Earth.
Lunar Orbiter 1 (USA)	8–66	Close-up photos of entire lunar surface; 1st photo of Earth from Moon.
Luna 12 (USSR)	10–66	Orbiter; sent back surface pictures.
Lunar Orbiter 2 (USA)	11–66	Close-up photos of entire lunar surface; deliberately crashed on Moon.
Luna 13 (USSR)	12–66	Soft landing; returned pictures to Earth.
Lunar Orbiter 3 (USA)	2–67	Close-up photos of entire lunar surface; photographed *Surveyor 1*.
Surveyor 3 (USA)	4–67	Soft landing; surface soil tests; televised pictures to Earth.
Lunar Orbiter 4 (USA)	5–67	Extensive close-up photos of entire lunar surface; near polar orbit.
Lunar Orbiter 5 (USA)	5–67	Finished mapping entire lunar surface.
Surveyor 5 (USA)	9–67	Soft landing; photographs and chemical analysis of surface.
Surveyor 6 (USA)	11–67	Soft landing; surface soil tests; televised pictures to Earth.
Surveyor 7 (USA)	1–68	Soft landing; returned over 21,000 pictures of lunar surface.
Zond 4 (USSR)	3–68	Orbiter; possible test vehicle for manned flights.
Zond 5 (USSR)	9–68	Circled the Moon and returned to Earth; biological specimens aboard.
Zond 6 (USSR)	11–68	Similar to *Zond 4* mission; biological experiments and photographs.
Luna 15 (USSR)	7–69	Unmanned landing.
Apollo 11 (USA)	7–69	1st manned landing, exploration; rock samples.
Zond 7 (USSR)	8–69	Orbiter returned to Earth.
Apollo 12 (USA)	11–69	Manned landing; exploration; rock samples.
Luna 16 (USSR)	9–70	Unmanned landing; brought back soil core.
Zond 8 (USSR)	10–70	Orbiter returned to Earth.
Luna 17 (USSR)	11–70	Unmanned landing; brought back soil core; unmanned roving vehicle, *Lunokhod 1*, operated 10 months.
Apollo 14 (USA)	1–71	Manned landing; exploration; rock samples.
Apollo 15 (USA)	7–71	Manned landing; exploration, rock samples.
Luna 20 (USSR)	2–72	Unmanned landing; soil core returned.
Apollo 16 (USA)	4–72	Manned landing.
Apollo 17 (USA)	12–72	Last manned landing.
Luna 21 (USSR)	1–73	Unmanned landing; second lunar rover, *Lunokhod 2*.
Luna 22 (USSR)	5–74	Lunar orbiter.
Luna 24 (USSR)	8–76	Unmanned landing; brought back 2-meter long soil core.

In the picture of the lunar lander in Figure 6.7, the sky is black. This is a sign that the Moon has no atmosphere. Many other visible clues, such as the sharp shadows of mountains and valleys and at the terminator (the dividing line between night and day) and the instant disappearance of stars when they pass behind the Moon, had indicated a lack of atmosphere long before manned landings on the Moon.

For the Moon to maintain an atmosphere, the atoms and molecules in the atmosphere cannot have velocities greater than that needed to escape. At the top of an atmosphere, where there is less chance of collisions, atoms and molecules with velocities greater than the escape velocity will fly off into space, escaping the Moon altogether. Velocities of atoms and molecules depend on the temperature of the atmosphere and the mass of the individual particles. The greater the temperature, the greater the velocity; the more massive the particle, the slower the velocity. Consequently, hot atmospheres composed of low-mass atoms and molecules are most susceptible to being lost. Atmospheric atoms and molecules are also influenced by the mass and radius of the Moon. These determine the magnitude of the gravitational attraction of the Moon and, therefore, the value for the escape velocity. A planet or moon can retain an atmosphere if its escape velocity is greater than the average velocity of the atoms and molecules composing the atmosphere. The Moon lacks an atmosphere because its mass is low and its surface is hot.

Since the Moon does not have the protective coat of an atmosphere, its surface is bombarded by the entire spectrum of solar radiation. Although the Moon's average temperature, 250 K (−10°F), is about the same as the Earth's would be if the Earth had no atmosphere, lunar surface temperatures can reach as high as 400 K (261°F), well above the boiling point of water. On the other hand, if the astronauts wanted to "cool off" in the shade, they would find that the surface temperature in the shade of a large boulder, even at lunar noon, can be 200 degrees cooler than in sunlight. The high temperatures on the sunlit side of the Moon are the result of the lunar surface absorbing radiation while it is exposed to the Sun during the 2-week lunar day. The low temperatures, 100 K (−279°F), found at midnight result from the Moon facing away from the Sun for 2 weeks, which allows the Moon to radiate infrared radiation back into space.

FIGURE 6.7

Lunar Lander on the Moon

The Apollo spacecraft consisted of a command module and a lunar lander. The command module, manned by one astronaut, circled the Moon while two astronauts descended to the surface in the lander. The lower part of the lander served as a launch pad for the upper section.
SOURCE: NASA.

The Moon's Surface Features

Nearly all of the Moon's visible features are the result of impacts (Figure 6.8). On Earth, processes such as plate tectonics, volcanism, and erosion ensure that most of the Earth's surface is young, just a few hundred million years old. The Moon's surface, on the other hand, has been geologically inactive for the last few billion years. It does not exhibit any signs of tectonic activity; most of its visible surface has been shaped by outside forces.

Craters. The study of the lunar surface is a study of impact cratering. A **crater** is a bowl-shaped cavity resulting from an interplanetary collision between a planet or satellite and a rock from space. The projectile, called a **meteorite,** explodes like a hand grenade on impact. It is fragmented, melted, and vaporized; its remains are scattered all around the impact site (Figure 6.9). Some material ejected outward falls back to the surface at great distances from the impact site, forming an **ejecta**

Meteorite: The remnant of a small, solid rock that survived the passage through the Earth's atmosphere and crashed into the surface; when in space the rock is called a *meteoroid.*

Ejecta blanket: The area surrounding a crater covered by the material that was thrown radially outward during an impact; most of the material is deposited close to the crater rim.

(a)

(b)

■■■ FIGURE 6.8

Near and Far Sides of the Moon

(a) A near-side view of the Moon from an Earth-based telescope. *(b)* The left half of this *Apollo 17* picture of the Moon is the heavily cratered lunar far side.

SOURCES: Part (a) from Lick Observatory, University of California, Santa Cruz. Part (b) from NASA.

blanket. This debris consists of **brecciated,** or crushed, rock and liquid rock that quickly solidifies to form beads of glass. The larger, slower moving ejecta accumulate near the impact point and, together with the underlying rock that is heaved upward and outward near the edge of the impact, form a circular rim.

In fact, nearly all craters are circular. The explosion occurs so quickly, in just a fraction of a second, that the disturbance causing the explosive ejection propagates faster than the meteorite travels. Therefore, the angle of the incoming meteorite has little effect on the crater shape. The size of the crater, however, depends on both the size of the meteorite and its collisional speed. For typical speeds near 10 km/s, crater diameters are 10 to 15 times the diameter of the impacting meteorite. Craters will be larger, of course, for high-velocity impacts than for low-velocity impacts.

To understand the *morphology,* or the form and structure, of lunar craters, the cratering process can be visualized as occurring in three major stages: compression, excavation, and modification. Compression is the initial contact and penetration of the lunar or planetary surface by the meteorite. The impact generates a compression, or shock, that moves radially away from the impact point in all directions except up. The shock crushes, heats, and melts rock as it pushes its way deeper into the surface. At terrestrial crater sites, for instance, geologists find mineral forms produced by high temperatures and pressures normally found deeper in the crust and mantle. Compression results in the near complete disintegration of the incoming meteorite. Excavation refers to

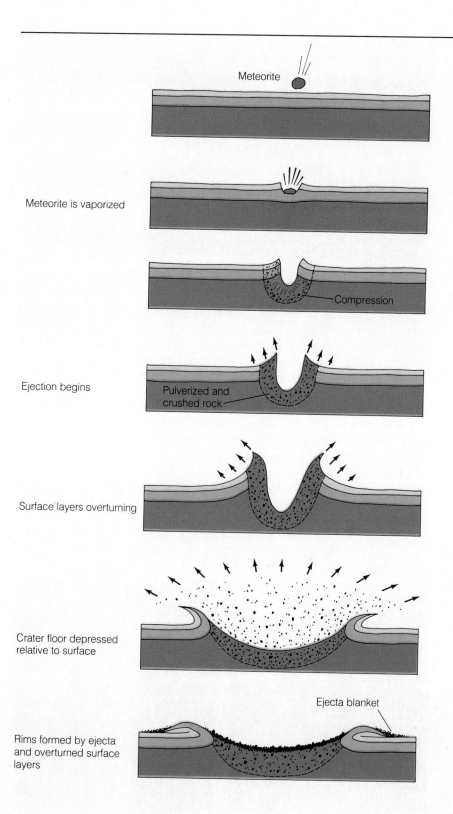

Meteorite

Meteorite is vaporized

Compression

Ejection begins

Pulverized and
crushed rock

Surface layers overturning

Crater floor depressed
relative to surface

Ejecta blanket

Rims formed by ejecta
and overturned surface
layers

FIGURE 6.9

Formation of a Crater

A meteorite strikes the surface of the
Earth compressing the ground. Material
near the surface is free to move upward
and is therefore ejected away from the
impact site.

■ FIGURE 6.10

Rim Profile

The rim of an impact crater exhibits inverse stratigraphic layering.

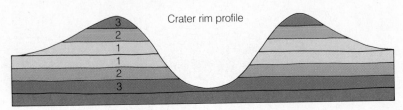

(a) Before meteoritic impact: level surface

Crater rim profile

(b) After impact: depression and reverse layering

the radial ejection of material around the cavity, or hole, forming the ejecta blanket and rim of the crater. About one-third of all material involved is ejected away from the blast site. This can amount to 1000 to 10,000 times the mass of the colliding meteorite. The rim deposits exhibit an inverse stratigraphic sequence (Figure 6.10). The topmost pre-impact surface material is ejected the farthest from the site and forms the lowest rim layer. The next deepest pre-impact surface layer is not ejected as far and falls on top of the highest layer to form the next rim layer. Successive pre-impact surface layers are similarly deposited, forming an inverse rock sequence.

Debris from impacts produces ejecta blankets consisting of *secondary craters* and *rays* (Figure 6.11). The secondary craters are often elongated because the speed of the ejected fragments is much slower than that of the impacting meteorite and because the impact angle of the debris is sometimes very shallow. Rays are bright streaks emanating radially

■ FIGURE 6.11

Secondary Craters and Rays

(a) Crater Euler in Mare Imbrium showing an ejecta blanket consisting of rays, crater chains, and secondary crater clusters. *(b)* Young crater exhibiting fresh rays.

SOURCE: NASA.

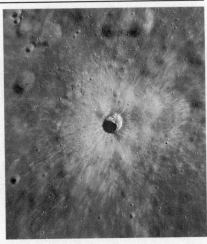

(a)

(b)

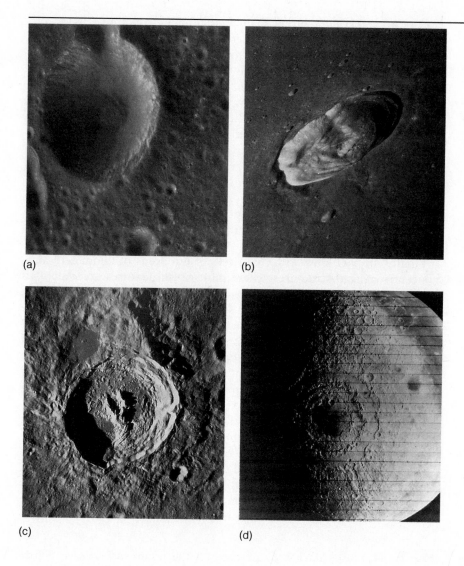

(a)

(b)

(c)

(d)

■■■■ FIGURE 6.12

Crater Types

(a) A small bowl-shaped crater surrounded by smaller craters. *(b)* The moderate-sized crater Arago showing concentric terraces due to wall collapse. *(c)* A
large crater with central peaks and terraced walls; note the shadows cast by the
central peaks. *(d)* The Orientale Basin.

SOURCE: NASA.

away from the primary crater like the spokes of a wheel. Rays consist
of fine particles of ejecta, very small secondary craters, and local surface regolith disturbed by the falling debris.

Whereas compression and excavation are instantaneous, postcrater-
ing modification may go on for long periods after the impact. Modification results in a variety of crater structures that correlate with crater
diameter. Small craters a few kilometers in diameter are simple bowl-
shapes with smooth inner walls and floors. The outer walls slope gently
into the surrounding landscape. Slightly larger bowl-shaped craters
show accumulations of material on the floor at the center (Panel a in
Figure 6.12). This is evidence of *slumping* and is simply debris that
never rose completely out of the crater and just rolled back down. The
cause of slumping is, of course, gravity pulling the rocks down the inner
slopes of the crater walls.

Craters on the Moon larger than about 10–15 km exhibit a more complex structure. As the walls of craters become steeper with more violent impacts, the gravitational stresses on the walls increase. For small craters the strength of the surrounding rock is able to support the walls and keep them from falling in. When the gravitational stresses become greater than the strength of the rock, major landslides occur. In addition, the melt from the impact will drain back down the walls and form a pool that soon solidifies. The landslides can enlarge a crater and partially fill it with debris from the rim. The collapsed walls involve the shifting of concentric slices of wall rock that creates concentric terraces (Panel b in Figure 6.12). For even larger craters, from about 20 to 40 km, subsequent modification can result in a strong inward radial movement of rock, causing a structural upheaval near the center of the crater (Panel c). The resulting central uplift, which can be a cluster of peaks, is called a **central peak.**

Central peak: Mountains near the centers of large craters caused by the radial modification of the floor and walls after impact; the inward flow meets near the center causing a central upheaval.

Finally, impact sites with diameters of hundreds of kilometers form concentric-ringed structures. These multiringed features are generated as large areas of the surface subside at the end of a major cratering event. The largest visible ringed structure on the Moon is Orientale Basin on the Moon's western limb, the outer edge of the visible part of the Moon (Panel d in Figure 6.12). Impact craters with diameters of more than 300 km are called *basins.* The outermost ring of Orientale Basin, called the Cordillera Mountains, is about 1000 km in diameter and rises about 7 km above the surrounding plains, and the inner ring, the outer Rook Mountains, is 620 km in diameter.

The present system of naming craters was devised in 1651 and uses names of notable scientists, philosophers, and writers, particularly those connected with lunar study. Some earlier geographers of the Moon, however, used names based on Earth geography. A few of these, such as the Alps, Apennines, and Carpathian, survive today (Figure 6.13). Refer to the map of the Moon in the Observer's Handbook for the names of some prominent lunar features.

■ FIGURE 6.13

Alpine Valley

A cigar-shaped depression about 120 km long and as wide as 10 km in places in the lunar "Alps" on the edge of Mare Imbrium.

SOURCE: National Space Science Data Center, Mr. Leon J. Kosofsky, principal investigator.

Maria. The large dark gray patches on the lunar surface (see Figure 6.8) visible even with the unaided eye were once thought to be large seas, hence the name *maria* (singular *mare*) meaning "seas" in Latin. We know today that these "seas" are vast solidified lava beds and that their dark color is due to a black oxide of iron and titanium. Maria are mainly found on the side of the Moon facing the Earth.

Two types of maria can be identified: circular maria, such as Imbrium and Crisium, and irregular depressions, such as Oceanus Procellarum. Enormous impacts produced the circular maria; they are just very large craters. For instance, the circular outline of all but the western rim of the largest lunar basin, Mare Imbrium, can still be seen (Panel a in Figure 6.14). The impacts that produced the maria fractured and weakened the surface, allowing lava from the interior of the Moon to cover the surface. These mare lava flows did not occur at the same time. Close inspection of the maria shows *flow fronts*, indicating lava flows on top of lava flows (Panel b). These *basaltic*, or fluid, lavas also

(a)

(b)

flowed out of some basins to fill surrounding regions, producing irregular basins. Oceanus Procellarum, for example, is a vast lava flood plain probably covered by lavas resulting from the Imbrium and other surrounding basin impacts.

Volcanism. The dark floors of the maria are the result of volcanic activity in which fluid lava flowed out of fissures and spread across the surface of the Moon. Do large volcanoes exist on the Moon? If so, are they currently active or dormant? Evidence of current volcanic activity on the Moon consists of over 1200 sightings of "transient" events; these are visual telescopic observations of color changes. Astronomers at Lowell Observatory in 1963, for instance, observed a red glow near the crater Aristarchus, and Apollo data suggest gas emission in this region. These are just 2 of over 300 observations associated with this single crater. No obvious volcanic eruptions have been observed on the Moon, however.

No towering volcanoes or large shield volcanoes exist on the Moon, but volcanic features, although small, are evident on the lunar surface. Long *sinuous rilles* are common on the Moon (Figure 6.15). These may be lava tubes that fed lava from the basins or fissures to other regions on the surface. During the lava flow, the outside of the flow cooled and solidified first, forming a solid "tube" surrounding the still hot lava inside. Once the flow ceases, the tubes collapse, forming long rilles. Often

■ FIGURE 6.14

A Circular Mare and Flow Fronts

(a) Mare Serenitatis is the circular mare at the lower left. All but the western outer ring of the impact that produced Mare Imbrium, 1300 km in diameter, can be seen to the right of Mare Serenitatis. *(b)* Flow fronts on the floor of Mare Imbrium; their apparent thinness indicates a very fluid lava that quickly spread across the basin floor.

SOURCES: Part *(a)* from Lick Observatory, University of California, Santa Cruz. Part *(b)* courtesy NASA.

▆▆ FIGURE 6.15

Sinuous Rilles

A sinuous rille, called Hadley Rille, in the region of the *Apollo 15* landing site.

SOURCE: NASA.

▆▆ FIGURE 6.16

Mare Nubium and the Lunar Highlands

The highlands are heavily cratered while the maria in comparison have relatively few craters.

SOURCE: Hale Observatories.

sinuous rilles are seen to flow from fissures on the surface or to start in breaks in the walls of large craters that have been filled with lava.

The Moon does not show any tectonic activity; no evidence exists for mountain ranges or trenches caused by plate collisions. All of the mountains on the Moon are simply crater walls. To understand why the Moon has not been tectonically active, scientists must try to reconstruct the history of the Moon. The first step in this reconstruction is to determine the age of the different features seen on the Moon.

Ages of Surface Rocks. Rock formations and fossils allow the construction of a complete stratigraphic time sequence for the Earth. Although the exploration of the Moon has not been extensive enough to determine a time sequence for lunar rock formations, craters can be used as a chronometer to construct a lunar relative stratigraphic sequence. Furthermore, absolute ages are known for several locations on the Moon. As a result, scientists are able to convert a lunar relative stratigraphic sequence into an absolute time sequence for the entire lunar surface.

The principle behind the use of craters as age indicators is easily seen by comparing the surfaces of the maria with the heavily cratered, or *highland*, regions on the Moon (Figure 6.16). The maria are clearly less densely cratered than the surrounding regions. To see how researchers deduce relative ages for maria and the highlands, let's compare craters to snowflakes. If during a mild snow storm 100 snow flakes fall on 1 square meter (m^2) of a sidewalk every hour, we would conclude that a sidewalk with 2000 snowflakes per m^2 has been exposed to the storm for 20 hours. At the same time, a sidewalk with 100 snowflakes per m^2 has been exposed for only 1 hour, or $\frac{1}{20}$ of the time. Similarly, the maria show about 20 times fewer large craters than the highlands. The most straightforward explanation for this is that the maria surfaces have not been exposed to impact cratering as long as the highlands—the maria must be younger surfaces.

It is not immediately obvious from crater counts, however, whether the Moon has been exposed to a constant or variable bombardment rate throughout its history. Astronomers can estimate how many craters are being produced on the Moon currently by taking an inventory of interplanetary objects, such as meteoroids and comets, and estimating how many are colliding with the Earth and the Moon. This inventory of interplanetary debris shows that if the Moon had been exposed to the same bombardment rate that it is experiencing today, the entire lunar surface would only be about as densely cratered as the maria. Consequently, the high density of craters in the lunar highlands must be due to a very intense meteoritic bombardment of the lunar surface that occurred before the maria flooded.

Beyond this statement of the possibility of an interplanetary meteoritic blizzard and the determination of the relative ages of various regions of the Moon's surface, absolute ages cannot be established just by counting craters. The absolute ages of the lunar surface come from the radiometric dating of the lunar rock samples brought back to Earth by Apollo astronauts and Russian robot space probes.

The radiometric ages for lunar rocks are derived from the rubidium-strontium, uranium-lead, thorium-lead, and potassium-argon radioactive decays. Ages are given in Table 6.4 and divide into three groups: the mare basalts (3.2–3.8 billion years), highland breccias (3.9–4.3 billion years), and very old, pristine rocks (4.4–4.6 billion years). the youngest rocks are the mare basalts; the mare lava flows occurred *after* the formation of the lunar highlands.

The correlation of absolute ages with measured surface densities of craters confirms that an interplanetary meteoritic blizzard produced the very heavily cratered terrain of the highlands. Figure 6.17 shows that the most heavily cratered terrains are indeed the oldest. It also indicates that the high surface densities of craters were created in a very short time; that is, between about 4.6 and 4.0 billion years ago meteorites were intensely bombarding the Moon's surface. This bombardment reset the radioactive "clocks" to between 4.3 and 4.0 billion years, heavily fractured surface rocks, and covered the lunar surface with regolith. Subsequently, between 3.8 and 3.2 billion years ago, the bombardment gradually declined in intensity. The youngest basin dated is Oceanus Procellarum, and its surface density of craters is what we would expect if it were exposed to the present bombardment rate for 3 billion years. Crater counts indicate that the youngest basins may only be 2.5 billion years old.

We see evidence for features younger than the maria in young craters exhibiting bright rays. The age of the crater Copernicus has been estimated at 900 million years from *Apollo 12* rock samples that are

■■■ TABLE 6.4 **Ages of Lunar Rocks**

Mission	Location	Age (billions of years)
	Mare basalts	
Apollo 11	Mare Tranquillitatis	3.6–3.7
Apollo 12	Oceanus Procellarum	3.2–3.4
Apollo 15	Mare Imbrium	3.3–3.4
Apollo 17	Mare Serenitatis	3.6–3.8
Luna 16	Mare Fecunditatis	3.4–3.5
Luna 24	Mare Crisium	3.3
	Breccia	
Apollo 14	Fra Mauro	3.9–4.0
Apollo 15	Hadley-Apennines	3.9–4.0
Apollo 16	Descartes	3.9–4.3
Apollo 17	Taurus-Littrow	4.0–4.3
Luna 20	Apollonius	3.9
	Ancient rocks	
Apollo 12, 16, 17	Various rocks	4.4–4.5
Apollo 17	Rock #72417	4.6

■■■ FIGURE 6.17

Crater Density versus Age

The ages of rocks collected by Apollo (A) and Luna (L) spacecraft are shown. The surfaces with the greater number of craters per unit area are the oldest. The age of the crater Copernicus is estimated from ejecta at the *Apollo 16* site, and its density of craters is obtained from the crater floor.

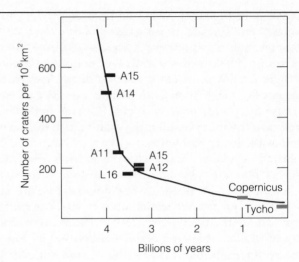

thought to be ejecta from this crater and from crater counts of its floor. The crater South Ray, which also exhibits bright rays, is near the *Apollo 16* landing site and is estimated to be only 2 million years old. Another small bright ray crater seen on the far side, named Bruno, exhibits very sharp detail. Although it has not been dated, it is possible that a bright flash on the Moon seen by Irish monks in A.D. 1178 was from the meteoritic impact that formed Bruno.

The Interior and History of the Moon

The most fundamental result of the Soviet Luna and American Apollo programs was the determination of the great ages of lunar rocks. Whereas almost all Earth rocks are less than 3 billion years old, nearly all lunar rocks are older than 3 billion years old. Moon rocks, therefore, fill a gap in the study of the very earliest times in the solar system that we cannot fill by studying Earth rocks. In fact, much of lunar research has consisted of sifting through rock samples, looking for primordial material.

Surface Rocks. The Moon's crust is a relatively simple collection of rocks compared to that of the Earth. Since no water exists on the Moon, no sedimentary rocks were found. In fact, water is not even bound up in lunar rocks as it is in even the driest of Earth's rocks. All lunar samples are igneous rocks; they all seem to have been molten at some time in the past.

The lunar rocks collected by astronauts are divided into three types: highland rocks, breccias, and mare basalts. The highland rocks are mainly *anorthosite*, a low-density calcium-rich aluminum silicate ($CaAl_2Si_2O_8$). All highland rocks are older than 3.9 billion years; most are between 4 and 4.4 billion years old, but a few are 4.6 billion years old. Lunar breccias are cohesive clusters of rock fragments and regolith stuck together by the heat and pressure generated by impact processes. Breccias have ages similar to highland rocks. Mare basalts, extruded between 3.8 to 3.2 billion years ago, are similar to common volcanic rock on Earth, but differ, as does lunar anorthosite, from Earth's rocks in several important ways. In general, lunar rocks are depleted in **volatile elements** such as water, mercury, zinc, lead, and gold but are enriched in **refractory elements** such as chromium, titanium, magnesium, and calcium. These differences have important implications concerning the origin of the Moon (see Chapter 11 for details).

Planetary astronomers realized early in the study of lunar rocks that the low-density anorthosite would float to the surface of the Moon if the Moon were molten. The great age of highland anorthosite suggests that a *magma ocean* initially covered the entire Moon, and the chemical differences between the anorthositic crust and the mare basalts indicate that the upper several hundred kilometers of the magma ocean were differentiated. As the Moon cooled, the anorthosite was the first rock to solidify because of its high melting temperature. Consequently, it floated to the surface and formed the lunar crust.

During the Moon's first half billion years, the anorthosite crust experienced an intensive meteoritic bombardment as indicated by the concentration of highland rock ages at about 4 billion years (Figure 6.18). Near the end of this bombardment, about 4 billion years ago, very large impacts produced the circular basins. At the same time, these impacts ruptured the Moon's surface, allowing the basins to flood with interior lavas. The chemical composition and density of mare basalts indicate that they originated below the 60 km thick layer of anorthosite but at depths not over 400 km. During the basin-flooding stage, between about 3.2 and 3.8 billion years ago, the intensity of the meteoritic bombardment steadily decreased. Except for a few large impacts, such as those that formed the craters Copernicus and Tycho, the Moon has been geologically subdued for the last 3 billion years (Table 6.5).

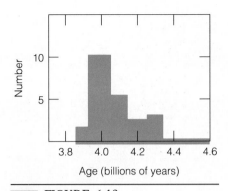

■■■ FIGURE 6.18

Relative Frequency and Ages of Highland Rocks

The abrupt minimum age of 4 billion years signals the reduction in the intensity of the meteoritic bombardment. These highland rocks were obtained by the *Apollo 15, 16,* and *17* missions.

Volatile element: An element or compound characterized by a low melting temperature; it is loosely bound to the rock structure and therefore easily escapes upon heating.

Refractory element: An element or compound characterized by a high melting temperature.

■■■ TABLE 6.5 Geological History of the Moon

1. Accretion of the Moon	≈4.6 billion years ago
2. Differentiation of global magma ocean Anorthosite crust formed	4.6–4.4 billion years ago

3. Intense meteoritic bombardment
     Highlands created
     Large meteorites created large basins
	4.4–3.8 billion years ago*

4. Partial melting of interior and basin flooding	3.8–3.2 billion years ago
5. Internal cooling and cessation of volcanism	3.2 (2.5)–0 billion years ago

*Intense bombardment probably started 4.6 billion years ago but left no record.

Interior. Planetary astronomers obtained information about the Moon's interior from seismic studies, from heat flow experiments, and from the geochemistry of lunar rocks. These data constrain predictions of the state of the lunar interior in just the same way such data for the Earth constrain predictions of the Earth's interior. For instance, when the density of highland rocks, 2.95 g/cm³, or mare basalts, 3.3–3.4 g/cm³, is compared to the average density of the Moon, 3.34 g/cm³, we conclude that the Moon is nearly homogeneous; that is, the Moon has nearly the same density throughout.

The Moon can be divided into three separate regions: regolith, crust, and mantle (Figure 6.19). The Moon may also have a small iron-rich core. The 10-meter thick regolith in the highlands actually covers a 1–2 km thick region of rock fragments and fracturing, called the *megaregolith*, produced by the intense early bombardment of the highlands. Below the crust is a thick, rigid lithosphere that reaches depths of approximately 1000 km. The lower limit of the lithosphere can be determined from depth measurements of moonquakes. Most earthquakes, for instance, occur at depths of about 100 km at the boundary of the solid lithosphere and the asthenosphere, the hot, fluid layers of the mantle. Most moonquakes occur between 800 and 1000 km below the surface. By analogy, scientists conclude that moonquakes also occur at a similar boundary. The Moon does not exhibit tectonic plates because the thickness of the lunar lithosphere prevents any interaction with a fluid mantle that could produce individual plates.

The extent of the partial melting in the Moon's interior is not known. The Moon, however, cannot have a large molten core. Seismographs left on the near side of the Moon by the Apollo astronauts have detected seismic waves generated by meteoritic impacts that have occurred on the far side. The lack of S waves received at the near-side stations clearly indicates a molten interior, but not enough moonquakes have occurred to pinpoint the exact size of the core. The data are consistent with an iron core of no more than 400 km in radius. Temperatures pre-

■■ **FIGURE 6.19**

Internal Structure of the Moon Consistent with Known Constraints

The upper part of the mantle is probably partially molten, but an iron-rich core is conjecture at present.

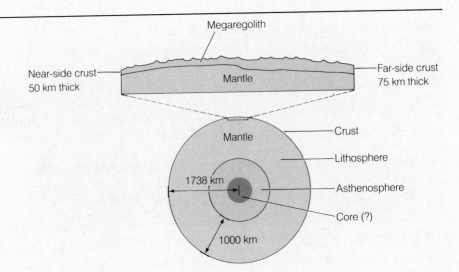

dicted for the lunar interior are above the melting point of iron but are much lower than the Earth's temperature; central temperatures are near 1500°–1600°C, about three times lower than that of the Earth. The Moon has cooled more than the Earth because it is smaller; it has a greater surface area, from which to radiate energy, relative to its volume.

The detection of an extremely small lunar magnetic field came as no surprise because of the Moon's slow rotation and lack of a significant iron core. Astronomers were surprised, however, when they discovered a remnant magnetic field in lunar rock samples. These paleomagnetic fields show random orientations that suggest that the rocks were magnetized before being excavated by meteoritic impact and spread all over the surface. Apparently, the Moon was able to generate a magnetic field billions of years ago. This is consistent with the suspected molten interior, caused by radioactive heating in the early Moon, and with the fact that the Moon was probably rotating faster then than it is now.

Although scientists have been able to study the Moon in detail and even deduce the conditions at its center, the planet Mercury is much more difficult to study. In fact, only one spacecraft has even been sent to Mercury. Analysis of the data it collected revealed a hot, Moon-like world.

▰▰▰MERCURY

Observations of Mercury have always been difficult because it is always found near the Sun in the sky and because it is a small planet. Mercury can never be observed in a dark sky from the Earth. Spacecraft observations in 1974 revealed a planet that is both Moon-like and Earth-like. Mercury exhibits a lunarlike surface saturated with impact craters, but it appears to have a large molten iron core. Nevertheless, both Mercury and the Moon appear to have progressed through very similar histories. Table 6.6 summarizes the basic data for Mercury.

The Orbit and Rotation of Mercury

Mercury is the closest planet to the Sun in the solar system, being only 58 million km, on the average, distant. Its orbit, however, is quite eccentric with an eccentricity of 0.206; by comparison, the Earth's orbital eccentricity is only 0.0167. At perihelion Mercury is only 46 million km from the Sun, and at aphelion it is nearly 70 million km away. This means that sunlight striking the Mercurian surface is more than twice as intense at perihelion than at aphelion.

Mercury rotates on its axis in the same direction as the Earth, which normally causes an east-to-west motion of the Sun on the sky during the Mercurian day. At perihelion, however, Mercury swings around the Sun so fast, 212,400 km per hour, that it causes the Sun to move *eastward* on the sky faster than Mercury's rotation causes the Sun to move westward. Watching sunrise on Mercury near perihelion, you would see the Sun rise slowly in the east, stop its westward motion, move east-

TABLE 6.6 Mercury Data

Orbital semimajor axis	0.39 AU (57.9 million km)
Perihelion distance	0.31 AU (45.9 million km
Aphelion distance	0.41 AU (69.7 million km)
Eccentricity	0.206
Orbital period (sidereal)	87.97 days
Rotational period	58.65 days
Inclination	0°
Diameter	4878 km (0.382 Earth diameters)
Mass	3.3×10^{23} kg (0.055 Earth masses)
Mean density	5.4 g/cm^3
Escape velocity	4.3 km/s (9600 MPH)
Surface temperature (mean)	620 K (350°C = 660°F)
Maximum	700 K (430°C = 800°F)
Minimum	100 K (−170°C = −280°F)

ward and set in the east, and then rise again. All this would occur over a few days' time. The Sun itself would also appear more than twice as large as it does from the Earth and would change its size by almost 50% as Mercury revolves around it.

The rotational period of Mercury was *not* known prior to 1965! This exemplifies the difficulty of studying a planet that is always seen in the glare of the Sun. For about 200 years astronomers thought that Mercury's rotational period equaled its orbital period of 87.97 days (references to "days" will always be in Earth days). Observers based this rotational period on observations of spotlike features apparently seen on the surface of Mercury (Figure 6.20). Radar observations of Mercury made in 1965 showed that Mercury actually rotates with a period of 58.65 days.

FIGURE 6.20

Mercury from an Earth-based Telescope

Prior to 1965, we thought Mercury rotated slowly since its surface features did not move noticeably during a 24-hour observation period. Furthermore, since these features did not seem to move when observed after 1 Mercurian year, we believed that Mercury exhibited synchronous rotation like the Moon. Note that Mercury exhibits phases as does Venus.

SOURCE: New Mexico State University Observatory.

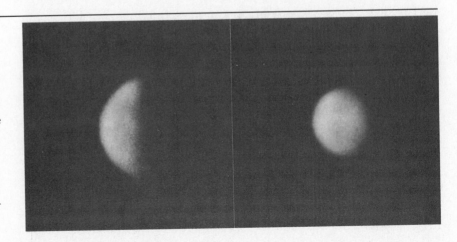

The fact that one side of Mercury moves toward us and the other side moves away from us as Mercury rotates causes reflected radar signals to change their wavelength. To understand this, imagine yourself in a coal mine car on a track along a straight tunnel. If the car is stationary and you clap your hands, say, once every second, you will eventually hear an echo of your claps, once every second, as the sound bounces off the distant tunnel wall. Now suppose the coal car moves at a steady speed toward the end of the tunnel, and you again clap at a rate of one clap per second. After hearing the echo of the first clap, you will hear the echo of the second clap *less* than a second after the first. Because the coal car has moved closer to the end of the tunnel, the sound of the second clap had less distance to travel so that you heard it sooner than if you were stationary. The same will happen with subsequent claps. In the case of Mercury, the side of Mercury rotating toward the Earth will reduce the wavelength of the reflected radar waves because the surface is rushing toward the signals while the opposite occurs on the side of Mercury rotating away from the Earth.

Although Mercury does not rotate about its axis with the same period as it orbits the Sun, it does exhibit a form of synchronous rotation. Mercury orbits the Sun twice while it rotates on its axis 3 times. This is an example of 2-to-3 *spin orbit coupling*. The Moon, for comparison, exhibits 1-to-1 spin orbit coupling. The Mercurian spin orbit coupling has a curious effect on the length of the Mercurian day.

Whereas the length of the lunar day (sunrise to sunrise) is the same as its orbital period, the Mercurian day is twice its orbital period. Figure 6.21 schematically follows Mercury through 2 revolutions about the Sun. At position 1 the Sun is rising on Mercury. As Mercury orbits the Sun counterclockwise in Figure 6.21, it also rotates counterclockwise so that at position 3, 44 Earth days after sunrise, it is local noon. Another 44 days brings sunset at position 5. Midnight occurs at position 7, and sunrise, at position 9, occurs 176 days later. Note that from position 1 to the position marked "X" Mercury has rotated on its axis once relative to the stars, but the Sun is only in approximately a "2:00 P.M." position on the sky.

Exploration of Mercury

Nearly all of our data about Mercury was collected by the *Mariner 10* spacecraft. *Mariner 10* was launched on November 3, 1973, flew by Venus in February 1974, and arrived at Mercury in March 1974. The trajectory of *Mariner 10* was such that its elliptical orbit around the Sun had a period of 176 days, or exactly 2 Mercurian "years." This meant that every 176 days *Mariner 10* and Mercury crossed paths. The spacecraft flew by Mercury three times before using up all of the fuel needed to orient itself. During these three passes *Mariner 10* photographed about 55% of the Mercurian surface with the same resolution Earth-based telescopes can photograph the Moon (Figure 6.22). Since the spacecraft always flew by Mercury on its dark side, it could only photograph the incoming and outgoing illuminated half-hemispheres. Furthermore, since *Mariner 10* passed by Mercury exactly every 2 Mercu-

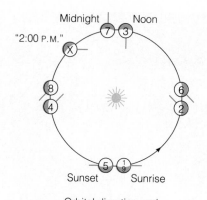

Orbital direction and rotational direction are counterclockwise.

■ **FIGURE 6.21**

The Mercurian Day

Mercury rotates counterclockwise as it orbits the Sun counterclockwise in this view. The magenta bar marks the position of an observer on Mercury.

(a)

(b)

━━━ FIGURE 6.22

Photographs from *Mariner 10*

(a) The "incoming" hemisphere of Mercury. *(b)* The "outgoing" hemisphere of Mercury.

SOURCE: NASA.

rian "years" or 3 Mercurian "days," it photographed the same regions on each flyby.

Mariner 10 carried cameras, magnetometers, and spectrometers. The magnetometers measured the magnetic field around Mercury, and the spectrometers measured radiation from many wavelength regions. Infrared measurements determined the surface temperature while spectra of reflected sunlight from the Mercurian surface provided indirect evidence of the nature of the surface material. Ultraviolet measurements could detect the presence of hydrogen, helium, carbon, oxygen, neon, and argon gases in a very thin Mercurian atmosphere. These instruments also measured the interaction of the Mercurian magnetic field with the solar wind and detected a magnetosphere.

The atmosphere of Mercury is so sparse that it is hardly worth calling an atmosphere. The fact that Mercury is a small planet and is so close to the Sun ensures its meager atmosphere. Since Mercury's escape velocity is low, 4.25 km/s (9600 MPH), and since its surface temperatures are very high, atoms and molecules find it easy to escape. At noon when Mercury is at perihelion, temperatures soar to 700 K (800°F). Although the highest temperatures recorded are above the melting temperature of lead, typical afternoon temperatures at intermediate latitudes near perihelion are about 200 K cooler. Consequently, we would not expect to find "pools of lead" or other metals on the Mercurian surface. (If pools could form, they would evaporate because of the lack of a substantial atmosphere). In fact, the soil itself acts as an insulator, making the subsurface rock 100–200 K cooler just inches below the surface. Temperatures at sunset, however, rapidly cool to 100 K ($-280°F$) by midnight. Mercury exhibits the largest temperature range of any planet in the solar system; these extremes in temperature between noon and midnight are simply due to the lack of an insulating atmosphere. Although *Mariner 10* detected traces of gases to heights of 600 km above the surface, the total atmospheric pressure from all these gases is a factor of 2×10^{12} *less* than the Earth's sea level pressure. These gases probably are produced by the decay of radioactive elements or captured from the solar wind. A quantity of helium, for instance, only lasts 200 days on the surface before escaping.

Although the magnetic field detected by *Mariner 10* was only one-hundredth of the Earth's, it is strong enough to form a magnetosphere and deflect part of the solar wind. Mercury's magnetic field, like the Earth's, is a dipole, oriented roughly along the spin axis of the planet. The field strength, however, is not strong enough to develop radiation belts such as the Earth's Van Allen belts. If the magnetic field were a remnant field, like that of a bar magnet, rather than produced by a dynamic mechanism, Mercury's interior would have to be very cool. Astronomers estimate that by virtue of its probable supply of radioactive elements, Mercury could generate enough heat to keep a large core at least partially molten to ensure the convective motions necessary to generate a planetwide magnetic field.

The Surface of Mercury

The *Mariner 10* photographs of Mercury revealed a Moon-like surface with craters, valleys, large cliffs, and plains. Cartographers working with the photographs to create maps of Mercury assigned names to the topographic features in accordance with the recommendations of the Working Group for Planetary System Nomenclature of the International Astronomical Union. Large craters are named after authors, artists, and musicians such as Hawthorne, Michelangelo, and Schubert. Mercurian valleys are named after radio telescope observatories such as Arecibo, Goldstone, and Haystack. Large cliffs bear the names of sailing ships associated with scientific exploration on Earth such as Discovery, Endeavour, and Santa Maria. Finally, Mercury's names in different languages, Tir, Odin, and Borealis, for instance, are used for Mercurian plains.

Craters. Mercury exhibits the full range of crater shapes. It has simple bowl-shaped craters, craters with terraced walls and central peaks, and ringed basins (Figure 6.23). Nevertheless, several differences exist between Mercurian and lunar craters. The transitions between morphological types occur at smaller diameters on Mercury. Furthermore, Mer-

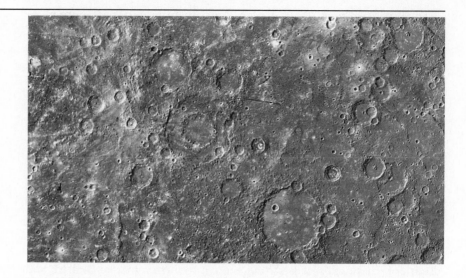

Mercurian Craters

Several prominent ray craters, a multiple-ring crater (center), and old, worn craters are seen here near the south pole of Mercury.

SOURCE: National Space Science Data Center, Dr. Bruce C. Murray, principal investigator.

curian ejecta blankets cover from 20% to as little as 5% of the surface area covered by lunar ejecta blankets. These differences are due to Mercury's larger surface gravity. Crater walls are subject to greater gravitational stresses on Mercury than on the Moon. The larger surface gravity means that ejected particles will not travel as far on Mercury as on the Moon.

The largest ringed basin, Caloris Basin, is about 1200–1400 km in diameter (Figure 6.24). Caloris is the same size as the Moon's Imbrium Basin and looks very similar to the Orientale Basin on the Moon (see Panel d in Figure 6.12). Caloris, from the Latin for "heat," received its name because it is the hottest place on Mercury; it lies directly under the Sun when Mercury is at perihelion. Most double-ringed basins on Mercury are much smaller in diameter.

■ FIGURE 6.24

Caloris Basin on Mercury

Only half of Caloris Basin was photographed by *Mariner 10*. A vast lava plain called Odin Basin lies outside the outer rim of Caloris Basin.

SOURCE: NASA.

Many old, worn craters are visible on Mercury's surface (Figure 6.23). These are not similar to the ghostlike craters on the Moon that have been partially flooded with lava. These Mercurian craters are assumed to be old because of the large number of small craters covering their floors. None of them show central peaks, even though they are large enough, and their rims are smooth and worn looking, not terraced. Scientists suspect that these craters may have formed at a time when the surface of Mercury was more fluid, allowing a fluidlike, gravity-driven readjustment to occur after the impacts.

Plains. The most heavily cratered surfaces on Mercury are the plains between larger craters called "intercrater" plains. Although they are characterized by a high density of small craters, the intercrater plains are not completely saturated with craters (Figure 6.25) as are the oldest lunar surfaces. Why do we have this difference? Perhaps thicker Mercurian ejecta blankets are more efficient in burying smaller craters than are the thinner lunar ejecta blankets. It is also possible that during part of an intensive bombardment the Mercurian surface melted and small impacts left little or no trace. The large, old, worn craters without central peaks or rings support this idea. In a similar vein, the entire surface of Mercury could have been resurfaced by gigantic lava floods that destroyed the record of the very earliest and heaviest bombardment. Subsequent cratering, because it was not as intense, could not completely saturate the surface.

The Mercurian "smooth" plains are similar to lunar maria, however (Figure 6.25). They cover about 15% of the photographed Mercurian sur-

■■■ FIGURE 6.25

Intercrater and Smooth Plains on Mercury

The heavily cratered intercrater plains (lower left) are contrasted with the relatively smooth plains (upper right). Intercrater plains are heavily peppered with small craters.

SOURCE: National Space Science Data Center, Dr. Bruce C. Murray, principal investigator.

face but are not as dark as lunar maria. Consequently, they are not as
apparent in photographs as the striking lunar maria are. The smooth
plains of Mercury are clearly younger than the intercrater plains but
are more heavily cratered than lunar maria. It is difficult to date the
Mercurian plains relative to the lunar maria because it appears that,
since Mercury is more massive and larger than the Moon, the cratering
rate of Mercury was greater than the Moon's. This means that a Mercurian lava plain that is 3.5 billion years old would be expected to have
accumulated more craters than a lunar mare of the same age. The Mercurian smooth plains appear to be similar to lunar maria in that they
represent surfaces that have been covered by vast lava floods and then
peppered with craters and ejecta.

Scarps. The surface features that surprised astronomers most were
the **scrarps,** or rounded cliffs, the largest of which are about 3 km high
and 500 km long (Figure 6.26). A scarp is a *thrust fault* in which one
block of rock rides over another as a result of compression (Figure 6.27).
Scarps usually imply a reduction in surface area. Since scarps cover a
significant fraction of Mercury's surface, astronomers conjecture that
Mercury experienced global shrinkage when it cooled after an initial
molten state. Furthermore, since some scarps have displaced existing
craters while others have been covered by craters, Mercury's conjec-
tured global shrinkage probably spanned a long time interval.

Ages. Since planetary astronomers do not have samples of Mercurian
rocks, they cannot directly assign absolute ages. Thus they cannot say
how long the intense period of meteoritic bombardment took on Mercury or how young the smooth plains are. Even comparisons with the
Moon are not useful because it experienced a different bombardment
rate. It is also likely that the surface evolution, such as the timing and
extent of the lava flooding of plains, and the interior evolution may

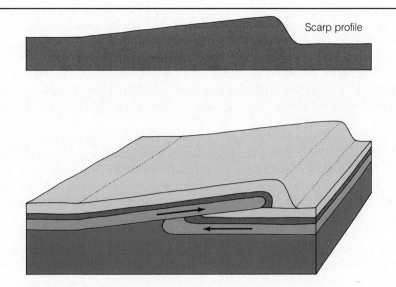

Scarp profile

FIGURE 6.27

Geometry of a Scarp

Compression, or contraction, causes one
sheet of rock to override another.

have been significantly different on Mercury than on the Moon. Yet relative ages can be assigned to various Mercurian surface features.
Clearly, the intercrater plains are the oldest surfaces on Mercury, and
the smooth plains are the youngest. Not all intercrater plains are the
same age; that is, they have different surface densities of craters covering their surfaces. The same can be said for the smooth plains; some
are older than others.

The Interior of Mercury

Models of Mercury's interior are ultimately based on the calculated average density of Mercury, the existence of a weak magnetic field, and
the extensive network of scarps on the surface. No seismic data or heat
flow measurements are available for Mercury. Thus all of the evidence
about the interior is indirect.

Although the average density of Mercury is nearly the same as the
Earth's, part of the Earth's high average density is due to compression.
The larger the planet, the greater are its internal pressures, and the
more its internal matter is compressed. The effect of compression can
be deleted mathematically and the average *uncompressed* planetary
densities compared. Uncompressed densities better reflect the actual
chemical composition of the planet. Astronomers find that the Earth's
average uncompressed density is about 4.3 g/cm^3 while Mercury's is
still 5.4 g/cm^3. Because Mercury is so small, compression is not an important factor in its average density.

The higher average uncompressed density for Mercury implies that
Mercury must be composed of a greater fraction of heavy elements than
the Earth. Furthermore, radar, near infrared, and optical spectra of reflected sunlight off of Mercury's surface are similar to those off of the
Moon's surface. Consequently, Mercury's surface is probably composed
mainly of silicates. If Mercury has a silicate crust with a density of
about 3 g/cm^3 and an iron core with a density of 8–9 g/cm^3, a mixture

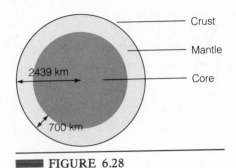

■■■ FIGURE 6.28
The Structure of Mercury

of about 60% iron and 40% silicon results in an average density of 5.4 g/cm³. This is a simple model and assumes that the iron and silicon are separated. Compare this with the Earth, which is about 40% iron, and the Moon, which is about 10% iron. Furthermore, the radius of Mercury's iron core could be as large as 1750 km, or about the size of the Moon! A reasonable model of the Mercurian interior, therefore, is one with an iron core with a radius of 1750 km and a silicon-rich mantle of about 700 km (Figure 6.28).

Mariner 10 detected a weak magnetic field around Mercury; it was about 1% of the Earth's magnetic field strength. The existence of any magnetic field on Mercury is significant because of its very slow rotation. Since planetary magnetic fields are thought to be generated by a rotating metallic core, the presence of a magnetic field is more evidence suggesting a large metallic core; a large, fluid core makes up for the slow rotation.

The network of scarps indicates that the entire planet contracted by about 1–2 km. If the entire planet were molten and then cooled, a decrease in volume would be expected. Furthermore, if the entire planet were molten, then heavy elements, such as iron and nickel, would separate from the lighter silicon and sink to the center, resulting in an iron core and a silicon crust. Recall that the existence of a large, iron-rich core for the Earth was evidence that the Earth was probably molten in its early history and differentiated. Models of Mercury indicate that when Mercury formed, radioactive elements could have generated enough heat to melt the entire planet and still retain a partially molten core today.

The melting of Mercury would have caused the planet to expand. Melting had to occur before the intensive bombardment finished, otherwise expansion fractures on the surface would be visible. Mercury's surface, however, shows signs of contraction in the form of scarps. Furthermore, some surface features, such as the large, worn craters, support the conjecture that the surface of Mercury was molten in the past.

It appears then that during the initial epoch of an intensive bombardment, Mercury was heated to temperatures high enough to melt the entire planet. As the planet cooled, some impacts created craters with unusual morphology in a molten surface. Furthermore, since Mercury is larger than the Moon, it took longer to cool and perhaps could supply lava to the surface for a longer period of time. Consequently, the surfaces of Mercury may be much younger than simple comparisons with the Moon would indicate.

■■■**SUMMARY**

The close proximity of the Earth and Moon to each other generates gravitational interactions that raise tides on both worlds. These tides have acted to brake the Moon's rotation, slowing it to its present 27⅓-day spin, equal to its orbital period. The tides have also acted to slow the rotation of the Earth from as little as 5 hours several billion years ago. At the same time, the tidal bulge on the Earth accelerates the Moon in the direction of its orbital motion, causing it to spiral away slowly from the Earth.

Craters and maria are the most prominent features on the Moon. The craters exhibit a variety of structures that are the result of modifications of the terrain following the impacts that produced the craters. The maria are the largest craters; the impacts that produced the maria fractured and weakened the crust, allowing dark-colored lava to flow to the surface.

Within about 200 million years of the formation of the Moon, differentiation of a global magma ocean occurred in which an anorthositic crust and an iron- and magnesium-rich mantle formed. Between about 4.4 and 3.8 billion years ago, the anorthositic crust was subjected to an intense meteoritic bombardment. This produced the heavily cratered highlands and the large impacts that produced the large lunar basins. The low-lying basins were subsequently flooded with lava from the mantle; flooding could have lasted until as recently as 2.5 billion years ago. As the Moon cooled, volcanism stopped as the lithosphere became thicker and thicker, reaching over 1000 km below the Moon's surface. Below the solid lithosphere, the Moon has a small molten region. The average density of the Moon and the small magnetic field of the Moon argue against the existence of a large metallic core, and seismic studies are consistent with a small or nonexistent core. Except for space meteoritic bombardment, the Moon has undergone very little change since the flooding of the basins.

Visually, Mercury is much like the Moon. Its surface is littered with hundreds of thousands of craters that exhibit the same overall morphology as lunar craters. Although less prominent than their lunar counterparts, Mercurian lava plains also spread across its surface. The surface density of craters is used to estimate relative ages on Mercury as on the Moon. The oldest surfaces are the Mercurian intercrater plains, the youngest surfaces are the smooth marialike plains.

To date, *Mariner 10* is the only spacecraft to explore Mercury and since it did not bring back surface samples, astronomers have no rock samples from which to establish absolute ages of Mercurian surface features. Because of Mercury's larger size and, therefore, longer cooling time, it is likely that events on the surface and interior have been spread out longer in time relative to the Moon.

The differences between lunar and Mercurian surfaces indicate different evolutionary histories. Old, worn-looking craters indicate that the surface of Mercury experienced melting on a large scale; perhaps the entire planet melted. The vast network of scarps on Mercury strongly suggests that Mercury experienced a global shrinkage as well; this would be expected if the planet melted and then slowly cooled.

The average uncompressed density of Mercury indicates that the planet has a large metallic core. The small magnetic field, enough to generate a magnetosphere, discovered around Mercury also supports the existence of a large metallic core, since the core must be large to generate a magnetic field with Mercury's slow planetary rotation.

Like the Moon, Mercury has virtually no atmosphere. It harbors just traces of gases probably produced by radioactive decay in the mantle and crust and trapped solar wind particles. The lack of atmosphere and close proximity to the Sun cause Mercury to experience the greatest temperature extremes in the solar system; temperatures range from 700 K at noon at perihelion to 100 K at midnight.

Mercury is locked into a 2-to-3 spin orbit coupling with the Sun; it spins on its axis 3 times as it orbits the Sun twice. The slow rotation and short orbital period produce a Mercurian day of 176 Earth days. Although Mercury rotates in the same direction as the Earth, producing an east-to-west daily motion of the Sun, Mercury's orbital eccentricity and slow rotation cause the Sun to exhibit retrograde motion in the Mercurian sky.

CHAPTER CAPSULE

Topics and Terms	Review and Remarks
Tidal force	It causes tides on the Earth and the Moon. It slows the rotation of the Earth and the Moon and accelerates the Moon in its orbit.
Cratering process	Compression Excavation Modification
Geological history of the Moon	Accretion: 4.6 billion years ago Differentiation of magma ocean (surface only?) and formation of silicate crust

(continued)

CHAPTER CAPSULE (continued)

Topics and Terms	Review and Remarks
	Intensive meteoritic bombardment formed the highlands and large basins during the first 600 million years.
	Basin flooding created the maria during the next billion years.
	Internal cooling and cessation of volcanism
Geological history of Mercury	Accretion: 4.6 billion years ago
	Differentiation of entire planet and formation of silicate crust; the old, worn craters were produced at this time.
	Intensive meteoritic bombardment formed the oldest terrain, and global crustal contraction formed the scarps.
	Volcanic flooding created the smooth plains.
	Internal quiescence
Spin orbit coupling	This is the ratio of the orbital period to the rotational period:
	It is 1:1 for the Moon—the Moon rotates once for every orbit around the Earth.
	It is 2:3 for Mercury—Mercury rotates three times for every two orbits around the Sun.
	The coupling is caused by tidal interactions between the orbiting bodies.

REVIEW QUESTIONS

1. How has our knowledge of the Moon and Mercury changed since the birth of the space age? Why have the Moon and Mercury been discussed in the same chapter? What are their most obvious similarities? What are their most obvious differences?

2. What characteristics differentiate the Terrestrial and the Jovian planets? Can you guess why the planets should be so different? (*Hint:* Look at the densities of the planets in Table 6.1.)

3. Describe the *long-term* affects of the tidal interaction between the Earth and the Moon. Can you think of one *obvious observable* result of this interaction?

4. Photographs taken from the Moon's surface always show a dark sky. Can you tell why?

5. What are the youngest features on the surface of the Moon that are observable from Earth?

6. Arrange the following in order of time of formation on the Moon: (a) the highlands, (b) the rays of Tycho and Copernicus, and (c) the maria.

7. Are the Moon's highland craters the result of volcanism, impact, some other mechanism, or a combination of the three?

8. Until the 1960s astronomers thought Mercury's rotation was synchronous with its orbital motion. How could this idea have persisted until recently?

9. Neither the Moon nor Mercury has a significant atmosphere. Why?

10. The Moon's craters have higher rims, longer ray systems, and larger ejecta blankets than those of Mercury. What is responsible for the difference?

11. From Table 6.1 determine which planet comes closest to Earth. Which planet is most easily observed from Earth (that is, which planet is situated so that we can observe its surface to best advantage)? Explain your answers.

12. Table 6.1 shows relative high densities for the terrestrial planets compared to those of the Jovian planets. Figure 6.1 shows the terrestrial planets to be small compared to the Jovian planets. Can you reconcile this with the chemical compositions given in Table 6.1?

FOR FURTHER READING

Burnham, R. 1989. How Apollo changed the Moon. *Astronomy*, July, 40.

Chapman, C. R. 1988. Mercury's heart of iron. *Astronomy*, Nov., 22.

Cordell, B. M. 1986. Mars, Earth, and ice. *Sky & Telescope*, July, 17.

Greenberg, D. A. 1987. Modeling tidal power. *Scientific American*, Nov., 128.

Kitt, M. T. 1987. Sculpting the Moon. *Astronomy*, Feb., 82.

Runcorn, S. K. 1987. The Moon's ancient magnetism. *Scientific American*, Dec., 60.

ASTROPROBE 6

Craters: Scars on the Earth's Surface

It may be surprising to learn that in the early part of the twentieth century many astronomers attributed the craters on the Moon to volcanic eruptions while geologists thought craters on Earth were due to impacts with large objects. Today, nearly all lunar craters are thought to be due to impacts while both impact and volcanic craters are found on Earth. Estimates for the number of impact craters currently recognized on Earth vary from about 60 to 120. Table 6A.1 lists some of the known impact craters, and Figure 6A.1 gives their locations.

Most of the craters listed in Table 6A.1 have been documented as impact craters only in the last 30 years. Systematic searches of aerial and satellite photographs of deserts and regions of ancient rock formations, such as the Canadian Shield in northeastern Canada, have uncovered many circular features that have been confirmed as impact craters by later surface studies. Even craters originally thought

TABLE 6A.1 **Large Terrestrial Impact Craters**

Name	Location	Diameter (km)	Age (millions of years)
Araguainha Dome	Brazil	40	<250
Bosumtwi	Ghana, Africa	10.5	1.3
Brent	Ontario, Canada	3.8	450
Carswell Lake	Saskatchewan, Canada	37	485
Charlevoix	Quebec, Canada	46	360
Clearwater East	Quebec, Canada	22	290
Clearwater West	Quebec, Canada	32	290
Deep Bay	Saskatchewan, Canada	12	100
Gosses Bluff	Australia	22	130
Henbury	Australia	0.15	?
Kara	USSR	50	≈60
Manicouagan	Quebec, Canada	100	210
Manson	Iowa	32	< 70
Meteor Crater	Arizona	1.2	0.03
Monturaqui	Chile	0.5	?
New Quebec	Quebec, Canada	3	5
Popigai	USSR	100	30
Puchezh-Katunki	USSR	80	180
Ries	Germany	24	15
Serpent Mount	Ohio	6.4	300
Sierra Madera	Texas	13	100
Siljan	Sweden	45	360
Steinheim	Germany	3	15
Sudbury	Ontario, Canada	140	1850
Vredefort	South Africa	100	1970
Wells Creek	Tennessee	14	200

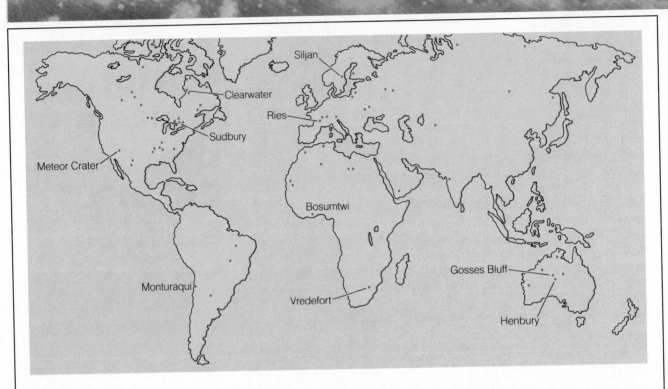

■ FIGURE 6A.1

Geographical Distribution of Impact Craters

A few of those listed in Table 6A.1 are labeled.

to be of volcanic origin have been restudied and found to be impact craters. The difficulty in identifying impact craters is recognizing structural features that are unique to impacts. Part of the recent increase in the number of craters recognized as impact craters is due to the establishment of criteria for their recognition.

One of the most thoroughly studied impact craters in the world is Meteor Crater in northern Arizona. First noticed by scientists in 1891, the debate over its origin, volcanic or impact, raged for over 40 years. By 1930 only 10 other impact structures were recognized in the whole world. The question was how can you tell the difference between impact and volcanic craters? Three features of a crater definitely confirm an impact origin:

■ The blanket of rock in the rim exhibits inverted layers relative to the surrounding rock (Figure 6A.2).

■ Minerals that were formed under high pressure and evidence of melting are present.

■ Meteorites (see Chapter 10) representing pieces of the impacting object are present.

These criteria are the natural result of the impact process, but not of volcanic processes.

The impact process is violent because the incoming projectile is traveling so fast. Possible collisional velocities of large objects in the solar system range from about 10 km/s (24,000 MPH) to 70 km/s (170,000 MPH). The energies involved are equivalent to that released in megaton thermonuclear explosions. The impact converts the energy of motion of the projectile into a strong shock wave that compresses the target material, reaching pressures of several million times the surface pressure on the Earth. These high pressures cause rock to vaporize and melt. The impacting projectile also experiences these high pressures, and it deforms, breaks apart, and vaporizes almost instantly. The impact ejects high-velocity particles made up of incandescent and molten fragments of the target and the projectile.

A crater assumes its final shape during the excavation phase, where the remains of the projectile and target material are ejected in all directions from the impact point. At the very end of the excavation phase, the moving ejecta will leave at very steep angles, and some will fall back to form a layer of loose debris on the floor of the new crater. Soon after the excavation, the central regions of large craters can lift upward, forming hills and small mountains at the center.

Once they are formed, erosion and infilling can modify the appearance of craters. Gravity places stress on the walls of the craters, causing landslides that fill in the floor and can give the walls a terraced appearance. Very old craters on Earth can have had their appearances drastically changed by wind and water erosion and can therefore be difficult to identify today.

When we look at the Moon's surface, we see thousands of craters (Figure 6A.3), but on the Earth only a hundred are known. Why the difference? The solar system contains a large body of small objects called asteroids and comets, and collisions are continually occurring between these small bodies and planets. During the solar system's first billion years, the number of collisions was many orders of magnitude greater than today. The craters seen on the Moon are the visible remains of the last stages of the formation of the Moon. The Moon's surface has been inactive for the last few billion years, and the craters there have been exposed to very little erosion. The Earth must have been subjected to a similar bombardment that would have produced millions of craters. The Earth's surface, however, is active. In fact, most of the rocks on the surface have been reprocessed through tectonic processes and subjected to erosion, volcanism, and crustal deformation, all of which tend to bury craters. These forces have erased all evidence of the early bombardment. Insufficient time has passed to erase the signs of all impacts, however. The oldest areas of the Earth's surface are mostly 1 to 3 billion years old, and some retain old impacts. These craters still postdate the final inten-

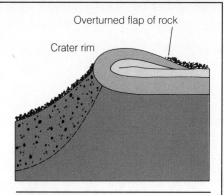

■ FIGURE 6A.2

Schematic Representation of the Overturned Flap Geology Found at the Rims of Impact Craters

■ FIGURE 6A.3

The Lunar Surface

The heavily cratered lunar surface shows the results of the final accretion of the Moon.

SOURCE: Lick Observatory, University of California, Santa Cruz.

sive bombardment of the Earth's surface. Only relatively young craters and older craters on ancient surfaces are visible now. Some of these are described next.

SOME RECOGNIZED TERRESTRIAL CRATERS

Meteor Crater, Arizona

Meteor Crater has been called by several names in scientific and popular literature: Canyon Diablo Crater, Coon Butte Crater, Crater Mound, and the Barringer Crater, as well as Meteor Crater (Figure 6A.4). Meteor Crater is one of the most recent terrestrial large craters caused by impact. The crater is about 25,000 years old. It exhibits the classic overturned rock formation on its rim, and fragments of the colliding object have been found up to 5 km away, but the search for any remains of the projectile that might be buried below the crater floor has been in vain.

Scientists estimate that the colliding object was about 30 m in diameter and traveled at a speed of 15 km/s (36,600 MPH) at impact. The explosion was equivalent to several million tons of TNT and excavated about 200 million tons of rock. The crater is about a kilo-

FIGURE 6A.4

Meteor Crater

One of the youngest impact craters in the world, Meteor Crater was used as a training site for the Apollo astronauts.

SOURCE: Meteor Crater Enterprises, Inc., Northern Arizona.

meter across and 200 m deep with a rim extending 30 to 60 m above the surrounding plains. Aerial photographs show the crater to be polygonal in shape. This is due to the structure of the rock formations at the impact site.

Canadian Craters

About 20 known impact craters are located on an old section of the Earth's crust called the Canadian Shield. The ages of the craters range from about 100 million years to almost 2 billion years, and they range in diameter from 2 to 140 km. Most of the Canadian craters have only been confirmed as impact craters since 1950. It is difficult to locate circular features with raised rims because the craters have filled with sediment over millions of years, and many have had their appearance extensively modified by the scouring action of glaciers.

The Deep Bay Crater exhibits those characteristics that make it difficult to locate ancient craters on Earth (Panel a in Figure 6A.5). As its name implies, it is a deep bay, which lies in the southeast corner of Reindeer Lake in Saskatchewan. Deep Bay is round and perfectly symmetrical and quite out of character for the lake. Close geological inspection revealed that it was caused by a tremendous explosion. Much of the rock in the inner walls was shattered and fragmented, but no raised rim existed. Although Deep Bay's only resemblance to a crater from the air is its circularity, aerial photography can be done in such a way as to produce stereoscopic images that allow investigators to detect raised rims of possible craters. Deep Bay is typical of the Canadian craters, which are so old that their rims have been eroded away.

■■■ FIGURE 6A.5

Impact Craters in Canada

(a) Deep Bay. *(b)* Clearwater lakes. This pair of craters was produced in a twin impact event about 290 million years ago. *(c)* Manicouagan, an old, eroded crater. Shown here is an annular lake around the central uplift.

SOURCE: Energy, Mines and Resources, Ottawa, Canada.

(a)

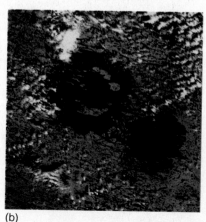

(b)

(c)

The largest Canadian craters exhibit central uplifts similar to the central peaks seen in large lunar craters. The central uplift in the Manicouagan Crater, for instance, rises 300 m above the surrounding landscape (Panel c in Figure 6A.5).

The oldest Canadian Shield crater, the Sudbury Structure in Ontario, was discovered in 1883 (Figure 6A.6). A land surveyor in the Sudbury region noticed a large disturbance of his compass needle, which usually indicates a large underground area of a metallic ore. When a railway was built through the region, large deposits of an important copper ore were discovered. Most surprising was the discovery of nickel in the ore. At that time only about 1000 tons of nickel per year were produced in the world. As it turned out, nickel steel is

■ FIGURE 6A.6

Sudbury Structure

This Landsat image of Sudbury hints at its elongated shape. The insert is a schematic illustration of its surface structure.

SOURCE: Energy, Mines and Resources, Ottawa, Canada.

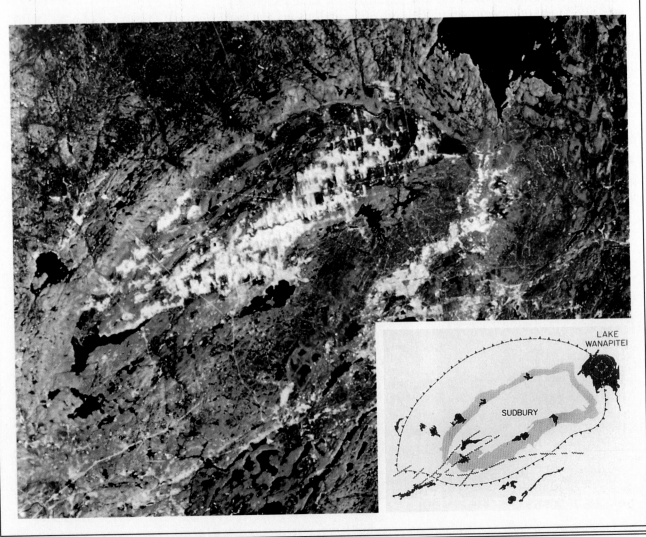

superior to iron steel as armor plating for ships, and the U.S. Navy began to order nickel ores from Sudbury, creating an enormous demand for nickel. Since the late nineteenth century, Sudbury has generated billions of dollars worth of nickel, copper, iron, platinum, and other heavy metals.

Geologically, Sudbury is confusing; in particular, the presence of solidified molten rock was a source of puzzlement for a long time. In fact, it took 80 years of intensive study before geologists realized that the confusion could be cleared away by assuming that Sudbury was an impact crater. The recognition came from geologists who had studied other known impact craters. It appears that the impact was violent enough to fracture the crust so that magma from below could flood the crater, an explanation that accounted for the solidified molten rock. In this respect Sudbury is similar to the large lunar basins that were flooded with magma. The impacting meteorite was at least 4 km (2.5 mi) in diameter, forming a crater 140 km (85 mi) across and 3 km (2 mi) deep.

The unusual amount of nickel and iron is attributed to the meteorite. That is, the large quantities of metallic ore in this region are extraterrestrial in nature! This may be of interest to future space travelers and miners because it may be possible in the future to travel to asteroids and mine them for metallic ores (see AstroProbe 11 for more on the resources of the solar system). It appears that small asteroids could supply needed ores for centuries.

German Craters

Unlike the remote Canadian craters, several impact craters in Europe have been "lived in." Ries Crater in southern Germany, about halfway between Frankfurt and Munich, is a large, multiringed structure inside of which is the old city of Nördlingen. The innermost crater walls, defining a diameter of 24 km, are marked by forests at the higher elevations. Large broken rock lies in great disarray around the rim, and larger boulders have been found as far away as 20 km (35 mi) as if they were ejected radially away. At first, geologists believed this structure was volcanic, but eventually rock fragments were identified as being similar to the ejecta found near Meteor Crater in Arizona. The crater is 0.75 km deep now, but at the time of impact the colliding body may have excavated a hole 2 km deep.

The Ries Crater was formed about 15 million years ago by an object about 3 km in diameter colliding at approximately 15 km/s. The object probably had a low density because Ries Crater is very shallow compared to its diameter; perhaps it was a comet (see Chapter 10 for more on comets). A high-density object would have penetrated

■■ FIGURE 6A.7

Steinheim Basin in Germany

The town of Steinheim lies near the central uplift in the center of the crater. Most of the outer walls have been eroded.

SOURCE: Albrecht Brugger, Stuttgart, West Germany.

more into the Earth, giving a deeper hole, and ejected material at a high angle, producing high walls.

Within 30 km and in a straight line from Ries Crater are two smaller impact craters, Steinheim, with a diameter of 4 km, and Stopfenheim, with a diameter of 9 km (Figure 6A.7). All three appear to be the same age, and astronomers have suggested that they may be the result of a break-up of a large, single body into three pieces.

Australian Craters

A most interesting feature on the Australian landscape is the Gosses Bluff impact structure (Figure 6A.8). It is a ring-shaped rise and appears to be the central uplift area of a crater that may once have been as large as 20 km across. The outer ring has been severely eroded over the last 130 million years, the approximate age of the crater. Just after the formation of large craters, gravitational readjustment of the walls and all the area interior to the walls is such that the material moves radially inward, meeting at the center. The meeting at the center produces central uplifts or central peaks.

A cluster of over a dozen craters near the old Henbury Cattle Station in Australia's Northern Territory about 115 miles southwest of Alice Springs was discovered in 1931 (Figure 6A.9). It was brought to the attention of scientists after a brilliant fireball was observed in South Australia. Just before midnight the whole sky was as bright as day for several seconds as a meteor nearly disintegrated as it flew

■ FIGURE 6A.8

Gosses Bluff, Australia

SOURCE: Robin Brett, USGS.

■ FIGURE 6A.9

Henbury Craters, Australia

SOURCE: Paul Hodge, University of Washington.

through the atmosphere. The meteorite created a crater only 18 inches across. Because of the public interest in this event, the existence of a group of craters near Henbury was mentioned to the staff of the Southern Australian Museum. The craters were not easy to distinguish because they had been filled with sediment, and trees and shrubs grew inside them. Nevertheless, not only were craters found, but several hundred kilograms of meteorites also were collected. The largest of the craters is about 140 m across and only about 15 m deep. In the center of the smallest crater, which is 9 m across, 200 kg of iron meteorites were found, the first instance of a meteorite being found *inside* a crater. These craters may only be a few thousand years old. It has been speculated that they could have been formed by a shower of meteorites from a larger object that broke up during its flight through the atmosphere.

Cratering has had an important impact on the surfaces of planets. In the very early times of planetary formation, impacts melted and cracked the surfaces of planets and moons. Impacts may have contributed to separations of continents and oceans on the Earth and may have strongly affected evolution by acting as a catalyst for mass extinctions of life.

CHAPTER 7

Venus and Mars

OUTLINE

Venus
The Orbit and Rotation of Venus
Exploration of Venus
Venusian Surface Features: Cratering
   and Tectonism
The Atmosphere of Venus
   Atmospheric Composition,
     Structure, and Evolution
   Atmospheric Dynamics
   The Venusian Magnetosphere

Mars
Exploration of Mars
   Earth-based Observations
   Spacecraft Observations
Martian Surface Features
   Craters
   Canyons and Channels
   Volcanism
   The Nature of the Martian Surface:
     The Viking Landers
   The Geological History of Mars
The Atmosphere of Mars
   Global Circulation
   Water
The Moons of Mars

Summary

Chapter Capsule

Review Questions

For Further Reading

▅▅▅▅▅**ASTROPROBE 7:**
   Terraforming

Mars from Phobos.
ARTIST: MariLynn Flynn.

V ENUS AND MARS ARE ROCKY WORLDS with atmospheres rich in carbon dioxide. Their surfaces show numerous signs of tectonic activity. Both planets possess volcanoes: probably active on Venus, extinct or dormant on Mars. Until spacecraft orbited the planets, plunged through their atmospheres, and landed on their surfaces to sample air and dirt, humans could hardly imagine how unlike the Earth Venus and Mars were. Venus, completely covered in yellow-white clouds, had been envisioned by some as a humid, swampy world. Mars, with its 24^h37^m rotation and obvious seasons, produced visions of ancient, canal-carving civilizations. Who could have guessed that the clouds of Venus were corrosive acid or that the dust-ridden atmosphere of Mars was unbreathable? This chapter is mainly devoted to the description of the surface features and atmospheres of Venus and Mars. Comparisons with the Earth will emphasize the differences in the planetary environments of the three planets. These differences are due to their varied tectonic and interior histories and to long-term changes in planetary atmospheres.

VENUS

Even though Venus comes closer to the Earth than any other planet, it has a long history of fooling observers. Since it is both a morning and evening object, early observers thought that Venus was two different planets, Hesperus and Phosphorus. During the last 300 years, its thick layer of clouds prevented astronomers from visually inspecting its surface and led to a host of theories and qualitative descriptions of the mysterious Venusian surface. Before the space age investigations of the 1960s and 1970s, Venus was described variously as a humid, swampy world teeming with life, as a world covered completely by water, and as a hot, dry, global desert. From these and many other equally varied descriptions, it was not even clear that everyone was talking about the same planet! Such diverse speculations and theories existed because astronomers had very few quantitative observations of Venus and were therefore not constrained by contrary evidence.

Let's first describe the bulk properties of Venus and then study the history of its exploration by unmanned spacecraft. The description of the surface and atmosphere of Venus rests almost entirely on this space age exploration. Table 7.1 provides an overview of the basic properties of Venus.

The Orbit and Rotation of Venus

The nearly circular orbit of Venus brings it within 41 million kilometers of the Earth, closer than any other planet. The earliest record of observed markings on the visible disk of Venus were made by the Italian astronomer Franciscus Fontana (1585–1656). Today astronomers know that the shadings he saw were features in the clouds that cover the entire planet, rather than surface markings. The clouds around Venus never exhibit any breaks that would allow astronomers to peek at the Venusian surface below. Consequently, it is not possible to determine

■■ TABLE 7.1 **Venus Data**

Orbital semimajor axis	0.72 AU (108.2 million km)
Perihelion distance	0.728 AU (108.9 million km)
Aphelion distance	0.718 AU (107.5 million km)
Eccentricity	0.007
Orbital period (sidereal)	224.7 days
Rotational period	243.0 days (retrograde)
Inclination	177°
Diameter	12,104 km (0.949 Earth diameters)
Mass	4.9×10^{24} kg (0.815 Earth masses)
Mean density	5.24 g/cm³
Escape velocity	10.4 km/s (23,270 MPH)
Surface temperature (mean)	+750 K (475°C = 890°F)
Maximum	+750 K (475°C)
Minimum	+750 K (475°C)

the rotation rate of the planet visually. Radar signals, however, can penetrate the Venusian clouds as easily as airport radar on Earth can penetrate the overcast on a cloudy day. Astronomers have used the 305 m (1000 ft) antenna at the Arecibo Observatory in Puerto Rico (Figure 7.1) to measure the rotational period of Venus by observing changes in the frequency of the reflected radar waves, as they did for Mercury. The rotational period of Venus is a slow 243.0 days—longer than its 224.7-day sidereal, or orbital, period! As in the last chapter, "days" refer to

■■ FIGURE 7.1

The Arecibo Radio Telescope

This is the largest telescope in the world, measuring 305 meters across a bowl-shaped valley in Puerto Rico.

SOURCE: National Astronomy and Ionosphere Center. The Arecibo Observatory is part of the National Astronomy and Ionosphere Center which is operated by Cornell University under contract with the National Science Foundation.

Earth days. Furthermore, this slow rotation is **retrograde;** that is, in the opposite direction of Venus' revolution around the Sun.

Although Venus rotates more slowly than Mercury, the Venusian solar day, 116.8 days, is shorter than Mercury's. This is a consequence of retrograde rotation. Imagine standing on Venus with the Sun directly overhead (position 1 in Figure 7.2). After revolving halfway around the Sun, position 3, Venus has not yet rotated halfway around on its axis. Since the Sun will be directly overhead again before Venus has rotated exactly halfway on its axis (position 5), noon occurs less than halfway through its rotation period, or less than 121.5 days after sunrise. Therefore a hypothetical Venusian would see the Sun (if it could be seen through the clouds!) rise in the *west* and set in the *east* 58.4 Earth days after it rose.

A brief inspection of Table 7.1 shows that both Earth and Venus have similar physical properties. For instance, the average density of Venus, 5.24 g/cm³, is nearly the same as the Earth's average density. Even taking the crushing mass of the overlying rock into account, the uncompressed density of Venus, 4.2 g/cm³, is just slightly less than the Earth's uncompressed density. Models of the interior of Venus are very similar to those of the Earth because of the similarities in diameter, mass, and average density. In fact, interior models are based more on the similarities with the Earth than on data about Venus. For instance, Venusian soil samples indicate that the crust has a density similar to the Earth's crust, about 3 g/cm³. Astronomers assume therefore that Venus is differentiated like the Earth and has an iron core. Because of the apparent similarity of the interiors of the Earth and Venus, astronomers expected to find signs of mountains, volcanoes, and lithospheric plates once space probes arrived at Venus.

Exploration of Venus

During the last two decades, the Soviet Union and the United States have sponsored over 20 spacecraft missions to Venus and have left just as many probes littering its surface (Table 7.2). The American *Mariner 2* spacecraft began the era of direct planetary exploration when it flew within 35,000 km of Venus in December 1962. Data from *Mariner 2* and from the subsequent *Mariner 5* and *Venera 4, 5,* and *6* missions suggested a hot, carbon dioxide–rich atmosphere with extremely high surface pressures. These surprisingly high pressures and temperatures of the Venusian atmosphere presented difficult engineering problems for spacecraft designers. What scientists did not know was that the atmospheric pressures were high enough to crush the sturdiest spacecraft. They discovered later that spacecraft also had to be cooled while descending through the atmosphere because the excessive temperatures caused malfunctions of key electronic components.

In December 1970, *Venera 7*, modified to withstand the most extreme surface conditions estimated from earlier missions, landed on the surface and successfully transmitted data—but for only 23 minutes! It measured an incredibly high surface temperature of 750 K (475°C = 890°F). *Venera 8* was even more successful; it transmitted from the sur-

Retrograde rotation: Planetary rotation in the opposite direction of the Earth's rotation; clockwise as viewed from the north celestial pole.

■ FIGURE 7.2

The Solar Day on Venus

Venus takes 112.35 days, half of its sidereal period, to move in its orbit from position 1 to position 3. At the same time, Venus has not yet rotated halfway around its polar axis; this takes 121.5 days (position 5). Noon (position 4) occurs 4.4 days after position 3.

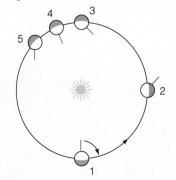

TABLE 7.2 Successful Spacecraft Missions to Venus

Spacecraft	Encounter Date	Type	Accomplishment
Mariner 2 (USA)	12-62	Flyby	Temperature measurements; no magnetic field detected.
Venera 4 (USSR)	10-67	Hard lander	Atmosphere mostly carbon dioxide (CO_2)
Mariner 5 (USA)	10-67	Flyby	Measured mass and size; structure of upper atmosphere.
Venera 5 (USSR)	5-69	Hard lander	Atmospheric temperature, pressure, and composition.
Venera 6 (USSR)	5-69	Hard lander	Atmospheric temperature, pressure, and composition.
Venera 7 (USSR)	12-70	Soft lander	1st spacecraft to land on another planet; surface pressure estimated at 90 times Earth's.
Venera 8 (USSR)	7-72	Soft lander	Low surface winds; soil analysis; "clear" below clouds.
Mariner 10 (USA)	2-74	Flyby	1st pictures of Venus from spacecraft; confirmed upper clouds' rotation of 4 days; went on to Mercury.
Venera 9 (USSR)	10-75	Orbiter/lander	1st photo of Venusian surface.
Venera 10 (USSR)	10-75	Orbiter/lander	One surface photo; high CO_2 abundance; radar maps.
Pioneer Venus 1 (USA)	12-78	Orbiter	Radar map of surface.
Pioneer Venus 2 (USA)	12-78	Hard landers	Four entry probes; lightning; atmospheric composition.
Venera 11 (USSR)	12-78	Soft lander	Measured temperature, pressures, and wind velocities.
Venera 12 (USSR)	12-78	Soft lander	Measured temperature, pressures, and wind velocities.
Venera 13 (USSR)	3-82	Soft lander	1st colored pictures; soil analysis.
Venera 14 (USSR)	3-82	Soft lander	Colored pictures; soil analysis.
Venera 15 (USSR)	10-83	Orbiter	High-resolution radar map of northern hemisphere.
Venera 16 (USSR)	10-83	Orbiter	High-resolution radar map of northern hemisphere.
Vega 1 (USSR)	6-85	Flyby/balloon	Atmospheric dynamics; went on to Halley's comet.
Vega 2 (USSR)	6-85	Flyby/balloon	Atmospheric dynamics; went on to Halley's comet.
Magellan (USA)	8-90	Orbiter	High-resolution radar map of Venus.

face for almost an hour and discovered that the clouds had a lower boundary between 35 and 50 km below which the sky appeared clear. Despite the clarity of the atmosphere beneath the clouds, light levels at the surface were similar to those on a very cloudy day on Earth. Furthermore, measured surface wind velocities were very low, just a few miles per hour. Subsequent missions confirmed the high temperatures and pressures, photographed the surface (Figure 7.3), and obtained data consistent with sulfuric acid being a principal constituent of the cloud particles. Sulfuric acid on Earth is partly responsible for the eye irritations associated with smog and, as a concentrated acid, is very corrosive.

In 1978 the Soviets and Americans sent seven spacecraft to Venus. The Pioneer Venus entry probes gathered data consistent with the existence of droplets of concentrated sulfuric acid in the clouds. The Pioneer Venus orbiter mapped the surface with radar, discovering two continent-sized surface features, volcanoes, mountains, and deep valleys. The Veneras and the Pioneer Venus entry probes detected a large number of radio pulses that were interpreted as powerful lightning discharges. These radio pulses originated either in the cloud layers in thunderstormlike activity or nearer the surface, perhaps associated with volcanism. Low-frequency noise bursts detected were interpreted as "thunder."

In 1982, *Venera 13* and *14* scooped up and analyzed the Venusian soil, finding it very similar to volcanic rock on Earth. In the following year, the *Venera 15* and *16* spacecraft began to map the Venusian surface with radar at latitudes north of 30°; they were able to resolve details on the surface as small as a few kilometers across. They found craterlike circular features, huge mountain ranges, and ridges. They also detected hot spots with temperatures greater than 975 K (700°C = 1300°F), perhaps indicating sites of active volcanism.

The most recent Soviet missions to Venus were *Vega 1* and *2* that dropped off two balloons and landers on their way to a rendezvous with Halley's Comet in 1986. The balloons floated in the middle of the Venusian cloud bank for 46 hours as they gathered data about horizontal and vertical wind speeds, temperature structure, and cloud properties. The balloons traveled over 4000 km in winds of more than 150 MPH. They clearly demonstrated that the atmosphere of Venus rotates in the retrograde sense, as does Venus itself, but much faster than the planet.

All told, the data gathered directly from all of the surface landers are equivalent to a 9-hour visit, and the data from probes and balloons are equivalent to about a 5-day balloon trip; astronomers also have many years of radar mappings from *Pioneer Venus*, *Vega 15* and *16*, and Arecibo. The *Magellan* spacecraft (launched in 1989) will add greatly to the radar data. *Magellan* will map about 90% of the surface of Venus, resolving features as small as 250 meters across. These radar images give scientists their best "view" of the Venusian surface.

Venusian Surface Features: Cratering and Tectonism

Radar images of Venus cover nearly the entire planet. The Pioneer Venus orbiter provided the most comprehensive radar map of Venus (Figure 7.4). Venus has two continent-sized landforms, several very deep basins, a small elliptically shaped region called Beta Regio, and several smaller elevated areas. (See Table 7.3 for the classical names used for planetary features.) Apart from these distinctive features, over 70% of the imaged surface can be described as *rolling plains* that lie within ± 1 km of the mean radius of Venus, 6052 km. By comparison, only 20% of the Earth's surface lies within ± 1 km of its mean radius while 80% is characterized by two distinct types of terrain: deep ocean basins and elevated continents. Similar elevation extremes on Venus represent only a small fraction of its surface area.

The extremely high surface temperatures of Venus ensure that the vast plains of Venus are drier than the driest Earth desert. The *Venera 13* and *14* close-up views of the Venusian plains near Beta Regio show a rocky desert with boulders, gravel, flat outcrops, and evidence of a regolith, or soil (Figure 7.5). Soil samples by the Veneras indicate that they landed on rocks with a chemical composition similar to the Earth's solidified lavas. Furthermore, the plains of Venus exhibit "radar-bright" regions that may be solidified lava flows. Radar-bright regions are rough, highly scattering surfaces that are good reflectors of radar waves and therefore look bright to radar because much of the emitted radar signal is returned. The rough surface is thought to result from flowing lava whose surface cools to a thin crust that breaks up as the flow

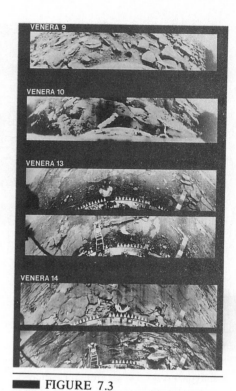

■ FIGURE 7.3

Venera 9, 10, 13, and *14* Views of Venus

SOURCE: NASA.

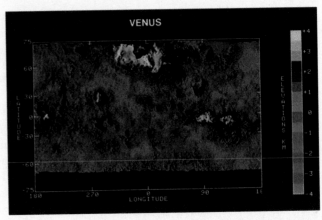

■ FIGURE 7.4

Color Contour Radar Maps of Earth and Venus

The heights indicated by the colors are shown in the columns on the right; white represents the highest terrain while blues and purples represent the lowest. These map projections exaggerate the surface areas of features at high latitudes. East is to the right and north is at the top.

SOURCE: NASA.

■ TABLE 7.3 Classical Names of Geological Features on Planets

Chasma: Very large linear chasm

Mons/montes: Mountain/mountain range

Planitia: Low plain

Rupes: Cliff

Tholus: Small domed hill

Labyrinthus: Network of linear depressions

Patera: Volcano with irregular edges

Planum: Large plateau

Terra: Landmass

Vallis/valles: Valley/valleys

moves on. The jagged pieces of solidified lava form a rough, reflecting surface. The main plain-forming material on Venus appears to be basaltic, or fast flowing, lava chemically similar to terrestrial basalts.

Radar images of the plains and basins from radio telescopes and satellites also show many well-defined circular features (Figure 7.6). Over 100 impact craters were found by *Venera 15* and *16*. Astronomers use the number of craters in the plains to determine their age as they did the plains and maria· on Mercury and the Moon. The estimates for the ages of the plains range from about 300 million years to a billion years; that is, they are younger than the lunar maria but older than the Earth's ocean floors. The plains also exhibit large circular features with diameters from 200 to 600 km called *coronas* (Panel b in Figure 7.6). Many appear to be surrounded by large areas of basaltic lava flows. Planetary scientists think that coronas lie above past volcanic hot spots, or *mantle plumes*, which are isolated columns of upwelling magma originating deep in the mantle. The magma below the coronas has pushed its way to the surface, deforming and fracturing the surface in the process. Cooling of the hot spot could have caused the crust over it to subside, forming collapsed circular basin-like features.

The highlands of Venus are characterized by two continent-sized land masses, Ishtar Terra and Aphrodite Terra, and by an apparent volcanic region called Beta Regio. Aphrodite Terra stretches for nearly 10,000 km along the equator of Venus and consists of two mountainous regions separated by a low area. The most geologically interesting features on Aphrodite are three deep chasms found in the middle of the continent, the deepest of which lies 2.9 km below the mean radius. Although this is only one-third as deep as the deepest trench on Earth, suggesting weak, if any, plate subduction on Venus, much of Aphrodite Terra exhibits numerous features that are similar to the boundaries of diverging, or separating, plates on Earth. Detailed radar imaging of Aphrodite shows features reminiscent of those found along the Mid-Atlantic Ridge. Indeed, Aphrodite Terra may be a region of present crustal spreading on Venus.

The highest points on Venus are three high peaks in Maxwell Montes, 11.5 km, 11.3 km, and 9.5 km above the mean radius; they are located on Ishtar Terra, the smaller of the two continent-sized landmasses. Ishtar is about as high as the Tibetan plateau on Earth and is the size of the continental United States. Although the mountains compare with Mt. Everest, which rises about 12 km above the Earth's mean radius (which is 2.5 km below sea level), the range of elevation from the lowest point to the highest on Venus is only 14 km; on Earth it is about 20 km. The larger range of elevation on Earth is due to the deep trenches found where plates collide; such trenches appear to be absent on Venus. Just to the east of Maxwell Montes, however, is a region of complex and hilly terrain. High-resolution Venera radar imaging of Ishtar Terra (Figure 7.7) shows that this complex region of folded mountains and ridges is reminiscent of the Himalayas and the Appalachians. Compressions of the crust formed both of these terrestrial mountain ranges. By analogy with the Earth, Ishtar appears to be the result of extensive horizontal movement of the Venusian surface, which has produced a complex region of troughs and ridges. To the west of Maxwell Montes on the flat plateau region of Ishtar Terra are two large craters or calderas that might be the source of the basaltic floods covering the continent.

Several lines of evidence suggest that Venus has *active* volcanoes. First is the variable sulfur dioxide content of the atmosphere. A combination of Earth-based observations and Pioneer Venus data indicates that the atmospheric sulfur dioxide content has decreased by a factor of 50 since 1978, probably through chemical reactions in the atmosphere. The temporary high sulfur dioxide content is attributed to violent volcanic eruptions before 1978. Secondly, all of the gases outgassed by Earth volcanoes have been detected in the Venusian atmosphere. Finally, electrical discharges measured by the Pioneer Venus probes as they descended through the atmosphere were concentrated over the suspected volcanoes on Beta Regio (Figure 7.8). The signals were very similar to those generated by lightning in terrestrial volcanic plumes.

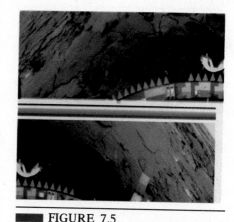

■■ FIGURE 7.5

Venera 14 **Color Pictures of the Surface of Venus**

SOURCE: Tass from Sovfoto.

■■ FIGURE 7.6

Venusian Craters and Coronas

(a) The largest impact crater discovered in the northern hemisphere is Klenova, 144 km across. *(b)* This corona is over 400 km in diameter and is thought to be a collapsed crustal feature.

SOURCE: NASA.

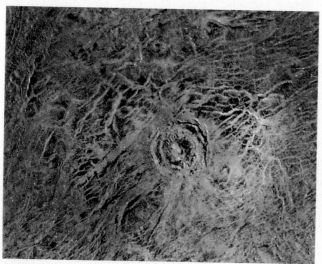

(a)

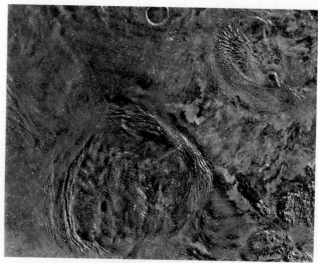

(b)

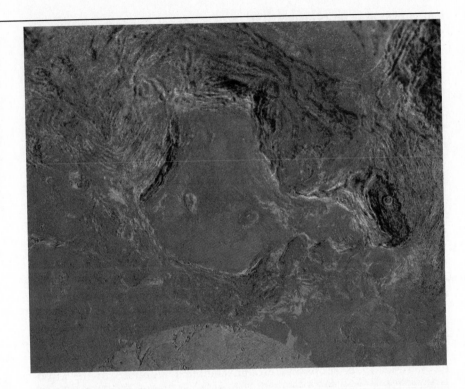

■ **FIGURE 7.7**

Ishtar Terra

High-resolution radar map of Ishtar Terra. North is at the top and east is to the right. The central plateau of Ishtar Terra is the large purple area in the center of the picture. Two large caldera sit atop the plateau. The large crater Cleopatra is seen just east of the high peaks of Maxwell Montes, the brown area on the eastern edge of the plateau.

SOURCE: Alfred S. McEwen, U.S. Geological Survey.

■ **FIGURE 7.8**

Arceibo Radar Image of Venus

This area of Venus shows evidence of extensive volcanic activity with few, if any, impact craters. Lava flows appear to surround the circular volcanic crater in the center of the picture.

SOURCE: D. B. Campbell, National Astronomy and Ionosphere Center. The Arecibo Observatory is part of the National Astronomy and Ionosphere Center which is operated by Cornell University under contract with the National Science Foundation.

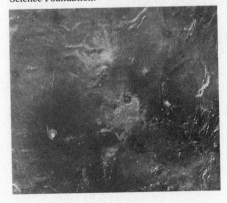

Radar images of Beta Regio show it to be a large dome-shaped area of possible volcanic origin; it is about 2100 km long and is associated with a major rift system. From early radar imaging of this region, astronomers have long described it as dominated by two large *shield* volcanoes, both about 5 km high and separated by a narrow saddle. Shield volcanoes arise from thousands of fluid lava flows forming large flattened domes, similar in shape to ancient war shields lying on the ground. The Hawaiian Islands are examples of terrestrial shield volcanoes. They are the tops of volcanic domes built up from the bottom of the ocean and are the result of mantle plumes. A long trough extends south of Beta Regio for several thousand kilometers toward two smaller highland areas; this suggests that Beta Regio may be a large crustal rift, or splitting, caused by a swelling of the crust above a hot spot.

These observations suggest that Venus evolved more like the Earth did rather than like Mercury or the Moon. Venus shows evidence of limited crustal movement similar to the Earth's plate tectonics. Crustal separation appears to have shaped Aphrodite Terra, and collisions appear to have built at least part of Ishtar Terra. Several large volcanoes on the surface are suspected of being active. The extent of crustal movement on Venus seems to be less than the Earth has experienced; for instance, deep trenches caused by subduction appear to be absent. In this respect Venus is characterized more by hot spot tectonics than by plate tectonics. Since most of the surface features associated with suspected hot spots are circular, they may resemble regions on the Earth like Africa, in which slow moving or stationary plates lie over hot spots. Moreover, Venus appears to have experienced extensive basaltic volcanism, which may be responsible for the surface of the smooth plains and even the large plateau on Ishtar Terra. Planetary geologists are uncertain why tectonism on Venus has apparently been subdued. The lithosphere could be too thick to respond to mantle convective currents or too thin to maintain individual plates for a long period of time. Perhaps the high surface temperatures and slow rotation somehow restrict plate tectonics. It is hard to imagine that the slight differences in radius, mass, and possibly chemical composition between the Earth and Venus might favor hot spot tectonics to plate tectonics.

The Atmosphere of Venus

Venus is encircled by a thick, choking, carbon dioxide–rich atmosphere and has the hottest planetary surface in the solar system. How can a planet that is physically very similar to the Earth and not much closer to the Sun be so different from the Earth? Why is Venus perpetually covered with clouds? Why is the surface hot enough to melt lead? The answers lie in the Venusian atmosphere.

Atmospheric Composition, Structure, and Evolution. The atmosphere of Venus is mainly carbon dioxide (96.5%) with a little nitrogen (3.5%). The adjective "little" describing the amount of nitrogen is misleading. The atmosphere of Venus is 90 times more massive than the Earth's, so that 3.5% actually corresponds to much more nitrogen than is in the Earth's atmosphere even with the Earth's high abundance of 78% nitrogen. Trace amounts of the inert gases as well as water vapor, various sulfur compounds, and exotic chemicals, such as hydrogen chloride and hydrogen fluoride, also are present (Figure 7.9). Because of the wide variety of chemicals in the Venusian atmosphere, the atmospheric chemistry is very complex. For instance, sulfuric acid in the clouds can react with hydrogen fluoride to form fluorosulfuric acid, one of the most corrosive substances known. It is no wonder that space probes have had such a difficult time surviving in the atmosphere of Venus.

The main cloud deck, composed of sulfuric acid droplets, sulfur particles, and other sulfur compounds, lies between 50 and 70 km with haze layers below and above. High atmospheric temperatures produce a lower boundary by evaporating sulfuric acid rain. As the droplets grow, they begin to fall out of the clouds like rain on the Earth, but soon encounter very high temperatures and evaporate long before reaching the ground. Clouds on Venus are more similar to mist or fog than to thick Earth clouds. But, because they are 20 km thick, Venusian clouds are nearly opaque to visible light. Complex chemical cycles within the cloud layers, between the clouds and the atmosphere, and between the atmosphere and the surface produce sulfuric acid, hydrogen chloride, and other compounds. The main source of the sulfur compounds, for instance, is probably volcanic eruptions.

Space probes descending through the Venusian atmosphere continuously measured temperatures and pressures. These data allow astrono-

■ FIGURE 7.9

Chemical Composition of the Venusian Atmosphere

Trace elements include water vapor, sulfur dioxide, carbon monoxide, hydrogen sulfide, hydrogen chloride, hydrogen fluoride, oxygen, and inert elements.

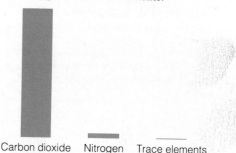

Carbon dioxide 96.5%   Nitrogen 3.5%   Trace elements < .01%

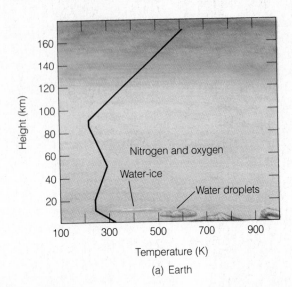

(a) Earth

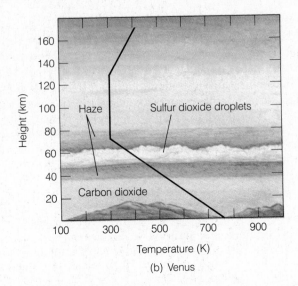

(b) Venus

FIGURE 7.10

Atmospheric Structures of the Earth and Venus

The main differences between the structures of the two atmospheres are the levels of clouds, temperature distribution with height, and the absolute values of temperatures and pressures.

mers to compare the atmospheric structures of Venus and the Earth (Figure 7.10). The most significant differences are the extremely high Venusian temperatures and pressures. Temperatures reach 750 K and pressures reach 1320 lb/in², or 90 times the Earth's sea level atmospheric pressure. Why is Venus so hot? Venus should have a surface temperature only 50 K greater than the Earth's because it is 30% closer to the Sun. Its atmosphere, of course, would warm Venus because of the greenhouse effect. On Earth the absorption of sunlight by the ground and atmosphere and the reradiating of infrared radiation warms the surface by about 40 K. On Venus, the carbon dioxide atmosphere, assisted by the sulfuric acid of its clouds as well as by sulfur dioxide and small amounts of water vapor, effectively traps the relatively small amount of solar energy (2.5%) that reaches the surface, raising temperatures hundreds of Kelvins (Figure 7.11).

Although the atmosphere of Venus now maintains extremely high temperatures via the greenhouse effect, how did Venus develop such an

FIGURE 7.11

Incident, Reflected, and Absorbed Solar Radiation

Only 25% of the incident solar radiation on Venus is not reflected back into space. Of this, 15% is absorbed by the clouds, 7.5% is absorbed by the atmosphere and haze above and below the clouds, and only 2.5% reaches the surface.

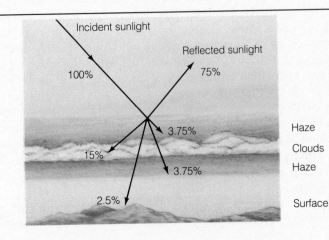

oppressive atmosphere? Scientists believe that the secondary atmosphere of the Earth resulted from volcanic eruptions. Because both planets probably had similar geological histories, Venus too probably generated a secondary atmosphere by volcanic outgassing. Because of the higher initial temperatures on Venus, its atmosphere could hold more water vapor than the Earth's atmosphere. As more and more water vapor was injected into the Venusian atmosphere through volcanism, the greenhouse effect caused temperatures to rise higher and higher. Each further increase in temperature allowed more water vapor to reside in the atmosphere. Eventually, temperatures became so high that the water vapor was never able to condense into liquid water. The atmospheric water vapor was dissociated in the upper atmosphere by sunlight, which is about twice as intense on Venus as on the Earth. Astronomers assume that it did not rain on Venus because they do not have any "visual" evidence of water flowing on the Venusian surface as they do for Mars, for example.

The apparent lack of oceans on Venus also encouraged a high atmospheric carbon dioxide content. On the Earth, for instance, oceans were responsible for removing the carbon dioxide from our secondary atmosphere. Water that evaporated from the oceans took carbon dioxide out of the atmosphere when it rained. Ultimately, the carbon dioxide, after dissolving in surface rock, ended up on the ocean floor as limestone. Today, of course, carbon dioxide is also removed by plants; it does not appear possible, however, that Venus has ever developed plant life. The lack of liquid water on Venus prevented carbon dioxide from being washed out of the atmosphere. Thus Venus is hot and its atmosphere is mainly carbon dioxide because of a "runaway" greenhouse effect.

Although the Earth's atmosphere is comfortable at present, the levels of carbon dioxide in the atmosphere are steadily increasing. Plants can absorb about half of any increase in atmospheric carbon dioxide, but the other half apparently just enters the atmosphere and tends to increase temperatures. As mentioned in AstroProbe 5, even small changes in carbon dioxide may significantly influence the Earth's climate. The study of the Venusian atmosphere has put scientists on guard for a similar, although perhaps not as extreme, occurrence of a runaway greenhouse effect on the Earth.

Atmospheric Dynamics. Little similarity exists between the atmospheres of Venus and the Earth. Their atmospheric structures and compositions are fundamentally different. Contrary to what a lot of people might expect, the very long rotational period of Venus does not produce a large difference between "daytime" and "nighttime" temperatures for two reasons. First, Venusian clouds reflect most of the sunlight striking the atmosphere and very little reaches the surface to influence the temperature. Second, the atmosphere of Venus is so thick and massive that it responds very slowly to changes in solar radiation even though the atmosphere has months to increase the temperature differences as the Sun beats down on the sunlit side of the planet. Venus is like an oven set to a temperature of 750 K. Nighttime on Venus does not bring any relief from the insufferable temperatures.

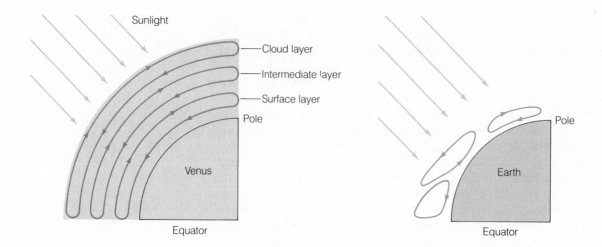

FIGURE 7.12

Meridian Circulation of Venus and the Earth

While the Earth's hemispheric wind flow divides into several cells, the Venusian winds may travel from the equator all the way to the poles in one large atmospheric cell. Spacecraft data are consistent with the upper two cells; the surface cell is inferred.

FIGURE 7.13

***Pioneer Venus* Ultraviolet Picture of Venus**

The large sideways "Y-shape" is a typical large-scale feature seen in ultraviolet images of the upper clouds of Venus.

SOURCE: NASA.

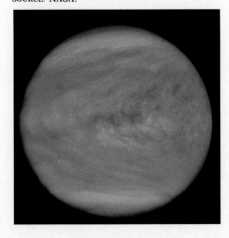

The slow rotation of Venus produces a very weak Coriolis effect compared to the Earth's. The Coriolis effect on Earth prevents a parcel of air, heated at the equator, from reaching the poles. The very weak Coriolis effect on Venus allows air from the equator to reach high latitudes, resulting in a simple equator-to-pole circulation (Figure 7.12). As on the Earth, the north-to-south circulation is the result of the imbalance between the excess solar radiation absorbed at the equatorial regions relative to the poles. This circulation is also distinctly different from the Earth's because the main atmospheric cell driven by solar radiation is high in the clouds where Venus absorbs most of the Sun's energy. Very little solar energy reaches the lower levels of the atmosphere.

The first observations of an east-to-west atmospheric rotation were Earth-based ultraviolet pictures of Venus. These pictures revealed large-scale features that look like the letter "Y" or "C" (Figure 7.13) and move around the planet approximately every 4 days. The tracking of small-scale features on *Mariner 10* and *Pioneer Venus* ultraviolet pictures confirmed the very rapid rotation of the upper atmosphere and upper clouds. The Venusian atmosphere rotates as a solid body at the cloud level with speeds of 220 MPH over the equator and zero over the poles. Wind speeds decrease with altitude, and winds move from east to west at all latitudes. Near the surface, wind speeds are only a few miles per hour.

The Venusian Magnetosphere. The magnetic field of Venus is at least 10,000 times weaker than the Earth's. Scientists expected that Venus would have a very weak magnetic field, if any, because its rotation is so slow. Consequently, the solar wind can impinge directly onto the upper atmosphere of Venus. Spacecraft, however, have detected a magnetospherelike environment around Venus. *Pioneer Venus* detected the presence of over a dozen ions, including oxygen, carbon dioxide, carbon monoxide, nitrogen, and helium ions, in the upper atmosphere of Venus. These atomic and molecular ions collide with the solar wind particles to form a turbulent region in which the solar wind particles slow down and are forced around the planet. Consequently, solar wind particles do not actually reach the surface of Venus as they do on Mercury and the Moon.

▬MARS

Whereas the observation of phases of Venus by Galileo cast serious doubts on the Ptolemaic world system, the detailed calculations of the orbit of Mars by Kepler destroyed the Greek system. The fascination with Mars became acute when observers realized that Mars is apparently very similar to the Earth; Mars has a day slightly longer than 24 hours, seasons, polar ice caps, clouds, and surface markings. Maps of Mars drawn in the late nineteenth century showed linear markings called "canals" that generated speculation that ancient civilizations were struggling to survive on a dying planet. As it turned out, the actual facts obtained by spacecraft about Mars were just as bizarre as the speculations (see Table 7.4 for basic data on Mars).

Exploration of Mars

Mars has a rich history in both Earth-based and spacecraft observations. Astronomers have been able to peer at the surface of Mars for more than three centuries and have watched Mars pass through nearly 200 cycles of spring, summer, fall, and winter. Nations have sent a dozen spacecraft to photograph Mars and sample its air and soil. In the future, humans may explore and live on Mars.

▬ TABLE 7.4 **Mars Data**

Orbital semimajor axis	1.52 AU (228 million km)
Perihelion distance	1.38 AU (207 million km)
Aphelion distance	1.67 AU (249 million km)
Eccentricity	0.093
Orbital period (sidereal)	1.88 years (687.0 days)
Rotational period	$24^h37^m23^s$
Inclination	25.2°
Diameter	6787 km (0.53 Earth diameters)
Mass	6.4×10^{23} kg (0.107 Earth masses)
Mean density	3.94 g/cm³
Escape velocity	5.0 km/s (11,190 MPH)
Surface Temperature (mean)	220 K (−53°C = −63°F)
Maximum	295 K (22°C = 72°F)
Minimum	190 K (−83°C = −117°F)

■■ **FIGURE 7.14**

Complete Circuit of Mars

These photographs of Mars were taken from the Earth during the 1971 opposition.

SOURCE: International Planetary Patrol Program photograph furnished by Lowell Observatory.

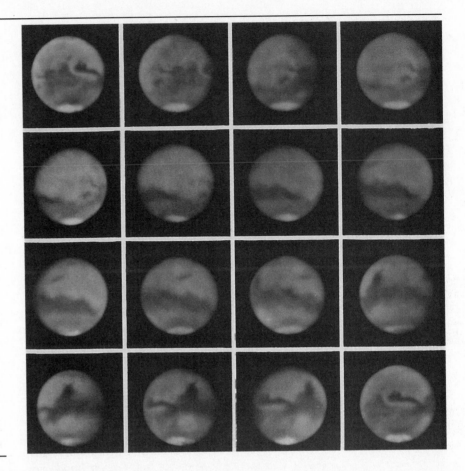

■■ **FIGURE 7.15**

The Orbits of Earth and Mars

The locations of Mars in its orbit for its southern hemisphere seasons. The bold lines connecting the two orbits represent the relative positions of the Earth and Mars at opposition, which occurs every 780 days. Favorable oppositions, such as in 1986 and 1988, occur every 15–17 years. At these times Mars can come as close as 55 million kilometers.

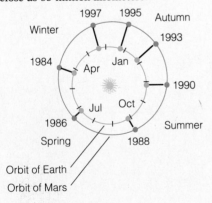

Earth-based Observations. The exploration of the surface of Mars began in 1609 when Galileo observed Mars through the recently invented telescope. Because Mars is not blanketed by a thick layer of clouds as Venus is, observers could readily identify surface markings on Mars (Figure 7.14) and could therefore measure the length of the Martian day. The rotational period of Mars is an Earth-like $24^h37^m23^s$; its solar day is 2 minutes and 13 seconds longer. Christian Huygens (1629–1695) in 1659 was the first astronomer to measure a Martian rotational period of 24 hours, and William Herschel (1738–1822) in the late eighteenth-century estimated a rotational rate for Mars just 14 seconds shorter than today's accepted value. These measurements can best be done when Mars is at opposition, when Earth and Mars are as close as their orbits allow (Figure 7.15).

Two very prominent features on Mars are the *polar caps*. Careful observation of the Martian surface over the centuries revealed changes in the brightness and color of surface markings that correlated with the annual growth and shrinkage of the Martian polar caps. The south polar cap shrinks more than the north polar cap because Mars is closer to the Sun at the time of the southern hemisphere summer. The caps recede very rapidly in late spring but retreat gradually in the summer. The rapid retreat of the polar caps indicates that the *seasonal* cap is a very thin layer of ice, probably of carbon dioxide ice on the surface. The *permanent* polar caps are thick layers of mainly water-ice that remain year round. These regular changes in the polar caps and in the brightness and color of other visible features on Mars clearly indicate that Mars has seasons. Mars experiences seasons similar to the Earth's because the rotational axis of Mars is tilted 25°.2 with respect to its orbital plane, nearly the same as the Earth's tilt. Since the Martian year, 687 days, is almost 2 Earth years, Martian seasons are almost twice as long as Earth's seasons.

The Englishman, William Dawes, published the first useful map of Mars in 1864, and the Italian astronomer Giovanni Schiaparelli (1835–1910) used a biblical and mythological nomenclature, still in use today, to identify different features on Mars (Figure 7.16). A remarkable aspect of these Earth-based maps of Mars is that their dark and light areas show almost no correlation with the topographical features discovered with spacecraft. Only an impact basin, part of a large canyon, and a low-elevation plains region appear to be associated with bright and dark areas on the old maps. Today astronomers believe that the dark areas are coarse surface material that is free of dust while the bright areas are covered with dust. Observed seasonal changes are probably caused by global winds redistributing the dust. In fact, dust storms, made up of fine dust particles lifted into the Martian air by the wind, are observed as yellow clouds.

White clouds were first reported in 1858 by the Italian astronomer Angelo Secchi (1818–1878). Often these are seen as stationary white spots just on the nighttime side of the terminator and are composed of carbon dioxide ice crystals. The largest clouds can persist for weeks and can be 2000 km across. The largest white cloud is the *polar hood* over the north pole. The polar hood covers the entire pole and about half of

■ **FIGURE 7.16**

Map of Mars

Classical names were used for features visible from the Earth. Some of these names, such as Hellas, Argyre, Chryse, and Tharsis, are used today to identify topographical features.

SOURCE: NASA

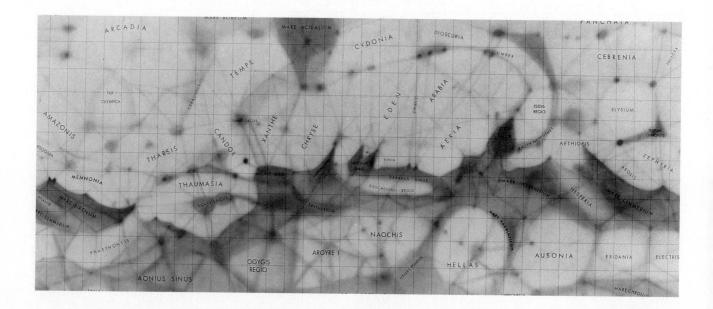

the northern hemisphere in winter. It prevents us from watching the northern polar cap grow in the fall, but the cloud dissipates in the summer.

The most widely proclaimed and debated features on Mars were the "canals." They were also the most quickly forgotten. Schiaparelli was the first to make an extensive map of these seemingly straight lines that he perceived as covering the surface of Mars like a spider's web (Figure 7.17). Later Schiaparelli called them by the Italian word "canali" meaning channels, but it was translated into English as "canals," implying constructed waterways. To some scientists and lay observers at the time, this suggested the existence of a civilization on Mars. Of course, not all astronomers agreed; many seasoned Mars observers never saw canals.

The idea of an ancient Martian civilization was popularized at the turn of the century by fiction writers and especially by the wealthy astronomer Percival Lowell (1855–1916). Lowell established an observatory in Flagstaff, Arizona, now called the Lowell Observatory, and dedicated his life to observing Mars and its canals. He wrote several popular accounts of research on Mars, *Mars, Mars and Its Canals*, and *Mars the Abode of Life*, that became best sellers. He believed that the Martian "canals" were waterways supplying the dry deserts with water from the polar caps. Even as late as the 1960s and 1970s, explanations of the envisioned linear markings were still being proposed. Some astronomers suggested that they could be giant rift valleys, similar to the Earth's mid-ocean ridges, or giant cliffs of hard rock that resist erosion, or even long chains of sand dunes, such as those found in Saudi Arabia. Spacecraft missions to Mars proved that the Martian canals do not exist as geological or "Martian-made" landforms. Martian canals were the result of the human mind trying to make sense out of what it sees. A series of dots, for instance, can be interpreted as a straight line depend-

■■ FIGURE 7.17

Map of Martian "Canals" by Percival Lowell

SOURCE: Lowell Observatory photograph.

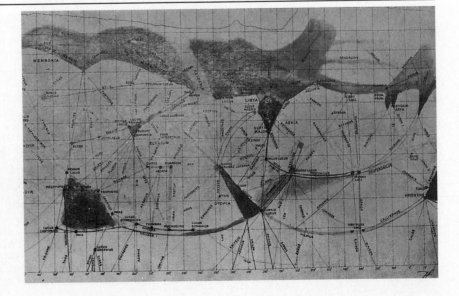

ing on the observer's vision, the quality of the telescope, and the state of the Earth's atmosphere. Unmanned spacecraft sent to Mars revealed the real surface of Mars.

Spacecraft Observations. The first successful missions to Mars were accomplished by *Mariner 4, 6,* and *7,* which took nearly 220 pictures of Mars (Table 7.5). Although the photographs were very indistinct, they showed a cratered terrain similar to the Moon's. Astronomers prematurely concluded that Mars did not have Earth-like landforms and that the dominant terrain was a cratered surface. *Mariner 9,* however, revealed a planet that was hardly Moon-like.

Mariner 9 entered an orbit around Mars in November 1971 and, at first, saw very little. Almost two months before *Mariner 9* reached Mars, a dust storm began to spread over the whole planet, leaving only four dark spots visible. Two Soviet spacecraft, *Mars 2* and *3,* also arrived at Mars during the 1971 global dust storm, but the science sequence programmed into the Soviet spacecraft could not be altered; they were only able to take photographs of a dust-laden Mars. As the dust settled, *Mariner 9* could see more and more of the four dark spots. All four turned out to be very large volcanoes; one, Olympus Mons, is the largest known volcano in the solar system. *Mariner 9* also discovered an immense canyon and a vast network of dry riverbeds. Mars was unlike anything astronomers or writers had imagined.

The last American spacecraft to Mars, the Vikings, arrived at Mars in the summer of 1976. They were combined orbiters and landers. The orbiter pictures revealed spectacular details beyond the resolving power of the Mariner cameras, and the landers gave us the first close-up photographs of the Martian surface and of the Sun setting on another world (Figure 7.18). In light of the historical debate about life on Mars, it is not surprising that the Viking landers carried experiments designed to detect the presence of life. Five experiments were carried out: one was

■■■ TABLE 7.5 **Spacecraft Missions to Mars**

Spacecraft	Encounter Date	Type	Accomplishment
Mariner 4 (USA)	7-65	Flyby	Atmospheric structure; 22 pictures; lots of craters.
Mariner 6 (USA)	7-69	Flyby	74 photos; high carbon dioxide content.
Mariner 7 (USA)	8-69	Flyby	Another 125 photos.
Mariner 9 (USA)	11-71	Orbiter	7,329 photos of surface and moons.
Mars 2 (USSR)	11-71	Orbiter/lander	1st soft landing on Mars.
Mars 3 (USSR)	12-71	Orbiter/lander	Successful soft landing; orbiter photos.
Mars 4 (USSR)	2-74	Flyby	A few pictures.
Mars 5 (USSR)	2-74	Orbiter	20 pictures; functioned for 20 orbits.
Mars 6 (USSR)	3-74	Lander	Soft landing; returned data obtained during descent.
Mars 7 (USSR)	3-74	Lander	Missed planet.
Viking 1 (USA)	6-76	Orbiter/lander	Surface and orbiter photos; volcanoes, past fluid flow.
Viking 2 (USA)	9-76	Orbiter/lander	Same as *Viking 1*; both had biological experiments.
Phobos 2 (USSR)	1-89	Orbiter/lander	Photos of Mars and Phobos; radio contact lost before mission completed.

designed to identify a wide range of compounds, one was designed to photograph life-forms as small as a few millimeters, and three were to look for metabolic activity of Martian life-forms. These experiments, however, failed to produce conclusive evidence for or against life on Mars. No tiny (or large!) Martians were photographed, nor were any organic compounds detected. Although biologists can probably rule out Earth-like life-forms, they cannot rule out the possibility of an alien life-form adapted to the characteristics of the Martian environment.

Martian Surface Features

Astronomers have discovered more variety in surface landforms on Mars than on any other planet besides the Earth. Mars has a cratered terrain similar to the lunar highlands, smooth plains and basins, new crater types, volcanoes, canyons and valleys, channels, and ice-covered polar caps. Overall, Mars shows a general north-south topographical asymmetry: *heavily cratered terrain* dominates the Martian southern hemisphere while relatively smooth *volcanic plains* dominate the northern hemisphere. In most places, the boundary between the heavily cratered terrain and the volcanic plains is a cliff about 1 to 2 km high.

The density of craters in the northern volcanic plains ranges from two to three times that of the lunar maria to smooth, craterless plains; the density of craters in much of the southern hemisphere, however, is comparable to that in the lunar highlands. Astronomers assume that Mars experienced a period of intense meteoritic bombardment some 4.6–4 billion years ago, as did the Moon and probably all of the planets in the solar system. Although astronomers do not have Martian rock samples from which to obtain radiometric ages, they assign ages to the Martian surface by using an adjusted crater density versus age relation (Figure 7.19). An adjustment is required because Mars is closer to the asteroid belt (see Chapter 10) and therefore probably experienced more meteoritic impacts than the Moon. The smooth volcanic plains are some of

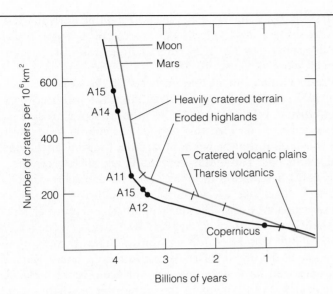

FIGURE 7.19

Crater Density versus Age for Lunar and Martian Surfaces

The cratering rate for Mars was higher than for the Moon; consequently, for surfaces of the same age, the Martian surface shows a greater number of craters. (A11 indicates rocks collected by the *Apollo 11* mission and so forth.)

the youngest surfaces on Mars, perhaps as young as several hundred million years old; the southern cratered terrain is more ancient, dating back 4 billion years.

Although the northern plains are about 3–5 km lower in elevation than the southern cratered terrain, the Tharsis and Elysium regions in the north are elevated areas (Figure 7.20). In fact, if Mars had oceans, the northern hemisphere would be covered with water, except for the Tharsis and Elysium uplifts, and the southern hemisphere would be a vast continent, larger than any on Earth. The Tharsis Rise or uplift, is a huge bulge 10 km high and 5000–6000 km across and is about 2 billion years old. The Elysium Rise is 4 km high and 1500 km in diameter and is about a billion years older than the Tharsis Rise.

Craters. The heavily cratered terrain exhibits two distinct types of craters: large degraded craters and small fresh craters. Craters with diameters greater than 20 km are generally very eroded, and some are barely visible as shallow circular depressions. Their floors are flat and

FIGURE 7.20

Color Contour Maps of Earth and Mars

White represents the highest landforms and purple the lowest. Notice the high Tharsis rise with several volcanic peaks (left) and the deep, circular Hellas basin. Landmarks, such as craters, valleys, volcanoes, and basins, are named after villages on Earth, scientists (mostly astronomers), rivers, and the word for Mars in different languages.

SOURCE: NASA.

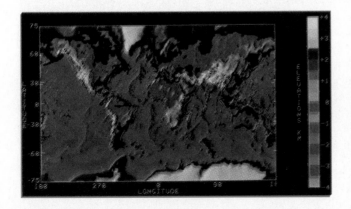

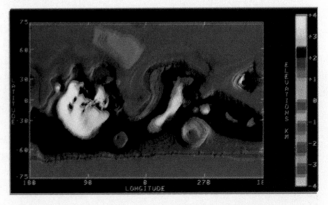

featureless and are lower than the surrounding terrain. The rims of these large craters are level with the surrounding terrain. The smaller craters are fresh looking. They have distinct raised rims and internal detail such as terraced walls. The large craters represent a very early era of crater bombardment that occurred at the same time as a period of extensive crater erosion, or obliteration. Crater obliteration was due to water erosion, volcanic activity, and the cratering process itself. Only the largest craters survived this period. The smaller craters seen today formed after the initial heavy bombardment and after the obliteration of craters subsided. Large Martian craters are ancient craters.

The general description of lunar impact craters also applies to Martian craters. Mars has everything from small bowl-shaped craters to very large impact basins. The most distinctive feature of Martian craters is their ejecta pattern. Lunar and Mercurian ejecta are characterized by ballistic features resulting from material thrown up and away from the site of the impact. The ejecta around the small Martian craters are characterized by *flows* across the surface (Figure 7.21). This "fluidized" ejecta pattern is evident for craters larger than about 5 km in diameter and is indicative of water or water-ice in the crust of Mars. The lower limit of 5 km may indicate that liquid water is about 1 km deep; that is, a permafrost of water-ice may exist down to a depth of about 1 km, below which it is warm enough for liquid water to exist. Only the larger meteorites crash into the surface with enough force to reach the liquid water level. The impacts must have liberated *liquid* water because, if the water came just from ice, the ice in the upper layers would vaporize on impact, and the surrounding ice would not necessarily melt, leaving only a relatively small amount of water to impart fluid properties to the ejecta.

■ FIGURE 7.21

Fluidized Ejecta Pattern of Martian Craters

(a) These ejecta patterns surround the craters with steep outward-facing cliffs. The smallest craters do not show the fluidized ejectra pattern. The largest crater in this photograph is about 15 km across. *(b)* Crater Yuty, 18 km (11 mi) in diameter, has a central peak and obvious fluid-like flows.

SOURCE: NASA.

(a)

(b)

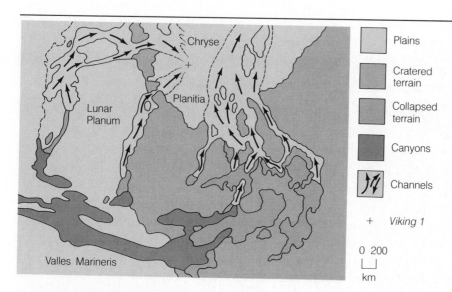

Plains

Cratered
terrain

Collapsed
terrain

Canyons

Channels

+   Viking 1

0 200

km

■ FIGURE 7.22

**Map of Canyons and Outflow
Channels around Chryse Basin**

Sublimation: The process by which a
solid (an ice, for example), when
heated, becomes a gas without passing
through the liquid phase. Dry ice (frozen carbon dioxide) is an ice that sublimes at Earth's temperatures and pressures. Water ice sublimes under the
low temperature and pressure environment of Mars today.

■ FIGURE 7.23

**Martian Landslides in Ganges
Chasma in the Valles Marineris**

The aprons of debris on the canyon floor
are the result of flows caused by the collapse of the canyon walls. The multiple
layers show that the wall collapsed at intervals. The partly transected crater on
the far rim is 16 km across.

SOURCE: NASA.

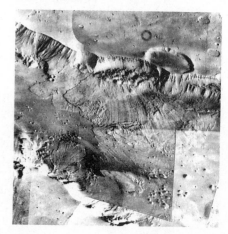

Canyons and Channels. On the eastern slope of the Tharsis Rise is
a system of interconnected canyons 4000 km long called the Valles Marineris, or the Valleys of Mariner (Figure 7.22). It starts as a network of
linear depressions, called Noctis Labyrinthus, at the top of the Tharsis
Rise and then drops through a half dozen very large canyons with cliffs
7 km high. The elevations continue to drop toward the east and, at the
eastern edge of the canyon, Mariner Valley merges with a series of
channels. These in turn flow down slope into the large basin Chryse
Planitia whose center lies 14 km below the crest of the Tharsis Rise.
The individual canyons can be 200 km across, and three parallel canyons in the central portion of the Valles Marineris are more than 700
km in width. The Grand Canyon, by comparison, is one-tenth as long
and one-third as deep as the Valles Marineris.

The floors of the canyons are generally flat, and landslide debris covers areas where the walls of the canyons have collapsed (Figure 7.23).
Landslides are probably caused by melting and **sublimation** of ground
ice and by groundwater seepage. The removal of ice or water will leave
behind a loose material easily subject to sliding if triggered by a physical event such as a crater impact, "marsquake," or even wind under-
cutting the canyon walls.

To the north of the canyons, numerous *outflow channels* several
hundred kilometers long and tens of kilometers across can be mapped
(Figure 7.22). Geologists distinguish channels from canyons in that
channels show clear evidence of fluid flow. Unlike Earth channels, the
Martian channels start abruptly without tributaries. The appearance of
the "headwaters" of these channels gives the impression that the surface collapsed as fluid flowed away (Panel a in Figure 7.24). The magnitude of the outpouring of water, as evidenced by teardrop-shaped islands and deeply scoured surfaces, suggests catastrophic flooding (Panel
b). Glacial and wind erosion are also suspected of contributing to the
formation of the large outflow channels. The channels generally flow

(a)

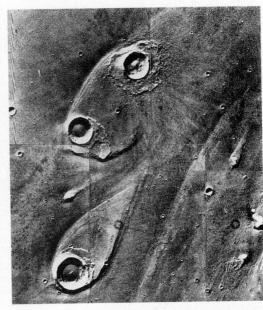

(b)

■■■ FIGURE 7.24

Martian Channels

(a) The channel with a diameter of 20 km starts abruptly from a depression 40 km across. Inside the depression is *chaotic terrain* indicative of surface collapse.
(b) Several teardrop-shaped islands are visible. The catastrophic water flow produced the long tails pointing downstream.

SOURCE: NASA.

north into Chryse Planitia. Smaller channels that also start abruptly are found near the Elysium Rise.

Numerous small branching channels are found exclusively in the heavily cratered terrain of the southern hemisphere. These appear to have been carved out of the landscape by rapidly flowing water, as gullies are on Earth. The southern branching channels exhibit all levels of degradation indicating extensive fluid flow during the initial meteoritic bombardment as well as after the bombardment declined.

Volcanism. Martian volcanoes resemble shield volcanoes on Earth, such as those comprising the Hawaiian Islands, but are many times larger. For instance, the three Tharsis volcanoes, Arsia, Pavonis, and Ascraeus Mons, sit on the 10 km high southeast flank of the Tharsis Rise and reach heights of 24–27 km. Olympus Mons itself reaches 27 km but starts from the 3 km level of the Tharsis Rise. Olympus Mons is by far the largest known volcano in the solar system. Its base is a steep cliff with a diameter of 550–600 km, and its volcanic crater, or **caldera,** is nearly 80 km across at the top (Figure 7.25). Several features indicate that the Tharsis Rise is actually an uplifting of the surface of Mars. The canyons of the Valles Marineris suggest the splitting of the surface expected from an uplift. Secondly, the immense Tharsis shield volcanoes are located on the rise. These volcanoes must have been located above deep mantle plumes that supplied their magma. Finally, the Tharsis volcanoes are consistent with an enormous volume of lava. Olympus Mons, for instance, is greater in volume than all of the Hawaiian Islands combined.

The large domes, such as the Tharsis and Elysium Rises, are a consequence of a *lack* of plate motion, which allowed lava flows caused by

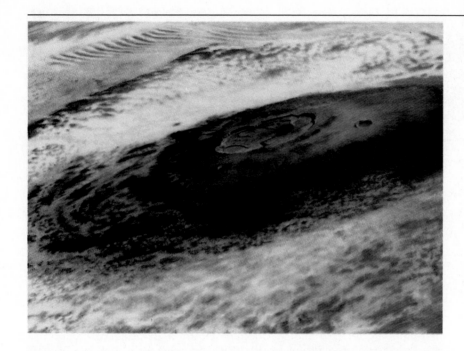

■■■■■ FIGURE 7.25
**View of the Summit and
Volcanic Crater of Olympus Mons**
Clouds form as wind carries air to high
elevations. The complicated caldera indi-
cates a varied history of eruptions.
SOURCE: NASA.

hot spots to concentrate in one area over a long period of time. Geologists find no evidence of plate subduction or separation on Mars, such
as long, linear "ocean" trenches or "mid-ocean" ridges. Nor does Mars
have mountain chains that indicate plate collisions. Furthermore, the
lower surface gravity of Mars allows its surface to support larger structures, such as the huge Tharsis volcanoes. Consequently, the range in
elevation on Mars is ~30 km, much greater than on Venus or the Earth.

The Nature of the Martian Surface: The Viking Landers. The
Viking 1 lander landed in Chryse Planitia, a young basin, and the *Viking
2* lander landed in Utopia Planitia, a northern hemisphere plains region
(Figure 7.26). The topography of the *Viking 1* landing site can be char-
acterized as rolling plains whereas the *Viking 2* landing site is flatter.
Rock sizes at the sites ranged from a few centimeters to several meters.
Most of the rocks are angular and pitted, similar to lavas in which gases
have escaped while the lava cooled. Much fine-grained material is
spread over the surface and has probably been deposited by the wind.
Obvious drifts and wind tails are seen. The yellowish brown color of the
Martian surface appears to be due to an iron-rich clay in which an iron
oxide, called limonite, stains everything yellow-brown.

The Viking landers observed several temporal changes during their
operational lifetime on the Martian surface. Major dust storms caused
changes in the nearby drifts. Close inspection of the drifts reveals layering and indicates that the drifts are stable and that they are being
eroded away by the wind. During the winter a white frost covered the
ground at the landing sites. Both landers analyzed surface materials,
found very similar compositions, and sampled debris that probably had

(a)

(b)

■■■ FIGURE 7.26

Views of the Martian Landscape from the Viking Landers

(a) Viking 1 lander view of Chryse Planitia. The landscape shows many small rocks and is dominated by sand drifts. *(b) Viking 2* lander view of a frost-covered Utopia Planitia.

SOURCE: NASA.

been distributed around the planet by the global dust storms. Compared with the Earth and Venus, Mars appears to have an iron-rich chemistry with much magnesium and sulfur but little aluminum and potassium. When some of the samples were heated, water evaporated in amounts ranging from a few tenths of a percent to several percent. Water is very probably stored in near-surface rock or regolith.

The Geological History of Mars. Mars probably experienced a very heavy meteoritic bombardment during the last 500 million years of planetary formation (see Chapter 11 for a detailed description of planetary formation). During this time, the surface became completely covered with craters of all sizes, and Mars developed an atmosphere from volcanic outgassing (Table 7.6). The atmosphere was dense enough at first to support liquid water on the surface. The evidence for this is the branching channels seen in the heavily cratered highlands in the south. This thick atmosphere together with water and volcanism eroded most of the cratered surfaces, destroying the small craters and leaving the largest craters in a degraded condition. Smaller craters now visible on the surface were produced near the end of the bombardment. Apparently, at this time, the efficiency of the erosional processes was greatly reduced. Mars also differentiated at this time, forming a small iron-rich core. The differentiation of Mars is supported by the difference between its surface density, about 3 g/cm^3, and its average density of 3.9 g/cm^3.

During the next billion years, much of the northern hemisphere was resurfaced by extensive lava floods. The outflow channels flowing into Chryse Planitia formed at this time, probably due to subsurface melting of ice induced by the extensive volcanic activity that flooded the plains. Following the widespread volcanism in the northern hemisphere, two great uplifted regions formed, first the Elysium Rise and then the giant Tharsis Rise. The formation of the Tharsis uplift split the surface of Mars and produced the giant Valles Marineris. Near the end of this period, the large Tharsis volcanoes formed, rising higher and higher with each layer of lava. These volcanoes appear to have been active over the last 2–3 billion years and may be dormant now. The floors of the calderas of the Tharsis volcanoes are less cratered than their flanks while the volcanoes themselves are less cratered than other regions of the Tharsis Rise. From the number of craters, the Tharsis Rise appears to be several billion years old while the larger volcanoes may be less than 100 million years old.

■ TABLE 7.6 **Geological History of Mars**

1. Heavy meteoritic bombardment
  Large craters formed
  Smaller craters formed near end of
   bombardment
 Mars differentiated, forming a small iron-rich
  core
 Secondary atmosphere outgassed
	4.6–4 billion years ago

2. Northern hemisphere covered by lava floods
  Outflow channels produced by catastrophic
   flooding
	4–3 billion years ago

3. Tharsis and Elysium uplifts form
  Valles Marineris forms
  Great Tharsis volcanoes form
	3–2 billion years ago

4. Tharsis volcanoes extinct (or dormant?)	2–0 billion years ago

Astronomers suspect that the core of Mars is small and even solid because it has a negligible magnetic field even though it rotates nearly as fast as the Earth. The actual size of the core is uncertain because only one of the Viking seismographs operated, and it only detected a couple of "marsquakes" over a period of several years. The lack of seismic activity and plate tectonics suggests that the lithosphere of Mars is very thick and that the core and lower mantle may be solid.

During the first billion years of the geological history of Mars, liquid water flowed over its surface. The disappearance of water is intimately tied to the evolution of the atmosphere.

The Atmosphere of Mars

The Martian atmosphere differs from the Earth's atmosphere in two important respects: its composition is mainly carbon dioxide, and its surface temperatures and pressures are much lower than the Earth's. The chemical composition of the Martian atmosphere is similar to that of Venus (Figure 7.27). Unlike Venus, however, the average surface pressure on Mars is 150 times *less* than the Earth's average surface pressure. Because the Martian atmosphere is so thin, atmospheric warming caused by the greenhouse effect is very small, even though the Martian air is mainly carbon dioxide. Recall that the greenhouse effect warms the Earth's surface by about 40°C compared to what it would be without an atmosphere. The greenhouse effect on Mars causes only a modest 3°C warming. In addition, the combination of a thin atmosphere and its great distance from the Sun results in a frigid global mean surface temperature of 220 K (−53°C = −63°F) for Mars. The lowest temperature on Mars is 190 K at the south pole during winter; the warmest it gets on Mars is a comfortable 295 K (72°F) in the summer hemisphere. Finally, because the upper atmosphere of Mars lacks significant amounts of ultraviolet-absorbing molecules such as ozone, the temperature structure of the Martian atmosphere is very simple (Figure 7.28).

■ FIGURE 7.27

Martian Atmospheric Composition

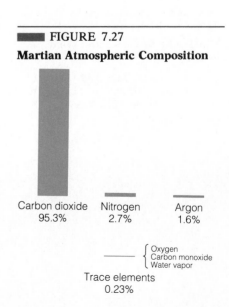

Carbon dioxide 95.3% Nitrogen 2.7% Argon 1.6%

{ Oxygen
Carbon monoxide
Water vapor

Trace elements 0.23%

■ FIGURE 7.28

Atmospheric Structure of Mars

Mars has carbon dioxide–ice clouds, water-ice clouds, and dust clouds. The lack
of significant amounts of ozone and other
ultraviolet-absorbing molecules in the
Martian atmosphere ensures a simple
temperature stratification. Temperature
structure of Earth's atmosphere is shown
for comparison (see also Figure 7.10).

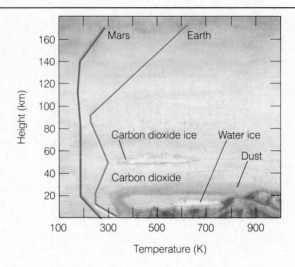

Global Circulation. Evidence of a dynamic Martian atmosphere includes the global dust storms, passing storm fronts at the Viking landing sites, existence of active sand dunes, and light and dark streaks extending from craters (Figure 7.29). The light and dark streaks extend
downwind of craters and other elevated landforms. When air flows
around a crater, for instance, the flow is broken up into two components, one on each side of the crater rim. These flows eventually converge downwind of the crater where the dust is deposited. Since the
directions of the streaks are an indication of the direction of surface
winds, astronomers use the global pattern of streaks as "wind socks" to
map wind directions.

■ FIGURE 7.29

**Martian Sand Dunes and Wind
Streaks**

(a) A "transverse" dune field 130 by 65
km long having ridges 1 to 2 km apart.
(b) Dark streaks in a crater field.
SOURCE: NASA.

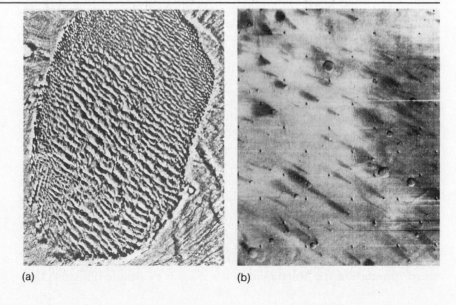

(a)

(b)

The global circulation of Mars is more similar to the Earth's than to that of Venus. Since Mars rotates at about the same rate as the Earth, planetwide circulation is influenced by Coriolis forces, giving east-west winds and cyclonic storms. The Martian circulation pattern is also influenced by topographical features, such as the large uplifts and volcanoes, that can divert wind flow over a large region of a hemisphere. The circulation pattern of Mars has two unique features. One is caused by the extremely cold polar temperatures and the other by large temperature differences between the dayside and nightside of Mars. Winter temperatures become so cold at the poles that carbon dioxide freezes out of the atmosphere, blanketing the winter hemisphere in dry ice and causing a 20% decrease in the atmospheric pressure. This creates a seasonal flow of air from pole to pole, or from high pressure to low pressure, as one pole thaws and the other freezes. The second unique circulation feature is strong winds blowing across the Martian terminator. Because the Martian atmosphere is so thin, it does not have the capacity to store heat. For instance, the Viking landers measured large daily temperature changes of 60 K. The thin Martian atmosphere permits rapid cooling at night and quick heating in the daytime. Recall for comparison that the thick Venusian atmosphere had the opposite effect; it maintained an almost constant surface temperature. On Mars, the very rapid cooling of the air after sunset causes large temperature differences between the day and night hemispheres; this produces strong winds that tend to blow from the cold nightside to the warm dayside.

Finally, planetwide dust storms can completely disrupt global wind patterns. Major dust storms begin in the southern hemisphere during its summer when Mars is near perihelion and receives the greatest amount of solar energy on its surface. This produces larger than usual temperature differences between dayside and nightside and, therefore, generates very strong surface winds that can lift significant amounts of dust to heights of 30 to 40 km. The largest dust storms can cover the entire planet in about three weeks (Figure 7.30). Mars then stays covered with opaque dust for two to three months, after which the dust gradually subsides and the air clears.

FIGURE 7.30

A Martian Dust Storm

A small dust storm in the Solio Planum region in the southern hemisphere. This small storm occurred between two global storms observed in 1977.

SOURCE: NASA.

Water. One of the most fascinating mysteries of Mars is the present lack of visible water, despite the overwhelming evidence for water on Mars from outflow channels, branching drainage systems, fluidized crater ejecta, and frozen polar caps. Furthermore, the wide distribution of Martian channels throughout the heavily cratered terrain implies that the water flow was widespread and that the sources of water were dispersed. Where is the Martian water today? This is especially puzzling since astronomers believe that the secondary, or outgassed, atmosphere of Mars was fundamentally similar to that of the Earth and Venus.

The release of water vapor, carbon dioxide, sulfur, and nitrogen by volcanic outgassing produced the secondary atmospheres of the Earth and Venus. The Venusian atmosphere evolved under the influence of a runaway greenhouse effect while the Earth's atmosphere evolved through a complex interaction between air, oceans, land, and plant life.

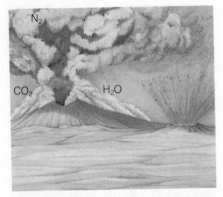

(a) Secondary atmosphere

(b) Thick atmosphere and rains

(c) Cold and dry

■■■ **FIGURE 7.31**

Atmospheric Evolution on Mars

(a) Secondary atmosphere of water, carbon dioxide, and nitrogen. *(b)* Rains and reduction of carbon dioxide in the atmosphere; nitrogen is lost to space. *(c)* Reduced temperatures and pressures prohibit liquid water on the surface.

Astronomers estimate that the secondary atmosphere of Mars was thick enough to have produced an atmospheric pressure at its surface about twice the Earth's present surface pressure. Calculations indicate that the amount of water outgassed on Mars was too much for the atmosphere to hold, allowing it to rain. How long did it rain on Mars?

High pressures and temperatures above the freezing point of water are necessary for water to exist in a liquid state. If the atmospheric pressure above liquid water is too low, the individual molecules of water easily escape from the liquid. For instance, water boils at a temperature of 100°C at sea level but where atmospheric pressure is lower, as on high mountains, water boils when it is just warm to the touch. At low enough atmospheric pressure, therefore, water can just boil or evaporate away. The atmospheric pressure on Mars is currently so low that the boiling point of water is 0°C—the same as its freezing point. Consequently, water on Mars behaves as dry ice (frozen carbon dioxide) does on Earth; it sublimes, passing from an ice to a gas without entering a liquid phase. Today, no liquid water can exist on the surface of Mars.

What about in the past? Astronomers believe Mars experienced high temperatures during its early history because meteorite impacts and heat from internal radioactive elements warm the surfaces of new planets. The Martian outgassed atmosphere was much thicker than today's atmosphere. The thicker atmosphere would have contributed to the surface heat via the greenhouse effect as it did on the Earth and Venus (Figure 7.31). Under these conditions, rains on Mars produced the branching drainage systems seen in the old, heavily cratered terrain. At the same time, the presence of liquid water and rain on Mars reduced the amount of atmospheric carbon dioxide by washing it out of the atmosphere; this would reduce the atmospheric pressure and the effectiveness of the greenhouse mechanism. If the carbon dioxide was not replaced by more outgassing, atmospheric pressures and temperatures would decrease until liquid water could not exist on the surface.

Astronomers believe this happened because significant crater obliteration appears to have stopped near the end of the meteoritic bombardment, about 4 billion years ago. Since volcanic activity, induced by meteoritic impacts, releases gases in primitive atmospheres, carbon dioxide would not be replenished unless volcanism continued on a large scale or if plate tectonics occurred. On the Earth, for instance, carbon dioxide is continuously recycled when the carbon dioxide–rich carbonate rock is driven into the mantle where plates collide. Here the rock is heated to temperatures high enough to liberate the carbon dioxide, which subsequently escapes through volcanic eruptions. Mars, however, shows no signs of plate tectonics and no evidence of large-scale *ancient* volcanism needed to replace the carbon dioxide. The large volcanoes seen today on Mars all formed after the decline in the meteoritic bombardment.

Atmospheric temperatures and pressures probably decreased on Mars during the first 1–2 billion years of its history, evaporating all liquid water on the surface. The evaporated water eventually condensed out of the atmosphere to reside in the polar caps as ice, and any subsurface water froze to depths of about 1 km. The time scale for these events is still uncertain; it is not known whether the Martian atmosphere was thick and warm for a billion years or for hundreds of millions of years.

The Moons of Mars

The American astronomer Asaph Hall (1829–1907) discovered the moons of Mars, Phobos ("Fear") and Deimos ("Dread") during the close opposition of 1877 (Figure 7.32). He named them after the attendants of the god Mars in Homer's *Iliad.* It is interesting to note that Jonathan Swift in *Gulliver's Travels* (1720) referred to the two moons of Mars over 150 years before they were discovered. Swift did not have any mystic powers of prediction; as early as 1610, Johannes Kepler suggested that Mars had two moons. Kepler was intrigued with geometric progressions and since Venus did not have any moons, Earth had one moon, and Jupiter showed four moons, Kepler thought that Mars must have two moons. Swift was probably aware of Kepler's speculation because he quoted Kepler's third law of planetary motion in *Gulliver's Travels.*

The moons of Mars are mere pebbles compared to the Earth's Moon. The average diameter of Phobos is 21 km and that of Deimos is 13 km; both are very irregular in shape (Table 7.7). As seen from Mars, Phobos is about one-third the size of the Moon as seen from the Earth. Phobos has an orbital radius that brings it as close as 6000 km above Mars. Consequently, Phobos cannot be seen from high latitudes at the surface of Mars. The angular diameter of Deimos is about one-sixth that of Phobos, and Deimos would appear only as a bright star in the Martian sky. Because Phobos takes almost 8 hours to orbit Mars, an observer would be able to see Phobos cross the Martian sky two to three times a day while Deimos, which requires a little over 30 hours to orbit, would take 5½ days to go from "new" Deimos to "new" Deimos.

Phobos and Deimos orbit Mars in synchronous rotation with their long axes pointing toward Mars. The Martian tidal effect on Phobos may be slowing it down. Astronomers estimate that within 100 million years Phobos may crash into Mars. Deimos, on the other hand, appears to be slowly moving away from Mars as the Moon is slowly moving away from the Earth.

■ FIGURE 7.32

Phobos with Mars in the Background

Phobos is much darker than Mars and irregularly shaped. Mars is obscured by a global dust storm. This photograph was taken by the Soviet *Phobos 2* spacecraft.
SOURCE: NASA.

■ TABLE 7.7 **The Moons of Mars**

	Phobos	**Deimos**
Semimajor axis	9377 km	23,463 km
Orbital period	7^{h}39^m	30^{h}17^m
Size	21 × 20 × 18 km	25 × 12 × 10 km
Mass	1.3 × 10^{19} g	1.8 × 10^{18} g
Mean density	≈2 g/cm^3	≈2 g/cm^3
Escape velocity	15 m/s (16 MPH)	10 m/s (11 MPH)

(a)

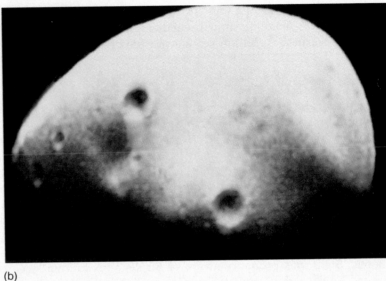

(b)

FIGURE 7.33

Phobos and Deimos

(a) Phobos is dominated by the large crater Stickney, named after Hall's wife, and shows grooves radiating away from the crater. *(b)* Deimos' surface is more subdued than that of Phobos.

SOURCE: NASA.

FIGURE 7.34

High-Resolution View of Deimos

This photograph, which was taken from 45 km away, covers an area 2 km by 2 km and shows a cratered but subdued terrain.

SOURCE: NASA.

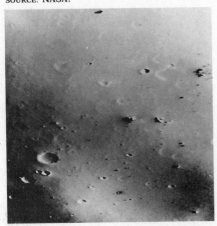

Both moons show heavily cratered surfaces with crater densities similar to the lunar highlands; such densities indicate ages greater than 4 billion years (Figure 7.33). The surface of Phobos is dominated by three relatively large craters: Stickney (10 km in diameter), Hall (5 km), and Roche (5 km). The largest crater on Deimos, on the other hand, is only 2.3 km in diameter. Both moons lack complex craters. This is expected because the transition between simple and complex craters is determined mainly by gravity; both moons have very low surface gravities. The crater rims on both moons are mainly upturned rock without many secondary craters. This is also expected because low gravities would allow ejecta produced by a meteorite impact to escape the moons. The ejecta, however, are not able to escape the gravitational field of Mars and will continue to orbit the planet. This orbiting debris will eventually be recaptured by the moons. It was impacts from the recaptured debris that produced a thick regolith, probably at least 5–10 m deep, on each moon. That Deimos has a thicker regolith is evident by the observation that almost all craters on Deimos are filled with debris. In general, the craters on Deimos are more subdued and show flatter floors than those on Phobos (Figure 7.34).

Besides their lack of complex craters, the other nonlunar characteristic of the Martian moons is the *grooves* on Phobos. They radiate in all directions away from the large crater Stickney and converge on the opposite side of Phobos. The largest grooves, 700 m across and 90 m deep, are closest to Stickney. The typical groove is 100–200 m wide and 10–20 m deep. The grooves are probably the result of the tremendous impact that formed Stickney. Both the grooves and Stickney appear as old as the rest of the surface of Phobos.

The Viking orbiters were able to fly by both moons several times at very close range. In addition to taking detailed pictures of their surfaces, the orbiters were able to measure the masses of the moons. The average densities calculated for the moons of Mars are about 2 g/cm³.

These low densities imply that their chemical composition must include light elements, or volatiles, such as water. Astronomers suspect that Phobos and Deimos are very similar in composition to "carbonaceous chondrites," a type of meteorite rich in water and carbon material.

▬SUMMARY

Venus and Mars are more Earth-like than any other planets in the solar system. Together with Mercury and the Earth, they comprise the Terrestrial planets. Venus, Mars, and the Earth are small, rocky worlds with atmospheres (Figure 7.35).

Both Venus and Mars have carbon dioxide–rich atmospheres while the Earth's atmosphere is mainly nitrogen and oxygen. All three planets developed secondary atmospheres by volcanic outgassing. The atmosphere of Venus evolved through a runaway greenhouse mechanism that eventually evaporated all liquid water and maintained a high carbon dioxide content. Its present atmosphere is 90 times more massive than the Earth's and many times hotter. The atmosphere of Mars allowed rain to shower the planet for a period that lasted from 500 million years to perhaps 1 to 2 billion years. Volcanic outgassing on Mars was not able to provide enough carbon dioxide and other gases to allow the greenhouse mechanism to keep temperatures high. Eventually the water evaporated and froze in the polar caps or below the surface. The atmosphere of Mars is now 150 times less dense than the Earth's and much colder. The Earth's atmosphere, on the other hand, evolved through complex interactions between the air, oceans, land, and life.

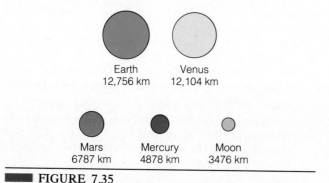

Earth
12,756 km

Venus
12,104 km

Mars
6787 km

Mercury
4878 km

Moon
3476 km

▬ FIGURE 7.35

Relative Sizes of the Earth, Venus, Mars, Mercury, and the Moon

The surface of Venus is characterized by rolling plains while Mars claims the largest landforms known in the solar system. Venus has two large continent-sized landforms and probably active volcanoes. It also shows evidence of lithospheric plate separation and collision. Mars, on the other hand, shows no evidence of plate motion but has two immense crustal uplifts on which several large volcanoes reside. Tectonism on Venus and Mars is dominated by hot spot tectonics where mantle plumes fed lava to their surfaces. Both planets experienced extensive basaltic, or fluid, lava flows that covered much of their surfaces.

That Venus is more active tectonically than Mars is not surprising given its similarity to the Earth's size, mass, and average density. It is puzzling, however, that plate tectonics appears to play only a minor role on Venus. The physical properties of Mars, however, lie between those of the Moon and Mercury and those of the Earth and Venus. It is not surprising that the surface evolution of Mars has been different. On the other hand, Venus, Mars, and the Earth as well as Mercury have differentiated, resulting in iron-rich cores and low-density crusts.

The Venusian atmosphere is characterized by clouds that completely cover the planet and lie between 50 and 70 km above the surface. These clouds are composed of sulfuric acid droplets as well as other sulfur compounds. Active volcanoes are the probable source of the sulfur. Mars also has clouds. The low-level Martian clouds may be composed of water-ice while the higher clouds are carbon dioxide–ice. During the Martian southern hemisphere summer, dust storms develop that can engulf the entire planet in a matter of weeks.

Venus exhibits relatively simple atmospheric dynamics with stacked equator-to-pole circulation cells caused by its very slow rotation. The atmosphere and the planet rotate in a retrograde direction. Mars exhibits circulation patterns more similar to the Earth's, but has a unique pole-to-pole circulation, caused by the extremely low polar temperatures, and nightside-to-dayside circulation, caused by the large temperature differences between day and night.

Venus has a steady climate. It is always hot on the surface with very light surface winds and no seasons. Mars and the Earth exhibit seasons as well as daily weather variations on the surface. Early observers of Mars detected polar caps that expand and shrink with the seasons and surface markings that change brightness and color with the seasons.

Although spacecraft sent to Mars could not identify the surface markings seen from the Earth with topographical features, they did discover huge volcanoes, large canyons, numerous craters, and dried river beds.

Mars also has two small elliptically shaped moons, Phobos and Deimos, while Venus has no moon.

CHAPTER CAPSULE

Topics and Terms	Review and Remarks		
	Earth	*Venus*	*Mars*
Atmosphere	Secondary atmosphere via outgassing	Secondary atmosphere via outgassing	Secondary atmosphere via outgassing
	It rained.	Too hot to rain—caused high CO_2 abundance	It rained.
	Continuous geological activity	Continuous geological activity	Volcanism ceased early.
	Moderate greenhouse effect	Runaway greenhouse effect	Minimal greenhouse effect
	Life evolved; produced oxygen.		Surface froze.
	Breathable N_2-O_2 atmosphere	Oppressive CO_2 atmosphere	Thin CO_2 atmosphere
Circulation	Hemispheric cells	Equator to pole	Hemispheric cells Pole-to-pole Nightside-to-dayside
Clouds	H_2O clouds	Sulfuric acid clouds	CO_2 and H_2O (?) clouds Global dust clouds
Temperatures	Moderate temperatures	Very hot—day and night	Very cold; can be warm at times
Surface features	Continents and ocean basins	Two large continents	Volcanic domes
	Ocean trenches	Rolling plains	Riverbeds and channels (dry)
	Volcanoes—active	Volcanoes (active?)	Extinct large volcanoes
	Some craters	Some craters	Many craters
Tectonics	Plate tectonics	Hot spot tectonics	Hot spot tectonics

REVIEW QUESTIONS

1. Though each is a Terrestrial planet, Mars, Venus, and the Earth appear quite different. Compare both the compositions of these planets and their atmospheres.

2. The rotational period of Venus was not known until the 1960s while that of Mars has been known for hundreds of years. What could account for the difference in these discovery dates?

3. The rotation of Venus is peculiar in several ways. What are they? What is special about the rotational period of Mars?

4. Compare the surface features of Venus and Mars to those of Earth. The vertical relief of Mars is greater than the vertical relief of both Venus and the Earth. Can you tell why?

5. Though the atmospheric compositions of Venus and Mars show similarities (they are mostly CO_2), their

minor constituents and densities are very different. What could account for this difference?

6. The Earth has little CO_2 in its atmosphere while that of Venus is mostly CO_2. Why should the atmospheres be so different while the planets themselves are so similar in size and apparent composition?

7. Neither Venus nor Mars has liquid water on its surface at present. Can you say why? (*Note:* The reason for each is very different.)

8. Compare the surface temperatures of Venus, Earth, and Mars. Why should they be so different?

9. There are several striking similarities among the surface features of Venus, the Earth, and Mars. Name some of them.

10. There are significant differences among the surface features of Venus, the Earth, and Mars. Describe them.

11. Venus cannot really be said to have seasons while Mars has seasons very similar to those of Earth. What causes this difference?

12. What evidence do we have that liquid water has existed on Mars at some time in the past? In what form does water exist on Mars now? Why can liquid water not exist, for long, on the surface of Mars now?

13. Describe the major surface features of Venus.

14. Describe Olympus Mons and Valles Marineris. Compare them to similar features on Earth.

15. Mercury and the Moon have very heavily cratered surfaces. Mars has a number of craters but not nearly as many as Mercury and the Moon, and the Earth has fewer still. Are these differences due to original formation or to subsequent events? Explain.

16. Compare observations that have been made of Mercury, Venus, and Mars since the birth of the space age.

FOR FURTHER READING

Bazilevskiy, A. T. 1989. The planet next door. *Sky & Telescope*, Apr., 360.

Carroll, M. 1985. The first colony on Mars. *Astronomy*, June, 6.

———. 1987. The changing face of Mars. *Astronomy*, Mar., 6.

———. 1988. Digging deeper for life on Mars. *Astronomy*, Apr., 6.

Dick, S. J. 1988. Discovering the moons of Mars. *Sky & Telescope*, Sept., 242.

Haberle, R. M. 1986. The climate of Mars. *Scientific American*, May, 54.

Hartmann, W. K. 1989. What's new on Mars. *Sky & Telescope*, May, 471.

Kasting, J. F., O. B. Toon, and J. B. Polluck. 1988. How climate evolved on the terrestrial planets. *Scientific American*, Feb., 90.

Phillips, J. L., and C. T. Russell. 1988. The ashen light of Venus. *Sky & Telescope*, Mar., 250.

Schultz, P. H. 1985. Polar wandering on Mars. *Scientific American*, Dec., 94.

Wall, S. D. 1989. Venus revealed. *Astronomy*, Apr., 26.

ASTROPROBE 7

Terra-forming

The concept of **terraforming**, large-scale planetary engineering to produce Earth-like environments, has its roots in imaginary Martians. Percival Lowell became infatuated with the idea of Martian canals and their implication of a dying Martian civilization. Lowell believed the canals were part of a planetwide irrigation system for transporting water from the Martian polar caps to dry equatorial regions (Figure 7A.1). Although everyone now realizes that neither canals nor Martians exist, Lowell's speculations helped give rise to the concept of terraforming.

Mars, in fact, is the most likely planet to be a candidate for terraforming because it is so Earth-like. It has a similar rotational period; it experiences seasons; it has polar ice caps of water; it exhibits clouds and dust storms; and it has an atmosphere. What are we waiting for? Let's go to Mars! You already realize, of course, that the Martian atmosphere is unbreathable and that it is *very* cold on Mars. Before humans can walk on the Martian surface unprotected, planetary engineers have much work to do.

DE-TERRAFORMING THE EARTH

Humans have been experimenting with planetary engineering for at least the last century. What they have been doing is actually a form of "de-terraforming" in which the environment is polluted in a variety of ways (Figure 7A.2). Lakes, rivers, and groundwater, for instance, are showing the effects of acid rain; atmospheric carbon dioxide levels are ever-increasing due to industrial fossil fuel burning; species of animals are being destroyed by chemical wastes and developments; and atmospheric ozone is being depleted. At the same time scientists are desperately trying to warn the world of these dangers, they are also trying to develop techniques to help control the Earth's climate. Atmospheric scientists, for instance, have had some success in modifying hailstorms and hurricanes by seeding clouds with silver iodide, which acts as an artificial ice. Unfortunately, scientists do not yet know enough about climatic cause and effect to try climate modification techniques on a large scale. Someday it may be possible to control the rainfall and wind patterns of an entire continent, ensuring, for instance, the agricultural needs of humans or preventing natural disasters.

The goal of global climate control has been aided by the study of other planetary atmospheres in the solar system. Venus, for instance, has taught us a great deal about the greenhouse effect and the role manmade chemicals play in enhancing it. Observations of the atmospheric circulation on Venus, Mars, and Jupiter have provided important tests for models used to describe the Earth's atmosphere. Some of these observations and tests form the basis for the scientific

FIGURE 7A.1

Percival Lowell

Lowell's observations of Mars and his ideas on Martian canals led to the first dreams of terraforming a planet.

SOURCE: Lowell Observatory photograph.

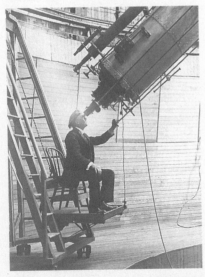

community's concern over the de-terraforming experiments inadvertently being done here on Earth. At the same time, when astronomers, atmospheric scientists, and biologists study the planets, they are drawn to the idea of modifying these planets to suit the needs of humans. Let's now concentrate on the ideas, some of them quite exotic, involved in terraforming the planets.

TERRAFORMING PLANETS

How would planetary engineers change the surface of a planet to make it hospitable to humans? Let's restrict the discussion to changes in the environment and ignore physical changes, such as in a planet's mass or diameter, or orbital changes, such as in its semimajor axis or inclination. The techniques of planetary engineering will involve the following:

- Changing the chemical composition and structure of the atmosphere.
- Changing the insolation, or the amount of sunlight absorbed by the surface.
- Changing the character of the surface.
- Changing the rotational rate of a planet.

Changing the atmosphere can be done biologically, as plants have done on Earth, or by brute force, such as by adding light elements transported from other parts of the solar system. The amount of sunlight absorbed at the surface can be changed using plants or a dark soil as a covering or using, for instance, giant space mirrors that can concentrate sunlight on the planet's surface. The surface can be transformed by making it rain or by large-scale engineering projects. Trying to change the rotational rate of a planet may require a tremendous amount of energy, perhaps beyond our capabilities even in the future.

Before describing the details of some of these techniques, let's consider the basis for the desired changes; that is, what are the biological conditions, or limits, on factors such as temperature, atmospheric composition, and light levels that must be met by an environment designed to support human life? First, a terraformed planet must have an average temperature in the range of 260 K to 310 K for humans to survive (Figure 7A.3). Second, oxygen must be present in the atmosphere as well as nitrogen and small amounts of carbon dioxide; the oxygen requirement means that extensive plant life on the planet's surface is necessary. Third, light levels can vary from a hundredth to about twice that on Earth, but ultraviolet radiation must not be higher. Fourth, water must cover at least 10% of the surface

■ FIGURE 7A.2

An Example of De-Terraforming

Smoke from a coal-burning electric power generator contains sulfur particles that eventually fall out of the atmosphere as acid rain.

SOURCE: Steve McCutcheon/Visuals Unlimited.

■ FIGURE 7A.3

A Human Environment

The Earth has all of the right conditions conducive to a comfortable life.
SOURCE: Phillip Flower.

to ensure enough fresh water. Finally, planetary engineers will need to keep wind velocity and dust content low, and extreme volcanic activity and meteoritic bombardment rates must be avoided. The techniques of terraforming can go beyond these limits because some terrestrial organisms are able to survive in very cold or very hot environments and even without oxygen. Such organisms may prove useful in the initial stages of terraforming.

It is natural to start a study of terraforming with Mars since it appears so Earth-like. Can the red planet be terraformed into a "blue" planet—one with water, comfortable temperatures, and a thick, oxygen-rich atmosphere? Ideas to achieve just this range from detonating nuclear bombs in volcanic craters to throwing dirt on the polar caps. Increasing the temperature of Mars goes hand in hand with increasing atmospheric pressure and the density of the air. The connection is through the greenhouse effect in which a planet's atmosphere can absorb energy radiated by the surface and warm the surface by reradiating the energy back down to the surface. For instance, if Mars were warmer, the carbon dioxide–ice in the polar caps would evaporate, adding carbon dioxide to the atmosphere. Increasing carbon dioxide would add to the atmosphere's ability to trap heat through the greenhouse effect and, therefore, warm the surface (Figure 7A.4). Unfortunately, Mars does not appear to have enough frozen carbon dioxide to increase the density of the atmosphere enough to raise average temperatures more than about 10 K. Since water produces a more intense greenhouse effect than carbon dioxide, planetary engineers will need to melt the polar ice caps.

Melting the ice caps would first add water *vapor* to the atmosphere because liquid water would evaporate at the low pressures of the present Martian atmosphere. The water vapor would increase the surface temperatures via the greenhouse effect and cause more evaporation and eventually more melting of the polar ice caps. The trick, of course, is to initiate the melting of the ice caps. One way to do this would be to cover the polar caps with a dark substance, thereby increasing the amount of solar radiation absorbed and raising the temperature of the ice caps. A possible source of black "dirt" could be the moons of Mars. Both Phobos and Deimos are covered with a black, carbon-rich regolith. Perhaps engineers could build electromagnetic cannons, called mass drivers, that would shoot buckets of the black "soot" onto the polar caps. Another possibility involves building huge orbiting mirrors that would concentrate sunlight onto the poles. Both methods appear feasible with today's technology. Even if planetary engineers could raise surface temperatures to a comfortable level, they would need to produce oxygen in the currently carbon dioxide–rich atmosphere of Mars. Oxygen is needed to

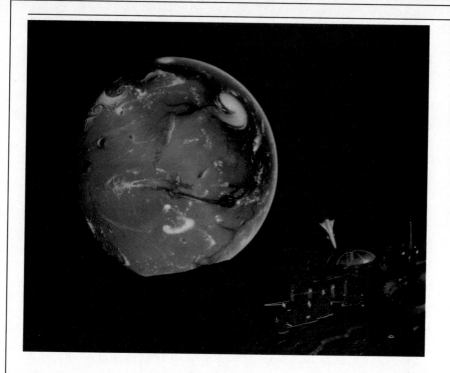

■■■ ■ FIGURE 7A.4

**An Artist's Conception of
a Terraformed Mars**

Here Mars is viewed from a space port
on its moon Phobos.

SOURCE: Adolf Schaller, copyright © Dream-
time Productions.

produce ozone to shield organisms from ultraviolet radiation and to
support human metabolism.

On a planetary scale, plants are required to increase the oxygen in
an atmosphere. Plants use carbon dioxide and sunlight to produce
oxygen through photosynthesis. The normal green plants you see everyday simply could not survive on Mars in its present condition.
Some forms of lichen and blue-green algae, however, may be able to
exist in certain places on Mars. Blue-green algae, for instance, do not
require oxygen; lichen is very resistant to ultraviolet radiation; and
both can survive in very dry climates. The idea is to sow these plants
into carefully chosen areas, add water, and allow them to spread.
Estimates on how long it would take to produce the minimum
amount of oxygen needed to breath are on the order of 100,000 years!
Scientists might be able to speed up the process dramatically by ge-
netic modification of specific terrestrial oxygen-generating organisms. Furthermore, experiments by the Viking landers suggest that
oxygen may be released from the Martian soil when water is added.
This may indicate that terraforming Mars would not be as difficult
as it appears. Once some oxygen and ozone are produced, more efficient oxygen-producing plants can be seeded to speed up the process
even more. Although it is impossible to give reliable estimates for the

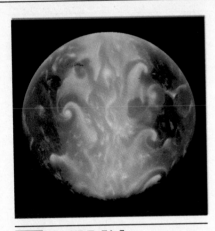

■ FIGURE 7A.5

An Artist's Conception of a Terra-formed Venus, Showing an Equa-torial Ocean

SOURCE: Adolf Schaller, copyright © Dream-time Productions.

time needed to produce an oxygen-rich atmosphere, studies indicate time spans of 10,000 to 100,000 years might be required.

Warming Mars and generating oxygen are still not enough; the existing atmospheric carbon dioxide must be greatly reduced. This is achieved on Earth by plants that use carbon dioxide and by rain, vast amounts of rain, that wash carbon dioxide out of the atmosphere. It is imperative to flood Mars. This is only possible if temperatures and air pressures are high enough to support liquid water. One source of water, of course, is the polar caps; another is the frozen water below the surface. Perhaps warming Mars will generate catastrophic flooding of Chryse Planitia and other low regions as has happened in the past. This would produce vast oceans, ensuring a planetwide supply of fresh water and rain. Comets are another potential source of water (see Chapter 10); millions of comets are believed to exist beyond the orbit of Pluto. Sending them inward to collide with Mars would increase the water content of Mars as well as add other elements, such as oxygen and carbon, to its atmosphere and surface. Of course, moving comets is a feat in itself!

Venus is another candidate for terraforming. Successful terraforming of Venus would result in a second Earth in the solar system. Planetary engineers would need to eliminate the hot, deadly, carbon dioxide–rich atmosphere of Venus and increase its rotational rate. Some scientists envision placing genetically modified algae in the atmosphere; these would carry out photosynthesis *in* the clouds, converting carbon dioxide and water into oxygen and carbon compounds. As the amount of carbon dioxide decreased, the heating of the atmosphere via the greenhouse effect would also decrease (Figure 7A.5). To produce water, planetary engineers would need to import huge quantities of hydrogen, perhaps from the atmospheres of the Jovian planets. Increasing the spin rate of Venus can only be done through collisions; asteroids or comets (see Chapter 10) could be aimed at Venus from billions of miles away. The subsequent collisions, if properly done, could increase the spin rate. An increased spin rate would generate a magnetic field, providing a planetary magnetic field that would protect inhabitants from solar radiation. Time scale? The most recent estimates place the length of time needed to terraform Venus at 16,500 years!

Although some of the ideas presented here may sound like a science fiction novel, most are based on NASA studies of the environment of Mars and the known behavior of terrestrial organisms. While these preliminary studies indicate that terraforming is possible, the time scale is thousands of years and longer. Terraforming, for instance, is not the solution to the problems associated with the world's population growth. Instead of terraforming an entire planet, it may be possible to build a small "planet" with the proper environmental conditions for humans; that is, it may be possible to build colonies in space.

SPACE SETTLEMENTS

In the early 1970s, Professor Gerard K. O'Neill of Princeton University published several papers outlining the building of large, self-sufficient human colonies in *space*. Building a space settlement is more "terramaking" than terraforming. It is the construction of a habitable environment beyond the confines of the Earth. The most amazing aspect of O'Neill's space settlements is that they are technically feasible today.

Designing space settlements requires the same considerations as terraforming a planet. Settlements must contain breathable oxygen and plants to produce oxygen and remove carbon dioxide; they must maintain proper temperature and light levels yet protect the inhabitants from solar radiation, particles from solar flares, and meteoroids; and they must generate "artificial" gravity to provide needed physical stress on the inhabitants.

The most reasonable place to build settlements is in a special location called the "L_5" point (Figure 7A.6). This is a stable location in the Moon's orbit lying 60° behind the Moon, as viewed from Earth. This is one of five stable points in the Earth-Moon system in which an object will remain in the same position relative to the Moon and the Earth. The L_5 point "follows" the Moon in its orbit about the Earth. The choice of L_5 for a settlement is dictated by the need to mine the raw material on the Moon for the settlement. It is much easier to lift raw material off the Moon than off the Earth. Because the escape velocity of the Moon is almost 5 times less than the Earth's, it would require about 20 times less energy to move material from the Moon than from the Earth. Furthermore, mining the Moon does not affect the environment on the Earth. Moreover, lunar rocks are rich in oxygen (about 40%) and in useful metals (about 20–30%), such as aluminum. Consequently, the raw material for building the structure of a settlement is best obtained from the Moon (see AstroProbe 11).

Earth materials will be needed initially to provide the transportation system (rockets), the mining facility on the Moon (nuclear power station, mining equipment, auxiliary and maintenance equipment, and crew quarters), a material extraction and fabrication facility at L_5 from which to process the lunar raw material for the major construction of the settlement, and the transfer station in Earth orbit (space station and construction facilities). When the habitat is built,

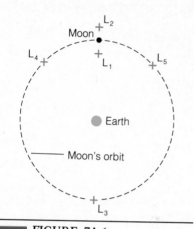

FIGURE 7A.6

L_5 Geometry

Special locations called the Lagrangian points arise from the gravitational interaction between the Earth and the Moon. An object placed at any of the Lagrangian points will remain in a fixed location relative to the Earth and the Moon as the entire system revolves around the Sun.

hydrogen, carbon, and nitrogen, which are needed for the atmosphere, water, and chemical recycling systems and are not available from the lunar soil, must come from the Earth. The Earth will also supply plants, animals, and, of course, colonists.

The settlements may be constructed in a variety of shapes, from dumbbells and spheres to doughnuts and cylinders (Figure 7A.7). These physical structures must be designed to contain an atmosphere and to protect the inhabitants from exposure to harmful solar radiation. Sunlight, of course, is needed, and the amount of sunlight inside a settlement is easily controlled by louvered mirrors. The ability to control the amount of sunlight shining, for instance, on plants will allow scientists to use optimal growing rates. Raw lunar material can be used as shielding on the outside of the settlements to protect inhabitants from harmful radiation and from damage by collisions with meteoroids. An impact by any meteoroid traveling at a high velocity (about 90,000 MPH is average) will produce a crater or hole in any shielding. A hole, of course, will result in a loss of air from the settlement. For instance, a settlement built for 10,000 inhabitants

■■■■ FIGURE 7A.7

**Basic Design Shapes
for Space Settlements**

SOURCE: Based on Figure 4–2, page 40 in NASA SP-413, *Space Settlements: A Design Study*, ed. R. D. Johnson and C. Holbrow (Washington, D.C.: NASA, 1977).

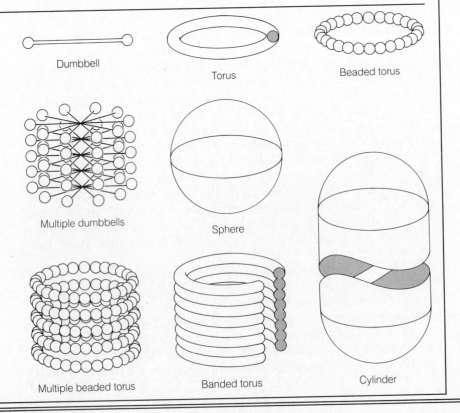

Dumbbell

Torus

Beaded torus

Multiple dumbbells

Sphere

Multiple beaded torus

Banded torus

Cylinder

would lose 60% of its air in one day from a hole 1 m in diameter. The Earth and Moon pass through regions with large numbers of meteoroids several times a year; these are the remnants of comets (see Chapter 10). During such passages, a settlement may experience hundreds of impacts per hour. Nevertheless, as long as the settlement can detect and locate meteoroid impacts, meteoroids as massive as a million grams do not pose a severe threat to kilometer-sized settlements.

Humans also need the physiological stress on their bones and muscles caused by gravity. The effects of a prolonged absence of gravity are not fully understood, but results from long-term space flights indicate, for instance, that decalcification (decrease in bone mass) occurs at a rate of 1 to 2% per month. Returning to Earth gravity after extended space missions also causes problems: astronauts have experienced increases in heartbeat, changes in muscle reflexes, and difficulties with blood circulation. Some level of gravity clearly is needed in a space settlement. To generate "artificial" gravity in a settlement requires that the settlement rotate. A rotating torus, as shown in Figure 7A.8, generates the sensation of weight on the inside surface of the outer rim of the torus. As a colonist moves toward the center of the torus through connecting tubes, the effects of rotation will decrease until "zero-gravity" is reached in the center. Spacecraft would dock and special zero-gravity factories would be located at the center.

Finally, the environmental design of a settlement must satisfy the physical needs of people without subjecting them to damaging psychological stress. Diversity and variability must be the goal of environmental planning so that individuals can tailor their living areas to their needs. Trade between the Earth and the colony is an absolute necessity because small colonies (those with less than 100,000 inhabitants) cannot be self-sufficient. The many services and goods Earth people take for granted will not necessarily be available to colonists. Emphasis must be placed on transportation and communications. For instance, a trip to Earth from a colony located at L_5 would take several days, making frequent family visits difficult. Schools for children, medical services, entertainment, and government must be planned for. A space settlement would be an isolated community and would have to deal with problems all colonies have had to deal with in the past.

As you can see, the planning of a space colony is complex. It is not just a matter of building a structure to house people and equipment. Consider the allocation of space. As in any city on Earth, much of the area will be residential. Space is also needed for businesses (offices and shops), schools, hospitals, and assemblies (community halls, churches, and recreation and entertainment areas), and for public

■ FIGURE 7A.8

Space Habitat Design Using a Rotating Torus

Rotation produces an artificial gravity equal to the Earth's surface gravity at the outer rim of the torus. The large mirror reflects sunlight into the colony.

SOURCE: NASA.

■ FIGURE 7A.9

Inside a Space Habitat Design Using a Sphere for the Habitat

SOURCE: NASA.

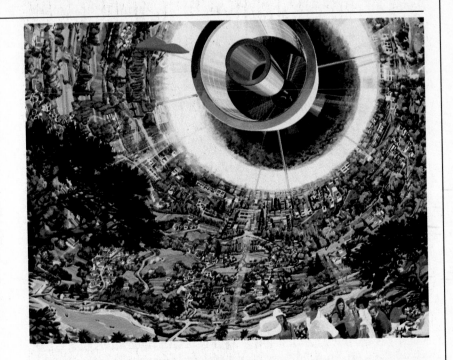

open spaces, such as parks. Room must be provided for service industries, the transportation system, and mechanical and electrical subsystems, such as for communications, waste and water treatment, and electricity. Finally, space must be provided for growing plants, animals, and food processing (Figure 7A.9).

You may ask whether space colonies are needed. Even if terraforming were a necessity, humanity would not reap its benefits for thousands of years; but a space settlement can be built in 10 to 20 years. Although the Earth has limited resources, the solar system by comparison has unlimited resources (more on resources in AstroProbe 11). To use these resources, humans will necessarily need to venture into the solar system. This economic need will naturally develop into a need for space settlements. In fact, one possible way to reduce population expansion pressures in the twenty-first century is to build many large space settlements. This is, of course, very long range planning, but the building of safe space settlement can be done—and it can be done now.

The Outer Planets

OUTLINE

Jovian Planets: Characteristics
Chemical Composition and Internal
    Structure
Internal Energy Sources
Rotations and Orientations

Jupiter and Saturn
Exploration of Jupiter and Saturn
Jupiter and Saturn: Features and
    Observations

Uranus and Neptune
Discovery and Exploration
Uranus
Neptune

Pluto
Discovery
Pluto and Its Satellite
The Origin of Pluto

Summary

Chapter Capsule

Review Questions

For Further Reading

███████ASTROPROBE 8:
    Remote Sensing of the Planets

*The Sword of Herschel: Saturn from
Mimas.*
ARTIST: Kim Poor.

T HE GIANT, OR JOVIAN, PLANETS, Jupiter, Saturn, Uranus, and Neptune dominate the outer expanse of the solar system. They are characterized by thick, colorful atmospheres of mainly hydrogen and helium gases. Jupiter and Saturn were known to astronomers of antiquity, but Uranus and Neptune were discovered only during the last two centuries. Unlike the Jovian planets, the outermost planet, Pluto, is a small, cold world, so remote that spacecraft have not been sent to it. The planet itself was discovered only in 1930 and its moon in 1978.

JOVIAN PLANETS: CHARACTERISTICS

Astronomers classify Saturn, Uranus, and Neptune as Jovian planets because they are more similar to Jupiter than to any Terrestrial planet. Next to the Sun, Jupiter is by far the most massive object in the solar system (Table 8.1), and the combined mass of all the Jovian planets is over 200 times that of the Terrestrial planets. These giant planets are at great distances from the Sun: Jupiter must travel for nearly 12 Earth years to orbit the Sun once; Saturn takes over 29 years; Uranus needs 84 years; and Neptune crawls around the Sun once every 165 years. These great distances make it very difficult to study the Jovian planets with Earth-based telescopes. Consequently, most of our data on the detailed physical characteristics of the Jovian planets come from spacecraft measurements.

TABLE 8.1 **Characteristics of the Jovian Planets**

Property	Jupiter	Saturn	Uranus	Neptune
Semimajor axis	5.2 AU	9.5 AU	19.2 AU	30.1 AU
Eccentricity	0.048	0.056	0.047	0.009
Orbital period	12 years	29 years	84 years	165 years
Rotational period	0.41 days	0.44 days	0.72 days	0.67 days
Inclination	3.1°	26.7°	97.9°	29.6°
Diameter	142,796 km	120,000 km	51,200 km	48,600 km
(in Earth diameters)	11.2	9.41	4.0	3.8
Mass	1.9×10^{27} kg	5.7×10^{26} kg	8.7×10^{25} kg	1.0×10^{26} kg
(in Earth masses)	318	95	15	17
Mean density	1.3 g/cm³	0.7 g/cm³	1.2 g/cm³	1.8 g/cm³
Escape velocity	59.6 km/s (136,000 MPH)	35.6 km/s (79,650 MPH)	21.3 km/s (47,395 MPH)	23.8 km/s (52,760 MPH)
Surface temperature	163 K −110°C −166°F	133 K −140°C −220°F	78 K −195°C −319°F	80 K −193°C −315°F

Chemical Composition and Internal Structure

Even though the Jovian planets are huge, massive bodies, their densities are amazingly low. The average density of Saturn is 0.7 g/cm³, less than that of water—it could float in a very large ocean! Clearly, Jovian planets cannot be composed mainly of rock as the Terrestrial planets are. The spectroscopic study of stars (Chapter 13), including the Sun, reveals that 99% of all atoms in the universe are hydrogen and helium. Therefore, these are the only low-mass, or "light," elements abundant enough to be major constituents of the Jovian planets. Indeed, spectroscopy of Jupiter shows that it is about 83% hydrogen and 27% helium with hydrogen molecules (H_2) outnumbering helium atoms 9 to 1 (Figure 8.1). Mixed with the hydrogen and helium are traces of methane (CH_4), ammonia (NH_3), water (H_2O), and compounds, such as ethane (C_2H_6) and hydrogen cyanide (HCN), all combinations of light elements. Saturn's atmosphere also consists mainly of hydrogen and helium, but the abundance of helium in Saturn's upper atmosphere is significantly lower than in Jupiter's; for every helium atom in Saturn's atmosphere, astronomers detect 14 hydrogen molecules (Table 8.2). Although the atmospheric abundances of Uranus are similar to Jupiter's, helium has not been detected spectroscopically in the reflected light from Neptune. Astronomers assume, however, that the Neptunian atmosphere is also mainly hydrogen and helium.

These giant orbs of hydrogen and helium are, for the most part, not gaseous. In the atmosphere of Jupiter, for instance, hydrogen is very rarified, but deeper inside, it is highly compressed. As the densities increase deeper and deeper inside Jupiter under the pressure of the great overlying mass, the hydrogen molecules are squeezed closer and closer together and behave more and more like a liquid. About one-fourth of the way to the center, all hydrogen is liquid in a compressed state called **liquid molecular hydrogen.** Because the hydrogen gas will *gradually* transform into liquid molecules with depth, no fixed boundary is expected between the gaseous atmosphere and the underlying liquid "mantle."

Deeper into Jupiter's interior, where pressures reach values a million times that at the Earth's surface, the hydrogen molecules are broken into individual atoms. At even greater depths and higher densities, the hydrogen atoms are ionized, freeing electrons that behave as free electrons do in a metal. The mobility of electrons in metals, for instance, is responsible for electrical conductivity. Since the electrons in this high-density state of hydrogen have similar properties, it is called **liquid metallic hydrogen.** Because of the vast volume of metallic hydrogen in Jupiter and Saturn, it may be the most common metal in the solar system, yet none is found on Earth!

The centers of the Jovian planets are probably "rocky" cores composed of heavy elements mixed with water, methane, and ammonia (Figure 8.2). These cores are massive: about 15 times the mass of the Earth in Jupiter, about 25 times Earth's mass in Saturn, and a few

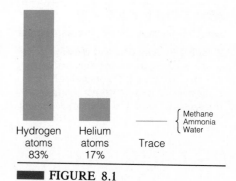

FIGURE 8.1

The Chemical Composition of Jupiter's Atmosphere

Percentages by *mass* are shown.

Liquid molecular hydrogen: A highly compressed state of hydrogen in which molecules of hydrogen still show random movement but are partially restricted (as with molecules of a liquid); hydrogen assumes this state only under very high pressures.

Liquid metallic hydrogen: A very highly compressed state of hydrogen in which the hydrogen electrons are no longer bound to an individual proton but are free to migrate throughout the liquid; the ability of the electrons to move gives this state of hydrogen the electrical properties of a metal.

TABLE 8.2 Hydrogen and Helium Abundances by Number

Planet	Hydrogen Molecules	Helium Atoms
Jupiter	9	1
Saturn	14	1
Uranus	7	1

■■■■ ■ FIGURE 8.2

Interior Models of the Jovian Planets

Each has a rocky core and a mantle composed of either liquid metallic hydrogen or liquid water, ammonia, and methane. Atmospheric gases represent a large fraction of their radii. The interiors of Uranus and Neptune are assumed to be similar.

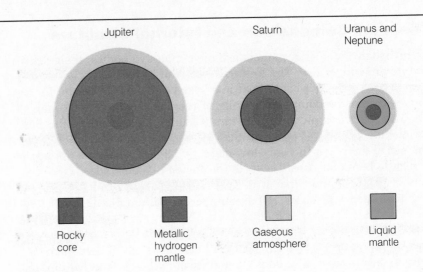

Jupiter   Saturn   Uranus and Neptune

Rocky core   Metallic hydrogen mantle   Gaseous atmosphere   Liquid mantle

Earth masses in Uranus and Neptune. At the very centers of Jupiter and Saturn, however, where pressures may be tens of millions of Earth atmospheres and temperatures tens of thousands of Kelvins, the term "rocky" is used to describe a mixture of light and heavy elements such as oxygen, silicon, and metals. We do not know the exact mixture, but we know that there is a strong concentration of mass at their centers. Furthermore, because of the great compression, the cores may not be much larger in diameter than the Earth, even though they are much more massive. At the centers of Uranus and Neptune, on the other hand, where temperatures and pressures are expected to be more similar to those at the center of the Earth, scientists expect molten or even solid rocky cores.

Jovian planets differ from each other in several other ways. For instance, if Jupiter and Saturn are composed mainly of light elements, how can Jupiter be nearly twice as dense as Saturn? This is due to Jupiter's greater mass; its interior is simply more compressed than Saturn's. This is also why Jupiter is only 18% larger in diameter than Saturn, even though it is three times more massive. Uranus and Neptune, on the other hand, are not massive enough to generate the high pressures required to compress hydrogen molecules into a liquid state. As a result, the middle third of these two smaller Jovian planets is a hot, dense, liquid mantle of water, ammonia, and methane. The "smallness" of Uranus and Neptune is due to a high abundance of water. Because the atoms making up the molecules of water, ammonia, and methane are more compact than those of hydrogen and helium, Uranus and Neptune are about three times smaller than if they were made of primarily hydrogen and helium. In fact, they are slightly larger than a hypothetical sphere of pure water of the same mass.

Although these giant spheres reside in the distant cold regions of the solar system, far from the warmth of the Sun, their liquid interiors are anything but cold. In fact, the Jovian planets have an excess of internal heat.

Internal Energy Sources

From their study of the Terrestrial planets, astronomers realize that collisions with meteorites during planetary formation generated a great deal of heat. This also occurred for the Jovian planets but on a much larger scale. Furthermore, the great compression of planetary material caused by the huge masses of the Jovian planets also contributes to the high temperatures. The heat content of Jupiter and Saturn, for instance, is so high that more energy flows through their atmospheres from below than they receive from the Sun. Jupiter emits about 1½ times the energy it receives from the Sun while Saturn emits over 2½ times what it receives. Earth's surface, by comparison, receives 5000 times as much energy from the Sun as from the flow of internal heat to its surface.

In absolute terms, the internal energy source in Jupiter is about twice as large as Saturn's. Nevertheless, because Saturn's mass is less than a third of Jupiter's mass, Saturn actually radiates more energy per gram of material than Jupiter does. This implies that Saturn has an additional source of energy. The additional heat appears to be related to the observed deficiency of helium in Saturn's atmosphere. Astronomers expect both planets contain the same mix of chemical elements; in particular, their hydrogen and helium abundances should be nearly the same. Helium atoms, however, are able to sink in Saturn's atmosphere and upper mantle because temperatures are cooler there than they are in Jupiter. The *friction* between the sinking helium atoms and the gaseous and liquid hydrogen can provide an additional source of heat.

The internal heat source of Uranus is so weak that it is not detectable, but Neptune is known to emit a small amount of excess energy. Small heat sources are expected for these Jovian planets because they are smaller and less massive than either Jupiter or Saturn.

Rotations and Orientations

Although the Jovian planets are much larger and more massive than the Earth, they all rotate faster than the Earth, and all except Uranus rotate in the same direction as the Earth. Uranus is unique in this respect due to a most unusual orientation of its rotational axis. Uranus is tilted so much, 98°, that its poles point nearly along its orbital plane (Figure 8.3). In effect, Uranus lies on its side. This unusual posture produces unusual seasons. A Uranian pole, for instance, faces alternately toward and away from the Sun during its year. One pole experiences a 42-year season of perpetual light while the other pole plunges into 42 years of increasing darkness. In fact, if you were anywhere on Uranus outside a region 8° north or south of the equator, you would be on the poleward side of an arctic or antarctic circle. Sunrise and sunset at the Uranian solstices, for instance, is experienced only in areas within 8° of the equator.

The south pole of Uranus is currently facing the Sun and, therefore, the Earth. How do astronomers know that they are studying the south pole of Uranus and not its north pole? This is simply a matter of con-

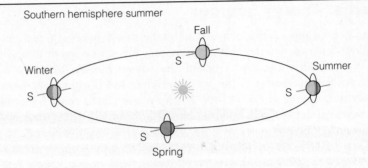

**The Tilt of the Rotational Axis
of Uranus**

Uranus orbits on its side. At the solstices
either its north or south pole nearly faces
the Sun while the equator faces the Sun
at the equinoxes. The seasons indicated
for the southern hemisphere of Uranus.

■■■■ **FIGURE** 8.4

Collision with Uranus

A large object colliding with Uranus near
either of its rotational poles could have
tipped the planet on its side. Its moons
could have formed out of the debris of
such a collision.

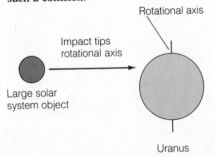

(a) Before collision

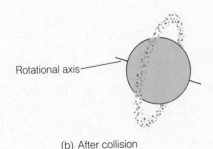

(b) After collision

vention; astronomers have agreed to call all planetary rotational poles
that point above the ecliptic (in the direction of the Earth's north celestial pole) north poles and all pointing below the ecliptic south poles.
The Uranian pole facing the Earth now is tilted about 8° below the
ecliptic; therefore it is a south pole.

The orientation of Uranus has interesting implications for the history
of the Uranian system. Chapter 11 argues that when the planets formed,
their rotational axes were nearly perpendicular to their orbital planes.
What happened to Uranus? It appears that some large object knocked
Uranus over (Figure 8.4). This must have happened very early in the
formation of Uranus because all of its moons orbit in its equatorial
plane. If the moons were already orbiting Uranus before the cataclysmic event, they could not have rearranged themselves in the tilted
equatorial plane in nearly circular orbits.

The main type of markings on the visible disks of Jovian planets are
bands that run parallel to the equator. These are especially pronounced
for Jupiter and can be seen with even a small telescope. Larger telescopes and space probes reveal distinct features within the bands that
can be seen to move across the visible disk of Jupiter. As early as the
seventeenth century, astronomers used cloud features to measure the
rotational period of Jupiter, and by 1690 they found that regions near
Jupiter's equator rotate faster than regions at higher latitudes. The difference in rotation with latitude indicated to observers that they were
not looking at a solid surface; they were seeing clouds. Furthermore,
this *differential rotation* indicates that the rotation of the clouds does
not necessarily represent the rotation of the planet itself.

How can astronomers determine the rotation of a Jovian planet if
they can only see clouds? All of the Jovian planets have magnetic fields.
The magnetic field of Jupiter is about 20,000 times greater than the
Earth's; Saturn's is somewhat less than Jupiter's; and the magnetic
fields of Uranus and Neptune are about as strong as the Earth's. The
Earth appears to generate its magnetic field by the rotation of a metallic core. Similarly, astronomers expect that Jupiter generates its magnetic field by the rotation of its metallic hydrogen mantle. The faster
rotation and larger mass of conducting material in Jupiter would ac-

count for the stronger field strength and immense size of the Jovian magnetosphere. If you could see Jupiter's magnetosphere from the Earth, it would cover a region in the sky about 15 times that of the apparent diameter of the full moon. Jupiter's magnetosphere can extend 100 Jupiter radii (7,000,000 km) toward the Sun, and its tail downwind from the Sun extends all the way to the orbit of Saturn, about 4.5 astronomical units! Aside from its vast size and strength, the shape and structure of the Jovian magnetosphere are similar to the Earth's. The Jovian magnetic field can be detected from the Earth by the long wavelength radiation emitted by high-speed particles trapped in Jupiter's magnetosphere. The radiation is the type expected from charged particles, such as electrons, protons, and other ions, *spiraling* in a magnetic field. Astronomers assume that the rapid rotation of the other Jovian planets also generates their magnetic fields. Furthermore, since the source of the magnetic field is the interior, the rotational period of the magnetic field is identified as the rotational period of the planet. For Jupiter, this is $9^h55^m30^s$. As Table 8.3 indicates, the clouds do appear to be rotating at nearly the same rate as the planet.

Knowledge of Saturn's magnetic field came from *Pioneer 11* observations. The physical dimensions and the properties of the radiation field in the magnetosphere of Saturn are intermediate between Jupiter and the Earth. Furthermore, whereas the magnetic axes of Jupiter and Earth are tilted about 10° with respect to their rotational axes, Saturn's magnetic axis is aligned within 1°. The orientation of the rotational and magnetic axes of Uranus and Neptune, on the other hand, are very different from those of the Earth, Jupiter, or Saturn. The magnetic poles of Uranus and Neptune are tilted about 60° and 50°, respectively, relative to their geographic poles (Figure 8.5). Although Figure 8.5 shows the Uranian magnetic pole pointing upward, its orientation will change as the planet spins on its axis. The direction of the north magnetic pole, for instance, will swing from above the ecliptic to below and back again in one rotational period.

It is clear from this study of the characteristics of the Jovian planets that Jupiter and Saturn form a natural pair as do Uranus and Neptune. Furthermore, astronomers know much more about Jupiter and Saturn than they do about Uranus and Neptune. This, of course, is a natural consequence of the distances to these remote worlds. This division is also used in the next two sections in which the two pairs are treated separately, starting with Jupiter and Saturn.

TABLE 8.3 Rotation Rates

	Jupiter	Saturn
Equatorial	9^h51^m	10^h14^m
Mid-latitudes	9^h56^m	10^h50^m
Magnetic field	9^h56^m	10^h39^m

FIGURE 8.5

Planetary Magnetic and Rotational Axes

Rotational axes are labeled following the convention in which north is used for a rotational axis that points above the ecliptic (Earth's north). The magnetic field orientations are represented by bar magnets and a thin line. The plane of the ecliptic is represented by the dashed line and the direction of rotation of the planet by the arrowhead on the equator of each planet.

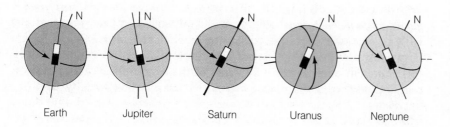

Earth   Jupiter   Saturn   Uranus   Neptune

◼️ FIGURE 8.6

Atmospheric Bands on Jupiter

Jupiter's light and dark bands are visible
through even a small telescope.

SOURCE: Lick Observatory, University of California, Santa Cruz.

◼️ JUPITER AND SATURN

Humans have known about Jupiter and Saturn since antiquity. They
are distinctly bright in the nighttime sky and rank first and second in
the solar system in diameter and mass. Although astronomers determined the gross properties, such as diameter, mass, and average density, of these large Jovian planets relatively early in their studies, a tremendous amount of knowledge has been added in the last decade from
the flyby missions of four spacecraft.

Exploration of Jupiter and Saturn

Because Jupiter and Saturn have large diameters, astronomers have
been able to observe many of their atmospheric details during the last
350 years. The visible disk of Jupiter, the largest of the Jovian planets
and the closest to the Earth, exhibits the greatest detail. Observers with
even small telescopes are quick to notice the alternating light and dark
bands parallel to the equator (Figure 8.6). Before radio observations in
the 1950s, a very large, easily viewed oval, called the Great Red Spot,
was used to measure Jupiter's rotation rate. Less prominent features,
such as white ovals, irregular patches, and streaks, can be seen to move
across the disk of Jupiter when it is studied with large instruments.
Most of the features seen on Jupiter are variable. The bands vary in
color, width, and intensity over time intervals as short as a few months.
Even the long-lived Great Red Spot changes; it became so indistinct in
the late eighteenth century that no one observed it for about 50 years.

Infrared observations reveal that Jupiter radiates more energy than it
receives from the Sun. Observations at visual wavelengths produce a
Planck distribution similar to the Sun's because the visual light seen
from Jupiter or any other planet is reflected sunlight (see Chapter 4).
The radiation emitted by a planet itself, however, peaks far into the
infrared and reveals the planet's cold temperature. At even longer wavelengths, in the radio part of the electromagnetic spectrum, observers
can detect Jupiter's magnetosphere.

Saturn, of course, is famous for its beautiful ring system. Galileo
must have been surprised when he viewed Saturn for the first time
through his telescope in July 1610. In fact, his observations were so
mysterious that he did not immediately publish them, except in the
following anagram:

smiasmrmilmepoetaleumibunenugttauiras.

Translated and deciphered, this means *"I have observed the highest
planet to be triple-bodied"* (Figure 8.7). Galileo saw a bright central disk
with two smaller yet fainter disks one on each side, almost touching the
larger disk. He could not detect any motion of the three disks with respect to each other. Within 50 years of these first observations, astronomers determined that the two small "disks" were actually part of a
flat system of rings; but Galileo and other early observers did not know
what to make of them. Remember that the first telescopes were very

◼️ FIGURE 8.7

Galileo's Views of Saturn

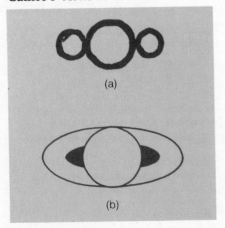

(a)

(b)

■■■■ TABLE 8.4 **Spacecraft Encounter Dates for the Outer Planets**

Spacecraft	Jupiter	Saturn	Uranus	Neptune
Pioneer 10	1973	—	—	—
Pioneer 11	1974	1979	—	—
Voyager 1	1979	1980	—	—
Voyager 2	1979	1981	1986	1989

crude instruments (see Module 2, "Astronomical Instruments and Telescopes") and looking through them was worse than looking through a cheap dime-store plastic toy telescope with crinkled cellophane covering the lens.

Spacecraft exploration of the Jovian planets faces several problems. First is simply their tremendous distance from the Earth; it takes years for a spacecraft to reach them. Second, a wide belt of small, rocky bodies between Mars and Jupiter, called asteroids, must be navigated safely. Since astronomers knew that hundreds of thousands of asteroids, ranging in size from a few centimeters to hundreds of kilometers, inhabited this belt, they were not certain that a spacecraft could survive a passage through it. Finally, a spacecraft must plunge through the intense Jovian radiation field to view the planet at close range. Again, astronomers were not sure a spacecraft could survive.

The first spacecraft designed to explore the outer solar system were *Pioneer 10* and *11* (Table 8.4). Their purpose was to study the interplanetary environment beyond Mars, including the asteroid belt, the radiation field of Jupiter, and the rings of Saturn. The survivability of these spacecraft could not be ensured; these were real pioneers. Planetary astronomers and spacecraft engineers were both anxious and excited when *Pioneer 10* passed through the wide asteroid belt between July 1972 and February 1973 and later when it swept through Jupiter's intense radiation fields. Although some scientific instruments were saturated by the influx of particles and radiation in the radiation belts, and a few pictures were lost due to spurious computer commands induced by the radiation, *Pioneer 10* survived both the asteroid belt and Jupiter's magnetosphere. *Pioneer 11* followed suit exactly one year later and, as it swung by Jupiter, changed its trajectory to rendezvous with Saturn in 1979.

Pioneer 10 and *11* photographed regions of Jupiter inaccessible to Earth-based telescopes and discovered a great variety of structures at the boundaries of the atmospheric bands (Figure 8.8). The spacecraft measured global temperatures far below freezing and confirmed that Jupiter and Saturn radiate more energy than they receive from the Sun. The Pioneer spacecraft were the first to measure the helium abundance of Jupiter and Saturn and found that the ratio of helium to hydrogen is similar to that of the Sun for Jupiter but slightly smaller for Saturn. They also found that the magnetic field of Jupiter was thousands of

(a)

(b)

■■■■■ ■ FIGURE 8.8

Views of Jupiter from
Pioneer 10 and Voyager _1_

(a) Pioneer 10 view in 1973. _(b) Voyager 1_
view in 1979.

SOURCE: NASA.

times stronger than the Earth's and discovered the close alignment between Saturn's magnetic poles and its axis of rotation.

A rare distribution of the outer planets, which occurs every 179 years,
provided an opportunity in the late 1970s for long-lived spacecraft to
explore several planets and satellites in one mission. For a period of
several years, all of the Jovian planets were positioned on the same side
of the solar system. This alignment made it possible for one spacecraft,
over a period of 10 years, to fly by Jupiter, then Saturn, and finally
Uranus and Neptune. _Voyager 1_ and 2 were designed to do just this, and
their first stop was Jupiter.

The design of the Voyagers was based on the proven Mariner spacecraft, but they had to be "hardened" to withstand possible radiation
damage in the magnetic environment of Jupiter. This required radia-
tion-resistant materials, spot shielding of especially sensitive areas on
the spacecraft, and the selection of highly reliable electronic components. After all, the electronic and mechanical components had to last
at least a decade. The Voyagers also had to be equipped with their own
electric power generators because solar panels would be ineffective at
these great distances. Their thermoelectric generators used a radioactive plutonium oxide; as the plutonium decays, it generates heat that is
converted into electricity.

The Voyager missions were probably the most spectacular unmanned
spacecraft missions in history. _Voyager 1_ made a detailed study of the
motion of material in the Great Red Spot and discovered complex interactions between small white spots and the Great Red Spot (Figure
8.9). It found that the temperature above the Great Red Spot was much

cooler than the surrounding regions. *Voyager 1* also detected cloud-top lightning bolts, and on Jupiter's moon Io it photographed the first known active volcano in the solar system outside the Earth. In addition, *Voyager 1* discovered a ring around Jupiter and sent back detailed pictures of Jupiter's other moons showing a variety of surface features, some of which have never before been seen on any planet or moon in the solar system (see the next chapter for more on the Jovian moons). The *Voyager 2* mission showed that the cloud formations, or weather, on Jupiter changed over short periods and observed Jupiter and its satellites from different angles. It studied the ring of Jupiter in greater detail and found that the ring may extend down to the cloud tops. Most of the volcanoes on Io were still active when *Voyager 2* flew by.

Both *Pioneer* and *Voyager* have long passed Jupiter and Saturn. *Pioneer 10* and *11* and *Voyager 1* are not targeted for any other planet and are traveling fast enough to escape from the solar system. *Voyager 2* made stops at Uranus (1986) and Neptune (1989) and is now journeying into the outer reaches of the solar system. One more mission, called *Galileo*, was launched in 1989 and will reach Jupiter in December 1995. *Galileo* will orbit the giant planet, observe its moons, and deploy a probe into Jupiter's atmosphere.

Jupiter and Saturn: Features and Observations

The Pioneer and Voyager observations provided astronomers with the data necessary to determine the temperature structure of the upper regions of Jupiter's atmosphere (Figure 8.10). The lowest temperature, 100 K, occurs above the cloud tops where atmospheric pressures are about 1/10 of the Earth's sea level pressure. Deeper in the atmosphere where pressures are equal to 1 Earth atmosphere, temperatures rise to

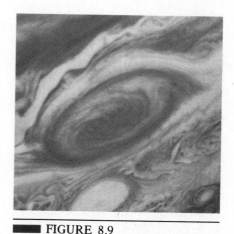

FIGURE 8.9

Jupiter's Great Red Spot

Note the white spots below the Great Red Spot and the clumping of clouds just to the left of the Red Spot and on both sides of the white spot.

SOURCE: NASA.

FIGURE 8.10

Atmospheric Temperature Structures of Jupiter and Saturn

The chemical composition of the clouds is conjecture. Jupiter's clouds are more compressed than Saturn's because of Jupiter's greater surface gravity.

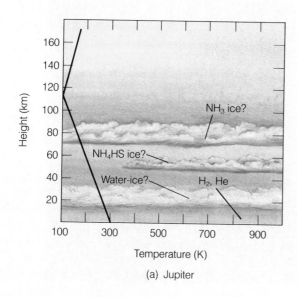

(a) Jupiter

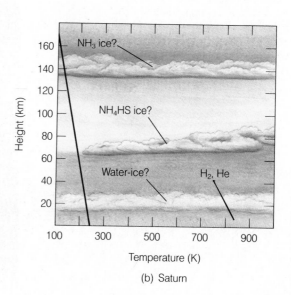

(b) Saturn

MathTools 2: Temperature °F/°C/K

160 K and appear to increase steadily downward. Temperatures as high as 260 K were measured in a few breaks in the clouds; these are presumably from very deep in the atmosphere.

The lowest temperature in Saturn's atmosphere, 83 K, occurs at the cloud tops (Figure 8.10). It is colder at Saturn's cloud tops than Jupiter's because Saturn is farther away from the Sun. Deeper in the atmosphere, at a pressure of 1 Earth atmosphere, temperatures rise to 133 K, still colder than Jupiter. The clouds of Saturn are also more spread out and extend to a higher altitude than Jupiter's clouds because of Saturn's lower surface gravity. The higher the surface gravity, the more compressed the atmosphere. This may explain the subdued appearance of Saturn's cloud features (Figure 8.11); since observers must look through extended cloud decks and haze layers, less detail is visible. In fact, features in Saturn's clouds are so difficult to see that, during the last 100 years of observation, observers have only detected 10 spots that could be seen clearly enough to estimate Saturn's rotational rate. Generally, only one or two of Saturn's bands are visible from the Earth.

Every feature seen in pictures of Jupiter and Saturn is a cloud, but neither the Pioneer nor the Voyager spacecraft penetrated the clouds to determine their compositions. The estimates of cloud compositions are based on the spectroscopically determined chemical composition of the atmospheres, the temperature and pressure structure, and known chem-

■■■ FIGURE 8.11

Jupiter, Saturn, and the Earth

The three planets are shown to scale. Notice that the atmospheric bands in Saturn's atmosphere are less distinct than those in Jupiter's. Saturn has a subdued appearance because its clouds are more spread out within its atmosphere so light reflected off the clouds must pass through more layers of haze.

SOURCE: NASA.

ical reactions between the atoms and molecules in the atmosphere. Atmospheric modeling suggests that the upper most clouds are ammonia ice crystals. The next lower layer, invisible to us, may be ammonium hydrosulfide (NH_3SH) ice with water-ice clouds below that (see Figure 8.10).

One of the most remarkable observations made by the Pioneer and Voyager spacecraft was the very small temperature difference between the dayside and nightside and between the equator and poles of these planets. This suggests that the atmospheric circulation of these giant planets is not dominated by differential solar heating as it is in the small atmospheres of Venus, Earth, and Mars. Internal energy sources probably play an important, but at the moment, unclear role.

Astronomers, however, have no doubt that rapid rotation is mainly responsible for the observed zonal cloud features. The most prominent of these are the alternate light and dark bands seen at low latitudes in both hemispheres. The light bands, called **zones,** are white to pale yellow tinged with red, and the dark bands, called **belts,** are browns mixed with blues. The Voyager infrared measurements of the zones and belts found that the temperatures at the tops of the zones are lower than at the tops of the belts, indicating that the zones are higher in the atmosphere than the belts. The zones are probably upper-level high pressure regions while the belts are low pressure regions; this implies rising motions in the zones and flow from the zones to the belts (Figure 8.12). Zones are probably light in color because ammonia crystallizes and forms light-colored clouds as atmospheric gases rise to cooler levels. The belts then represent regions of descending gas where the ammonia crystals evaporate to uncover deeper and therefore warmer regions of the atmosphere.

The origin of the particular colors of zones and belts is unknown. Since helium, hydrogen, ammonia, methane, and water are colorless, the colors must be due to trace amounts of other compounds, such as phosphorus (red), sulfur molecules (purples and yellows), and perhaps organic, or carbon-containing, compounds (yellows and greens). Furthermore, because the chemical reactions producing the particular mol-

Zones: Light-colored bands of high pressure running parallel to the equators of Jupiter and Saturn; zones are believed to be regions of rising gas.

Belts: Dark-colored bands of low pressure running parallel to the equators of Jupiter and Saturn; belts are believed to be regions of descending gas.

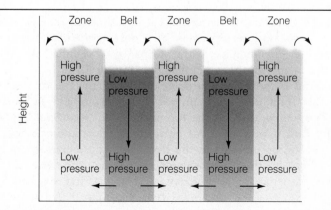

■■■■ FIGURE 8.12

Jovian Atmospheric Circulation between Belts and Zones

The deduction that zones are high pressure regions implies rising motions in the zones.

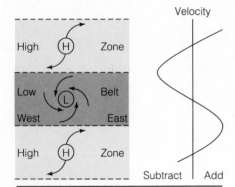

FIGURE 8.13

Wind Direction at the Boundaries of Zones and Belts

Coriolis forces in the northern hemisphere produce winds flowing eastward at the upper boundary of the zones and westward at the lower boundary. The velocity profile to the right shows the resulting wind speeds in the bands.

FIGURE 8.14

Voyager Picture of the Great Red Spot and a White Oval

The circulation is counterclockwise in both features. Turbulent features are seen to the west (left) of the Great Red Spot and the white oval. The turbulence is caused by eastward-moving clouds being deflected downward and then around the features.

SOURCE: NASA.

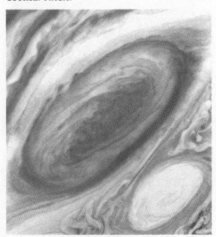

ecules are temperature sensitive, visible regions in the belts and zones are different colors because they are at different temperatures and, therefore, at different heights in the atmosphere. Blue features are the lowest; browns and whites are higher; and the highest features are reddish in color.

An intriguing possibility is that some of the cloud colors may be due to life. Many of these colors are similar to those of organic molecules developed in experiments by Harold Urey and Stanley Miller in the 1950s at the University of Chicago. They subjected a mixture of hydrogen, water vapor, ammonia, and methane to electrical discharges, simulating lightning in the Earth's primitive atmosphere. The results were organic, or carbon-based, molecules, including basic building blocks of life, such as amino acids. Although their experiments were designed to investigate early life on Earth, similar conditions appear to exist in Jupiter's atmosphere today. Since these conditions may have existed for several billion years, primitive life may have developed.

A more fundamental question about the zones and belts is, Why do Jupiter and Saturn have atmospheric bands in the first place? First of all, their rapid rotation ensures a rapid flow from west to east. If the zones are places of rising gas, then the gases will tend to diverge, or spread, at the tops of the zones. Because Jupiter is rotating, the Coriolis effect will divert the parcels of air to the right of their direction of motion in the northern hemisphere and to the left in the southern hemisphere. Since both planets rotate more than twice as fast as the Earth, the Coriolis effect is much stronger than in the Earth's atmosphere. Whereas the Earth exhibits up to three large atmospheric cells in each hemisphere, Jupiter and Saturn are expected to exhibit many more. Furthermore, as can be seen in Figure 8.13, in Jupiter's northern hemisphere the flow on the northern edge of a zone adds to the general rotation while the flow at the southern edge subtracts from the flow. Consequently, wind speeds are expected to increase and decrease with latitude. This is, in fact, what is observed when the motions of small features in individual zones and bands on Jupiter are tracked. Surprisingly, this is not the case with Saturn. Very little correlation is seen between zone and belt boundaries and wind speeds. The zonal winds on Saturn, however, reach speeds of 2880 MPH, four times faster than the winds of Jupiter.

The zonal winds of Jupiter and Saturn produce a variety of large and small features with long lifetimes. The most distinguishable cloud feature on Jupiter, for instance, is the stormlike swirl called the Great Red Spot found in the southern hemisphere (Figure 8.14). It is at least 300 years old and is twice the diameter of the Earth. The intensity of the color of the Great Red Spot can vary from prominent to faint over a decade. The temperature at the top of the Great Red Spot is very cold, indicating that it reaches great elevations. The standard view is that gases are spiraling upward in the Red Spot, but astronomers have no direct evidence for this. Time sequence imaging of the Red Spot shows that the winds rotate counterclockwise with a period of about 6 days.

It is not clear exactly what the Great Red Spot is. Astronomers generally refer to it as a huge atmospheric "storm" that may be driven by the alternate flow of gases in the belt above and the zone below it, spinning it like a wheel. The long lifetime of the Great Red Spot may be related to the fact that Jupiter has no solid surface. On Earth, for instance, tropical storms and hurricanes dissipate rapidly once they reach land where the friction between the rapidly flowing air and the land surface decreases wind strength. The rapid and steady zonal flow and the lack of friction deep in the atmosphere appear to be able to drive and maintain storms on Jupiter for decades and even centuries.

Jupiter's southern hemisphere exhibits three large white ovals just south of the Great Red Spot. Other smaller white spots in the southern hemisphere as well as small brown spots in Jupiter's northern hemisphere are also visible. The three large white storms are only 40 years old and exhibit the same counterclockwise rotation as the Great Red Spot. Prior to 1939 the band occupied by the white ovals was a light-colored zone. During 1939–1940, three spots appeared, and a dark cloud began to spread from each. Eventually, the dark clouds replaced the light zone. The white ovals and the Great Red Spot exhibit wakelike disturbances just to their west. The turbulence is obvious in close-up photographs of the Great Red Spot (Figure 8.14). Time sequence imaging of the region around the Great Red Spot clearly shows clouds bunching up at the western edge of the Great Red Spot, and very small white spots flow around the Great Red Spot from the east. They pause at the western edge and either continue west or swing around the Great Red Spot. At the eastern edge of the Great Red Spot, they typically split up with one segment continuing east and the other entering into the circular, upward flow of the Great Red Spot.

The bands, the zonal wind flow, the Great Red Spot, and the white ovals are quasi-permanent features that exhibit changes in color, brightness, and size over a few years. The bands change in width while the Great Red Spot and white ovals on Jupiter appear to be contracting. The Great Red Spot, for instance, was about 45,000 km across 100 years ago but is now only 25,000 km across. Furthermore, all long-term features in the Jovian atmosphere drift in longitude. You can see in Figure 8.15 that the Great Red Spot moved westward while the white spots

■■ FIGURE 8.15

Cylindrical Projections of *Voyager 1* and *2* Photographic Sequences

Compare the *Voyager 1* picture *(top)* with the *Voyager 2* picture *(bottom)* taken 4 months later. The Great Red Spot drifted westward (left) while the white ovals drifted eastward. You can also see changes in the positions of the brown spots located in the northern hemisphere and in the colors and widths of the zones and belts.

SOURCE: NASA.

■ FIGURE 8.16

The Dark Side of Jupiter

The limb is outlined by polar aurorae while lightning bolts show up as spots on the dark side.

SOURCE: NASA.

moved eastward during the 4-month interval between the *Voyager 1* and *2* flybys.

Regularly spaced white, cometlike plumes at about 10°N latitude can also be seen in Figure 8.15. These begin as rapid eruptions of clouds followed by a spreading of the bright cloud westward and toward the equator. The low temperatures measured for the plume heads indicate that they are very high in the atmosphere, suggesting that the plumes are rapidly rising clouds. The nucleus of a plume can be several thousand kilometers across and show smaller features that look like thick Earth cumulus clouds. It is puzzling that the plumes are seen only in the Jovian northern hemisphere. Perhaps the existence of large-scale features, such as the Great Red Spot and the white ovals, prevent the development of plumes in the southern hemisphere. Similar plumes are seen in Saturn's atmosphere but rise about 10 times faster.

The Voyagers detected aurorae, meteors, and lightning on the dark side of Jupiter. Aurorae appear to originate at several layers starting about 700 km above the clouds. These were observed only at the poles, as is true for aurorae on Earth (Figure 8.16). Meteors were seen burning up in the Jovian atmosphere as they plunged through the gaseous envelope while lightning was observed in clusters of bolts uniformly distributed around the dark side. The clustering is indicative of electrical storms.

■ URANUS AND NEPTUNE

Humans have been aware of Mercury, Venus, Mars, Jupiter, and Saturn since prehistoric times because these planets are visible to the unaided eye. Astronomers of early civilizations could follow their motions in the heavens, and eventually the analysis and subsequent explanations of these motions resulted in no less than the scientific revolution. Thus scientists developed a very good understanding of planetary motion in complete ignorance of the existence of Uranus and Neptune. Their discovery came almost 200 years after the invention of the telescope. Uranus was discovered during a systematic telescopic survey of the sky, even though it is just visible to the unaided eye when it is near perihelion. Its discovery was the key to the discovery of Neptune and of the more distant Pluto. Certain peculiarities in the observed orbit of Uranus inspired astronomers to look specifically for these two outer planets using mathematical predictions of their orbits and positions.

Discovery and Exploration

William Herschel (1738–1822) was a professional musician and an amateur astronomer who delighted in viewing the heavens with his homemade telescopes. In England in 1781 he began an ambitious program of observations by which he hoped to determine the structure of the universe. His immense task required that he conduct a complete survey of the heavens and record the position of every object in the sky that he could see with his telescopes. After observing nearly 15,000 stars as part of his survey, Herschel observed an object on March 13, 1781, that had a distinct visible disk. He knew that stars were so far away that they could only be seen through his telescopes as pinpoints of light. His continued observations of the object convinced him that it moved relative to the stars. Herschel had discovered the seventh planet.

At first, neither Herschel nor anyone else believed that the new object was a planet. Herschel himself thought that he had discovered a comet (see Chapter 10 for more on comets). No one expected a seventh planet. For several thousand years astronomers had known only six planets: Why should the solar system have more? Herschel's discovery took everyone by surprise, but continued observations and refined orbital calculations eventually convinced astronomers that Herschel's object was indeed a planet.

The new object was named Uranus at the suggestion of the German astronomer Johann Bode (1747–1826). Bode argued that the name Uranus would make the solar system a mythological family since Uranus was the husband of Earth, the father of Saturn, and the grandfather of Jupiter. Jupiter, in turn, was the father of Mercury, Venus, and Mars. Actually Herschel suggested the name "Georgium Sidus," or George's star, in honor of King George III of England. Although Herschel later gracefully agreed to Bode's suggested name, George III felt that Herschel's heart was in the right place and rewarded him with a nice stipend and a prestigious position. Sometimes even astronomers have need of a bit of political shrewdness.

Uranus actually had been observed at least twice before Herschel's observations, once in 1690 and again in 1756. These observations were found in old catalogs and notebooks in which the observer recorded the position of Uranus and, thinking that it was just a star, never checked its position later to see if it had moved with respect to other stars. Seven years of continuous observations between 1781 and 1788 and these two old positions should have been sufficient for astronomers to calculate a very accurate orbit of Uranus using Newton's laws of motion and gravity (Figure 8.17). But the positions of Uranus predicted from the computed orbit were always significantly different from the latest observed positions. Even by the first decade of the nineteenth century, after astronomers had discovered a total of 17 observations of Uranus made before 1781 and had 40 years of new observations, the calculated orbits could not accurately predict the position of Uranus. Clearly, something was wrong.

A few astronomers immediately suspected that Newton's theory of gravity was incorrect. Since the mathematical basis for the orbit calculations for Uranus was the theory of gravity, the computed orbits were, in effect, predictions of the theory. If the predictions were wrong, so was the theory. This apparent refutation of Newton's theory of gravity turned into a major triumph, however.

Although some astronomers in the middle of the nineteenth century questioned Newton's theory, most astronomers did not. The latter group believed that an unknown planet lay beyond Uranus, a "trans-Uranian" planet, and thought that it was changing the orbit of Uranus by its gravitational attraction. They reasoned that when Uranus was

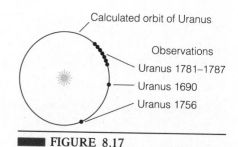

■ FIGURE 8.17

Computing Orbits

The observed positions of Uranus in its orbit for the years 1690, 1756, and 1781–1787 are shown. The calculated orbit is a closed line that passes through all of these observed positions. If astronomers can find an orbit through these positions, they assume that the planet will travel over other parts of the calculated orbit. In this way, the location of a planet can be predicted.

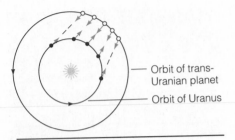

■ FIGURE 8.18

Suspected Accelerations of Uranus by an Unknown Planet

The arrows between Uranus and the trans-Uranian planet represent gravitational forces that accelerate and decelerate Uranus; the longer the arrow, the stronger the force. Every time Uranus "passes" the trans-Uranian planet, its orbital velocity is changed slightly. This causes slight changes in its orbit.

■ FIGURE 8.19

Visual Observations of Uranus

This drawing of Uranus was made by amateur astronomer Stephen O'Meara on July 23, 1981, using the Harvard Observatory's 9-inch Clark refractor.

SOURCE: Stephen J. O'Meara, Assistant Editor, *Sky & Telescope* magazine.

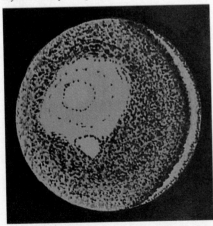

moving toward the unknown outer planet, which moved in a more distant orbit, the gravitational attraction between the two planets would accelerate Uranus in the direction of the trans-Uranian planet. As Uranus swung by the outer planet, as illustrated in Figure 8.18, Uranus was decelerated. These constant accelerations and decelerations produced *perturbations*, or small changes, in the orbit of Uranus. If astronomers knew the orbit, location, and mass of the trans-Uranian planet, they could calculate its gravitational effect on Uranus using Newton's law of universal gravity. The problem encountered by nineteenth-century astronomers was just the opposite; given the differences between the observed positions and the predicted positions, they had to find the perturbing planet.

The Englishman John Adams (1819–1892) and the Frenchman Urbain Leverrier (1811–1877) independently solved the problem of finding the trans-Uranian planet. Both men labored over the detailed computations for the unknown planet's orbit from which they could predict its position for any date. With the solutions in hand, however, neither mathematician could find anyone in his own country to look for the planet! Frustrated by his fellow Frenchmen's refusal to search for the planet, Leverrier sent his calculations to Johann Galle (1812–1910) at the Berlin Observatory. On the night of September 23, 1846, the first night that Galle looked for the trans-Uranian planet with Leverrier's calculated position, he found it! Although French astronomers insisted that the planet should be called Leverrier, Leverrier himself suggested the mythological name Neptune (see AstroProbe 9 for more on the mythological names of planets). Today both Adams and Leverrier are credited with the discovery of Neptune, the eighth planet, and the calculated orbit represents a triumph for Newton's theory of gravity.

As with Uranus, astronomers have discovered records of observations of Neptune in the notebooks of astronomers who did not recognize it as a planet. In all fairness to some of these observers, the early telescopes did not give as crisp, sharp images of planets or stars as even the most inexpensive telescope made today. Poor optics can produce a bloated, fuzzy image of a star that would look like a disk. The earliest record of a possible observation of Neptune may have been made by Galileo! In January 1613, Neptune happened to be located near Jupiter in the sky. While recording the positions of the moons of Jupiter, Galileo recorded the appearance of a faint object with about the right brightness for Neptune. Galileo even noted that this object seemed to move relative to the stars. Apparently he was not sure enough about the motions to realize the importance of his observation.

On January 24, 1986, *Voyager 2*, still functioning after 8½ years in deep space, flew by Uranus. It approached the Uranian system head-on; Uranus, with its rings facing *Voyager 2*, looked like a bull's eye target. *Voyager* took approximately 7,000 pictures of Uranus, its satellites, and rings as it passed quickly through the Uranian system. Before the *Voyager* encounter, observers had reported seeing spots, bands, and a dark polar region (Figure 8.19); 5 satellites had been discovered between 1787 and 1948 and 9 thin rings by 1978; methane and hydrogen had been detected; and astronomers suspected a high helium content. The *Voyager* mission verified the banded structure of the clouds of Uranus, discovered 10 more satellites and 2 more rings, verified the existence of helium, and discovered a strong and unusual magnetic field.

Voyager 2 has been traveling through our solar system since its launch in September 1977, more than a decade ago. It has moved silently among the planets in a semidormant state, conserving fuel and energy, but occasionally making an observation or performing an engineering test. When it approached a planet, it reawakened: computers relayed instructions, rockets fired, and cameras moved. In the summer of 1989, *Voyager 2* wakened for the last time before voyaging beyond the known solar system when it flew by the eighth planet. It photographed a beautiful blue planet having a huge atmospheric storm similar to Jupiter's Great Red Spot and showing high, frosty white cirrus clouds. *Voyager 2* also discovered 6 small moons, 3 rings, and an unusual magnetic field.

Uranus

Astronomers have usually grouped Uranus with Jupiter and Saturn because Uranus is larger and more massive than the Earth, has a low density, is surrounded by many moons and rings, has a short rotational period, and exhibits Jovian atmospheric phenomena. For instance, Uranus has a zonal wind circulation with winds moving east to west (Figure 8.20). In internal structure, mass, and diameter, however, Uranus, like Neptune, differs appreciably from Jupiter and Saturn.

Although the atmosphere of Uranus is similar to Jupiter and Saturn in that it does show some indication of zonal flow parallel to its equator, it is somewhat surprising. Since the Sun is shining down on the south pole of Uranus, winds might be expected to circulate from the south pole toward the equator and possibly toward the north pole. It is clear from the observed banded appearance photographed by *Voyager 2* that this is not the case; the circulation is symmetric about the axis of rotation. The zonal wind circulation of Uranus emphasizes the importance of planetary rotation in global circulation. At the same time, it is fair to point out that Uranus is so far from the Sun that solar heating is minuscule; it is so small that it is not able to drive global atmospheric circulation.

Each of the planets viewed through a telescope exhibits a characteristic color. Venus is white due to its sulfuric acid clouds; Mars is red due to its iron-rich soil; and Saturn is yellow-white due to light-colored ammonia ice crystals. Observers usually describe Uranus as blue-green, and *Voyager's* color pictures show a light blue with a tint of green (Figure 8.21). The color of Uranus is due to methane gas. The low temperatures in the Uranian atmosphere allow methane ice crystals to form, and they form deeper in the cold Uranian atmosphere than do the ammonia clouds in the Jovian or Saturnian atmosphere. This means that the sunlight reflected off the deep Uranian methane clouds passes through a greater amount of atmosphere than on Jupiter or Saturn. Since a major absorbing constituent of this atmosphere is methane,

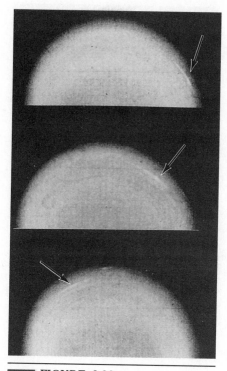

FIGURE 8.20

Bands on Uranus

In these Voyager pictures, the south pole of Uranus is at the left of center on the disk pointing toward the viewer. Bands can be seen at lower latitudes, and a convective plume can be seen to rotate from right to left in the upper part of the disk.

SOURCE: NASA.

■ FIGURE 8.21

Uranus in Color

Uranus would look this blue-green color to us if we were in orbit about the planet.
SOURCE: NASA.

which absorbs red light, the reflected solar light is predominantly blues and greens.

Neptune

If Uranus and Neptune were placed side by side, they would appear very much the same. The similarities between Uranus and Neptune start with size; both have diameters about four times larger than the Earth's. Neptune, however, is slightly more massive than Uranus. Consequently, Neptune's greater average density implies that it has a greater fraction of heavy, rocklike material than Uranus does. Still, Neptune, like Uranus, is more compressed for its mass than are Jupiter and Saturn. It appears, therefore, that water may be an important component of the interiors of both Uranus and Neptune.

Although the interior structures of Uranus and Neptune are probably similar, astronomers would normally expect Neptune's atmosphere to be colder (about 15 K colder) than the atmosphere of Uranus because Neptune is 1½ times farther from the Sun. Unlike Uranus, however, the more massive Neptune radiates more energy than it receives from the Sun. This, in turn, warms the atmosphere despite its greater distance from the Sun.

The great distance to Neptune makes it difficult to see distinct features on the planet because it is small and faint. Any cloud features on the visible disk of Neptune would be just at the threshold of visibility even with the largest telescopes using optimum magnifications. Observers have claimed to see atmospheric bands but these were very faint and at the limit of detectability. Observers have also reported a variable haze layer that sometimes enshrouds half of the planet. The haze can dissipate and re-form in a matter of weeks. At the same time, photographs from Earth-based telescopes made at infrared wavelengths show distinct cloud features. Consequently, astronomers expected to see a banded planet when *Voyager 2* flew by Neptune. The amount of detail observed, however, was a pleasant surprise to astronomers and a fitting end to the 12-year mission of the Voyager spacecraft.

The *Voyager 2* flyby in August 1989 revealed a beautiful blue planet with definite but subdued atmospheric bands and several distinct cloud features. The blue color was expected because Neptune looks blue when viewed through a telescope on Earth and because Neptune's relatively high abundance of methane ensures the absorption of red sunlight as it passes through the Neptunian atmosphere.

The southern hemisphere of Neptune is dominated by a large blue oval, wide light and dark bands encircling the planet, lesser ovals, and wispy clouds (Figure 8.22). The large blue oval, or spot, is about the size of the Earth and lies about 20° south of Neptune's equator. It is probably a giant rotating storm system, reminiscent of Jupiter's Great Red Spot. Its rotation appears to be counterclockwise as with the Great Red Spot (Panel b). During the flyby, a dark feature was observed to develop and extend westward from the blue spot. It may be a sign of atmospheric turbulence in the flow of air around the storm or it could be a flow of material from the storm. Because Neptune is so faint and its

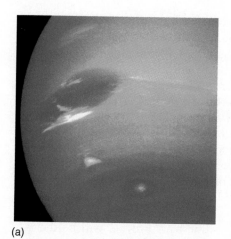

(a)

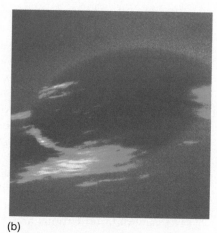

(b)

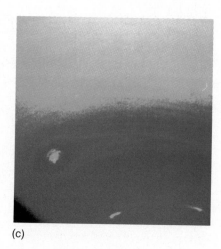

(c)

features are not very distinct, it is hard to see enough detail over a long enough period of time to follow trends in the atmosphere. Several smaller cloud systems are also visible. The largest is a small oval in the middle of a wide dark band at about 55° south of the equator (Panels a and c). This also appears to be a cloud system, similar perhaps to the white spots seen in the atmosphere of Jupiter.

Great turbulent waves are not seen surrounding the spots probably because of an extended, thin haze covering the planet. The haze is detected at infrared wavelengths reflected by methane gas. The planet-wide haze envelope is probably caused by ultraviolet radiation splitting molecules of methane (CH_4), which later recombine into more complex molecules such as ethane (C_2H_6) and acetylene (C_2H_2). These compunds then drift to lower altitudes and form a hazy covering over the deeper clouds.

The dark bands and storms are highlighted by wispy, cirruslike, white clouds. These are high in the atmosphere, and because of the low atmospheric temperatures (55 K = −360°F), they are probably methane ice crystals. Although methane clouds were expected, the high cirrus were a surprise. These appear to be much higher in the atmosphere than the large blue spot and other storm systems. At the same time, some of these methane cirrus are associated with the large blue spot. A bright patch of clouds lies just to the south of the large blue spot and one covers a small region of the northwest boundary; these two have remained in the vicinity for several months. Furthermore, white cirrus clouds have been seen to appear rapidly over the large blue spot and dissipate over several hours, clearly indicating the dynamic nature of the Neptunian atmosphere.

About a week before Voyager's close encounter with Neptune, scientists detected radio emission from the planet's magnetic field. Tracking the signal as the planet rotated allowed astronomers to determine the length of the Neptunian day, which lasts 16 hours and 7 minutes. This is just a little shorter than the 17 hours and 40 minutes scientists expected based on the difficult visual observations from Earth. Voyager scientists were surprised, however, to find that the orientation of the

■■■ FIGURE 8.22

Neptune

(a) Embedded in the middle of Neptune's southern hemisphere is a dark blue oval and several other ovals and spots. *(b)* A close-up of the large blue spot. This storm system rotates counterclockwise. *(c)* This close-up of Neptune by *Voyager 2* shows a large white spot and two white clouds near the south pole of Neptune.

SOURCE: Jet Propulsion Laboratory.

magnetic field was tilted 50° with respect to Neptune's rotational axis (Figure 8.5). This is similar to the 59° tilt of the magnetic field of Uranus. In the case of Uranus, scientists felt that this was a peculiar system anyway and perhaps the odd orientation of the magnetic field was an aftereffect of a collision sometime in its past. It has been suggested that maybe the magnetic field of Uranus is changing polarities as Earth's field does. We now know of two planets with apparently peculiar orientations of their magnetic fields; it is unlikely that both have had identical histories or are passing through the same magnetic reversal phase. The reasons for these particular orientations are unknown; much work on the understanding of the generation of planetary magnetic fields is needed before we will be able to give satisfactory explanations to these apparently peculiar systems.

The new data on Uranus and Neptune by *Voyager 2* will be the last planetary information from space probes traveling in these dark outer regions of the solar system for decades to come.

PLUTO

In mythology, Pluto was the ruler of the dark underworld; appropriately, Pluto, the ninth planet, was discovered in the distant dim and gloomy regions of the solar system. Actually, several names for the ninth planet were seriously considered by Lowell Observatory, where the discovery was made; Minerva, Cronus, and Pluto were the most popular. The ninth planet could very well have been called Minerva after the goddess of wisdom, but that name was already given to an asteroid. Cronus was also a good possibility, but it is the Greek name for the god Saturn! Interestingly, the symbol for Pluto, ♇, is a combination of the letters P and L, the initials of Percival Lowell. Although Lowell's theories concerning life on Mars are well known, few realize that his dedication to the trans-Neptunian problem eventually led to Pluto's discovery in 1930. (See Table 8.5 for a summary of the basic information that we know about Pluto.)

Discovery

After the discovery of Neptune, astronomers were in a position to compute an orbit for Uranus in which they could take into account the gravitational perturbations caused by the previously unknown planet Neptune and, of course, by the giants Jupiter and Saturn. The newly calculated orbits for Uranus still did not accurately predict the movement of the planet. Could another planet, a "trans-Neptunian" planet, be orbiting still farther from the Sun? Astronomers eventually accepted this hypothesis, and several attempts were made to calculate the orbit of the unknown planet. Only brief searches, however, were conducted, and all appeared unsuccessful. As a result of these initial failures, astronomers in the late nineteenth and early twentieth centuries were generally skeptical about the existence of a ninth planet. At this time,

■■■ TABLE 8.5 **Pluto Data**

Orbital semimajor axis	39.4 AU (5.9 billion km)
Perihelion distance	29.7 AU (4.4 billion km)
Aphelion distance	49.2 AU (7.4 billion km)
Eccentricity	0.248
Orbital period (sidereal)	248.6 years
Rotational period	6.39 days
Inclination	94°
Diameter	≈2300 km (≈0.18 Earth diameters)
Mass	≈1.2 × 10²² kg (≈0.002 Earth masses)
Mean density	≈2.1 g/cm³
Escape velocity	≈1 km/s (≈2240 MPH)
Surface temperature	50 K (−220°C = −364°F)

however, Percival Lowell (1855–1916) became intensely interested in the problem of a trans-Neptunian planet.

Lowell launched two searches for the trans-Neptunian planet at Lowell Observatory. The first search, between 1905 and 1910, was a photographic survey of a narrow strip along the ecliptic. Although it was unsuccessful, Lowell gained important insights into how to plan and conduct photographic planetary searches. Most importantly, Lowell learned that random searches were useless; he needed a prediction for the position of the planet. Consequently, during Lowell's second search between 1910 and 1915, he relied on extensive computations, of the type done by Leverrier but carried much further, to calculate the orbit of the suspected planet. His calculations, done in Boston with a team of mathematicians, were used to direct the photographic search at the observatory in Arizona. Although the trans-Neptunian planet was not identified during this second search, inspections of the survey photographs 15 years later revealed that the planet was unknowingly photographed twice in 1915.

To understand the immensity of the task of identifying a planet from a tiny point of light on a **photographic plate,** you must realize that every photographic plate developed during these early surveys contained tens of thousands of stars. Lowell had two plates taken several weeks apart of each region of the sky to be searched. He would then scan the plates with a magnifying glass looking for a planet. If he had photographed a part of the sky where the planet was located, the planet would appear on one plate and not be visible on the other, or, if visible, it would be in a different location. Imagine how easy it would be to miss two specks on over 400 plates!

Photographic plate: Glass that has a light-sensitive coating, called an emulsion, cemented onto it; when the emulsion is exposed to light and then developed, it produces a permanent record of an image, called a negative, just as a 35 mm camera does. Astronomers generally study the glass negatives directly, rather than prints made from the negatives.

FIGURE 8.23

Clyde W. Tombaugh

Clyde Tombaugh at the 37-cm (13-in) telescope dome carrying a 36-by-43 cm plate holder. This photograph was taken in the summer of 1931 at the Lowell Observatory.

The third, and successful, search for the trans-Neptunian planet by Lowell Observatory was begun in 1929 by Clyde Tombaugh (1906–), a young amateur observer whom the observatory hired for the planetary search. During the 14 years between the second and third searches, Lowell Observatory built a new telescope especially for the purpose. It was small by today's standards, but it gave exceptionally clear images over a large region of the sky. The photographic plates used with this telescope, however, were huge, measuring 36-by-43 cm (14-by-17 inches) and containing hundreds of thousands of stars (Figure 8.23). Lowell Observatory also improved the method of comparing plates by purchasing an instrument called a *blink-microscope comparator*. With a blink microscope an observer is able to look at identical regions on two plates at the same time. While you peer at the plates through a microscope eyepiece, the comparator mechanically shifts your view from one plate to the other and back again. If an object is on one plate but not on the other, it appears to blink on and off as the comparator switches views.

On February 18, 1930, Clyde Tombaugh was blinking a pair of plates with 400,000 stars each. After he had searched about one-fourth of each plate, he noticed one image appearing and disappearing on the blink microscope. Another image nearby was doing the same thing. If both images were in the field of view of the microscope eyepiece, the image would appear to jump back and forth. Tombaugh hoped that his image was that of the ninth planet that had moved between the time he took the first and second plates. Comparison with other plates taken in January 1930 confirmed that the object did indeed move (Figure 8.24). Clyde Tombaugh had discovered the ninth planet in the solar system.

After the discovery of Pluto, other observatories began reexamining their old plates. They soon discovered that Pluto, like Uranus and Neptune before it, had been observed before its official discovery; Pluto had been photographed as early as 1908. In fact, plates taken intentionally for a search for the trans-Neptunian planet in 1919 did record images of Pluto. The search was based on calculations by William H. Pickering (1858–1938) of Harvard University. The image of Pluto on the plates was missed by the individual who examined the plates. This, of course, was a great disappointment to Pickering. Clyde Tombaugh, now an emeritus professor of astronomy at New Mexico State University, was the last person to discover a planet. Only three others before him, Herschel, Adams, and Leverrier, had also discovered planets.

Pluto and Its Satellite

Although Pluto was the last planet discovered and has an orbit with the largest semimajor axis, it is currently not the most distant planet from the Sun. Figure 8.25 shows the orbits of Saturn, Uranus, Neptune, and Pluto for two orientations. In Panel a, you are looking down on the solar system with the planets revolving around the Sun in a counterclockwise direction. The orbits of Uranus and Neptune are more nearly circular than the orbit of Pluto. In fact, Pluto has the most eccentric planetary orbit known in the solar system. Although Pluto lies more than 49 AU

from the Sun at aphelion, it is closer to the Sun at perihelion than Neptune ever gets. Pluto is currently closer to the Sun than Neptune and will remain so until 1999. Panel b shows that although Pluto can be closer to the Sun than Neptune, the two planets cannot collide because the orbit of Pluto is tilted with respect to that of Neptune.

Astronomers have never seen any surface feature on Pluto from the Earth. Clyde Tombaugh recognized Pluto only by its motion on the celestial sphere, not by a visible disk. Even viewed through the largest telescopes in the world, Pluto is just a point of light, featureless and without dimensions. How then were the data about Pluto in Table 8.5, such as diameter and rotation period, obtained? All of the information is hidden in the light from Pluto. For instance, Pluto's light is not steady. When observed over several days, Pluto changes its brightness regularly, passing through a cycle of bright, dim, and bright every 6.4 days. Since Pluto is too large to have an irregular shape, which could cause light variations, astronomers assume that Pluto's surface is not uniform (Figure 8.26). Pluto may have a hemisphere of bright ice or a dark coating, or it may have a few large bright spots located here and there.

Light variations can also be used to determine the diameter of Pluto. In particular, **occultations,** which occur when a star is eclipsed by a planet, present an opportunity for astronomers to measure the diameter of a planet by simply measuring how long the star is behind the planet. An occultation of a star by a planet is similar to a solar eclipse in which the Moon blocks out the Sun. Similarly, Pluto blocks out the light from the distant star it occults. Because Pluto is so small, however, occultations of stars are rare and are difficult to observe due to its distance. When occultations do occur, astronomers try to find a location from

FIGURE 8.24

A Small Area from Two Plates of Pluto

Pluto is marked with an arrow on each plate. Since the star fields are the same, you can see that Pluto has moved. These plates also give you a sense of how difficult it is to detect a faint planet on plates with thousands of star images.

SOURCE: Lowell Observatory photograph.

Occultation: An eclipse of a planet or star by the Moon or a planet.

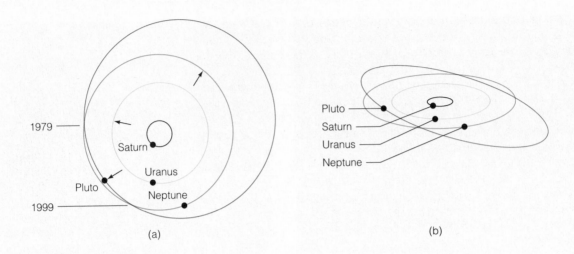

(a)   (b)

FIGURE 8.25

Orbits of the Outer Planets

(a) View of the orbits of Saturn, Uranus, Neptune, and Pluto as seen from above the solar system. The short arrows point to the perihelion positions of Uranus, Neptune, and Pluto. Pluto's orbit is very eccentric and is actually closer to the Sun than Uranus for about 20 years. *(b)* An almost edge-on view of the orbits of the outer planets that illustrates the tilt of Pluto's orbit, 17°, to the ecliptic. Consequently, Pluto and Neptune cannot collide. The relative positions of the planets are for 1989.

which to view the occultation so that the star passes through the middle of Pluto's disk. This is not always possible for two reasons. One is that relatively large telescopes are needed to observe Pluto; it is not easy to move large telescopes. Second, astronomers do not know the exact position of Pluto in its orbit well enough to predict the locations on Earth of Pluto's shadow. The position of Pluto at the time of the occultation must be calculated from Pluto's orbit as determined from the measured positions of Pluto on many photographic images of the planet taken before the suspected occultation. Pluto's position is uncertain, however, because the light producing the image is not from Pluto alone. It is from Pluto and its moon, and the light from even a faint moon will distort the image, leading to uncertainty in its position on the plate and finally to imprecise locations on the Earth from which to view the occultation.

Despite these difficulties, astronomers have observed grazing occultations of stars by Pluto in which the star passed behind the upper or lower limb of Pluto. Although astronomers could not determine Pluto's diameter, they did discover that Pluto has an atmosphere. Although methane had been detected spectroscopically before the occultation data were obtained, it was not clear if the spectra were produced by a

FIGURE 8.26

Rotation of Pluto

Pluto's 6.4-day variation in brightness may be caused by a highly reflective region on its surface that faces the Earth periodically as Pluto rotates on its axis. In this figure, Pluto is rotating toward us as it moves in its orbit.

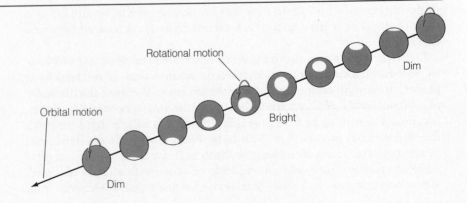

gaseous methane atmosphere or by sunlight reflecting off methane ice. Some astronomers now suspect that the atmosphere of Pluto may contain substantial amounts of other elements, the likeliest major candidate being carbon dioxide.

Some constituents of Pluto's atmosphere may not be present throughout its 248-year revolution about the Sun. These gases do not escape; they just freeze. At aphelion, a distance of 7.4 billion km (49.2 AU) from the Sun, Pluto is the coldest planet in the solar system. Methane freezes there. On the other hand, at perihelion Pluto is 60% closer to the Sun and attains its highest temperature. Since Pluto reached perihelion in 1989, it is now about as warm as it ever gets. If any ices or frosts are going to evaporate from the surface and form an atmosphere, now is the most probable time. As Pluto moves away from the Sun and temperatures drop, the gases will eventually condense out of the atmosphere into ice.

The fact that Pluto has a moon and that its orbit about Pluto is unusual presents astronomers with another method for determining the physical properties of Pluto as well as of its moon. The discovery of the moon occurred in 1978, when the U.S. Naval Observatory began a series of photographic observations of Pluto to improve its orbital data. In June, while examining the photographic plates, James Christy noticed an appendage to the image of Pluto (Figure 8.27). Christy and his co-workers examined older photographs of Pluto and took a series of new photographs. They discovered that the appendage moved around Pluto with a period of about 6 days. Their conclusion was the only logical explanation: the appendage was a satellite of Pluto. The official name of Pluto's moon is Charon, after the mythological boatman who ferried souls of the dead across the river Styx to the underworld ruled by Pluto.

Scientists have successfully measured the period of Charon and find that it is in synchronous rotation about Pluto; that is, Charon's orbital period is 6.4 days, the same as the rotation period of Pluto. Furthermore, Charon's orbit is nearly perpendicular to the plane of the solar system (Panel a in Figure 8.28). Charon, however, is not responsible for the 6.4-day variation in the light output from Pluto because its orbital orientation is such that it has passed in front of Pluto only recently for the first time since its discovery. Charon's orbit may indicate something very interesting about Pluto. The fact that Charon is in synchronous rotation implies that Charon probably lies near Pluto's equatorial plane. Therefore, the rotational axis of Pluto may be tipped over.

The peculiar orientation of Pluto and Charon as they orbit the Sun produces (1) transits of Charon in front of Pluto and (2) occultations of Charon by Pluto as seen from the Earth (Panel b in Figure 8.28). These events occur for a 5-year interval every 124 years. Fortunately, the most recent 5-year period for these transits and occultations occurred between 1985 and 1990; the last time this happened was during the Civil War and the next time will be in the twenty-second century. Each of these 4¼-hour transits and occultations causes the light from the Pluto-Charon system to decrease; the light variations can be used to determine the diameters of both. The analysis of the transit and occultation data is complicated. The first and last events are grazing where only

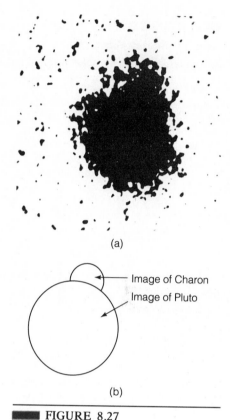

(a)

(b)

■ FIGURE 8.27

Pluto and Charon

(a) Photograph of Pluto showing the elongation, or bump, on its highly magnified image. *(b)* Orientation of the images of Pluto and Charon in the photograph.

SOURCE: Part (a) official U.S. Naval Observatory photograph.

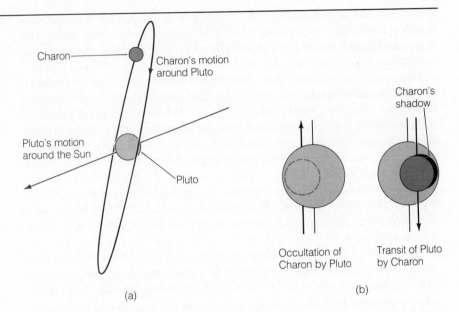

■ FIGURE 8.28

Orbit of Charon About Pluto

(a) The large arrow shows the direction of Pluto's motion around the Sun. Charon orbits Pluto in a clockwise direction in this drawing. (b) The orientation of Pluto and Charon between 1985 and 1990 as seen from the Earth. Charon was occulted by Pluto and transited the planet about once a week during this 5-year period.

part of Pluto or Charon is eclipsed. When Charon is in front of Pluto, part of the light from Pluto is blocked by Charon itself and part by Charon's shadow. In addition, Pluto and Charon do not have uniform surfaces. Pluto appears to have bright and dark spots while the presence of water-ice may cause the hemisphere of Charon that always faces Pluto to be brighter than the side that always faces away from Pluto, which apparently lacks water-ice. All of these factors must be introduced into the analysis of the observations before physical data can be obtained.

The most interesting aspect of the mass of Pluto listed in Table 8.5 is that Pluto could not be Lowell's trans-Neptunian planet! Its mass is much too small to produce appreciable gravitational perturbations on the orbits of Uranus or Neptune. In fact, recent studies of the perturbations of Uranus due to a trans-Uranian planet have shown that no significant perturbations really exist. Nevertheless, the discovery of Pluto was clearly the result of Lowell's dedication to the search.

Because of Pluto's low mass and small diameter, astronomers question whether it deserves the title "planet." Pluto is actually smaller than the Moon and the four large satellites of Jupiter, although after the first good estimates of the diameter of Pluto were made in 1950, astronomers thought that it was larger than Mercury; these estimates were as high as 6000 km. Although Pluto should perhaps be called a "minor planet" or "planetesimal," traditionally, it has been called a planet and will probably always receive that designation.

The Origin of Pluto

Pluto more closely resembles a small icy moon (see Chapter 9) than a rocky Earth-like planet. Since Pluto's orbit brings it close to the orbit of Neptune, the idea that Pluto was once a satellite of Neptune has been popular since soon after Pluto's discovery. But how could Pluto have been ejected from the Neptunian system into its present eccentric orbit? According to an early suggestion, Pluto, as a moon of Neptune, interacted with Triton, another moon of Neptune, in some complicated manner that ejected Pluto and drastically changed the orbit of Triton. Astronomers have always had problems with this idea because the orbits of Neptune and Pluto do not actually intersect. Furthermore, recent mass estimates for Pluto do not seem to lead to any plausible chain of events that would eject Pluto and, at the same time, change Triton's orbital direction. Nevertheless, Pluto could have been a moon of Neptune that collided with or was tidally disrupted by a large primitive solar system object. If the object was massive enough—several times the mass of the Earth—it could have changed the orbits of Neptune's moons, Triton and Nereid, and ejected a disrupted Pluto. Charon could then be one of the tidally disrupted pieces of the original Pluto. On the other hand, instead of emerging from a collision with a phantom body roaming the solar system, Pluto may have simply originated as a satellite of the Sun like the other planets. The idea of Moon-sized objects in the outer solar system is consistent with current theories about the formation of planets (see Chapter 11).

▰ SUMMARY

Jupiter and Saturn have been known since ancient times because they are easily seen in the night sky. Uranus was discovered by chance while Neptune was found at a location predicted by Newton's laws of motion and gravity. These planets are characterized by large masses and large diameters; low average densities; gaseous, cloudy atmospheres; no solid surfaces; and very rapid rotation.

The atmospheres of the Jovian planets are composed of nearly 100% hydrogen and helium with detectable traces of methane and ammonia. All features seen in pictures of the disks of the Jovian planets are atmospheric clouds. Cloud features include zones, belts, the Great Red Spot on Jupiter, the large blue oval on Neptune, white and brown spots, ovals, and plumes. Saturn's features are more difficult to see than Jupiter's because the cloud layers are spread over a greater altitude range on Saturn, producing a haze that masks details in the cloud structure.

The atmospheres of Jupiter and Saturn also show differential rotation with the equatorial regions rotating slightly faster than the polar regions. The internal rotation of Jupiter, Saturn, and Neptune is measured from the radio radiation emitted by the particles trapped in their magnetic fields. It is assumed that these magnetic fields are generated in the interiors by the rapid rotation of their mantles.

Although hydrogen and helium gases form the extensive atmospheres, the interiors of these giant planets are believed to consist of large liquid mantles; the immense pressure of overlying matter compresses the atoms and molecules to densities typical of liquids. The high internal temperatures maintain the fluid properties of hydrogen and helium even at very high densities in Jupiter and Saturn. The density is so high in these planets that hydrogen behaves as a metal. The interiors of Uranus and Neptune are cooler and consist mainly of liquids rich in oxygen, carbon, nitrogen, and hydrogen, such as water (H_2O), methane (CH_4), and ammonia (NH_3). The large liquid mantles of the Jovian planets probably surround massive rocky cores.

Because the interior of a Jovian planet gradually becomes liquid, its atmosphere is never in contact with a solid surface. The atmospheres of the Jovian planets are characterized by high-speed east and west winds in light zones and dark belts. Atmospheric zones and belts reflect the motions generated by the strong Coriolis effects caused by rapid rotation. Chemical reactions, which are not completely understood, produce the rich variety of color in the atmospheres, especially visible in Jupiter's atmosphere.

Jupiter and Saturn are truly giant planets. Jupiter is more than 300 times more massive than the Earth, Saturn is almost 100 times more massive, and both are about 10 times larger in diameter than the Earth.

Uranus and Neptune are usually grouped with Jupiter and Saturn because they are similar to those two planets, yet many differences exist. The masses of Uranus and Neptune are much lower than those of Jupiter and Saturn, and Uranus and Neptune are more compressed for their masses. Because of their lower masses, the internal temperatures, pressures, and densities of Uranus and Neptune are also much lower, almost Earth-like, when compared to conditions inside Jupiter and Saturn.

Uranus is unique in that it is tipped on its side, leaving its rotational axis pointing nearly in its orbital plane. Possibly, a large object collided with Uranus about the time it formed, tipping it over. The debris of the collision may have formed into the moons of Uranus.

The Jovian planets are still cooling; that is, they are still emitting heat leftover from their formation 4.6 billion years ago. Jupiter, Saturn, and Neptune emit more energy than they receive from the Sun. By comparison, Earth receives thousands of times as much energy from the Sun as it emits through its surface. Saturn's surprisingly strong heat source is related to its slight atmospheric helium deficiency; friction between sinking helium atoms and the other atmospheric atoms generates an additional source of heat.

Pluto, the most distant known planet in the solar system, is not at all similar to either the Terrestrial planets or the Jovian planets. Indeed, it is more like the cold, icy moons of Jupiter and Saturn (described in Chapter 9). Pluto, however, has its own moon, Charon. The orientation of the orbit of Charon suggests that Pluto, like Uranus, may be tipped over with its rotational axis pointing along its orbital plane. Pluto may also possess a variable atmosphere due to the thawing and freezing of atmospheric gases caused by its very eccentric orbit. Some scientists conjecture that the Pluto-Charon system may have escaped from Neptune's satellite system during an encounter with a large object.

▬CHAPTER CAPSULE

Topics and Terms	Review and Remarks

Jovian planets	Characteristics of the Jovian planets (Jupiter, Saturn, Uranus, and Neptune):
	    Large masses and diameters
	    Low average densities
	    Cloudy atmospheres of mainly hydrogen and helium
	    Rapid rotation

Atmospheres	Cloud features include zones; belts; red, white, and brown spots; ovals; and plumes. They rotate differentially with equatorial regions rotating faster than polar regions. A strong Coriolis effect produces high-velocity east-west winds, generating bands.
Planetary structure	They all have gaseous atmospheres. Jupiter and Saturn have mantles of liquid metallic hydrogen. Uranus and Neptune have mantles of liquid water, methane, and ammonia. They all probably have cores of heavy elements (solid?).
Planetary energy sources	Jupiter, Saturn, and Neptune emit more energy than they receive from the Sun.
Pluto	It is physically similar to the icy moons of Jupiter and Saturn. It has one moon—Charon. It is tipped over—its rotational axis lies near its orbital plane. It has an atmosphere, at least when it is at perihelion.

REVIEW QUESTIONS

1. Hydrogen is the primary chemical constituent of the Jovian planets and the Sun. What does this suggest about the difference between their evolution and that of the Terrestrial planets?

2. Pluto is not usually classified as a Jovian planet. Can you suggest why? (*Hint:* See Table 6.1.)

3. The temperatures of the clouds of Jupiter and of Saturn are not controlled primarily by the Sun. Can you explain why?

4. Except for Uranus, the Jovian planets all have similar orientations. What is so different about the orientation of Uranus?

5. What is unexpected about the observational history of Jupiter's Great Red Spot? Sketch the Earth and Jupiter, with its Red Spot, to scale to show their relative sizes.

6. Which planets did *Pioneers 10* and *11* visit? Where are these probes now? Which planets did *Voyagers 1* and *2* visit?

7. What is the origin of the belts and zones of Jupiter? Why are similar features not as easily observed on Saturn?

8. Compare Jupiter's magnetic field with that of Earth.

9. Which of the major planets was the first to be discovered (since antiquity)? Which was the first to be predicted?

10. It is often suggested that Pluto might have been a satellite of Neptune at some time in the past. Discuss the evidence to support this.

11. Which planets have been observed to have ring systems?

12. Why is Uranus likely to have more extreme seasons than the other Jovian planets?

13. As observed from Earth, what are the characteristic colors of the major planets?

14. Describe the affects of the tidal interaction between Pluto and Charon.

15. Which planet is, on the average, most distant from the Sun? Which is most distant now? Explain.

16. How was the rotational period of Pluto first determined? What makes Pluto's rotation peculiar?

FOR FURTHER READING

Beatty, J. K., and A. Killian. 1988. Discovering Pluto's atmosphere. *Sky & Telescope*, Dec., 624.

Berry, R. 1986. Voyager: Discovery at Uranus. *Astronomy*, May, 6.

Croswell, K. 1986. Pluto: Enigma on the edge of the solar system. *Astronomy*, July, 6.

———. 1986. The pull of planet X. *Astronomy*, Aug., 30.

Ingersoll, A. 1987. Uranus. *Scientific American*, Jan. 38.

Lanzerotti, L. J. 1989. The planets' magnetic environment. *Sky & Telescope*, Feb., 149.

Levy, D. H. 1986. Clyde Tombaugh is 80: A look back at Pluto. *Astronomy*, Feb., 26.

McLaughlin, W. I. 1989. Voyager's decade of wonder. *Sky & Telescope*, July, 16.

O'Meara, S. J. 1985. A visual history of Uranus. *Sky & Telescope*, Nov., 411.

Vasyutim, V. V., and A. A. Tishchenko. 1989. Space coloristics. *Scientific American*, July, 84.

ASTROPROBE 8

Remote Sensing of the Planets

Once humans realized that the Moon and planets were worlds, perhaps like the Earth, they have wondered what those alien landscapes were like. The first step in satisfying this curiosity was the invention of the telescope. As astronomers built larger and larger telescopes, they saw greater and greater detail. The Earth's atmosphere, however, limits the detail attainable with Earth-based telescopes. The great distances to moons and planets also greatly limit our views; in fact, the Moon is the only object in the solar system on which astronomers can identify geological features, such as craters, valleys, and mountain ranges, with Earth-based optical telescopes. All other moons, seen through even the largest telescopes are mere points of light. Astronomers wanted a closer look, and this became possible with the advent of rockets and satellites.

Thousands of satellites have been placed in orbit about the Earth, and more than 70 spacecraft have left the Earth to explore the solar system. Astronauts have set foot on the Moon, and robot landers have landed on the surfaces of Venus, Mars, and the Moon. The Apollo missions to the Moon brought back rock samples, movies of the adventure, and thousands of pictures. All other space probes to the Moon (except the Russian Zond missions) and to other planets were one-way missions that never came back; nevertheless, astronomers obtained a wealth of information from these probes in the form of pictures and data. The detection of radiation from distant objects with instruments, such as satellites and spacecraft, located far from the observer is called **remote sensing.** Remote sensing of a planetary surface requires an imaging system (basically a camera), a way to transmit the images from the spacecraft to Earth, receivers to record the transmitted spacecraft data, and facilities on Earth to convert the data into pictures.

An imaging system consists of an optical array of lenses to focus the image to be recorded, a shutter to expose the image, and a sensor, either film or electronic, on which the image is recorded. The great advantage of remote sensing of planets is that the spacecraft are close enough to "see" much greater detail, than is ever possible from the Earth. A measure of the ability of an imaging system to see small objects is called its *spatial resolution*. The greater the resolution, the smaller the object that can be detected. The resolution of an imaging system depends on the quality of the focusing lenses and, of course, on how close the spacecraft is to the planet or moon. For example, the Viking orbiters could only resolve features larger than about 10 m on Mars but passed so close to Deimos (within 50 km) that they could detect features as small as 1 m across.

After a spacecraft or satellite images a scene, it must convert it into a form that can be transmitted, or "radioed," back to Earth. The Jet Propulsion Laboratory in Pasadena, California, operates the Deep

Space Network for NASA. This network consists of large antennas and powerful transmitters at stations located in the Mojave desert at Goldstone, California; near Madrid, Spain; and near Canberra, Australia (Figure 8A.1). NASA scientists use the antennas of the Deep Space Network to send information to and receive data from interplanetary spacecraft. The antennas of the Deep Space Network and on spacecraft, however, transmit and receive data using *direct wave* transmissions in which the transmitting and receiving antennas must be "visible" to each other. Because these antennas transmit signals in a very narrow beam, they do not need much power. This is especially critical for spacecraft that must be as light as possible at launch. Once astronomers receive the transmissions from spacecraft, they decode the data and reconstruct the images.

Let's examine several imaging systems used in the exploration of the solar system to see how the image data are transmitted back to Earth.

IMAGING SYSTEMS

The key to the transmission of image data is converting a picture into electrical currents and voltages, which can then be transmitted as a radio signal. This conversion is done by *imaging systems;* the systems used for visual photography include film, vidicon (television) cameras, facsimile cameras, and charge coupled devices to record the image.

Film, of course, is a familiar medium to most of us, but the problem of using it in most planetary missions is that the missions do not return to Earth for the film to be developed. The advantage of film is that it gives the highest resolution images. For this reason it was used on the unmanned Lunar Orbiter missions that mapped the surface of the Moon in search of landing sites for the Apollo missions. The film was developed on the spacecraft with a system similar to that used today in Polaroid cameras. Once the film was developed, the negative was scanned with a microscopic spot of high-intensity light (Figure 8A.2). After the light from the spot passed through the film, its intensity was measured by a light-sensitive electronic device called a *photomultiplier tube.* (See Module 2, "Astronomical Instruments and Telescopes") for more on photomultiplier tubes.) A photomultiplier tube converts light intensity to electrical current; the strength of the current is proportional to the intensity of the light transmitted through the film.

Vidicon cameras are similar to television cameras in which the image of a scene is focused onto a photosensitive plate. The plate has the property of having high electrical resistance when no light is shining on it and low resistance when photons of light strike it. Since

■ **FIGURE 8A.1**

NASA Deep Space Tracking Antenna

This 26-m (85-ft) antenna is located near Canberra, Australia. The three NASA tracking sations, Goldstone, California; Madrid, Spain; and Canberra, are stationed at 120° intervals around the Earth so that at least one antenna will always have direct view of a spacecraft or satellite.

SOURCE: NASA.

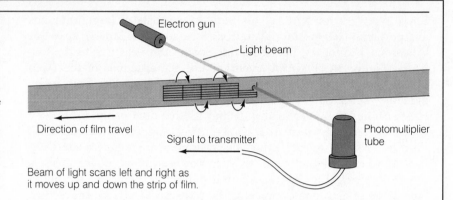

■■■ FIGURE 8A.2

**The Imaging System
of the Lunar Orbiter**

The beam of light scanned the film in
two directions: across and then down
the film. The scanning of one exposure
took about 22 minutes.

an image is simply an area of varying light and dark, an image forms
spots of different electrical resistance when it is focused onto the
plate. For instance, the vidicon cameras on the Viking Orbiters were
photosensitive surfaces 11 mm square that constructed images composed of 1.25 million individual spots. Each spot is called a *pixel*, an
abbreviation for picture element. Converting the image to electrical
currents requires scanning the photosensitive plate, in this case, with
a beam of electrons. The scanning is done horizontally across the surface, then down the width of a pixel and across again; it is repeated
until the entire photosensitive surface is scanned, which takes about
4.5 seconds for the Viking Orbiters' cameras. When the narrow electron beam strikes a spot on the plate with low resistance, corresponding to a bright area of the imaged scene, it generates a large
flow of electrons because the resistance is low; a dark spot in an image produces a correspondingly low current. Each of these currents
produces a small voltage, which is stored in the on-board computer.
Consequently, one image, or frame, consists of 1.25 million voltage
readings.

Spacecraft facsimile cameras are similar to those used to transmit
newspaper wire photographs by radio or by phone and to those used
by atmospheric scientists to generate weather maps from satellite
images. Facsimile cameras differ from vidicon systems in that the
scene is scanned directly; that is, a small slit allows light from only
a tiny portion of the scene, again called a pixel, to be exposed to a
photomultiplier tube. Each exposed tiny pixel is assigned a "gray"
level based on the intensity of light from the pixel. A value of "0"
corresponds to black while a value of "255" corresponds to white.
Figure 8A.3 shows a facsimile photograph of a Martian crater with
the values for each pixel of the picture. Notice that the dark shadow
in the crater has pixel values of "0" while the bright sunlit areas have
values near "255." While the Viking Orbiters used vidicon cameras,
the Viking landers used facsimile cameras. The different cameras

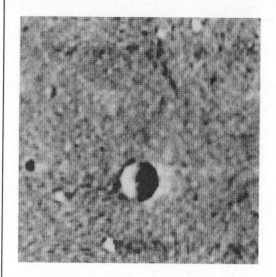

```
153 160 135 126 110 102 113 118 125 135 140 143 130 120 122 120 113 115 135 142 112 108 112 109  99 108 127 132 133 127
150 154 139 120 106 110 119 119 126 136 144 139 130 119 116 116 105 112 130 130 105 103 110 106 103 115 129 133 136 130
115 130 136 115 110 118 116 116 122 125 129 129 127 116 115 123 113 116 132 129 112 108 116 118 116 120 126 127 130 123
 96 116 133 119 120 122 119 127 132 120 125 125 116 115 122 126 116 119 132 132 118 110 115 122 119 119 126 127 126 116
108 119 130 127 129 125 120 132 133 112 120 126 122 119 116 120 118 112 109 118 119 113 110 123 122 122 126 126 125 118
119 125 132 130 129 127 116 119 122 110 118 126 122 119 116 116 122 110  96 108 116 115 122 122 120 123 126 127 125
132 119 126 125 120 133 132 118 113 116 125 119 110 132 116 120 116 116 122 122 112 115 119 122 123 127 125
122 118 129 132 129 142 135 108  98 113 122 126 129 122 120 116 113 110 110 118 125 137 127 115 116 119 125 118 118 135
119 122 136 140 140 139 132 113 103 110 115 122 120 120 120  96 102 112 116 119 122 120 129 123 126 127 133 116 112 133
113 110 123 143 146 133 133 127 115 113 113 120 127 115 113 109 102  95 109 110 116 120 120 128 123 126 120 125 132 136 137
122 115 122 147 150 129 120 115 115 118 112 113 110 100 113 113 102 106 110 116 132 123 115 113 123 147 157 137 126 129
133 125 126 136 129 115 112 110 119 125 115 108 103 113 125 126 108  95 103 109 120 111 115 118 135 136 120 126 133
125 116 118 123 123 115 110 116 122 119 113 106 113 106 113 127 123 115  95 103 106 112 125 123 123 115 109 125 133
126 127 116 112 125 127 127 127 112 118 129 126 130 127 113 119 115 118 106 132 119 115 112  96  99 109 116 136 127 120 118 118 119 129 130
129 137 127 119 120 127 127 127 112 118 129 126 130 127 113 116 132 119 136 149 150 135 118 127 127 130 135 132
122 136 132 116 112 120 133 120 122 135 122 127 135 118 112 120 119 109 110 119 125 135 144 137 120 122 127 130 136 136
118 136 137 116 115 125 120 133 132 140 137 130 112 119 162 142 112 119 116 132 130 116 132 130 130 125 132 136 137
118 127 139 132 125 137 149 144 133 120 106 112 136 146 127 120 133 146 127 130 137 133 137 132 137
112 115 133 139 125 142 157 133 108 119 108 108 119 126 125 129 129 136 135 129 133 129 122 122 130 120 130 147 169 152
119 118 133 133 133 136 132 127 118 115  95  81 119 110 120 126 127 133 126 116 127 147 149 137 126 127 127 130 132 136 135
119 137 147 129 116 119 122 105 102 120 118 125 126 126 129 112 103 126 142 140 160 132 126 133 130 129 144 149 144 147
103 112 132 133 135 132 136 120 116 109 126 115 119 133 164 133 105 109 126 137 130 123 132 135 132 133 142 154 159 146
129 122 133 133 123 130 139 126 109  93  62  62  99 129 119 110 116 120 119 130 152 156 143 129 135 145 143 133
122 139 150 143 132 113 132 113  92  54  95 175 140 166 159 127 106  91  64 91 136 167 163 147 160 153 132 135 127 110
115 133 150 150 154 125  91 108 154 171 178 183 164 133 115  99  55  16  13  14  23  84 129 167 200 183 150 153 169 163
127 143 140 139 136 103  84 137 207 200 190 191 177 142 108  88  11  14  13  10   0  28  93 176 211 198 161 147 149 167
136 146 130 127 108  75  95 180 248 225 188 171 156 123  89  68  41  10  17  23   0   6  51 166 205 212 174 153 177 171
116 127 110 110  96  85 142 203 255 255 242 171 140  98  72  40   7   0   6  18   0  20 113 176 193 170 160 171 161
127 123 108  93  86 102 174 255 255 203 164 137  82  75  57   3   0   0  10   0   0  14  93 140 160 152 159 161 146
109 108 106  95  89 133 208 255 255 246 180 146 129  65  61  67   1   0  18  14   0   0  10  78 126 160 153 159 159 144
103 101 108 103  71 127 214 254 255 255 217 169 127  74  74  81  18  10  40  23   0   0   7  74 130 173 164 160 161 156
 98 115 103  92  54  95 177 255 255 255 232 184 147 119 109  95  45  31  31  18   0   0   6  71 142 181 171 170 178 171
108 123  72  45  50  88 156 221 255 229 218 197 177 133  92  53  33  28  10   0   0   0  69 150 169 152 157 177 176
154 135  65  35  62  93 135 205 245 224 244 214 153  96  64  45  38  42  27   6   0  28 116 183 169 149 156 170 164
144 109  85  72 102 132 146 201 248 229 252 225 156 101  68  57  62  41  34   3   0  85 186 221 195 180 186 177 154
101  84  95  82 103 120 123 146 215 205 214 205 163 122  84  62  59  47   0   0  45 152 215 214 193 193 101 160 149
 93 106 110 103 120  98  93 127 164 264 207 195 154 122  95  75  47  40  13   0  18 118 190 195 170 150 146 144 140 152
105 115 112 122 109  57  75  98 102 171 191 173 142 110  65  35  16  20  13  23  89 161 181 167 146 130 132 130 133 143
 92 112 110 125 127 113  74  85  95  85 120 132 120 126 112  52  27  24  50  86 115 143 167 159 150 142 123 136 126 127 135
106 112 110 125 120 119 110 102  98  98 112 106 112 122  88  74  85 112 152 166 153 150 136 133 130 136 126 135
133 112 109 122 112 115 118 119 119 115 105 128 122 116 123 113 160 157 176 173 157 143 120 125 127 122 126 146 144 136
126 113 102 120 112 110 113 110 113 112 116 125 133 136 125 119 173 104 147 122 130 132 129 112 132 137
118 125 132 126 149 140 110 115 125 127 115 126 149 133 142 132 143 156 163 143 135 125 132 139 147 133 143 143 130 127
127 116 130 137 127 115 113 135 150 136 118 127 153 154 147 123 125 139 139 152 130 122 126 144 140 149 136 129 113 123
```

---

were used because the facsimile cameras used on Viking were about 100 times slower than the vidicon cameras. Speed was important for the orbiters because their orbital motion would cause blurring during long exposures.

The most recent imaging systems use charge coupled devices (CCDs), invented in 1969 by Bell Laboratories (see AstroProbe 14 for more on CCDs). A CCD is physically structured as an array of light-sensitive elements. A scene is focused onto the CCD "chip," and all of the elements record light intensities at the same time. Therefore, each element represents a pixel. An element produces an electrical charge proportional to the amount of light that strikes it. Although no scanning is necessary since all of the pixels are exposed at once, the electrical charge of each pixel must be measured, one at a time, and converted into a voltage.

All of these imaging systems convert light from imaged scenes into voltages. Then the spacecraft converts these voltages into numbers that can be sent through its communication systems to Earth.

▇▇DATA TRANSMISSION

The electrical voltages produced by the imaging systems are examples of *analog signals*, which can have an infinite range of values. These analog signals are converted to *digital signals*, which can have only a limited range of values; most digital signals today are binary and use either a "1" or a "0." The advantage of converting images to a digital format is that computers can easily manipulate binary num-

▇▇ **FIGURE 8A.3**

A *Mariner 6* Photograph of a Martian Crater and Its Numerical Representation

The dark shadows are represented by low pixel values, near 0, while bright, sunlit regions are represented by high numbers, near 255.

SOURCE: NASA.

bers (see AstroProbe 14 for more on binary numbers and their manipulation by computers).

Analog signals are converted to digital (binary) for transmission to Earth. The spacecraft has a very accurate clock and a voltage generator that produces a slowly increasing voltage starting from zero volts. When converting the analog voltage of a pixel to a binary number, the clock times how long it takes for the voltage generator to build up to the voltage measured in the pixel by sending electrical pulses to counters that count in binary. For example, the binary equivalent of the number 1 is 0001, of the number 2 is 0010, the number 3 is 0011, and the number 4 is 0100. Each number is represented by a different set of zeros and ones. Each of the digits, either 1 or 0, is called a bit. Here only 4 bits are used and numbers as high as 15 (1111) can be represented; if 8 bits are used, numbers as high as 255 (11111111) can be represented (see AstroProbe 14). The spacecraft counter will increment each time it receives an electrical pulse from the clock, counting 0001, 0010, 0011, 0100, 0101, and so on. When the pixel voltage and the generated voltage are the same, the clock stops sending pulses and the counters stop; the pixel voltage is now represented by a binary number. This binary number is then transmitted to Earth.

NASA spacecraft and the Deep Space Network transmit and receive at two frequencies: 2295 million cycles per second and 8418 million cycles per second. A "cycle per second" is called one hertz (abbreviated Hz) so the frequencies are 2295 MHz and 8418 MHz; MHz is read megahertz. Signals sent at these frequencies are called carrier signals because they "carry" information, such as data, voice, or video. This information is "applied" to the carrier in such a way as to vary, or *modulate*, some characteristic of the carrier, such as its amplitude or frequency. For instance, radio stations transmit signals at frequencies much higher than voice or music frequencies, which are from 20 Hz to about 20,000 Hz. If the stations transmitted at these low frequencies, everyone would hear the music from all nearby radio stations at once! At the same time, if you were to listen to the high frequency of a radio transmitter, you would hear nothing. The transmitter impresses the information to be sent on the carrier.

An AM radio station modulates its carrier by changing the carrier's amplitude; it **A**mplitude **M**odulates. A loud sound corresponds to a large amplitude while a soft sound to a small amplitude, as illustrated in Panel b in Figure 8A.4. An FM radio station modulates its carrier by changing its frequency; it **F**requency **M**odulates. Loud and soft sounds cause small changes in the frequency of the carrier (Panel c). Satellites can frequency modulate their carriers, so that sending a binary number with a frequency-modulated signal may look simi-

■■■ FIGURE 8A.4

Modulation of Carrier Waves

(a) A carrier wave of fixed frequency. *(b)* Amplitude modulation of the carrier wave. *(c)* Frequency modulation of the carrier wave.

(a) Carrier wave of fixed frequency

Amplitude

(b) Amplitude-modulated wave

(c) Frequency-modulated wave

lar to that shown schematically in Figure 8A.5. Here a binary "1" is represented by a frequency slightly less than the carrier frequency while a binary "0" is represented by a frequency slightly greater than the carrier frequency. Receivers on Earth are able to detect the slight differences in frequency and convert the signal into binary ones and zeros.

Once the signal is received by the antennas of the Deep Space Network, the images are reconstructed from the binary data. The pictures are just arrays of numbers that can be represented as different degrees of light and dark. How then are colored pictures obtained? A colored picture is made on Earth, not on the spacecraft. Scientists use the three primary colors, red, blue, and green, combinations of which produce other colors. The imaging camera on a spacecraft includes a set of three *filters*, one red, one blue, and one green. Each allows only one color to enter the camera. Consequently, when the red filter is placed in front of the lens, the camera measures the intensity of only the red light from the scene it is imaging. The same is true for the blue and green filters. For instance, an image of Mars will look very bright through the red filter because its surface is reddish. On the other hand, an image of the Earth focusing on the oceans will look bright through a blue filter but faint through a red filter. Three pictures, one for each filter, are taken of the same scene in rapid succession, and each one is transmitted to Earth.

Scientists on the Earth must then combine the red, blue, and green images into a single picture. The individual pixel values in each color give the relative brightness of the image as it appeared through each filter. Once the images are carefully aligned so that the pixels representing the same location in the image are matched, colors can be assigned to the combined pixels by "mixing" the colors; that is, different intensities of each pixel combine to give different colors. When three pictures of a scene of Mars are combined, mixing the different intensities of each set of three pixels, corresponding to red, blue, and green, results in a particular color for that location in the image (Figure 8A.6). For instance, if the intensity from the red image is high and intensities from the blue and green images are very low, the color defined by the combined pixels is red.

Color is also used in a different way to give images recorded at wavelengths not visible to the eye. For instance, infrared thermal mapping of Mars gives digital data representing intensities at infrared wavelengths. High intensities correspond to high temperatures, low intensities to low temperatures. Of course, the human eye cannot record different shades of temperature. Pictures of thermal data are simply color coded. For instance, the picture of Mars in Figure 8A.7 is a thermal map in which the color red represents warm

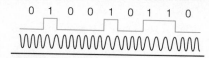

■ FIGURE 8A.5

Frequency Modulation of Digital Data

The binary bit "1" is represented with a slightly lower frequency than the carrier while the binary bit "0" is represented by a higher frequency.

■ FIGURE 8A.6

Assembly of a Color Picture

These pictures from the red, blue, and green filters show the same location of Mars. The frames do not match up perfectly because the spacecraft moved in orbit between exposures.

SOURCE: NASA.

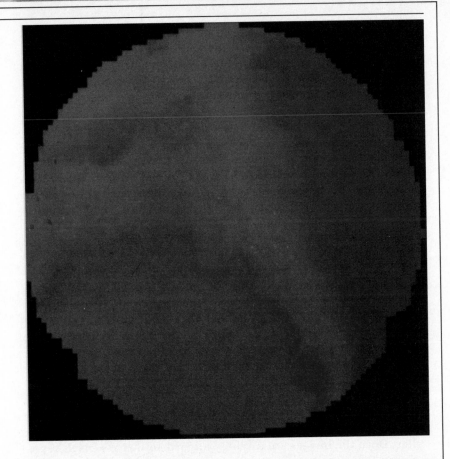

FIGURE 8A.7

Visual Representation of Infrared Thermal Mapping Data of Mars

Temperatures are represented by colors: blues are coolest and reds hottest. Notice the large pixel sizes near the limb of Mars; this indicates that the infrared images had a low resolution.

SOURCE: USGS Planetary Data Facility, Hugh Keiffer, Branch Chief.

temperatures and the color blue cool temperatures. Oranges and greens correspond to temperatures in between. Therefore, the colors are not the result of combining three images of Mars. The colors result from simply assigning a color to a range in pixel values. Reds may range from 200 to 255 while blues may range from 0 to 75. This is similar to color contour maps where different colors or shades of colors are assigned to different elevations. This method is used to display data that would otherwise be difficult to assimilate.

Earth-based observations will continue to play an important role in the observations of planets; in particular, they are an important source of data on changes in planetary conditions that occur over very long periods of time. Satellites can also make such observations if they are in orbit about a planet or moon, but spacecraft generally observe for only a limited number of months, although a few exceptional missions last a few years. Nevertheless, the resolution provided by even short term flyby missions contains a vast amount of information unattainable from the Earth.

CHAPTER 9

Satellites and Rings

OUTLINE

Discovery

Satellites of the Jovian Planets
The Moons of Jupiter
Galilean Satellites
Small Jovian Satellites
The Moons of Saturn
The Classical Moons
Co-orbitals and Lagrangians
The Moons of Uranus and Neptune

Planetary Rings
The Rings of Saturn
The Rings of Jupiter, Uranus, and
Neptune

Summary

Chapter Capsule

Review Questions

For Further Reading

▬▬▬▬ASTROPROBE 9:
Planetary Pedigree

Cassini's Division.
ARTIST: Don Dixon.

■ TABLE 9.1
Diameters of the Jovian Satellites

Moon/Planet	Diameter
Ganymede	5300 km
Titan (Saturn)	5120
Mercury	4900
Callisto	4800
Io	3600
Triton (Neptune)	3500
Moon (Earth)	3500
Europa	3100
Pluto	2300

THE JOVIAN PLANETS ARE MINIATURE SOLAR SYSTEMS in themselves, characterized by impressive systems of intricate rings and icy moons. Two satellites are larger than Mercury and half a dozen are larger than Pluto (Table 9.1). Most satellite surfaces are mixtures of ice and rock, which show the scars of meteoritic impact and reflect the satellites' histories of destruction and re-formation. Jupiter boasts a moon with the only active volcanoes outside the Earth's, while Saturn claims a moon with an atmosphere denser than our own. Saturn displays a magnificent set of thin, flat rings composed of a myriad of ice-covered rocks and dust, while Jupiter, Uranus, and Neptune are encircled by lesser ring systems. The appearance and dynamics of these rings are the result of involved interactions between ring particles and satellites; some of the smaller moons act to confine ring particles into narrow ringlets while larger moons can gravitationally generate gaps between the rings. As with the Jovian planets themselves, much of our knowledge of satellites and rings, including discoveries of new moons and rings, comes from the data collected during the journeys of the Voyager spacecraft.

DISCOVERY

The Galilean satellites of Jupiter—Io, Europa, Ganymede, and Callisto—were the first bodies in the solar system, other than the five visible planets, discovered by humans. Galileo observed these satellites for the first time in January 1610. Their names, as well as those of many other satellites of Jupiter, are taken from the names of the mistresses of the mythological god Jupiter (see AstroProbe 9 for more on the mythology behind planet and satellite names). The orbits of the Galilean satellites are all in Jupiter's equatorial plane and are oriented nearly on edge relative to the Earth (Figure 9.1). Consequently, the moons usually appear in a straight line parallel to Jupiter's equator when viewed through a telescope. Their orbital periods range from about 2 days for Io to nearly 17 days for Callisto, and an observer looking through a small telescope can see them move during a few hours' observing. Occasionally, observers can watch one disappear behind Jupiter or see a dark shadow of a moon cross the face of Jupiter.

Jupiter is so bright and its other satellites so small and faint that astronomers did not discover a fifth moon of Jupiter until 1892, nearly 300 years after Galileo's observations. This was accomplished at Lick Observatory in California by the American astronomer Edward E. Barnard (1857–1923), and between 1904 and 1974 observers discovered eight more moons. The Voyager spacecraft uncovered three tiny moons orbiting Jupiter inside the orbits of the Galilean satellites. These discov-

■ FIGURE 9.1

Telescope View of the Galilean Satellites of Jupiter

SOURCE: Lick Observatory, University of California, Santa Cruz.

eries and the detailed pictures of the Galilean satellites by the Voyagers essentially opened up a new solar system to study.

Galileo, of course, was the first person in history to see Saturn's rings, but, as mentioned in the last chapter, the optics of his telescopes were so poor that he was not sure what he was viewing (Figure 9.2). Furthermore, because the objects did not seem to move, Galileo and others did not keep close watch on Saturn. When Galileo observed Saturn in 1612, he was again surprised; this time he saw only one object. The rings in 1612 were oriented on edge as viewed from the Earth and were too thin to see (Figure 9.3).

Although Saturn's rings were extensively viewed for the 50 years following the 1612 observations, little progress was made toward an explanation of their structure. In 1656, the Dutch astronomer Christian Huygens (1629–1695) announced his theory of a thick, solid ring surrounding Saturn. Giovanni Domenico Cassini (1625–1712), however, discovered that an inner bright portion of the ring was separated from an outer dim portion by a dark band. Cassini interpreted the dark band as a gap in the ring, now called the Cassini division. By the end of the

FIGURE 9.3

Orientations of Saturn's Rings

Saturn's rings are tilted 27° relative to its orbital plane as seen from the Earth. Whenever the rings are on edge, they disappear from view.

SOURCE: Lowell Observatory photograph.

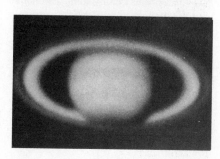

■ FIGURE 9.4

Divisions of Saturn's Rings

The detailed structure of the rings in this drawing made in 1856 by Warren De la Rue (1815–1889) bears a striking resemblance to the Voyager photographs.

seventeenth century, the consensus among astronomers was that the rings were composed of a large number of very small "rocks" revolving around Saturn.

At the end of the eighteenth century, the French mathematician Pierre Simon de Laplace (1749–1827) replaced the idea of multiple particle rings with the concept of numerous thin solid rings, like concentric hula hoops of different diameters. Laplace's thin ring theory implied that more divisions besides Cassini's were possible. Detailed observations of the rings of Saturn spurred by Laplace's theory led to drawings showing Saturn's rings with many divisions (Figure 9.4). Johann Franc Encke (1791–1865), for instance, observed a dark band, now known as the Encke division, in the outer, or A, ring (Figure 9.5). In 1850 a thin, dark, shadowy ring inside the inner, or B, ring was discovered. It is called the C ring but is sometimes referred to as the "crepe" ring because observers were able to see the edge of Saturn through the ring, indicating that the ring was thin and perhaps not solid. Further observations of the rings occulting stars and dimming, not completely blocking, starlight helped repudiate the solid ring theory. Finally, in 1859, the Scottish physicist James Clerk Maxwell (1831–1879) mathematically proved that for the rings to exist for a long time they must be countless, independently orbiting satellites.

While the rings of Saturn claimed much theoretical and observational attention, observations of Saturn when the rings were on edge led to discoveries of satellites. Huygens discovered the largest Saturnian satellite, Titan, in 1655. Cassini discovered two moons in 1671 and two more in 1684. One of these moons, Iapetus, was unique in that it was only seen when it was west of the planet. Cassini correctly interpreted this to mean that Iapetus had light and dark hemispheres and that it always kept the same face toward Saturn. Consequently, when Iapetus was east of the planet, its dark hemisphere was facing the Earth. More than 100 years passed before two more moons were discovered and another 60 years before the small outer moon, Hyperion, was seen for the first time. The discovery of the distant moon Phoebe in 1899 was the

■ FIGURE 9.5

Classical Ring Nomenclature

Rings A, B, C and the Cassini division were known in the eighteenth century. The Encke division, near the outer edge of the A ring, was seen by some astronomers but not confirmed until 1978.

last pre-spacecraft discovery of a Saturnian moon; Phoebe was discovered with the then recently invented technique of photography.

Three spacecraft flew by Saturn between 1979 and 1980: *Pioneer 11*, *Voyager 1*, and *Voyager 2*. *Pioneer 11* discovered two additional rings as did the Voyager spacecraft. The rings were photographed at high resolution and exhibited thousands of "ringlets", or thin rings (Figure 9.6). Embedded within the rings, astronomers found "ringmoons," or mountain-sized satellites, that act to confine ring particles. A tremendous effort is now being made to understand the dynamics of the rings of Saturn; since astronomers have also discovered rings around Jupiter, Uranus, and Neptune, rings represent a fundamental class of planetary structure.

While many astronomers in the seventeenth and eighteenth centuries were searching for divisions and gaps in the rings of Saturn, more discoveries awaited the patient eye of William Herschel, the discoverer of Uranus (Table 9.2). Although Herschel started as an amateur astronomer, soon after his discovery of the seventh planet he was elected a Fellow of the Royal Society and awarded an annual income from the king of England. Herschel was then able to devote all of his time to building telescopes and observing. In 1787, just six years after the discovery of Uranus, Herschel discovered the two outermost moons of Uranus, Oberon and Titania. The faint inner moons of Uranus were not discovered until much later. In 1851, another British astronomer, William Lassel (1799–1880), discovered the next two inner moons, Ariel and Umbriel. Astronomers had to wait almost another century before the Dutch-born American astronomer, Gerard Kuiper (1905–1973), discovered the small inner moon Miranda in 1948. Finally, in 1986 the *Voyager 2* spacecraft discovered 10 more, even smaller, moons closer to Uranus than Miranda.

The remote Neptune has only two major moons. William Lassell discovered the largest of Neptune's satellites, Triton, in 1847 less than a year after Neptune's discovery. Over 100 years later, Kuiper discovered

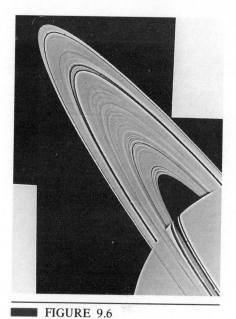

■ FIGURE 9.6
Ringlets of Saturn

High-resolution *Voyager 1* picture of Saturn's rings showing many small rings.
SOURCE: NASA.

■ TABLE 9.2 **Planetary and Satellite Discovery**

Planet	Satellite	Year Discovered	Discoverer
Uranus		1781	Herschel
	Oberon	1787	Herschel
	Titania	1787	Herschel
	Umbriel	1851	Lassell
	Ariel	1851	Lassell
	Miranda	1948	Kuiper
	Small moons	1985–1986	*Voyager 2*
Neptune		1846	Adams, Leverrier
	Triton	1847	Lassell
	Nereid	1949	Kuiper
	Small moons	1989	*Voyager 2*
Pluto		1930	Tombaugh
	Charon	1978	Christy

a small outer moon, Nereid. Most recently, *Voyager 2* discovered 6 small inner moons during its flyby in 1989.

▰▰SATELLITES OF THE JOVIAN PLANETS

Astronomers have discovered nearly 60 satellites with diameters greater than 10 km (6 mi) orbiting the four Jovian planets. About 26 of these were recently discovered from images taken by the Voyager spacecraft. Except for the unusual orbit of Neptune's two primary moons, the larger satellites orbit in the equatorial plane of the parent planet and in the same direction as the planet rotates. A few smaller moons, however, orbit well out of the equatorial plane and, in some cases, revolve in the opposite direction of the planet's rotation. Many of the moons have icy, cratered crusts and centers of water and rock. Several moons, however, are far from icy: Jupiter's volcanic Io and dense Europa and Saturn's gas-covered Titan. Before the Voyager missions, these moons were mere specks of light seen through telescopes; today astronomers see them as real worlds with craters, mountains, valleys, and volcanoes.

The Moons of Jupiter

Jupiter has 16 known moons. The 4 Galilean satellites and the 4 small innermost moons revolve in the same direction as Jupiter rotates. Their orbits lie in Jupiter's equatorial plane and have small eccentricities. The 8 small, irregularly shaped moons farther from Jupiter (Figure 9.7) have more inclined orbits with the outer 4 revolving in the direction opposite Jupiter's rotation (see Table 9.3).

Galilean Satellites. The Galilean satellites are the largest in the Jovian system. Callisto and Ganymede are the largest of the four. Both

▰▰▰ FIGURE 9.7

Relative Sizes and Distances from Jupiter of the Jovian Moons

The numbers in the circles indicate the moon's average densities.

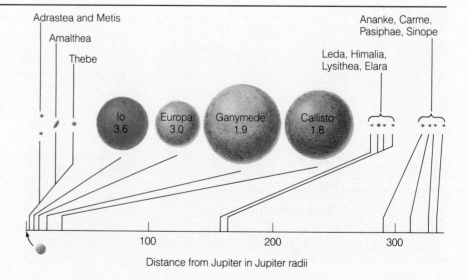

██████ TABLE 9.3 **Satellites of Jupiter**

Name	Radius (km)	Density (g/cm³)	Orbital Radius (Jupiter radii)	Orbital Period	Year Discovered
Metis	20	—	1.79	7^h5^m	1979
Adrastea	10	—	1.81	7^h5^m	1979
Amalthea	135 × 85 × 75	—	2.55	11^h44^m	1892
Thebe	40	—	3.11	16^h5^m	1979
Io	1816	3.55	5.95	1.77 days	1610
Europa	1563	3.04	9.47	3.55 days	1610
Ganymede	2638	1.93	15.1	7.16 days	1610
Callisto	2410	1.83	26.6	16.69 days	1610
Leda	≈5	—	156	240 days	1974
Himalia	90	—	161	251 days	1904
Lysithea	≈20	—	164	260 days	1938
Elara	40	—	165	260 days	1904
Ananke	≈15	—	297	1.67 years	1951
Carme	≈22	—	319	1.89 years	1938
Pasiphae	≈35	—	329	2.01 years	1908
Sinope	≈20	—	332	2.08 years	1914

have average densities just under 2 g/cm³ and are about the same size as Mercury. Their surfaces produce reflection spectra that indicate a high water-ice concentration. The crusts on these two moons may be 90–95% water-ice. The interiors of Callisto and Ganymede are probably silicate-rich rock, on top of which is a mantle of high pressure ice and a thin crust of normal ice.

The surface of Callisto is saturated with craters larger than 100 km across, suggesting a very ancient surface (Panel a in Figure 9.8). The

██████ FIGURE 9.8

The Surfaces of Callisto, Ganymede, and Europa

(a) The concentric rings of the impact basin Valhalla are the dominant feature in this photograph of Callisto; the white ejecta probably indicate young craters on an icy surface. *(b)* The dark areas on Ganymede are ancient terrain. The younger light areas are separated from the old terrain by systems of grooves. The prominent ray system is probably water-ice ejected by a recent impact. *(c)* The icy surface of Europa is completely covered with cracks; only a few craters have been seen.

SOURCE: NASA.

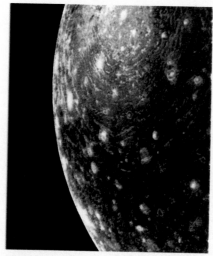

(a)

(b)

(c)

(a)

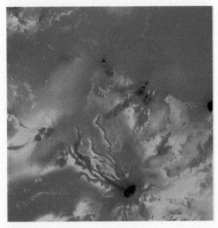

(b)

■■■ FIGURE 9.9

Io and Its Volcanoes

(a) The sulfur-laden surface of Io. Io's yellow and red colors are probably due to different forms of sulfur. At low temperatures, sulfur is yellow-white while at high temperatures it is a deep red. *(b)* Long lava flows like the one visible in this *Voyager 1* picture typically radiate from the dark spots on Io's surface.

SOURCE: NASA.

craters on Callisto are relatively flat compared to craters on worlds with rocky crusts. Presumably this is due to subsequent modification of the terrain by partial flows of the icy crust caused by the heat of meteoritic impact. Several multiringed basins are also seen on the surface of Callisto, indicative of large meteoritic impacts. Ganymede, by contrast, shows a mixed surface of both old, heavily cratered terrain and young terrain with crater densities about the same as the lunar maria (Panel b). About 60% of the surface is a unique grooved, light-colored landform. The grooves, which extend across terrain of many ages, are alternating valleys and ridges with elevations of only a few hundred meters. They may be the result of tectonic breaking and stretching of the crust, similar to the crustal motions observed in Earth. Whatever produced the grooves ceased operating billions of years ago.

The inner two Galilean moons, Europa and Io, are rocky worlds about the same size as our Moon. Both have densities of about 3 g/cm³. Europa has an almost pure ice crust, and it is conceivable that it has a global ocean of liquid water between its frozen crust and a rocky mantle. Its surface geology is completely different from any other known moon. Only three craters (all about 20 km across) are visible on Europa's surface. Either the surface is young or the record of cratering has not been preserved. The latter may be true since the surface is nearly pure ice and could have been a liquid ocean during the intense bombardment era; if the ocean froze much later, it would retain no trace of the bombardment. The most unique topography on Europa is the global network of linear features that crisscrosses its surface (Panel c in Figure 9.8). These are surely the result of tectonic activity and perhaps were associated with a cracking of the icy crust as Europa cooled.

Io is the most geologically active satellite known in the solar system (Panel a in Figure 9.9). Nine volcanic eruptions detected by *Voyager 1* and *2* from eight volcanoes have been studied in detail. Volcanic plumes rose several hundred kilometers above the Ionian surface and spread material up to 600 km away. The plumes are mainly molten sulfur and sulfur dioxide (SO_2). The eruptions are actually similar to terrestrial geysers where water turns to steam when it comes into contact with hot rocks. Astronomers conjecture that liquid sulfur dioxide on Io provides the necessary explosive pressure when heated rapidly below the surface. Eruptions issue from vents, dark caldera, and shield volcanoes, and lots of surface flows and magma deposits are seen around the active volcanic sites (Panel b). Astronomers estimate that the volcanoes on Io eject enough material to cover its entire surface with a layer of sulfur-rich debris 10 m thick every million years. This is enough magma to wipe out any trace of ancient as well as recent bombardments.

Io is bursting with activity compared to our Moon, a geologically quiet world about the same size as Io. How can Io be so geologically active in these cold and remote regions of the solar system? Although Io is slightly farther from Jupiter than the Moon is from the Earth, Jupiter is 318 times more massive than the Earth. Jupiter's huge gravitational force on Io can introduce tremendous tidal distortions, which alternately stretch and squeeze Io as it orbits Jupiter. Calculations

▬ TABLE 9.4 **Galilean Satellites**

Satellite	Density	Crater Density	Features	Distance from Jupiter
Callisto	1.83 g/cm^3	High	Craters	Farthest
Ganymede	1.93 g/cm^3	Moderate to high	Grooves and craters	
Europa	3.04 g/cm^3	Low	Cracks	
Io	3.55 g/cm^3	Very low	Volcanoes	Closest
Moon (Earth's)	3.4 g/cm^3	High to low	Craters and basins	—

suggest that the tidal friction between the interior rocks is severe enough to generate the heat needed to drive Io's volcanism.

The Galilean satellites exhibit strong correlations between their surface appearances, average densities, and distances from Jupiter (Table 9.4). Callisto is the farthest from Jupiter, and its surface is the most saturated with craters. Moving closer to Jupiter, Ganymede has fewer craters than Callisto while Europa and Io have essentially none. Whereas Callisto does not have any cracks on its surface, except the ringed impact structures, Ganymede and Europe exhibit surfaces that have evolved by internal processes—Europa more so than Ganymede. Io's surface, on the other hand, is completely dominated by internal processes. Finally, the moons closest to Jupiter have the highest average density. These correlations suggest that the surfaces of the three outer Galilean satellites froze at different times. Callisto's surface froze first, recording the end of an intense bombardment era. Ganymede's surface froze later as the bombardment diminished, and Europa's surface froze last, after the bombardment ceased.

It appears that the satellites closest to Jupiter were heated more than the more distant satellites. Meteoritic impacts were a likely mechanism for this heating. The gravitational field of a large planet, such as Jupiter, focuses the number of interplanetary objects near the planet and increases impact velocities. Consequently, a satellite near Jupiter is subjected to a greater density of meteoroids than a more distant satellite. For instance, the expected bombardment rate for Io is five times that for Callisto, just because Io is closer to Jupiter. Furthermore, impacts on satellites closer to Jupiter will be more energetic and will therefore generate more heat. On top of this, Io is also subjected to intense tidal heating, which is certainly the reason it is still geologically active. Tidal effects could also be partly responsible for Europa's unique surface.

Small Jovian Satellites. The eight outermost Jovian moons are all dark (reflecting 2–3% of any incident light), relatively small, very remote, and, consequently, very difficult to observe. The outermost four, which exhibit retrograde rotation around Jupiter, may have been cap-

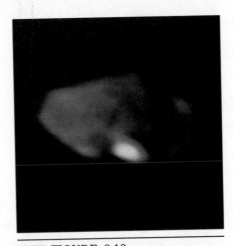

■ FIGURE 9.10
Voyager View of Amalthea

Amalthea is an irregular dark reddish
moon that is probably heavily cratered.
The bright spots are craters.

SOURCE: NASA.

tured by Jupiter. If so, these outer moons may be examples of very primitive solar system material.

Amalthea is the largest of the four inner Jovian satellites. Our knowledge of Amalthea is limited because it is small and close to Jupiter, making it difficult to observe. In addition, the Voyager spacecraft did not fly very close to Amalthea (Figure 9.10). It is in synchronous orbit around Jupiter with its blunt end always pointing toward Jupiter. Amalthea is also dark, reflecting only 5% of any incident light. It is probably heavily cratered, but only two large craters have been detected. Both are bowl-shaped craters about 80 km in diameter and may be the largest bowl-shaped craters in the solar system.

The innermost Jovian moons, Adrastea and Metis, are small and dark and lie just outside the bright ring of Jupiter. In fact, they could be large chunks of the Jovian ring system. They are also "co-orbitals"; that is, they share the same orbit. This phenomenon will be explored in detail in the next section when the moons of Saturn are studied because Saturn also has several co-orbitals.

The Moons of Saturn

The seventeenth, eighteenth, and nineteenth centuries saw the discovery of nine Saturnian satellites, the "classical moons of Saturn," which orbit beyond Saturn's great ring system (Table 9.5). Prior to the Voyager missions in the 1980s, these moons were just very faint points of light, hardly visible in a telescope. Astronomers knew the orbits of these moons, their periods, and their distances from Saturn, but they had little to say about the individual satellites aside from the detection of a methane-rich atmosphere on Titan and brightness variations of a few moons. The Voyager missions, of course, changed that. The Voyager images allowed planetary scientists to study the surface features of dozens of new worlds, a feat impossible with Earth-based observations.

The Classical Moons. All of Saturn's moons orbit in the planet's equatorial plane except for the distant Iapetus and Phoebe; Phoebe is the only moon that orbits retrograde (see Table 9.6 for a summary of satellite data). The densities of the Saturnian moons are consistent with a half–water-ice and half-rock composition (Figure 9.11). Meteoritic bombardment has played a very important role in the evolution of these moons because they are deep within the strong gravitational field of Saturn. The cratering rate for Mimas, for instance, is believed to have been 20 times greater than for Iapetus. In fact, the flux of meteoroids caused by Saturn's strong gravitational field must have been so high during the initial heavy bombardment of Saturn that disruption of the inner satellites could have been common. After disruption, the mutual gravitational attraction of the disrupted pieces would cause the satellite to re-coalesce. This disruption and re-coalescence probably occurred several times for each of the larger satellites.

Titan, the largest moon in the Saturnian system, is the second largest in the solar system and is larger than Mercury. Yet its low density im-

■ TABLE 9.5
Classical Moons of Saturn

Phoebe	Dione
Iapetus	Tethys
Hyperion	Enceladus
Titan	Mimas
Rhea	

■ TABLE 9.6 **Satellites of Saturn**

Name	Radius (km)	Density (g/cm³)	Orbital Radius (Saturn radii)	Orbital Period	Year Discovered
Atlas	20 × 10 × ?	—	2.30	14ʰ27ᵐ	1980
Prometheus	70 × 50 × 37	—	2.32	14ʰ43ᵐ	1980
Pandora	55 × 45 × 33	—	2.4	15ʰ6ᵐ	1980
Janus	110 × 95 × 80	—	2.5	16ʰ34ᵐ	1966
Epimetheus	70 × 58 × 50	—	2.5	16ʰ34ᵐ	1966
Mimas	197	1.4	3.1	22ʰ34ᵐ	1789
Enceladus	251	1.2	3.9	1.37 days	1789
Tethys	530	1.2	4.9	1.89 days	1684
Telesto	15 × 10 × 8	—	4.9	1.89 days	1980
Calypso	12 × 11 × 11	—	4.9	1.89 days	1980
Dione	560	1.4	6.3	2.74 days	1684
Helene	17 × 16 × 15	—	6.3	2.74 days	1980
Rhea	765	1.3	8.7	4.52 days	1671
Titan	2575	1.88	20.3	15.95 days	1655
Hyperion	205 × 130 × 110	—	24.6	21.28 days	1848
Iapetus	730	1.2	59.0	79.3 days	1671
Phoebe	110	—	215.7	1.51 years	1899

plies an interior much richer in ices than any Terrestrial planet. Titan is also the only satellite in the solar system known to have a dense atmosphere; in fact, its atmosphere is denser than that of any Terrestrial

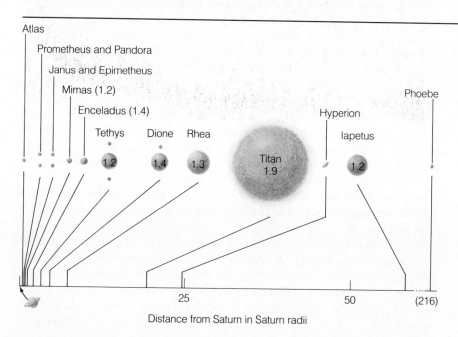

Atlas
Prometheus and Pandora
Janus and Epimetheus
Mimas (1.2)
Enceladus (1.4)
Tethys   Dione   Rhea   Phoebe
1.2   1.4   1.3
Titan
1.9
Hyperion
Iapetus
1.2

25   50   (216)

Distance from Saturn in Saturn radii

■ FIGURE 9.11

Relative Sizes and Distances from Saturn of the Saturnian Moons

The numbers are the measured average densities of the moons. Phoebe is 216 Saturn radii away from Saturn. Titan's atmosphere is shown as a blue haze.

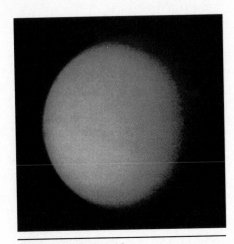

■ FIGURE 9.12

Featureless Titan

The surface of Titan is hidden below its
reddish haze and thick clouds.

SOURCE: NASA.

planet except Venus (Figure 9.12). Nitrogen is the principle component
of Titan's atmosphere with methane probably playing the role water
plays in the Earth's atmosphere. On the Earth, temperatures and pressures allow water to exist in its solid, liquid, and gaseous (water vapor)
forms. On Titan, temperatures and pressures may also allow methane
to exist in all three forms: Titan may be covered with methane clouds;
its polar caps may be frozen methane; it may rain methane, and its
surface may be covered with pools of methane. Unfortunately, the surface of Titan lies about 200 km below the cloud tops and is hidden by
thick, dark orange clouds. The surface temperature is a cold 95 K, but
the surface pressure is 1.6 times the Earth's.

The Voyager spacecraft obtained pictures of the surfaces of seven of
the other classical moons. All of them show the scars of an intensive
meteoritic bombardment while some show signs of tectonic activity.
Their surface appearance ranges from heavily cratered terrain, similar
to that found on the Moon and Mercury, to plains as smooth as lunar
maria. Although Saturn's moons do not exhibit the striking correlations
between average density, semimajor axes, and surface appearance
found for the Galilean satellites of Jupiter, the four moons just inside
Titan's orbit, Rhea, Dione, Tethys, and Enceladus, tend to show more
evidence for resurfacing than the more distant moons (Figure 9.13).
Dione, for instance, has more smooth plains than does Rhea while Enceladus has the youngest surfaces of the four. Enceladus also has
grooved terrain similar to Jupiter's Ganymede, indicating possible crustal tectonics. The exact mechanism for producing the smoother surfaces
is unknown at present, but probably includes heat sources that partially
melted the surface ices, destroying evidence of craters. An early source
of heat could be that left over from the initial bombardment, which
should have been more intense for these moons closer to Saturn.

The two most heavily cratered moons are tiny Mimas and distant Iapetus (Figure 9.14). Mimas has one very large crater, called Herschel,
that represents an impact by a meteorite that was almost large enough
to disrupt Mimas. Iapetus has one very dark hemisphere that reflects as
little as 2 to 4% of all incident light. Astronomers have no idea what
the composition of the dark material is, but since the dark hemisphere
faces the direction of Iapetus' orbital motion, the source of the dark
covering may be external to the moon. No topographical details are
visible in the dark hemisphere. Rhea and Dione also have dark hemispheres, but they are on the trailing hemisphere instead of on the leading hemisphere as with Iapetus. The dark terrain on these two moons
is called "wispy" terrain and may be tectonic in origin or may be recently outgassed ices. The wispy terrain is not seen on the leading hemisphere, perhaps because the higher cratering rate obliterated any signs
of tectonics.

Phoebe, the outermost satellite of Saturn, is only 220 km in diameter
and is very dark, reflecting only about 5% of incident light. It is in a
nonsynchronous, retrograde orbit. Phoebe was too far away for Voyager
pictures to reveal any surface detail. Hyperion lies between Titan and
Iapetus and has a very irregular profile compared to the similar-sized

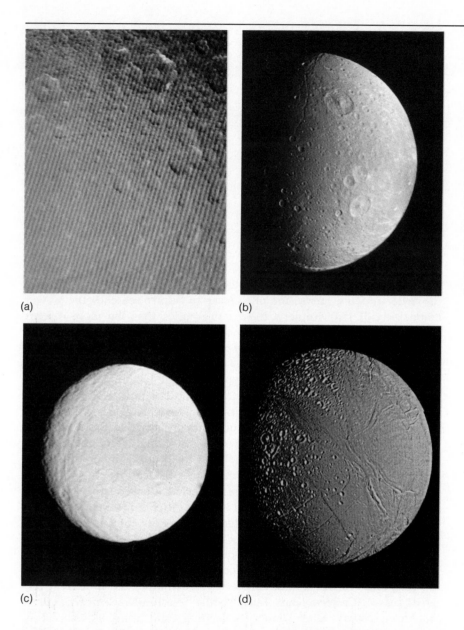

(a)

(b)

(c)

(d)

■ FIGURE 9.13

Rhea, Dione, Tethys, and Enceladus

(a) Voyager 1 photomosaic of Rhea, the most heavily cratered of Saturn's moons. The largest crater is about 300 km across; central peaks can be seen in several craters. *(b) Voyager 1* picture of Dione showing a heavily cratered surface. The largest crater is 100 km in diameter. *(c) Voyager 2* picture of Tethys showing Ithaca Chasm, a valley that extends nearly two-thirds the distance around Tethys.
(d) Heavily cratered terrain as well as lightly cratered plains and ridged areas is visible in this picture of Enceladus. High-resolution pictures show the grooves cutting across older cratering.

SOURCE: NASA.

Mimas and Enceladus. It does not appear to be in synchronous orbit and may be tumbling. Hyperion could be a fragment of a larger parent body. It has at least one large crater, about 120 km across, several craters in the 40–50 km range, and several major scarps.

Co-orbitals and Lagrangians. All of the moons inside the orbit of Mimas were discovered from Pioneer and Voyager images. The largest are the *co-orbital* satellites, Janus and Epimetheus. These are called co-orbitals because they "share" their orbit. Actually their orbital periods differ by a few minutes, which means that one orbits slightly closer to

■■■ FIGURE 9.14

Iapetus and Mimas

(a) Voyager 2 picture of Iapetus showing the contrast between the dark hemisphere and the bright hemisphere. *(b) Voyager 1* picture of Mimas showing the large crater 130 km in diameter with its central peak about 6 km high.

SOURCE: NASA.

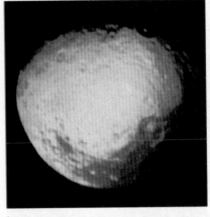 

(a)   (b)

■■■ FIGURE 9.15

Orbital Changes for the Co-Orbitals Janus and Epimetheus

The two moons approach each other at the top. The length of the blue arrows represents the orbital speeds of the satellites. The magenta arrows show the gravitational forces causing the moons to switch orbits.

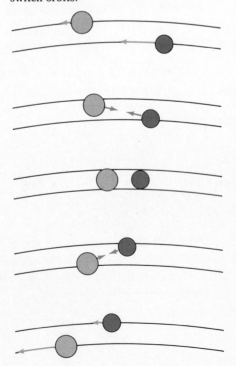

Saturn than the other; the difference is about 50 km. Every few years the faster moving moon, the one closer to Saturn, catches the slower moon. (Recall that Kepler's third law implies that the more distant moons revolve at a lower velocity than nearby moons.) Although the radius of each moon is greater than the distance between their orbits, a collision never takes place.

As the faster, or trailing, moon approaches the leading moon, it gravitationally pulls the slower moon toward it. The pull tends to reduce the orbital radius of the leading moon, placing it in a smaller orbit closer to Saturn. Similarly, the trailing moon is pulled to a more distant orbit (Figure 9.15). The effect becomes stronger as the moons come closer together, but before they collide, the leading moon begins to move away from the trailing moon. Since the leading moon is in a smaller orbit, it has a shorter orbital period. Consequently, the two moons separate and actually switch orbits. After a few years, they repeat this performance as the faster moon again catches the slower moon.

Five other moons also share orbits. Tethys shares its orbit with Calypso and Telesto while Dione is accompanied by Helene. Like the co-orbitals, these moons do not collide with each other but for a very different reason. Calypso leads Tethys while Telesto always trails Tethys, and Helene always leads Dione. The leading and trailing moons occupy special orbital locations, called **Lagrangian points** (Figure 9.16). The leading point is called "L_4" and the trailing point is called "L_5." L_4 and L_5 are located in the orbits 60° ahead and 60° behind Tethys and Dione as measured from Saturn. The Lagrangian points are special because once a moon finds itself at one of the Lagrangian points, it stays in that position relative to the other moons in the same orbit.

All the inner moons are icy, irregularly shaped, and have bright surfaces. Except for Janus and Epimetheus, their surface features could not be detected at the resolution of the Voyager cameras. The irregular shapes of these satellites may indicate a very violent past; they may all have been parts of larger parent bodies.

The Moons of Uranus and Neptune

Mythology and classical literature play an important part in the naming of astronomical objects. The names of the planets, for example, form a mythological family (see AstroProbe 9). The moons of Uranus, however, are named after characters in the works of Shakespeare and Pope. Oberon and Titania are from Shakespeare's *A Midsummer Night's Dream*; Miranda and Ariel are from *The Tempest*; and Umbriel is from Pope's *The Rape of The Lock*. The 10 new moons discovered by *Voyager 2* are also named after characters in Pope's poem and several Shakespearian plays.

Prior to the *Voyager 2* encounter, astronomers deduced that the five major moons of Uranus had diameters between 500 and 1600 km (Figure 9.17 and Table 9.7) and had icy but dark surfaces. The *Voyager 2* pictures showed that all of the major moons of Uranus have high surface crater densities, indicating an early epoch of intense meteoritic bombardment. As with Saturn's and Jupiter's moons, astronomers expect the moons closest to Uranus experienced very high impact rates, which probably caused the disruption of at least the inner three major moons. It is likely, for instance, that Miranda was disrupted by collisions several times and accreted after each disruption by the mutual gravitational attraction of the debris.

In addition, except for Umbriel, the moons of Uranus exhibit a clear increase in geological activity with proximity to the planet, but unlike the Galilean moons of Jupiter, the average densities of the Uranian moons do not appear to correspond to distance from Uranus (Figure 9.18). The low densities of the moons, however, imply a half–water-ice, half-rock composition. Moreover, astronomers must be cautious of any interpretations of the Voyager pictures because *Voyager 2* could only photograph the southern hemispheres of the moons; therefore astronomers can only guess what is to be found on the other hemispheres.

Miranda, the smallest, least dense, and closest of the five major moons to Uranus, displays the most bizarre geological forms found in the solar system thus far (Figure 9.19). Miranda's surface consists of two very different types of terrain: heavily cratered terrain and slablike banded and ridged terrain. The slablike regions are confined to roughly

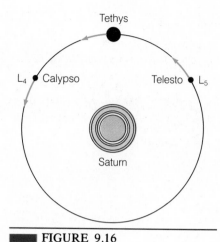

■■■■ FIGURE 9.16

Lagrangian Points

Two stable locations, L_4 and L_5, form an equilateral triangle with the three bodies.

Lagrangian points: Five stable locations in the orbital plane of two bodies revolving around each other in which a third body of negligible mass can remain in the same relative position to the two larger bodies.

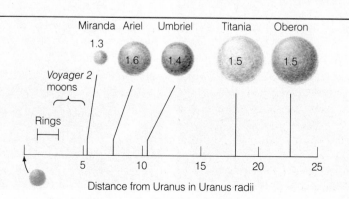

■■■■ FIGURE 9.17

The Major Moons of Uranus

The numbers indicate known average densities of the moons.

TABLE 9.7 **Satellites of Uranus**

Name	Diameter (km)	Density (g/cm³)	Orbital Radius (Uranian radii)	Orbital Period
Cordelia	~40	—	1.9	8^h4^m
Ophelia	~50	—	2.1	9^h4^m
Bianca	~50	—	2.3	10^h28^m
Cressida	~60	—	2.4	11^h9^m
Desdemona	~60	—	2.4	11^h22^m
Juliet	~80	—	2.5	12^h
Portia	~80	—	2.6	12^h21^m
Rosalind	~60	—	2.7	13^h27^m
Belinda	~60	—	2.9	15^h2^m
Puck	~170	—	3.4	18^h17^m
Miranda	484	1.26	5.1	1.41 days
Ariel	1160	1.65	7.5	2.52 days
Umbriel	1190	1.44	10.4	4.14 days
Titania	1610	1.54	17.0	8.71 days
Oberon	1550	1.50	22.7	13.46 days

FIGURE 9.18

Oberon, Titania, Umbriel, and Ariel

(a) At the center of the picture are two young rayed craters on Oberon with dark patches in their centers. The mountain or central peak on the lower left edge of the moon is 20 km high. *(b)* The surface of Titania has several prominent faults across its surface and is heavily cratered. Its neutral gray color is characteristic of Uranian satellites. *(c)* Umbriel's surface is dark with only a few light regions. *(d)* Ariel's surface has old, cratered terrain, young rayed craters, smooth terrain, and grooves.

SOURCES: Part (a), USGS Planetary Data Facility. Parts (b), (c), and (d), NASA.

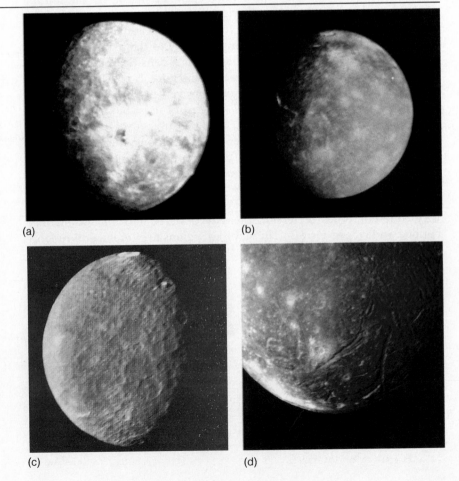

(a)

(b)

(c)

(d)

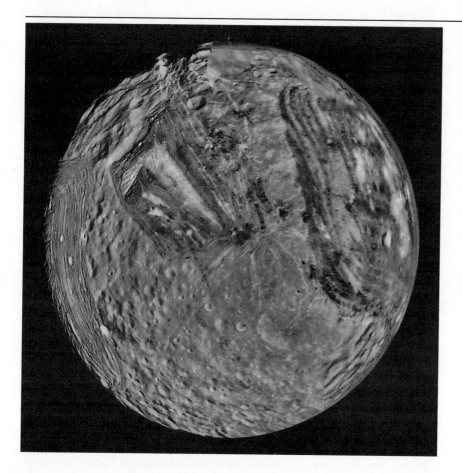

Miranda

This *Voyager 2* image of Miranda shows its banded and cratered terrain.
SOURCE: NASA.

rectangular areas and consist of racetrack patterns of grooves and ridges. The grooves and ridges are seen to "turn" at the corners of the rectangular regions. The slablike region with the V-shape appears to reach over the edge of Miranda in a deep valley connecting it with unknown terrain in the northern hemisphere. These features appear to be the result of tectonic processes, which were very localized yet involved large areas on the surface of Miranda, and may be related to the satellite's early history. Recall that Miranda was probably disrupted several times in the past. After a collision with a large meteorite, Miranda would have been broken into pieces of ice and rock. The material that remained in the same orbit would reassemble within a few tens of thousands of years. It may be that large chunks of dense rock in the rebuilt Miranda have worked themselves slowly toward the center, displacing some of the ice that would melt in the interior. The rectangular areas on the surface may be the response of the surface to such sinking. This is, of course, a guess as to the origin of the bizarre surface features on Miranda and should be viewed with cautious skepticism.

The inner 10 moons of Uranus are all less than 170 km in diameter; most are between 40 and 80 km across. Because they are so small, scientists can only determine their sizes, orbital periods, and semimajor

■■■ FIGURE 9.20

The Satellite System of Neptune

Except for the small inner moons, Neptune's satellite system is unlike those of the other Jovian planets.

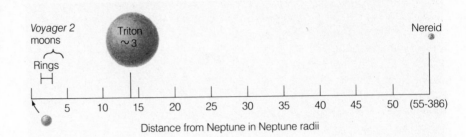

Distance from Neptune in Neptune radii

axes. Only the tiny moon Puck was imaged with enough detail to resolve a few craters.

Even at the immense distance of Neptune, astronomers have been able to discover two of its moons, Triton and Nereid, from Earth (Figure 9.20 and Table 9.8). Whereas the moons of Uranus have circular orbits in the same plane, those of Triton and Nereid are very irregular. Triton's orbit is retrograde and very inclined while Nereid's orbit is very eccentric.

Neptune's satellite system differs in significant ways from those of the other Jovian planets. Instead of being surrounded by a dozen or more regular satellites, Neptune has two "odd" satellites and just a few inner moons. Compared to the other Jovian planets, it is unusual for a planet to have (1) a large moon—Triton—in an inclined retrograde orbit, but at the same time a nearly perfectly circular orbit; and (2) another major moon—Nereid—with an extremely eccentric orbit. Consequently, astronomers suspect that something unusual took place in the Neptunian system. For instance, if a large object passed close to Neptune, it could have strongly interacted with Neptune's moons, drastically altering their orbits or even destroying some of them. In the early epochs of the solar system when planets were forming, many moderately large objects were probably orbiting the Sun. It is possible that one of these objects may have knocked over Uranus, and a similar event may have occurred at Neptune.

■■■ TABLE 9.8 **Satellites of Neptune**

Name*	Diameter (km)	Orbital Radius (Neptune radii)	Eccentricity	Orbital Period
1989 N6	~50	1.98	—	7^h6^m
1989 N5	~90	2.06	—	7^h30^m
1989 N3	~140	2.16	—	8^h0^m
1989 N4	~160	2.55	—	9^h30^m
1989 N2	~200	3.03	—	13^h18^m
1989 N1	~420	4.84	—	26^h54^m
Triton	2720	14.1	0.005	5.87 days
Nereid	~1000	55–386	0.75	359.88 days

*Names for the satellites 1989 N1 to 1989 N6 discovered by *Voyager 2* are temporary.

Triton may have been one of these large bodies that was captured by Neptune (Figure 9.21). One possibility is that Triton, while in a heliocentric orbit about the Sun, collided with one of the regular moons of Neptune. A collision is required because it would cause Triton to reduce its speed enough to allow Neptune to capture it; a capture without a collision requires very special circumstances and therefore is not likely. The resulting collision could have placed Triton into a highly eccentric orbit with a semimajor axis as high as a thousand Neptunian radii. After the collision, Triton would have been in a molten state because its highly eccentric orbit would take it alternately close to and then far away from Neptune, producing immense tides on Triton. Calculations show that the tides raised on Triton would not only heat Triton but would *reduce* the orbital eccentricity to nearly zero in about a billion years. Recall that for the Moon, Earth tides are slowly accelerating the Moon away from the Earth. For a retrograde orbit, the effect is just the opposite; Triton's orbit has been slowly changed so that it is in a circular orbit and much closer to Neptune than it was originally.

The slow change in Triton's orbit over a billion years would allow it to perturb the orbits of any existing moons orbiting Neptune. For instance, Triton would have crossed the orbit of Nereid a hundred thousand times in a billion years and gradually changed Nereid's orbit through random encounters. Smaller moons could have been destroyed by Triton as it swept through the Neptunian satellite system over and over by perturbing their orbits so that they were accreted by either Triton or Neptune. This model of the capture of Triton and its orbital evolution predicts that the only regular satellites in the Neptunian system should lie within the orbit of Triton, which is basically what *Voyager 2* discovered. A collision of Triton with one of the moons of Neptune appears to be a reasonable explanation of Triton's peculair orbit and the lack of major moons beyond Triton.

Triton is massive enough to have an atmosphere and a differentiated interior. The atmosphere of Triton is mainly nitrogen with some methane and may extend 800 km above the surface. Below 5 km is a hazy layer that might be caused by the condensation of atmospheric gases.

The *Voyager 2* pictures of Triton revealed an icy surface, spotted with frozen (methane?) lakes, active "nitrogen" volcanoes, and other features never before seen in the solar system. Panel a in Figure 9.22 shows the diversity of terrain features seen on Triton's surface. The northern hemisphere is in shadow in this image while the southern hemisphere basks in the Sun's feeble light. Near the border of the two hemispheres are long, straight ridges reminiscent of grooves on other Jovian moons. The southern hemisphere does not show any large impact craters—suggesting that the crust of Triton has been resurfaced recently. About 50 dark "wind" streaks, some over 150 km long, cover part of the southern hemisphere (Panel b). They remind astronomers of the wind streaks seen on Mars (compare with Figure 7.29). Triton's streaks originate at very dark spots several kilometers in diameter. The sources do not appear to be impact craters as on Mars; they may be vents where gas has erupted and ejected dark particles into Triton's thin nitrogen-rich atmosphere. Two plumes of gas, one 8 km high, have been detected in

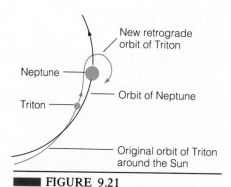

FIGURE 9.21

Hypothetical Capture of Triton by Neptune

If Triton approached Neptune from the Sun side, it could be captured in a retrograde orbit about Neptune. The dynamics of such a capture is more complicated than shown here and would involve a collision with at least one other large object.

■■■ FIGURE 9.22

Triton

(a) The southern hemisphere of Triton.
(b) Triton's southern hemisphere shows about 50 dark plumes, which may be caused by "ice" volcanoes. *(c)* A view of a large basin modified by flooding and melting. A small crater can be seen near the center. *(d)* Dark, irregular areas that may be surrounded by frost.

SOURCE: Jet Propulsion Laboratory.

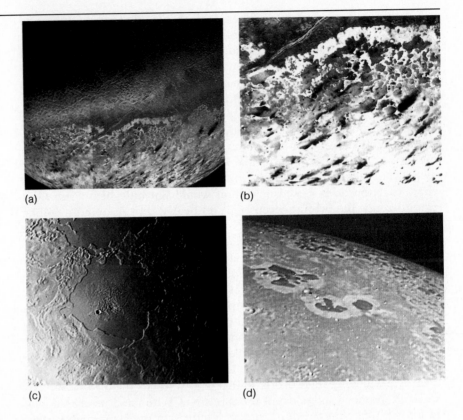

(a)

(b)

(c)

(d)

Voyager photographs. Scientists surmise that subsurface nitrogen can turn from a solid ice to an expanding gas, a process called sublimation, with a slight temperature rise beneath the surface.

What could cause temperature variations to fuel nitrogen eruptions? Neptune's rotational axis is tipped 29° relative to the Sun (Earth's axis is tipped 23½°) and the orbit of Triton is inclined 21° to this. Consequently, Triton's polar regions can point steeply toward the Sun—by as much as 50°. This occurs several times during a complicated 600-year cycle of seasons on Triton and leads to extreme variations in the amount of sunlight absorbed by the surface. These extreme tilts could cause significant temperature variations on the surface of the moon and force subsurface nitrogen to sublime. The gases released into the atmosphere would then tend to migrate toward the colder pole and freeze out, similar to what happens on Mars. This may have something to do with the apparent difference in the terrain seen near the border of the light and dark region in Panel a in Figure 9.22; the northern hemisphere might be covered with a thin layer of frozen nitrogen. The southern hemisphere of Triton will be tilted it steepest toward the Sun at the end of this century and will experience a "major" summer.

Figure 9.22 also shows several unique surface features on Triton. Panel c shows a depression that may be an old impact basin, similar to the lunar maria. In this case, however, flooding was probably by melted ice instead of lava. Panel d shows three dark areas surrounded by

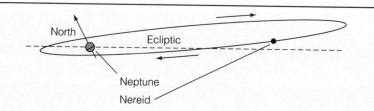

FIGURE 9.23

Orbit of Nereid

Although Nereid's orbital motion is direct, its orbit is tilted about 28° with respect to the equatorial plane of Neptune and is very eccentric.

brighter material. The bright "rims" might be frost, and the darker central regions may be material that was somehow heated, evaporating the frost covering. Most of the shapes on the surface of Triton are probably water-ice. Ices of methane and nitrogen could not sustain vertical structures of 100 to 300 meters seen on Triton.

The surface of Triton does not show signs of the intense meteoritic bombardment that it must have experienced during its first billion years. The crater density is what is expected if Triton were geologically inactive and just recorded the drizzle of meteorites over the last few billion years. It may be that signs of current geological activity are driven by seasonal variations.

Voyager 2 did not obtain high-resolution pictures of the other satellites of Neptune, including Nereid. Nereid's orbit is as unusual as that of Triton. It is the most elliptical orbit of any known satellite in the solar system. Its perigee is 1,390,500 km from Neptune, and its apogee is 9,733,500 km (Figure 9.23). Five of the newly discoverd moons of Neptune, however, appear to have regular orbits in the planet's equatorial plane. The orbit of the smallest of the six, 1989 N6, is only tilted about 5° to the equatorial plane, nearly the same as Earth's Moon. The largest of the small, inner satellites, 1989 N1, is about the same size as Uranus' moon Miranda.

PLANETARY RINGS

Saturn has millions of moons. Each ring particle is a small moon orbiting Saturn. The same is true of Jupiter, Uranus, and Neptune. The Pioneer and Voyager missions discovered not only new moons and details of the rings never before imagined but also new phenomena associated with small moons and ring particles.

The Rings of Saturn

Before the Voyager missions, astronomers believed the rings of Saturn consisted of three smooth, continuous rings, A, B, and C, composed of small, icy particles of various sizes. The Cassini division divided rings A and B, and the Encke division was located near the outer edge of the A ring. This picture was based on observations from the Earth where, under the best conditions, astronomers could only discern features larger than about 3500 km across; that is, any gaps in the rings must

342

CHAPTER 9

■■■ FIGURE 9.24

Close-up View of Saturn's Ring Structure

The F ring can be seen as the thin line just outside the major rings. Both the Cassini and Encke divisions are clearly visible.

SOURCE: NASA.

be more than 3500 km wide to be seen from the Earth. The Pioneer pictures have a resolution of 400 km while the Voyagers pick out details as small as 1–2 km across. These high-resolution pictures radically changed our view of the rings of Saturn.

The most surprising discovery concerning the rings was the detail in the ring structure (Figure 9.24). The rings are not continuous as previously thought, but seem to be concentric ringlets composed of small particles. Even the Cassini division has ringlets within it. Astronomers have also discovered several other fainter rings. Inside the C ring, a tenuous ring, called the D ring, extends to within a few thousand kilometers of the top of Saturn's atmosphere (Figure 9.25). The most distant ring, the E ring, has its highest concentration of particles near the orbit of Enceladus but extends smoothly for 50,000 km on either side of its orbit. The E ring particles are very small and probably spherical, possibly made of water-ice. The E ring could be the result of ices ejected from Enceladus due to an impact or, even more interesting, may possibly be due to eruptions of some sort of water volcanoes or geysers on Enceladus. Another newly discovered ring, the G ring, lies just inside the orbit of Mimas. The G ring is faint, several thousand kilometers wide, and has very poorly defined boundaries.

Just outside the A ring is a remarkable, very narrow ring called the F ring (see Figure 9.24). The F ring shows bright stands that twist and kink, giving it a braided appearance (Panel a in Figure 9.26). Two small satellites, Prometheus and Pandora, bracket the F ring (Panel b). These moons are called "shepherding" satellites because they act to confine the ring particles by slightly changing the orbital eccentricities of the particles. Although the gravitational interaction is slightly more complicated than that between co-orbitals, the net result is that the outer shepherding moon tends to slow down the ring particles at the outside part of the ring while the inner shepherding moon tends to speed up the ring particles at the inside of the ring. Consequently, the outer par-

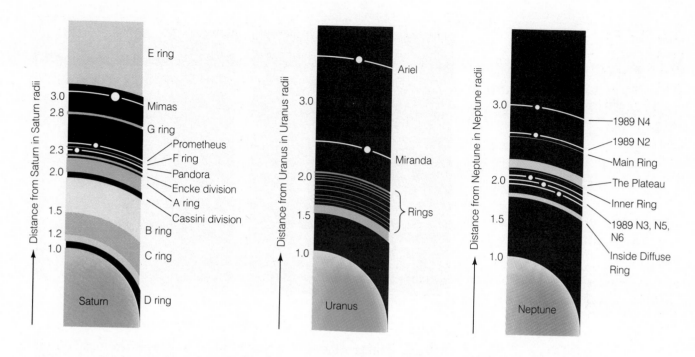

**Rings of Saturn, Uranus,
and Neptune**

ticles move inward while the inner particles move outward. As the particles move toward each other, they collide and reduce their in-and-out motions, forming a confined, narrow ring.

Except for the diffuse E ring, which is a few thousand kilometers thick, the rings of Saturn are surprisingly thin, less than 100 m. Observers have know that they were less than several thousand kilometers thick for several hundred years because the rings disappear whenever they are viewed on edge. Except for the very small particles in the E ring, most ring particles are between a few centimeters and several meters across. Collisions between individual ring particles cause the rings to be several times thicker than the larger particles. The collisions simply change individual orbits slightly so that the particles do not move in perfectly circular orbits in a single thin plane. The individual particles appear to be predominantly water-ice or at least covered with water-ice.

What causes the ring structure imaged by the Voyager cameras? Why do planets have rings anyway? The answer to the first question involves a special gravitational interaction that occurs between ring particles and distant satellites; the answer to the second question involves another gravitational interaction that occurs when two objects come too close to each other.

The Cassini division is an example of what can happen if the orbital period of ring particles is half that of a distant large moon. The moon in this case is Mimas. Mimas orbits Saturn once every 22^{h}34^m while a ring particle in the Cassini division revolves around Saturn once every 11^{h}17^m. Consequently, every 22^{h}34^m a Cassini division particle will line up with Mimas in exactly the same configuration at the same place in its orbit. The ring particle will feel the same gravitational tug from Mi-

344

FIGURE 9.26

Saturn's F Ring

(a) Twists and kinks in the F ring. *(b)* Prometheus and Pandora are less than 1800 km apart in this picture.

SOURCE: NASA.

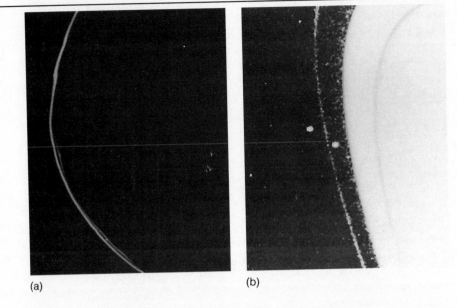

(a)   (b)

Resonance: Gravitational tugs by one body on another that repeat; that is, they occur with the same strength at the same relative configuration.

mas every other time it is in this location. The repeated tugs will impart a slight change in velocity to the particle and, therefore, slowly change its orbit. Eventually, the particle will drift out of its original orbit, vacating the Cassini division. This relationship between the orbital periods of ring particles and satellites with the associated gravitational interaction is called a **resonance**. Ring particles will also feel "resonance tugs" if their orbital periods are exact ratios, such as ½, ⅓, and ¼, of the sidereal periods of other satellites. Ring particles outside the Cassini division, of course, also feel gravitational tugs from Mimas, but these are random in that they do not occur at the same places with the same strengths and, consequently, have no net effect on the orbit over long periods of time.

Even with the wealth of data from the Pioneer and Voyager spacecraft, the amount of information astronomers have about the rings is still limited, especially about their behavior in time. Consequently, an understanding of the observed structures depends heavily on models of the rings, which involve gravitational resonances, collisions between ring particles, and shepherding effects. Current models can explain many of the features seen, for instance, in the A ring. Some features in the rings are not gaps but *waves* that are part of tightly wound spirals, like the grooves on a phonograph record, and appear to be generated by satellite resonances. The waves produced by the effect of resonances depend on the particle density in the ring, the thickness of the ring at the location of the waves, and even the mass of the total ring. The models not only predict structures within the rings but also their evolution, or changes with time. The tests of these models, of course, are comparisons with the Voyager data and, someday, with future observations.

Why do planets have rings? Why don't the ring particles merge together by their mutual gravitational attraction and form a small moon?

A moon approaching or orbiting a planet feels tidal forces acting over the moon's diameter. These tend to stretch the moon along the line between the moon and planet as happens in the Earth-Moon system. Imagine two small spheres in space held together only by their mutual gravitational attraction and approaching a planet with one sphere in front of the other. As the two spheres approach closer and closer to the planet, the tidal forces tending to separate them become stronger and stronger. Eventually, the spheres will reach a point above the planet in which the stretching tidal forces will be as large as the gravitational forces holding the two spheres together. As the two spheres move closer to the planet, they will then separate. The location at which they separate is called the **Roche limit,** after Edouard Roche (1820–1883), a French mathematician who formulated the problem.

A solid body, such as a rocky or icy moon, is also held together by the strength of its rock and ice. Consequently, it would have to be closer to a planet than the "classical" Roche limit before tidal forces dominate. Very small bodies, however, can exist inside a planet's Roche limit because the tidal stresses across it are small, producing tidal forces that are weaker than the electrostatic forces between individual atoms holding the body together. Once within the Roche limit and struck by a large meteorite, for instance, a body would be disrupted and could never re-coalesce if it stayed within the Roche limit. The Roche limit for large icy moons orbiting Saturn is about 2½ Saturnian radii from the center of Saturn. This is just outside the inner boundary of the A ring.

The rings, therefore, could be the result of a moon, or moons, migrating inside the Roche limit and then being disrupted by a large meteoritic impact. For instance, the total amount of material in Saturn's rings could make a satellite 250 km in diameter. On the other hand, the rings could be leftover planetary material from the formation of Saturn itself. This material was located inside the Roche limit and could not coalesce into moons. At present, scientists cannot make a convincing choice between these two alternatives.

Roche limit: The outer boundary of a zone in which a satellite may break up due to tidal forces generated by the planet it orbits; Roche originally calculated this limit for a liquid satellite. Pronounced "rōsh."

The Rings of Jupiter, Uranus, and Neptune

Pioneer 11 observations gave scientists a clue that Jupiter might have a ring. Subsequently, *Voyager 1* looked for and discovered the rings, and *Voyager 2* studied them in detail (Figure 9.27). The "bright" ring is only a few thousand kilometers wide, between 1.72 and 1.81 Jupiter radii from Jupiter, and is less than 30 km thick. The distribution of ring particles appears to be smooth. A second, very diffuse ring may extend all the way to the surface of the planet. The third component of Jupiter's ring system is a "halo" of particles extending more than 10,000 km above and below the bright ring.

Astronomers are able to estimate the particle sizes in rings by analyzing the light scattered off the ring particles. The pictures of the rings of Jupiter, for instance, were taken looking back toward the Sun when the spacecraft was behind Jupiter. The light seen is the result of *forward*

Jupiter's Ring

This is a mosaic of six *Voyager 2* images of the ring viewed from behind Jupiter inside Jupiter's shadow. The gaps are due to the partial coverage of the images.

SOURCE: NASA.

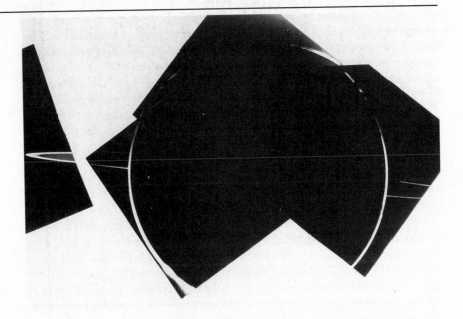

scattering by the ring particles. The amount of forward scattering indicates the sizes of the particles that scattered the light. For example, if the particles are large, they will block the light, resulting in very little forward scattering; if they are very small, light will pass through. From examining photographs taken at different wavelengths, scientists have found that Jupiter's ring particles appear to be small, a few larger particles probably are mixed with the smaller ones. Further analysis of reflected light from Jupiter's ring particles indicates that the particles are rocky, most likely silicates, rather than ice covered as Saturn's ring particles are.

The rings of Uranus were discovered by accident from an airborne observatory 41,000 feet over the Indian Ocean on March 10, 1977. The flying observatory was a NASA C-141 jet airplane, called the Kuiper Airborne Observatory, equipped with a 1-meter telescope, light-detecting instruments, and computers (Figure 9.28). A team of astronomers from Cornell University, headed by James L. Elliot, were to observe an **occultation,** or eclipse, of a star by Uranus. During an occultation of a star by our Moon, for instance, the star instantaneously disappears as it slips behind the sharp edge of the Moon. A planet with an atmosphere, however, does not have a sharp, distinctive edge because atmospheric gases thin with height above the planet. Consequently, a star will gradually dim as it passes behind increasingly thick layers of the atmosphere. The manner in which the light from the star fades indicates how the temperature and pressure change with height in a planet's atmosphere. Also, the length of time the occultation takes provides a remarkably accurate measure of a planet's diameter. The astronomers had these measurements in mind while preparing for the occultation.

While checking their instruments before the occultation started, Elliot and his colleagues were surprised when the star dimmed briefly.

Kuiper Airborne Observatory

SOURCE: NASA Ames.

Then another dimming occurred and another; this happened five times before the occultation and again after the occultation. These events were also recorded by four other groups observing the same occultation from different locations in the world. The observers concluded that the star must have passed behind five faint rings surrounding Uranus (Figure 9.29).

Further occultation work from Earth-based telescopes revealed a total of nine thin rings (Panel a in Figure 9.30 and Panel b in Figure 9.25). *Voyager 2* discovered two more. Like Saturn's rings, the rings of Uranus appear to be tens of meters thick. But, unlike Saturn's rings, most particles in the Uranian rings appear to be larger than a meter across. All are very dark, in contrast to the bright ring particles orbiting Saturn. Although most of the mass of the Uranian rings is tied up in large chunks, a fine dust is distributed throughout the ring system. This dust is probably the debris from countless collisions that have occurred between the ring particles over the eons.

The predominant characteristic of the 11 known Uranian rings is their narrowness. The density of particles in the narrow rings is high enough to block out the light from a star passing behind them. In this sense, they are most similar to Saturn's F ring. The F ring, you will recall, was confined by two shepherding satellites. It is not surprising, therefore, that astronomers discovered shepherding satellites, Cordelia and Ophelia, confining the outermost Uranian ring, known as the epsilon ring (Panel b). No other shepherding satellites were seen, however. If they exist, they must be smaller than 20 km in diameter because that was the lower limit to *Voyager 2's* detecting ability at Uranus.

Voyager 2 discovered two bright narrow rings, a faint, wide ring, and a broad sheet of small ring particles around Neptune (Figure 9.31 and Panel c in Figure 9.25). The rings are seen backlighted by the Sun, a viewing geometry that enhances the visibility of dust and allows fainter, dusty parts of the rings to be seen. The exposures were 10 minutes

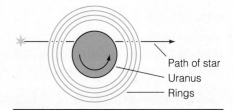

FIGURE 9.29

Occultation Geometry

Uranus and its rings present a bull's eye view to Earth observers; a star passing behind Uranus would also pass behind its rings.

FIGURE 9.30

Voyager 2 Views of the Rings of Uranus

(a) The outermost, or epsilon, ring is shown at the bottom left corner of the picture. *(b)* The two satellites, Cordelia and Ophelia, are seen on either side of the epsilon ring. These act to confine the ring particles.

SOURCE: NASA.

(a)

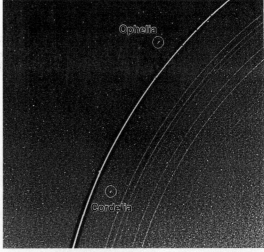

(b)

■ FIGURE 9.31

Neptune's Ring System

The 10-minute exposures needed to detect the faint rings caused the image of Neptune to be overexposed.

SOURCE: Jet Propulsion Laboratory.

■ FIGURE 9.32

Ring Arcs

Three ring arcs are seen along the Main Ring of Neptune.

SOURCE: Jet Propulsion Laboratory.

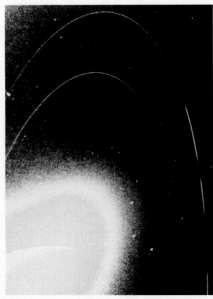

long, indicating the low light levels in this remote region of the solar system. The outer, or the "Main Ring," lies about 62,000 km from Neptune, which is at about the same distance as satellite 1989 N4. The next ring inward, the "Inner Ring," is 53,000 kilometers from Neptune, near satellite 1989 N3. The innermost ring, called the "Inside Diffuse Ring," is a broader ring 42,000 km from the center of Neptune. Figure 9.31 also shows a broad, diffuse sheet of fine material, called "The Plateau," just outside the Inner Ring. Particles are approximately the size of smoke particles in The Plateau. The other rings contain a greater proportion of larger ring particles.

Figure 9.32 shows what appears to be a new phenomenon in planetary ring science. The Main Ring shows obvious concentrations of ring particles seen as thick, bright segments, or arcs, along the ring. Astronomers suspected the existence of arcs from occultation observations from Earth but thought that the arcs would not be part of complete rings. Observations showed that stars dimmed before an occultation by Neptune but not after when they should have passed behind the other side of a suspected ring. It appears that the observed arcs were actually part of a complete ring that was not thick enough to dim the stars enough to be detected.

Current thinking attributes ring arcs and twists and kinks (such as exhibited by the F ring around Saturn) to collisions within the rings and to gravitational effects of nearby satellites and of moonlets inside the rings. The collisions within a ring could shake loose debris, which would then form clumps. The clumps, however, would eventually spread out along the ring—on a time scale of decades. Perhaps the peculiar orbits of Nereid and Triton gravitationally influence the rings in such a way as to produce temporary arcs or clumps along a ring. Rings are orbiting piles of small particles. They change their position in time by chance encounters with small satellites and by random internal stirring—they are not solid and static.

The known ring systems in the solar system are distinctly different. Jupiter's rings are composed of very small particles, about the size of dust grains, and are probably made of silicates. At Saturn, temperatures are cold enough for grains of ice to remain frozen; consequently, Saturn's ring particles are icy and bright. Saturn's particles are also larger than those at Jupiter. The rings of Uranus, on the other hand, are dark and probably have a coating of carbon-rich material. The Uranian ring particles are the largest of the three on the average. Furthermore, while Jupiter's rings are very tenuous, the rings of Saturn, Uranus, and Neptune are densely packed. The rings of Uranus and Neptune are very narrow and separated by large gaps whereas the major rings of Saturn are wide and separated by narrow gaps. The rings at Uranus are very similar to Saturn's F ring as are Neptune's rings. Neptune's ring system is the only one to show significant clumping, or arcs.

The intricacies of the ring systems of the solar system provide astronomers with a laboratory for particle dynamics. The interpretation of the observed ring structures is incomplete at present. It involves the combination of gravitational resonances with the gravitational and collisional effects within the rings themselves. Planetary rings may be relics from the early solar system and are perhaps representative of the particles that formed the planets.

▰ SUMMARY

Each of the Jovian planets is like a miniature solar system, holding many satellites, some as large as the smaller Terrestrial planets, in orbit about it. In addition, each has a system of rings consisting of small particles revolving in a flat, disklike structure.

Sixteen moons orbit Jupiter, at least 17 orbit Saturn, 15 orbit Uranus, and 8 orbit Neptune. Most of these moons orbit in the same direction as the planet rotates and in the planet's equatorial plane; the exceptions are distant, small Jovian moons and the largest moons orbiting Neptune.

The Jovian moons lie within the strong gravitational fields of the massive parent planets and have been exposed to enhanced meteoritic bombardments. These bombardments may have been so intense that several of the moons may have been completely disrupted many times throughout their history. Once disrupted, they re-coalesced under the mutual gravitational attraction between the pieces.

Many of the Jovian moons have icy surfaces. This implies that the "solidification" of satellite surfaces

was really a freezing of the surface ice. Nevertheless, hard ice can form the various types of craters.

Four large Jovian moons, known as the Galilean satellites, exhibit clear correlations between average density, surface appearance, and distance from Jupiter. Moons close to Jupiter are denser and have younger surfaces that reflect different solidification times. The innermost Galilean moon, Io, is one of only two solar system objects outside the Earth with known active volcanoes. The correlations are probably due to different heating histories of the satellites. The moons closer to Jupiter experienced a more intense bombardment, became hotter, and, as a result, took longer to cool. The moons that cooled first were able to record the peak of the intense bombardment while those that cooled later had liquid or slushy surfaces that were unable to form permanent surface features such as craters.

Saturn's satellite system contains the only moon in the solar system known to have a thick atmosphere; Titan's atmosphere is denser than the Earth's. Titan has a nitrogen-rich atmosphere in which methane may play a role similar to that of water in the Earth's atmosphere. Saturn's other moons have average densities indicative of half-ice, half-rock compositions.

The Saturnian satellite system has several examples of co-orbital satellites and Lagrangian satellites, while the most unusual satellite pairs are the shepherding satellites. These are small moons that act to confine ring particles into narrow ringlets. Uranus has at least one pair of shepherding satellites, while Jupiter has a co-orbiting pair of moons.

Jupiter, Saturn, Uranus, and Neptune have ring systems. Jupiter's rings are composed of tiny silicate particles. Saturn has three major broad rings easily visible from the Earth that are composed of bright,

icy chunks as large as a meter across. The 11 rings of Uranus appear to be composed mainly of relatively large, dark rocks. Most rings are very thin, being tens of meters thick. Whereas Jupiter's rings are very diffuse, the rings of Saturn, Uranus, and Neptune are dense enough to block out light.

In addition to the large gaps visible from the Earth, planetary rings exhibit rather intricate structures. The multitude of ringlets seen in Saturn's rings, in the "gaps" between Saturn's rings, and in the narrow rings of Uranus and Neptune appear to be strongly associated with gravitational resonances between ring particles and the larger moons. The major portions of the ring systems lie inside the planet's Roche limit.

CHAPTER CAPSULE

Topics and Terms	Review and Remarks
Satellite systems	The Jovian planets are characterized by many moons: Jupiter has 16. Saturn has 17. Uranus has 15. Neptune has 8.
Satellite orbital configurations	Co-orbital Shepherding Lagrangian
Surfaces	Most moons have icy surfaces as evidenced by: Reflectance spectra Snow-white ejecta of visible craters Apparent postimpact modification due to the heat generated during impact.
Galilean moons of Jupiter	Io has the youngest surface and is closest to Jupiter; its active volcanism is caused by tidal stretching. Europa, Ganymede, and Callisto have surfaces that froze at different times—Callisto's first and Europa's last. Their physical properties and appearance correlate with their distances from Jupiter.
Planetary rings	They are composed of particles of many different sizes. Tidal forces (Roche limit) prevent coalescence of ring particles into moons. The ring particles orbit the planet in its equatorial plane. The rings exhibit intricate structure, including ringlets, gaps, and twists, that is caused by gravitational resonances with moons.

◼︎REVIEW QUESTIONS

1. Each Galilean satellite of Jupiter has its own peculiar surface features. Describe each of them. Why are these moons referred to as "Galilean"?

2. Io has characteristics that make it unique among the satellites discovered so far. Describe Io's peculiar surface. Why does Io have few meteor craters?

3. Why should the Galilean satellites display such different surfaces? Can you compare their differences with those of the planets? (*Hint:* See Table 9.4.)

4. The rings of Saturn were originally designated as "A," "B," and "C." Compare the appearance of these rings as they appear from Earth and as they appear in pictures received from the *Voyagers*.

5. We now know of thousands of ringlets in the Saturnian system. Why are the ringlets not visible from Earth? Of what material are they composed?

6. Where are the Encke and Cassini divisions found?

7. What are co-orbitals and Lagrangian satellites?

8. Why are "ringmoons" sometimes referred to as shepherding satellites?

9. What is the most abundant chemical compound found in the satellites of the outer solar system?

10. What is Titan and why is it special?

11. Compare the ring systems of the Jovian planets.

◼︎FOR FURTHER READING

Beatty, J. K. 1987. Pluto and Charon: The dance goes on. *Sky & Telescope*, Sept., 248.

Chaikin, A. 1986. Voyage among the ice worlds. *Sky & Telescope*, Apr., 338.

Cuzzi, J. 1984. Ringed planets: Still mysterious—I. *Sky & Telescope*, Dec., 511.

———. 1985. Ringed planets: Still mysterious—II. *Sky & Telescope*, Jan., 19.

Cuzzi, J. N., and L. W. Esposito. 1987. The rings of Uranus. *Scientific American*, July, 52.

Esposito, L. 1987. The changing shape of planetary rings. *Astronomy*, Sept., 6.

Johnson, T. V., R. H. Brown, and L. A. Soderblom. 1987. The moons of Uranus. *Scientific American*, Apr., 48.

Morrison, D. 1985. The enigma called Io. *Sky & Telescope*, Mar., 198.

Simon, S. 1986. The view from Europa. *Astronomy*, Nov., 98.

ASTROPROBE 9

Planetary Pedigree

All of the names of the planets and most of their moons derive from Greek mythology. In many cases the Roman name for a Greek deity is used today. For example, Mercury is used for the Greek Hermes, Saturn for the Greek Cronus, Earth for the Greek Gaea, and Jupiter for the Greek Zeus. In Greek mythology, all of the Greek gods and goddesses derive from four primeval deities: Chaos (Infinite Space), Gaea (Earth), Tartarus (Lower World), and Eros (Love). Gaea, of course, is "Mother Earth," the sustenance of universal life. The Lower World is the abode for the souls of all, good or bad, who perished from the Earth. Before entering the Lower World, souls had to pay a fee to cross the river Styx in the boat of the repulsive, old ferryman Charon. Hence derives the Greek custom of placing a silver coin in the mouth of every corpse before burial. Eros was the personification of love, who represented a unifying influence on the conflicting elements of Chaos and allowed harmony and order in the world.

Most of the mythological characters whose names have been used for the planets and moons of the solar system were descendants of Earth. The first unfathered offspring of Earth were Pontus (The Sea) and Uranus (The Heavens). Our planetary pedigree derives from the descendants of Uranus and Earth. The union of Uranus and Earth produced many sons and daughters, the most renowned being the Titans, who for a while ruled heaven and Earth (Table 9A.1). Of particular importance were two of the Titans, Saturn and Rhea. Saturn fought his father Uranus and wrested the throne of the gods for himself.

Saturn took his sister Rhea for his wife and produced many children, including Jupiter, Pluto, Neptune, and Hera. Hera is noteworthy because she became the wife of her brother Jupiter and gave birth to Mars, Venus, and Mercury. Thus the deities whose names adorn the planets of the solar system are the children, grandchildren, and great-grandchildren of Earth (Figure 9A.1).

The names of the moons of the planets, except for those of Uranus, read like a mythological family tree. The moons of Mars, Phobos and Deimos, are the mythological sons of Mars and Dione (granddaughter of Uranus). Mars, a wild, ungovernable son of Jupiter, was the Greek god of war. His two sons were also filled with a lust for violence and desolation: Deimos means "fear" or "terror" and Phobos means "dismay" or "flight from fear." The Romans honored Mars second only to Jupiter and said that Mars was the father of Romulus and Remus, the male ancestors of their race.

Pluto (the Greek Hades) fought alongside his brother Jupiter in the War of the Titans in which Jupiter defeated his father Saturn and the other Titans. Jupiter then appointed Pluto to be governor of the Lower World. Thus Charon, the ferryman of the river Styx, was a

▬▬▬ TABLE 9A.1 The Titans

Oceanus	*Rhea*
Coeus	Themis
Crius	Mnemosyne
Hyperion	*Phoebe*
Iapetus	*Tethys*
Theia	*Saturn*

The names of planets or moons are in italic type.

natural choice for the name of Pluto's moon. Charon, by the way, was a grandson of the deity Chaos.

Neptune (the Greek Poseidon) ruled the oceans and the names of the planet's moons, Triton and Nereid, reflect this watery connection. Triton, the son of Neptune and Amphitrite, had a half-fish, half-human form. Triton has been described as having green hair, hard scales, gills below the ears, a human nose, a broad mouth with sharp animal teeth, and a fish's tail instead of feet. Nereid was one of the 50 daughters of Nereus, a sea god, who was himself the son of Earth and her son Pontus.

The moons of Jupiter and Saturn are a conglomerate of Greek gods, goddesses, and monsters (Table 9A.2). Many of Jupiter's moons are named for the mothers of Jupiter's children. Several of Saturn's moons were named after sons and daughters of Earth and Uranus: Hyperion, Iapetus, Rhea, Phoebe, and Tethys. The name Titan, of course, refers to the Titans. The moons Telesto and Dione of Saturn and Europa and Metis of Jupiter were the daughters of two Titans, Oceanus and Tethys. The daughters were ocean nymphs, inferior female divinities, who inhabited the seas. Among the mythological progeny of Oceanus and Tethys were all the rivers of the world.

Atlas, Prometheus, and Epimetheus, were the sons of Iapetus. Prometheus and Epimetheus sided with Jupiter during the War of the Titans while Atlas fought with the Titans. After the Titans were defeated, Jupiter punished Atlas by sending him to the Lower World where he was condemned to hold the world on his shoulders. Epimetheus was also the husband of Pandora, the central figure in another myth.

Pandora was actually the creation, the masterpiece, of Hephaestus, god of fire and a son of Jupiter and Hera. Hephaestus was a master craftsman who wrought many marvelous works for both gods and humans. He created Pandora at Jupiter's command with help from all the gods and goddesses; thus Pandora was given and had everything. Jupiter, however, wanted revenge on Prometheus because Prometheus had entered Olympia unnoticed one day and taken glowing charcoal from the fiery chariot of the Sun, which he gave to humans, thus introducing them to fire. Jupiter actually gave Pandora as a gift to Epimetheus, Prometheus' brother, who was more easily deceived; Prometheus had warned his brother never to accept gifts from Jupiter. Pandora brought with her a box from Jupiter that contained all sorts of evils and diseases, such as Toil, Sorrow, Quarrel, Insanity, and Passion. Not knowing what the box contained, Pandora opened it, and before she could close it, all had escaped, except Hope.

Prometheus and Pandora play the role of Adam and Eve in some forms of Greek creation myths. Just as Eve ate of the apple that led

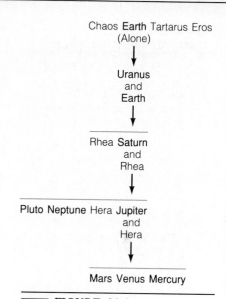

■ FIGURE 9A.1

Planetary Pedigree

Arrows originate with parents and some of their offspring are shown below the horizontal line. Chaos, Earth, Tartarus, and Eros are the four primeval Greek deities from whom all other gods and goddesses derive.

■ **TABLE 9A.2**
Moons of Jupiter and Saturn

Jupiter	Saturn
Metis	Atlas
Adrastea	Prometheus
Amalthea	Pandora
Thebe	Janus
Io	Epimetheus
Europa	Mimas
Ganymede	Enceladus
Callisto	Tethys
Leda	Telesto
Himalia	Calypso
Lysithea	Dione
Ananke	Helene
Carme	Rhea
Pasiphae	Titan
Sinope	Hyperion
	Iapetus
	Phoebe

to the expulsion of humans from the Garden of Eden, Pandora brought all kinds of evil on humanity. Typical male-oriented mythologies!

Mimas and Enceladus were two of the powerful Giants Earth sent to destroy Jupiter and the Olympians (Jupiter's home was on Mount Olympus). Although Earth was allied with Jupiter and the Olympians in the battle against the Titans, she was unhappy at the treatment given the losers; after all, they were her grandchildren! These giants were of human form except their lower parts, which were those of a scaly dragon. With the help of Hercules, a mortal, the Olympians defeated the Giants.

Europa and Dione were two of the many mothers of Jupiter's children. In order to seduce Europa, Jupiter disguised himself as a magnificent white bull, tricked Europa into climbing on his back, and carried her off to Crete. Their son was King Minos of Crete. Pasiphae, one of Minos' daughters (through Hyperion), gave birth to the Minotaur, a monster that was half-man and half-bull, after mating with a bull (her passion for the bull was Jupiter's doing). To hide him from the public, the Minotaur was placed in the Labyrinth built by Daidalos. Dione, another of Jupiter's mistresses, was the mother of Aphrodite as well as the mother of Phobos and Deimos through Mars.

Io, Callisto, Leda, Metis, and Elara, were also mothers of children of Jupiter. Jupiter seduced many maidens, but he had to do it secretly because his wife Hera was naturally very jealous. For instance, Jupiter had to turn Io into a heifer to disguise her from Hera. Hera, however, asked for the cow, and Jupiter could not refuse lest he give himself away. Hera sent a gadfly that infected Io and drove her mad. Io wandered the world until she reached Egypt where she regained her sanity and, as one myth suggests, came to be worshiped as the Egyptian Isis.

The most distant moon of Jupiter is aptly named Sinope. She was the only woman to resist Jupiter's advances. When he offered to grant any wish that she might make, she cunningly wished for her virginity.

Many of the gods and goddesses whose names are borne by planets and moons also have associations with the stars and constellations. For example, Leda, a mortal and the wife of King Tyndareos of Sparta, was much loved by Jupiter. On one busy night, Leda was "embraced" by both her husband and Jupiter and eventually gave birth to Castor, Pollux, Helen (of Troy fame), and Clytemnestra. Clytemnestra became the wife of Agamemnon, and Helen, of course, was responsible for the Trojan War. Pollux was the son of Jupiter and was therefore immortal. Pollux was very close to his brother and when Castor was killed in a feud, Pollux begged Jupiter to allow him share his immortality with Castor. Jupiter agreed and each brother spent one day on Olympus and one day on Earth. Castor and Pollux reside in the sky as the brightest stars in the constellation Gemini, "the Twins."

Callisto also was awarded the skies after embracing Jupiter. In order to hide his illicit act, Jupiter turned Callisto into a bear. Hera discovered her and had her killed in a hunt, but Jupiter took pity on Callisto and placed her in the sky as the constellation Ursa Major, "the Great Bear."

Greek mythology is complex and contradictory; consequently, you may come across several variations of the stories related here. As noted earlier, Greek and Roman mythological figures survive today as celestial figures called constellations (see the *Observer's Handbook*). "Modern" names of planets and constellations derive from powerful myths that were an important part of ancient lives.

CHAPTER 10

Asteroids, Meteorites, and Comets

OUTLINE

Asteroids and Meteorites
The Discovery of Asteroids
Physical Nature of Asteroids
Meteors and Meteorites
Asteroid Orbits

Comets
Early Observations
Comets and Halley
The Modern View
The Origin of Comets

Summary

Chapter Capsule

Review Questions

For Further Reading

ASTROPROBE 10:
Extinctions: Dinosaurs and Comets

Nucleus of Halley's Comet.
ARTIST: Kim Poor.

OUR STUDY OF THE SOLAR SYSTEM up to now has emphasized the nine planets and their varied moons. The solar system also contains hundreds of thousands, even millions, of small bodies called asteroids and comets. These objects are rocks and ices that never accumulated into planets. Most asteroids lie between Mars and Jupiter in the asteroid belt, while most comets lie far beyond the orbits of the known planets in the Oort cloud. Asteroids and comets are of interest not only because they represent very primitive material that can help astronomers unravel the mysterious beginnings of the solar system, but also because the survival of humans could depend, in part, on the wanderings of these abundant objects; collisions between large asteroids or comets and the Earth could terminate most life on Earth.

ASTEROIDS AND METEORITES

Once a year professional and amateur astronomers declare a national "Astronomy Day," usually in May. That evening thousands of amateurs cart their homemade or store-bought telescopes to the dark countryside and spend the evening among fellow stargazers and the interested public scanning the skies for celestial delights. Although Astronomy Day festivities are usually for fun, many amateurs are serious observers. In fact, astronomy is one of the few sciences in which amateurs have made and continue to make important contributions. William Herschel, for example, was an amateur astronomer when he discovered Uranus, and many **asteroids** have been discovered by amateur astronomers. The story of the asteroids and the important participation of amateurs begins with a curious contribution to planetary astronomy by the German astronomer Johann Titius (1729–1796).

Asteroids: Any of the numerous small, rocky bodies orbiting the Sun; most lie between the orbits of Mars and Jupiter. Sometimes referred to as "minor planets."

The Discovery of Asteroids

Titius discovered a mathematical series that appeared to predict the relative distances of the known planets from the Sun. This series can be reproduced by writing down the numbers 0, 3, 6, 12, 24, . . . where each successive number after zero is doubled. Now add 4 to each number and then divide by 10 to get 0.4, 0.7, 1.0, 1.6, . . . (Table 10.1). This series closely approximates the relative distances from the Sun of the visible planets, except for the value of 2.8 between Mars and Jupiter. (The series breaks down for Neptune and Pluto, but they were not known to Titius.) In 1772, Johann Bode (1747–1826) came across this

TABLE 10.1 The Titius-Bode Law and Planetary Distances

	Known Planets at the Time of Titius and Bode							Unknown Planets		
	Mercury	*Venus*	*Earth*	*Mars*	*?*	*Jupiter*	*Saturn*	*Uranus*	*Neptune*	*Pluto*
Actual distance from the Sun	0.39	0.72	1.00	1.52	—	5.20	9.54	19.2	30.1	39.5
Series value	0.40	0.70	1.00	1.60	2.80	5.20	10.00	19.6	—	38.8

series, used it in an introductory astronomy book, and promoted it as a valid scientific law. Consequently, this series has become known as the "Titius-Bode law."

How can this series of numbers have any relationship to planetary distances? Astronomers in the eighteenth century realized, of course, that a series of numbers does not make a scientific law. The Titius-Bode law was not based on voluminous observational or experimental data. So they did not search for a "missing" planet between Mars and Jupiter—until the discovery of Uranus. The next number in the Titius-Bode law after Saturn, 19.6, was very close to 19.2 AU, the distance of Uranus. Perhaps the Titius-Bode law did mysteriously "predict" planetary distances. Some astronomers began to take the idea of a trans-Martian planet seriously and, by the end of the eighteenth century, had started searching for it.

Success soon followed. The Sicilian astronomer Giuseppe Piazzi (1746–1826) discovered a trans-Martian planet on the first day of the nineteenth century. On January 1, 1801 Piazzi noticed an unfamiliar object in a star field that he was studying. On the next night, he saw that the new object had moved westward. It continued this retrograde movement for two weeks and then changed to direct motion. By March, however, the object was too close to the Sun to observe. Furthermore, communications from Sicily were so slow that no one was able to confirm the presence of the new object.

While the new object was in the glare of the Sun and invisible to observers, the brilliant mathematician Karl Fredrick Gauss (1777–1855) computed an orbit for the trans-Martian planet by applying Newton's laws of motion and gravity to the few observations by Piazzi. Using Gauss's orbital prediction, astronomers rediscovered the object, now called Ceres, on January 1, 1802. The semimajor axis of Ceres was 2.767 AU. Initially, this seemed to be another confirmation of the Titius-Bode law. More interesting to astronomers, however, was the nature of Ceres. Herschel was the first to estimate its diameter: Ceres was only hundreds of kilometers across—much smaller than the major Jovian moons! That meant Ceres was the smallest known planet in the solar system. Moreover, the inclination of its orbit was greater than that of any other known planet at that time. While astronomers were puzzling over the nature of the tiny trans-Martian planet, an amateur astronomer discovered another one.

On March 28, 1802, Heinrich Olbers (1758–1840), a physician and amateur astronomer in Bremen, discovered a small object, which he named Pallas. Pallas was nearly the same distance from the Sun as Ceres. Furthermore, this second object had an even more inclined orbit and was smaller than Ceres. Instead of finding a single trans-Martian planet, observers had found two small planets. In fact, Herschel did not believe that Ceres and Pallas were planets such as Earth, Mars, or Uranus. He coined the term *asteroid*, meaning "starlike," to distinguish them from the major planets.

If astronomers discovered two small objects where they expected one large planet, perhaps more small asteroids exist. Maybe many more. Olbers suggested that pieces of a large trans-Martian planet, somehow disrupted in the past, are spread all over that part of the solar system. Although this may seem farfetched, professional and amateur astronomers have discovered thousands of asteroids since Olbers's day. Only about 3000 have well-determined orbits while 6000 have approximate orbits. Although numerous, if all of the known asteroids were lumped together, they would not make a planet larger than Pluto.

Olbers himself discovered another asteroid, Vesta, in 1807. Since then, hundreds of asteroids have been discovered by amateurs. A German artist Hermann Goldschmidt (1802–1866), for instance, discovered 14 asteroids, and Joel Hastings (1866–1925), a New England Unitarian minister, discovered 39 asteroids between 1905 and 1914. More recently, the Japanese amateur Takeshi Urata discovered the asteroid 2090 Mizuho in 1978.

Most undiscovered asteroids are probably too faint for the majority of amateurs to discover today. Nevertheless, amateurs still play a very important role in asteroidal research. Amateurs are particularly needed, for example, for occultation observations that are used to determine the physical nature of asteroids.

Besides being given names by their discoverers, asteroids are assigned a number in order of discovery: 1 Ceres, 2 Pallas, 3 Juno, 4 Vesta, 624 Hektor, 2090 Mizuho.

Physical Nature of Asteroids

Asteroids are small and remote. No spacecraft has landed on an asteroid to sample its surface or has flown by one to measure its diameter. The information on the size, chemical composition, and number of asteroids has been garnered through painstaking observations from Earth-based telescopes. Additional hints on the chemical composition of asteroids come from extraterrestrial rocks found on Earth, some of which may be fragments of asteroids.

Thousands of small asteroids revolve about the Sun between the orbits of Mars and Jupiter. Exactly how small are they? Most are very small indeed. Ceres is the largest of the known asteroids, being just under 1000 km in diameter. Although astronomers know of thousands of very small asteroids, only 30 have diameters larger than 200 km. The diameters of even the largest asteroids are very difficult to ascertain. Imagine trying to estimate the diameters of rocks the size of Iceland and smaller from several million kilometers away, many times the distance to the Moon. A few asteroids have come close enough to Earth for direct visual measurements of their diameters, but, for the most part, astronomers rely on other methods for diameter determinations. The most accurate technique, but one applicable to only a few asteroids, involves occultations of stars by the asteroids. A second technique, less accurate but relatively easy to apply, uses visual and infrared observations.

As an asteroid passes in front of a star during an occultation, observers see the star wink out of sight, stay hidden for a few seconds, and then reappear. The time it takes for an asteroid to pass in front of a star is a measure of the asteroid's size; the longer the occultation, the larger the asteroid. Asteroids, however, do not necessarily pass *directly* between us and the star, with the star passing behind the exact center of

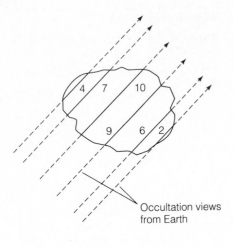

Occultation views
from Earth

Approximate shape of asteroid

■ FIGURE 10.1

Occultation Geometry

Observations from several locations on
the Earth would give several different
timings for the occultation (numbers next
to the solid lines are in seconds). The
lengths of the solid lines are proportional
to the length of time the star was behind
the asteroid as seen from the different
sites. Many such observations result in an
estimate of the size and shape of the asteroid.

the asteroid. Consequently, a single occultation is best observed from
several locations on Earth; at each location, a different part of the asteroid occults the star (Figure 10.1). When all the observations of a single occultation are combined, astronomers obtain an accurate diameter
and sometimes even the shape of the asteroid. Because of the massive
effort involved in observing an occultation and because occultations are
seldom visible from major observatories, professional astronomers rely
heavily on observations by amateurs. Although occultation diameters
are very accurate, only about a dozen diameters have been determined
in this way.

Most diameters are determined from observations of reflected visual
light and infrared emission from asteroids. In general, the larger the
asteroid, the more sunlight it will reflect, and, therefore, the brighter it
will appear. One catch to this rule is that when two asteroids of the
same size are compared, a darker asteroid will appear fainter because
it reflects less sunlight. It reflects less because dark surfaces absorb
more radiation than light-colored surfaces. The fact that the absorption
heats the surface and causes it to emit infrared radiation allows astronomers to determine relative darknesses of surfaces. That is, a darker
asteroid emits more radiation in the infrared *relative* to that reflected at
visual wavelengths than the emitted and reflected radiation from a
light-colored asteroid of the same diameter. From visual and infrared
observations, astronomers have obtained diameters for over a thousand
asteroids (Figure 10.2).

Diameters of asteroids from occultations, visual and infrared observations, and direct measurements range from tens to hundreds of kilometers. Asteroids are small. Scientists estimate that several hundred
thousand asteroids have diameters greater than 1 km. Only a handful,
however, have measured densities; these range from 2.3 to 3.6 g/cm³. If
these densities are typical, the total mass of all asteroids is about 2000
times less than the Earth's mass. Indeed, if the asteroids were once part
of a planet, the planet must have been very small, smaller, for instance,
than any of the Galilean satellites of Jupiter.

How would an asteroid look up close? Imagine yourself in a spacecraft approaching an asteroid. First you would notice that it rotates.
Typical rotational periods for asteroids are about 8 hours, but some
spin rapidly, once every few hours, and others take as long as 100 hours
to turn once. When viewed from the Earth, rotational rates of asteroids
are measured by observing periodic changes in their brightness. Near
an asteroid, however, you could easily measure the asteroid's rotational
rate because you could certainly identify many craters on its surface.
The surfaces of asteroids are probably similar to the cratered surfaces
of the moons of Mars, Phobos and Deimos, which are about the right
size for asteroids. Asteroids would also appear to be tumbling rather
than spinning because they are irregularly shaped.

If it were possible to land on an asteroid, what would its surface be
like? For the most part, asteroid surfaces are very dark; most reflect
only a few percent of the incident sunlight striking their surfaces, making them darker than lunar maria. Unfortunately, no spacecraft has
ever landed on an asteroid, so chemical analyses of asteroid surfaces

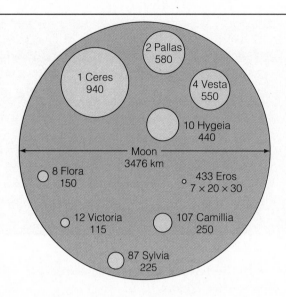

FIGURE 10.2

Diameters of Asteroids Compared to the Moon.

The number below each asteroid's name is its diameter in kilometers.

can only be done from the spectra of reflected sunlight. These *reflectance spectra* do not produce the sharp absorption lines from which individual elements can be identified; instead, broad spectral regions, or bands, thousands of Ångstroms wide are seen. These bands are caused by minerals on the surface and often cannot be unambiguously identified. Despite this, the majority of asteroids can be divided into three distinct groups. Most have carbon-rich surfaces in which dark carbon compounds are mixed with silicates. Most of the rest lack the carbon ingredients and have lighter colored surfaces composed mainly of silicates. A few percent of the asteroids show reflectance spectra of metal-rich minerals, and are probably composed mainly of iron and nickel.

These broad compositional categories form the basis of asteroid classification. Carbon-rich asteroids are called C-asteroids; those rich in silicate are called S-asteroids; and those with metallic surfaces are called M-asteroids. These are broad categories because individual mineral types cannot be unequivocally identified. These categories, however, correspond to certain laboratory spectra obtained from extraterrestrial rocks found on the Earth, suggesting a link between the two.

Asteroid classification: C = carbon rich
S = silicate rich
M = metals

Meteors and Meteorites

On a clear, dark night you can always see "shooting stars." Typically, a half dozen are visible every hour and, occasionally, more than 60 in an hour. Astronomers refer to shooting stars as **meteors.** Meteors are the brief trails of light that mark the destruction of small particles heated to incandescence by friction with air molecules as they plunge through our atmosphere. Before these particles enter our atmosphere, they are called **meteoroids.** The brief view of meteors tells us that meteoroids travel only a short distance in the atmosphere before disintegrating. Almost all are destroyed before they reach a height of 80 km. Only the

Meteor: The glowing trail of a meteoroid passing through the Earth's atmosphere; a "shooting star."

Meteoroid: A small, solid rock in space.

FIGURE 10.3

A Meteoroid, Meteor, and Meteorite

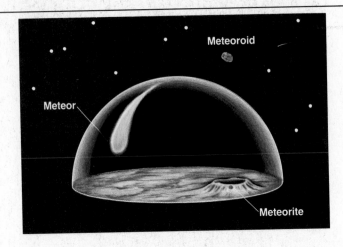

Meteorite: A part of a meteoroid that survived the passage through the Earth's atmosphere and fell to the surface.

Widmanstätten patterns: Patterns of interlocking long crystals in iron alloys.

larger pieces reach the Earth's surface. These rocks that fall from the sky are called **meteorites** (Figure 10.3).

A large meteoroid entered the Earth's atmosphere soon after midnight on February 8, 1969. Some of the inhabitants of the small village of Pueblito de Allende in north central Mexico witnessed a brilliant blue-white light crossing the sky, leaving a glowing trail behind it. The light separated into two flares, and soon both erupted in an explosive fireworks display of light. Thousands of stones and pebbles fell from the sky. In the morning, the inhabitants found hundreds of unusual rocks strung along an oval area about 50 km long and 10 km wide.

Since someone saw this meteoroid descend through the atmosphere and fall to the ground, astronomers call the associated rocks (collectively called the Allende meteorite) *falls*. If someone simply comes upon a meteorite lying on the ground or buried in the soil, it is called a *find*. About two-thirds of all meteorites are finds. Very bright meteors with trains that persist for as long as half an hour are called *fireballs* (Figure 10.4); if the fireball breaks up during atmospheric entry, it is called a *bolide*.

The realization that meteorites are rocks from space dates only from the nineteenth century. Even though meteorites had been collected for hundreds of years, and even worshipped, scientists were very skeptical of rocks falling from the skies. In 1803, several thousand fragments of a large meteorite were seen to fall near the small French village of L'Aigle. The investigation team sent to study these falls prepared a convincing report that clearly supported the view that meteorites came from space. A century of further study revealed that meteorites are not like Earth rocks.

Meteorites are classified into three main types: irons, stony-irons, and stones. **Irons** are composed of iron and nickel. When a thin sliver of an iron meteorite is cut and polished, it exhibits long crystals interlocked into a pattern called **Widmanstätten** (Figure 10.5). The Widmanstätten patterns provide a very important clue to the conditions under which irons formed. The large crystals seen in these patterns are similar to those found in mixtures of nickel and iron that have been heated and

FIGURE 10.4

Fireball of 1972

A meteoroid just skipped along the edge of the Earth's atmosphere and bounced back into space.

SOURCE: James M. Baker/Visuals Unlimited.

then cooled very slowly. Thus they indicate long cooling times as well as high temperatures. Since metal conducts heat well and, therefore, can cool quickly, at one time the irons must have existed deep inside a large object, called a *parent body,* insulated from the cold of space.

Stony-irons are rare. As their name indicates, they are part iron and part silicate (Table 10.2). The silicates of some stony-irons resemble the Earth's mantle material and perhaps formed where silicates contacted the surface of an iron core or blobs of iron near the core of a parent

FIGURE 10.5

Widmanstätten Patterns in an Iron Meteorite

SOURCE: Meteor Crater Enterprises, Inc., Northern Arizona.

TABLE 10.2
Composition of Meteorites

Type of Meteorite	Iron and Nickel (Percent)	Silicate (Percent)
Iron	100	0
Stony-iron	50	50
Stone	10–15	85–90

Carbonaceous meteorite: A stony meteorite rich in carbon and other elements with low melting temperatures; believed to be the very old, virtually unaltered remains of the early history of the solar system.

FIGURE 10.6

Hypothetical Structure of a Parent Body

Shown here are the regions from which the different kinds of meteorites probably formed after the parent body suffered violent collisions and fragmented.

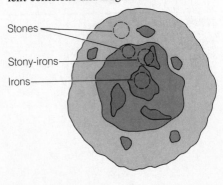

Stones

Stony-irons

Irons

■ Unmodified or slightly modified silicates with water and carbon

■ Partially melted and differentiated silicates

■ Iron and nickel

body. The silicates of other stony-irons resemble crustal silicates, such as surface lavas. It is not clear how this crustal material could mix with the iron. Perhaps violent collisions between asteroids fused silicate and iron.

The **stone** meteorites are composed mainly of silicates with only 10 to 15% iron and nickel. Stones are generally light gray in color, reflecting their silicate-rich compositions, and are hard to distinguish from Earth rocks. The most common stones, the *chondrites*, contain BB-sized round granules called chondrules that appear to be melted droplets. In fact, all of the irons and stony-irons and most of the stones represent material that was melted or partially melted. Furthermore, all known meteorites are old, dating to 4.4 to 4.6 billion years; they represent very primitive solar system material that originated at the time the planets in the solar system formed.

Carbon-rich meteorites called **carbonaceous meteorites** are a less common type of stone. These are very dark, due to the relatively high (a few percent by weight) carbon content. The carbon is in the form of complex organic molecules, often containing water, but with very little iron. One of the most remarkable aspects of carbonaceous meteorites is that they contain substances, such as proteins and amino acids, recognized by biologists as fundamental to life. Since meteorites originate in space, their organic molecules were formed without the presence of life. Furthermore, carbon from meteorites could have played a very important role in the development of life on Earth. Scientists estimate that several hundred tons of meteoritic matter fall onto the Earth each *day*. Most of this is in the form of microscopic pieces of meteoroids chipped off during their flights through the Earth's atmosphere. As these pieces have floated down to the surface over billions of years, they may have added significantly to the supply of carbon on the Earth.

Although it is clear that meteorites originated in space, what is known about their parent bodies? Several lines of evidence point toward asteroids as strong candidates for the parent bodies. From the properties of meteorites, scientists deduce that some of the parent bodies were large enough to differentiate. Iron and nickel sank to the centers while lighter, silicate-rich material formed the mantle and crust (Figure 10.6). These parent bodies were then disrupted by violent collisions; meteorites are pieces of these parent bodies. Since meteorites are old, the parent bodies must have been formed early in the solar system. Furthermore, meteorites have been exposed to space for varying lengths of time before colliding with the Earth. Meteoroids orbiting the Sun are constantly exposed to energetic solar wind particles called *cosmic rays*. These energetic particles collide with the meteoroids and leave microscopic tracks. The longer a meteoroid is exposed to space and cosmic rays, the more tracks are made. The *exposure times* for meteorites estimated from the number of tracks range from as low as 100,000 years to as high as a billion years. Thus some meteorites have just recently been liberated from their parent bodies. Consequently, the parent bodies of the meteorites must have been located where collisions are common. In addition, although the parent bodies were hot enough to produce differentiation, the absence of alloys produced by high pressures suggests that the parent bodies were small objects, probably about the size of asteroids. Finally, the classification and spectra of meteorites and asteroids suggest a common origin. Asteroids are classified as carbon rich, silicate rich, and metallic; these correspond to the carbonaceous, stony-iron and stone, and iron meteorites. In fact, the reflectance spectra of many asteroids are very similar to laboratory spectra of meteorites.

On top of all this evidence, astronomers have been able to calculate the orbits of three meteoroids that collided with the Earth and left meteorites. Their orbits are shown in Figure 10.7 and extend beyond the orbit of Mars to an environment in which asteroids can grind themselves down from parent bodies of a thousand kilometers to small chunks of rock.

Asteroid Orbits

The largest asteroids, such as Ceres, Pallas, and Vesta, have orbits between Mars and Jupiter, as do most of the known asteroids. The semimajor axes of asteroid orbits range mainly between 2.1 to 3.3 AU; this zone of asteroids between Mars and Jupiter is called the **asteroid belt** (Figure 10.8).

Not all asteroids stay within the asteroid belt. The eccentricities and orbital inclinations of the asteroids are larger, on the average, than those of the planets. Some of the asteroids near the inner regions of the asteroid belt, for instance, cross inside the orbit of Mars. Astronomers also know of about 30 asteroids that actually cross the Earth's orbit. Most of these Earth-crossing, or *Apollo*, asteroids (named after 1862 Apollo, a member of this group) are only a couple of kilometers in diameter; the largest is 8 km across. The Earth-crossing orbits of the

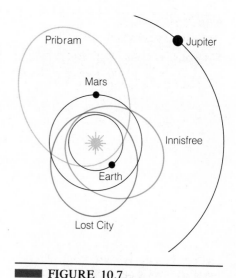

■ FIGURE 10.7

Orbits of Meteoroids That Have Entered the Earth's Atmosphere

Asteroid belt: Region in the solar system between the orbits of Mars and Jupiter containing most of the known asteroids.

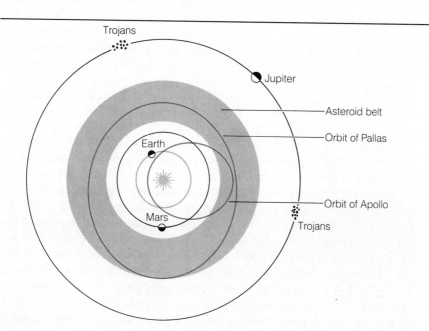

■ FIGURE 10.8

The Asteroid Belt

Most asteroids orbit the Sun between the orbits of Mars and Jupiter, but a few have perihelion distances closer to the Sun. Asteroids such as Apollo cross the Earth's orbit.

Apollo asteroids improve the prospect of a collision between an asteroid
and the Earth. An Apollo asteroid 1 km in diameter hitting the Earth
would produce a crater 10–50 km across and release as much energy as
30,000 1-megaton nuclear bombs. An extraterrestrial rock about 30 meters in diameter, for example, produced the 1 km diameter Meteor Crater in Arizona (Figure 10.9). A collision with such a small object in a
populated region on Earth would be disastrous. A collision with a larger
asteroid could wipe out most life on Earth (see AstroProbe 10).

Collisions between asteroids and close encounters between asteroids
and Mars are probably the main source of the Earth-crossing Apollo
asteroids. Jupiter is responsible for the collisions between asteroids
within the asteroid belt. In 1866 the American astronomer Daniel Kirkwood (1814–1895) noticed gaps in the distribution of asteroids in the
asteroid belt. He noted further that the gaps were located at distances
where orbital periods are ½ and ⅓ of Jupiter's period. Subsequent
analyses have shown that more gaps are present and are located where
the orbital periods are exact ratios, such as ¼, 2/7, and ⅖, of the orbital
period of Jupiter (Figure 10.10). These gaps are called the **Kirkwood
gaps.** Kirkwood's explanation for the gaps was similar to that used to
explain the gaps in Saturn's rings; repeated gravitational tugs by Jupiter on the asteroids gradually pulled them out of these particular orbits.

The existence of the Kirkwood gaps is evidence that collisions occurred in the asteroid belt. Even if all the asteroids initially orbited the
Sun in circular orbits, Jupiter's clearing out of the Kirkwood gaps
would produce eccentric orbits. Asteroids in these new orbits would
cross the orbits of other asteroids and in time collide with them. Some
of the debris from these collisions would continue on in nearly the same
orbit while some would be forced into new orbits. Eccentric orbits can
bring asteroids closer to Mars, for instance, which can perturb their

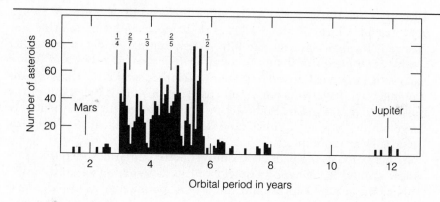

■■■ FIGURE 10.10

Kirkwood Gaps

Most asteroids lie between 2 and 3 AU from the Sun and have orbital periods between 3 and 6 years. The number of asteroids is smallest at periods of about 3, 4, 5, and 6 years. These are integral fractions, ¼, ⅓, ⅖, and ½, of Jupiter's orbital period.

orbits even more, deflecting them toward the inner regions of the solar system.

Collisions and perturbations have also sent asteroids toward Jupiter. In fact, two groups of asteroids accompany Jupiter around the Sun. One group orbits the Sun ahead of Jupiter and the other is behind Jupiter. These asteroids occupy the L_4 and L_5 stable Lagrangian points in Jupiter's orbit. We described a similar situation with Saturn's moon Tethys; Tethys has two moons at the L_4 and L_5 Lagrangian positions in its orbit. The asteroids in Jupiter's orbit are called "Trojans" because they are named after the heroes of the Trojan War, such as Hektor, Achilles, and Agememnon.

Other groups of asteroids also travel together. Astronomers have identified about 100 different *families* of asteroids in which members of each group have similar orbital characteristics. The larger families have as many as 60 members in the same orbit around the Sun. Current thinking is that the members of a family are actually pieces of one or more larger asteroids that suffered a collision. They are the debris that continued to orbit the Sun in nearly the same direction as one of the colliding asteroids.

The first explanation for the existence of asteroids was Olbers's explosion of a trans-Martian planet, but astronomers do not know of a mechanism that could blow a planet to pieces. The prevailing view today is that a planet never did form between Mars and Jupiter, and that the larger asteroids were the parent bodies of today's meteorites. The gravitational influence of Jupiter probably prevented small objects from accumulating into planet-sized worlds. Perhaps much of the original material between Mars and Jupiter was gravitationally ejected by Jupiter out of the region and even out of the solar system altogether. The largest objects that seemed to have formed are 500–1000 km asteroids. During the last 4.6 billion years, these probably have suffered numerous collisions that have ground them down to small pieces.

Two very distant objects suggest that more asteroids may orbit the Sun beyond Jupiter and Saturn. In 1920, Walter Baade (1893–1960) discovered 944 Hidalgo, a small (~50 km in diameter) dark object that revolves around the Sun in a very eccentric orbit between the orbits of Mars and Saturn (Table 10.3). In 1977, Charles Kowal discovered 2060

■■■ TABLE 10.3 **Distant Objects**

Orbital Parameters	944 Hidalgo	2060 Chiron
Semimajor axis	5.9 AU	13.7 AU
Eccentricity	0.66	0.38
Aphelion	9.6 AU	18.9 AU
Perihelion	2.0 AU	8.5 AU
Period	14.2 years	50.7 years
Inclination	42°	7°

Chiron, a relatively large asteroid-like body orbiting between Saturn and Uranus. Chiron is about 180 km in diameter and is in an orbit that brings it through Saturn's satellite system approximately every 10,000 years. Such passes probably account for its eccentric orbit, and future passes through the Saturnian system will either send it hurtling toward the inner solar system as an Apollo asteroid or send it flying out of the solar system altogether. Both objects hint at the existence of relatively large objects beyond Jupiter and Saturn that are difficult to detect because they are so faint.

In 1989, photographs of 2060 Chiron showed an atmosphere-like fuzziness around it, bringing suspicion on its designation as an asteroid. This cloud around Chiron and the orbital parameters of Hidalgo and Chiron, especially the large eccentricities and inclinations, are reminiscent of very special objects observed by humans for thousands of years—comets.

COMETS

Astronomers, mainly amateurs, discover about a dozen new **comets** every year, and one of these usually can be seen with the unaided eye. Some are spectacular, such as the famed Halley's comet of 1910, others are just fuzzy patches on a clear, dark night. Imagine yourself a hunter in the year 10,000 B.C. You are very familiar with the sky because you use celestial motions as a clock and calendar. You know that the stars, Sun, and Moon appear punctually as expected and that even the planets "wander" in a regular fashion. One night you look up and see a bright comet to the west with a long tail pointing away from the horizon (Figure 10.11). What would be your reaction? Awe? Fear? Interest?

Early Observations

The Chinese reacted with fear. Perhaps the Chinese were more disturbed than fearful, but they generally interpreted the appearance of comets as omens of bad tidings (Figure 10.12). The Greeks also interpreted comets as messengers of ill tidings. They thought that comets foretold natural disasters, such as droughts. Such sour feelings toward comets may seem surprising because comets do not do anything menacing: they do not flash across the sky, or make terrifying sounds, or emit bright sparks of light. A comet moves very slowly relative to the stars, rising and setting as the stars do. On the other hand, comets are occasional celestial visitors, appearing in the sky without warning. Some are visible for a few days, others for weeks or months. They appear anywhere in the sky, not just near the ecliptic as the planets do. The inability to predict the appearance or location of such magnificent celestial visitors was certainly unsettling for early astronomers.

Furthermore, humans tend to remember occasional events as important occasions. Remember your senior class prom, your high school graduation, and your acceptance letter to college. Your prom was not just another dance, your graduation was not just another school function, and your acceptance letter was not just another piece of junk mail.

FIGURE 10.11

Comet West Seen Near the Horizon

SOURCE: Hans Vehrenberg/Hansen Planetarium.

FIGURE 10.12

Comets as Depicted in Many Cultures

At upper right is a Chinese silk painting of a comet appearing in 168 B.C.

SOURCE: Anne Norcia.

FIGURE 10.13

Halley's Comet as Recorded in the Bayeux Tapestry

This return in A.D. 1066 coincided with the Battle of Hastings in which William the Conqueror and his Normans conquered England. King Harold of England was killed in the battle.

SOURCE: The Granger Collection.

These were singularly important events; you remember them. Similarly, the appearance of a bright and unexpected comet would be remembered. If another event, such as a death in the royal family, a defeat in battle, or a natural disaster happened at the same time a comet was visible, superstitious people would tend to associate the comet with the event (Figure 10.13).

While comets were eliciting fear, celestial observers could not decide if comets were celestial objects or simply atmospheric phenomena. Although many Greeks, as long ago as the sixth century B.C., believed that comets were celestial and existed well beyond the Earth's atmosphere, Aristotle (384–322 B.C.) thought that comets were manifestations in our atmosphere. Aristotle's erroneous idea persisted to the end of the Middle Ages. Nevertheless, by the fifteenth century, astronomers were making quantitative measurements of the positions, sizes, lengths and diameters of tails, and brightnesses of comets. In 1531 European astronomers realized that the tail of a comet always points away from the Sun (Figure 10.14). Although this view was new to Europe, Chinese writings dated 700 years earlier refer to the same idea. Even the Roman philosopher Seneca (4 B.C.–A.D. 65) appeared to favor such a view. Astronomers also realized that comets shone by reflected sunlight rather than by their own source of light.

A brilliant comet appeared in the skies in 1577. Although it produced mass hysteria in Europe, Tycho Brahe calmly tried to determine whether the comet resided in the Earth's atmosphere. Tycho saw no reason why a comet's tail would always point away from the Sun if the comet were inside our atmosphere. His detailed measurements of this comet clearly placed it far outside the Earth's atmosphere and even beyond the Moon. As a result of quantitative measurements of comets, such as those by Tycho, astronomers knew by the end of the sixteenth century that comets were occasional celestial visitors, that they shone by reflected sunlight, and that their tails always pointed away from the Sun. The nature of comets and their tails was as yet unknown, however.

Comets: Small bodies of ice and dust in orbit about the Sun; if they pass close to the Sun, their vaporized ices can develop long extensions, called tails, and a large cloud of dust and gas, called a coma, that surrounds the comet.

■ FIGURE 10.14

Comet Tails

Peter Apian's *Astronomicum Caesarem* detailed his observations of the comet of 1531 (Halley's comet) and showed that the tails of comets are directed away from the Sun.

SOURCE: Donald K. Yeomans.

It was also still a mystery why comets could appear anywhere in the sky and at any time.

Comets and Halley

Great progress in the understanding of comets was made in the late seventeenth century by the English scientist Edmund Halley (1656–1742). Halley identified 24 comets for which he had reliable observations, and he painstakingly calculated orbits for them using Newton's recently published laws of motion and gravity. The results of his endeavor were remarkable. He confirmed the observation that, unlike the planets, comets were not restricted to the region near the ecliptic. He also found that more than half the comets he studied revolved around the Sun in the opposite direction of the planets. Finally, the perihelion distances for these comets were all within about 1 AU of the Sun. Moreover, Halley noticed that 3 of the comets, those of 1531, 1607, and 1682, had very similar orbits. Could these, in fact, be the same comet? Halley deduced that the probability of these three comets being separate comets in nearly identical orbits was practically nil. He concluded, therefore, that the orbits were really a single ellipse representing the orbit of one comet and predicted that the comet would return in 1758.

During 1758 an international effort was mounted to view the return of the comet of 1682. Johann Palitzsch, a German farmer and amateur astronomer, discovered the comet on Christmas night in 1758. This comet bears Halley's name in honor of his achievement in predicting its return. Halley's triumph was also a triumph for Newton's physics because the return of the comet of 1682 was a calculated consequence of Newton's laws of motion and gravity.

TABLE 10.4 Returns of Halley's Comet

Date	Historical Events
240 B.C.	Romans destroy Carthaginian fleet off Sicily.
164 B.C.	Hipparchus creates first major star catalog.
87 B.C.	Civil war in Rome about 88 B.C. Julius Caesar saw this appearance as a boy.
12 B.C.	Near the time of Christ.
A.D. 66	Jewish state revolts against Rome.
141	Rome and Jews at war again; Ptolemy prepares geocentric theory.
218	Roman emperor Macrinus dies.
295	Roman empire still around.
374	Huns invade eastern Europe; this and the last three appearances recorded only by the Chinese.
451	Attila and the Huns defeated at Châlons by Roman general Aetius; appearance reported all over Europe.
530	Very few records of the comet from either Chinese or Europeans.
607	Only recorded by Chinese; what's going on in Europe?
684	First known drawing of Halley's comet; later reproduced in the *Nuremberg Chronicle* in 1493 by Schedel.
760	Charlemagne is empire building in France.
837	Muslims suppress a revolt of Jews and Christians in Toledo, Spain.
912	Muslim rule in Spain begins its golden era.
989	Vikings exploring at this time.
1066	Battle of Hastings; poor Harold.
1145	Second Crusade.
1222	Fifth Crusade ends.
1301	French parliament meets for the first time.
1378	"Great Schism" begins in Roman Catholic Church.
1456	War of the Roses in England; Ottoman Turks stopped at Belgrade.
1531	Astronomers show that comet tails always point away from the Sun.
1607	Jamestown established; forks for eating introduced; Kepler observed Halley's comet.
1682	La Salle claims Louisiana Territory for France; Halley observes "his" comet.
1759	French and Indian War in North America; Voltaire publishes *Candide*.
1835	Mark Twain is born; Texas revolts against Mexican rule.
1910	Mark Twain dies; tail of Halley's comet grazes Earth.
1986	Humans still exist on surface of the Earth; spacecraft are sent to meet Halley's comet.

As for Halley's comet itself, astronomers have collected records for its last 30 appearances. The first reliable record of a return of Halley's comet is a Chinese manuscript indicating that it was viewed in 240 B.C. The comet has been seen approximately every 76 years since then. Halley's comet has received worldwide attention several times during the last 2000 years because of its spectacular displays, its correlation with some important events in history, and, more recently, its predictability. Since this comet has been viewed by humans for thousands of years, it is interesting to compile a historical time line showing what the world was doing during the comet's returns (Table 10.4). During its last return in 1986, scientists decided to see what Halley's comet was doing and sent an armada of five space probes to rendezvous with this famous comet.

Meteor shower: Many meteors over a period of several nights that seem to radiate from a common point in the sky; showers are caused by the Earth passing through the debris of a comet.

A most remarkable aspect of comets has been deduced from "shooting stars." Several times during the year more than 60 meteors per hour can be seen on a clear night. Such a display of meteors is called a **meteor shower.** Although individual meteors were identified with asteroids at the beginning of this chapter, meteor showers are intimately associated with comets. Astronomers made this connection after a comet named Biela disappeared in 1866. This comet was first seen in 1772, but astronomers were not able to obtain enough observations to calculate a reliable orbit. The comet was rediscovered in 1826, and since it was visible for several weeks that year, astronomers were able to compile enough observations to compute a reliable orbit and found that its orbital period was only 6.6 years. Comet Biela was too close to the Sun in the sky to observe in 1839. The next time astronomers looked for it, in 1846, they were surprised: Instead of seeing a single comet, they saw two comets! Comet Biela had separated into two pieces. Observers also saw it double in 1852, but were unable to view it in 1859 because again it was too close to the Sun. In 1866 it was gone.

Although Comet Biela was not seen, it was still orbiting the Sun—in thousands of pieces. In November of 1866, 1872, 1885, and 1892, the remains of Comet Biela treated the world to spectacular meteor showers. After Comet Biela broke apart, the pieces continued to orbit the Sun, more or less clumped together. When the Earth intercepted this swarm of cometary debris, spectacular meteor showers occurred. After a few orbits, the pieces gradually spread out along the orbit reducing the intensity of the showers. You can still see meteors from the remaining pieces of Comet Biela during the Andromedid meteor shower in the middle of November every year (see Appendix A).

Generally, the most favorable time to observe a meteor shower is after midnight. At that time, the nighttime side of the Earth faces the swarm of cometary debris, which is swept up by the Earth as it plunges through the swarm (Figure 10.15). In the evening, on the other hand,

■ **FIGURE 10.15**

Meteor Shower Geometry

Meteors seen after midnight are swept up by the Earth as it passes through the orbit of the meteoroids; only those moving fast enough to overtake the Earth are seen before midnight. Consequently, the best time to see many meteors is after midnight.

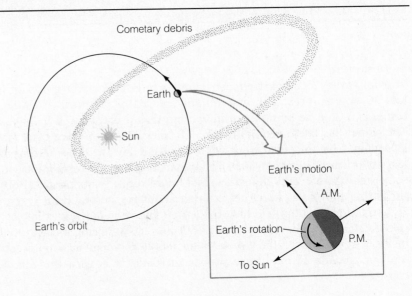

observers are on the trailing side of the Earth, and the only meteors seen are from particles that are moving in the same direction as the Earth and are fast enough to catch up with it. Furthermore, since the orbit of the cometary pieces lies in a certain direction in space, all meteors that are part of the shower appear to come from the same point in the sky, the **radiant** (Figure 10.16). About 15 comets have been identified with known meteor showers.

The probable cause for the breakup of Comet Biela was the tidal stresses produced by the Sun when the comet was near its perihelion. Astronomers witnessed a more recent breakup of a comet in 1976 when Comet West broke into four pieces (Figure 10.17). Other comets have been seen to split after passing close to Jupiter. The discovery during the 1840s that comets break apart led to the idea that comets were not solid, compact chunks of rock, like asteroids, but loose conglomerates of dust particles and ice.

The Modern View

In the 1950s, the American astronomer Fred Whipple proposed the *icy-conglomerate* model for comets in which he envisioned a comet as ice and dust packed together into a single mass. His model allowed astronomers to understand the behavior of comets when they were near the Sun as an interaction of sunlight and the ices of the comet. At the same time, Ludwig Biermann of Germany postulated the existence of a continuous outflow of charged particles from the Sun called the *solar wind*. He noticed that material was being accelerated away from comets as if a gas were "blowing" away from the Sun. The existence of the solar wind has since been verified by Earth-orbiting and interplanetary spacecraft. The solar wind explains the development, structure, and changes observed in cometary tails.

Comets are hard to study because most of the brightest comets and, therefore, the easiest to observe appear unpredictably, allowing very little time to plan observational programs. Halley's comet, for instance, is the only **periodic comet** that is large and bright enough to be seen regularly with the unaided eye. Consequently, it has been difficult to accumulate data on comets. Nevertheless, a dramatic increase in our

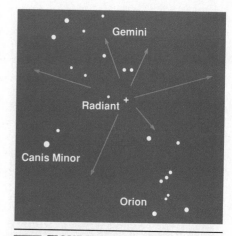

■ FIGURE 10.16

A Radiant

Shown here is the radiant for the Orionids (see Appendix A), which occur every year in October.

Radiant: Point in the sky from which meteors appear to diverge as they approach us due to cometary debris traveling parallel to each other.

Periodic comets: Comets whose elliptical orbits are well determined; that is, astronomers can predict when they will return. Generally, they are comets with orbital periods less than 200 years and are also called "short-period" comets.

■ FIGURE 10.17

Comet West Breaking into Four Pieces

SOURCE: New Mexico State University Observatory.

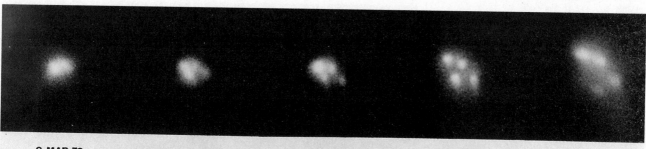

8 MAR 76   12 MAR 76   14 MAR 76   18 MAR 76   24 MAR 76

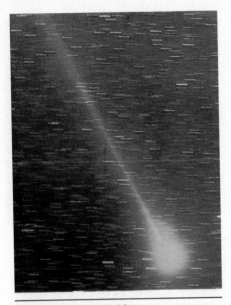

 FIGURE 10.18

Comet Giacobini-Zinner

This comet was discovered in 1900 by M. Giacobini and independently rediscovered by E. Zinner in 1913. Since the telescope followed the motion of the comet and not the stars when this photograph was taken, the stars show up as short streaks.

SOURCE: NASA/Science Source, Photo Researchers.

Nucleus (of a comet): The solid part of a comet composed of ices and dust grains.

knowledge of comets has resulted from spacecraft missions in 1985 and 1986 to two comets, Comet Giacobini-Zinner and Halley's comet.

In September 1985, the International Cometary Explorer passed through the tail of Comet Giacobini-Zinner (Figure 10.18). Because the spacecraft was originally designed to monitor the solar wind, it was not equipped to photograph the comet. It was, however, perfectly equipped to study the comet's particle and magnetic environment. The fleet of spacecraft sent to investigate Halley's comet consisted of a European, two Japanese, and two Soviet spacecraft. This international armada gathered information about the chemical composition and temperature of the comet, the interaction between the comet and the solar wind, and its size and shape. The Japanese spacecraft stayed far away from the comet to study its faint outer regions. The Soviet and European probes hurtled themselves through the most dangerous inner regions.

The danger lay in colliding with dust particles surrounding the comet. Even microscopic dust grains are dangerous because the relative speeds of the dust and spacecraft averaged 70 km/s (157,000 MPH!). A small dust grain could knock a spacecraft out of control. In fact, the European spacecraft *Giotto*, as it passed near the comet, was sent wobbling for 32 minutes before it could reorient itself. Both Soviet craft lost more than 50% of their electrical power due to heavy dust damage to their solar panels.

Astronomers divide comets into several distinct regions: *nucleus*, *coma*, *tail*, and *hydrogen cloud* (Figure 10.19). All but the nucleus are transient phenomena; they only occur when the comet is near the Sun. The coma, tail, and hydrogen cloud are the result of the interaction of the nucleus with sunlight and the solar wind. The source of the atoms, molecules, and particles that make up the coma, tail, and hydrogen cloud is the nucleus itself.

The **nucleus** of a comet cannot be seen from Earth as anything but a point of light. Consequently, astronomers must infer sizes of comets from the brightness of the nucleus, as is done with asteroids. Before the spacecraft missions to Halley's comet, cometary diameters were thought to range from .1 km to about 10 km, with perhaps a few larger comets; estimates for the diameter of Halley's comet were between 3 and 5 km. From the *Giotto* and *Vega* images, however, Halley's comet was found to be much larger: approximately 16 km × 8 km (Figure

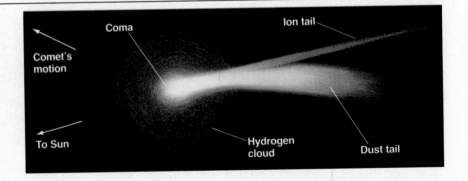

 FIGURE 10.19

The Structure of a Comet

The hydrogen cloud, coma, and tail are temporary structures seen only when the comet is near the Sun. At the center of the coma is the small nucleus.

10.20). Furthermore, Halley's comet is much darker than thought, reflecting only 2 to 4% of the sunlight reaching it. If this is true for other comets as well, then it appears that astronomers have systematically underestimated cometary diameters by as much as 50%, a significant surprise from the comet missions!

The nucleus is a loose, porous conglomerate of dust embedded in ice and probably having a density about 10 to 25% that of ice. The *Giotto* and *Vega* spacecraft analyzed micrometer-sized dust particles from near Halley's nucleus and detected iron, oxygen, silicon, magnesium, sodium, sulfur, carbon, and an abundance of hydrogen. The oxygen, magnesium, silicon, and iron are elements common in silicate rock. The silicate and carbonaceous matter apparently is trapped in large cavities within ice crystals. Halley's comet, for instance, appears to be about 80% water-ice; most of the rest is carbon dioxide–ice. The nucleus of Halley's comet is presumed to be covered by a layer of black carbonaceous material. The origin of this black crust can be understood if the changes in a comet are followed as it revolves around the Sun.

Imagine standing on the surface of Halley's comet, protected from the vacuum of space. Far from the Sun, Halley's comet is just a cold, jet black, airless, peanut-shaped "iceberg." As you explore its surface, your footprints would cover its black crust. Occasionally, you would kick up white snow that lies underneath the crust. The surface gravity is so low that you could send a dirty snowball in orbit about the Sun by simply throwing it upward. In your explorations you would notice large cavities, or vents. Most of these are in roughly linear arrangements several kilometers long. Finally, as you watched the stars, you would notice that you are slowly spinning, but not in a regular manner. Halley's comet rotates once along its long axis about every 7 days and once around its short axis about every 2 days (Figure 10.21).

As the comet nears the Sun, you begin to feel the heat of sunlight; so does the comet's surface. As the surface heats, you would notice, here and there, puffs of gas sending ice crystals and dust grains upward, like popcorn in a popper. The gas is caused by the abrupt change in the ice from a solid to a gas as the ice **sublimes.** As the gas pressure builds below the carbonaceous crust, bubbles of gas burst through the surface. Some of the ice crystals and dust fall back to the surface as a sooty snow while some of it is thrown far away to form a thin envelope surrounding the nucleus. The fallen sooty snow forms a black crust covering the nucleus.

As the comet moves to within 3–4 AU of the Sun, the puffs of gas turn into jets; the strongest erupt out of the large vents you noticed earlier. The jets are geyserlike eruptions, ejecting tens of thousands of kilograms of water vapor, carbon dioxide, and dust into space. Halley's nucleus ejected more than 16 tons of water every second during the flybys. The *Giotto* spacecraft identified at least seven jets on the comet (Figure 10.22). Most of the jets were located on one hemisphere; as the nucleus rotated, the sources of the jets were illuminated, and they became more active. Conversely, when the jets were turning away from the Sun, they became relatively quiescent. These discrete outpourings of gas and dust form a huge envelope surrounding the nucleus, called the **coma,**

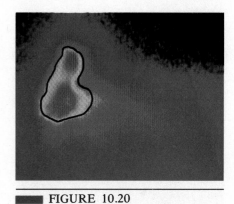

FIGURE 10.20

***Vega* Image of Halley's Comet**

The shape of the comet is drawn over the color-contoured image.

SOURCE: Tass from Sovfoto.

Sublime: The process by which solids, when heated, become gases without passing through the liquid phase; carbon dioxide–ice ("dry ice") is a common solid that sublimes at room temperature. Water-ice will sublime only at very low pressures.

Coma (of a comet): The diffuse envelope of dust and gas surrounding the nucleus; the gas and dust are liberated from the nucleus when it is near the Sun.

FIGURE 10.21

Halley's Rotation

Halley's comet rotates about two axes at once. See close up, it would appear to tumble.

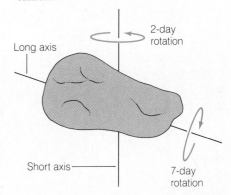

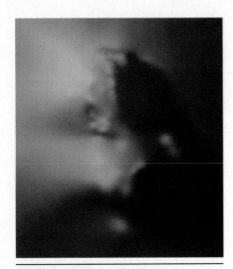

■ FIGURE 10.22

Giotto **Image of Halley's Comet**

This image of the nucleus of Halley's comet is composed of 7 images taken by the Halley Multicolor Camera on board the European Space Agency's *Giotto* spacecraft on March 13, 1986.

SOURCE: Copyright © 1986 Max-Planck-Institut für Aeronomie, Lindau/Harz, FRG. Courtesy H. U. Keller.

Tail (of a comet): Gas and dust grains forced away from the coma by the solar wind and the pressure of sunlight.

hundreds of thousands of kilometers across. The coma grows as the comet nears the Sun.

You would find the exploration of Halley's comet treacherous now. The jets on the sunlit side are very violent, reaching maximum eruption in the comet's early afternoon. In fact, they are responsible for peculiar orbital variations observed for comets. From your vantage point on the surface, you would notice the comet swinging in one direction, then another, as geysers erupt. The jets act as small rockets, giving the comet little pushes, which change its orbit slightly. The net effect of the jet action is to make it difficult to predict the exact date of the next return of a comet. For example, although Halley's comet has an average orbital period of 76 years, it has ranged from 74.4 years to 79.3 years. Gravitational perturbations due to the planets in the solar system also add slight changes in the orbital periods of comets.

As the comet moves even closer to the Sun, and you peer through the gas and dust of the coma, you would notice long extensions, or **tails,** of dust and gas appearing to emanate from the nightside of the comet. The tail of gas is long and extends nearly straight back; the tail of dust gently curves away from the nucleus. Both can extend for millions of kilometers. Although the dust and gas are mainly ejected by the jets toward the Sun, they are forced back and away from the Sun by solar radiation and the solar wind.

The gas, or ion, tail consists of charged molecules in which one or more electrons have been removed by solar ultraviolet radiation. The blue color of the ion tail comes from the emission by carbon monoxide (CO) ions. The solar wind also consists of particles but moving at speeds of 400–500 km/s. These particles escape from the Sun along magnetic field lines that stretch away from the Sun's surface (see Chapter 12 for more on the Sun's magnetic field). Since these magnetic field lines rotate with the Sun, they are drawn out in a very tight spiral pattern like the grooves in a phonograph record. As a comet nears the Sun, ultraviolet radiation ionizes the molecules in the outer layers of the coma, and they collide with the solar wind particles and the magnetic field lines. As the comet plunges through this magnetic environment, the magnetic field lines fold around the comet and are pushed back behind the comet by the solar wind (Figure 10.23). The ions of the coma follow the magnetic field lines away from the nucleus and in the opposite direction of the Sun. Consequently, the ion tail acts like a "solar" wind sock, indicating the direction of the solar wind. Occasionally, the magnetic field lines flowing back from the coma are "pinched" together, form a closed loop of magnetic field lines, and detach from the ion tail. As the disconnected tail drifts away, more magnetic field lines fold around the coma, generating another ion tail.

The dust grains are electrically neutral and therefore do not interact with the solar magnetic field. The grains, however, are subject to collisions with the solar wind and to the pressure of solar radiation. Pressure from light can be understood by visualizing light as a stream of photons, each of which can produce a force on a dust grain. Since this force is directed away from the Sun, the collisions push the dust grains away from the nucleus and cause them to take a new orbit that is

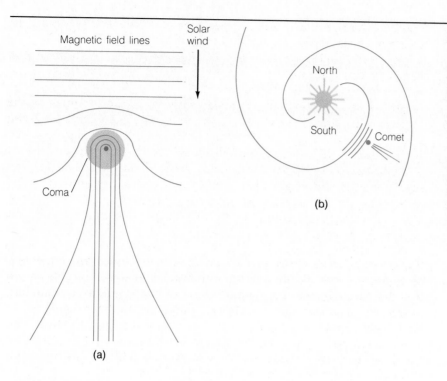

(a)

(b)

FIGURE 10.23

A Comet and the Solar Magnetic Field Lines

(*a*) The solar wind and the Sun's magnetic field are represented by parallel lines. They interact with the ions in the comet's coma and sweep around the comet. The coma ions flow along the magnetic field lines behind the comet forming the ion tail. (*b*) This is a schematic representation of the spiral pattern of the solar interplanetary magnetic field.

slightly farther from the Sun than that of the nucleus (Figure 10.24). Dust tails are simply dust particles that have been ejected from the nucleus and are traveling in a slightly different orbit from the nucleus.

At your station on Halley's comet, you saw it as a cold, dark world when it was far away from the Sun. As it moved nearer to the Sun, you saw the nucleus become more active, developing a coma and then tails

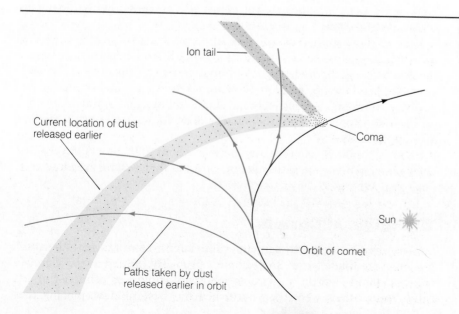

FIGURE 10.24

Path of Dust Grains after Leaving the Coma

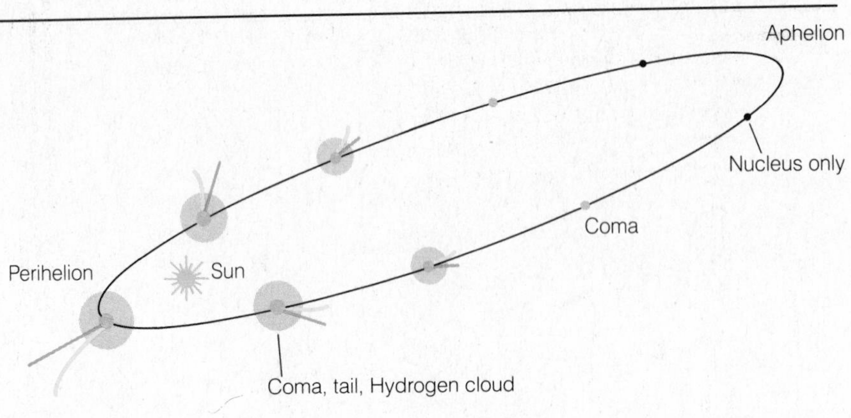

■ FIGURE 10.25

Development of a Comet

Far from the Sun the comet is only a
cold, dark nucleus. Near the Sun the
coma and tail(s) become visible and
brighten as the comet nears perihelion.
These changes are reversed after perihelion.

Hydrogen cloud (of a comet): Immense
sphere of hydrogen gas surrounding the
nucleus and coma of a comet; visible in
the ultraviolet.

(Figure 10.25). The closer to the Sun the comet moved, the larger the
coma became and the longer the tail. What you were not able to see
was the development of a gigantic cloud of hydrogen gas surrounding
the nucleus and coma. The **hydrogen cloud** can be tens of millions of
kilometers across and can be detected in ultraviolet light. The hydrogen
atoms originate in the water vapor ejected into space by the jets. The
water molecules are disassociated by ultraviolet sunlight into hydrogen
and oxygen atoms in the outer part of the coma.

Most comets pass through the stages from naked nucleus to coma to
tail as they approach perihelion. The extent of activity a particular
comet exhibits depends on how close its perihelion is to the Sun and
how active the nucleus becomes. Consequently, astronomers see a wide
variety of cometary forms (Figure 10.26). Since some of the dust ejected
by the jets falls back onto the nucleus, after many orbits around the
Sun comets build up a thick layer of dark carbonaceous material that
acts to insulate the frozen ices beneath. Astronomers suspect that this
layer can become so thick that it eventually prevents the development
of a coma and a tail.

After Halley's comet passes perihelion and heads back toward the
outer reaches of the solar system, its activity diminishes. Its tails steadily shrink as do the hydrogen cloud and coma. By the time it reaches
aphelion, just beyond the orbit of Neptune, Halley's comet is once again
a slowly tumbling, porous iceberg. This is the normal state of comets;
for most of a comet's orbit, the nucleus does not have a coma, a tail, or
a hydrogen cloud.

Halley's comet is one of many comets. About 700 comets have well-
determined orbits, but astronomers estimate that several hundred billion exist. Where do they come from?

The Origin of Comets

Comets are considered to be primordial solar system matter—the stuff
planets were made from. Some comets probably formed in the vicinity
of Uranus and Neptune, where astronomers know ices can exist naturally. Their orbits were then perturbed by these planets, placing the

(a)

(b)

(c)

(d)

(e)

FIGURE 10.26

Cometary Structures

(a) Halley's comet in 1910 exhibited a long thick ion tail. *(b)* Halley's comet in December 1985 showed a short ion tail. *(c)* By March 1986, Halley's comet developed a long ion tail and a dust tail. *(d)* Brook's comet shows a straight ion tail. *(e)* Comet West shows a very broad dust tail and a narrow, inconspicuous ion tail.

comets in very eccentric orbits about the Sun. The region of formation of comets is also expected to extend very far from the Sun, beyond the orbits of the known planets. In fact, comets are predicted to orbit the Sun as far away as 100,000 AU, nearly half the distance to the nearest star. These orbiting comets are thought to form a roughly spherical cloud, called the **Oort cloud** after the Dutch astronomer J. Oort who introduced this model in 1950. Scientists estimate that 1 to 2 trillion comets exist in the Oort cloud! At these great distances from the Sun, comets preserve the record of the chemical composition and physical conditions that existed when planets formed. Comets preserve this record much better than planets because, by virtue of their small sizes, they did not undergo internal heating that could cause differentiation and surface tectonics. They are in virtually a pristine state.

Oort cloud: Reservoir of cometary nuclei orbiting the Sun at distances of up to 100,000 AU.

The basis of Oort's model is the distribution of semimajor axes of comets with periods of more than 200 years; these range from 20,000 AU to 100,000 AU. Although comets in the Oort cloud are much too faint to detect, other properties of comets indicate that the Oort cloud exists. Since comets orbit the Sun in elliptical orbits, it is reasonable to assume that they all were formed in the solar system, instead of being captured by the Sun as they passed the solar system. Moreover, the number of short-period comets appears to be what would be expected of a population of comets with semimajor axes of tens or hundreds of thousands of astronomical units. That is, short-period comets, such as Comet Encke (3.3 yr period) and Halley's comet, were at one time long-period, Oort cloud comets. These comets, however, had perihelia inside the orbit of Jupiter, and near passes to Jupiter and the other Jovian planets changed their long-period ellipses to the short-period ones they have now (Figure 10.27). Before the Jovian planets can change cometary orbits, however, the Oort cloud comets must be "fed" into the inner regions of the solar system.

The average period of a hypothetical Oort cloud comet is a few million years. Typically, about 5 to 10 stars pass within tens to hundreds of thousands of astronomical units of the solar system every million years. This means that 10 to 30 stars will pass near the solar system while a comet is traveling in the slowest part of its orbit, tens of thousands of astronomical units from the Sun. Each passing star can alter the orbit of this comet. The net effect of all stars acting on all comets is a complete randomizing of cometary orbits. This is the reason why comets can lie outside the ecliptic and explains why astronomers think that the Oort cloud is more or less spherical. Finally, whenever a star passes near the Sun, it can change the orbits of thousands of cometary nuclei and send them hurtling toward the Sun. Once they have perihelia in the inner solar system, the Jovian planets modify their orbits even more.

Thus the overall picture is one of a population of a trillion cometary nuclei orbiting the Sun with aphelion distances of up to 100,000 AU. Passing stars perturb cometary orbits so that some change their perihelia to within the orbit of the Jovian planets, whose gravitational effects on these comets modify their orbits further, trapping them within the inner solar system.

FIGURE 10.27

Orbital Perturbations Caused by Jupiter

If a long-period, Oort cloud comet passes too close to Jupiter, the gravitational attraction of Jupiter will deflect its orbit and trap it inside the orbits of the nine planets.

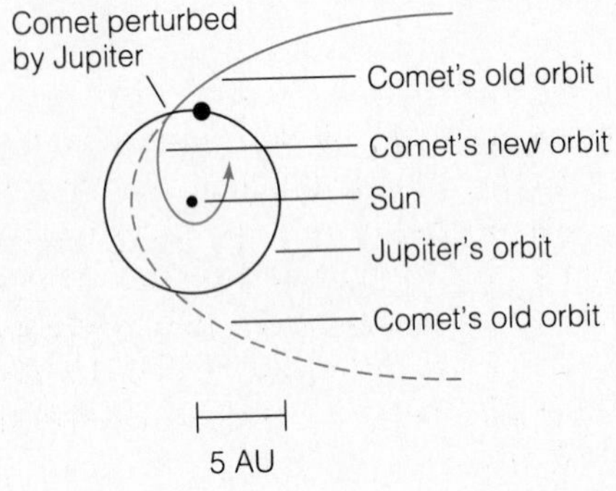

Once in the inner regions of the solar system, they will make hundreds to thousands of passes around the Sun, as Halley's comet has. During each pass, the comet will be stripped of part of its mass by the sublimation of ices. If the carbonaceous coating in the comet becomes thick enough, it may prevent dust and ices from forming a coma and stop jets from becoming active near perihelion. The comet would then be "dead" and would not be easily visible. Some of these dead comets may make up part of the Apollo asteroids. In fact, one of these comets could indeed be a harbinger of disaster.

At the turn of the century a comet may have collided with the Earth. On June 30, 1908, a brilliant fireball was seen followed by a tremendous explosion near the Tunguska River in the Central Siberian Uplands of Russia. It flattened trees over an area of a thousand square kilometers, thousands of nearby caribou died, reindeer herders about 80 km away were blown out of their tents and some were knocked unconscious, a heat wave from the blast was felt 100 km away, seismographs recorded the shock 1000 km away, and millions of tons of dust were thrown into the atmosphere. When Soviet scientists investigated the site of the explosion, they found trees stripped of leaves and branches and toppled over in a radial direction from the blast center. They found no crater. Nor did they find any obvious remains of the object that caused the explosion. When large meteorites produce craters on Earth, some of the meteorite is generally buried in the ground and pieces are strewn for miles around the site.

The most reasonable explanation for the explosion is that a cometary nucleus entered the Earth's atmosphere and detonated violently about 8 km above the surface. Heating of the comet by friction with atmospheric gases built up pressures that caused the material to expand explosively. Because the comet was mainly ice, it was vaporized in the explosion, leaving no substantial remains. The explosive force is estimated to have been equivalent to that of a 10-megaton nuclear bomb. A cometary nucleus about 50 m in diameter could produce just such an explosion.

The Tunguska explosion was certainly not the only time the Earth has collided violently with comets or asteroids. The Earth still shows the scars of about 200 meteoritic impacts (AstroProbe 6), and new evidence suggests that the Earth may experience a catastrophic impact periodically (AstroProbe 10). The fossil record indicates that most species of life on Earth could have been destroyed by such impacts.

■■■SUMMARY

The apparent ability of the Titius-Bode law to "predict" the distances of planets from the Sun inspired the search for a planet between Mars and Jupiter. Instead of finding one planet, astronomers found thousands of asteroids. Measured diameters of asteroids range from a few kilometers to nearly a thousand kilometers. Although most asteroids orbit between Mars and Jupiter in the asteroid belt, some travel to the inner solar system, crossing the orbits of the Earth and Mars. Others have been trapped by Jupiter and orbit the Sun at the Lagrangian points around Jupiter's orbit. Observations of moderately large asteroid-like objects, such as Hidalgo and Chiron, hint at a possible substantial population of small bodies beyond the orbit of Saturn.

Jupiter is also responsible for gaps, called the Kirkwood gaps, in the distribution of asteroids in the asteroid belt. These gaps are due to gravitational resonances between the orbital periods of the asteroids and that of Jupiter. These resonances also produce chaotic conditions in the asteroid belt. As a result asteroids have been colliding with each other for billions of years, grinding themselves down to smaller and smaller pieces.

Meteorites are fragments of asteroids that have survived the frictional passage through the Earth's atmosphere. The analysis of the chemical composition of meteorites suggests that they were once part of moderately large parent bodies that existed in the asteroid belt. These parent bodies were sufficiently large to retain internal heat long enough for iron to melt and sink to the center, but not too large or too massive to subject the iron to high pressures.

Comets have enjoyed a long history of observation by humans, but an understanding of the nature of comets has come very slowly; only recently have spacecraft ventured near comets. Comets are small, porous conglomerates of ice and dust that form a vast cloud, called the Oort cloud, surrounding the solar system. Most comets have orbits that take them tens to hundreds of thousands of astronomical units from the Sun. Consequently, they spend millions of years orbiting the Sun just once. The periodic comets have very elliptical orbits. Although they were once Oort cloud comets, gravitational perturbations by Jupiter have trapped them in orbits with much smaller semimajor axes and shorter orbital periods.

The cometary phenomena of coma, tail, and hydrogen cloud only occur when comets near the Sun. As radiation from the Sun causes the cometary ices to sublime, jets of gas and dust develop into a luminous coma surrounding the nucleus. As comets near the Sun, the solar wind, solar magnetic field, and solar radiation push the dust and gas in the outer coma back away from the Sun. The dust left in the orbits of comets and the pieces of comets tidally destroyed by the Sun produce wonderful meteor showers when the Earth intercepts their orbits.

▉▉CHAPTER CAPSULE

Topics and Terms	Review and Remarks
Asteroids	They were discovered during a search inspired by the Titius-Bode law.
	Thousands of asteroids orbit the Sun between Mars and Jupiter, but some cross the orbit of the Earth.
	Diameters of asteroids range from meters to 1000 km.
Kirkwood gaps	The asteroid belt has gaps where no asteroids orbit.
	The gaps are due to gravitational resonances between the asteroids and Jupiter.
Meteorites	These are fragments of asteroids that survived passage through the Earth's atmosphere.
	Meteorites appear to have originated in large bodies that chemically differentiated.
Cometary phenomena	Comets exhibit tails, a coma, and a hydrogen cloud when they near the Sun.
	Two kinds of tails are observed: a yellow dust tail and a blue ion tail.
	Pressure from the solar wind and radiation produces cometary tails.
	The gaseous coma and hydrogen cloud form as the Sun heats the nucleus of the comet.
Structure of comets	They are small, porous conglomerates of ice and dust only tens of kilometers across.
Oort cloud	Comets form a vast cloud tens to hundreds of thousands AU from the Sun and spend millions of years orbiting the Sun once.
	Interstellar perturbations cause Oort cloud comets to enter the inner solar system.
	The Jovian planets cause gravitational changes to the orbits of some comets so that they orbit the Sun with shorter periods.

REVIEW QUESTIONS

1. The Titius-Bode law works well with the known planets if Ceres is included and Neptune is ignored. At what distance does it predict the next possible planet? With Kepler's third law, determine the period of the tenth planet.

2. What factors would make a tenth planet, as determined in question 1, very difficult to observe? Should astronomers look for it based on this prediction?

3. What determines whether a body is designated as a major planet, an asteriod, a meteoroid, or a comet? Compare these classifications.

4. Explain the difference between the terms *meteor*, *meteorite*, and *meteoroid*.

5. What roles do radioactive dating and the fact that meteorites show differentiation play in determining their history?

6. What are the Apollos and Trojans?

7. Meteor showers are apparently the result of comet debris entering the Earth's atmosphere. Appendix A shows two showers with no known comet origin, *two* showers for Comet Halley, and only one shower for each of the other comets listed. How do you account for the fact that Comet Halley has two showers associated with it while the other comets have only one? Also, why do you suppose there are no comets associated with two of the showers?

8. The nucleus of Comet Halley was found to be about 16 km × 8 km. The tail of a comet can be millions of kilometers in length. What conditions would you expect to exist in the tail of a typical comet?

9. What happened to Comet Biela?

10. A comet is usually named after its discoverer(s). Comet Halley is an exception to this rule. Explain why.

11. Describe the ion and dust tails of a typical comet. What part of the radiation from the Sun affects each of these tails? Can the chemical content of either of these tails be determined from their radiation? Why do these tails point *away* from the Sun?

12. Other than scientific curiosity, why are astronomers so intersted in determining the nature of comets and asteroids?

FOR FURTHER READING

Balsiger, H., H. Fechtig, and J. Geiss. 1988. A close look at Halley's comet. *Scientific American*, Sept., 96.

Berry, R. 1986. Giotto encounters Comet Halley. 1986. *Astronomy*, June, 6.

———. 1987. Search for the primitive. *Astronomy*, June, 6.

Berry, R., and R. Talcott. 1986. What have we learned from Comet Halley? *Astronomy*, Sept., 6.

Brandt, J. C., and M. B. Niedner, Jr. 1986. The structure of comet tails. *Scientific American*, Jan., 48.

Davies, J. K. 1985. Is 3200 Phaethon a dead comet? *Sky & Telescope*, Oct., 317.

Delsemme, A. H. 1989. Whence come comets. *Sky & Telescope*, Mar., 260.

Sinnott, R. 1989. An asteroid whizzes past Earth. *Sky & Telescope*, July, 30.

Special Issue of *Sky & Telescope*. 1987. Anatomy of a comet. *Sky & Telescope*, Mar.

ASTROPROBE 10

Extinctions: Dinosaurs and Comets

■ FIGURE 10A.1

The Cretaceous-Tertiary Boundary

The K-T boundary exposed at Petriccio, Italy lies just above the white Cretaceous limestone. The 50 Lira coin is about 2 cm in diameter.

SOURCE: Alesandro Montanari, University of California at Berkeley.

Why did the dinosaurs die out after dominating the Earth for 150 million years? Did a global catastrophe cause a sudden demise of the dinosaurs 65 million years ago? Or was their extinction less abrupt, caused perhaps by a gradual change in climate? The disappearance of the dinosaurs certainly changed life on Earth dramatically. It signaled the end of a reptilian era and the beginning of a mammalian era. But many life-forms besides the dinosaurs also became extinct: all of the great marine reptiles and flying reptiles; almost all marine plankton; about one-fourth of shallow water invertebrates; some land plants; and a few primitive mammals. In fact, nothing weighing more than 25 kg survived the extinction. The dinosaurs were just part of a great **mass extinction.** This particular mass extinction marks the boundary between the Cretaceous and Tertiary periods (see Chapter 5 for more on geological periods) and is called the late Cretaceous extinction (Figure 10A.1). The geological boundary between the two periods is called the K-T boundary instead of C-T because "C" is used for the Cambrian period.

In 1979, a team of researchers from the University of California at Berkeley found evidence suggesting that the Earth collided with a large comet or asteroid 65 million years ago (Figure 10A.2) Their first clue was a layer of clay that is exceptionally rich in the element iridium and is found worldwide in sediments 65 million years old. Iridium is very rare in the Earth's crustal rock but 10,000 times more abundant in comets and meteorites. Iridium is an element that has a chemical affinity for iron so that, when the Earth differentiated and the iron sank toward the center of the Earth, iridium went with it. If a comet or asteroid 10 km in diameter struck the Earth, the violence of the collision would scatter debris all over the globe. The present iridium-rich clay found at the K-T boundary is thought to be part of this debris that settled on land and on the ocean floor after the hypothesized collision.

The catastrophic impact hypothesis proposed by the late physicist Luis Alvarez, his geologist son Walter Alvarez, and their colleagues is that the collision enveloped the Earth in a cloud of opaque dust and soot. In their model, the soot was the product of massive burning of large areas on the Earth's surface caused by the resulting gigantic fireball. As the dust and soot floated in the atmosphere for months after the collision, they blocked out sunlight, drastically slowing photosynthesis and, consequently, starving much life on Earth. The hot flight through the atmosphere and the violent impact would also produce huge amounts of nitrogen oxides that eventually would fall to Earth in a very acidic rain, contaminating oceans, lakes, and streams. The acidity of the oceans would become high enough to dissolve calcium carbonate shells of ocean animals, and the strong acid

FIGURE 10A.2

Collision between an Asteroid and the Earth

Such a collision may have caused or at least contributed to a mass extinction of life on Earth 65 million years ago.

SOURCE: *Astronomy* Magazine, Kalmbach Publishing Company.

on land would dissolve most trace metals in the soil, poisoning the water supply. This destructive picture is very similar to the "nuclear winter" models describing the global events following a major nuclear war. Nuclear winter models predict the extinction of most life on Earth.

In the last decade, more evidence has surfaced in support of the catastrophic impact hypothesis. Other elements, which have chemical properties similar to iridium, have been detected in the K-T boundary layer in what appear to be extraterrestrial abundances. Evidence for an impact is also found worldwide in the K-T layer in small spherules of melted rock, indicating that rock was heated to very high temperatures, and in shocked quartz, implying that rock was stressed by very high pressures. These are natural by-products of a meteoritic impact and are found at the sites of known terrestrial impact craters (see AstroProbe 6 for locations of terrestrial craters). Furthermore, large quantities of soot have recently been identified in the K-T boundary layer. Finally, the Berkeley scientists point out that a mass extinction occurred 65 million years ago when the K-T boundary deposits were accumulating.

Although the evidence for a catastrophic impact 65 million years ago seems very strong, paleontologists are not entirely convinced that it caused the demise of the dinosaurs. Paleontologists point out that extinctions are common. In fact, 99% of all **species** that lived on

Species: The basic category of biological classification; composed of related individuals that resemble each other and are able to breed among themselves but not with other species.

■■■ FIGURE 10A.3

Stepwise Extinctions

Extinctions appear to occur in "steps" in which several species are wiped out at about the same time. The time on Earth in which a species lived is shown by a vertical line. Its time on Earth is known from the location of its fossils in the geological record. The insert shows how a catastrophic extinction would look in the fossil record.

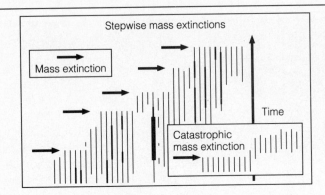

Earth at one time or another have vanished. What you see today represents 1/100 of all the life-forms that have ever existed on Earth for the last few hundred million years. Figure 10A.3 is a schematic representation of the history of the existence and extinction of individual species. Each vertical line indicates when a species existed, the line's thickness represents the species' relative abundance, and the line ends when that species ceased to exist. These lines just reflect the fossil record; fossils of an extinct species simply are not found above a certain layer in the rocks in the Earth's crust. What is evident in such graphs is the "stepwise" nature of the extinctions in which *several* species "suddenly" disappear from the fossil record. On the average, the "sudden" disappearance of these species is spread over about 3 million years. These extinctions are called *background extinctions* and are found throughout the fossil record.

Two important factors influencing the survivability of an organism in "background times" are its geographic range and the number of species within a class of organisms. Species with restricted geographic range are more susceptible to environmental changes than widespread species. For instance, if all the species of a plant or animal were located at very high latitudes, then a single ice age could wipe them all out. Similarly, a species-rich organism has a better chance of surviving for long periods than a species-poor plant or animal. For instance, turtles with 19 species are more likely to survive than a reptile of only a single species. Due to the ever-changing environmental conditions on Earth through climate changes, plate tectonics, and even extraterrestrial events, background extinctions represent a normal phenomenon of life on Earth.

Occasionally, background extinction processes are replaced by widespread, or mass, extinctions. Five times in the last 500 million years, life on Earth has experienced mass extinctions in which as much as 90% of *all* living species were destroyed. These occurred in the following periods:

Late Ordovician	≈440 million years ago
Late Devonian	≈360 million years ago
Late Permian	≈250 million years ago
Late Triassic	≈240 million years ago
Late Cretaceous (K-T)	≈65 million years ago

The late Permian was a massacre in which 96% of all marine species were wiped out while the late Cretaceous marked the end of the dinosaurs. Mass extinctions are markedly different from background extinctions in that the traits of individual species that would normally enhance survivability during background times are ineffective during mass extinctions. That is, the ability of a species to adapt to its environment will not necessarily save it during a mass extinction. It appears that mass extinctions represent times in which the physical conditions experienced by species are greatly altered.

Mass extinctions have played a major role in the evolution of life on Earth, not only because many species are wiped out, but because evolution, after a mass extinction episode, is diverted into a direction that normally would not have occurred in background times. An elimination of an entire species creates opportunities for change in plant and animal life by opening up ecological niches that were previously occupied by a now extinct species. For instance, mammals now dominate the Earth instead of reptiles because the late Cretaceous mass extinction of the largest reptiles that ever roamed the Earth, the dinosaurs, opened up vast ecological slots into which mammals readily expanded (Figure 10A.4). Evolutionary patterns are greatly influenced by rare but important mass extinctions causing shifts that have little to do with successful adaptations during background times. The extensive chronicle of extinctions found in the fossil record is the reason scientists question the catastrophic impact hypothesis as the cause of the late Cretaceous mass extinctions. In fact, the dinosaurs themselves appear to have been dying out for several million years before the late Cretaceous mass extinction, and some dinosaurs appear to have survived a few million years after the hypothesized impact 65 million years ago.

Is there any evidence for terrestrially induced changes in the Earth's environment that could cause severe biological stress to plant and animal life? Variation in climate is an obvious terrestrial factor that could indeed generate conditions that would stress a species. Ice ages are times when the Earth periodically changes from an ice-free condition to one with polar caps, plunging much of the Earth into a deep freeze (see AstroProbe 5). Furthermore, wind patterns and

■ **FIGURE 10A.4**

The Last Days of the Dinosaur

A small dinosaur (Dromaeosaurus) scavenges the carcass of a long dead dinosaur (Chasmosaurus) in a dried river bed in what is now Alberta, Canada. The scene is set in the late Cretaceous.

SOURCE: Painting of "Carcass of the horned dinosaur *Chasmosaurus* with small scavenger *Dromaeosaurus*" by Elenor M. Kish from *A Vanished World—The Dinosaurs of Western Canada* by Dale A. Russell (Ottawa, 1977). Reproduced with permission of the National Museum of Natural Sciences, Ottawa, Canada.

ocean currents are intricately entwined and a change in either could drastically affect local climates. For instance, tectonic changes could occur that would change ocean currents in such a way that a normally nutrient-rich current is replaced by a nutrient-poor current. The marine life that depended on the nutrient-rich waters would perish. Then their decaying carcasses could deplete the water's oxygen supply, affecting other sea life; if carbon dioxide–producing marine organisms also die, the carbon dioxide content of the atmosphere might change significantly. Changes in the amount of solar energy striking the Earth's surface can produce similar results by inducing changes in wind patterns that, in turn, affect ocean currents. Although the Earth's climate appears very sensitive to environmental changes and can deteriorate rapidly, the return to stable, stress-free conditions are not necessarily as fast or even guaranteed.

Volcanoes have also been suspected of promoting extinctions. For instance, a huge lava flood in India, which consists of over 100 individual lava flows, suggests a very active period of fissurelike eruptions. These lava beds have been dated at 66 million years—the same time as the late Cretaceous mass extinctions. If volcanic eruptions are violent enough and widespread, they may be able to produce the same level of disturbance in the atmosphere and oceans as that attributed to a catastrophic impact. The driving mechanism for occasional global volcanism is thought to be instabilities in the Earth's mantle. Both the late Permian (250 million years ago) and the late Cretaceous (65 million years ago) extinctions, for instance, appear to have been preceded by a long period of terrestrial magnetic stability. Apparently, the changes in the Earth's mantle and core that cause reversals in Earth's magnetic field eventually migrate upward to the crust and result in extensive volcanism. Global volcanism as the cause of mass extinctions is a very controversial hypothesis, however.

Detailed studies of the five major mass extinctions indicate that three are probably related to changes in climate rather than to catastrophic impact. During the late Ordovician extinction (440 million years ago) and the late Devonian (360 million years ago), for instance, the world experienced deep, cold ice ages. The late Permian (250 million years ago) appeared to be a time of lowering sea levels, stressing marine life and probably indicating extensive glaciation. Many scientists support the idea that extinctions are associated with changes in ocean chemistry and in large temperature fluctuations. Ice ages, for instance, occur periodically and could readily cause extinctions. Both a violent impact or extensive volcanism could upset the chemistry of the world's oceans, putting the environment off-balance so that the normal small changes in climate could cause drastic temperature fluctuations.

The late Triassic mass extinction, on the other hand, appears to have been very "rapid"; it could have taken place in less than 850,000 years. Although a large meteor crater located in Quebec seems to have been caused by an impact at about the same time, no other evidence supports a catastrophic impact 240 million years ago. The weakest case for a terrestrial cause of a mass extinction is for the late Cretaceous extinction. Sea levels decreased during this time, but scientists cannot find evidence of extensive glaciation or growth of polar caps. As noted at the beginning of this AstroProbe, the strongest evidence for an extraterrestrial cause for mass extinctions is for the late Cretaceous extinctions.

In their investigations of extinctions, scientists have discovered what appear to be periodicities in extinction episodes. For instance, paleontologists at the University of Chicago found a pattern in the extinction of marine organisms that suggests extinctions occur every 26 to 31 million years (Figure 10A.5). Studies of huge lava plains also suggest that massive flooding, indicative of global volcanism, occurs every 32 million years, on the average, and at roughly the same time as major extinctions. Clearly, the situation is complex and more data are required to confirm these periodicities. If extinctions are periodic, what could cause them? Since no phenomena on Earth, such as volcanism or tectonic movements, are known to be periodic, astronomers have looked to the heavens for a possible explanation.

One hypothesis blames periodic extinctions on *showers* of comets occurring about every 30 million years. In this hypothesis, the Sun is

FIGURE 10A.5

Extinction Pattern as Indicated by Marine Species

The percentage of species destroyed is shown as a function of geological time. A large "spike" upward indicates a large extinction event, and the five mass extinctions are labeled. Smaller spikes can be seen, and mathematical analyses of data such as these suggest that extinctions occur every 30 million years or so on the average. (Based on data of John Sepkowski reexamined by Chicago paleontologists David Raup and George Buyajian.)

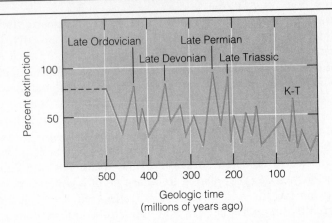

FIGURE 10A.6

The Far Side Cartoon

SOURCE: THE FAR SIDE cartoon by Gary Larson is reprinted by permission of Chronicle Features, San Francisco, CA.

THE FAR SIDE   By GARY LARSON

The real reason dinosaurs became extinct

considered to have a small and distant companion star, called Nemesis, that orbits the Sun every 30 million years. When the hypothetical Nemesis is at its closest distance from the Sun, it passes through or near the Oort cloud, perturbing the orbits of millions of comets and sending them toward the inner solar system to destroy life on Earth. Detailed calculations of the resulting orbits suggest that, like cometary orbits, the orbital period of Nemesis would vary, not by a few years as for comets, but by a few million years. The irregularity of such an orbit would ensure enough variability to be consistent with the data on extinctions. Yet another hypothesis suggests that the solar system periodically passes through dense regions of our Galaxy and disturbs the Oort cloud, sending more comets to Earth. Both hypotheses are consistent with showers of comets that last 1 to 3 million years, in apparent agreement with estimates of the time scale seen in the stepwise extinction patterns.

The jury is still out with a final decision on whether an asteroid or comet or global volcanism caused the extinction of the dinosaurs (Figure 10A.6). Certainly, an extraordinary event appears to have happened at the end of the Cretaceous period. It may be that a violent collision caused a major environmental change on the Earth that finished off the dinosaurs who were in decline at that time. Regardless of the final decision on the cause of dinosaur extinction, the catastrophic impact hypothesis had a tremendous effect on paleontological, geochemical, and astrophysical research. Scientists have made new and detailed investigations of extinction, critically reevaluating old results and collecting new data. The answer to why the dinosaurs and three-fourths of the species living on Earth disappeared 65 million years ago may indicate what the future holds for us.

Origin of the Solar System

OUTLINE

Characteristics of the Solar System

The Formation of Planets and Moons
The Distribution of Elements in the
    Solar Nebula
Planetary Accretion
The Formation of Planetary
    Satellites

**Subsequent Development of the
    Planets**

Summary

Chapter Capsule

Review Questions

For Further Reading

████████ASTROPROBE 11:
The Solar System: Resources for
the Future

Formation of moon.
ARTIST: Don Dixon.

MORE THAN 5 BILLION YEARS AGO the atoms and molecules making up the planets, moons, asteroids, and comets of our solar system were dispersed in a gigantic interstellar cloud of gas and dust. Many of the present-day characteristics of the planets provide important clues about the conditions that existed in this cloud in the distant past. These characteristics permit astronomers to reconstruct the early history of the solar system and to describe how diffuse atoms and molecules came together to form the Sun and planets.

CHARACTERISTICS OF THE SOLAR SYSTEM

Jupiter and Mars, Iapetus and Io, Comet Halley and Ceres are obviously different. A prodigious planet and a pygmy world, a frozen moon and a molten satellite, a dirty snowball and a rocky orb, they are all part of the great diversity of the solar system. Despite their differences, they all have the same celestial lineage. The ancestral "genes" of the bodies of the solar system came from the stars.

Stars manufacture the raw material for planetary formation. They create elements as massive as iron at their centers, while more massive elements are explosively created at the end of the "life" cycle of massive stars and are violently ejected into interstellar space (see Chapter 16 for more on the synthesis of elements). Today, astronomers find this raw material for new star systems concentrated in enormous clouds scattered throughout the Galaxy. These clouds are so cold that atoms are bound together into molecules; hence they are called *molecular clouds*. Astronomers refer to the fragment of a molecular cloud out of which the solar system formed as the **solar nebula.**

Ultimately, astronomers want to know the chemical composition of and the physical conditions in the solar nebula at the time of the formation of the Sun and planets. Since the Sun and planets formed out of the same fragment, the chemical composition of today's Sun is assumed to be the same as that of the early solar nebula. Table 11.1 lists the most abundant elements in the Sun; they include the familiar elements found in the rocks of the Terrestrial planets (nickel, iron, silicon, aluminum, and calcium) and in the atmospheres of the Jovian planets (hydrogen, helium, nitrogen, and carbon). Thus this table gives the pro-

Solar nebula: The isolated, collapsed fragment of a molecular cloud out of which were formed the Sun, planets, and lesser bodies in the solar system.

TABLE 11.1 **Abundances of Some Elements in the Sun**

Element	Atomic Mass	Percent by Mass	Element	Atomic Mass	Percent by Mass
Hydrogen	1.0	78.5	Sulfur	32.1	0.04
Helium	4.0	19.7	Nickel	58.7	0.009
Oxygen	16.0	0.86	Calcium	40.1	0.007
Carbon	12.0	0.40	Aluminum	27.0	0.007
Iron	55.8	0.14	Argon	39.9	0.003
Silicon	28.1	0.10	Copper	63.5	0.00006
Nitrogen	14.0	0.09	Tin	118.7	0.000001
Magnesium	24.3	0.08	Uranium	238.1	0.00000007
Neon	20.2	0.06			

portions of the raw materials in the solar nebula that were available for the formation of the planets in our solar system.

Each step, each event that led from a cloud of elements to a star, planets, and lesser bodies must be pieced together from clues provided by the family of worlds now orbiting the Sun. The first clue is that the solar system is at least 4.6 billion years old. The oldest Moon rocks and meteorites are this old, and the oldest Earth rocks are nearly as old. This clue clearly implies that our roots lie in the remote past. To reconstruct the events that led to the formation of the planets, astronomers must use the techniques of a successful detective, such as the legendary Sherlock Holmes. They must pay close attention to the present state of the solar system, as Holmes would survey the scene of a crime.

One obvious clue is that all the planets orbit the Sun in the same direction, counterclockwise as viewed from the direction of the north celestial pole. The rotation of the Sun and most of the planets is also counterclockwise. The retrograde rotation of Venus is, of course, an obvious exception, as is that of Uranus and Pluto. Most astronomers, however, agree that a possible violent collision knocked Uranus on its side causing it to appear to rotate backwards. If this did happen, and perhaps to Venus also, then it may provide a clue about the early **dynamical** conditions in the solar nebula when the planets were nearly full-sized.

Another clue is the fact that the planets revolve around the Sun in nearly the same plane. That is, the solar system is flat, or *coplanar;* most of the orbital planes of the planets are within a few degrees of the ecliptic and of the Sun's equatorial plane. A noteworthy exception is the orbit of Pluto; smaller bodies, such as asteroids and comets, also have inclined orbits. Pluto's peculiar orbit may be the result of a unique event, as noted in Chapter 8. But this clue, like the orientation of Uranus, may tell scientists how the solar nebula behaved dynamically before it reached its present state. On the other hand, the elliptical and inclined orbits of asteroids and comets are probably the result of many perturbations and collisions occurring long after their formation. Consequently, their orbits may indicate more about late developments in the solar nebula.

The fact that planetary orbits, on the whole, are nearly circular is yet another clue. Pluto and Mercury, of course, have somewhat more eccentric orbits than the rest of the planets. Again, Pluto's eccentricity may simply reflect its own peculiar history. Mercury's orbit is perhaps more difficult to understand than Pluto's, and it may indicate how important the dynamical conditions close to the nearly formed Sun were.

More clues can be found in the satellite systems of the Jovian planets—they resemble miniature solar systems. The moons generally orbit in the same direction as the parent planet rotates and in the planet's equatorial plane. Jupiter's outer moons and Neptune's two outer satellites are obvious exceptions. As Sherlock Holmes takes note of seemingly irrelevant evidence, astronomers must also make note of these exceptions for possible future use.

The above clues describe the *orbital-rotational* characteristics of the solar system (Table 11.2). They provide important information about

Dynamics: The study of the motions of material bodies under the action of forces; in this case, the study of the motions of the bodies in the solar nebula.

■ TABLE 11.2 **Orbital-Rotational Characteristics of the Solar System**

1. Planetary orbital motions are in the same direction.
2. Planetary rotation is in the same direction as planets revolve around the Sun, and the Sun spins in this same direction—counterclockwise as viewed from the north celestial pole.
3. Planetary orbits are coplanar and lie in the Sun's equatorial plane.
4. Planetary orbits are nearly circular.
5. Major satellite systems resemble miniature solar systems.

Dust grains (dust): Solid microscopic particles composed of silicates, carbon, or metals, such as nickel and iron.

the early dynamical state of the solar nebula. In fact, these clues have allowed astronomers to piece together an important part of the story: The early solar nebula was rotating, it was flat or became flat, and the motions in the nebula were organized. Indeed, these are the characteristics of the gravitational collapse of a rotating fragment of a molecular cloud.

Imagine the solar nebula collapsing under the mutual gravitational attraction of its individual atoms, molecules, and **dust grains.** You must assume that the solar nebula was rotating because the solar system is rotating now. This is an example of a current condition in the solar system resulting from an initial condition. Although an individual dust grain in the solar nebula has motion directed toward the center due to the collapse, it also partakes in the rotation of the cloud. Consequently, instead of traveling straight toward the center of the rotating cloud, it rotates around the center while moving inward. Furthermore, the rotational motion is maximized in the equatorial plane and minimized along the rotational axis. To understand this, visualize a spinning potter's wheel on top of which is a clay vase (Panel a in Figure 11.1). If the vase is covered by a flat plate, a marble placed at the edge of the plate will fly off as the vase spins around. A marble placed at the exact center of the plate, however, will tend to stay put, unaffected by the spinning. Imagine sliding the plate off the vase as a magician quickly pulls a tablecloth off a table without spilling the china; the marble at the center will fall straight down regardless of the spinning of the vase. Similarly, a dust grain at a pole of a rotating cloud will tend to fall straight toward the center, more so than a grain located at the equatorial plane of the cloud. As a result of the combined motions of all of the dust grains, the solar nebula flattens at the poles as it collapses (Panel b).

The solar nebula also rotates faster and faster as it shrinks. This is analogous to figure skaters who spin faster and faster as they pull their arms closer to their bodies. When the equatorial rotation is fast enough, however, the material there will orbit about the center of the solar nebula without moving closer to the center. The slowly rotating solar nebula, therefore, collapses into a flat *disk* of dust and gas (Figure 11.2). The dust, molecules, and atoms in the center will form a sun; in the equatorial plane they are available to form planets, moons, asteroids, and comets. Note that if the solar nebula were not rotating, all of the chemical elements and dust would collapse to the center leaving nothing for planetary formation.

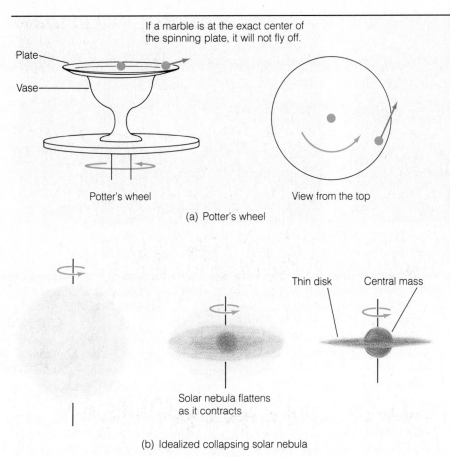

If a marble is at the exact center of
the spinning plate, it will not fly off.

Plate

Vase

Potter's wheel

View from the top

(a) Potter's wheel

Thin disk   Central mass

Solar nebula flattens
as it contracts

(b) Idealized collapsing solar nebula

FIGURE 11.1

**Motions in a Collapsing
Solar Nebula**

(a) A spinning potter's wheel illustrates
the motions in a rotating and collapsing
solar nebula. The marble at the center of
the plate covering the vase will fall into
the vase if the plate is quickly removed.
The marble near the edge will be thrown
out due to the rotation. *(b)* The rotational
motion is greatest near the equator of the
solar nebula and least at its poles. Therefore the solar nebula flattens as it contracts.

This, of course, is not the whole picture. A slowly rotating, collapsing
solar nebula accounts for the orbital-rotational characteristics of most
planets. But just as Sherlock Holmes picks up and analyzes a fallen
strand of hair or spilled pipe ash, astronomers must now pick up pieces
of the planets to obtain more clues. They begin by noticing that the
planets can be divided into two broad classes: the Terrestrial planets,
Mercury, Venus, Earth, and Mars, and the Jovian planets, Jupiter, Saturn, Uranus, and Neptune.

The Terrestrial planets are "rocky" worlds. Their rocks consist of silicates in their crusts and mantles and metallic iron in their cores. Only
a small fraction of their planetary material is composed of hydrogen,
helium, water, and carbon-containing compounds. These are found below the surface as carbonate rock, on the surface as water and ices, and
in the atmosphere as gases. The atmospheres of Venus, Earth, and Mars
are predominantly carbon dioxide and nitrogen and represent a very
thin layer of gases covering these rocky worlds.

The Jovian planets are mixtures of gas, ice, and rock. Their atmospheres are predominantly composed of hydrogen and helium and represent 20 to 50% of their radii. Their mantles make up most of the rest

(a)

(b)

■ FIGURE 11.2

Examples of a Flattened Rotating Disk

(a) A rotating galaxy seen face on. *(b)* A rotating galaxy seen on edge. The solar nebula is a scaled-down version of a galaxy. The central mass that formed the Sun is analogous to the central bulge seen in the galaxy. The disk of the solar nebula is analogous to the thin disk of stars around the galaxy's central bulge.

SOURCES: Part (a), Hale Observatories. Part (b), Palomar Observatories.

of the planet and vary in detail, ranging from metallic hydrogen and helium to mixtures of water, ammonia, and methane, but all consist of mainly low-mass elements. Observations and models of Jovian planets suggest that they may have rocky cores.

Pluto is the most difficult planet to classify. It appears to be neither a Terrestrial planet nor a Jovian planet, but rather an ice-covered world similar to the icy Jovian moons. Comets are also probably similar in composition to the moons of the Jovian planets, while asteroids are small rocky worlds without ice.

These clues reveal that chemical composition and size change with distance from the Sun. Terrestrial planets are rocky and small, Jovian planets are "gaseous" and large (Table 11.3). Individual Terrestrial planets themselves exhibit distinct chemical differences. The decrease in average uncompressed density with distance from the Sun indicates that denser rocks were more plentiful closer to the center of the solar nebula than farther away.

Finally, the rocky and icy surfaces of planets and moons show the results of an extensive meteoritic bombardment. This is another important clue telling us about events that took place when the planets reached nearly full-size and the Terrestrial planets and most satellites developed solid surfaces.

Just as Sherlock Holmes can present his solution to a mystery after gathering and analyzing all the clues, astronomers can give an event-by-event description of the formation of planets from dispersed atoms, molecules, and dust. As Holmes uses his knowledge of pipe ash or current fashion to fill gaps here and there in his information, astronomers rely on observations, laboratory experiments, and mathematical models

■ TABLE 11.3 **Physical Characteristics of the Solar System**

1. Chemical composition varies with distance from the Sun; inner planets are rocky and outer planets gaseous.
2. Planetary size increases with distance from the Sun.
3. Solid planetary and satellite surfaces show signs of intensive cratering.

to fill in their information gaps. Although scientists may miss a detail here or there or lack complete understanding of some physical processes, the picture of the formation of the planets given in the next section is probably close to what actually happened 4.6 billion years ago, and most astronomers believe that it may be typical for planetary formation in other star systems.

THE FORMATION OF PLANETS AND MOONS

Astronomers agree that the planets, moons, asteroids, and comets formed out of a fragment of a molecular cloud about 4.6 billion years ago and that the formation was by the **accretion** of solid particles. To understand the fundamental processes that transformed a large cloud of dust and gas into a star surrounded by a rotating system of planets and lesser bodies, astronomers must examine the environment in which these objects formed. To this end, it is important first to describe the distribution of chemical elements and temperature in the solar nebula at the time of planetary formation; it will then be possible to look closely at the process of accretion that actually consolidated the dust and gas into planets.

Accretion: Growth in size by accumulating matter.

The Distribution of Elements in the Solar Nebula

As the slowly rotating solar nebula collapsed, two important changes took place. Most of the nebular matter accumulated at the center where it formed a hot concentration of matter called the *protosun*. Billions of molecules, atoms, and dust grains reached the center after falling millions of kilometers. During their fall they attained very high velocities, and their ensuing violent collisions onto the central condensation raised the temperature of the protosun to thousands of Kelvins. The second major change was the formation of the disk, deduced in the last section from the orbital characteristics of the planets. The outer part of the disk far from the protosun remained cold; the hot protosun, however, raised the temperature of the inner part of the disk to thousands of Kelvins (Figure 11.3).

At all temperatures throughout the disk, hydrogen and helium could exist as gases. On the other hand, only "high-temperature rock," such as metallic iron and nickel and aluminum-rich silicates, could exist as solids, or **condensed** matter, at the high temperatures near the protosun. That is, all other rock-forming material and ices were vaporized into their individual atoms. Farther from the protosun, at intermediate temperatures, "low-temperature rock," such as carbon compounds and iron-bearing silicates, could also exist as condensed matter. Only at great distances from the protosun, where temperatures were very low, could ices of water, ammonia, and methane and ice-coated dust grains exist as condensed matter. Thus if you could have scooped up matter from different regions of the solar nebula before the planets formed, you would have found hydrogen and helium gases everywhere in the disk, high-temperature rock near the protosun, low-temperature rock beyond

To simulate heat generation by impact, hammer nails into wood; feel the head of the hammer when you are finished—it will be warm to the touch.

Condensation: The process by which substances change from a gaseous or vapor phase to their liquid or solid phases; above a certain temperature, called the condensation temperature, the substance is a vapor. Rock-forming substances have high condensation temperatures, 1300–1600 K; ices have low condensation temperatures, 100–300 K.

■■■■■ FIGURE 11.3

The Distribution of Temperature in the Early Solar Nebular Disk

The temperatures at the locations of the planets are indicated by dots. The horizontal axis is a logarithmic scale (see MathTools 1). Ices could only exist at temperatures below 200 K, beyond the orbit of Jupiter.

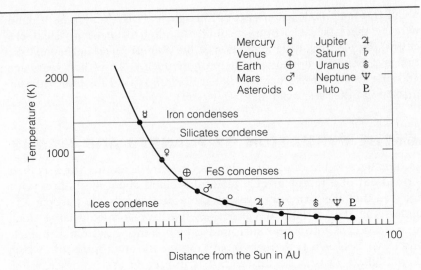

a certain distance, and ices and ice-coated grains only at great distances from the protosun.

Such a mixture of elements, rocks, and ices condensing at different temperatures in the heated disk is called a *condensation sequence*. Because iron is the most abundant of the massive elements (see Table 11.1), it plays an important role in the condensation sequence. For example, at temperatures below 1300 K, iron exists as metallic iron by itself or alloyed with nickel. Below about 1000 K, iron combines with silicon and oxygen to form silicates, such as olivine (Fe_2SiO_4), which is abundant in the Earth's crust. Below about 600 K, iron sulfide (FeS), suspected to be a component in the Earth's core, condenses into solid grains, while water can be incorporated into iron minerals below about 500 K.

The condensation sequence is reflected in the compositions of the planets. For instance, the raw material for Mercury was higher in density than that available for Mars because the solar nebula at Mercury was much warmer than at Mars. Near Mercury, high-density metallic iron and nickel and some silicates existed as condensed matter while lower density materials were vapors. At the lower temperatures near Mars, the variety of material was greater, including low-density silicates and minerals with water incorporated. Beyond the asteroids, temperatures were low enough that ices could exist side by side with rocky material and gases; planetary cores and mantles formed from mixtures of ices and rocks. In addition, the elements making up the gases and ices (hydrogen, helium, carbon, nitrogen, and oxygen) were much more abundant than the heavier elements (see Table 11.1). The outer planets that formed, therefore, did so as large, low-density worlds.

Not only did the temperature in the disk vary with distance from the protosun, the temperature also changed over time. Once the solar nebula stopped contracting and heating, the disk cooled. During the cooling, the once-vaporized elements in the disk could condense into solid grains, even near the protosun. Consequently, additional low-density material could easily be incorporated into the Terrestrial planets. The low masses of the Terrestrial planets, however, did not permit them to attract or keep large atmospheres of the light elements, such as hydrogen and helium. These light atoms moved fast enough to escape the relatively weak gravity of these small planets. At the same time, the lower temperatures in the outer regions of the disk made it easy for Jovian planets to capture and keep the light elements.

Today, very little gas is left between the planets. At some stage in the evolution of the solar system gas must have been cleared away. Astronomers do not fully understand how this cleansing took place. Observations of young stars indicate that they pass through a brief phase, lasting from a few thousand to a few million years, in which they eject a tremendous amount of matter into the surrounding interstellar space. This phase is called the *T Tauri wind*, named after a young star in the Taurus constellation that exhibits this behavior (see Chapter 15 for more on star formation and T Tauri winds). Such an outburst may purge a young solar system of any unaccreted gas. Unfortunately, observations cannot tell whether the T Tauri wind occurs before, during, or after planet formation. Another possibility involves a tidal effect on the nebula by planets, a kind of "reverse shepherding" effect. Recall that rings can be maintained by two shepherding satellites in which the outer satellite causes ring particles to move inward and the inner satellite causes particles to move outward. Once growing planets become large, they affect the disk gas and dust in a similar manner. First, a planet reaches its full size after it accretes all nearby dust and gas, clearing out a doughnut-shaped volume along its orbit. Second, the remaining disk material outside the inner part of the cleared region will be pushed inward, away from the planet; the material outside the outer part of the cleared area will be pushed outward, again away from the growing planet. Although large volumes of gas can be cleared in this manner and although part of this material will naturally fall toward the protosun, it appears that a T Tauri–like wind is necessary to rid the solar system of the rest.

At this point in the reconstruction of the events that took place 4.6 billion years ago, many of the orbital-rotational characteristics of the solar system and major differences between the chemical compositions of the Terrestrial and Jovian planets are accounted for. Let's now investigate how the dust grains and gases actually combined to form planets and moons.

Planetary Accretion

Picture the solar nebula 4.6 billion years ago as a swarm of dust grains, each about 0.0001 cm across, circling the newly forming Sun. Their individual orbits were nearly circular so the *relative* speeds of the grains were very small. The interactions between the dust grains took the form of very gentle collisions. Dust grains would nestle up to each other and form fluffy clumps, or small **planetesimals,** by adhering to each other. These fluffy clumps ranged in size from about .1 cm to 1 cm and were

Planetesimal: Small (centimeters to hundreds of kilometers) bodies that condensed out of and grew in the solar nebula; they eventually accreted to form the planets, moons, asteroids, and comets found in the solar system today.

the first aggregated planetary matter; they were the seeds for planetary growth.

Further growth was accomplished by successive, gentle collisions between pairs of planetesimals. Imagine driving a "bumper" car at an amusement park where all the drivers drive conservatively at nearly the same speed without cutting across each other's lanes. Any bumping will hardly affect the motion of the cars. Similarly, because orbital speeds of neighboring planetesimals in the disk were still nearly the same, any collisions at this time were constructive, building larger and larger planetesimals without destroying planetesimals. The largest planetesimals had an advantage over the smaller ones because they were also able to build by gravitationally attracting the smaller planetesimals. For instance, a low-speed collision between a small and a large planetesimal would result in the planetesimals bouncing apart. If the rebound speed was low enough, the smaller planetesimal would fall back onto the larger one. Such collisions during this growth period led to planetesimals of asteroidal dimensions.

With the advent of large planetesimals, encounters between them introduced radical orbital changes. Imagine the bumper car drivers now crazily driving in all directions; the ensuing collisions send cars moving in all directions—chaos! In the solar nebula, encounters with large planetesimals produced just the same effect. Orbits became more eccentric, more inclined, and even retrograde (Panel a in Figure 11.4). The motions in the disk became wilder and wilder with time. Because the relative speeds of the planetesimals now were greater, collisions were more violent and disruptive. Only the largest planetesimals, those with gravitational field strengths great enough to hold the debris of collisions, would grow in time. The smaller planetesimals would be systematically destroyed. Direct collisions, however, were not the only way to destroy small planetesimals. They also could be ripped apart and their remains captured if they ventured within the Roche limit of a larger planetesimal (Panel b).

The largest planetesimals soon grew to planetary dimensions. The larger they grew, the more they stirred up the orbits of smaller planetesimals. Impacts grew even more violent and more destructive. It was

■ FIGURE 11.4

Wild Orbits and Planetesimal Destruction

(a) Encounters with large planetesimals produce eccentric orbits and, consequently, violent collisions. *(b)* A small planetesimal that passes within the Roche limit of a large planetesimal will be torn apart, and the remaining pieces will be accreted onto the large planetesimal.

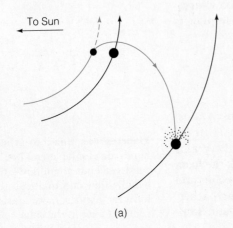

To Sun

(a)

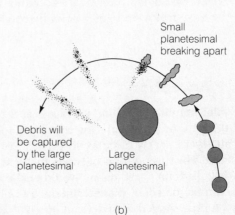

Small planetesimal breaking apart

Debris will be captured by the large planetesimal

Large planetesimal

(b)

at this time that impacts were probably responsible for determining the rotational rates and inclinations seen today in the solar system (Figure 11.5). Uranus, for instance, could have suffered a very violent impact that knocked it on its side. Venus may also have been struck at this time, reversing its rotation. These collisions had to have occurred late in the planet-building process because large planetesimals would be required to change a planet's spin orientation or rotational rate significantly.

Planetary accretion as described above may have been enhanced and accelerated in the outer part of the disk where temperatures were low enough for the condensation of water, ammonia, and methane ices. These ices, astronomers believe, would have had a greater tendency to adhere and clump than rocky material. Furthermore, the ices were several times more abundant than rocky substances. The largest planetesimals, which later became the cores of the Jovian planets, were mixtures of rock and ice. Because of their large sizes, they were able to capture and hold the abundant hydrogen and helium gases and, therefore, add significantly to their masses. This allowed them to sweep up even more debris and to grow even larger. Consequently, it is reasonable to expect that large planetesimals formed in the outer part of the disk (Figure 11.6).

The Terrestrial planets, on the other hand, not only were smaller because of less raw material, but they did not have sufficient mass to accrete large quantities of hydrogen and helium effectively. The planets that formed from the dust and gas close to the protosun were destined to become small worlds.

How long did it take for planets to grow from the first fluffy accumulations to their present sizes? The answer lies in measured abundances of xenon-129 in meteorites. Xenon-129 is the daughter nucleus of radioactive iodine-129, which has a half-life of 17 million years. Xenon-129 is also an inert gas and escapes into space unless the iodine is incorporated into the crystal structure of newly formed planetesimals. Because of iodine's relatively "short" half-life, finding xenon-129 in a meteorite indicates that iodine-129 could not have been created long before the meteorite was formed. Consequently, it appears that radioactive iodine-129 was injected into the solar nebula a short time before it collapsed. The most likely source of iodine-129 is a gigantic stellar explosion, called a **supernova**, which marks the destruction of a star. A supernova probably occurred near the solar nebula at the time of its collapse.

As the radioactive iodine-129 diffused through the solar nebula, it became part of the planet-forming material in the disk. Since the amount of iodine-129 was continuously decreasing due to radioactive decay, the asteroids that formed first would now have a greater amount of xenon-129 in their crystal structures than asteroids that formed later. Using the relative amounts of xenon-129 in meteorites, scientists have determined the relative ages of meteorites and found that all were formed within an interval of 100 to 200 million years. In addition, numerical studies of orbiting small planetesimals also show that they would accrete into planets in a few hundred million years. Astronomers con-

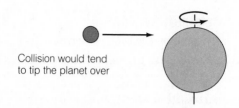

Collision would tend to tip the planet over

Collision would decrease planet's rotational rate

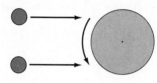

Collision would increase planet's rotational rate

■ FIGURE 11.5

Effects of Collisions on Inclinations and Rotational Rates

Collisions of planetesimals with planets would have changed planetary tilts and rotational rates. The present-day tilts and rotational rates are the result of numerous random collisions between planetesimals and growing planets.

Supernova: A tremendous stellar explosion that ejects most of a star into space leaving only a dense, compact core. (See Chapter 16 for a detailed description.)

■■■■ FIGURE 11.6

Hypothetical Planetary Systems

Terrestrial-like planets are represented by blue circles and Jovian-like planets by yellow circles. Numbers give the mass of the planets in Earth masses. Can you pick out our solar system? Although the theoretical model used to generate these fictitious solar systems was somewhat crude, they give us an idea of the range of possible solar systems we might discover someday. (Adapted from R. Isaacman and C. Sagan, 1977, *Icarus*, 31:510.)

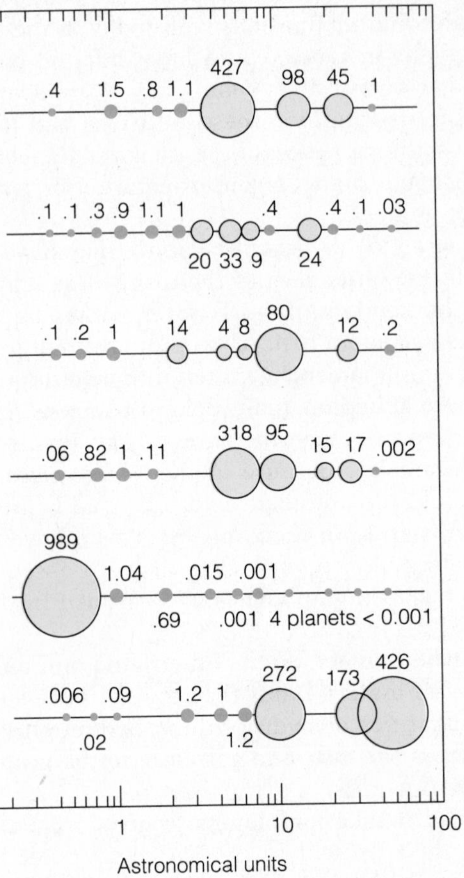

clude, therefore, that it only took a few hundred million years for the major planets to form.

The last step in planet building was the sweeping up of the remaining small planetesimals. For a few hundred million years the matter in the solar nebula was accreting into larger and larger objects. The numerous collisions that occurred after large planetesimals were formed resulted in many millions of small planetesimals distributed throughout the disk. Today, the record of the sweep-up is seen in the intensely cratered surfaces of the Moon, Mercury, Mars, and the satellites of the Jovian planets. The "initial intense bombardment" of the Moon described in Chapter 6 was actually the final stage of its formation. The analysis of lunar rock samples indicates that this final intense accretion of small planetesimals by the Moon lasted approximately 500 million years. Astronomers presume a similar time scale for the final intense bombardment of the other planets and moons in the solar system.

Up to this point our discussion has been confined to the formation of the planets; but seven of the nine planets in the solar system have satellites. Their origin must also fit naturally into the picture we have presented of the formation of the solar system.

The Formation of Planetary Satellites

Many differences exist among the known satellite systems in the solar system. The systems of large moons around Jupiter, Saturn, and Uranus, for instance, appear to be scaled-down versions of the solar system. The satellites are small compared to the planet they orbit, and they revolve around the planet in the same direction—the direction in which the planet itself rotates. Their orbits are nearly circular and lie in the equatorial plane of the planet. On the other hand, the moons of Earth, Mars, Pluto, and Neptune and some small Jovian moons do not fit the solar system analogy as well. Some of these satellites have retrograde orbits; others have very eccentric orbits; and some are highly inclined to planetary equatorial planes. In addition, the moons of Earth and Pluto are large compared to the planet they orbit. This variety suggests that planets may have developed satellite systems in several ways.

Certainly, the formation of an individual moon was by accretion as was planetary formation. The question is how did the moons end up where they are today? That is, did they form around the planet they now orbit, or did they form somewhere else in the solar nebula and were later captured? Astronomers have proposed three basic models for satellite formation (Figure 11.7):

1. Gravitational capture of a planetesimal
2. Fission of the planet in which a rapidly spinning planet separates into two or more objects
3. Co-accretion of the planet and satellite or satellites from small planetesimals in the same region of the solar nebula

The last two models are simply two different ways in which a moon may be formed at the same location as the planet it orbits. A variation of the gravitational capture model could be a direct collision of a planetesimal with a planet or an existing satellite followed by the accretion of the debris into a moon.

The large Jovian moons probably co-accreted with the planet they now orbit. The Galilean moons of Jupiter, for instance, may have ac-

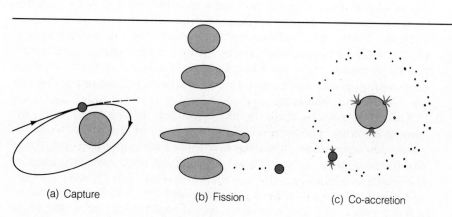

(a) Capture   (b) Fission   (c) Co-accretion

■■■ FIGURE 11.7

Satellite Formation Models

(a) Capture. *(b)* Fission of a rapidly spinning planet. *(c)* Co-accretion of planet and satellite.

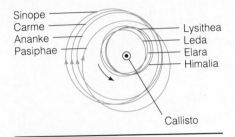

Sinope
Carme
Ananke
Pasiphae

Lysithea
Leda
Elara
Himalia

Callisto

■ **FIGURE 11.8**

The Orbits of Jupiter's Outer Eight Moons

The outer eight moons appear to be two groups of four moons; the outer four rotate retrograde.

creted out of a disk that formed around Jupiter as the local dust and gas collapsed onto Jupiter's core. The irregular moons of Jupiter and Saturn, on the other hand, were probably captured when they passed too close to the planet. The capture process may have involved a collision between an incoming planetesimal and an existing satellite. Both could have been disrupted and the debris later coalesced to form one or more satellites. The outer two groups of four moons of Jupiter with their eccentric and inclined orbits probably were produced in this manner (Figure 11.8). That is, instead of eight independent captures, two planetesimals could have been disrupted by direct collisions with existing moons. The debris then produced the eight small outer moons that now orbit Jupiter.

The small moons of Mars, Phobos and Deimos, are an interesting pair in that they are small, about the size of small asteroids, but orbit Mars in nearly circular orbits with little inclination. Their size suggests that they are captured asteroids, but their orbits suggest that they co-accreted with Mars. Astronomers do know, however, that their surfaces are very similar to asteroids and carbonaceous chondrites and their average densities are about half that of Mars. Thus these physical properties suggest that Phobos and Deimos were formed beyond Mars, probably in the asteroid belt, and were later captured.

What about our Moon? Was it captured as the moons of Mars appear to have been, or did it form with the Earth? The answer is not readily apparent. One of the primary scientific reasons for sending astronauts to the Moon was to learn the secret of the Moon's origin. The average density of the Moon is about the same as the average density of the Earth's mantle. This suggests that the Moon may be a piece of the Earth's mantle and was produced by the fission of the Earth. After the Apollo missions, scientists knew much more about the chemical composition and age of the lunar surface. In fact, the analysis of the Apollo samples and recent numerical simulations of the early Earth-Moon system suggest that none of the three models of satellite formation—capture, fission, or co-accretion—can account completely for the formation of the Moon!

The gravitational capture by the Earth of an object the size of the Moon intact is not physically possible unless the Moon was in about the same orbit as the Earth to begin with. In that case, it is more probable that the Moon would have collided with the Earth or would have been perturbed into a more eccentric orbit for which capture was impossible. Furthermore, if the Moon formed by the accretion of planetesimals from the same region of the solar nebula as the Earth formed, the chemical composition of the Moon should be the same as the entire Earth's, not just the Earth's mantle.

The attractiveness of the fission hypothesis has already been mentioned; a natural consequence of fission would be the similarity in the chemical composition of the Moon and the Earth's mantle. The idea of the Earth flinging out a portion of itself rests on the assumption that the Earth was spinning very fast when it formed. The spin rate thought to be necessary is less than 2 hours per rotation. Although it is reasonable to expect the Earth to have had a rapid initial spin, the Moon would have been flung out so fast that its orbit should be larger than it is now. Further difficulties arise in computer simulations of a rapidly spinning Earth in that they show that the ability of the Earth's rocks to adhere would prevent material from being flung off the Earth even at high spin rates.

Finally, the major drawback of the co-accretion model of lunar formation is that the Earth and the Moon have very different overall chemical compositions. Theorists have responded by devising elaborate mechanisms to create the Moon from iron-depleted material. But these are designed to work only for the Earth; they do not explain why planets such as Mars and Venus do not have large satellites or why Jovian planets do not have satellites much larger than the ones they do have. It is also very difficult for the co-accretion model to account for the lack of volatiles, such as mercury, lead, zinc, and water, in the Moon.

This brief description of the attempts to apply the three models of satellite formation to the Moon does not do justice to the immense effort that scientists have put into trying to understand the Moon's origin. Although astronomers are now confident that none of the three models, by itself, will explain the origin of the Moon, the work done on the individual models has recently led to a model of lunar formation that uses a combination of these models.

Although an object the size of the Moon swooping into the inner part of the solar system and intercepting the Earth's orbit could not be captured intact by the Earth, such an object might have collided with the Earth. At the time when the Earth and other planets reached their final sizes, many large planetesimals would have been orbiting the Sun, some in very eccentric orbits. As we have seen, the unusual axial tilt of Uranus and the peculiar orbits of Neptune's moons are attributed to possible encounters with large planetesimals. Theorists are now exploring the attractive idea that perhaps a large planetesimal collided with the Earth.

A planetesimal about the size of Mars striking the Earth nearly tangentially would produce a disk around the Earth of partially vaporized debris. The impact would have ejected matter from both the Earth's mantle and the planetesimal into space (Figure 11.9) and would have vaporized about half the planetesimal. The resulting disk of debris around the Earth would be composed of half Earth mantle and crust rock and half planetesimal rock. Furthermore, the debris would be depleted in volatiles, as the Moon is, because the high temperatures created by the collision would vaporize them. This debris then accreted to form our Moon. Thus instead of just gravitational capture, or just the fission of the Earth by rapid spinning, or simply co-accretion of the Moon and Earth, astronomers now propose a gravitationally induced collision, followed by the ejection of mantle material into orbit and the subsequent accretion of the debris into the Moon. Although this theory appears reasonable, too many uncertainties remain for astronomers to say that this is definitely how the Moon formed.

The formation of our Moon, other moons, and the planets is not the end of the story. The subsequent development of the individual planets and moons produced the variety of worlds of the solar system.

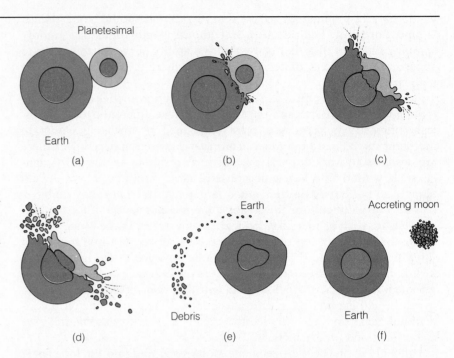

Collision between the Earth and a Large Planetesimal

Although the core of the planetesimal eventually merges with the Earth's core, a stream of debris is placed in orbit around the Earth. The debris is the vaporized fragments of the Earth's mantle and the planetesimal. The debris cooled and accreted to form our Moon. Panels a–d show details of the actual collision; Panels e and f are at a slightly smaller scale and show the accretion after the collision as the debris orbits the Earth. (Adapted from W. Benz, W. Slattery, and A. Cameron (Panels a–d) and M. Kipp and J. Melosh (Panels e–f), in *Origin of the Moon*, W. K. Hartman, R. J. Phillips, and G. J. Taylor, eds.)

■■■ SUBSEQUENT DEVELOPMENT OF THE PLANETS

The final stage in the formation of the planets was the accretion of the remaining planetesimals, but this raises a question. All the Terrestrial planets, including our Moon, experienced planetesimal bombardment. Why then are their surfaces so different? Mercury and the Moon exhibit the scars of this bombardment, but the Earth appears to have gone unscathed. Has the Earth simply eroded its scars away? It is not quite that simple; the differences in planetary surfaces are related to planetary size.

Every impact by a planetesimal with the surface of a planet or moon generated heat. In fact, the major source of heat early in the development of a planet, such as the Earth, was probably the accretion process itself. So much heat can be generated through these collisions that the outer layers of a young planet may have been hotter than its center— hot enough, in fact, to melt rock. Heat was also generated throughout a planet by radioactive decay in minerals rich in radioactive elements, such as uranium, thorium, and potassium. When these heat sources increased interior temperatures to a few thousand Kelvins, differentiation took place. For instance, once Earth's iron became molten, it sank to the center to form a molten core while the lighter silicates floated to the surface to form a solid crust. The solidified crusts of the Terrestrial planets recorded the final impacts of the remaining planetesimals. The record, however, varies because some planets cooled faster than others.

Large planets provided more insulation for the internal heat than small planets. Because the Moon and Mercury were smaller than the Earth and Venus, they cooled faster. A new planet's crust cools faster than its interior because the crust is exposed to space while the interior is insulated. Cooling will extend the solid upper mantle, called the *lithosphere*, deeper toward the center of the planet or moon. This will eventually halt tectonic activity because the lithosphere will become too thick to move or crack. The Moon, for instance, has a lithosphere 1000 km thick and shows no tectonic activity. The Earth, on the other hand, still has a thin lithosphere and is very active tectonically. If the Moon or Mercury ever had plate tectonic surface activity, it must have been long before the end of the planetesimal bombardment.

The Earth has probably gone through the following stages in its development:

1. Melting of its surface and differentiation
2. Solidification of its molten surface
3. Thin lithospheric tectonics and volcanism

The differentiation of the Earth was probably spread over time, occurring during solidification of the crust and even during early tectonics and volcanism. It is likely that the Earth experienced tectonic activity very early and that its lithosphere was too mobile from the very beginning to preserve large impact basins or the hundreds of thousands of impact craters. This mobility of the Earth's lithosphere resulted from its slow cooling; enough heat has been trapped in the Earth's interior to drive mantle convection and the associated tectonics for the last 4.6 billion years.

Small worlds, such as the Moon and Mercury, have gone further in their development, passing through three more distinct stages:

4. Thickening of the lithosphere
5. Cessation of volcanism
6. Quiescence

The Moon and Mercury have cooled faster than the Earth and have passed more rapidly through stages 1–3. Mars has probably reached stage 4 and perhaps volcanism has already stopped. Stages 4–6 are in the futures of the Earth and Venus as they continue to cool slowly.

Venus, Earth, and Mars also developed atmospheres. Geologists realize that volcanoes are sources of water vapor, carbon dioxide, and other gases. Volcanism must have been prevalent on young worlds as lava erupted from below cooling crusts. Another source of atmospheric gas was the bombardment by planetesimals that originated in the outer regions of the solar nebula. Their orbits could have been perturbed by the Jovian planets, allowing them to infiltrate the inner part of the solar nebula and become part of the final accretion of the Terrestrial planets. These planetesimals were rich in water, carbon dioxide, ammonia, and methane ices and were probably very similar to comets.

The atmospheric development after the final bombardment was unique for each Terrestrial planet and differed completely from that for the Jovian planets. It probably never rained on Venus; it rained only for a brief period on Mars; and it has been raining since the beginning on Earth. While Venus and Mars have carbon dioxide–rich atmospheres, the lower temperatures and oceans on the Earth prevented carbon dioxide from dominating the atmosphere. In addition, the Earth's atmosphere has been enriched in oxygen by the development and evolution of life. Mercury and the Moon, on the other hand, were too small ever to hold a substantial atmosphere; gases could easily escape because of their low surface gravities. The atmospheric development of the Jovian planets was simpler. The large masses that accumulated in the outer solar system were able to attract an enormous amount of the surrounding nebular gases and soon became enshrouded in thick envelopes of gas. Consequently, the chemical composition of the Jovian planet atmospheres more closely reflects the initial chemical composition of the solar nebula.

To sum up, the present state of the solar system includes planets and moons in various stages of development. Mercury and the Moon are quiescent; their surfaces are only disturbed by occasional meteorites, astronauts, or spacecraft. Mars has probably reached the stage of a thick lithosphere; it may also be volcanically inactive. The Earth and Venus still retain relatively thin lithospheres; both show signs of current tectonic activity. The Jovian planets, of course, did not pass through the kinds of phases associated with planets that have solid surfaces. The gaseous, dynamic atmospheres of the Jovian planets have probably exhibited fascinating cloud phenomena ever since their formation. In contrast, asteroids and comets are cold worlds; asteroids suffer only occasional collisions with themselves or with planets, and comets have surface eruptions only when they near the Sun.

▰SUMMARY

The solar system is the product of the collapse of a slowly rotating fragment of an interstellar cloud of dust and gas. This fragment, called the solar nebula, collapsed to form a central mass, which became the Sun, and a thin disk, which became planets, moons, asteroids, and comets. The collapse of the solar nebula resulted in (1) all planets revolving in the same direction around the Sun and (2) planetary orbits that were nearly circular and occupied a very narrow plane.

The collapse of the solar nebula and emergence of the Sun produced high temperatures at the inner part of the disk while the outer regions remained cold. As a result of this temperature distribution, different mixes of rock, ice, and gas for planet formation existed at different locations in the solar nebula. Rocks and gases dominated the inner regions while ices and gases were prevalent in the outer regions. Moreover, the ices in the outer regions were several times more abundant than the rocky material. Consequently, planets dominated by ices and gases formed in the outer regions, and predominantly rocky planets formed in the inner regions of the disk.

The manner in which the individual dust grains, molecules, and atoms in the solar nebula actually pieced together to form planets is not completely understood. In fact, the least understood aspect of planetary formation is the initial accumulation of dust grains into snowflakelike clumps. The initial growth was probably accomplished by successive gentle collisions, first between dust grains and later between larger planetesimals. When the largest planetesimals reached the size of asteroids, gravitational encounters between them produced large perturbations in their orbits and violent collisions. Under these circumstances, only the largest planetesimals survived, and out of these came the planets.

Satellite systems apparently formed in several ways. The major moons of the Jovian planets appear to have formed by accreting around the planet they orbited. Most of the irregular moons of the Jovian planets and the moons of Mars are probably captured planetesimals. Some of them may have been disrupted on capture, breaking into several pieces. Our Moon appears to have been the aftermath of a collision between a large planetesimal and the Earth. The collision ejected parts of the Earth and the planetesimal into orbit around the Earth, and this debris accreted into the Moon.

Astronomers attribute individual rotational rates and axial tilts of the planets to collisions with hundreds of thousands of planetesimals. Although most collisions were with planetesimals much smaller than the planet, collisions with large planetesimals may have been frequent. Our Moon and the unique axial tilt of Uranus may have been the result of collisions; the orbital characteristics of Neptune's satellites and the existence of Pluto may have been a result of a collision or a grazing collision; and the slow, retrograde rotation of Venus may also have been a result of a collision.

Once the Terrestrial planets reached their present sizes, further development over the last 4.6 billion years depended mainly on how fast they cooled. Planetary cooling rates, in turn, were controlled by the size of the planet; small planets cooled faster than large planets. As a planet cooled, its lithosphere thickened and extended deeper into the mantle. Eventually, the lithosphere become so thick that tectonic activity was not possible. This happened early for the Moon and Mercury and perhaps only recently for Mars. Venus and the Earth still have tectonically active lithospheres. The development of the Jovian planets, on the other hand, was controlled by the accumulation of enormous amounts of gas and dust from the solar nebula.

CHAPTER CAPSULE

Topics and Terms	Review and Remarks
Solar nebula	It was a fragment of an interstellar cloud of gas and dust. The collapse of the solar nebula formed a central mass, the Sun, and a thin disk. The disk eventually formed into planets, moons, asteroids, and comets.
Collapse	The collapse of the solar nebula resulted in: All planets revolving in the same direction around the Sun Circular planetary orbits All planets orbiting the Sun in a very narrow plane
Condensation sequence	Different mixes of rock, ice, and gas occurred in different parts of the disk: Heavy elements dominated the hot inner regions—rocky planets formed there. Ices were most abundant in the outer regions—gaseous planets formed there.
Formation of planets	Initial growth was characterized by gentle collisions. Later encounters were violent and caused large changes in orbits. Only the largest planetary bodies survived subsequent collisions and grew.
Formation of moons	Moons could have formed in several ways: Accretion around the planet they orbit Capture by a planet Collision and subsequent coalescence—this is probably how the Moon formed.
Special features	Individual rotational rates and axial tilts were probably due to collisions.
Planetary evolution	The evolution of a Terrestrial planet depended on how fast it cooled: Small planets cool faster than large planets. Cooling means a reduction in geological activity and solidification of lithospheres.

REVIEW QUESTIONS

1. Each planet has its own orbital and spin characteristics. A number of these characteristics, however, are similar for all of the major planets. What are they?

2. Several of the major planets have components of motion that are very different than those of the other major planets. What are those differences and what are their likely causes?

3. Review the physical characteristics of the Jovian planets and of the Terrestrial planets.

4. Why could the Jovian planets accrete hydrogen and helium atmospheres while the Terrestrial planets could not? In other words, what advantage did the larger planetesimals have in accreting extensive atmospheres?

5. At a microscopic level, what is the difference between a gas and a solid? Would solids likely form in one part of the solar nebula earlier than in other parts? Why?

6. What is the *condensation sequence* and what role did it play in the early stages of formation of the planets?

7. Why might planetesimal accretion occur in the outer parts of the solar disk earlier than in its inner parts?

8. Except for the Earth, water seems to be rare in the Terrestrial planets but is a common component of the outer solar system, particularly in the satellites of the Jovian planets. What could have caused this variation?

9. What is a T Tauri wind and how could it be partially responsible for reducing the amount of interplanetary gas and dust in the early solar system?

10. Many millions of small planetesimals must have been formed during the time the major planets were formed. Even more must have resulted from collisions of larger bodies. What has happened to these bodies?

11. Many of the moons in the solar system are thought to have been formed with the major planets. Others are thought to have been captured. What orbital characteristics point to the difference in the origin?

12. What part did planetary size play in determining the surface appearance of the Terrestrial planets?

13. Why do Mercury, Mars, and our Moon have thicker lithospheres than the Earth and Venus?

14. Why do Mercury, the Moon, and to a lesser extent Mars have heavily cratered surfaces while the Earth and probably Venus have few craters?

FOR FURTHER READING

Barnes-Svarney, P. 1988. The chronology of planetary bombardments. *Astronomy*, July 20.

Cole, S., and K. R. Majdacic. 1988. Creating the future. *Astronomy*, Jan. 18.

Croswell, K. 1988. Does Barnard's Star have planets? *Astronomy*, Mar. 6.

Meszaros, S. P. 1985. Sizing up the planets. *Sky & Telescope*, July, 404.

Nichols, R. G. 1989. From footprints to foothold. *Astronomy*, July, 48.

Ride, S. K. 1988. Leadership and America's future in space. *Astronomy*, Jan., 8.

Young, A. T. 1985. What color is the solar system. *Sky & Telescope*, May, 399.

The Solar System: Resources for the Future

Most of us realize that the Earth has finite mineral and fuel resources and that someday they will be exhausted. How long will it take for humans to extract all of the copper, nickel, or coal the Earth has to offer? Miners probably cannot extract all of a given mineral from the Earth, but mining can reach a point where the extraction is extremely expensive and environmentally damaging, making it economically infeasible to mine further. With these qualitative limits in mind, it is possible to estimate the mineral and fuel reserves in the Earth's crust. Since the rate at which the world is consuming these resources is known, scientists can estimate the "life expectancy" of a particular mineral or fuel. Such estimates give surprising results. Several economically important minerals are predicted to be depleted in less than 100 years: some of the more familiar are silver, mercury, tungsten, nickel, cobalt, zinc, tin, and copper. Although additional reserves of these minerals may be found in seabed deposits, for instance, they will be more difficult to extract and the process may be more damaging to the environment. Furthermore, these estimates are based on the rates of use by today's industrial countries. If the underdeveloped nations try to raise their standard of living to equal our own, consumption of minerals and fuels will skyrocket.

Some minerals and fuels, even though they are plentiful, can become economically and environmentally very expensive to exploit. Coal, for instance, exists in great quantities in the Earth's crust, but many problems are associated with its recovery and use. Many of the remaining coal deposits contain significant amounts of sulfur. Sulfur vaporizes during combustion, enters the atmosphere, and helps produce acid rain. After coal is burned, a few percent of it are left as ash, which must be disposed of. Smoke from coal furnaces also presents severe air pollution concerns and, of course, underground mining accidents cost the lives of miners every year while others suffer from various lung diseases. Environmental and health problems are also associated with the mining of other fuels and minerals.

As minerals and fuels become scarce, they also become more expensive both monetarily and environmentally. For instance, the world experienced an artificial increase in the price of oil in the 1970s when oil-producing nations cut their production. Many underdeveloped nations suffered economically from the inflated prices. At the same time, some minerals and fuels have become so scarce that low-grade deposits and undersea sources must be exploited, at great expense to the environment. Strip mining of coal and drilling for offshore oil are causing environmental damage to the Earth by ravaging the countryside and contaminating our beaches (Figure 11A.1). These woes are inflicted upon the Earth for the sake of maintaining our present standard of living. Imagine what will happen when the

■■■ FIGURE 11A.1
Strip Mining Operation
SOURCE: Tom Havill/Visuals Unlimited.

■■■ FIGURE 11A.2

Overpopulation

Hunger at an African relief center.
SOURCE: Science VU/Visuals Unlimited.

whole world reaches or tries to attain our standard of living. Even if nuclear fission energy could replace fossil fuels as our major source of energy, the mining for radioactive minerals and the disposal of radioactive wastes will present severe problems.

The inevitable scarcity of minerals and fuels in the future will also cause political problems. Some political and social scientists believe that the threat of nuclear war will increase greatly under conditions of mineral and energy depletion. The force behind these potentially catastrophic social changes is population growth. The world's present population of over 5 billion people could easily reach 10 billion people by 2035. Over 90% of these will be born into poverty and in less developed countries (Figure 11A.2). Can the world reduce its population growth so the population will stabilize at a level that the world's resources can support? Are there alternatives to industrial growth? Must we look forward to a static society in a "steady-state" world? This scenario is not inevitable if we can find the necessary resources to maintain and expand our industrial society. The place to look for these resources is out of this world.

■■■THE INDUSTRIALIZATION OF SPACE

Almost unlimited economic growth will be possible if space is industrialized. Space industrialization is the commercial, profit-making use of space, resulting in new products, goods, and services for those on Earth and, eventually, for those living in space. Several characteristics of the environment of space make it desirable and useful as an industrial base. First, satellites or space stations can see the entire facing hemisphere of the Earth. The world already makes use of this "view" with satellites used for telecommunications, weather reports, navigation, and the study of the Earth's mineral, food, and fuel resources. Profitable use of satellites will expand in the future as video telephone conversations become commonplace; the demand for remote access to libraries and other sources of information increases; remote medical consultation and diagnosis gain wider use; electronic mail becomes more popular; and the need for news services, such as facsimile transmissions, increases. Furthermore, data acquisition from Earth-orbiting satellites will become more common and necessary for harvest prognostication, land-use monitoring, food production and water budgeting, pollution alerts, weather forecasting, and eventually climate control (Figure 11A.3). Whole new, profitable, and rapidly growing industries have emerged with the launching of near-Earth satellites.

A second advantageous characteristic of space is the phenomenon of weightlessness. Weightlessness allows the use of manufacturing processes not possible on Earth, resulting in the production of higher quality products as well as new products that cannot be made on Earth. For instance, large, nearly perfect crystals, only obtainable in space, will be very valuable for the electronics industry; enzymes and vaccines requiring exacting purification and separation processes can only be made in Earth orbit; and ultrastrong fibers and high-strength magnets, to name only two products, can readily be manufactured in the weightlessness of space.

Thirdly, weightlessness in the near-Earth environment will allow the building of very large structures. This will be important for collecting the unlimited amount of solar power (yet another useful characteristic of space) since huge kilometer-sized solar panels will be needed. Such collecting stations could be designed to transmit the collected solar energy via microwaves down to Earth to be converted into electricity. Estimates suggest that as much as 20% of the electrical needs of the United States could be met with solar power from space in the early twenty-first century. Large collectors will also supply all the energy needs of any manufacturing facilities in space. Solar power is a very plentiful resource in space; it just needs to be collected.

A fourth characteristic of space is its "limitlessness." Consequently, it is a natural location for industrial waste products and for the removal of heat from any manufacturing structures. Most importantly, the Earth's environment will not be damaged by pollution-intensive processes in space no matter how large scale they are. The limitless-

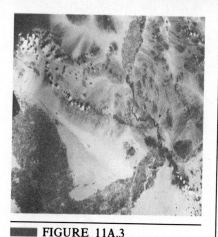

■ FIGURE 11A.3

Infrared Photograph of Farm Fields in Southern California and Mexico

Space photography is used to evaluate fields of crops, rangelands, forests, geologic structures, and other features on the Earth's surface. Here the red squares are farm fields.

SOURCE: NASA.

ness of space is also characterized by a vacuum. Many manufacturing techniques require vacuums and are currently limited by the small volumes of vacuums obtainable with expensive vacuum pumps.

The industrialization of space will require men and women to engage in the necessary activities to support industrialization. Habitable orbiting facilities will be needed (See AstroProbe 7) to house the men and women, and eventually their families, working in space. This human element will require medical, entertainment, and educational support industries staffed by other men and women. Eventually, this will lead to a continuous human presence in near-Earth space.

Currently, communications and Earth resources satellites are built and launched from the Earth using the natural resources of our planet. This industry does not at present appear to strain our resources, but other space activities, such as manufacturing facilities, giant solar collectors, and human settlements, will require a vast amount of resources. How can a presence of humans in space help alleviate the future mineral and fuel crises the world faces by using additional resources? The key to the success of the industrialization of space is the resources of the solar system itself. For life-in-space to be successful, the raw materials for the necessary facilities must come from the objects in the solar system—the Moon, asteroids, comets, planets, and other moons. Are there sufficient mineral and fuel resources to support the industrialization of space?

RESOURCES OF THE SOLAR SYSTEM

The nearest celestial resource to the Earth is, of course, the Moon. Humans have been to the Moon and brought back samples of its soil and rock (Figure 11A.4). A typical Apollo lunar sample, for instance, contained about 40% oxygen, 20% silicon, 12% aluminum, 6% titanium, 4% iron, 3% magnesium, and small amounts of other elements. Tied to lunar regolith and rocks is oxygen, a natural "waste" product of the processing of lunar material. The oxygen, of course, is needed to sustain life and for rocket fuel, the major means of transportation in space. Silicon is very important for the electronics industry and for making solar cells that can be used to generate electrical power from solar energy. Titanium is particularly important in the aerospace industry because it is a strong, but light, metal. The processing of titanium, however, requires very high temperatures, high vacuums, and lots of energy; all of these are expensive on Earth but cheap in space. The raw lunar material can be mined on the Moon, sent to near-Earth manufacturing facilities, and the final product taken down to Earth.

■ **FIGURE 11A.4**

Apollo Astronaut Collecting Lunar Samples

Nearly 400 kg of lunar rock samples were returned from the Moon by the Apollo astronauts.

SOURCE: NASA.

Mining the Moon will have two purposes. One is to obtain the necessary raw materials to build industrial sites in near-Earth orbit. The second is eventually to supply the Earth with minerals and fuel so that (1) Earth-based industrialization will not be stifled by its limited resources and (2) the Earth will not be polluted and contaminated by the wastes of the manufacturing process. Mining the Moon, moreover, would not need to be a large scale operation: a small base of about 100 people is all that would be needed to run a lunar mining facility (Figure 11A.5). To supply a million tons per year, only an area the size of eight football fields dug to a depth of ten meters is needed. Ten million tons of lunar regolith, for instance, contain enough material to build a space settlement for 10,000 humans. This indicates that the material needed to build manufacturing structures in near-Earth orbit can easily be obtained from the Moon.

The economic success of lunar mining depends on finding a cheap and efficient method for launching large amounts of ore from the lunar surface without expending large amounts of propellant. One method to accomplish this is to build an electromagnetic mass accelerator called a *mass driver*. No propellant is needed because the mass driver is made up of superconducting buckets magnetically levitated

■ FIGURE 11A.5

An Artist's Conception of a Future Lunar Base

A lunar mass driver is shown on the left; each cylindrical canister contains tens of kilograms of raw lunar material that will literally be thrown off the Moon.

SOURCE: Copyright 1985, Lunar and Planetary Institute, Houston. Art by Pat Rawlings.

above a track and accelerated by an electric motor (see Figure 11A.5). During acceleration the payload, tens of kilograms of lunar ore, is tightly held but is released upon reaching lunar escape velocity. As the bucket follows the curve of the lunar surface, the payload rises relative to the bucket and the surface and continues away from the Moon. These accelerated payloads would then be captured and transported to a manufacturing facility. This method eliminates any need to launch transport spaceships from the Moon's surface, and the required energy can be supplied by relatively small nuclear reactors.

Although the Moon contains many important minerals, it would not be able to support completely the industrialization of space because it lacks three important elements: hydrogen, nitrogen, and carbon. These are all essential for agriculture and initially will be supplied by the Earth. Hydrogen, nitrogen, and carbon, however, are plentiful in asteroids. Carbonaceous asteroids contain water mixed in minerals, organic compounds, and probably ice. Other classes of asteroids are rich in silicates, iron, and nickel and in some elements that are rare or difficult to extract on Earth. Hydrogen is also available in asteroids because it is implanted into the regolith grains by the solar wind and can be released just by heating. Although most asteroids orbit in the asteroid belt, where they would be too far away to mine economically, some come very close to Earth.

In fact, the retrieval of material from Earth-approaching (Apollo) asteroids may be cheaper and easier than retrieving lunar material. Large, kilometer-sized Apollo asteroids number about 40, but scientists expect that hundreds of thousands of smaller as yet undetected asteroids pass near the Earth's orbit. Some of these asteroids approach the Earth at low relative velocities and would be easy to mine because, due to the low surface gravities of these tiny worlds, a rocket could easily land and take off. As an example of the richness of minerals in asteroids, the world's largest concentration of nickel comes from the meteorite that produced the Sudbury Crater in Ontario, Canada. Asteroid mining, therefore, could eventually become a very important space industry for the Earth, providing not only hydrogen, nitrogen, and carbon for manufacturing facilities and settlements but also important minerals for the Earth.

That raw material that humans can use exists on the Moon and in asteroids is a fact. Can we venture off the Earth to live, work, and play in space—to reach out and take the mineral and energy resources the solar system has to offer? The first goal of the industrialization of space should be to provide the Earth with the material and energy resources necessary to bring the standard of living of all countries of the world to a decent level and to do this without punishing those countries already with a high standard of living. What should

the second goal be? That will take care of itself. With the vast resources available in the solar system, humans can construct space
settlements that will be able to hold the world's population by the
middle of the twenty-first century (Figure 11A.6). This seems incredible! Nevertheless, conservative analyses of resources and the pro-
ductivity of spacefarers point to this as a very real possibility. This
future is not built on the imaginations of science fiction writers who
use science and technology not yet invented, but on critical evalua-
tions of science, technology, and resources that exist today. This future provides hope for the children of the twentieth century—and it
lies in space.

■ **FIGURE 11A.6**

**An Artist's Conception of the
Interior of a Space Colony**

Rotation produces artificial gravity for
this torus, or doughnut-shaped, design
of a habitat for 10,000 people. The "horizon" follows the curved shape of the
torus.

SOURCE: NASA.

CHAPTER 12

The Sun

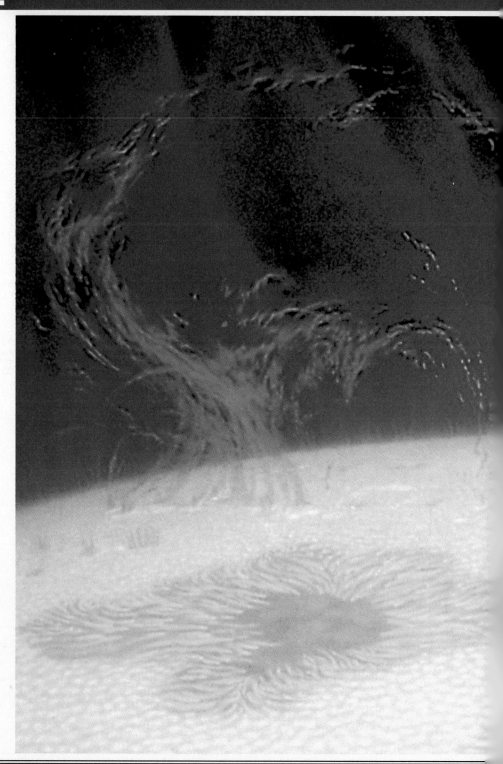

OUTLINE

Physical Characteristics of the Sun

Nuclear Reactions in the Sun

The Chemical Composition of the Sun

The Sun's Interior

The Sun's Outer Layers
The Photosphere and Sunspots
The Chromosphere
The Corona
Prominences and Flares

Summary

Chapter Capsule

Review Questions

For Further Reading

ASTROPROBE 12: Sun-Earth Connections

Solar Panorama.
ARTIST: Don Davis.

THE SUN IS ONE OF THE BILLIONS OF LUMINOUS SPHERES in the Galaxy that astronomers call **stars.** Stars create their own light. This is a characteristic shared by all stars and one that distinguishes them from planets and moons, which are seen by reflected light. Sunlight can play a very important role on a planet's surface. The oppressive atmosphere of Venus, for instance, is the result of the containment of solar energy while life on Earth could not exist without the energy received from the Sun. The source of the Sun's vast energy is invisible to us and lies deep at the Sun's center.

Life on Earth benefits so much from sunlight because the Sun is very close, *astronomically speaking*. The most distinctive feature of the Sun compared to other stars is that it is 150 million kilometers from the Earth, making it readily accessible for Earth-based astronomers to study in minute detail. Astronomers can see its surface bubbling with energy, showing dark spots, immense storms, and violent eruptions. The Sun is close enough that the effects of this surface activity can be felt on Earth through X-rays, radio radiation, and the solar wind.

The Sun's physical characteristics of mass, radius, temperature, chemical composition, and intrinsic brightness lie midway in the range of these properties exhibited by other stars. In this sense, the Sun is an ordinary star. Consequently, what astronomers learn about the physical processes that determine the structure and appearance of the Sun applies to most other stars. Thus this ordinary star, so important to life on Earth, is also important to astronomers for understanding other stars.

PHYSICAL CHARACTERISTICS OF THE SUN

How can the Sun keep shining day after day, with a seemingly endless supply of energy, as it has been for the last 4.6 billion years? A start to answering this question requires knowledge of the Sun's physical characteristics, such as its diameter, the amount of matter it contains, the temperature at its center, and its chemical composition (Table 12.1). Of these characteristics, two are critical for understanding the Sun's long-term energy generation: mass and luminosity. The Sun's mass is over 330,000 Earth masses! Out of this enormous amount of matter comes the fuel that the Sun uses to produce the energy we can see and feel. This large fuel supply hints at the reason why the Sun can shine on and on, day after day.

The Sun's **luminosity** is the total amount of energy the Sun emits each second in *all* directions outward from its surface. Picture the Sun enclosed by a sphere with a radius of one astronomical unit (AU). All the energy emitted by the Sun must pass through the surface of this sphere. The Earth, by virtue of its small size, can only intercept a tiny fraction of the Sun's energy. A measure of this tiny fraction is the **solar constant:** the amount of energy passing through 1 cm² of space at the Earth's orbit every second. The solar constant is about ⅐ of a **watt** per cm², or ⅐ of a **joule** per second per cm². This does not seem like much energy emitted each second; ⅐ of a joule is about the amount of energy expended salting a dinner. Suppose, however, that engineers could col-

Luminosity: The total amount of energy emitted every second by a star.

Watt: A unit of power, describing the rate at which energy is being used; measured in *joules* per second.

Joule: A unit of energy roughly equivalent to the energy expended placing a pound of beans in a grocery cart.

■ TABLE 12.1 Solar Data

Radius ($R_\odot$)	6.96×10^5 km
Mass ($\mathfrak{M}_\odot$)	1.99×10^{30} kg
Density	Mean: 1.41 g/cm^3 Core: $\approx$160 g/cm^3
Solar constant	0.136 watts/cm^2
Luminosity ($L_\odot$)	3.83×10^{26} watts
Surface gravity	27.9 times Earth's surface gravity
Escape velocity	617.7 km/s (1.38 million MPH)
Rotational rate	25.7 days at equator; $\approx$33 days at the poles
Temperature	Surface: 5800 K Core: $\approx$16,000,000 K
Age	4.6 billion years
Chemical composition	Hydrogen abundance: $X_\odot \simeq 0.78$ Helium abundance: $Y_\odot \simeq 0.20$ More massive elements: $Z_\odot \simeq 0.02$

■ FIGURE 12.1

Luminosity

The Sun's luminosity is found by multiplying the solar constant by the surface area, $4\pi R^2$, of a sphere with a radius, R, of 1 AU

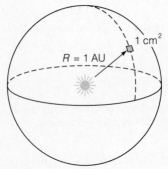

Surface area of sphere = 2.8×10^{27} cm^2

lect all the energy that strikes the hemisphere of the Earth facing the Sun and convert it into electricity. The energy collected each second would be equivalent to the power output of a billion nuclear reactors! Let's extend this comparison to include all the square centimeters on the sphere with a radius of 1 AU surrounding the Sun, by multiplying the solar constant by the surface area of the sphere (Figure 12.1). This yields 3.83×10^{26} watts for the Sun's luminosity and is represented by the symbol $L_\odot$, where the "$\odot$" stands for the Sun. Does the Sun's luminosity represent a lot of energy? If the entire surface of the Earth were covered with nuclear reactors, they would be able to generate only one ten-millionth of the power output of the Sun. The Sun must have a vast store of fuel available to generate this much energy for so long a time.

Before answering the question of how the Sun can shine brightly day after day, let's first use the solar constant to determine another important physical characteristic of the Sun—its surface temperature. Recall from Chapter 4 that the Stefan-Boltzmann radiation law states that the total amount of energy passing through 1 cm^2 of the Sun's surface every second equals the Stefan-Boltzmann constant (represented by "σ" in Chapter 4) multiplied by the surface temperature of the Sun raised to the fourth power: σT^4. Since the surface area of the Sun is 46,000 times smaller than that of the sphere with a radius of 1 AU, the amount of energy passing through 1 cm^2 at the Sun's surface must be 46,000 times *larger* than the solar constant, or 6400 watts per cm^2. Inserting this into the Stefan-Boltzmann law gives a surface temperature of 5800 K. Although it is not important that you actually perform this calculation, you can understand its significance by realizing that the Stefan-Boltzmann law allows astronomers to determine the temperature of the Sun's surface without actually making the measurement at the Sun.

Although a temperature of 5800 K is high by terrestrial standards, it is "cool" compared to that at the center of the Sun. In fact, the explanation for the Sun's ability to generate energy is found deep within the immensely hot fiery furnace in the Sun's core.

NUCLEAR REACTIONS IN THE SUN

How is the Sun's energy generated? Where is the source of this energy? Humans have tried to answer these questions indirectly for 2500 years. The development of the ideas about the Sun's energy source closely parallels the history of the efforts to estimate the age of the Earth.

Greek philosophers realized that some geological formations, such as the delta of the Nile River, were very old. Every time the Nile River flooded, it left a layer of sediment, and thousands of layers meant thousands of years of flooding. By the Middle Ages western Europeans had lost much of Greek science and based their estimates of the age of the Earth on literal interpretations of the Bible, not on observations of nature. Nevertheless, by the late eighteenth century geologists were estimating time scales for processes, such as the carving of mountains and the accumulation of sediment, that invalidated biblical literalism. For example, layers of shale 2000 m thick were visible in many places in the world. Geologists knew that silt and clay that settle on the ocean floors each year produce deposits of shale less than a millimeter thick. This implied ages of millions of years for the deepest layers. By the beginning of the nineteenth century, geologists estimated that the Earth was at least 75 million years old. •

At the same time, physicists and astronomers could not imagine a process that could provide the Sun with so much energy for so long a time. In the eighteenth century Immanuel Kant (1724–1804) estimated that if the Sun generated heat by chemical means, such as burning coal, it could last only a few thousand years. This time scale was too short even for the biblical literalists! The German physicist Hermann von Helmholtz (1821–1894) tried to explain the Sun's energy generation in terms of the gravitational contraction of the Sun. His idea was that as the Sun formed out of the solar nebula, it contracted and compressed the matter at its center. Since compressing a gas will increase its temperature, a hot gas develops and radiates energy as heat is radiated from a hot fire. Helmholtz estimated that the Sun could generate energy for about 20 million years in this way. Although a long time, it still was not long enough for some geological processes to have taken place on Earth.

On top of this, at the beginning of the twentieth century, dating rocks by radioactive decay resulted in ages of nearly 4 billion years for Earth's oldest rocks. Radiometric ages of rocks containing fossils showed that life has existed on Earth for more than 3 billion years. Since life requires the energy from the Sun, the Sun must have been shining with nearly the same luminosity during that time. From studies of the origin of the solar system (see Chapter 11), scientists also realized that the Sun and Earth were formed at the same time. Clearly, the Sun is several billion years old.

The only known source of energy that could last billions of years was recognized only recently. When an electron and a positron (a positively charged electron) collide in nuclear experiments, they disappear in a flash of energy, and the amount of radiant energy can be calculated. All that is needed for the calculation are the masses of the colliding particles. The equation, first formulated by Albert Einstein, relating mass, m, and energy, E, is $E = mc^2$, where c is the speed of light, 3×10^5 km/s. Any energy derived from the annihilation of matter is called *nuclear energy*. Astronomers understood that if all of the Sun's mass was available for nuclear energy generation, the Sun could shine for tens of billions of years. Although no one at the beginning of the twentieth century knew how nuclear energy was generated or how much of the Sun's mass was available for energy generation, it was clear that the Sun must be a gigantic nuclear fire.

In 1939 Hans Bethe in the United States and Carl von Weizsäcker in Germany solved the problem of nuclear energy generation in the Sun by discovering a set of *nuclear reactions* in which four hydrogen nuclei **fuse** into a helium nucleus. Nuclear fusion reactions are written in the same manner as chemical reactions. The chemical symbols of the fusing elements are placed on the left-hand side and those of the products on the right-hand side. An arrow between the fusing elements and the products indicates the direction of the reaction, usually from left to right. The number to the upper left of a chemical symbol is the number of neutrons and protons in the nucleus. Figure 12.2 shows the nuclear reactions occurring in the Sun. In reaction a, two protons fuse to form a deuterium nucleus (^{2}D), composed of one proton and one neutron, a positron (e^+), and a neutrino (ν). The neutrino escapes the Sun because it does not interact strongly with matter. Reaction b is the fusion of a proton and a deuterium nucleus into a helium-3 (^{3}He) nucleus, which contains two protons and one neutron. A high-energy photon, or gamma ray (γ), is also produced in reaction b. After reactions a and b each occur *twice*, two ^{3}He nuclei fuse to form two protons and a helium-4 (^{4}He) nucleus consisting of two protons and two neutrons. This set of

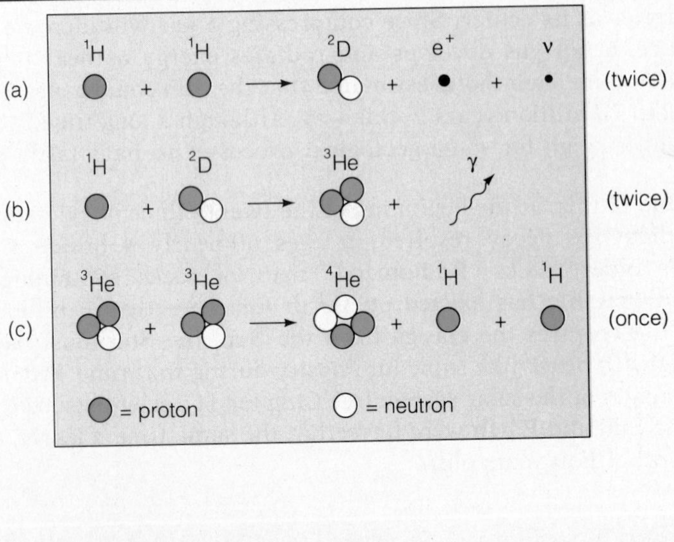

Fusion: A thermonuclear reaction in which nuclei fuse together to form a more massive nucleus; energy is released because the product nucleus is less massive than the reacting nuclei.

■■■ FIGURE 12.2

Proton-Proton Chain

Nuclear reactions a and b must occur twice before reaction c can occur. Six protons, ^{1}H, fuse to form a helium nucleus, ^{4}He, and two protons. The net result is the fusion of four protons into a helium nucleus. The remaining two protons in reaction c are available for further nuclear reactions.

reactions is part of the **proton-proton chain** occurring inside the Sun (see Appendix G for the complete proton-proton chain).

Each of the nuclear reactions in the proton-proton chain generates energy in the form of motion, called *kinetic energy*, of the product particles. The kinetic energy of a gas is a measure of its temperature. Heating a pan of water, for instance, causes the water molecules to move faster; the energy supplied by the stove burner increases the kinetic energy of the water molecules. The greater the kinetic energy of the molecules, the greater the temperature of the water. Similarly, the ^{3}He nucleus in equation b of the proton-proton chain has a greater kinetic energy than that of the proton and the deuterium nucleus. The ^{3}He nucleus transfers this energy to nearby nuclei through collisions. The continuous supply of kinetic energy provided by nuclear reactions keeps the Sun's interior hot.

Nuclear reactions create energy because the mass of the ^{4}He nucleus is less than the mass of the four protons from which it formed. For every 1000 grams of hydrogen involved in the proton-proton chain, only 993 grams of ^{4}He are produced. Where are the other 7 grams? It is not in the positrons or neutrinos; they are not massive enough. Most of the missing 7 grams has been converted into kinetic energy and a little into γ rays. The amount of kinetic energy can be calculated from Einstein's equation, $E = mc^2$. For the Sun to generate 3.83×10^{26} watts, it must convert about 6×10^{11} kg of hydrogen (about half the mass of Mt. Everest) to helium *every second*. Although this seems like a lot of hydrogen, the Sun has a lot—enough to last many billions of years.

Where in the Sun do these nuclear reactions take place? Understanding how the two protons fuse will help us locate the source of the Sun's nuclear power and determine how many billions of years the Sun can provide its essential energy. Let's start by investigating what the two protons in reaction a have to go through to fuse into deuterium. First, since both protons have a positive charge, the electromagnetic force (see AstroProbe 4) between them is repulsive. Second, the strength of the electromagnetic repulsion increases the closer the protons are to each other. This repulsion can be visualized as the wall of a crater separating the two protons (Panel a in Figure 12.3). For one proton to fuse with the other, it must "climb over" the crater rim, or barrier. The height of the barrier simply reflects the strength of the repulsive electromagnetic force between the two protons. Imagine the proton on the outside of the crater as a ball rolling up the rim. If it rolls fast enough, it will make it up and over the rim. For the protons this means that the faster they approach each other, the more likely they are to fuse. In fact, if they come within about 10^{-13} cm of each other, the strong nuclear force will bind them together despite the repulsive electromagnetic force.

Are the protons inside the Sun moving fast enough to fuse? Because of the tremendous amount of overlying mass compressing the gas in the interior, the temperatures inside the Sun are millions of Kelvins. These very high temperatures ensure that the protons move at very high speeds. Yet, the vast majority of protons in the Sun still cannot overpower the electromagnetic force.

■ FIGURE 12.3

Nuclear "Craters"

(a) The repulsive electromagnetic force between two protons is represented here as the rim of a crater. For two protons to fuse, the outside proton must move fast enough to climb the wall and unite with the other proton. *(b)* Radioactive elements can be represented by nucleons (protons and neutrons) in the upper part of a nuclear crater. Here the rim is thin and it is easier for a nucleon to tunnel out. *(c)* In a stable element the nucleons are deep within the nuclear crater where the walls are too thick to tunnel through.

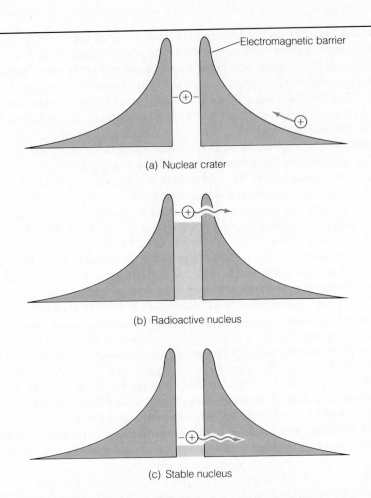

(a) Nuclear crater

(b) Radioactive nucleus

(c) Stable nucleus

Quantum mechanics: A mathematical theory in physics that starts with the assumption that energy is not infinitely divisible and goes on to describe atomic phenomena.

Two thousand years ago, Greek astronomers used the geocentric model of the universe as a tool to predict the motions of the planets. Although the Greeks described these motions in terms of spheres and circles, these were just mathematical constructs; they did not exist. Furthermore, the Greeks did not understand how planets could ride on spheres or move in circles. Modern scientists have since replaced the Greek geocentric model with Newtonian physics. Newtonian physics works well in the macroscopic world of humans and planets. It does not correctly describe events in the microscopic world of atoms and subatomic particles, however. Physicists have constructed another model to describe and predict events in the microscopic world; it is called **quantum mechanics.** Quantum mechanics predicts that the protons in the Sun fuse.

In the quantum mechanical description of matter, atomic particles can "tunnel" through the energy barriers between nuclear particles. Tunneling follows from our innate uncertainty of the location of subatomic particles (see the "uncertainty principle" in AstroProbe 4). It implies that the "outside" proton has a finite probability of tunneling through the electromagnetic barrier as it moves toward the other proton. The closer to the top of the crater a proton is, the greater the probability of it *finding* itself on the other side of the barrier. For instance, radioactivity can be described in terms of such probabilities. The decay of a radioactive element is simply part of the nucleus escaping. Picture a radioactive nucleus as one in which the protons and neutrons are close to the top of a barrier (Panel b in Figure 12.3). Since the rim is "thin" here, it is easier for part of the nucleus to quantum mechanically tunnel through; that is, the probability is relatively high that it will be on the other side of the barrier. In this simple picture, stable nuclei have nucleons (protons and neutrons) deeper inside the crater where the rim is "thicker" and tunneling is impossible (Panel c in Figure 12.3). This only gives a hint of the quantum mechanical explanation of radioactivity, but it does illustrate that the closer a proton is to the top of the crater rim, the greater is the probability for fusion. The ability of subatomic particles to tunnel allows nuclear reactions to occur at temperatures much lower than that required if the particles had to rely only on their speeds.

Since the temperatures in the Sun increase inward, as do the temperatures in the Earth, and because very high temperatures are needed for nuclear reactions to occur, the center of the Sun is the most likely location for nuclear energy generation. Too far from the center, the temperatures become so low that not even quantum mechanical tunneling can ensure nuclear reactions. Detailed computer models of the Sun indicate that only the inner 10% of the mass of the Sun has temperatures high enough for nuclear reactions to occur (see AstroProbe 15). This small fraction of the Sun's mass can supply the Sun with fuel for another 5 or 6 billion years.

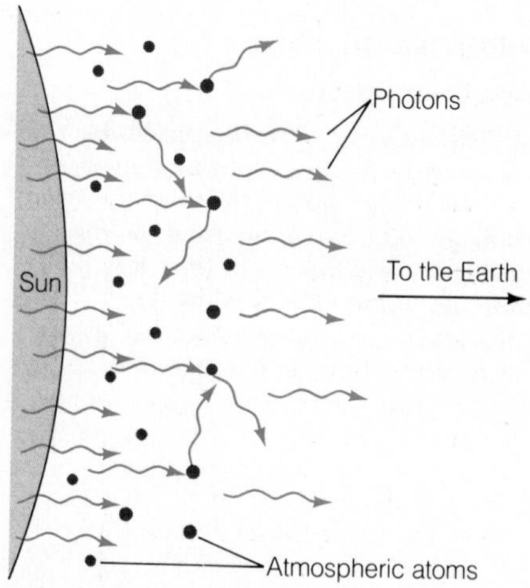

■■■ FIGURE 12.4

Spectral Line Formation in the Sun's Atmosphere

Photons absorbed by atoms in the Sun's atmosphere are eventually emitted in random directions. This represents a reduction of light intensity in the direction they were traveling before being absorbed.

■■■THE CHEMICAL COMPOSITION OF THE SUN

The hot gas in the Sun's core produces photons that reveal the chemical composition of the Sun. These photons are absorbed and reemitted millions of times before they reach the surface and pass through its outer layers where they travel radially away in all directions. Some of these photons that originated in the deep interior are absorbed by atoms in the Sun's outer layers and are taken out of the stream of light traveling toward the Earth. Even though a photon is almost immediately reemitted by an absorbing atom, the emission can be in any direction (Figure 12.4). Although a small fraction of the photons will be reemitted in the same direction that the light was originally heading, most of the reemitted photons will travel in other directions. Since photons are lost from the stream heading toward the Earth, the intensity of light at the wavelength of the absorbed photons is diminished relative to other wavelengths. Consequently, when astronomers record the spectrum of the Sun, they see absorption lines. More than 50,000 absorption lines have been identified in the spectrum of the Sun (Figure 12.5).

Although absorption lines clutter the solar spectrum, astronomers are able to identify individual series of lines associated with different elements. Recall from Chapter 4 that each element has its own spectral

Now may be a good time to review the sections in Chapter 4 that discuss atomic transitions and absorption spectra.

426

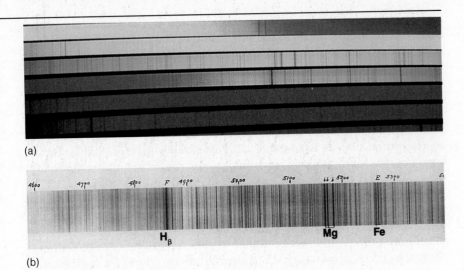

(a)

(b)

signature that produces a unique set of spectral lines. Scientists identify lines in the Sun's spectrum by heating an element, such as calcium, in a laboratory on Earth and photographing its spectrum. They then superpose this laboratory spectrum onto the solar spectrum and look for a match in the spectral lines. Of the known 109 elements, 67 are found in the Sun's spectrum. One of these, helium, was discovered in the Sun's spectrum before it was identified on Earth. Of the 38 missing elements, 10 are radioactive. The others are probably present, but either do not absorb photons with visible wavelengths or are so scarce that they do not absorb much light.

The analysis of the Sun's spectrum reveals that hydrogen and helium constitute about 98% of the Sun's mass while the elements more massive than hydrogen and helium comprise only about 2% (see Table 11.1). Astronomers use the letter Z to designate the fraction by *mass* of all of these more massive elements: for the Sun, $Z_\odot \approx 0.02$. The fractions of hydrogen and helium are designated by X and Y, respectively. These represent mass fractions. That is, although the Sun contains about 12 to 14 hydrogen atoms for every helium atom, the mass of a helium atom is nearly 4 times the mass of a hydrogen atom. Consequently, for the Sun $X_\odot \approx 0.78$ and $Y_\odot \approx 0.20$.

Spectral lines reveal much about the chemical composition of the Sun's outer layers, but they do not hint at the internal chemical composition of the Sun, which is quite different from the outer layers.

▰▰THE SUN'S INTERIOR

At the very center of the Sun, the site of nuclear energy generation, temperatures reach almost 16 million Kelvins, densities are as high as 160 g/cm³, and pressures are 200 billion Earth atmospheres. Even though the density is more than 10 times that of anything in the Earth and the pressures are immense, the ions and nuclei in the Sun are moving so fast that they behave as a gas. That is, they move freely and

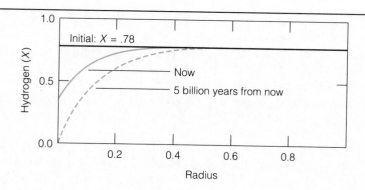

Nuclear Burning inside the Sun

The horizontal line at X = 0.78 represents the distribution of hydrogen throughout the Sun when it was formed. Over time nuclear reactions at the center deplete the hydrogen. The line marked "Now" gives the current distribution of hydrogen inside the Sun, and the dashed line is the predicted distribution 5 billion years from now. Note that the temperatures are only high enough for hydrogen depletion near the center of the sun. (See AstroProbe 15 for details on stellar model calculations.)

collide as atoms and molecules do in the air. In the Sun, however, ions and nuclei collide with tremendous violence. These violent collisions, of course, produce the energy-generating nuclear reactions. Nuclear reactions are changing the chemical composition in the Sun.

Since the Sun has been "burning" hydrogen for 4.6 billion years, the amount of hydrogen at its center is lower now than it was when the Sun formed. The central hydrogen abundance has been lowered to about X = 0.4 while the central helium abundance has been raised to about 0.58 (Figure 12.6). Furthermore, since the temperatures and densities decrease outward from the center, nuclear reactions have been less effective over time farther from the center. Figure 12.6 shows that the hydrogen and helium abundances are $X \approx 0.63$ and $Y \approx 0.35$ at a distance of one-tenth of a solar radius from the center. At the Sun's surface and throughout the outer layers of the interior, temperatures are far too low for nuclear reactions to occur. Consequently, the spectroscopic abundances noted in the last section are unchanged from the Sun's initial gaseous mix.

Radiative transport: The transfer of heat from hot regions to cold regions by electromagnetic radiation; heat from a fireplace, for instance, is transferred by radiation—you feel the infrared radiation as heat.

Since the temperature in the center of the Sun is greater than that in its atmosphere, heat flows from the center outward, as within the Earth. Heat transport over most of the Sun's interior is accomplished by **radiative transport.** In radiative transport, photons are emitted in hot regions and absorbed in cooler regions, thereby transporting energy from hot regions to cool regions. This is how heat is transported from a hot fireplace. In the Sun's interior a photon typically cannot travel more than a centimeter before being absorbed by an atom. Once absorbed, the photon is almost immediately reemitted, but it is reemitted in a random direction. Consequently, quanta of energy "zigzag" through the Sun, and, since the intensity of photons is always greater from hotter regions, the zigzags eventually lead toward the surface (Figure 12.7). This outward diffusion takes nearly 10 million years! In other words, if nuclear energy generation in the Sun stopped right now, humans would not notice it for millions of years.

Let's imagine speeding outward through the Sun at 100 MPH. It would take about 5 months to traverse the Sun's radiative region, which spans about 85% of the Sun's radius. All during this trip the temperatures and densities would continuously decrease outward from the center. For example, halfway through the Sun the temperatures and

Radiative Diffusion inside the Sun

A quantum of energy takes, on the average, 10 million years to pass through the Sun after being created in the center. Although a quantum may be initially emitted as an energetic X-ray photon, by the time it reaches the relatively cool surface of the Sun, its wavelength has been changed by all of the absorptions and emissions it has experienced in 10 million years.

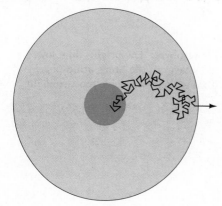

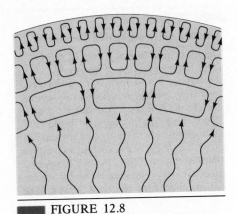

FIGURE 12.8

Convective Cells in the Sun

The rising and sinking motions of "bubbles" of gas produce convective cells below the photosphere. Arrows indicate the direction of motion of the gas in the convective regions.

densities have dropped to 4 million K and 1.3 g/cm³, respectively. This is too "cold" for nuclear reactions to occur via the proton-proton chain.

When interior temperatures decrease to hundreds of thousands of Kelvins far from the center, radiative transport is not able to transport all of the energy generated at the center. The reason is that more ions are able to capture electrons at these cooler temperatures and, consequently, become more effective absorbers of photons. In these regions the gas absorbs energy and heats up. Parcels of gas hotter than average bubble up toward the surface while being replaced by cooler, sinking gas. This physical movement of gas is called *convection* and is phenomenologically similar to the convective motion in the Earth's mantle (Chapter 5). The convective region, or zone, in the Sun covers the outer 15% of the Sun's radius; it would take about a month to pass through it traveling at 100 MPH. The rising and sinking parcels of gas circulate in convective cells (Figure 12.8). Astronomers expect, therefore, to find great activity at the top of the convection zone where gases rise and sink. In fact, the tops of these convective cells can be seen from the Earth.

THE SUN'S OUTER LAYERS

Astronomers define the atmosphere of the Sun as those layers in which emitted photons have a good chance of passing through the gas without being absorbed again. Such a definition is needed because the entire Sun is gaseous and does not have a solid surface separating an interior from an atmosphere as the Earth does. The Sun's atmosphere, therefore, is as deep as you can see into the Sun. Astronomers identify three distinct regions in the Sun's atmosphere: the photosphere, chromosphere, and corona. The photosphere is by far the brightest of the three; the chromosphere and corona normally can be seen only during solar eclipses when the bright glare of the photosphere is eliminated by the Moon. The major physical distinction between the three layers besides their brightness is their temperature, starting at about 6000 K in the photosphere and reaching millions of Kelvins in the corona. All three regions show evidence of intense magnetic activity, and detailed observations indicate that this activity follows a regular cycle, repeating itself every 11 years.

The Photosphere and Sunspots

Photosphere: The bright, thin, lowermost layer of the Sun's atmosphere from which we receive most sunlight.

The **photosphere** lies just above the Sun's convection zone and extends only a few hundred kilometers beyond it. The distribution of intensity with wavelength, or Planck curve, of the photons from the photosphere indicates a temperature of 5800 K, and this is identified as the temperature of the gas in the photosphere. Astronomers often refer to the photospheric temperature as the "surface," or "effective," temperature of a star.

The thin photosphere is the site of two prominent visible phenomena. The first is caused by the bubbling of the gases at the top of the convective region. Detailed photographs of the photosphere reveal a honey-

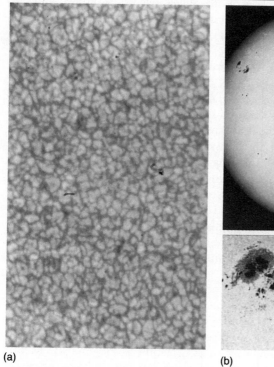

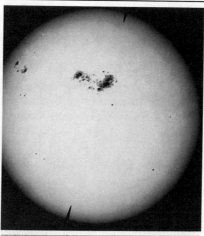

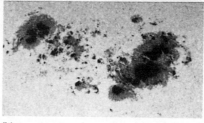

(a) (b)

■ FIGURE 12.9

Granulation and Sunspots

(a) Bright areas in the photograph are sites of rising gas; dark areas are regions of sinking gas. The gases rise with speeds of several km/s. *(b)* A complex sunspot group is seen on the Sun's surface along with several smaller sunspots.

SOURCES: Part (a), Project Stratoscope, Princeton University supported by NASA, NSF, and ONR. Part (b), Mt. Wilson photograph, Carnegie Institute of Washington.

combed pattern of bright spots surrounded by darker narrow lanes (Panel a in Figure 12.9). The bright spots, or *granules*, are typically 700–1000 km across. They are regions of rising gas while the darker surrounding lanes are where the gas sinks after cooling. Granules are the tops of convective cells. Astronomers call the honeycombed pattern of granules and dark lanes **granulation.** The lifetime of a typical granule in this pattern is only 8 minutes. Continuous observations of granules show them expanding, as hot gas reaches the top and spreads horizontally, and then fading away as if the convective cell below shifted, only to be replaced by another upwelling of hot gas. Granulation represents a dynamic and continuously changing distribution of convective cells.

Sunspots are the other visible phenomenon in the photosphere (Panel b in Figure 12.9). A typical spot is about 1500 km across, and the largest spots are nearly 50,000 km in diameter. Although sunspots, like granules, are transient, they last much longer. Individual sunspots are visible anywhere from a few hours to a few months. This was long enough for Galileo to notice that they moved across the face of the Sun. Astronomers today use this motion to study the Sun's rotation and find that the Sun rotates *differentially*, spinning faster at its equator than at its poles. Near the equator, the Sun rotates once every 25 days, but at intermediate latitudes, at about 30° for instance, it rotates once every 26½ days. Sunspots are rare at solar latitudes above 40°; the highest spot ever seen was at a solar latitude of 60°. The rotation at this latitude is about 30 days, and the expected rotation rate near the poles is about 33 days.

Granulation: Cellular pattern of convective cells seen in the Sun's photosphere.

Sunspots: Dark regions of intense magnetic fields in the Sun's photosphere.

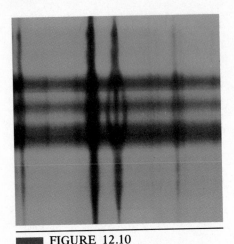

■■ FIGURE 12.10

The Zeeman Effect

Spectra of sunspots clearly show split lines. Here the normally unsplit lines of the surrounding photosphere are split into three lines over a sunspot.

SOURCE: National Optical Astronomy Observatories.

Sunspots are cooler than the photospheric gases and appear darker than the bright photosphere because, as the Stefan-Boltzmann law (Chapter 4) tells us, a cool gas emits less light at all wavelengths than a hot gas. The intensity difference between sunspots, such as those shown in Figure 12.9, and the surrounding photosphere implies that sunspots are approximately 1500 K cooler than the photosphere. Sunspots are also regions of intense magnetic fields. Astronomers detect magnetic fields in sunspots through spectra. The Dutch physicist Pieter Zeeman (1865–1943) discovered that gases immersed in a magnetic field produce spectral lines that are split into components with slightly different wavelengths. The splitting of spectral lines by an external magnetic field, called the *Zeeman effect*, is very well understood quantitatively. Astronomers can predict exactly the number of components a line will produce and calculate the separation, or spacing, of the components as a function of the strength of the magnetic field. Spectra of sunspots clearly show Zeeman splitting and suggest magnetic field strengths two to three thousand times stronger than Earth's magnetic field (Figure 12.10).

Groups of sunspots, some containing as many as 100 spots, exhibit distinct magnetic relationships to each other and to the Sun's magnetic poles. Sunspot groups are oriented in an east-west direction. The leading spots (the ones leading in the direction of rotation) of a group are of one magnetic polarity, and the trailing spots are of the opposite polarity. Furthermore, all the leading spots in one hemisphere have the same polarity as the hemisphere's magnetic pole. For instance, if the leading spots in the northern magnetic hemisphere are north magnetic poles, then the leading spots in the southern hemisphere will be south magnetic poles. On top of this, the polarities of the leading spots in each hemisphere reverse approximately every 11 years.

In 1843 Samuel H. Schwabe discovered that the location and the number of sunspots seen on the Sun vary over an 11-year period. He was looking for new planets crossing the Sun's disk and kept careful records of the appearance of the Sun for over 18 years. He found that at the beginning of an 11-year period sunspots form predominantly at latitudes of about ±35°. As time progresses, *new* spots form closer to the Sun's equatorial regions as the older, higher latitude spots fade. Near the end of an 11-year period, sunspots form predominantly within 8° of the Sun's equator. Figure 12.11 illustrates the variation in the location of sunspot formation for several 11-year periods. Because the graph looks like a collection of butterflies, it is called a *butterfly diagram*. Careful analysis of the butterfly diagram also shows that the number of sunspots formed at different times varies in 11-year periods (Figure 12.12). That is, the time between successive sunspot maxima or minima averages about 11 years.

The polarity of the Sun's overall, or global, magnetic field also follows an 11-year cycle—the north magnetic pole of the Sun switches to a south magnetic pole every 11 years. The Sun's global magnetic field is only slightly stronger than the Earth's magnetic field, but unlike the Earth's field, the Sun's field does not have a well-defined orientation. It

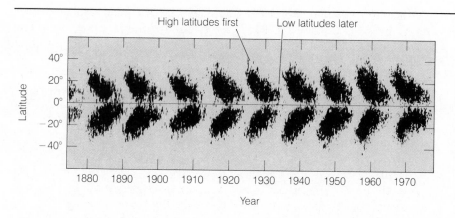

High latitudes first   Low latitudes later

■ FIGURE 12.11

Butterfly Diagram

Each set of "butterfly wings" represents
the location of new sunspots on the northern and southern hemispheres of the Sun
during an 11-year period. At the beginning of each period, sunspots form at predominantly high latitudes; at the end of
the period they form mainly at low latitudes.

SOURCE: Diagram prepared by the Royal Greenwich Observatory and is reproduced with the
permission of the Observatory.

does not have the symmetrical "dipole" shape of the Earth's global field
but looks to be a conglomerate of many localized fields.

In the last few paragraphs several phenomena were described that
appear to be linked with the Sun's 11-year magnetic period:

■ The location of newly formed sunspots

■ The number of sunspots

■ The polarity of leading sunspots

■ The reversing of the global solar magnetic field

To understand the link between these, let's examine the origin and development of sunspots.

At the beginning of an 11-year period, the Sun's magnetic field lines
can be envisioned as stretching north and south just beneath the photosphere and emerging out of the Sun at its poles. The emerging polar
magnetic fields spread over an area from the poles to latitudes of 50° to
60°, so they are not very localized. Because the gases below the photosphere are ions and, therefore, interact strongly with the magnetic field,
the ions drag the magnetic field lines with them as the Sun rotates. The
Sun's differential rotation winds and twists the subsurface field lines
into ropelike strands called magnetic *flux tubes*. After many solar rota-

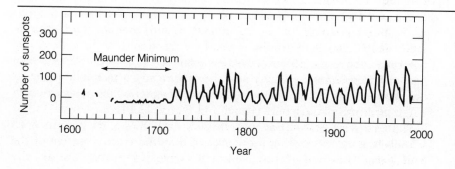

■ FIGURE 12.12

Sunspot Numbers

For the last several centuries, the average
number of sunspots seen each year has
varied within an 11-year cycle. In addition, every 80 years or so the number of
sunspots at sunspot maximum reaches a
maximum. The period between 1635 and
1715, the Maunder Minimum, correlates
with the Little Ice Age (see AstroProbe 5)
and hints at a possible Sun-Earth climate
connection (see AstroProbe 12).

■ FIGURE 12.13

Differential Rotation of Magnetic Field Lines

(a) Magnetic field lines of the Sun lie just beneath the photosphere. (b–d) Solar rotation slowly winds the subsurface magnetic field lines because the equatorial regions rotate faster than the higher latitudes.

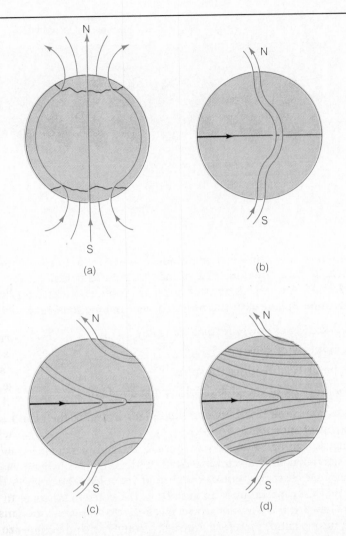

tions, the flux tubes are wound tighter and tighter, first at higher latitudes then at the lower latitudes (Figure 12.13). As the magnetic field lines are squeezed closer together, some of them thrust above the photosphere. The exact reason why this happens is not yet known. In fact, because of the complexity of the physical interaction between the ions in the Sun's atmosphere and its magnetic field, the magnetic environment of the Sun as a whole is poorly understood. When a flux tube protrudes above the photosphere, two sunspots are produced; one spot has a north magnetic polarity and the other a south magnetic polarity. Sunspots are simply the places where the magnetic flux tubes exit and enter the Sun's photosphere (Panel a in Figure 12.14).

The east-west orientation of sunspots and their polarities in each hemisphere are natural consequences of the differential rotation of the Sun. When the flux tubes pop into the atmosphere, they are already oriented east-west. At the same time, the direction (emerging or entering) of the leading spots in each hemisphere is the same as the direction

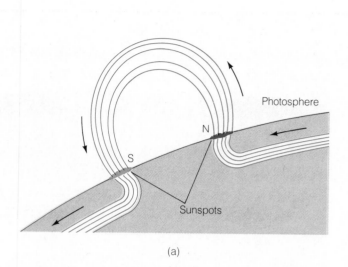
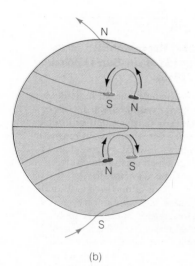

(a)   (b)

of the magnetic field at the pole in that hemisphere (Panel b). Consequently, the polarities of the leading spots are opposite in each hemisphere.

Even though sunspots disappear relatively soon after their formation,
their influence remains and eventually neutralizes the Sun's global
field. Once the strong magnetic fields of sunspots pop above the surface,
they expand upward. Photographs of the Sun's limb show huge arches
of matter that follow these extended magnetic fields (Figure 12.15). The
visible sunspots spread apart as the flux tubes stretch upward into the
Sun's atmosphere. After the sunspots themselves disappear, they leave
remnant "puddles" of magnetic polarity that continue to spread apart.
They spread in such a way that the trailing remnant moves toward the
pole and the leading remnant moves toward the equator. As the flux
tubes continue to expand upward, they push into the weak magnetic
field lines of the Sun's global magnetic field. Whenever two magnetic
field lines merge and are of opposite polarity, they neutralize themselves. Figure 12.16 shows the expanding magnetic field lines from sunspot groups on the western side of the Sun merge and neutralize a
global magnetic field line. Eventually, all of the magnetic field lines
connecting the magnetic poles of the Sun are similarly neutralized.
During this time the trailing remnant magnetic fields move to higher
and higher latitudes while the remnants near the equator neutralize
themselves. As the polar magnetic fields are neutralized, the polarity of
the migrating remnant fields becomes the new polarity of the polar
fields. Observations indicate this neutralization occurs near sunspot
maximum, and a new field of reversed polarity is generated soon after-
wards.

Figure 12.16 is a simplification of the real events—all of which are
not completely understood—occurring on the Sun during the 11-year
period. It is an attempt to help you visualize the destruction of the
Sun's global magnetic field. Of the preceding description, it is important to remember that (1) the magnetic fields of sunspots are much
stronger than the Sun's overall magnetic field and (2) the migration of

■ FIGURE 12.14

Magnetic Polarity of Sunspots

(a) The arrows show the direction of the
magnetic field lines. Where lines emerge
from the photosphere, the polarity is
magnetic north; where they enter the
photosphere, the polarity is magnetic
south. *(b)* Magnetic fields emerging form
the photosphere resemble horseshoe magnets. The leading polarities are reversed
in opposite hemispheres.

■ FIGURE 12.15

**Extended Magnetic Field over
a Sunspot Group**

The ionized matter in the Sun's upper atmosphere outlines the arching magnetic
field lines produced by a sunspot group.
The actual motion of the ionized gas is
down in both directions starting from the
tops of the loops.

SOURCE: National Optical Astronomy Observatories.

FIGURE 12.16

A Simplified Representation of the Neutralization of the Sun's Global Magnetic Field

As the magnetic field lines of individual sunspot groups expand outward, lines of opposite polarity (antiparallel) neutralize each other. *(a)* Growing sunspot magnetic fields are shown toward the end of an 11-year cycle in which part of the Sun's global field has been neutralized. *(b)* Magnetic fields of northern and southern hemisphere sunspot pairs merge and extend outward to eliminate the global magnetic field lines. *(c)* When the global magnetic field of the Sun has been neutralized, the same process generates a new global magnetic field but with the opposite polarity.

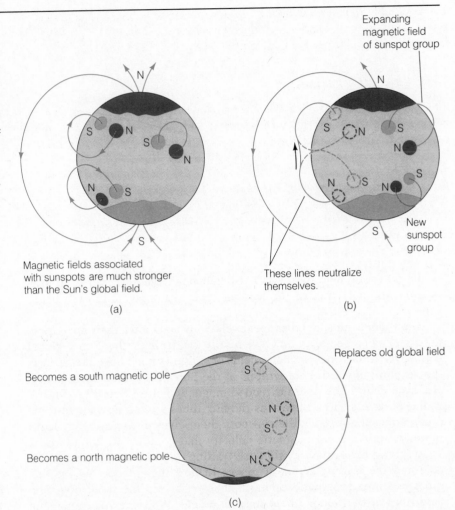

Magnetic fields associated with sunspots are much stronger than the Sun's global field.

(a)

Expanding magnetic field of sunspot group

These lines neutralize themselves.

New sunspot group

(b)

Becomes a south magnetic pole

Becomes a north magnetic pole

Replaces old global field

(c)

sunspot polarity to the poles eventually reverses the polar polarity. Furthermore, the 11-year period is not always exactly 11 years; it ranges between 9 and 11 years. Although this period is associated with several phenomena, the time for the global solar magnetic field to return to a given polarity is between 19 and 22 years. That is, if one pole of the Sun is a north magnetic pole, it will stay a north pole for about 11 years, then switch. It will stay a south magnetic pole for approximately 11 more years before switching back to a north pole. The same is true for the polarity of leading sunspots in a hemisphere. If they start out as north poles, then about 22 years later they are again north poles.

Although sunspots are the most obvious manifestations of solar magnetism, magnetism also plays important roles in the higher layers of the Sun's atmosphere. Whereas sunspots reside in the photosphere, their arching magnetic fields extend well above it. The highest layer of the atmosphere is a tenuous but vast region called the corona. Between the corona and the photosphere is a transition region, the chromosphere. Both the chromosphere and corona contain very few particles, but their temperatures are enormously high.

The Chromosphere

The **chromosphere** was noticed in ancient times during total solar eclipses as a pinkish skirt around the limb of the Sun. During solar eclipses, observers get only a brief view of the chromosphere and must be well prepared to obtain a spectrum of it. Since the chromosphere briefly flashes into view just before and after eclipse totality, the spectrum of the chromosphere is called the *flash spectrum* (Figure 12.17). Flash spectra show over 3500 emission lines. On the whole, these lines are from the same elements that produce the photospheric absorption line spectra. Although some of the emission lines result from atoms and ions in the chromosphere absorbing photons from the photosphere and reemitting them, most are produced by collisions in the chromosphere itself. The collisions excite the atoms and ions, causing electrons to move to orbitals farther from the nuclei. When the electrons drop back to their original orbitals, photons are emitted in random directions—some are emitted toward us. The most prominent emission line is the hydrogen-alpha (H_α) spectral line at 6563 Å. This emission line lies in the red part of the spectrum and is responsible for the chromosphere's pinkish color.

The first flash spectra obtained in the middle of the nineteenth century revealed a series of spectral lines that could not be identified immediately. Astronomers attributed the lines to a new element and named it after the Greek word for Sun *helio*—the element was helium. Helium was subsequently discovered on Earth 30 years later. Even lines due to *ionized* helium were seen in the flash spectra. Since the electrons in the helium atom are bound more tightly to the helium nucleus than, for instance, electrons to hydrogen or calcium nuclei, the presence of helium emission lines implied that the temperatures of the chromosphere must be higher than those in the photosphere. Recall that temperature refers to the rapid movement of the atoms and ions. Since most of the photons from the photosphere pass right through the sparse chromosphere, the excitation and ionization of elements in the chromosphere must be due to violent collisions between individual atoms and ions, causing electrons to change orbits.

Astronomers take pictures of the limb of the Sun during an eclipse to look for structures in the chromosphere. They also use a special device, called a *coronograph*, that uses a disk inside a telescope to block out the light from the photosphere. Such photographs of the edge of the Sun show that the top of the chromosphere, lying only 2000–3000 km above the photosphere, is very jagged. It exhibits spearlike projections, called *spicules*, that move up and down, dancing like the flames in a fireplace (Panel a in Figure 12.18). Spicules surge out of the lower chromosphere, rise thousands of kilometers, and collapse back down in a matter of minutes.

Chromosphere: A transition region between the relatively cool photosphere and the hot corona. Since the chromosphere can be seen as a pinkish glow briefly before totality during a solar eclipse, the Greeks used the word *chromo* meaning color to describe it.

■■■ FIGURE 12.17

Flash Spectrum of the Solar Chromosphere

The curved emission lines show the shape of the Sun's limb, which acted as the slit to the spectrograph (see Module 2, "Astronomical Instruments and Telescopes," for more on spectrographs).

SOURCE: Hale Observatories.

▓▓▓ FIGURE 12.18

Spicules

(a) Seen on the solar limb, spicules dance up and down over a time scale of a few minutes. *(b)* The chromosphere seen in H_α shows spicules outlining large regions called supergranules.

SOURCES: Part (a), National Solar Observatory/Sacramento Peak. Part (b), National Optical Astronomy Observatories.

(a)

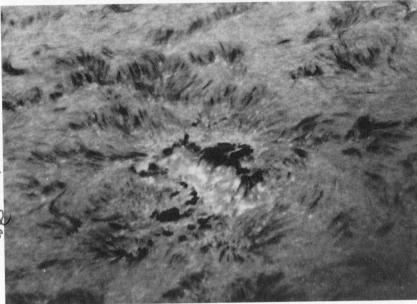

(b)

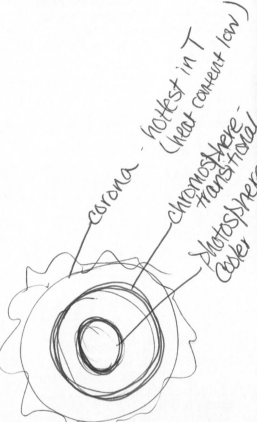

[handwritten annotations: corona – hottest in T (heat content low); chromosphere – transitional; photosphere – cooler]

Corona: The faintly luminous, outermost region of the solar atmosphere consisting of ionized gas at temperatures of several million Kelvins; derived from the Greek *korone* meaning crown.

Photographing the chromosphere looking directly at the disk of the Sun is a challenge. Astronomers know, however, that the H_α emission line is very bright; therefore, if they take a picture of the face of the Sun at only its wavelength, they will see only those features made up of hot hydrogen gas, that is, chromospheric gas. This can be done by placing a filter, which lets only light of H_α pass through, in front of a camera. Pictures in H_α show that spicules cover much of the Sun and that their distribution is not random. Spicules appear to be concentrated around the boundaries of large granules, called *supergranules* (Panel b Figure 12.18). Supergranules are about 30 times larger than granules and last several hours. The boundaries of supergranules are regions where gas is falling and are also areas of concentrated magnetic fields. It appears as if horizontal convective flow in the supergranules high in the chromosphere pushes the magnetic field toward the boundaries of the supergranules where astronomers find spicules. Although the origin of spicules still eludes astronomers, they must certainly be tied to the Sun's magnetic activity.

The Corona

Spicules originate in the chromosphere but shoot up into the **corona**, where temperatures reach a million Kelvins. Although the *temperature* of the corona is extremely high, its *heat* content is low. Scientists use the words temperature and heat for two different things. Heat is a form of energy that raises the temperature of an object. Heat increases the motions of atomic particles, and temperature is a measure of their motions. Temperature refers to a certain scale, such as Centigrade or Kelvin, that measures "hotness." When a gas is at a temperature of a million Kelvins, its individual atoms are moving very quickly indeed. In the chromosphere and corona, however, where the density of gases is so low, the heat content of these regions is also very low. Thus, if you could shield a cup of coffee from photospheric radiation, you would be hard pressed to heat it in the million-degree corona. In these upper layers of the Sun's atmosphere, so few atoms and ions exist that their collisions with objects, such as a cup of coffee, would be rare and, therefore, could hardly raise the temperature of the coffee.

How can temperatures in the very outermost layers of the Sun's atmosphere be as hot as the deep inner regions of the Sun? What source of energy could make the atoms and ions in the chromosphere and corona move so fast? The density of the gas is too low for nuclear reactions to occur. Sound may be responsible.

In the middle of the afternoon you suddenly hear a "boom" followed by a rattling of windows and shelves—you just heard and felt a sonic boom. It is caused, of course, by a jet flying faster than the speed of sound. The jet actually flies so fast that the molecules in the atmosphere are unable to move out of its way. Consequently, the air molecules bunch up, producing a narrow region of high pressure that moves through the air along with the jet. Scientists call this high pressure region a *shock wave*, and you hear and feel the shock wave as a sonic boom. Similarly, the turbulent churning of the photosphere by the Sun's convection zone produces sound waves that propagate upward. The density in the solar atmosphere decreases with height, and when a sound wave moves through such a density change, it speeds up. Eventually, it reaches the speed of sound, becoming a shock wave. Instead of shaking windows and shelves, the propagating solar shock wave shakes the atoms and ions in the Sun's atmosphere—it increases their speeds. Furthermore, the Sun's magnetic field seems to enhance the heating of the chromosphere and corona. Spicules, for example, eject matter continuously into the corona and are intimately associated with localized magnetic fields. Large sunspot regions can be sites of gigantic explosions that eject matter and energy into the corona (and even all the way to the Earth) and double the temperatures above the sunspots. Mechanical motion originating in the Sun's convection zone appears to be able to heat the chromosphere and, enhanced by strong magnetic fields, may generate enough energy to heat the corona to millions of Kelvins.

The corona is most readily seen during total solar eclipses when it appears as a huge ghostly white bonnet surrounding the darkened Sun and is visible for the length of the eclipse. Although astronomers can block out the Sun's disk with a coronograph, the faint outermost regions of the corona are lost in the scattered light in our atmosphere. Consequently, astronomers send large expeditions to solar eclipse sites to obtain a few minutes of data on the outer corona. Since the middle

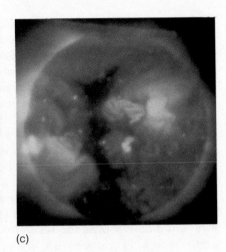

(a)

(b)

(c)

■■■ FIGURE 12.19

The Solar Corona

(a) At sunspot maximum the corona is very symmetric. *(b)* At sunspot minimum the corona appears flatter and shows streamers and plumes near the poles. *(c)* The corona shown in X-ray light exhibits hot regions (bright spots) located over sunspots and long, "cold" regions called coronal holes (dark area). Coronal holes are a source of solar wind particles.

SOURCES: Part (a), official U.S. Naval Observatory photograph. Part (b), National Center for Atmospheric Research/National Science Foundation. Part (c), NASA.

of the nineteenth century, astronomers have collected a total of about two hours of data in this way, but recently spacecraft have added immensely to our information about the corona. The corona is huge. It extends millions of kilometers beyond the photosphere. Balloon, aircraft, and spacecraft instruments have detected the corona out to 30 solar radii, or over 20 million km. The shape of the corona is extremely variable (Panels a and b in Figure 12.19). At sunspot minimum, the corona shows extension in the equatorial regions and rays in the polar regions. At sunspot maximum, the corona is more symmetric in all directions.

The spectrum of the corona also shows emission lines not just of ionized atoms, but of very highly ionized atoms. For example, a line at 5303 Å, in the green part of the spectrum, is due to 13 times ionized iron. Many lines of 9 to 15 times ionized iron, calcium, and nickel are produced in the visible spectral regions, and lines of highly ionized carbon, nitrogen, and oxygen, among others, are produced in the X-ray regions. A typical temperature of the corona, as indicated by these lines, is 1 to 2 million Kelvins. At these high temperatures the corona also emits X-rays intensely at 10 Å–30 Å, making the corona brighter in X-rays than the photosphere.

The high speeds of atoms and ions implied by these temperatures and the fact that the escape velocity is relatively low at distances of tens of solar radii ensure that some atomic particles escape the Sun. Normally, strong magnetic fields, such as those between sunspots, force the coronal ions to flow along closed magnetic lines, preventing their escape. Escaping coronal particles, however, flow out through *coronal holes* (Panel c in Figure 12.19), regions where magnetic field lines do not close back onto the surface but open outward into space. Coronal holes look dark in X-ray photographs and therefore appear to be void of matter, because the rapid escape of particles causes a cooling and results in low-intensity X-ray emission. Coronal holes were discovered in the mid-1970s with instruments aboard NASA's *Skylab* space station and were studied intensively in the 1980s with NASA's *Solar Maximum Mission* spacecraft. Although escaping coronal ions can drag weak magnetic field lines away from the Sun, producing an opening to interplanetary space, why the Sun produces open magnetic fields is still an unanswered question.

That particles, mainly protons and electrons, escape the Sun was no surprise since observations of comets decades ago strongly hinted at a **solar wind.** Spacecraft measurements indicate that the solar wind is a very high-speed, continuous stream of particles, traveling at 500 km/s (1 million MPH). It represents a loss of matter at a rate of about a million tons every second. Even at this high rate, however, the Sun has lost no more than 0.1 percent of its mass over the last 4.6 billion years. Strong particle flows from coronal holes represent an important contribution to the solar wind. Transient mass ejections, in which billions of tons of solar material are thrown outward, also contribute to the solar wind and are intimately associated with two violent phenomena in the Sun.

Solar wind: The steady stream of ions, mainly protons and electrons, flowing from the Sun.

Prominences and Flares

Photographs of the Sun's limb during eclipses or with a coronograph show huge luminous clouds of gas in the corona. These clouds, or *quiescent prominences*, form over sunspot groups and look like curtains or hedgerows silhouetted against the black of space (Figure 12.20). They represent coronal gases falling to the photosphere by following magnetic field lines toward the sunspots below. Quiescent prominences can exist for several months to a year. They are typically 40,000 km high and can extend horizontally for up to 200,000 km. They are often connected to the chromosphere by magnetic field lines that look like supporting arches. Sometimes quiescent prominences undergo active stages when much matter streams along the magnetic field lines after which the prominences seem to disappear. The old magnetic "framework" appears to remain intact because the prominences soon rebuild themselves in the old shape. The most beautiful type of prominence is the loop prominence in which coronal gas follows along magnetic field lines connecting sunspot groups (see Figure 12.15).

■■ **FIGURE 12.20**

Prominences

(a) A quiescent prominence silhouetted against the background of space. *(b)* A large surge prominence, in which matter was ejected from the Sun, is seen on the Sun's disk. *(c)* This ultraviolet *Skylab 4* picture of the Sun shows an erupting solar flare. Photographs from the previous day showed this to be a quiescent prominence.

SOURCES: Part (a), National Solar Observatory/Sacramento Peak. Part (b), Institute for Astronomy, University of Hawaii. Part (c), NASA.

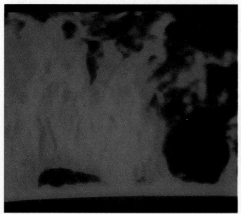 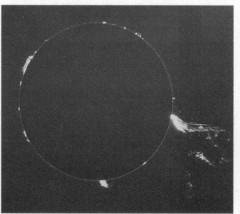 

(a)   (b)   (c)

Solar flare: Localized, short-lived, explosive bursts of light, X-rays, and particles from the vicinity of sunspots.

More active prominences are called *surge,* or *eruptive, prominences,* and even more violent than these are the **solar flares.** In surge prominences, coronal gases surge upward, typically at speeds of over 1000 km per hour, throwing matter several hundred thousand kilometers above the photosphere. Although surge prominences expand upward and appear to eject matter from the Sun, motion pictures of the prominences show that the gas is actually moving along closed magnetic field lines. Flares, on the other hand, represent violent ejections of matter. They were discovered with H_α photographs and appeared as a sudden brightening over a small region of the Sun's surface. They reach maximum intensity in minutes and then fade in minutes to hours. They release dangerous amounts of X-rays and eject bursts of particles, mostly protons and electrons. The radiation reaches the Earth in 8 minutes and the particles arrive 1 to 2 days later. The charged particles strike and excite atoms and molecules in our upper atmosphere, and the emissions that occur when these atmospheric atoms and molecules deexcite produce the aurorae. The X-rays generated by flares also ionize the Earth's upper atmosphere and interfere with radio communications, especially at the poles. At the same time, strong magnetic fluctuations on Earth caused by flares sometimes cause voltage pulses in electrical transmission lines and telephone cables.

Photospheric motions and intense magnetic fields appear to be the source of energy for flares, but the mechanism that transforms this energy into the observed violent ejections is poorly understood. Emissions of X-rays are first seen at what appear to be locations where magnetic loops are "anchored" to the photosphere at sunspots. The mechanism that generates the X-ray emission probably operates high in the corona at the top of the loop and acts to accelerate particles at near the speed of light along the loop toward the photosphere. These high-speed particles emit X-rays as they crash into the denser gas in the lower corona, chromosphere, and photosphere (Figure 12.21). The collisions between the high-speed particles and the ions in the Sun's atmosphere are so violent that they generate nuclear reactions from which very energetic photons and neutrons have been detected by spacecraft. The tremendous heating in the lower atmosphere (as high as 10 million Kelvins) results in an explosive rise of the ions into the corona, ejecting some into the solar wind.

Many questions concerning magnetic fields, coronal heating and holes, flares, and sunspots remain unanswered today. The most recent advances in our understanding of these phenomena have come about through important ultraviolet and X-ray observations from space. NASA's future space station will house the Advanced Solar Observatory, which will generate more data needed for a better understanding of the Sun. These questions are important from a practical standpoint because the Sun's emissions influence life on Earth and from a scientific standpoint because it is the closest star to the Earth. Furthermore, knowledge of the Sun will be directly applied to understanding the nature of stars.

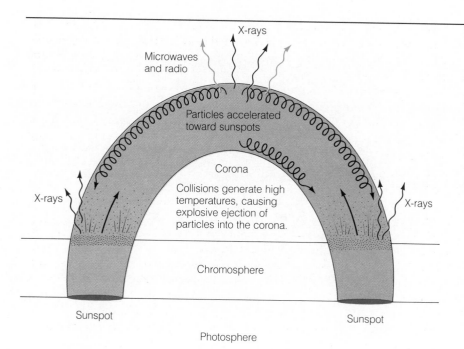

X-rays

Microwaves
and radio

Particles accelerated
toward sunspots

Corona

Collisions generate high
temperatures, causing
explosive ejection of
particles into the corona.

X-rays

X-rays

Chromosphere

Sunspot

Sunspot

Photosphere

Model of a Solar Flare

Electrons and protons are accelerated at
the top of the coronal loop by an unknown mechanism and spiral along magnetic field lines toward sunspots in the
photosphere. Collisions in the denser gas
of the lower corona and chromosphere
heat the gas to tens of millions of Kelvins,
causing an explosive ejection of material
into the corona.

▬▬ SUMMARY

The Sun is an immense sphere of gas in which all
atoms and nuclei move about freely, colliding with
each other just as molecules do in the air you are
breathing. Although the central density of the Sun is
more than 10 times greater than that inside the
Earth, the high temperatures inside the Sun keep the
atoms in a gaseous state.

High interior temperatures are also responsible for
the Sun's source of light and energy. Temperatures
of millions of Kelvins and high densities ensure that
nuclear fusion powers the Sun's tremendous energy
output. Nuclei release energy when they fuse because
the resulting nucleus is less massive than the nuclei
that fused. The lost mass, m, has been converted into
energy in the amount given by Einstein's equation $E
= mc^2$. Nuclear reactions can occur only near the
center of the Sun where temperatures are high
enough for individual nuclei to collide with enough
violence to fuse. Consequently, the chemical composition of the Sun's interior is continuously changing.
About half of the Sun's original hydrogen has been
converted to helium at the center. In another 5–6 billion years, all of the hydrogen will be exhausted at
the center of the Sun.

The energy generated in the center of the Sun
slowly works its way outward toward the surface.
Energy transport in the inner 85% of the Sun is accomplished by radiative transport. Through the
outer 15% of the interior of the Sun, energy is transported by convection (Figure 12.22). Evidence of convection can be seen in photographs of the photosphere that show the honeycombed pattern of
convective cells at the bottom of the photosphere.

The solar atmosphere is dominated by strong magnetic fields and their interaction with atmospheric
ions, of which sunspots are a major manifestation.
Sunspots have been recorded since the invention of
the telescope almost 400 years ago, and, except for a
lack of sunspots recorded between about 1645 and
1715 (the Maunder Minimum), the numbers vary
with an approximate 11-year period. The location of
new sunspots and their polarity are also linked to the
Sun's magnetic cycle. The reversal of the Sun's
global magnetic field is intimately associated with
the spreading of remnant sunspot magnetic sites and
the interaction of the strong magnetic fields of sun-

■■■ FIGURE 12.22

The Sun

This cutaway view shows the major structural features of the Sun. Sunspots would be at the "feet" of the loop and surge prominences and the solar flare. The chromosphere is a very thin region between the photosphere and corona.

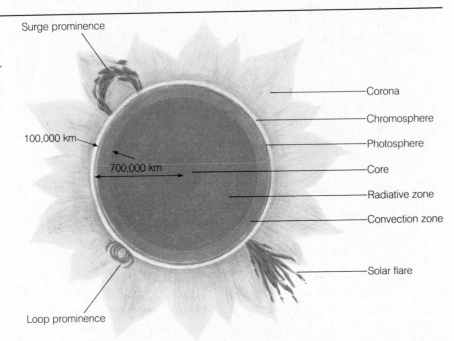

spots and the weak overall field of the Sun. Phenomena such as spicules, prominences, and flares are also associated with strong, localized magnetic fields.

The outermost layers of the Sun's atmosphere, the chromosphere and corona, are regions of very high temperatures but very low densities. Highly ionized atoms indicate temperatures of hundreds of thousands to millions of Kelvins. The corona is ejecting a continuous stream of particles called the solar wind.

The Sun is only one of billions of stars in the universe, but it is the only star for which astronomers can study sunspots, spicules, prominences, and granulation in minute detail. The foundation of our understanding of stars lies in our detailed observations of the Sun.

▆▆▆CHAPTER CAPSULE

Topics and Terms	Review and Remarks
The Sun	It is an immense sphere of hot gas; there are no solid surfaces inside the Sun. High interior temperatures ($>10^7$ K) are responsible for fusion reactions.
Nuclear reactions	They release energy by the conversion of mass: $E = mc^2$. This causes a gradual change in the chemical composition inside the Sun: the Sun will deplete its supply of hydrogen at its center in 5 to 6 billion years.
Energy transport	It takes millions of years for the energy released by nuclear reactions to reach the surface of the Sun. The inner 85% of the Sun transports energy by radiative transport. The outer 15% of the Sun transports energy by convection.
11-year sunspot cycle	The location, number, and polarity of sunspots change about every 11 years.
22-year magnetic cycle	The Sun's overall polarity cycles from north to south to north every 22 years.
Localized magnetic fields	These are responsible for sunspots and phenomena associated with spicules, prominences, and solar flares.

(continued)

CHAPTER CAPSULE (continued)

Topics and Terms	Review and Remarks
The photosphere	Spectra show thousands of absorption lines; 98% of the Sun is hydrogen and helium. The surface temperature of the Sun is 5800 K. The visible granulation pattern is evidence for convective energy transport.
The chromosphere	Flash spectra show emission lines due to highly ionized elements. Temperatures inferred from the spectra are hundreds of thousands of Kelvins.
The corona	Emission lines indicate temperatures of millions of Kelvins. The corona is visible during total solar eclipses. The solar wind escapes through coronal holes.

REVIEW QUESTIONS

1. What makes the Sun so important to astronomers?

2. Describe the Sun's photosphere, chromosphere, and corona.

3. Compare the Sun's chemical composition to that of the major planets in the solar system.

4. Suppose the Sun's temperature suddenly dropped to 95% of its current value. How would that affect the power (amount of energy per second) received by Earth? What effect would this likely have on us?

5. Why must the Sun have an energy source other than conventional fuels (such as coal or fuel oil) or gravitational contraction? How does nuclear energy solve this problem?

6. The burning of fossil fuels releases chemical energy. By what mechanism does the proton-proton chain produce energy? For about how long should this fuel last in the Sun?

7. Why are such high temperatures required for the proton-proton chain to be operative?

8. Discuss the chemical composition of the Sun as a function of distance from its center. Why are the changes in the composition of the core not communicated to the photosphere? Can we *directly* determine the composition of the Sun's core? Explain your answer.

9. Explain what is meant when it is said that *the Sun rotates differentially*. What is the most obvious consequence of this differential rotation?

10. Explain the properties of the sunspot cycle as demonstrated by the butterfly diagram. What other phenomena do we associate with sunspots?

11. Where do the absorption lines in the spectrum of the Sun originate? What parts of the Sun produce emission spectra?

12. What different conditions are responsible for the absorption and emission spectra produced by the Sun? (See question 11.) Which of these two distinct spectra do we normally observe?

13. Distinguish between quiescent prominences, eruptive prominences, and solar flares.

FOR FURTHER READING

Enslie, A. G. 1987. Explosions in the solar atmosphere. *Astronomy*, Nov., 18.

Giampapa, M. S. 1987. The Sun-stellar connection. *Sky & Telescope*, Aug., 142.

Harvey, J. W., J. R. Kennedy, and J. W. Leibacher. 1987. GONG: To see inside our Sun. *Sky & Telescope*, Nov., 470.

Kanipe, J., R. Ralcott, and R. Burnham. 1988. The rise and fall of the Sun's activites. *Astronomy*, Oct., 22.

Livingsten, W., O. Engvold, and E. Jensen. 1987. Old and new views of solar prominences. *Astronomy*, July, 18.

McIntosh, P. S., and H. Leinbach. 1988. Watching the premier star. *Sky & Telescope*, Nov., 468.

Paresce, F., and S. Bowyer. 1986. The Sun and the interstellar medium. *Scientific American*, Sept., 92.

Schaefer, B. E. 1988. The astrophysics of suntanning. *Sky & Telescope*, June, 595.

Williams, G. E. 1986. The solar cycle in Precambrian time. *Scientific American*, Aug., 88.

ASTROPROBE 12

Sun-Earth Connec-tions

Scientists have reached the conclusion that the long-term variability of solar radiation can affect the Earth's climate. To a lesser extent, they have linked transient events on the Sun to short-term changes in the Earth's weather. The term **climate** refers to the average state, or condition, of the atmosphere considered over long periods of time, while **weather** refers to the condition of the atmosphere at any particular time and place. Changes in the atmosphere and their effects can be nearly imperceptible and even go unnoticed for years. For example, the acidity of lakes and streams slowly increased over the last few decades as more and more pollutants spilled into the Earth's atmosphere and fell as rain (Figure 12A.1). Only recently has the magnitude of this change been realized. Acid rain is an example of an artificially created change caused by human activity. Natural climatic changes can be short term, such as a persistent drought or a series of severely cold winters (Figure 12A.2), or long lasting, such as an ice age. Climatic changes have happened in the past, are happening now, and will occur in the future.

SUN-CLIMATE CORRELATIONS

One of the first scientists to notice a possible Sun-Earth connection was the astronomer William Herschel (1738–1822). In 1801 he sug-

FIGURE 12A.1

Acid Rain

The solid marble figure outside the Field Museum of Natural History in Chicago shows the effects of acid rain over several decades. The photograph on the left was taken in January 1967 and the one on the right in June 1981.

SOURCE: Photograph at left, Field Museum of Natural History (negative number GN80924), Chicago. Photograph at right, Field Museum of Natural History (transparency number GN83213c), Chicago.

gested that the price of wheat in London was "controlled" by sunspots. Herschel observed that less rain fell in England when few sunspots were visible. Since less rain resulted in poor crop yields, the price of wheat rose with the short supply. Ever since Herschel's observation, scientists have been looking closely for possible influences of the Sun on the Earth's climate and weather.

Some long-term extremes in climate have been attributed to solar activity. AstroProbe 5 described the "Little Ice Age" (A.D. 1430–1850) as a period of generally cold climate, especially during winter in the Northern Hemisphere. This was a time when glaciers in the Alps, Scandinavia, and Iceland increased in size; winters were long and severe; and farming at very northern latitudes became impossible. During this frigid age, two very extended cold periods occurred: one near the beginning of the sixteenth century (1510–1520) and the other near the end of the seventeenth century (1670–1690). At the same time, solar activity, as measured by sunspot numbers, was at a minimum (Figure 12A.3). The Maunder Minimum (1645–1715) and the Spörer Minimum (1460–1550) shown in Figure 12A.3 coincided with the coldest periods of the Little Ice Age.

The estimates for sunspot numbers before 1600 shown in Figure 12A.3 derive from a relationship between the number of sunspots, the intensity of cosmic rays, and the abundance of radioactive carbon (^{14}C) rather than from actual counts of the number of sunspots. Cosmic rays are charged particles that originate in the Galaxy and arrive at the Earth from all directions. Solar activity appears to modulate cosmic ray intensity; it is lowest at sunspot maximum and highest at sunspot minimum. Cosmic rays produce ^{14}C, the radioactive isotope of carbon, by atomic collisions with atmospheric nitrogen-14. The isotope is assimilated in plants and trees in the form of carbon dioxide (CO_2) and decays with a half-life of 5700 years (see Chapter 4 for more on radioactivity). In a year of sunspot maximum

■ FIGURE 12A.2

Winter Storm

Winter storms cause damage to tree limbs and power lines.

SOURCE: A. J. Copley/Visuals Unlimited.

■ FIGURE 12A.3

The Little Ice Age

Shown here are sunspot numbers and temperatures during the Little Ice Age. The upper curve gives temperature values for London and Paris. The lower curve is an estimate of sunspot numbers based on a relationship between sunspot numbers, cosmic ray intensity, and radioactive carbon-14 abundance.

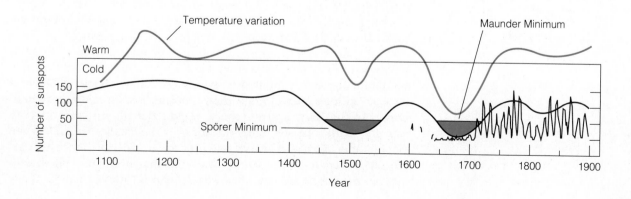

and few cosmic rays, relatively less ^{14}C is assimilated by plants compared to a year of sunspot minimum. Scientists use the carbon content measured in tree rings as an indication of the year-to-year variation of the radioactive carbon abundance in the atmosphere. Since this correlates with the number of sunspots, analysis of tree rings gives an estimate of variations in sunspot numbers in the past.

Terrestrial events can also influence climate. The year 1816, near the end of the Little Ice Age, was known as "the year without summer." In North America that year, snow fell in June and killing frosts came in July and August! The following winter was one of the most severe on record. In 1815, just prior to this cold winter, a large volcano, named Tamboro, erupted in Java. The dust from the eruption stayed in the atmosphere for a large part of a year. This could account for the cold weather in 1816 because the dust would reflect some sunlight, resulting in less heating of the Earth's surface. Perhaps the effects of the volcano were amplified by the already cold climate of the Little Ice Age.

Another possible Sun-Earth connection is that droughts in the High Plains of the United States appear to have been in phase with the solar cycle for the last 170 years. Droughts have occurred just after a sunspot minimum every 20 to 22 years since 1815. The sunspot minima in question are those in which the magnetic polarity of the leading sunspot in sunspot groups in the northern hemisphere of the Sun is a south pole. Figure 12A.4 shows how the sunspot cycle can be represented as a 22-year cycle by plotting the sunspot numbers as negative when the polarity of the Sun's northern hemisphere is a south pole and positive when it is a north pole. Figure 12A.5 shows the correlation between sunspot minima and the occurrence of drought, using the 22-year representation of the sunspot cycle. The last drought in this cycle occurred in 1976. About half the normal amount of rainfall fell during that drought in the Corn Belt of the United States. At the same time, England and continental Europe suffered their most severe drought in over a hundred years (Figure 12A.6). The prediction, of course, is that the next major drought associated with the solar cycle will occur in the late 1990s.

In the late 1980s, however, the United States suffered a drought. This was clearly out of phase with the 22-year sunspot cycle. It may be another example in which events on Earth appear to have a stronger influence on climate than the Sun. Recent computer simulations of the Earth's atmosphere suggest that the drought in 1988 was due to unusual sea temperatures over the Pacific Ocean between Hawaii and Mexico. A warm patch of air disturbed the Earth's atmospheric circulation in such a way that the jet stream, which usually lies over the United States, was displaced toward Canada. Since

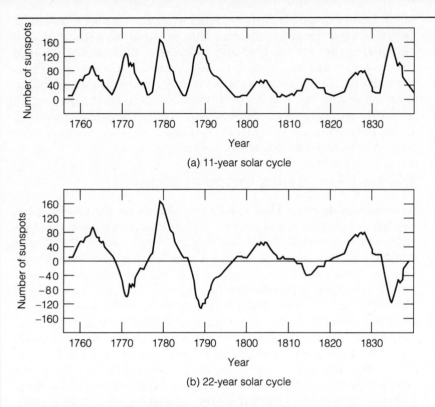

(a) 11-year solar cycle

(b) 22-year solar cycle

■ FIGURE 12A.4

The 22-Year Sunspot Cycle

(a) The 11-year solar sunspot cycle. *(b)* The 22-year solar cycle. The curve above the 0-line in Panel b indicates the 11-year cycles in which the northern hemisphere of the Sun had a north polarity; the curve below the 0-line indicates those in which the northern hemisphere had a south polarity.

rain storms generally follow the jet stream, moisture was deflected to the north away from the United States.

The temperature of the Earth's oceans also appears to follow the sunspot cycle. Sailors have been measuring the temperature of the oceans since 1850. These data suggest that the average temperature

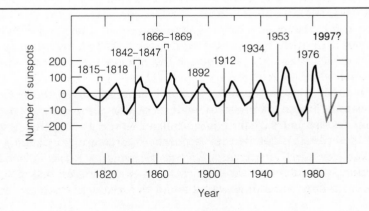

■ FIGURE 12A.5

Drought Cycle

Plotted against the 22-year solar cycle, the vertical lines indicate droughts occurring over the last 170 years. All droughts occurred after a sunspot minimum every 20–22 years.

FIGURE 12A.6

Drought of 1976

This dried-up bed of a reservoir illustrates the effects of the 1976 drought in England.

SOURCE: Keystone Press Agency Inc.

of the Earth's oceans is slightly higher when the number of sunspots during sunspot maxima is large. This occurred between 1835 and 1870 and again between 1945 and the present. During these periods, the average number of sunspots in a year of sunspot maximum reached over a 100—over 200 in the late 1950s—while the number of sunspots during maxima between these episodes stayed below 100. Although the correlation seems real, the temperature change is slight; during the years of high sunspot numbers, ocean temperatures were only as high as 0.6°C above normal.

SUN-WEATHER CORRELATIONS

Less convincing correlations have been proposed for variations in rainfall, temperature, and pressure. These correlations are very statistical in nature in that they are "buried" in the observational data and are therefore very difficult to detect without a lot of data manipulation. For instance, the amount of rainfall seems to correlate with the 11-year solar cycle—not the 22-year cycle. Greater than average rainfall in equatorial latitudes (±20°) tends to occur during periods of solar maxima, but less than average rainfall occurs in middle latitudes (20°–40°). The problem with these correlations is that not all locations show them. In some cases, local geographic features, such as a mountain range, appear to have a greater influence on the weather than solar activity does. These exceptions make it difficult to evaluate any suspected Sun-Earth correlation because at a given latitude some locations will show a correlation while others will not. If a location does not show a correlation, does it mean that local geography controls the weather, or does it imply that no correlation really exists? Annual mean temperatures also show solar-related variations. Surface air temperatures in the southeastern United States, for instance, have recently been studied and exhibit below average temperatures during sunspot maxima, at least since 1952. This correlation only applies to the last few sunspot cycles. What happened in the past? What will happen in the next few cycles? What happened in other parts of the world since 1952? It is too early to tell if this correlation will stand the test of more observations covering a longer period of time.

The annual mean surface pressure, primarily over the oceans, tends to be lower than normal at times of sunspot maxima in equatorial regions but higher than normal in temperate regions. Scientists describe this behavior of atmospheric pressure, particularly at higher elevations, in terms of *planetary standing waves*. Visualize pressure variations as waves with troughs and ridges that do not move, similar to standing waves found in a river downstream from

■ FIGURE 12A.7

Satellite Photograph of a Severe Storm System

SOURCE: Science VU/Visuals Unlimited.

large boulders. Some scientists try to explain planetary standing waves and the associated observed pressure variations in latitude and longitude as induced by solar activity. In particular, it is claimed that particles from the Sun may influence atmospheric pressure. Scientists point out that atmospheric pressure seems to respond within 2 to 4 days to major solar flares.

An even more difficult Sun-weather link to detect is the change in the paths, or tracks, taken by storms. In the Northern Hemisphere, these storm systems travel in a more or less eastward direction (Figure 12A.7). In sunspot maximum years, the east-west storm tracks lie closer to the equator by about 6° in latitude than in sunspot minimum years. At the same time, larger and more intense weather systems (associated with increased storminess and precipitation) also seem to occur in sunspot maximum years.

Explanations of these Sun-weather links hypothesize that somehow the variations in solar activity inject energy into the Earth's atmosphere by particles, bursts of radiation, and magnetic fields. Exactly how this energy is transformed into meteorological phenomena is unknown. Scientists are looking for links between solar activity and meteorological phenomena that may help to explain the interaction. One direct link between the Sun and the Earth is the radiation and particles ejected from the Sun by solar flares. Large solar flares send bursts of visual, ultraviolet, and X-ray radiation and high-speed charged particles to intercept the Earth. The emitted particles are known to be directly responsible for aurorae, the beautiful moving lights seen in northern latitudes, and geomagnetic storms (Figure 12A.8). Perhaps other changes in the upper atmosphere cause changes in the weather at the Earth's surface.

■■■ FIGURE 12A.8

Aurora Borealis or the Northern Lights

SOURCE: Steve McCutcheon/Visuals Unlimited.

The problem with short-term Sun-weather links caused by changes in particle flux or radiation from the Sun is that no acceptable linking mechanism between particles and radiation and the Earth's atmosphere has been identified. In short, no proposed mechanism is believable. This does not mean that there is no mechanism. It is just that scientists always feel uneasy about observations that cannot be explained, especially if the observations are as questionable as some of those mentioned above. Without a physical model as a guide, it is difficult to know which observations are significant and which are not and, therefore, which to include in weather predictions.

■■■SUN-EARTH CONNECTIONS?

Most scientists are willing to accept that there are changes in average atmospheric temperature associated with the sunspot cycle. The amount of solar radiation emitted by the Sun is known to vary during each sunspot cycle. Observers find that the solar constant, the total amount of energy reaching the Earth each second, decreases when sunspot groups cross the face of the Sun. Changes in the amount of radiation that reaches the Earth's surface changes the heat balance on Earth and can influence weather (see AstroProbe 5). Since the number of sunspots varies with an 11-year cycle, it is natural for scientists to look for correlations with sunspot numbers. Recent satellite measurements indicate that the solar constant is decreasing, but only by a small amount—about 0.1% to 0.2% in the last decade. If it occurred for a few decades, this is large enough to change the Earth's average ocean temperature significantly. It may be that a similar decrease in the solar constant during low solar activity, as measured by the number of sunspots, was responsible for the Little Ice Age. A large enough decrease could produce a twentieth-century "little ice age." How large a decrease is large enough is unknown at present.

Although it may appear reasonable to associate long-term Sun-climate change with solar radiation variations linked to the sunspot cycle, some of the observed correlations appear to break down after several solar cycles or apply to one location but not to another. It appears, for instance, that the correlation between sunspot minima and droughts may be changing, which may imply that there is no correlation. It may also suggest that conditions in the Earth's atmosphere slowly change on their own without solar influence on time scales on the order of hundreds of years. Furthermore, the changes in the amount of energy from the Sun due to solar activity are much smaller than the total energy emitted by the Sun. This suggests that the energy fluctuations from solar activity may trigger responses on Earth, indicating complex feedback mechanisms not directly related to the solar cycle. Feedback mechanisms can involve variations in such parameters as the amount of sunlight absorbed or reflected by land, water, ice, and snow; the amount of outgoing infrared radiation from Earth; temperature; precipitation; vertical and horizontal winds; atmospheric circulation; ocean currents; evaporation; and cloud cover. Chemical reactions in the upper atmosphere, for instance, caused by solar radiation and particles could change the ozone abundance or the number of cirrus cloud particles. Both influence atmospheric heating that could lead to changes in temperature, wind speeds, ocean currents, or circulation. Perhaps solar variations produce other unknown effects.

The details of a plausible, realistic physical mechanism explaining all of the observed correlations have not yet emerged. The Earth itself harbors a complex environment in which air, land, and sea interact in a very intricate manner. Solar activity is an outside influence that appears to be able to modulate the Earth's climatic equilibrium. The relationship between the Sun and the Earth's climate and weather is indeed complex, and our understanding of it will require a host of scientists and engineers working in a broad range of disciplines, such as meteorology, climatology, upper atmosphere physics, atmospheric electricity, chemistry, and physics, and using diverse measurements from instruments on Earth and from those carried aloft by balloons, airplanes, rockets, and spacecraft.

The hope, of course, is that we will someday understand the relationship between solar activity and the Earth's climate. The ultimate beneficiary of this understanding will be life on Earth.

Observing
the Stars

OUTLINE

Classification of Stars
Stellar Temperatures
Spectral Classes
The Chemical Composition of Stars

Magnitudes

Colors

Distances to Nearby Stars

Motions of Stars
Doppler Shifts
Proper Motions

Summary

Chapter Capsule

Review Questions

For Further Reading

ASTROPROBE 13:
Observatories and Observing

Globular Cluster.
ARTIST: Kurt C. Burmann.

ASTRONOMERS OF ANTIQUITY analyzed their visual observations of the apparent motions of stars to determine characteristics of the Earth, such as its axial tilt and rotational rate. Today astronomers use spectroscopic observations of these same stars to determine characteristics of the stars themselves. Since the mid-nineteenth century, when absorption lines in the spectrum of the Sun were identified as being due to known terrestrial elements, astronomers have been using detailed analyses of these lines to reveal not only the chemical composition of the Sun and stars but also their surface temperatures.

The first visual observations of stars concentrated on their positions, especially for detailed maps of the sky. Celestial maps divide the sky into 88 regions called *constellations*. Positional work on these stars eventually reached such a high degree of precision that astronomers were able to use standard surveying techniques to determine the distances to the nearest stars. Distances to the stars are not apparent from just looking at stars in the night sky. A star's apparent brightness depends on both its distance from Earth and its intrinsic brightness. Distance estimates showed that most constellation members are at great distances from each other and that their imagined outlines are due just to chance alignment of the stars.

The appearance of constellations also changes over time. Stellar spectra and the analysis of minute stellar motions on the celestial sphere disclose that stars move through space in many directions. These motions also reveal the direction that the Sun is moving in space and are the first hints of the dynamic nature of the universe. Such studies of the motions, temperatures, and chemical compositions of stars are critical steps to understanding their nature.

CLASSIFICATION OF STARS

Scientists are often faced with properties or characteristics of certain objects that vary in ways that they do not understand. Their first step in analyzing these variations is to *classify* the objects. When geologists in the seventeenth and eighteenth centuries were faced with a great variety of rocks, they classified them. They put different kinds of rocks into different "boxes" and eventually labeled the boxes with names, such as quartz, granite, and marble. Naturalists, when confronted with the seemingly infinite variety of life, did the same with insects, birds, fish, and mammals (Figure 13.1). As they learned more about a certain class of objects, such as birds, they subdivided the class. Birds are classified as woodpeckers, flycatchers, swallows, thrushes, and many others. Each of these can be subdivided even further. The robin is an example of a thrush. So are the bluebird, the varied thrush, the northern wheatear, and the several varieties of brown thrushes.

A close inspection of the spectra of stars reveals a variety of types. Some stellar spectra resemble the Sun's spectrum, but many others are very different. When faced with a confusing variety of stellar spectra in the late nineteenth century, astronomers classified them. The first results of stellar classification were the temperatures of stars.

■ FIGURE 13.1

Hawaiian Finches

These Hawaiian finches are grouped, or classified, on the basis of their bill.

SOURCE: Painting by H. Douglass Pratt. Reproduced courtesy of Bishop Museum, Honolulu, Hawaii.

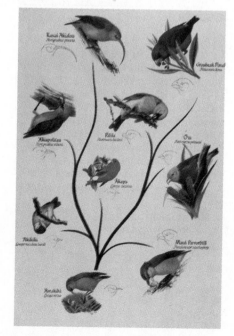

Stellar Temperatures

The chemical composition of the Sun follows from the identification of the chemical elements responsible for the absorption lines in its spectrum. Work done at the Harvard Observatory in the late nineteenth and early twentieth centuries revealed another use of stellar spectra. By arranging stellar spectra on the basis of the appearance of their absorption lines, Annie J. Cannon, a dedicated woman astronomer at the observatory, was able to determine another fundamental characteristic of stars.

Each element in a star's atmosphere can produce a distinct set of absorption lines corresponding to the allowed transitions of its electrons (refer to Chapter 4 for details). Absorption lines show up in the spectrum of a star as reductions in intensity, or dark lines (Panel a in Figure 13.2). Panel b shows a more schematic representation of absorption lines as downward spikes on a Planck curve. The Planck curve shows how many photons pass through the star's atmosphere at each wavelength. It represents the supply of photons from just below the photosphere that can be absorbed by atmospheric atoms. Hot stars, for instance, generate Planck curves with peaks in intensity at short wavelengths; they emit strongly in the ultraviolet part of the spectrum. Cool stars, on the other hand, emit strongly at infrared wavelengths, with little ultraviolet radiation. Consequently, an atom that is only capable of absorbing ultraviolet photons will not produce strong absorption lines in the atmosphere of a cool star.

The surface temperature of a star dictates what absorption lines atmospheric atoms can produce. This controlling influence of temperature can be illustrated by studying the behavior of the hydrogen atom

■ FIGURE 13.2

Absorption Lines

(a) A typical stellar spectrum in which the dark lines represent a reduction in the number of photons reaching the Earth. *(b)* The Planck curve of a star schematically illustrates the effect of absorption lines on the star's energy distribution. The downward spikes represent absorption lines near discrete wavelengths. An emission line is represented as a spike above the Planck curve corresponding to an additional source of photons near that wavelength.

SOURCE: Part (a), Lick Observatory, University of California, Santa Cruz.

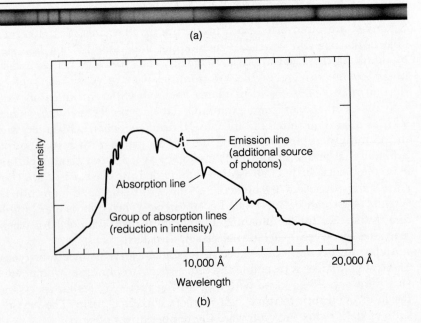

(a)

Emission line
(additional source
of photons)

Absorption line

Group of absorption lines
(reduction in intensity)

Intensity

Wavelength

10,000 Å   20,000 Å

(b)

at different temperatures. The analysis is easy for hydrogen because it is a simple atom, having only a single electron and a single proton. At high temperatures, tens of thousands of Kelvins, a star's Planck curve is dominated by high-energy ultraviolet photons. These photons are energetic enough and exist in large enough quantities to ionize most of the hydrogen atoms in a hot star's atmosphere. Hydrogen, therefore, cannot produce absorption lines in hot stars. At the other extreme, hydrogen cannot produce absorption lines in cool stars with temperatures of a few thousand Kelvins. At these low temperatures the hydrogen electron is in the orbit closest to the nucleus, and only ultraviolet photons can knock that electron into other orbits (see Figure 4.14). Photons emitted from these cool stars are not energetic enough to produce transitions that could result in absorption lines in the visible part of the spectrum. At temperatures in between these extremes, near 10,000 K, the ideal conditions exist for hydrogen atoms to produce absorption lines. Enough energetic photons are available to excite hydrogen atoms and place their electron in the second orbit, and absorption by electrons in this orbit produces lines in the visible part of the spectrum.

Spectral lines of hydrogen and other elements can appear as dark wide lines or lighter narrow lines, as shown in the spectrum in Figure 13.3. Also shown in Figure 13.3 is a portion of a Planck curve with absorption lines, showing "strong" lines and "weak" lines. The terms strong and weak refer to the darkness and widths, or the **strength,** of the lines. Line strength is a measure of how many photons are absorbed at the wavelength of the line. Spectral lines are strong when many atoms that can absorb photons are present; spectral lines are weak when only a few absorbing atoms are present. Of course, spectral lines can

Strength (of spectral lines): A measure of how many photons were absorbed by a certain transition; calculated by measuring the amount of light subtracted from the Planck curve at the wavelengths of the lines.

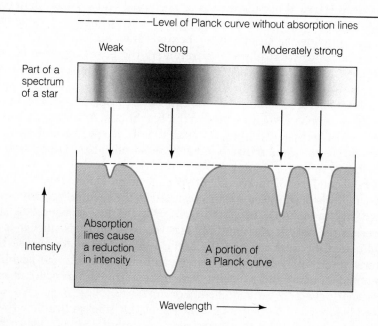

FIGURE 13.3

Line Strengths

■ FIGURE 13.4

Annie J. Cannon

SOURCE: Harvard College Observatory.

Women astronomers at Harvard Observatory played an important role in the history of spectral classification. Williamina P. Fleming developed the first classification scheme with classes A through Q. New spectra obtained with better equipment demanded a revision of Fleming's classification; Antonia C. Maury and Annie Cannon did just this. Although we use Cannon's scheme today, Maury was the first to suggest placing class B before class A and class O before class B. It is interesting to note that a reclassification of the original Harvard spectral types is currently being done by another woman astronomer—Nancy Houk of the University of Michigan.

Here are a few acronyms to help you remember the spectral sequence O, B, A, F, G, K, M:

Oh **B**e **A** **F**ine **G**irl **K**iss **M**e.

Oh **B**e **A** **F**ine **G**uy **K**iss **M**e.

Oh **B**oy **A**n **F** **G**rade **K**ills **M**e.

Old **B**oys **A**fter **F**orty **G**et **K**inda Mellow.

Our **B**est **A**stronomers **F**eel **G**ood Knowing **M**ore.

only be produced when an element is present in the atmosphere and will be stronger if more of that element is present.

When hydrogen lines are present, their appearance varies from spectrum to spectrum. Hydrogen makes its maximum contribution to a star's absorption spectrum in stars with temperatures of about 10,000 K. At higher and lower temperatures, hydrogen's contribution to the absorption of photons decreases, and its lines become weaker, even though the amount of hydrogen is roughly equal from star to star. Other elements behave in a similar fashion, but the temperature of their maximum contribution, or strongest lines, will differ. Helium, for instance, does not produce spectral lines in the visible part of the spectrum at temperatures below about 10,000 K. Neutral iron, on the other hand, produces many lines at low temperatures. Elements with many orbiting electrons, such as iron and calcium, also contribute absorption lines from their ionized states. Each element and ion have a characteristic temperature at which they are most effective in producing absorption lines.

This was not obvious, however, to astronomers at the end of the last century when they began to accumulate spectra of stars in both the Northern and Southern Hemispheres. In 1897 Annie J. Cannon (1863–1941) began to classify the spectra of southern stars taken by Harvard astronomers at their southern observing station in Arequipa, Peru (Figure 13.4). She published a catalog of 1122 stellar spectra arranged according to temperature; her scheme still forms the basis of the spectral classification of stars.

Spectral Classes

By 1890, just prior to Cannon's work, several thousand stellar spectra studied by Harvard astronomers were grouped and assigned letters of the alphabet from A to Q. This assignment was arbitrary; astronomers were just putting the spectra into "boxes." They did not know what to call the boxes or what physical parameters the boxes represented. For example, the spectra placed in the box A were dominated by strong hydrogen lines, and the K line of calcium was very prevalent. The spectra in box B showed neutral helium lines in addition to weak hydrogen lines. Some spectra, such as that of the bright star Arcturus, had more than 500 visible spectral lines. Comparison of the spectrum of Arcturus with that of the Sun showed remarkable similarities. Other spectra, however, were very different.

Careful analysis of thousands of spectra taken before 1896 and Cannon's analysis of southern spectra resulted in the spectral sequence published by Cannon: **O, B, A, F, G, K, M.** In this sequence, O stars represent the hottest stars and M stars the coolest. The sequence is not alphabetical because most of the early designations made before 1890 did not stand up to the test of better equipment. Details and peculiarities noted on many early spectra were not confirmed. The order of some classes also had to be switched. For instance, class B spectra were placed before class A spectra because the visible lines indicated a higher temperature, and class O spectra were eventually placed before both

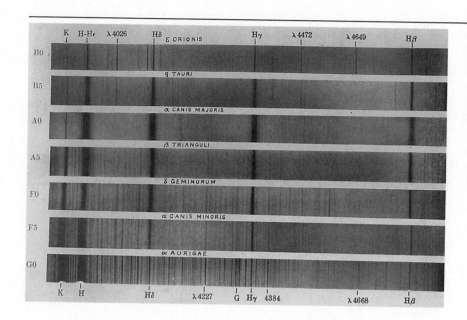

FIGURE 13.5

The Spectral Sequence

The strength of absorption lines determines the arrangement of the spectra shown here. Hottest stars are at the top and show few spectral lines. The coolest stars exhibit a profusion of lines due to metals. The three lines, H_β, H_γ, and H_δ, are due to hydrogen, and lines labeled H and K are calcium lines.

SOURCE: Royal Astronomical Society.

classes B and A. In other words, astronomers did not rename the boxes; they just moved the boxes around or eliminated boxes by placing the contents of one box into another. Using this scheme, Cannon and her colleagues at Harvard classified nearly 400,000 stars; Cannon herself classified about 5,000 stars a month between 1911 and 1915! Her classification scheme still remains the international standard.

Figure 13.5 shows part of the spectral sequence. Astronomers generally refer to hot stars, such as O, B, and A stars, as "early-type" stars and those closer to the cool end of the sequence, such as G, K, and M stars, as "late-type" stars. The terms "early" and "late" are holdovers from the erroneous idea that stars changed from O stars to M stars by cooling as they aged. Furthermore, each spectral class is divided into 10 subdivisions labeled 0 to 9, such as B0, B1, B2, . . . B7, B8, B9. The terms early and late are also applied to the subdivisions. A B1 star is called an early B star while a B8 is called a late B star.

The behavior of atomic transitions allows astronomers to assign temperatures to each spectral class and its subdivisions (Figure 13.6 and Table 13.1). The O stars, for instance, show strong ionized helium lines. These helium lines disappear at late O and are replaced by neutral helium lines. The neutral helium lines are prominent in the B stars while hydrogen lines develop in the late B stars. Hydrogen line strengths then decrease from late A through K stars. Ionized lines from metals, such as calcium, reach maximum strength in late F stars, and lines due to neutral metals, such as iron, begin to develop in F stars and become strong in later type stars. The coolest stars show absorption lines and wide absorption *bands* due to molecules, such as cyanogen (CN) in K stars and titanium oxide (TiO) in M stars.

The beauty of stellar spectra is that the temperature of a star can be ascertained just by careful visual inspection of its spectrum. The temperature signature of a star is written in the absorption lines of its in-

TABLE 13.1
Temperatures of Spectral Classes

Spectral Class	Temperature Range (K)
O	>30,000
B	10,000–30,000
A	7000–10,000
F	6000–7000
G	5000–6000
K	3500–5000
M	<3500

■ FIGURE 13.6

Strength of Absorption Lines

Relative line strengths are shown as a function of spectral type (lower axis) and temperature (upper axis). Each element has a characteristic temperature at which its absorption lines are strongest (highest point on the curves).

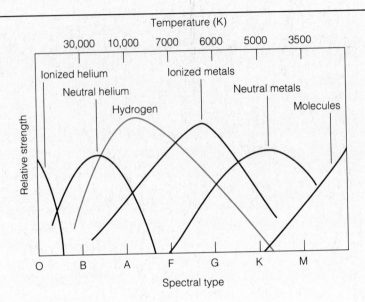

dividual elements. The classification sequence O, B, A, F, G, K, M is a temperature sequence from hot stars to cool stars. Since spectra also contain the signatures of individual elements, spectra are used for measuring the chemical composition of stars as well.

The Chemical Composition of Stars

Spectra of stars generally show the same lines as the spectrum of the Sun. Astronomers cannot assume, however, that other stars have the exact same mixture of elements as the Sun. Most stars consist mainly of hydrogen and helium. The percentage of hydrogen and helium ranges from about 96% to 99.99%. The main difference between stars lies in their *metal* abundance. Astronomers refer to any element more massive than helium as a "metal." The most abundant heavy elements are carbon, nitrogen, oxygen, and neon followed by iron, silicon, magnesium, and sulfur.

Metallicity: The abundance of elements other than hydrogen and helium; these are referred to as the "metals"; astronomers call elements, such as carbon, calcium, iron, nitrogen, and oxygen, metals and designate them collectively by the letter "Z." The metallicity of the Sun is $Z_\odot \approx 0.02$.

The variation in Z, or **metallicity,** from star to star is detected through the relative strengths of their absorption lines. Recall that absorption lines of a certain element are only produced if the conditions in the star's atmosphere are just right. Since the absence or presence of lines is due to a star's temperature or to the absence or presence of elements, the first step in estimating the abundance of an element is to determine the star's temperature. Once this is done, it is possible to concentrate on abundance variations. Figure 13.7 shows a portion of the Planck curves of two stars with the same spectral type, and therefore the same temperature, but with different metallicities. In one star the absorption lines of metals are clearly weaker and produce shallower spikes on the Planck curve. The area of the Planck curve that is missing due to the absorption of photons by a given element is a direct measure of the relative abundances in these two stars.

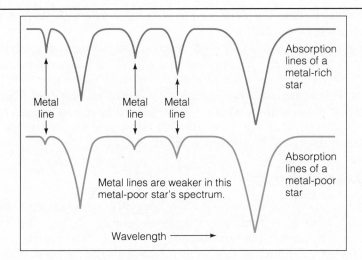

FIGURE 13.7

Metallicity Variations

A section of the Planck curves of two stars with the same temperature but different abundances of metals. The metal-poor star has weaker, or shallower, spikes in the Planck curve due to metals. The two strong lines in each spectra are due to hydrogen and helium, which do not vary greatly from star to star.

When stars are compared to the Sun, astronomers find that most of the stars near the Sun have metallicities from twice solar to about half solar, or from $Z = 0.04$ to 0.01. Stars with metallicities greater than $Z = 0.02$ are called *metal-rich stars*, and those with metallicities smaller than the Sun's are called *metal-poor stars*. Some stars have metallicities less than one-tenth of solar, $Z < 0.002$; they are called *extremely metal-poor stars*. In most cases these atmospheric abundances probably represent the abundance the stars had when they formed; that is, nothing appears to have happened to these stars to reduce or increase the abundance of the metals in their atmospheres.

At the same time, a small minority of stars exhibit very peculiar spectra that indicate more than just an increase or decrease in metallicity. Several types of stars show emission lines in their spectra together with the absorption lines. Observations of the Sun indicate that emission lines originating in the Sun's outer atmosphere can be observed only if the bright photosphere is blocked. The point is that observable emission lines in stars probably originate in thin outer layers. Furthermore, because the photosphere of other stars cannot be blocked out, the observed emissions probably originate in thin shells of gas surrounding the stars. Such shells of gas are observed around stars known to shed, or eject, some of their atmosphere (see Chapter 16). Another group of stars, similar to K and M stars, show unusually strong absorption bands due to *carbon molecules*. These stars are called carbon, or C, stars. Observers also find stars with hydrogen lines that are extremely faint or not visible at all, but their surface temperatures favor the presence of hydrogen lines. In these stars, helium is the most abundant element, so they are called helium stars. Since the abundances of other metals in both carbon stars and helium stars appear normal, the high helium and carbon content at their surfaces suggests that material from the interior somehow reached the surface. (As will be noted in Chapter 16, nuclear reactions inside some stars produce carbon as well as helium.) Perhaps these stars develop deep convection zones that reach to the center to dredge up carbon or helium.

Through the analysis of stellar spectra, astronomers can determine the surface, or effective, temperatures and chemical compositions of stars without any knowledge of their distances. Modern spectral classification is not the only way stars can be classified, however. The very first stellar classification scheme was based on the actual appearance of stars to the eye. Thus the boxes used in this scheme were arranged according to the visual brightness of the stars.

▬MAGNITUDES

Magnitude: A numerical scale for measuring stellar brightness; the larger the magnitude, the fainter the star. Abbreviated "mag." The magnitude scale is a logarithmic scale (see MathTools 1: Graphs and Plots 〈◺〉), allowing us to represent an enormous range of brightness with only a small set of numbers.

On a clear, cold, winter evening away from city lights, diligent observers could, with time and patience, count thousands of stars. They might first count a handful of stars that are very bright and mentally place these bright stars into a "box" representing stars at a certain brightness. Next they might pick out a few dozen stars that were fainter than the first group but still brighter than all of the other stars visible. These would make up a second "box." With the first and second groups of stars counted, it would be harder to count another group because so many would be visible. Nevertheless, this group would be distinctly fainter than groups 1 and 2 but still brighter than the majority of other stars in the sky. Counting all of the visible stars in this way would produce about six or seven brightness groups. In the second century B.C., the Greek astronomer Hipparchus did just this. When he counted the stars, he divided the visible stars into six groups. Astronomers now refer to these groups as **magnitude** groups. The stars in the first group are called first-magnitude stars; those in the second group are called second-magnitude stars, and so on. Hipparchus' faintest group was composed of sixth-magnitude stars. This classification system is still used today and is prevalent in almost all observational astronomy literature, from scientific journals to popular magazines.

The human eye defines the magnitude boxes. The response of the eye is such that a difference in magnitude of 1, say, from first magnitude to second magnitude or from third magnitude to fourth magnitude, is equal to a brightness change, as measured by modern instruments, of a factor of 2.512. This means that a first-magnitude star is 2.512 times brighter than a second-magnitude star. Similarly, a second-magnitude star is 2.512 times brighter than a third-magnitude star. Moreover, a first-magnitude star is 2.512×2.512 or 6.310 times brighter than a third-magnitude star (see Table 13.2). Every magnitude change of 1 corresponds to an increase or decrease by a factor of 2.512 in brightness. The magnitudes assigned to stars based on their appearance are called *apparent magnitudes* and are designated by the letter "*m*." A first-magnitude star has $m = 1$ while a sixth-magnitude star has $m = 6$.

The ratio of brightness b_1/b_2 for two stars, say, star 1 and star 2, can be calculated with the following equation:

$$\frac{b_1}{b_2} = 2.512^{\Delta m}$$

■ TABLE 13.2 **Magnitude Scale**

								Δ Mag	Brightness Ratio
1st mag star is 2.512					times brighter than a	2d mag star		1	2.512
1st " "	2.512 × 2.512		=	6.310	" " "	3d "		2	6.310
1st " "	2.512 × 2.512 × 2.512		=	15.851	" " "	4th "		3	15.851
1st " "	2.512 × 2.512 × 2.512 × 2.512		=	39.818	" " "	5th "		4	39.818
1st " "	2.512 × 2.512 × 2.512 × 2.512 × 2.512	= 100			" " "	6th "		5	100
5th " "	2.512				" " "	6th "		1	2.512
1st " "	100 × 100		=	10^4	" " "	11th "		10	10^4
1st " "	100 × 100 × 2.512		=	2.5×10^4	" " "	12th "		11	2.5×10^4
Brightness Ratios for Other Magnitude Increments									
1st mag star is 1.585					times brighter than a	1.5 mag star		0.5	1.585
1st " "	2				" " "	1.75 "		0.75	2
1st " "	3.981				" " "	2.5 "		1.5	3.981
1st " "	10				" " "	3.5 "		2.5	10
1st " "	25.119				" " "	4.5 "		3.5	25.119
1st " "	251.19				" " "	7.0 "		6.0	251.19

where Δm is the difference in the apparent magnitudes of the stars, $m_2 - m_1$. Scientists often use the symbol "Δ" to represent change in a quantity. This equation was used to calculate the brightness changes in Table 13.2. For example, if $\Delta m = 2$, then

$$\frac{b_1}{b_2} = (2.512)^2 = 2.512 \times 2.512 = 6.31$$

as calculated in the preceding paragraph. Note that the brightest stars have the smallest numeric values for their magnitudes.

Table 13.3 lists the apparent magnitudes of several celestial objects. Notice that stars and planets may have negative magnitudes. The Sun and Moon, for instance, are obviously much brighter than the brightest stars. The necessity for negative magnitudes arises because modern instruments find that some objects are many times brighter than first-magnitude stars on the scale of Hipparchus. Only negative magnitudes can represent the observed brightness ratios. The faintest stars visible to the unaided eye have magnitudes near $m = 6$ or 6.5. Telescopes or binoculars are necessary to view anything fainter than this.

The magnitudes listed in Table 13.3 are close to what the eye would measure. It is possible and extremely useful to filter out some of the light from stars and determine how bright a star appears in blue light and yellow light. Such observations allow astronomers to quantify a star's color.

■COLORS

While most stars appear white to our eyes, a few are definitely yellow-orange. When observers look at pairs of stars with telescopes, they see distinct color differences. Descriptions such as "a splendid gold and green," "a beautiful orange and blue," "a fine topaz and green" are com-

■ TABLE 13.3 **Magnitudes of Common Objects**

Magnitude Scale	Object	Magnitude
-30	Sun	-26.5
-25	Moon	-12.5
-20	Venus (brightest)	- 4
-15	Jupiter and Mars (brightest)	- 2.5
-10	Sirius (star)	- 1.4
- 5	Alpha Centauri (star)	0.0
0	Polaris (North Star)	2.0
5	Naked eye limit	6–6.5
10	Binocular limit	10
15	Pluto	15
20	Largest telescope limit	24
25		
30	Space telescope	28–30

■ **FIGURE 13.8**

Star Colors

The narrow images on the left side of the cones in this multiple-focus photograph of the constellation Orion are the in-focus images. (They appear as lines because the camera did not track, or follow, the stars during the exposure.) The largest ovals on the right side of the cones are the most out of focus images. Most of the bright stars in this picture are blue. The red star Betelgeuse in the upper left is obviously an exception. The pink object near the center is the Orion nebula, a glowing region of hydrogen gas.

SOURCE: David Malin.

mon for pairs of stars seen in the field of view of even a small telescope. Capturing the colors of stars on photographic film is difficult, however. In a properly focused picture of a star field, the bright stars are overexposed and their individual colors are washed out. Consequently, special photographic techniques are needed to record the colors of individual stars. Figure 13.8 shows a multiple-focus view of the constellation Orion. In this picture, varying the focus brings out the colors of both the faint stars and the bright stars. Orange Betelgeuse lies in the upper left and blue-white Rigel is in the lower right. Although the names of the colors are sufficient in everyday life, astronomers need a method of quantifying color.

Individual colors can be isolated through the use of filters. Easter baskets, for instance, are sometimes wrapped in red or yellow cellophane paper. The paper looks red or yellow because it filters out the other colors and allows only red or yellow light to pass through. Panel a in Figure 13.9 shows the location of the visible spectrum, red through violet, on a Planck curve of a star, and Panel b gives the light distribution measured from a star using an idealized blue filter. The wavelengths blocked by blue filters used by astronomers are actually more like that shown in the insert; the filters block most but not all of the radiation at other wavelengths. Astronomers have agreed to denote the magnitude of a star as m_B or just B, if the blue filter allows only light between about 4000 Å and 5000 Å to pass. Another widely used filter is yellow (5000–6000 Å), and the magnitude measured with it is designated m_V, or V, for visual.

The B and V magnitudes are important because they allow astronomers to measure a star's color quickly and accurately. Astronomers de-

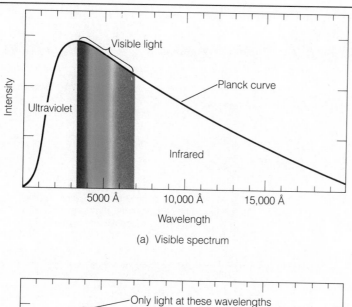

(a) Visible spectrum

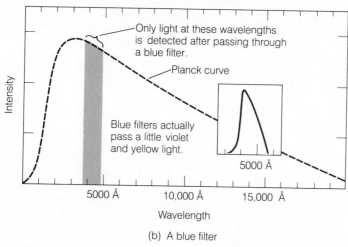

(b) A blue filter

fine the color, or *color index*, of a star as the difference between the B
and V magnitudes, $B - V$. Figure 13.10 shows idealized B and V measurements for two stars. The Planck curves for both stars are shown as
dashed lines. The intensity of light through the B and V filters happens
to be the same for the hot star. This means that the B and V magnitudes
are identical. For the hot star the color index is $B - V = 0.00$. The
Planck curve of the cool star shows that the intensity of light through
the yellow filter is greater than that through the blue filter. Since this
star emits more yellow light than blue light, the yellow intensity is
greater than the blue intensity, and the V magnitude will be numerically *smaller* than the B magnitude. Consequently, the color index of the
cool star will be a number greater than zero. For instance, the color
index of the orange star Betelgeuse, in the constellation Orion, is $B -$
$V = 1.56$; its temperature determined from spectra is about 3000 K. On
the other hand, the star Sirius, in the constellation Canis Major, has a

■■■ FIGURE 13.10

***B* and *V* Measurements for Two Stars**

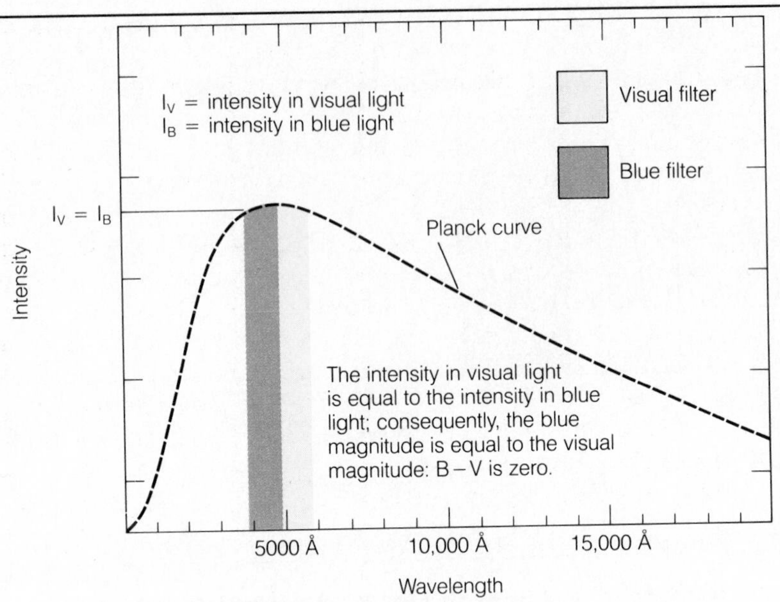

(a) A hot star

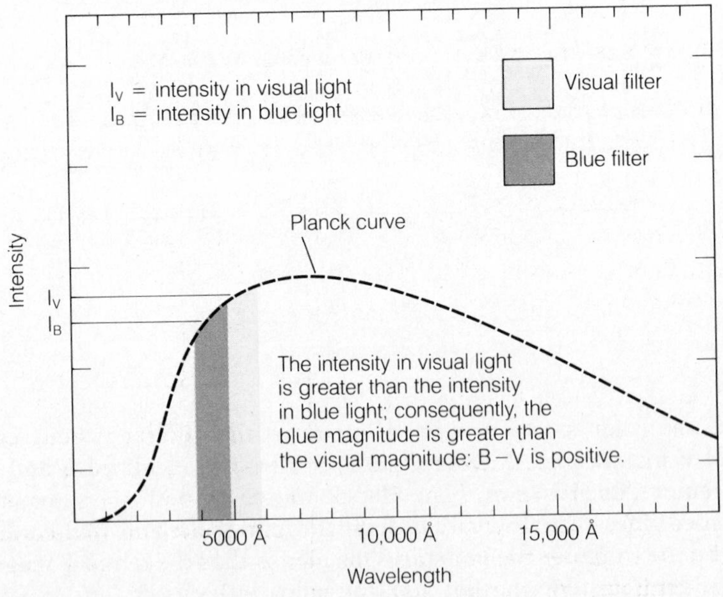

(b) A cool star

color index of $B - V = 0.00$; its temperature as determined from spectra is nearly 10,000 K.

Table 13.4 gives the relationship between spectral type, temperature, and color index. The hottest normal stars, the O stars, have temperatures about 40,000 K, and the coolest M stars register temperatures below 3000 K. The color index ranges from about -0.33 for the hottest stars to about 2.00 for the coolest stars. The sun, a G2 star, has a color index of about 0.6 for its temperature of 5800 K.

The *B* and *V* magnitudes are measurable for the faintest stars visible in the largest telescopes. Photographic measurements illustrate the power of *B* and *V* magnitudes for determining temperatures. Observers often photograph entire star fields with *B* and *V* filters. They then can measure the *B* and *V* magnitudes, and therefore the temperatures, for hundreds of stars at once. This would be a monumental task if astronomers had to take spectra of each individual star to determine its temperature. Nevertheless, it is important to realize that to construct a table showing the relationship between color index and temperature, such as Table 13.4, astronomers had to determine temperatures of many stars using spectra; that is, they had to determine the temperatures of bright stars with spectra and then measure their color index. In doing so, they used spectral classification to *calibrate* the relationship between color index and temperature. Once this relationship is known, observers can measure color indices of stars and thereby obtain their temperatures.

As we have seen, astronomers use spectral classification and magnitudes to determine temperatures and chemical compositions of stars. Before they can determine other physical properties, such as mass, luminosity, and size, however, they must know the distances to stars.

DISTANCES TO NEARBY STARS

Although astronomers have been able to measure the distances to stars only in the last 150 years, the basic technique for doing so has been known for millennia. Egyptian engineers used the technique in building the pyramids, Babylonians used it to build the Hanging Gardens, and civil engineering students walk all over university campuses learning it in their engineering laboratories. The technique involves right triangles—triangles with one angle equal to 90°. Astronomers use right triangles to survey the heavens.

Imagine yourself looking down on the solar system from an alien planetary system circling a distant star. Focus your attention on the Sun and the Earth. How would you describe the motion of the Earth? From this distant viewpoint the Earth would travel around the Sun in a nearly circular orbit; first on one side of the Sun, say, in January, and then on the other side of the Sun six months later in July. Form a right triangle with the base equal to the distance between the Earth and the Sun and with the distant star as the apex (Figure 13.11). The distance between the Sun and the star, *d*, is a line at right angles to the base. This distance is related to the apex angle *p* (Figure 13.12) as follows:

$$d = \frac{360°}{2\pi} \times \frac{1 \text{ AU}}{p}$$

Angle *p* is called the parallactic angle or simply *parallax*. Measured parallaxes are very small, just thousandths of a degree. Consequently, astronomers use a smaller angular measure than a degree. One degree is divided into 60 *minutes of arc* (abbreviated ′), and each minute of arc is

TABLE 13.4 Spectral Type, Temperature, and Color Index Scale

Spectral Type	Temperature (K)	B − V
O5	40,000	−0.33
B0	29,600	−0.29
B5	15,300	−0.16
A0	9,600	0.00
A5	8,200	0.14
F0	7,000	0.33
F5	6,500	0.43
G0	6,000	0.55
G5	5,100	0.88
K0	4,200	1.04
K5	3,900	1.5
M0	3,500	1.6
M5	3,000	1.8

MathTools 2: Angular Measurement

d = distance to star
p = angular separation
of the Sun and Earth
as seen from the star

FIGURE 13.11

Earth's Orbital Motion as Seen from the North Celestial Pole

divided into 60 *seconds of arc* (abbreviated ″). One degree then contains 3600 seconds of arc, or 3600″, so that the factor 360°/2π above becomes 206,265″. Since 360° has been expressed in seconds of arc, the angle p must also be in seconds of arc to maintain the distance units of AU. The above equation for distance simplifies to

$$d = \frac{206{,}265 \text{ AU}}{p''}$$

A star with a parallax of 1″ is 206,265 AU away.

Ask yourself this: If the above observation were made from an even more distant planetary system, how would the observed parallax change? Since the right triangle has a fixed base of 1 AU, the distance between the Sun and the Earth would appear smaller. Consequently, the parallax becomes smaller as the distance from the Earth increases. Furthermore, a star could be so far away that an observer orbiting around it could not see the Earth move around the Sun. In this case, the parallax could not be measured and, therefore, the distance to Earth would be indeterminable.

Ask yourself another question: If you were on Earth observing the distant star, how would you describe its apparent motion caused by the Earth's orbital motion? You can answer this question with your thumb. Extend your arm in front of you with your thumb pointing up. Now blink one eye, then the other. Your thumb will appear to move back and forth. Bring your thumb closer to your eyes and it will appear to move a greater distance back and forth as you blink. Your thumb *appears* to move because the background against which you view your thumb shifts slightly. That is, the right eye views the wall beyond your thumb from a slightly different perspective than the left eye. Mentally replace your eyes with the Earth's January and July positions and your thumb with a distant star. The distant star will appear to move back and forth as the Earth orbits the Sun. This apparent motion of a nearby star is viewed against stars so distant that their apparent motion can-

FIGURE 13.12

Angular Measure

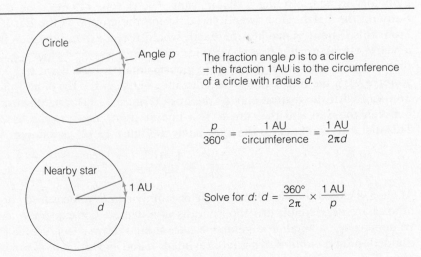

not be detected. It is as if you did the thumb-blink experiment with someone else's thumb across the room; you would be unable to detect any apparent motion. The apparent motion of nearby stars is called **stellar parallax.**

To determine the distance to a nearby star, astronomers need to measure the small parallactic angle. This means that astronomers must record a star's position in the sky relative to the background stars at least twice a year. One way to do this is to take photographs six months apart. Inspecting the photographs will reveal that a nearby star moves relative to other, more distant stars in the picture. It is a straightforward, but not an easy, job to measure how far the star moved between photographs. Almost simultaneously, three astronomers measured the first stellar parallaxes, not with photographs but at the telescope eyepiece (Table 13.5). These astronomers used an instrument called a *micrometer* to measure the distance, as seen in the eyepiece, between the star suspected of being nearby and the other stars in the field of view. As Table 13.5 indicates, parallax angles are small. In fact, the largest parallax ever observed is for Alpha Centauri, and it is only 0".76, or 4737 times smaller than a degree. How far away is Alpha Centauri? Its distance is simply

$$d = \frac{206,265}{p''}\text{AU} = \frac{206,265}{0".76}\text{AU} = 271,400 \text{ AU}$$

Consider traveling to Alpha Centauri on a spaceship traveling at the same speed as the *Voyager* spacecrafts, ~60,000 MPH. The trip to Alpha Centauri would take about 50,000 years. This is the closest star to the Sun!

The distance to Alpha Centauri can also be described in terms of time. This is often done in everyday life. For instance, we normally describe a trip to the airport by how long it will take rather than by the distance. Long-distance travel, such as a trip home for the holidays, is also described in terms of how many hours or days it takes to drive. Implicit in these time estimates are assumptions about driving speeds. Driving to the airport probably means city or expressway driving conditions, and long-distance trips probably mean an average speed near 50 MPH, or sometimes higher! In describing distances to stars in terms of travel times, it is convenient to assume a speed equal to the speed of light and to describe distances in terms of how far light travels in one year. This distance is called the *light-year* and equals 9.4×10^{12} km. Since 1 AU is 1.5×10^8 km, the distance to Alpha Centauri is 4.3 light-years; that is, traveling at the speed of light, it would take 4 years 2 months and about 20 days to reach the Alpha Centauri star system.

Stellar parallax: The apparent motion of stars caused by the Earth's motion around the Sun; the term *parallax* is also used to denote the angle (angle *p* in Figure 13.11) subtended by 1 AU at the distance of the star.

■■■ TABLE 13.5 **The First Parallax Measurements**

Astronomer	Year	Star	Reported Parallax	Actual Parallax
Bessel	1838	61 Cygni	0".31	0".31
Henderson	1839	Alpha Centauri	0".91	0".76
von Struve	1840	Vega	0".29	0".13

Parsec: A unit of distance used in astronomy; the distance (3.26 light-years) to a star that has a parallax of 1 second of arc.

Astronomers have replaced the light-year with another yardstick. Suppose a star has a parallax of exactly 1″. Its distance would be 206,265 AU, or 3.1×10^{13} km, or 3.26 light-years. Astronomers use this as a fundamental unit of distance and call it a **parsec.** The term parsec is an abbreviation of a "**par**allax of 1 **sec**ond of arc" and is written as "pc." Using this unit simplifies the mathematics of calculating distances. The distance equation reverts to

$$d = \frac{1}{p} \, \text{pc}$$

where p is measured in seconds of arc and d is obtained in parsecs. The distance to Alpha Centauri becomes 1/0.76 = 1.3 pc.

The smallest parallax angle astronomers are able to measure accurately is about 0″.01, which corresponds to a distance of 100 pc. Is this very far? As far as travel time is concerned, this distance corresponds to several hundred years even traveling at the speed of light. The vast distances between stars leaves very little room for optimism for travel between stars. One hundred parsecs is just the stellar neighborhood; the center of the Galaxy is over 8000 pc away and the nearest galaxies are over 50,000 pc away (see Chapters 17 and 18). Parallax measurements clearly can be done for only the Sun's neighbors in space. But such measurements are the foundation upon which astronomers determine the scale of the universe.

MOTIONS OF STARS

The motions of the stars that observers have studied since antiquity are reflections of the Earth's revolution and rotation. Real motions of stars are another matter. Some stars are moving toward us while others are moving away from us; some are moving parallel to us while still others are moving across our line of sight. An infinite number of combinations of these directions are possible. Sorting out stellar motions reveals the direction in space that the Sun is moving and is necessary for understanding the dynamic state of the Galaxy.

Doppler Shifts

The detection of stellar motions directed toward or away from the Earth requires measuring minute shifts in the wavelengths of light emitted by stars. A useful analogy involves the changes in sound from a moving train. Sound is made up of compressional waves, which, among other things, cause our eardrums to vibrate. The mind interprets these vibrations as sound. The pitch of a sound is the number of sound waves hitting our eardrums each second. The shorter the wavelength of the sound waves, or the more waves that strike our eardrums each second, the higher the pitch of the sound.

Now imagine standing on a train platform. You would hear a sound of a certain pitch from a horn of a stationary train in the train yard. When the train moves toward you, the sound waves would appear bunched closer together because successive sound waves are emitted by a horn that is closer and closer to you (see Figure 13.13). As a result, the sound from a train moving toward you would be at a higher pitch than that from a stationary train. In the opposite direction of the train's motion, the sound waves would be slightly farther apart than when the train was stationary because the horn is emitting waves as it moves away from that direction. If the train passed by, you would hear a lower pitch than that from the stationary train. This is the experience of anyone who has stopped at a railroad crossing. As a train passes through, the pitch of its horn lowers. Consider one other situation. Imagine yourself at the center of a circular track on which trains always move perpendicular to your line of sight. If a train sounds its horn as it circles, you would hear only a single tone that has the same pitch as that emitted by a stationary train. That is, sound waves do not bunch or spread apart in a direction perpendicular to the motion.

Now substitute a spectrograph for your ears and a star emitting light for a train sounding its horn. The change in pitch of a train's horn corresponds to a change in the color of a star. The color change is imperceptible to the eye, but astronomers can detect the change in a star's

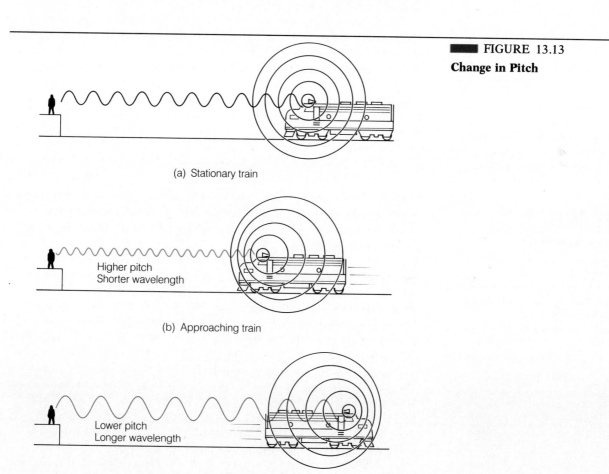

■ FIGURE 13.13

Change in Pitch

(a) Stationary train

Higher pitch
Shorter wavelength

(b) Approaching train

Lower pitch
Longer wavelength

(c) Departing train

spectrum. The wavelengths of light from a star heading toward the Earth are shifted to shorter wavelengths because they are bunched slightly together. This is a shift toward the blue part of the spectrum and is called a *blueshift*. The shift is toward the longer wavelengths, a *redshift*, for stars moving away from the Earth. For example, if an absorption line due to neutral calcium, which normally has a wavelength of 4426 Å, is shifted to a wavelength of 4426.2 Å, it must be moving away from us because the shift is toward longer wavelengths. The shifts in spectral lines due to a star's motion are called **Doppler shifts.**

Measuring a Doppler shift is not very difficult but requires a source of spectral lines that is not moving relative to the telescope. Whenever astronomers take a spectrum of a star, they also take a *comparison spectrum* of an element that produces many lines. The spectrograph has a source of light, usually an iron arc lamp, that produces emission lines. These are exposed just above and below the star's spectrum (Figure 13.14). Since the wavelengths of all of the iron lines are known precisely, the wavelengths of the lines in the star's spectrum can be calculated from comparing their locations with those of the iron lines. Because the comparison lines do not suffer from any stellar Doppler shift, they act as a stationary reference.

The Doppler shift depends only on the speed of the star producing the spectral lines. The faster a star is moving toward us, the more squeezed its spectral lines become in our direction. The Doppler shift is usually denoted by $\Delta\lambda$ (λ is the Greek letter lambda). If λ_0 equals the wavelength of a line when it is at rest and λ equals the measured wavelength in the spectrum of the moving star, then the Doppler shift is $\Delta\lambda = \lambda - \lambda_0$. The relationship between the Doppler shift and velocity is very simple:

$$\text{velocity} = \frac{\Delta\lambda}{\lambda_0} c$$

where c is the speed of light. The velocity is negative when the observed star is moving toward us; in this case, the observed wavelength of a line is shifted to values smaller than λ_0, making $\Delta\lambda$ negative. In the example above, $\Delta\lambda = 4426.2$ Å $- 4426$ Å $= 0.2$ Å and $\Delta\lambda/\lambda_0 = 0.2$ Å$/4426$ Å $= 4.5 \times 10^{-5}$. The velocity is then $+13.5$ km/s (30,240 MPH) away from us. Stellar velocities determined from Doppler shifts are called **radial velocities,** referring to the motion of the star radially away from or toward us.

It is very unlikely that a star would be moving directly toward or directly away from the Earth. It is probably also moving across our line

---

Doppler shift: The apparent change in the wavelength of radiation from a source due to the relative radial motion of the observer and the source.

Blueshift: motion toward the observer
Redshift: motion away from the observer

Radial velocity: The component of a star's velocity directed away from or toward the observer along the line of sight; measured from spectra using the Doppler shift of the spectral lines.

■■■ FIGURE 13.14

Calibration Spectrum

The spectrum of a star is sandwiched between spectra of iron. Since iron lines are emission lines of known wavelengths they permit the measurement of the wavelengths of the stellar lines.

SOURCE: Mount Wilson and Palomar Observatories.

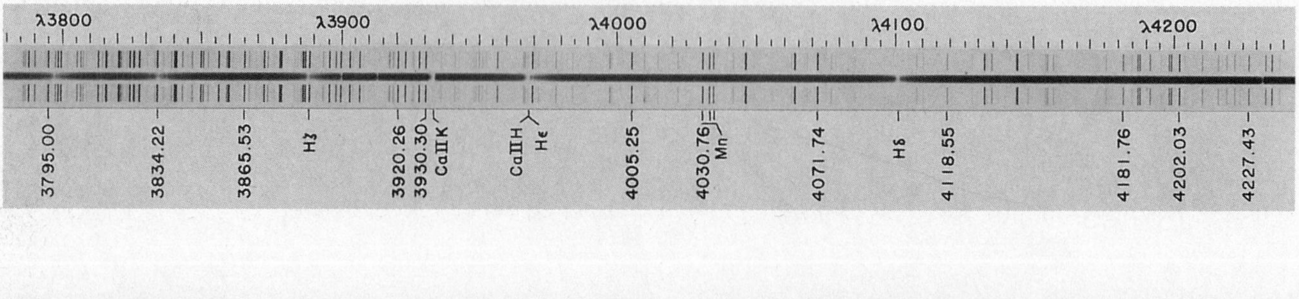

λ3800   λ3900   λ4000   λ4100   λ4200

3795.00 3834.22 3865.53 Hζ 3920.26 3930.30 CaIIK CaIIH He 4005.25 4030.76 Mn 4071.74 Hδ 4118.55 4181.76 4202.03 4227.43

of sight. Since spectra cannot detect this motion, astronomers must look carefully at changes in the positions of stars on the sky.

Proper Motions

Imagine jaywalking near a street corner, as shown in Figure 13.15. An alert policeman behind you realizes that your walking diagonally across the street is motion both away from him and across his line of sight. He could visualize your motion in two parts, or *components*. The component of motion away from him is a *radial motion;* the component of motion across his line of sight is a *tangential motion,* since the motion is tangent to his line of sight. In fact, if you crossed the street properly, you would have first walked to the corner, a radial motion, turned right, and crossed the street, a tangential motion. These are the components of jaywalking. Since both methods of crossing give the same result because they have the same starting and ending locations, they form a right triangle if the street blocks are perpendicular to each other.

Similarly, real stars may be moving in both radial and tangential directions at the same time. Astronomers do not have a method of directly measuring the true motion of a star in space. They can measure the radial component using Doppler shifts. In some cases, the tangential component can also be measured.

To obtain the tangential motion, astronomers must patiently watch stars move across the sky. The apparent motion of stars across our line of sight is called **proper motion** and is measured in seconds of arc per year ("/yr). Proper motion is determined by measuring the change in a star's position on two different photographs taken at two different times. Photographs taken exactly a year apart will eliminate any confusion between proper motion and parallax. This is why proper motion is defined in seconds of arc per year. The largest proper motion ever measured is 10.25 "/yr for the star called Barnard's star (Figure 13.16). Only several hundred stars show proper motions of more than 1"/yr. Most stars, however, are so far away that it would take centuries to

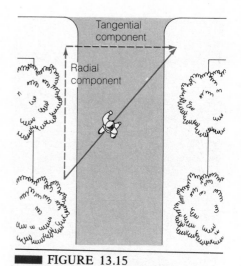

■ FIGURE 13.15
Tangential and Radial Motion

Proper motion: Annual motion of a star on the celestial sphere; measured in "/yr.

■ FIGURE 13.16
Proper Motion of Barnard's Star

These photographs were taken 10 years apart and show the change in position of Barnard's star during this period.

SOURCE: Lick Observatory, University of California, Santa Cruz.

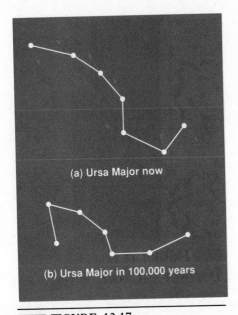

(a) Ursa Major now

(b) Ursa Major in 100,000 years

▬▬ FIGURE 13.17

**Proper Motion of the Stars
of the Big Dipper**

The arrows indicate the direction and
magnitude of measured proper motions.
Panel b shows the shape of Ursa Major
about 100,000 years from now.

Space velocity: The speed and direction of a star in space relative to the
Sun.

measure their proper motions. Even nearby stars have proper motions
so small that they require decades to measure accurately.

Figure 13.17 shows the proper motions of several stars of the constellation Ursa Major called the "Big Dipper." The direction of the arrow
at each star indicates the direction of the star's proper motion. The
length of the arrows indicates the magnitude of the proper motion. In a
few thousand years, the familiar shape of the Big Dipper will no longer
be recognizable.

When a star's radial velocity and its proper motion are known, astronomers are almost in a position to determine its actual speed and
direction of motion in space. Although proper motion depends on both
speed and the direction the star is moving relative to the Sun, it also
depends on the distance to the star. Consider two stars moving tangentially across our line of sight at the same speed. If one star is twice as
far away as the other, which one would show the larger proper motion?
The nearer star would appear to move a greater distance across our line
of sight in the same time interval and, therefore, exhibit the larger
proper motion (Panel a in Figure 13.18). Consequently, before astronomers can interpret a proper motion as a velocity, they must know the
star's distance. Once the distance to a star is known and its proper motion calculated, astronomers can calculate its velocity perpendicular to
our line of sight. This velocity is called the **tangential velocity.**

With both components of velocity known, the actual speed and direction of the star can be calculated. The tangential and radial components
represent two sides of a right triangle. The radial velocity will determine if the triangle is pointing toward or away from us, and the tangential velocity will give the direction of the motion on the sky. The hypotenuse of the triangle formed with the radial and tangential velocities
is the actual motion, or **space velocity,** of the star (Panel b). It gives the
direction and magnitude of the motion of the star—the space velocity
tells us where the star is going.

▬▬ FIGURE 13.18

Proper Motion and Distance

(*a*) Both stars move tangentially with the
same speed. One star is twice as far away
as the other. The nearer star exhibits the
greater proper motion. (*b*) The space velocity represents the actual speed and direction of travel of a star.

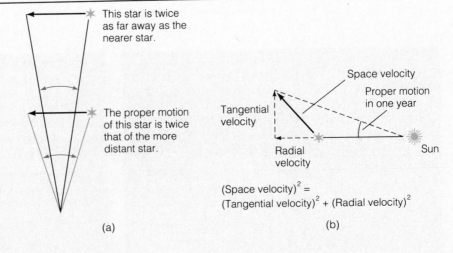

This star is twice
as far away as the
nearer star.

The proper motion
of this star is twice
that of the more
distant star.

Space velocity

Proper motion
in one year

Tangential
velocity

Radial
velocity

Sun

$$(\text{Space velocity})^2 = (\text{Tangential velocity})^2 + (\text{Radial velocity})^2$$

(a)   (b)

Astronomers have determined space velocities of hundreds of stars all over the sky. Imagine for the moment the Sun moving through space in a certain direction. Stars in its direction of motion would tend to show blueshifts. Stars on the opposite side of the sky, in the direction the Sun is coming from, will tend to show redshifts. And stars on either side will tend, as a group, to show proper motions in the direction opposite the Sun's motion. A similar streaming effect is experienced in a fast speedboat moving through a fleet of slow sailboats. When astronomers analyze radial velocities and proper motions of nearby stars, they find that the Sun is heading toward the bright star Vega near the boundary of the constellations of Lyra and Hercules (Figure 13.19).

What about the other stars? Where are they headed? Motions of individual nearby stars appear to be random, with stars moving in every direction. On a grander scale, the motions of stars follow a pattern. As will be shown in Chapter 17, this motion is part of a great rotation about the center of the Galaxy.

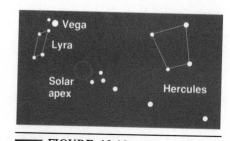

FIGURE 13.19

The Direction of the Sun's Motion in Space

This is where we are headed.

SUMMARY

The spectral classes O, B, A, F, G, K, M represent an ordering of stars in terms of their surface temperatures. The criteria for spectral classification are the presence and strengths of absorption lines in the visible part of the spectrum. The appearance of stellar lines depends primarily on temperature. Temperature determines the distribution of photons at different wavelengths, which controls how many atmospheric atoms are excited or ionized. This in turn determines the number and strengths of absorption lines. Since the appearance of spectral lines is independent of a star's distance from the Earth, astronomers can determine the temperature of any star for which they can obtain a spectrum.

Stellar spectra also allow astronomers to measure the chemical compositions of stars. The atmospheres of stars are predominantly composed of hydrogen and helium. The major variation in chemical composition lies in the abundances of metals, elements more massive than helium. Metallicities range from about 4% by mass to hundreds of times lower. About 2% of the Sun's atmospheric gases are metals.

Stellar spectra also reveal the radial motion of stars. Measurement of the Doppler shifts in stellar spectra lead to very precise velocities. When combined with proper motions and distances, radial velocities give the true velocity of stars through space.

Long before astronomers were able to obtain spectra of stars, they classified stars according to brightness by assigning magnitudes to stars. When magnitudes are obtained with filters, the color index, $B - V$, can be used to establish the temperature of a star. Although stellar spectroscopy is a very reliable temperature indicator, it is often too time-consuming for faint stars. Whereas it can take hours to obtain the spectrum of a single star, the color index can usually be determined with a few minutes observations.

It is important to remember, however, that the relationship between color index and temperature is calibrated with stellar spectra. That is, astronomers determine the temperatures of many stars by spectroscopy and measure the color indices of these same stars. This gives a set of colors for stars of known temperatures and allows the temperatures of stars too faint to observe spectroscopically to be determined by simply measuring their color indices.

Observations of planets, such as Venus and Mercury, established the value of the astronomical unit (see Chapter 3). This distance is necessary for astronomers to determine distances to stars through their observed parallaxes. Stellar parallax allows astronomers to estimate distances to stars about 100 parsecs (just over 300 light-years) away. Although these distances are small compared to the size of the Galaxy, they represent a very important step in gauging the size of the universe.

▰CHAPTER CAPSULE

Topics and Terms	Review and Remarks
Spectral classes	Stars are classified in terms of their surface temperatures. OBAFGKM is an ordering from high (O stars) to low (M stars) temperature.
Classification criteria	Stars are grouped according to the presence and strength of absorption lines in their spectra. These criteria are independent of the distance to the star—only spectra are needed to determine surface temperatures.
Chemical composition of stars	Spectra show that stars are predominantly hydrogen and helium, like the Sun. The abundances of heavier elements varies: Metals make up 2% of the mass of the Sun. Metallicities of stars range from about twice the Sun's to hundreds of times lower.
Radial velocity	The speed of a star directly toward or away from us; it is obtained from Doppler shifts.
Proper motion	The observed motion of a star on the celestial sphere, corrected for the orbital motion of the Earth.
Tangential velocity	The speed of a star across our line of sight; it is obtained from proper motions and known distances.
Space velocity	The speed and direction of a star in space
Magnitude	The magnitude system is a way of classifying stars in terms of their brightnesses. The color index, $B - V$, is a measure of a star's surface temperature.
Parsec	The standard unit of distance in astronomy (1 pc = 3.26 light-years)
Distance	Stellar parallaxes can currently be measured for stars closer than about 100 pc. Measured parallax angles are very small—less than 1 second of arc ($< 1/3600°$). A simple formula relates distance to parallax: Distance (pc) = 1/parallax (arc seconds).

▰REVIEW QUESTIONS

1. The primary chemical constituent of most stars is hydrogen, but stars whose photospheres are at 10,000 K have the strongest Balmer spectral lines. Does this imply that stars at that temperature have the greatest relative abundance of hydrogen? What property of a star determines the relative strengths of its spectral lines? (See question 11, Chapter 4.)

2. The spectral sequence is a listing of spectral classes in the order: O, B, A, F, G, K, and M. Why does the sequence have this peculiar ordering? What physical property of stars determines the particular ordering of the sequence?

3. What do we mean when we say the Sun has a metallicity of 0.02?

4. The star Sirius has an apparent magnitude of about −1.5 while Barnard's star has an apparent magnitude of about +9.5. Which of these stars appears brightest? About how many times brighter does one appear than the other? From the information given, can you say which of these stars is most luminous? Why?

5. Is there a connection between the apparent magnitude of a star and its color? Explain.

6. Why must the transmission characteristics of filters, such as the B and V filters used for color indices, be very carefully specified? Why do astronomers use color indices, in many cases, rather than detailed spectra to determine the temperatures of faint stars?

7. The color index of an A0 star (whose temperature is 10,000 K) is $B - V = 0.00$. Explain why the color index of a hotter star is negative and that of a cooler star is positive.

8. A heliocentric solar system was proposed more than 2000 years ago but, among other things, a lack of observable stellar parallax caused the idea to be

discarded. Why could ancient astronomers not observe stellar parallax?

9. If one angle of a right angle triangle is to be 1″, the hypotenuse must be 206,265 times as long as the side opposite the 1″ angle. If two light sources are 1 meter apart, from what distance would they appear to be 1″ apart? Give the answer in kilometers and miles.

10. The constellations of 2000 years ago were virtually the same as the constellations of today; that is, the Big Dipper would have appeared essentially the same then as it does now. How can this be when stars sometimes have space velocities in hundreds of kilometers per second?

11. The radial velocity component of a star can be determined without knowing its distance. Determining the tangential velocity component, however, requires a knowledge of the star's distance. Explain.

▰FOR FURTHER READING

Croswell, K. 1987. Visit the nearest stars. *Astronomy*, Jan., 16.

DeVorkin, D. H. 1989. Henry Norris Russell. *Scientific American*, May, 126.

Kaler, J. 1986. Origins of the spectral sequence. *Sky & Telescope*, Feb., 129.

———. 1988. Extraordinary spectral types. *Sky & Telescope*, Feb., 149.

Schombert, J. 1987. Surveying the northern sky. *Sky & Telescope*, Aug., 128.

Smith, D. H. 1985. New homes for monster telescopes. *Sky & Telescope*, July, 23.

———. 1989. An observatory at 90° south. *Sky & Telescope*, June, 598.

Sneden, C. 1989. Reading the colors of stars. *Astronomy*, Apr., 36.

ASTROPROBE 13

Observatories and Observing

See Module 2, "Astronomical Instruments and Telescopes."

Virtually all experimental data gathered by astronomers is through the detection of electromagnetic radiation from objects in space. The buildings equipped with the instruments and machines used by astronomers to gather this data are collectively called **observatories.** Prior to World War II an observatory was an optical telescope or a group of optical telescopes housed in buildings with peculiar domed tops. Today we are capable of detecting electromagnetic radiation of almost any wavelength: radio, ultraviolet, gamma rays, and X-rays, as well as visible and infrared (Figure 13A.1). The ultraviolet, gamma rays, and X-rays are detected with space satellite telescopes and balloon-borne telescopes. As a result, besides optical observatories, we have radio observatories and satellite control facilities.

OBSERVATORIES: WHO OWNS THEM AND WHO USES THEM

Telescopes available to American astronomers are operated by several types of organizations. The U.S. government supports, for instance, the National Optical Astronomy Observatories (NOAO) and the National Radio Astronomy Observatory (NRAO) through the National Science Foundation. The National Science Foundation is the government agency responsible for distributing government funds for science research and education in the United States. The National Optical Astronomy Observatories operate Kitt Peak National Observatory near Tucson, Arizona; Cerro Tololo Inter-American Observatory near La Serena, Chile; and the National Solar Observatory near Sunspot, New Mexico (Panel a in Figure 13A.2). The National Radio Astronomy Observatory supports radio telescopes in West Virginia, New Mexico, and Arizona (Panel b). Government support money is

FIGURE 13A.1

Two Observatories

(a) Telescope dome of the U.S. Naval Observatory in Flagstaff, Arizona.
(b) The 43-meter (140-foot) dish of the National Radio Astronomy Observatory in Green Bank, West Virginia.

SOURCES: Part (a), Hansen Planetarium. Part (b), NRAO/AUI.

(a)

(b)

(a)

(b)

also used by other agencies to run observing facilities, such as NASA's Infrared Telescope Facility (IRTF) in Hawaii, the Space Telescope Science Institute (STScI) on the campus of the Johns Hopkins University in Baltimore, Maryland, and the United States Naval Observatory with telescopes in Washington, D.C., and Flagstaff, Arizona.

Many universities support small- to moderate-sized telescopes on campus and at off-campus observing stations. The campus facilities range from small telescopes for student training and public viewing to moderate-sized research telescopes (Panel a in Figure 13A.3). Most astronomical research requires dark skies; this means locating telescopes far from city lights (Panel b). These observing stations may be only a few miles out of town or clear across the country. The University of Washington in Seattle, for instance, operates a moderate-sized research telescope just an hour and a half from campus and, together with the University of Chicago, New Mexico State University, Princeton University, and Washington State University, will operate a large 3.5-meter telescope in New Mexico. It is not uncommon for several universities to share the expense of building a major multimillion dollar observing facility. Universities also play an important role in running the national observatories. For example, 20 universities comprise the Association of Universities for Research in Astronomy, Inc. (AURA), which is responsible for overseeing the operation of the National Optical Astronomy Observatories and the Space Telescope Science Institute.

A few major observatories rely on private funds. The Lowell Observatory in Flagstaff, Arizona, was started by the wealthy Bostonian Percival Lowell. Similarly, Lick Observatory near San Francisco and the Hale Observatories near Los Angeles were started with private

■■■■ FIGURE 13A.2

American Observatories

(a) This is a view of the domes of several of the smaller telescopes of the Cerro Tololo Inter-American Observatory in Chile with the Andes Mountains of Chile in the background. The observatory also has 1.5-m and 4-m telescopes. (b) The Very Large Array (VLA) in New Mexico consists of 27 identical 25-meter (82-foot) reflector antennas arranged along three equally spaced radial arms, forming a Y-shaped array.

SOURCES: Part (a), National Optical Astronomy Observatory. Part (b), NRAO/AUI.

(a)

(b)

funds. These observatories as well as university facilities also receive
funds from the National Science Foundation, NASA, and other government agencies for instrument development, special research facilities and equipment, and future technologies research. Not all private observatories are dedicated only to research. Community
observatories, such as the Charles E. Daniel Observatory operated by
the Greenville County School District (Greenville, South Carolina),
concentrate on educating students and the public (Figure 13A.4).
And, of course, thousands of amateur astronomer observatories have
been built across the country. These are for pleasure as well as serious research.

Although it is true that with a modest investment just about anyone can enjoy the heavens, not everyone may use the major observatory facilities. Who uses these telescopes? Professional astronomers,
of course, use the telescopes at national observatories and university
facilities. These astronomers are usually university-trained men and
women with advanced degrees in physics, engineering, or astronomy.
The national observatories and many university facilities are open to
guest astronomers, but they must compete for time on telescopes.
Since the United States has over 3500 astronomers, not nearly
enough national and private observing facilities are available to accommodate all their needs. Clearly, astronomers who work at a national facility or at a university that supports an observatory have a
major advantage in that they essentially have a telescope in their
backyard. Even so, observatory staff astronomers may find themselves engaged in a fierce competition.

The competition is in the form of observing proposals. Astronomers
submit proposals that detail their project, giving the names of the
objects they wish to observe, the equipment needed, and the dates

and number of nights required to complete the project. These proposals are reviewed by both staff astronomers and outside astronomers. They are judged on the significance of the research and its feasibility. The number of nights spent observing varies greatly among the successful applicants for telescope time. A staff astronomer at a major observatory may spend over 100 nights a year at the telescope while a guest observer may only spend a couple of weeks each year observing. Usually, guest astronomers come from universities and must therefore teach as well as engage in research. Consequently, their research time is limited.

Let's imagine that we have had a proposal accepted by a major observatory and have been assigned observing time.

OBSERVING

We arrived at the observatory headquarters a couple of days ago and came up to the mountaintop this morning. Before arriving, we made most of the necessary preparations for our observing runs, such as selecting the objects to study, calculating their celestial coordinates, making charts, or small maps, of the portion of the sky we hope to observe (so that when we look through the telescope we will be able to identify the right star), and estimating how long to observe each object. Some observers design and build their own instruments and take them to the observatory. We spend the afternoon of our first observing night with an observatory engineer or staff astronomer who familiarizes us with the instrument we will use tonight (Figure 13A.5). The observatory staff has already attached the instrument to the telescope. An observatory has dozens of instruments, each with its own particular function, available to guest astronomers. The choice of observatory depends on the equipment available. We make the final checks before dinner; we do not want to spend time after supper checking equipment—that time is reserved for observing.

A couple of hours before sunset the telescope dome is opened (Panel a in Figure 13A.6). This permits the temperature inside the dome to reach the same temperature as the nighttime air. If the air inside the dome is warmer than the outside air, the rising warm air would distort our view of the stars as the heat from a radiator under a window distorts our view of the outdoors. After dinner we will meet with the observatory's telescope operator and describe the night's observing plan. Large telescopes cost millions of dollars to build and maintain, and to protect their investment, observatories have specially trained personnel to operate the telescope (Panel b). We will only be allowed to control the telescope after the telescope operator points the telescope in the general direction of the objects

■ FIGURE 13A.4

Charles E. Daniel Observatory

The Greenville County School District in South Carolina operates an observatory housing a .58-m Clark refractor.

SOURCE: Daniel Observatory, Roper Mountain Science Center.

■ FIGURE 13A.5

Instrument Check

An astronomer adjusts a photometer at the 1.3-m (50-inch) telescope at Kitt Peak National Observatory near Tucson, Arizona.

SOURCE: National Optical Astronomy Observatories.

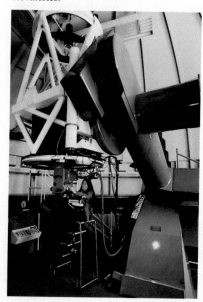

(a)

(b)

■■■ FIGURE 13A.6

Observatory Facilities

(a) The opened dome of the Palomar 200-inch in moonlight. (b) Console of the 3.9-m Anglo-Australian Telescope.

SOURCES: Part (a), Hale Observatories. Part (b), copyright © 1977 Anglo-Australian Telescope Board. Photo by David F. Malin.

we wish to observe. We will then be allowed to move the telescope at slow speeds to find the particular object we will be observing. This is where our charts are used; sometimes the field of stars is so crowded that it can take a while to locate the object we want to observe.

Everything is set—all the equipment is functioning properly and it is a clear night. Our project is to photograph very faint stars in a nearby galaxy. We can do this photographically using special astronomical photographic plates or electronically using special solid-state detectors. If we were to use photographic plates, we would make sure that the camera is in focus by photographing bright stars as soon as it becomes dark enough. Electronic photography requires several calibration exposures that provide important information about the camera that we will use later in analyzing the pictures. We soon develop our observing routine, moving from star field to star field. We have our "lunch" at midnight. Some observatories have dining halls while others just provide kitchen facilities. We have packed our lunch so that we can eat between observations.

Often the nights do not go smoothly; sometimes nothing goes right. We can always expect equipment troubles; we can fix the minor problems with the assistance of the telescope operators. If not, we will have to call the technician on night duty, if the observatory has one. If the technician cannot fix the problem, then we shut down and hope that the day staff can.

■■■■ FIGURE 13A.7

**The Morning After a Long
Night Observing**

Clouds fill the valley below; this is one
reason observatories are located high
on mountaintops.

SOURCE: Phillip Flower.

If all goes well, we complete our night's observing, sneaking in the
last photograph just before dawn (Figure 13A.7). The telescope operator will close the dome and place the telescope in its resting position. If we took photographs, we would develop them now. This can
take a couple of hours more. If we took electronic images, we would
collect our data, which was placed on magnetic tapes and possibly
do a little preliminary analysis to help plan our next night's work.
After we are finished, we are too tired to stay up for breakfast with
the observatory's day crew. We call it a day, or rather a night, and
sleep until early afternoon to be ready for another night's work.

Not all observing runs are successful. Besides equipment failure,
we could be rained out completely. The difficult nights are the partly
cloudy ones that may or may not clear. On these nights the telescopes close one by one with the largest telescopes last. Telescope
time on the big instruments is very valuable; even a couple hours in
the late morning are worth the wait. Of course, major observatories
are equipped with technical libraries at the observing site, and you
will always find a small collection of mystery and science fiction nov-
els to help pass the time on cloudy nights and week-long observing
runs.

Observing at radio observatories and with satellite telescopes is
similar except that the astronomer is not limited to nighttime observing, and equipment repair is much beyond the typical guest observer. Radio and satellite telescopes are generally more automated

than their optical counterparts, and astronomers have less interaction with the equipment. Nevertheless, the preparations for using these complex instruments are the same as the ones we made—objects, coordinates, and observing time.

At small university observatories, astronomers drive to the observatory in the late afternoon, observe all night or even just part of the night, and drive home the next morning. Usually, no technicians are available. The observing run is a couple of nights at most, depending on how far away the observing station is from home. If a campus observatory is available, astronomers check the equipment during the day between classes and decide, as late as after dinner, whether or not to observe that night.

The observing run is just the beginning of the study of the objects we have selected. We must now analyze the data we obtained. The light from astronomical objects contains all the information that we need to understand them. We must convert observations to numbers and then use our brains to unravel the secrets about the planets, stars, and galaxies that these numbers hold.

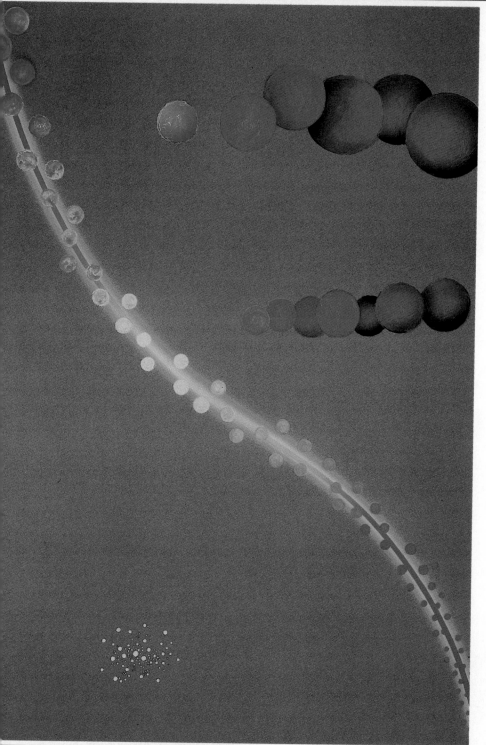

CHAPTER 14

Character-istics of Stars

OUTLINE

Absolute Magnitudes and Stellar Luminosities

The HR Diagram

The Masses of Stars
Binary Stars
The Mass-Luminosity Relationship

The Sizes of Stars

Summary

Chapter Capsule

Review Questions

For Further Reading

ASTROPROBE 14:
  Pixels and Stars: Stellar Imaging

HR Diagram.

ARTIST: Mark Paternostro. Courtesy *Astronomy* Magazine, Kalmbach Publishing Company.

WE CANNOT TOUCH STARS to measure their temperatures; we cannot survey stellar surfaces to measure their diameters; we cannot weigh stars to measure their masses; we cannot analyze atoms of stars to measure their chemical compositions; and we cannot travel to stars to measure their intrinsic light output. Yet astronomers can determine stellar temperature, diameter, mass, chemical composition, and luminosity even though stars are at great distances. Light from stars provides all of the information necessary to determine these physical characteristics. The last chapter described how astronomers analyze stellar spectra to measure the surface temperatures and chemical compositions of stars. This chapter describes how astronomers analyze light from stars to measure stellar luminosities, masses, and diameters. The five parameters—temperature, chemical composition, luminosity, mass, and diameter—fully describe a star and are fundamental to the study, discussed in the next two chapters, of the changes stars undergo as they mature and age.

▰ABSOLUTE MAGNITUDES AND STELLAR LUMINOSITIES

The Sun is an extremely brilliant star in the daytime sky because it is so much closer to the Earth than all other stars. What if the Sun were farther away? Could the Sun be seen with the naked eye at a distance of 10 parsecs? How does the Sun's *intrinsic* brightness compare to that of other stars? Apparent magnitude does not help here because it depends on both the star's intrinsic brightness and on its distance from the Earth. An intrinsically bright star can look faint if it is far away. The trick to comparing stars with the Sun is to mathematically "line them up" at the same distance from the Earth and then compare brightness.

Chapter 12 described how astronomers calculate the intrinsic brightness, or luminosity, of the Sun from the measured solar constant. Recall that the solar constant is the amount of solar radiation passing through one square centimeter of the surface of a sphere with a radius of 1 AU centered on the Sun. How would the amount of solar radiation passing through one square centimeter change if astronomers measured it from another planet in the solar system, such as Jupiter? Imagine now a large sphere centered on the Sun with a radius equal to that of Jupiter's semimajor axis, about 5 AU. The Sun emits the same amount of radiant energy whether it is observed from the Earth or from Jupiter. This same amount of energy must pass through the surfaces of both spheres, the one with a radius of 1 AU and the other with a radius of 5 AU. The Sun's radiant energy is spread over a greater area at the distance of Jupiter. Therefore less light must pass through each square centimeter of the surface area of the larger sphere. Consequently, the measured solar constant at Jupiter would be smaller than that measured at Earth. How much smaller? The number of square centimeters on the surface of a sphere with radius r is $4\pi r^2$. Since the sphere centered on Jupiter has 5 times the radius of the sphere centered on Earth, the Jovian sphere must have $5^2 = 25$ times the surface area. Therefore the Sun's light at Jupiter is spread over an area 25 times larger than that at Earth; a solar constant measured at Jupiter would be 25 times less than at Earth; and the Sun at Jupiter would appear 25 times fainter than at Earth.

This result can be stated more concisely as "the solar constant is inversely proportional to the distance from the Sun squared," or

$$\text{Solar constant} \propto \frac{1}{r^2}$$

This relationship between the solar constant, or the apparent brightness of the Sun, and distance follows the **inverse square** law (Figure 14.1). Brightness decreases with the square of the distance.

The inverse square law can be used to determine exactly how bright the Sun would appear at a distance of 10 pc ($=2.06 \times 10^6$ AU). The inverse square law implies that the Sun would appear $(2.06 \times 10^6)^2 = 4.25 \times 10^{12}$ times fainter than it does now. Table 14.1 shows the steps needed to calculate the apparent magnitude of the Sun as seen at a distance of 10 pc. For every factor of 10 increase in distance, the brightness of the Sun decreases by a factor of 100; but each factor of 100 in brightness corresponds to a change of 5 magnitudes. Viewed from a distance of 10 AU, for instance, the Sun would appear 5 magnitudes fainter, or as a -21.8-magnitude star, still very bright. At 100 AU, it would appear another 5 magnitudes fainter than this, or as a -16.8-magnitude star. At a distance of a million AU, the Sun would appear as a $+3.2$-magnitude star in the nighttime sky, 30 magnitudes fainter than it appears at 1 AU. Finally, at a distance of 2.06 million AU, the Sun would appear another 1.6 magnitudes fainter. The apparent magnitude of the Sun at 10 pc would be $+4.8$ magnitudes.

The choice of 10 parsecs was not arbitrary. Astronomers define the **absolute magnitude** (designated with an "M") of a star as the apparent

MathTools 2: Proportion a/b

Inverse square law: A mathematical relationship in which a property decreases with the square of the distance; astronomers use it to describe the decrease in light intensity with distance.

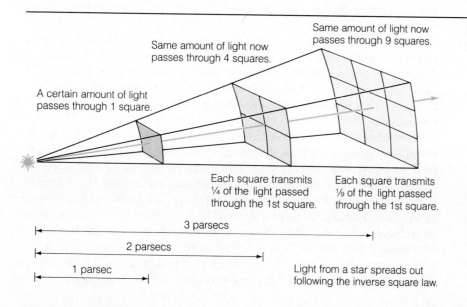

Same amount of light now passes through 9 squares.

Same amount of light now passes through 4 squares.

A certain amount of light passes through 1 square.

Each square transmits ¼ of the light passed through the 1st square.

Each square transmits ⅑ of the light passed through the 1st square.

3 parsecs

2 parsecs

1 parsec

Light from a star spreads out following the inverse square law.

■■ FIGURE 14.1

Inverse Square Law

■■■■ TABLE 14.1 Inverse Square Law Applied to the Sun

Distance	Brightness	Change in Magnitude (Δm)	Apparent Magnitude of the Sun ($m_\odot$)
1 AU	1	0	−26.8
10 AU	10^2 times fainter than at 1 AU	5	−21.8
100 AU	10^4 times fainter than at 1 AU	10	−16.8
10^3 AU	10^6 times fainter than at 1 AU	15	−11.8
10^4 AU	10^8 times fainter than at 1 AU	20	−6.8
10^5 AU	10^{10} times fainter than at 1 AU	25	−1.8
10^6 AU	10^{12} times fainter than at 1 AU	30	+3.2
2.1×10^6 AU	4.25×10^{12} times fainter than at 1 AU	31.6*	+4.8

*A change of brightness by a factor of 4.25 corresponds to a change of 1.6 magnitudes

■■■■ FIGURE 14.2

Stellar "Lineup"

Astronomers compare the brightness of other stars with the Sun by "lining" them up at a distance of 10 pc. They calculate their magnitudes at 10 pc using the inverse square law, their apparent magnitudes, and distances. The numbers next to the stars are their magnitudes, either apparent or absolute.

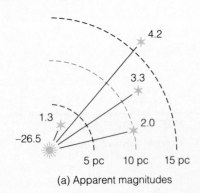

(a) Apparent magnitudes

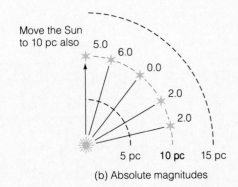

(b) Absolute magnitudes

magnitude it would have if placed at a distance of 10 pc from the Earth. The absolute magnitude of the Sun is, therefore, $M_\odot = +4.8$ magnitudes. If it were 10 pc away, the Sun would appear as an inconspicuous fifth-magnitude star, hardly worth noticing, but visible to the unaided eye.

Although the Sun would be visible if it were 10 pc away, the main goal is to compare the luminosities of other stars to the Sun's luminosity. Is the Sun intrinsically the brightest star, the faintest, or somewhere in between? With the distance to a star known, the steps in Table 14.1 lead to its absolute magnitude. This procedure uses the inverse square law to "line up" stars at a distance of 10 pc (Figure 14.2). Once positioned, the stars are compared to the Sun. For example, suppose that the absolute magnitude of a star is $M = +9.8$. This star is intrinsically 5 magnitudes fainter than the Sun. Since 5 magnitudes corresponds to a factor of 100 in brightness, the star's luminosity must be 100 times less than the Sun's: $L = 10^{-2}L_\odot = 3.8 \times 10^{24}$ watts. Similarly, a star with $M = -0.2$ will be intrinsically 100 times brighter than the Sun, while a star with $M = -5.2$ will be 10^4 times brighter than the Sun.

How does the Sun compare? The brightest stars have absolute magnitudes of $M \approx -10$; they are about a million times more luminous than the Sun. The faintest stars have absolute magnitudes of $M \approx +15$; they are about ten thousand times less luminous than the Sun. Therefore the Sun falls just below the midpoint of the range of stellar luminosities.

Remember, however, that these same stars can have very faint or bright apparent magnitudes depending on their distances from us. In fact, absolute magnitude, apparent magnitude, and distance are so closely related to each other that astronomers often denote distances with magnitudes. For instance, a star with an apparent magnitude equal to its absolute magnitude, $m - M = 0$, must be at a distance of 10 pc. This is just the definition of absolute magnitude. Suppose that a hypothetical star has $m - M = -5$. The star is 5 magnitudes fainter at 10 pc than at its actual distance from us. An example would be a star with $m = 5$ and $M = 10$ so that $m - M = 5 - 10 = -5$. How far away is such a star? First, it must be closer than 10 pc since it becomes fainter when we "move" it to 10 pc. Second, a difference of 5 magnitudes corresponds to a factor of 100 in brightness, but this, in turn, corresponds to a distance change of a factor of 10. Therefore, the star must be 10 times closer than 10 pc; it must be 1 pc away. Similarly, a star with $m - M = +5$ is 5 magnitudes brighter at 10 pc than at its actual distance. It must be 100 times fainter and at 10 times the distance of 10 pc. The star is 100 pc away. The difference $m - M$ denotes distance and is called the **distance modulus.** Table 14.2 gives the correspondence between the distance modulus and distance.

This analysis can be turned around and used for estimating the distance to any object with a known absolute magnitude. Suppose we identify a star that is identical to the Sun but in another galaxy. We can assume that its absolute magnitude is the same as the Sun's, +4.8. By measuring its apparent magnitude, we could easily calculate its distance using the distance modulus. In the next few chapters, certain stars will be introduced that can be easily identified at great distances, because of their unique properties, and can be used as distance indicators in this way.

THE HR DIAGRAM

Stars exhibit a tremendous range in luminosity, from millions of times brighter than the Sun to thousands of times fainter. Surface temperatures range from thousands of Kelvins to many tens of thousands of Kelvins. Nevertheless, when limited only to luminosity and temperature pairs for real stars, such as those listed in Appendix F, astronomers find that not all combinations are likely. A similar situation exists for humans; for instance, not all combinations of heights and weights are likely.

Consider the graph of heights and weights of astronomy students at Clemson University (Figure 14.3). No students who are 6'4" tall weigh 100 lb, and none who are 5'0" tall weigh 200 lb. Most students lie in a broad band, or a main sequence, going from lower right to upper left. Within this main sequence, student heights and weights follow the trend "taller is heavier." At the same time, subgroups lie outside the main sequence, such as the tall, thin students and the short, heavy students. On the whole, however, the distribution of student heights and weights is limited.

Similar trends exist for luminosities and temperatures of stars. Figure 14.4 is a graph of absolute magnitude (luminosity) and spectral type (temperature) of 130 of the brightest stars and stars nearest to the Sun. Recall that every change of 5 magnitudes corresponds to an increase or decrease of a factor of 100 in brightness. The magnitude range shown in Figure 14.4, from a little brighter than -5 to slightly fainter than $+15$, corresponds to a range of approximately 10^{10} in luminosity. The curving line of luminosity-temperature pairs from lower right to upper left through the middle of the graph is called the **main sequence.** Approximately 70% to 80% of all stars lie along the main sequence. The general trend along the main sequence is from faint, cool stars at the

TABLE 14.2 Distance Modulus

m − M	Distance
−5	1 pc
0	10 pc
+5	100 pc
+10	10^3 pc
+15	10^4 pc
+20	10^5 pc
+25	10^6 pc

Main sequence: A band in a graph of absolute magnitude (luminosity) versus spectral type (temperature) extending from the lower right to the upper left in which the majority of stars are found; like the Sun, the stars making up the main sequence are converting hydrogen into helium in their cores.

■■■■■ FIGURE 14.3

Height-Weight Diagram for Astronomy Students

The majority of students fall within a band in which heights and weights follow the trend "taller is heavier." Not all combinations of height and weight are found for humans.

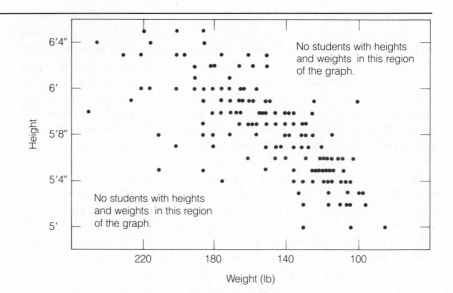

lower right to hot, bright stars at the upper left. Several subgroups clearly lie outside the main sequence. To the upper right is a group of bright, cool stars, and to the lower left is a "line" of faint stars. Most samples of stars generally include a main sequence and one or two subgroups. Stars simply do not exist for every possible luminosity and temperature combination. This chapter and the next two will investigate the reasons why this limitation exists.

Just as students can have different heights but weigh the same, stars can have different luminosities for the same temperature (Figure 14.4). When comparing a short student, for instance, with a tall student *of the same weight*, the difference between them is reflected in the physiques of the students—one student is thinner. What physical difference between stars reflects their vastly different luminosities for the same temperature? The Stefan-Boltzmann law (Chapter 4) implies that stars with the same temperature must emit the same amount of light each second through *each* square centimeter of their surfaces. How then can one star be brighter than another and still have the same surface temperature? A star with a greater surface area will have more square centimeters covering its surface than a star with less surface area. If these two stars have the same surface temperature, the star with the greater surface area, the larger star, will be brighter. The difference in luminosities between stars of the same temperature is reflected in their radii.

The fact that stars of the same temperature can differ enormously in luminosity and, therefore, in size was first noticed by the Danish astronomer Ejnar Hertzsprung (1873–1972) at the beginning of the twentieth century. A few years later the American astronomer Henry Norris Russell (1877–1957) plotted the available absolute magnitudes and spectral types as in Figure 14.4. In honor of these two astronomers, the graph of absolute magnitude versus spectral type is called the **Hertzsprung-Rus-**

Hertzsprung-Russell (HR) diagram: A graph of the absolute magnitudes versus spectral types of individual stars.

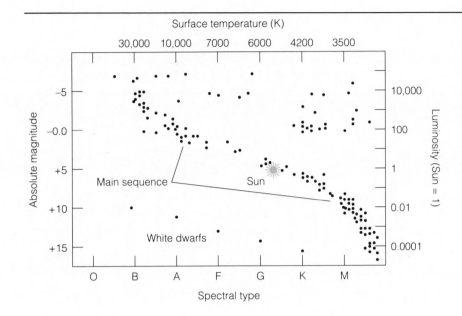

■■■ **FIGURE 14.4**

Luminosities and Temperatures of Stars

Luminosity and temperature pairs are plotted for the brightest stars in the sky and the nearest stars to the Sun. The luminosity scale to the right is relative to the Sun; the value 10,000, for instance, represents 10,000 times the Sun's luminosity. Most stars lie along the curving line from lower right to upper left called the main sequence. Several subgroups lie above the main sequence, and a line of white dwarfs falls below it. (Data from D. Popper, 1980, *Annual Review of Astronomy and Astrophysics*, 18:115.)

sell diagram. The Hertzsprung-Russell diagram, or HR diagram, has since become one of the most valuable tools for studying stars.

The hidden parameter in the HR diagram is the size of stars. The largest stars occupy the upper right corner of the HR diagram while the smallest stars lie at the lower left. This variety of stellar radii has led to a special terminology. Stars above the main sequence are called *giants*, and the brightest giants are called *supergiants*. These stars are larger than main-sequence stars of the same temperature. In the same manner of expression, main-sequence stars are called *dwarfs;* they are smaller than giants. The small stars in the lower left and below the main sequence are called *white dwarfs;* they are a special type of object described in Chapter 16.

Astronomers separate stars larger than dwarfs into four groups called *luminosity classes,* which are designated with Roman numerals from I to IV. A Roman numeral V is used for dwarfs. The supergiants, class I, fall into two classes, Ia and Ib. Figure 14.5 gives the approximate locations of each luminosity class on the HR diagram. Astronomers combine luminosity classes with spectral classes when describing a star. For instance, the Sun is a G2 V star. It is a G type star, subgroup 2, and a main-sequence star. A B0 supergiant could be a B0 Ia or B0 Ib while an M5 giant is classified as M5 III. Table 14.3 lists the classifications of a few prominent stars seen in the night sky. Astronomers assign the luminosity classification from spectra. The thinner, more extended atmospheres of large stars produce conditions that result in narrower, or sharper, spectral lines than those in their dwarf counterparts. Consequently, a spectroscopist can classify stellar luminosities as well as temperatures from the same spectra.

■■■ **TABLE 14.3 Luminosity Classification of Bright Stars**

Star	Classification
Aldebaran	K5 III
Capella	G5 III + G0 III (binary)
Rigel	B8 Ia
Betelgeuse	M2 Ia
Sirius	A1 V
Castor	A1 V
Procyon	F5 IV
Pollux	K0 III
Regulus	B7 V
Spica	B1 III + B2 V (binary)
Arcturus	K1 III
Antares	M1 Ib + B4 V (binary)
Vega	A0 IV–V
Altair	A7 V
Deneb	A2 Ia
Fomalhaut	A3 V
Polaris	F7 Ib

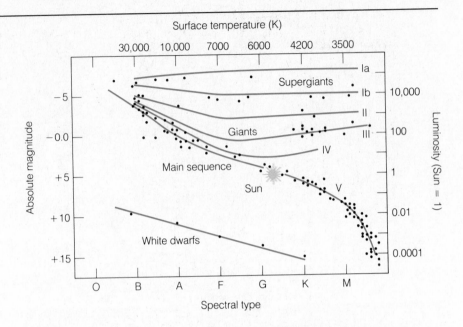

■ FIGURE 14.5

Luminosity Classes

The same data plotted in Figure 14.4 are shown here with the approximate locations of the different luminosity classes.

The next two chapters make extensive use of the HR diagram in describing the "lives" of stars. The HR diagram concisely describes stellar surface conditions, indicating the amount of light passing through the surface, the temperature of the surface, and the star's radius, or how far the surface is from the center. The HR diagram has one other hidden parameter that will determine to a great extent the location of individual stars on the HR diagram. We turn to it in the next section.

▬▬THE MASSES OF STARS

The orbit of a moon about a planet is the result of their interaction through the gravitational force. Since their masses control the strength of the gravitational force between them, orbital properties, such as semimajor axis and period, give information about the masses of the moon and planet. The point is that two gravitationally interacting objects are required to determine the mass of one or both. The same applies to stars. Observations of a single, isolated star in space cannot give direct information about its mass. The evidence of stellar mass is hidden in the observable effects of the gravitational interaction between stars. It is found in **binary stars,** pairs of stars that orbit about each other as do the Moon and the Earth.

Binary stars: Two stars revolving around each other and orbiting a common center of mass; also called double stars.

Binary Stars

Newton derived a form of Kepler's third law that specifically included the mass of the orbiting objects:

$$\mathfrak{M}_A + \mathfrak{M}_B = \frac{a^3}{P^2}$$

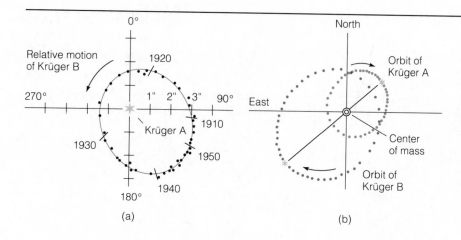

(a)

(b)

■■■■■ FIGURE 14.6

The Krüger 60 Binary System

(a) The measured relative positions of the faint component, Krüger 60 B, are shown relative to the brighter component, Krüger 60 A, from 1910 to 1955. The orbital period of this system is nearly 45 years. *(b)* Krüger 60 A and B orbit about their common center of mass. As they orbit, they are on exactly opposite sides of the center of mass. The center of mass is one focus in each of the elliptical orbits. (Adapted from van de Kamp, *Principles of Astrometry*, 1967.)

Here $\mathfrak{M}_A$ and $\mathfrak{M}_B$ are the masses of the orbiting stars A and B in solar masses; a is the semimajor axis of the orbit in astronomical units; and P is their orbital period in years. For instance, if a = 4 AU and P = 4 years, then the sum of the masses of the two stars making up this system is

$$\mathfrak{M}_A + \mathfrak{M}_B = \frac{4^3}{4^2} = \frac{64}{16} = 4\ \mathfrak{M}_\odot$$

The observed motion of one star about the other reveals the semimajor axis of a binary system. Since one star is usually brighter than the other, astronomers measure the position of the fainter star relative to the brighter (Panel a in Figure 14.6). If the distance to the system is also known, the semimajor axis in astronomical units can be calculated. The orbit so determined is a *relative orbit* because, although the motion of the brighter component is ignored, both stars actually revolve about a center of mass; that is, both are moving. In the hypothetical system of stars A and B above, only the *sum* of the masses of the stars is known. One star could be 3 $\mathfrak{M}_\odot$ and other 1 $\mathfrak{M}_\odot$, or both could be 2 $\mathfrak{M}_\odot$, or they could be some other combination of masses. Relative orbits do not provide enough information to determine individual masses.

Astronomers need to determine the individual, or *absolute*, orbits of the two stars about the center of mass of the system before they can obtain individual masses (Panel b in Figure 14.6). The location of the stars in a binary system relative to the center of mass is analogous to the positions of two children on a teeter-totter. The heavier child must sit closer to the center for the teeter-totter to balance (Figure 14.7). If we could observe the motion of both stars in a binary system relative to stationary, more distant stars, we could plot their positions and in time draw their individual orbits. The center of mass of the system is the common focus of the two elliptical orbits. Observations would immediately show that one orbit is smaller than the other; the star with

■ FIGURE 14.7

Center of Mass

Although binary stars are in motion, they obey the same relationship between mass and distance from the center of mass as do two people on a teeter-totter. The more massive object is closer to the center of mass.

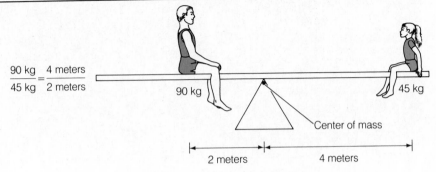

$$\frac{90 \text{ kg}}{45 \text{ kg}} = \frac{4 \text{ meters}}{2 \text{ meters}}$$

For a balanced teeter-totter: twice the mass, half the distance from the center of mass, •

(a)

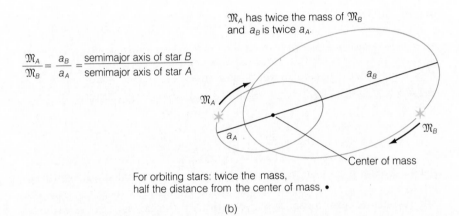

$\mathfrak{M}_A$ has twice the mass of $\mathfrak{M}_B$ and a_B is twice a_A.

$$\frac{\mathfrak{M}_A}{\mathfrak{M}_B} = \frac{a_B}{a_A} = \frac{\text{semimajor axis of star } B}{\text{semimajor axis of star } A}$$

For orbiting stars: twice the mass, half the distance from the center of mass, •

(b)

the smaller semimajor axis must be the more massive (Panel b in Figure 14.7). In fact, as with children on teeter-totters, the relationship between mass and distance from the center of mass is very simple:

Distance from the center of mass is inversely proportional to mass, or

MathTools 2: Proportion a/b

$$d \propto \frac{1}{\mathfrak{M}}$$

Suppose that, in our hypothetical binary system in which the sum of the masses of the components is 4 $\mathfrak{M}_\odot$, star B orbits three times farther from the center of mass than star A. Star B must be one-third the mass of star A, and the total mass of the system must be four times the mass of star B: 1 $\mathfrak{M}_B$ for component B and 3 $\mathfrak{M}_B$ for component A. Since the sum of the masses is 4 $\mathfrak{M}_\odot$, $\mathfrak{M}_B$ must equal 1 $\mathfrak{M}_\odot$, leaving 3 $\mathfrak{M}_\odot$ for star A.

The relative orbit can only give information about the sum of the masses of the two stars. The absolute orbits give the rest of the information necessary to determine individual masses.

What are the chances of finding binary systems? Forty-six stellar systems, including the Sun, lie within 5 pc of the Sun. Of these, 33 are

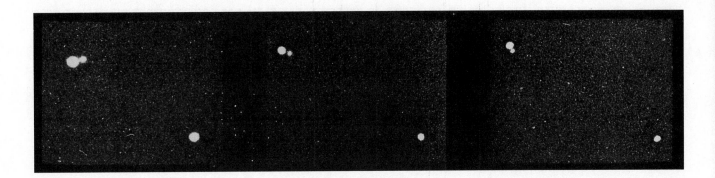

single stars, 24 stars belong to binary systems (12 binaries), and 3 stars make up a triple star system. Thus, of a total of 63 stars, nearly half are members of multiple-star systems. Although binary stars are very common, they were not discovered until soon after the invention of the telescope. In 1650 the Italian astronomer Giovanni Riccioli (1598–1671) discovered that Mizar, the middle star of the handle of the Big Dipper, appeared as two stars in the telescope. Mizar was the first binary system discovered. It was not until the beginning of the nineteenth century, however, that astronomers noticed that stars in binary systems moved relative to each other (Figure 14.8). They soon recognized the potential of binary stars for providing information about stellar mass.

Nearby binaries are identified by their visual appearance as stars close together in the sky. Astronomers must be cautious, however, because some pairs of stars just happen to lie in nearly the same direction from Earth and appear as a double-star system. In these *optical doubles*, one star is closer to the Earth than the other and they are not gravitationally bound to each other. Mizar, in fact, forms an optical double with Alcor, a star just visible to the eye on a clear night.

The nearest binary systems are commonly visible as two individual stars; these are called, appropriately, **visual binary stars.** We designate the individual components by capital letters A and B; for example, Alpha Centauri A and Alpha Centauri B. The relative orbit is constructed from a series of measurements that include the distance of one component from the other and the *position angle*, the angle between north and the fainter component measured toward the east (Figure 14.9). As with the orbital determination of planets, such as Neptune and Pluto, astronomers do not need to observe the positions of the stars throughout their entire orbit to determine the size and shape of the relative orbit. Since the shortest orbital periods are under 2 years, it is certainly possible to observe some binary systems through many orbits. The longest periods, on the other hand, are thousands of years. About 70,000 visual binaries are known and about 1,000 orbits have been observed. But only a dozen absolute orbits are well enough established to give accurate mass determinations. The masses range from just under 0.1 $\mathfrak{M}_\odot$ to 2.2 $\mathfrak{M}_\odot$.

Surprisingly, not all visual binaries are easily recognized. If the components are too far apart, 10^3 to 10^4 AU, and the orbital periods are thousands of years, we can only detect them through their common proper motion through space. At the other extreme, some binaries have

■ **FIGURE 14.8**
Relative Motion

This series of photographs shows the orbital motion and the proper motion of the Krüger 60 binary system over a 12-year period. The star to the lower right in these photographs is a background star that is too far away to show any proper motion.
SOURCE: Yerkes Observatory.

Visual binary: A double star in which both components are individually visible.

■■■ FIGURE 14.9

Position Angle

An individual measurement of a position of a binary star component includes the separation of the stars and the position angle, the angle between north and the fainter component measured toward the east (clockwise in this diagram).

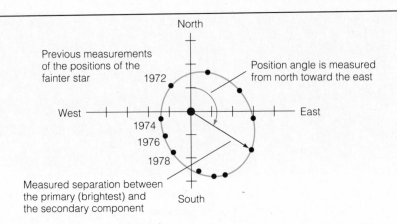

Previous measurements of the positions of the fainter star

Position angle is measured from north toward the east

Measured separation between the primary (brightest) and the secondary component

Astrometric binary: A double star in which one companion is "invisible"; the binary nature of the star is detected by periodic changes in the position of the primary component as it moves through space and around the center of mass.

one component that is "invisible." They are close enough that the binary nature of these systems is deduced from the motion of the visible companion about the center of mass of the pair. These binary systems are called **astrometric binaries.** The adjective "astrometric" is derived from the term *astrometry*, a branch of astronomy that deals with the measurement of the positions of stars.

The motion observed in astrometric binaries is similar to the motion of the ends of a bowling pin that has been thrown spinning in the air. The center of mass of the pin, which is located near the base, will make an arc in the air, but the two ends will spin about the center of mass (Panel a in Figure 14.10). Both ends make a wiggly line through the air as they spin around the moving center of mass. This kind of motion for stars was first observed for the brightest star in the sky, Sirius. Friedrich W. Bessel (1784–1846) discovered the peculiar motion of Sirius in 1844. Panel b in Figure 14.10 shows its motion during the last century. The path of Sirius is wiggly because it is moving around the center of mass defined by Sirius and its fainter companion, Sirius B. Since astronomers have photographed the faint companion to Sirius in this century, the Sirius system is now classified as a visual binary system.

The analysis of the orbits of the stars in an astrometric binary is difficult since only one star is visible. With only optical data, astronomers cannot determine individual masses. In many cases, observations include spectroscopic data. These additional data give valuable information on the motions of both components in binary systems and, together with the optical observations, allow astronomers to determine individual masses. Detailed analyses of about 20 astrometric binaries give masses from 0.1 $\mathfrak{M}_\odot$ to 1 $\mathfrak{M}_\odot$.

Some binary systems are so far away that the two stars appear as a single image in even the largest telescopes. At the same time, their great distances ensure that any "wiggly" motion due to a faint companion is imperceptible. Nevertheless, astronomers can still distinguish very distant binaries from single stars. Recall that, when a single star is moving away from or toward us, its Doppler shift is constant, being either a redshift or a blueshift. If a star is also orbiting another star at the same time, its Doppler shift will vary periodically. That is, when the star is

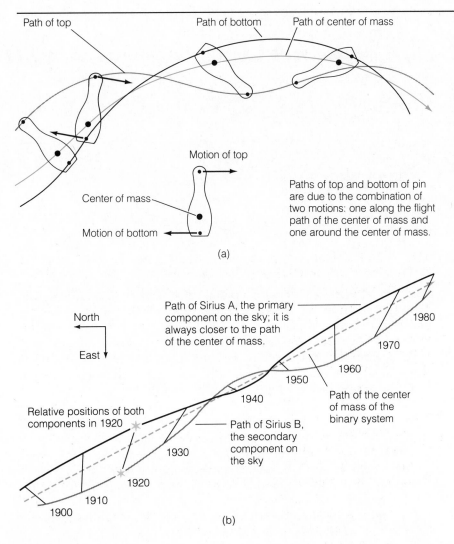

Path of top

Path of bottom

Path of center of mass

Motion of top

Center of mass

Motion of bottom

Paths of top and bottom of pin are due to the combination of two motions: one along the flight path of the center of mass and one around the center of mass.

(a)

North

East

Path of Sirius A, the primary component on the sky; it is always closer to the path of the center of mass.

1980

1970

1960

1950

Path of the center of mass of the binary system

1940

Relative positions of both components in 1920

Path of Sirius B, the secondary component on the sky

1930

1920

1910

1900

(b)

▆▆▆ FIGURE 14.10

Astrometric Motion

(a) The paths of both ends of a bowling pin make wiggly lines through the air as they both spin about the center of mass of the pin and move through the air. (b) The dotted straight line represents the motion of the center of mass of Sirius A and Sirius B. The short straight lines connect the positions of the two stars at the time indicated. Since Sirius A is twice the mass of Sirius B, its path is twice as close to the center of mass as that of Sirius B.

moving toward us *in its orbit*, its radial velocity has an added blue shift. When it is moving away from us *in its orbit*, its radial velocity has an added redshift. The spectral lines shift to the red, then to the blue, and back to red. These shifts are in addition to the system's Doppler shift produced by its space velocity. Binaries detected through variations in their spectra are called **spectroscopic binaries.**

The orbital period for a spectroscopic binary is the time it takes for the observed spectral lines to cycle through the red to blue to red variations. The periodicity of the orbital motion in radial velocity is clearly seen in a plot of radial velocity versus time. Such a graph is called a **radial velocity curve.** Figure 14.11 shows the radial velocity curve for one component of a spectroscopic binary in which the star moves in a circular orbit. This binary system is moving away from us at 100 km/s, and the orbital speed of the visible component is 15 km/s. The 15 km/s

Spectroscopic binary: A double star detected by periodic shifts of spectral lines and occasionally by overlapping of two normal spectra (double-line spectroscopic binary).

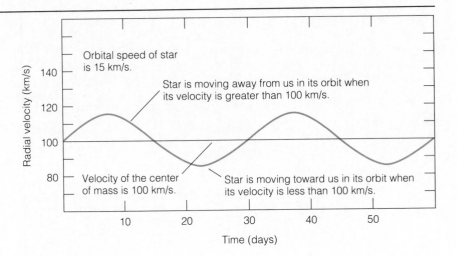

■ FIGURE 14.11

Radial Velocity Curve for a Circular Orbit with One Component Visible

Although this binary system is moving away from us at 100 km/s, the measured radial velocity varies between 85 km/s and 115 km/s because the orbital speed of the stars is 15 km/s. Here only the radial velocity of one component is shown.

■ FIGURE 14.12

Double-Line Spectroscopic Binary

These are two spectra of the binary star Kappa Arietis. The upper spectrum shows every line double because both stars are bright enough for us to record their spectra. One star is moving away from us, and the other is moving toward us in their orbits. The lower spectrum shows the same system when the individual stars are moving across our line of sight and, therefore, do not contribute to the measured radial velocity. Why must both stars be moving across our line of sight at the same time?

SOURCE: Lick Observatory, University of California, Santa Cruz.

is added to the measured system radial velocity when the star is moving directly away from us in its orbit. It is subtracted from the system radial velocity when the star is moving directly toward us in its orbit. When the star is moving across our line of sight, it does not contribute to the measured radial velocity, and the spectrum shows only the system velocity, 100 km/s. Since the radial velocity curve repeats every 30 days, the orbital period of this system is 30 days.

Because of their large distances from us and the requirement that they must be close together (otherwise we would detect them as visual binaries), orbital periods for spectroscopic binaries are short, tens to hundreds of days and even less. If both components are bright, their period is visible from two sets of spectral lines (Figure 14.12). The observed spectral lines themselves crisscross, oscillating between their maximum and minimum values.

The shape of a radial velocity curve depends on the orbital eccentricity and the orientation of the orbit in space. Circular orbits produce sinusoidal radial velocity curves, like the one shown in Figure 14.11, while elliptical orbits distort this shape. As a result, careful analysis of the radial velocity curve of a spectroscopic binary gives the shape of the orbit. Unfortunately, individual masses cannot be determined because the orbit is tilted, or inclined, with respect to the plane of the sky by an unknown amount (Figure 14.13). This means that the size of the semi-

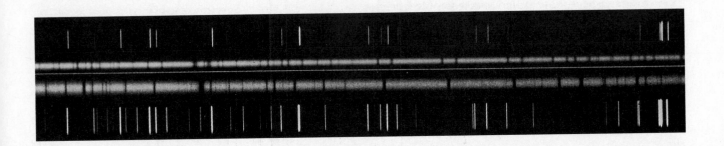

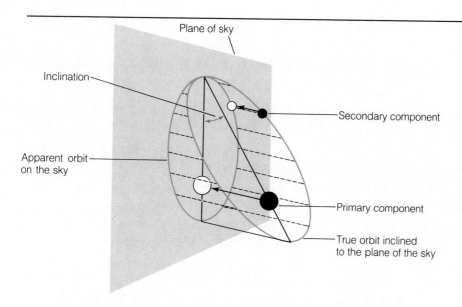

Plane of sky

Inclination

Apparent orbit
on the sky

Secondary component

Primary component

True orbit inclined
to the plane of the sky

■ **FIGURE 14.13**
Orbital Inclination

Observed orbits are only projections of
the real orbits onto the sky. If astronomers are unable to determine the inclination, as with spectroscopic binaries, they
always underestimate the size of the orbit
and the masses of the individual stars.
Thus the true orbit is always larger than
the apparent orbit.

major axis is always underestimated. Consequently, the masses from
spectroscopic binaries are all lower limits; actual masses are larger.

Suppose a spectroscopic binary system were tilted 90° with respect to
the plane of the sky. The orbit is on edge from our viewpoint. In such a
system, one star would pass in front of the other, causing an eclipse.
During the eclipse, the total brightness of the system decreases. During
one orbital period two eclipses occur; once when one component passes
in front of the other and again when it passes behind. When the hotter
star is eclipsed, the decrease in light is greatest; this is called the *primary minimum* in brightness. If the eclipsed star is the cooler of the
two, the decrease in light is less than during the primary minimum;
this is called the *secondary minimum*. These eclipsing systems are called
eclipsing binaries.

The first observed eclipsing binary was Algol, the second brightest
star in the constellation Perseus. Astronomers first noticed its variable
brightness in 1669 and were able to show in 1783 that the brightness
changed periodically every 2 days 20 hours and 40 minutes. Algol is a
naked eye eclipsing binary; the dates and times of the minima of Algol
are published every month in *Sky & Telescope* magazine. It takes about
2 hours for the eclipse, during which time Algol fades by 1.3 magnitudes, becoming about one-third as bright. The eclipse in the Algol system occurs between a B8 dwarf and a fainter G5 subgiant. The primary
minimum is very faint, or "deep," and occurs when the cooler, yellow
subgiant covers the hotter main-sequence star. Detailed analysis of the
Algol system reveals that it is a triple-star system. The B8 V and G5 IV
pair are very close to each other, only about 10 million km apart, while
the third component, a 2 $\mathfrak{M}_\odot$ A star, is about 2.5 AU away and takes
about 2 years to orbit the eclipsing pair A and B.

The light variation in eclipsing binaries when plotted against time is
called a **light curve.** Figure 14.14 shows a hypothetical light curve and

Eclipsing binary: A double star in
which the orbital plane is viewed
nearly edge on from the Earth so that
the stars eclipse each other.

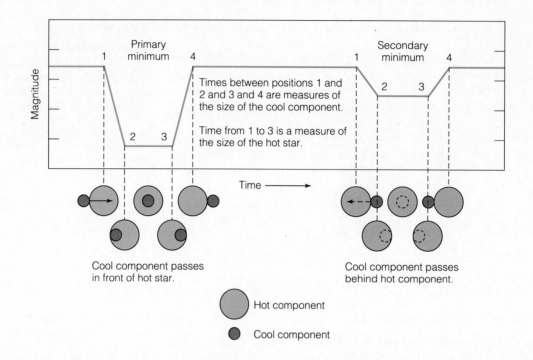

Times between positions 1 and 2 and 3 and 4 are measures of the size of the cool component.

Time from 1 to 3 is a measure of the size of the hot star.

Cool component passes in front of hot star.

Cool component passes behind hot component.

Hot component

Cool component

■■■ FIGURE 14.14

Light Curve for an Eclipsing Binary System

Shown here are the primary and secondary minima and the relative positions of the stars in an eclipsing binary. When the cooler star crosses in front of the hotter star, we observe a primary minimum. The secondary minimum is a smaller drop in brightness as the cooler star is eclipsed.

Types of binary systems:

- Visual binaries
- Astrometric binaries
- Spectroscopic binaries
- Eclipsing binaries

the relative positions of both stars during the eclipses. During the primary minimum, light from the system decreases between positions 1 and 2. At position 1 the cool component begins to move in front of the hot component, and at 2 it is completely in front. Between positions 2 and 3 the light from the system stays constant and is a minimum. It begins to rise as the stars come out of eclipse between positions 3 and 4. The secondary minimum is a repeat of the primary minimum except that less light is blocked as the cooler star is eclipsed. Detailed analyses of light curves can give the exact orbital inclination (always near 90°) and eccentricity. The times between positions 1 and 2 and positions 1 and 3 also allow astronomers to calculate the relative sizes of the stars. Finally, if spectroscopic data are available in addition to the light curve, absolute orbits can be calculated and, as a result, individual masses and radii.

Binary stars offer the only means of deriving the masses of stars. The types of binary stars, visual, astrometric, spectroscopic, and eclipsing, represent a sequence from wide pairs to close pairs. The wider apart the pairs are, the easier it is to detect them; the closer together the pair, the faster they orbit each other and the greater are their Doppler shifts. Of course, distance from us is also important in their detectability, more so for visual detection than for spectroscopic detection. Many binary stars themselves belong to multiple-star systems. Algol, for instance, is part of a triple-star system. The bright star Castor, in the constellation Gemini, is part of a sixfold system (Figure 14.15). It consists of three pairs, A, B, and C, with orbital periods of 9.2, 2.9, and 0.8 days. Pair A and B orbit each other in 380 years at a distance of 85 AU, and pair C orbits A and B in several thousand years at a distance of about 1000 AU.

Astronomers can determine stellar masses only for visual binaries and eclipsing binaries. Individual masses for the components of spectroscopic binaries are lower limits because the inclination of the systems is unknown. Table 14.4 lists a few masses for visual and eclipsing binaries and lower limits for several spectroscopic binaries.

Now that mass has been added to the list of stellar characteristics, a close look at the HR diagram and in particular at the main-sequence stars is warranted. This will reveal that trends along the main sequence reflect trends in stellar mass.

The Mass-Luminosity Relationship

Just as taller students generally are heavier, brighter main-sequence stars are more massive. Figure 14.16 shows this trend for 140 stars between the masses of about 0.1 $\mathfrak{M}_\odot$ to about 30 $\mathfrak{M}_\odot$. Nearly all of the stars are main-sequence stars; no reliable masses exist for giants or supergiants. This predominance of main-sequence stars is expected because most stars in the sky are, in fact, main-sequence stars. The trend between mass and luminosity shown in Figure 14.16 is called the **mass-luminosity relation.** It shows that the main sequence is a progression in mass as well as in temperature and luminosity. Faint, cool main-sequence stars have low masses; bright, hot main-sequence stars have high masses. Stellar mass is another "hidden" parameter in the HR diagram.

Just as there were exceptions to the general trends in the height-weight distribution in the student population, stars show exceptions to the main-sequence mass-luminosity relationship. Measured masses and

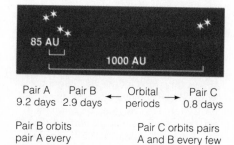

All three pairs are spectroscopic binaries.

85 AU

1000 AU

Pair A   Pair B   ← Orbital → Pair C
9.2 days   2.9 days   periods   0.8 days

Pair B orbits pair A every 380 years.

Pair C orbits pairs A and B every few thousand years.

FIGURE 14.15

The Castor Sextuple System

This system consists of six stars in three pairs that are gravitationally bound.

Mass-luminosity relation: The empirically determined trend for main-sequence stars: the more massive a star is, the brighter it is.

TABLE 14.4 Masses of Stars in Binary Systems

Name	Spectral Class		Period	Separation	Masses ($\mathfrak{M}_\odot$)	
	A	*B*			*A*	*B*
Visual binaries:						
Sirius	A1 V	White dwarf	50 years	20.5 AU	2.3	1.0
Krüger 60	M4 V	M6 V	45 years	9.5 AU	0.27	0.16
Alpha Centauri	G4 V	K1 V	80 years	23.5 AU	1.1	0.9
Spectroscopic binaries:						
Gamma Persei	G8 III	A2 V	5350 days	Unresolved	>4.7	>2.7
Alpha Virginis	B2 V	B3 V	4 days	>9 R$_\odot$	>7.5	>4.5
Beta Scorpii	B1 V	B2 V	6.8 days	Unresolved	>16.0	>9.6
32 o²Cygni	K3 Ib	B3 V	1141 days	Unresolved	>9.2	>7.6
Eclipsing binaries:						
Sigma Aquilæ	B3 V	B3 V	2.0 days	15 R$_\odot$	6.8	5.4
AR Cassiopeiæ	B3	A0	6.1 days	35 R$_\odot$	11.9	3.0
Algol	B8 V	G5 III	2.8 days	16 R$_\odot$	5.2	1.0
W Ursa Majoris	F8	F7	0.33 days	2.5 R$_\odot$	1.3	0.7

■■■■ **FIGURE 14.16**

Mass-Luminosity Relation

Mass and luminosity are plotted for 147
main-sequence stars and 3 white dwarfs.
Mass increases as luminosity increases
along the main sequence. The insert
shows this trend on the HR diagram.
White dwarfs obey a different mass-luminosity relation; they are underluminous
relative to main-sequence stars of the
same mass. (See MathTools 1: Graphs
and Plots 〰 for a review of logarithmic graphs.)

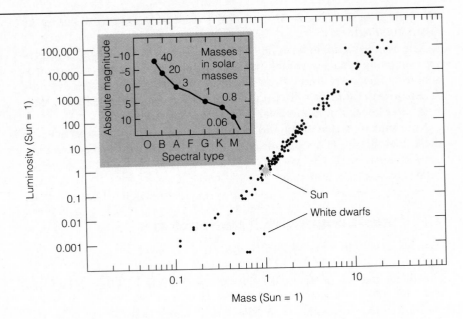

luminosities for white dwarfs show that they are underluminous compared to main-sequence stars of similar mass. White dwarfs are also
underluminous compared to main-sequence stars of the same temperature. Giants and supergiants, on the other hand, are expected to be
brighter than their main-sequence counterparts in mass (see Chapter
16). These deviations from the main-sequence mass-luminosity relationship are important clues to understanding the changes that occur in
stars as they use up hydrogen fuel at their centers. Chapter 16 will also
reveal that main-sequence stars, white dwarfs, and giants all have different sources of energy, and that this is responsible for the different
luminosities of stars with the same mass.

Figure 14.16 indicates that the mass range among stars is only two
orders of magnitude while the range in stellar luminosity is many orders of magnitude. Luminosity is clearly a very sensitive function of
mass. Earlier in this chapter it was noted that different combinations
of luminosity and temperature implied different stellar radii. Direct determination of stellar radii is very difficult, however.

■■■THE SIZES OF STARS

From their study of the HR diagram, astronomers realize that stars
vary in size. The Sun is the only star for which we can see an angular
diameter. All other stars are so far away that they appear as points of
light without any visible diameter. How then can astronomers assign
numerical values to the radii of supergiants, giants, and dwarfs? The
Stefan-Boltzmann law allows an estimate to be made based on a star's
luminosity and temperature. It states that the star's luminosity is pro-

portional to its surface area ($4\pi R^2$) and to the energy emitted by each square centimeter (σT^4): $L = 4\pi R^2 \sigma T^4$, or

$$R^2 = \frac{L}{4\pi\sigma T^4}$$

Comparing a star's radius with the Sun's radius eliminates the need to keep track of the constants, 4π and σ, in this equation.

$$\frac{R^2}{R_\odot^2} = \frac{L}{L_\odot}\left(\frac{T_\odot}{T}\right)^4$$

For example, if a star were half the temperature of the Sun but 100 times brighter, its radius would be the square root of $(100)(2^4) = 1600$ or $40\ R_\odot$. On the other hand, a star at twice the temperature of the Sun and 100 times fainter has a radius equal to the square root of $(0.01)(\frac{1}{2})^4$ or $0.03\ R_\odot$. Radii estimated from the radiation laws are indirect measurements because they do not involve an observational measurement of the size of the star and are only as accurate as the measured luminosities and temperatures.

One direct method uses the light curves and radial velocity curves of eclipsing binary systems. Since the radial velocity curve gives the speed of the orbiting stars and the observed light curve gives the times of the eclipses, astronomers can easily calculate how far the stars travel during an eclipse and, therefore, their diameters. Figure 14.17 shows that the time from position 1 to position 2 is the time needed for the cooler star to move a distance equal to its diameter. Since both stars are moving, the cooler to the right and the hotter to the left, the diameter of the cooler star is equal to the product of the relative velocity of the stars times this time interval. A similar analysis applies to the hotter star.

Eclipses of objects completely unrelated in any physical way to each other provide a second way to measure stellar radii. The Moon, for instance, sometimes passes in front of distant stars and eclipses them. Since a star has a finite diameter, it does not instantaneously disappear when the Moon occults it but fades gradually. It takes a short amount of time for the disk of the star to pass completely behind the limb of the Moon. The diameter of the star is derived from the duration of its decrease in brightness. The largest stars take only about $\frac{1}{5}$ of a second, but astronomers are able to sample the light from the star every $\frac{1}{100}$ to $\frac{1}{1000}$ of a second. These observations are complicated because the light from a star does not have a smooth distribution but, due to the optics of the telescope, appears under very high magnification as a set of concentric rings. (See Figure 12 in Module 2, Astronomical Instruments and Telescopes.) Therefore the actual reduction in brightness is not a smooth continuous decrease. Furthermore, the edge of the Moon is irregular, causing an even more complex light pattern. This can partially be overcome by observing the occultation from different sites on Earth.

A third method of measuring stellar diameters involves improving the ability of a telescope to resolve images of stars. Draw two dots on a piece of paper so close together that seen across the room they appear as only a single dot. If you approach the two dots, you will eventually

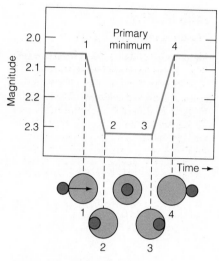

Time between positions 1 and 2 is the time it takes the cooler star to move a distance equal to its diameter.

Time between positions 1 and 3 is the time it takes the cooler star to move a distance equal to the diameter of the hotter star.

■ **FIGURE 14.17**

Primary Eclipse

The time it takes the cool component to pass from position 1 to position 2 and from 3 to 4 is a measure of the size of the cool component. The time it takes the cool star to pass completely in front of the hot component, from position 1 to position 3, is a measure of the size of the hot component.

■ FIGURE 14.18

Stellar Interferometer

Shown here is an optical interferometer that brings light to a common focus that is reflected off two mirrors placed at both sides of the telescope. Interference patterns from different parts of the star disappear when the mirrors are moved far enough apart.

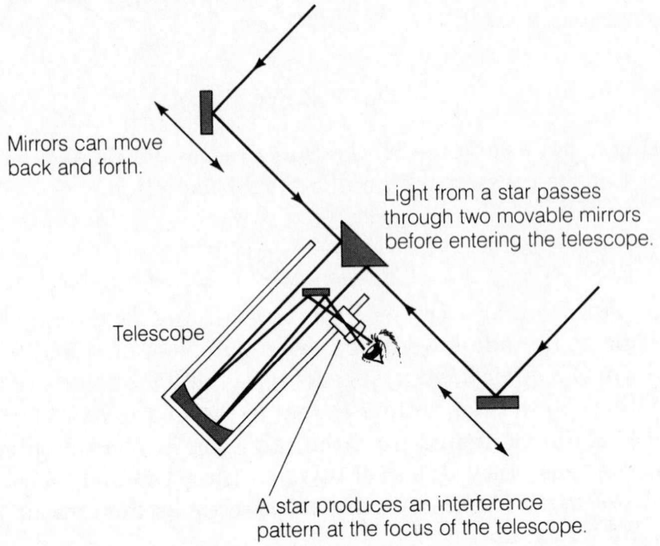

Mirrors can move back and forth.

Light from a star passes through two movable mirrors before entering the telescope.

Telescope

A star produces an interference pattern at the focus of the telescope.

Interferometer: An instrument, usually consisting of two or more detectors, that is used to improve the resolving ability of a telescope.

see them as two dots again—you have *resolved* the dots. Astronomers improved the resolution of the Mt. Wilson 2.5-meter telescope by adding two mirrors about four meters apart and brought the light from both mirrors to a common focus. Such a device is called an **interferometer** (Figure 14.18).

The ability of a large telescope to resolve two images or see a star as a disk depends on the turbulence of the Earth's atmosphere. This means that angular sizes smaller than about 1 second of arc cannot be measured. But, except for the Sun, no star is large enough or close enough to show up as a disk larger than 1 second of arc. Although we cannot see stellar disks even with an interferometer, the light collected from stars can reveal their radii. When trying to see the image of a star as a disk, astronomers are really trying to locate the edges of the disk to obtain the angular size of the star. Light entering an interferometer from the right and left edges of a star will arrive at each mirror at slightly different times and will have traveled slightly different distances to the common focus. The light from the edges will produce an interference pattern, an alternating light and dark intensity pattern

■ TABLE 14.5 **Stellar Radii**

Star	Name	Spectral Type	Radius ($R_\odot$)
Aldebaran	Alpha Tauri	K5 III	48
Antares	Alpha Scorpii	M1 Ib	700
Arcturus	Alpha Boötis	K1 III	26
Sirius	Alpha Canis Majoris	A1 V	2
Vega	Alpha Lyræ	A0 IV–V	4
—	VV Cephei	M2 Ia	~1200

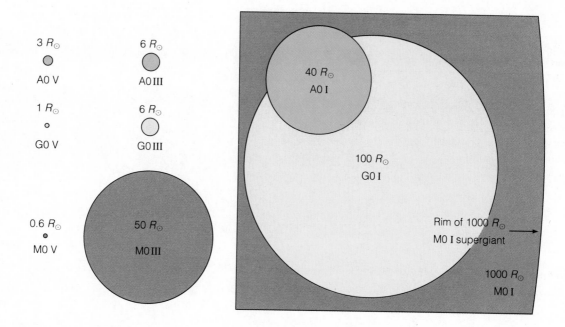

Relative Sizes of Stars

Here the sizes of dwarfs, giants, and supergiants of spectral type A0, G0, and M0 are compared. Moving from left to right at one of the spectral types is the same as moving vertically upward in the HR diagram. The radius of the M0 supergiant is too large to show completely.

caused by the light from one edge of the star interfering, or merging with, the light from the other edge. Interference patterns are caused by point sources of light; and in this case, the point sources are the edges of the star. Increasing the distance between the mirrors of the interferometer will eventually cause the interference pattern to disappear. At that time the star is no longer a point source to the interferometer. The angular extent of the star, the spacing of the mirrors, and the wavelength of light observed are related so that the star's radius is determinable if we know its distance.

Thus eclipsing binary systems, lunar occultations, and interferometers all provide direct methods of determining stellar radii. Table 14.5 lists several examples of these radius measurements, and Figure 14.19 shows the relative sizes of dwarfs, giants, and supergiants of different spectral classes.

■ SUMMARY

Table 14.6 lists the luminosities, masses, radii, and temperatures for stars in different spectral and luminosity classes. The range in mass listed is relatively small, from $\sim 0.2\ \mathfrak{M}_\odot$ to $\sim 50\ \mathfrak{M}_\odot$, while stellar radii can vary considerably, $0.01\ R_\odot$ to $\sim 1000\ R_\odot$. Stellar luminosity exhibits the greatest range, covering more than 10 orders of magnitude. For comparison, the last line of Table 14.6 lists these values for the Sun.

Absolute magnitudes of stars can be calculated from a star's apparent magnitude and its distance, using the inverse square law. Since the Sun's absolute magnitude and luminosity are known, we compare stellar absolute magnitudes to the Sun's to obtain luminosities, remembering that a difference of 5 magnitudes means a factor of 100 in brightness.

Binaries, or double stars, are the only means astronomers have for determining stellar mass. Luckily, binaries are very common—nearly half of all stars belong to binary and multiple-star systems. If

■■■ TABLE 14.6 **Characteristics of Stars**

Luminosity Class	Spectral Class	$L/L_\odot$	$\mathfrak{M}/\mathfrak{M}_\odot$	$R/R_\odot$	Temperature (K)
V	05	5×10^5	40	20	40,000
	B0	2×10^4	18	10	29,600
	A0	100	3	3	9600
	F0	7	2	1.3	7000
	G0	1.2	1.1	1.05	6000
	G2	1.0	1.0	1.0	5800
	K0	0.4	0.8	0.9	4200
	M0	0.06	0.5	0.6	3500
	M5	0.001	0.2	0.3	3000
III	B0	~1000	~25	16	30,000
	A0	~200	~5	6	10,000
	F0	~16	~2	4	7200
	G0	~30	2.5	6	5700
	K0	~40	4	16	4500
	M0	~100	6	~50	3500
I	B0	3×10^5	50	20	28,600
	A0	2×10^4	16	40	10,000
	F0	8×10^3	12	60	7800
	G0	6×10^3	10	100	5500
	K0	1×10^4	13	200	4500
	M0	3×10^4	17	1000	3200
White dwarfs	—	10^{-2}–10^{-6}	<1	0.01	6000–10,000
Sun	G2 V	$L_\odot = 3.8 \times 10^{26}$ watts	$\mathfrak{M}_\odot = 2 \times 10^{30}$ kg	$R_\odot = 7 \times 10^5$ km	$T_\odot = 5800$ K

we can see both components of a binary, it is a visual binary. An astrometric binary is one in which we can see only one component. The invisible component is massive enough to cause measurable motion of the visible component around the center of mass. Spectroscopic binaries, which are either so distant from us or so close to each other that they appear as one star in the telescope, are detected by periodic shifts in their spectral lines. Spectroscopic binaries only reveal lower limits to individual masses because we cannot determine the inclination of their orbits. Eclipsing binaries are binaries seen edge on in which the stars eclipse each other; they can be detected through light variations. We use the radial velocity curve and the light curve of a spectroscopic eclipsing binary to extract enough information about the orbits to determine individual masses.

The HR diagram introduced in this chapter is a graph of absolute magnitude (luminosity) versus spectral type (temperature). It concisely displays the various types of stars, such as main-sequence stars, giants, and supergiants. It also shows that not all luminosity and temperature pairs are possible for stars. Two parameters, mass and radius, are "hidden" among the data plotted in the HR diagram. Mass increases along the main sequence: faint, cool dwarfs have low masses while bright, hot dwarfs have high masses. The radii of stars in the HR diagram increase diagonally from the lower left to the upper right. Figure 14.20 shows lines of constant stel-

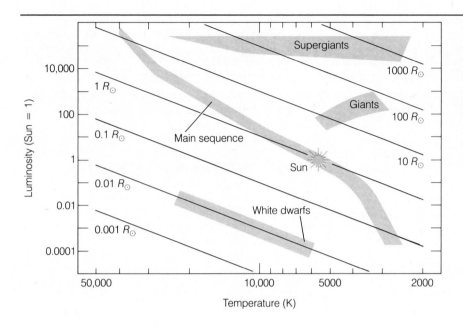

Stellar Radii on the HR Diagram

Lines of constant radius are plotted on an HR diagram with luminosity and temperature on the axes. From the radiation laws we have $R^2 \propto L/T^4$. Notice that the main sequence is not exactly parallel to a line of constant radius; radii increase slightly along the main sequence.

lar radii. Radii, luminosities, and temperatures are plotted in Figure 14.20 because they are mathematically related through the radiation laws.

Stellar radii can be obtained directly from timings of eclipses in eclipsing binaries, from lunar occultations, and from interferometry.

■■■CHAPTER CAPSULE

Topics and Terms	Review and Remarks
Absolute magnitude	The apparent magnitude a star would have if it were 10 pc away. It is obtained from known distances and apparent magnitudes.
Double stars	Visual: both stars are visible and the relative orbit is directly observable. Astrometric: one star is visible, and the other is inferred from the motion of the visible companion. Spectroscopic: one star is visible, and the other is inferred from the Doppler shift of the observed spectrum of the system. Eclipsing: one star is visible and the other is inferred from eclipses. Optical: two stars are visible but they are not true double stars.
Observations of binary systems	Relative orbits Absolute orbits Radial velocity curves Light curves
Hertzsprung-Russell diagram (HR diagram)	A plot of magnitude (luminosity) versus spectral type (temperature) It exhibits the luminosity classes: White dwarfs, dwarfs, giants, and supergiants. The hidden parameters are mass and radius: Mass increases along the main sequence from faint stars to bright stars. Radius increases diagonally from lower left to upper right.

REVIEW QUESTIONS

1. Why do astronomers use absolute magnitude rather than apparent magnitude when discussing the characteristics of a star or when comparing stars?

2. If the Sun were at a distance of 10 pc, it would have an apparent magnitude of +4.8. What would its apparent magnitude be if it were at a distance of 100 pc? At what approximate distance would its apparent magnitude be at the visibility limit of the human eye?

3. If a star at 100 pc has an apparent magnitude of −0.20, what is its absolute magnitude? By what factor is this star more or less luminous than the Sun? If this is a main-sequence star, what is its spectral class?

4. An A0 V star has an apparent magnitude of +10. From information given in the text, determine the absolute magnitude, mass, and diameter of this star. How far away is it?

5. Imagine a horizontal line across the top of an HR diagram. Compare the properties of stars at opposite ends of this line. Repeat for stars at opposite ends of a vertical line near the right side of an HR diagram.

6. How are stars of similar diameter distributed on an HR diagram? Where are the largest and smallest stars located? How are masses and diameters distributed along the main sequence?

7. Compare the physical properties of Proxima Centauri and Betelgeuse if Proxima is an M5 V star and Betelgeuse is an M2 Ia star.

8. A G2 Ia star has the same temperature as the Sun but it has an absolute magnitude of about −10. Compare the luminosities and diameters of these two stars.

9. Binary stars can be classified as visual, astrometric, spectroscopic, or eclipsing. How are each of these types identified? Can one binary be more than one of these types? For which HR diagram stars does the mass-luminosity relation hold?

10. In general, the two minima of the light curve of an eclipsing binary will not be of the same depth. Explain what property of the two stars makes these minima different.

FOR FURTHER READING

Croswell, K. 1985. When stars coalesce. *Astronomy*, May, 67.

Hopkins, J. L., and R. E. Stencel. 1986. Epsilon Aurigae. *Astronomy*, Feb., 6.

Kaler, J. 1986. M stars: Subgiants to dwarfs. *Sky & Telescope*, May, 450.

———. 1986. The K stars: Orange giants and dwarfs. *Sky & Telescope*, Aug., 130.

———. 1986. Cousins of our Sun: The G stars. *Sky & Telescope*, Nov., 450.

———. 1987. The temperate F stars. *Sky & Telescope*, Feb., 131.

———. 1987. White Sirian stars: Class A. *Sky & Telescope*, May, 490.

———. 1987. The B stars: Beacons of the skies, *Sky & Telescope*, Aug., 146.

———. 1987. The spectacular O stars. *Sky & Telescope*, Nov., 464.

Levy, D., and P. Jedicke. 1987. Betelgeuse. *Astronomy*, Apr., 6.

MacKeown, P. K., and T. C. Weekes. 1985. Cosmic rays from Cygnus X-3. *Scientific American*, Nov., 60.

Schild, R. E. 1988. Coloring the electronic sky. *Sky & Telescope*, Feb., 144.

Tomkin, J., and D. L. Lambert. 1987. The strange case of Beta Lyrae. *Sky & Telescope*, Oct., 354.

ASTROPROBE 14

Pixels and Stars: Stellar Imaging

Most astronomy books are filled with photographs of planets, comets, stars, and galaxies. Pictures certainly catch the attention of the reader, and their abundant use emphasizes the importance of photography to astronomy. After the development of the telescope, one of the most important tools that astronomers have applied to astronomical research is photography. Before they developed the ability to record the light gathered with the telescope permanently, astronomers made all measurements at the telescope. They jammed their eyes to the eyepiece and counted the stars in the Milky Way, measured the positions of stars and planets, and drew pictures of planets, comets, and galaxies. Photography allows astronomers to do all this and much more, more accurately and in less time. With the camera, observers can photograph many stars at once and measure their positions and brightnesses; measurements are more accurate because they are not limited by what equipment can be placed at the telescope eyepiece; and the photographs provide a permanent record of the observations. Furthermore, in the last decade astronomers have found methods to analyze photographs and new ways to record images that reveal previously hidden details. At the same time, these methods generate an overwhelming amount of data. Only with the help of high-speed computers can astronomers assimilate and begin to understand their observations.

▅▅▅PHOTOGRAPHY

When film is exposed to light, the light produces photographic images through chemical action. These chemical reactions take place in the film's **emulsion,** a layer of gelatin consisting of many tiny grains of silver bromide. The emulsion is coated onto a plastic or glass base. Astronomers prefer the glass base, or plate as we call it, for several reasons. Many astronomical cameras require large plates; 51 centimeter (20-inch) square plates are often used for surveys (Figure 14A.1). It is difficult to support a large piece of plastic film in a camera without the film sagging. Furthermore, some cameras purposefully bend glass plates to a slight curve because the optics of some telescopes give the best images on a curved surface. Plates snap back to their original flat shape after being curved, but large pieces of film treated similarly will buckle and stretch irreversibly. Furthermore, many astronomical emulsions are thicker than commercial emulsions and tend to shrink during processing; they need the firm support glass provides.

The light falling onto a photographic plate produces a chemical separation of silver and bromine. This process, unfortunately, is very inefficient—only a few percent of all photons falling on the emulsion

▅▅▅ FIGURE 14A.1

Photographic Plates

A 36 by 43 cm (14 by 17 inch) plate and a 20 by 25 cm (8 by 10 inch) plate are compared to a 35 mm negative.

SOURCE: Evan Flower.

FIGURE 14A.2

Star Images

This is a highly magnified image of a star field. Bright stars are large and dark while faint stars are much smaller and less distinct.

SOURCE: Phillip Flower.

Negative: The developed emulsion showing the metallic silver grains that were struck by photons; it reverses the relationship between light and dark of the original subject.

Bit: A single digit, either 0 or 1, in a binary number system; the numbers we use, such as 2, 5, and 6, can be represented by a series of bits.

actually separate the silver and bromine. Furthermore, each grain of silver bromide must be struck more than once before the atoms separate. Once the separation occurs, it is made permanent by "developing" the plate. This process leaves clumps of metallic silver in the emulsion. The excess bromine atoms and undeveloped grains of silver bromide are then washed away in a process called "fixing" that prevents further chemical reactions. Developing and fixing leave a permanent image, a **negative;** the places where light struck are blackened, and the places where the light did not strike are clear, or transparent.

Once we have a negative, what can we do with it? Obviously, prints can be made just as a camera shop makes prints from the film we take for developing. Prints are used to identify objects, to help classify them, to study their structure, or simply to count them. For some purposes, however, the original photographic plates are more useful than prints. Observers often make measurements, such as positions, spectral line identification, radial velocities, and magnitude, with special measuring machines that require the support that glass plates provide. In addition, the image quality of a print is not as high as that of the original negative. Consequently, astronomers usually measure directly from negatives. For instance, we measure the spacing between spectral lines for line identifications and radial velocities right from the original plate. We can also measure the brightnesses of stars from photographic plates by measuring the diameters of star images. The brighter the star, the larger the image. Bright stars generate many photons that strike the silver bromide grains in the emulsion and make large clumps of silver (Figure 14A.2). Of course, when astronomers publish results obtained from measurements of plates, they generally show prints of their negatives.

Measurements made directly from negatives, such as the distance between two spectral lines or the diameter of a stellar image, generally follow relatively straightforward and well-defined procedures. Astronomers, however, did not realize the extent of hidden information in photographs until the 1970s when they discovered "digitizing" and the power of the computer.

DIGITAL IMAGE PROCESSING

A computer only handles two numbers, "1" and "0"; it interprets these electronically as "on" and "off." We call 1 or 0 a **bit** and can represent a number by a series of bits. A typical personal computer represents a number by 8 bits. Here are some examples of numbers represented by 8 bits:

0 is 00000000.

1 is 00000001.

2 is 00000010.

3 is 00000011.

4 is 00000100.

8 is 00001000.

15 is 00001111.

255 is 11111111.

Using two numbers, 0 and 1, in this way is also called binary notation. The value of an 8-bit number is calculated using "powers of 2." The value for the *power* of 2 is "0" if the farthest digit to the right is 1, "1" if the next digit to the left is 1, and reaches "7" for the farthest digit to the left. The 1 at the first, second, third, and fourth places from the right, for instance, represents the numbers 1 $(= 2^0 = 1)$, 2 $(= 2^1)$, 4 $(= 2^2)$, and 8 $(= 2^3)$, respectively. The number 2, 00000010, is just $2^1 = 2$ while the number 15 is $2^3 + 2^2 + 2^1 + 2^0 = 8 + 4 + 2 + 1 = 15$. Notice that if a bit is 0, then that power of 2 is not used. The largest number represented by 8 bits is 255; that is, $255 = 128 + 64 + 32 + 16 + 8 + 4 + 2 + 1$. Try to construct 8-bit binary numbers for numbers 5, 6, and 7 and even larger numbers. All operations performed by a computer involve the manipulation of binary bits.

Digitizing is the process of converting a picture into numbers, or digits. In the simplest representation of a picture with numbers, we divide the picture into small segments and represent each segment by a 1-bit number, either 0 or 1. The number "0" represents black while "1" represents white or transparent. A picture, therefore, can be represented as a rectangular or square array with each element of the array being a 1-bit number. In Figure 14A.3, a black square on a white background is pictured together with its "digital image." The digital image is an array of numbers that the computer stores. In Figure 14A.3 each picture element, or **pixel**, is represented by a single digit, 0 or 1. This single digit representation of pictures is useful today in optical-character-recognition applications where a typewritten page is scanned by a camera and a computer converts the recorded images, black and white shapes, into letters. The images of objects, such as stars and galaxies, are not simple black shapes but generally show many *gray levels*. In this case we can represent each segment by an 8-bit number from 0 to 255. The number "0" represents black as before, while "255" now represents white or transparent; numbers in between are shades of gray. The picture is now

Pixel: Abbreviation of the term *picture element;* an individual component element of a digital image.

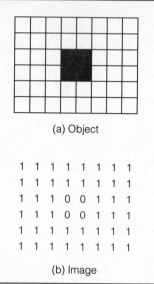

(a) Object

```
1 1 1 1 1 1 1 1
1 1 1 1 1 1 1 1
1 1 1 0 0 1 1 1
1 1 1 0 0 1 1 1
1 1 1 1 1 1 1 1
1 1 1 1 1 1 1 1
```

(b) Image

■■■ FIGURE 14A.3

Digital Image of a Black Square on a White Background

The group of numbers in Panel b is called the digital image; it is a numerical representation of the object and background. The grid in Panel a gives the size of the pixels in the digital image; the square is represented by four pixels. The digital image is stored in the computer as an *array* of 48 numbers, 6 × 8 array.

stored in the computer as an array of 8-bit numbers. The resulting range of pixel values, 0 to 255, allows us to display many gray levels and, consequently, to see much detail.

To digitize a photographic plate or print, we illuminate the plate from behind or the print from above and scan across it with a device called a *microdensitometer*, which measures light intensity as a camera's light meter does. You can envision the scanning process as dividing the picture into tiny square segments and measuring how much light passes through a plate or is reflected off a print in each segment. We construct the final digital picture by assembling all of the tiny squares together like the pieces of a puzzle. When we scan a star on a plate, for instance, we measure very little or no light passing through the star; in areas free of stars, we measure all of the light passing through the negative.

Before scanning a plate or a print, we must choose the size of the squares to sample. This is the size of the pixel whose value represents the transparency of a small segment of the picture. We make the pixel size smaller than the smallest object on the plate or print we wish to study. Figure 14A.4 shows the results of several scans over a black triangle on a white background using different pixel sizes. With the large pixel size, a pixel may sample part of the triangle and part of the background at the same time, resulting in pixel values between the black and white limits of 0 and 255. Consequently, the digitized image exhibits several shades of gray (Panels a and b). Furthermore, using large pixels does not allow us to define the edges of the triangle very well. As the pixel size becomes smaller, the boundaries of the triangle become sharper. We are *resolving* image detail as the boundaries of objects become clearer.

Normally, we are interested in only a small portion of an entire plate, perhaps a small galaxy or a comet. Even digitizing small areas results in a tremendous amount of data; a 3-by-3-inch square on a plate typically needs an array of a thousand pixels on each side, or 10^6 pixels. If each pixel is 8 bits, we generate nearly 10 million bits of data. Clearly, a computer is needed to store this much data and, once stored, a computer is needed to manipulate the data. In fact, the whole point of digitizing a picture is to obtain an image in numerical form that a computer can manipulate. The set of techniques, or operations, used to manipulate image data is called **image processing.** We take pieces of data that make a picture and extract information from them. Image processing is to picture data as graphing is to tabulated data.

Image processing is a rapidly developing branch of computer graphics and involves many powerful techniques. Only a few basic operations that are widely used in astronomical image processing

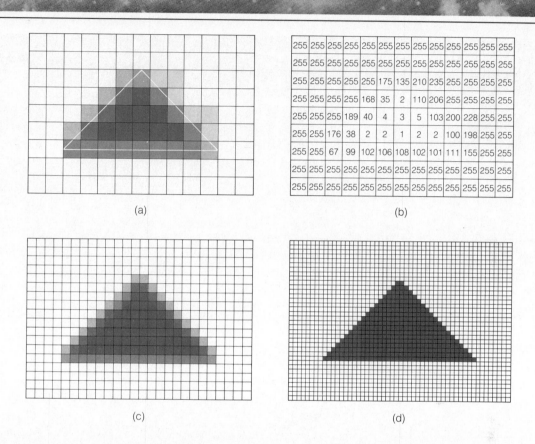

(a) (b)

(c) (d)

will be mentioned here. One operation we can perform on an image of a star, for instance, is adding all its pixel values. This is a measure of the apparent brightness of a star. A bright star, for instance, will cover a large area and will be represented by a large number of pixels compared to a faint star. Furthermore, a bright star will have darker array values at its center than a faint star because more photons struck the emulsion. This operation is simple—just add all of the pixel values that represent the star. We must, of course, determine where the star ends and the background sky begins. Since the image is clear at a pixel value of 255, we simply do not count pixels with values near 255. This kind of operation, one that counts or displays pixels with certain values, is called *density slicing*. Density slicing is used to isolate and highlight features of interest. Color coding an image is another form of density slicing. We simply choose a range of pixel values, such as between 150 and 175, and color these pixels red; we then choose another range, say, between 176 and 200, and color these blue. In this way we can distinguish between features with different intensity characteristics. The map of Venus in Figure

FIGURE 14A.4

Digitizing

(a) A black triangle (its outline is shown) is digitized using a large pixel; you may guess that the object is a triangle, but you could not draw its exact outline. *(b)* A digital image of the triangle in Panel a; since the pixel size is large, pixel values reflect measuring both the black triangle and the white background at the same time at the boundaries of the triangle. *(c)* The outline of the triangle becomes clearer as the pixel size is reduced. *(d)* The boundaries of the triangle are clear once very small pixels sizes are used.

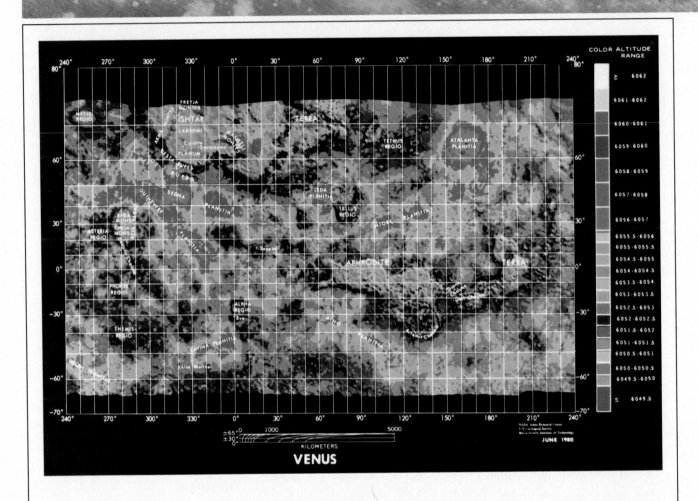

COLOR ALTITUDE RANGE

	≥ 6062
	6061-6062
	6060-6061
	6059-6060
	6058-6059
	6057-6058
	6056-6057
	6055.5-6056
	6055-6055.5
	6054.5-6055
	6054-6054.5
	6053.5-6054
	6053-6053.5
	6052.5-6053
	6052-6052.5
	6051.5-6052
	6051-6051.5
	6050.5-6051
	6050-6050.5
	6049.5-6050
	≤ 6049.5

VENUS

■■■■ **FIGURE 14A.5**

Color Density Slicing

A map of Venus in which different heights are represented by different colors. The color bars on the right give the elevations (distances from the center of Venus) for each color.

SOURCE: NASA.

14A.5 is an example of density slicing. In this case different colors represent different intensity values of radar images of the planet. The intensity values refer to heights above the surface of Venus.

Suppose a picture is washed out, like the overexposed pictures we all have taken with our cameras. By washed out, we mean that the pixel values fall only in a small range, such as from 175 to 200, and therefore represent only a few shades of gray. The image will be just a gray, featureless picture. To improve the contrast so that we can pick out details, that is, so we can distinguish many shades of gray, we stretch the range of the values of the pixels in the original image. We do this mathematically by assigning the highest pixel value the number 255, or white, and set the lowest value to 0, or black. The pixel values are now spread from 0 to 255 instead of from 175 to 200. This procedure is similar to adjusting the contrast on a television set. It allows our eyes to recognize features by displaying more gray lev-

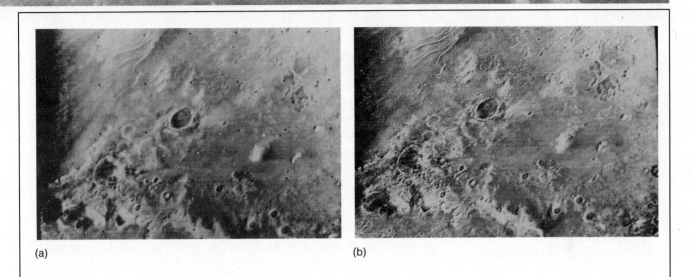

(a)   (b)

els. This important operation is called *contrast enhancement*. An example of contrast enhancement is shown in Figure 14A.6 where a *Mariner 7* picture of Mars is enhanced to show greater detail on the surface of the planet.

Although we are able to manipulate digitized picture elements derived from photographic negatives or prints in many ways to extract information, the information extracted is limited because the photographic process itself is limited. First, the response of the emulsion is not linear; that is, twice as many photons do not produce an image twice as dark. Each photographic plate must be tested to establish exactly how the darkness of an image varies with the intensity of light that produces an image. This is particularly difficult to do for the brightest and faintest objects imaged. Second, as mentioned earlier, emulsions are very inefficient; at best they can record only a few percent of the photons that strike the emulsion. This means that only the largest telescopes are capable of recording the very faintest images and only at considerable effort by the observer. Happily, within the last 20 years scientists have developed technology that provides both linear responses and increased sensitivity.

CHARGE COUPLED DEVICES

Astronomers are now able to obtain direct digitizing of a scene without first photographing it. The most recent type of digital image sensor used by astronomers is the **charge coupled device** or CCD. A CCD is an array of thousands of tiny silicon detectors arranged in a square or rectangle (Figure 14A.7). As many as 640,000 tiny detectors in an 800 × 800 array can fit on a 2-inch square CCD. The individual light-

■ FIGURE 14A.6

Enhancement Contrast

Two *Mariner 7* images of Mars are shown. The scene in Panel b shows more detail after the range of the pixel values has been extended. No new data have been created; the information shown in the image on the right is all in the image on the left. It is up to us to extract that information.
(a) Original data. *(b)* After contrast enhancement.

SOURCE: NASA.

■■■■ ■ FIGURE 14A.7

Charge Coupled Device

This small wafer is an array of 640,000 tiny silicon detectors.

SOURCE: National Optical Astronomy Observatories.

sensitive silicon detectors become the picture elements—the pixels are built into the device. When observers expose a CCD to light, photons strike the individual detectors and build up electric charges that can readily be measured. The picture is stored by converting the electric charge in each detector into a number, and the number becomes part of an image array. The final result is a digitized image, called a *frame*, of what we exposed to the CCD.

Besides the convenience of not having to scan a picture, the CCD has many other advantages. First, the electrical charge built up in each bin is directly proportional to the number of photons falling into the bin; that is, twice the photons means twice the electrical charge. This linearity allows accurate determination of the relative brightnesses of objects in the frame. Second, CCDs are very efficient. More than 60% of the photons that strike a detector are registered. This means that a picture of a field of stars or a galaxy can be taken in a fraction of the time needed with conventional emulsions. Furthermore, a small 1-meter telescope equipped with a CCD can detect fainter stars than a giant 5-meter research telescope using a photographic plate to record images. Third, we know the exact location of each detector in the array and can transform this into precise positional measurements of the objects we are imaging. Fourth, CCDs are small, lightweight, and do not require any mechanical parts. Finally, the image data can be read immediately into a computer in a form that can be manipulated to extract more information.

Charge coupled devices will not immediately replace the photographic plate, however. Although the size of a CCD is an advantage in weight and packaging convenience, it is a disadvantage when trying to image a large field of stars. We still do not have a detector that can rival the ability of the photographic plate to record huge areas of the sky. In addition, photographic plates are still relatively inexpensive compared to CCDs. A research-quality CCD costs thousands of dollars. Nevertheless, CCDs are finding their way into consumer products such as 35 mm cameras and video cameras. Amateur astronomers have successfully used these less expensive CCDs to construct their own homemade image processing systems.

Both the photographic plate and the CCD are powerful devices for recording faint images. Most important, both produce data that can be digitized and analyzed through digital image processing, which reveals information completely hidden from the human eye.

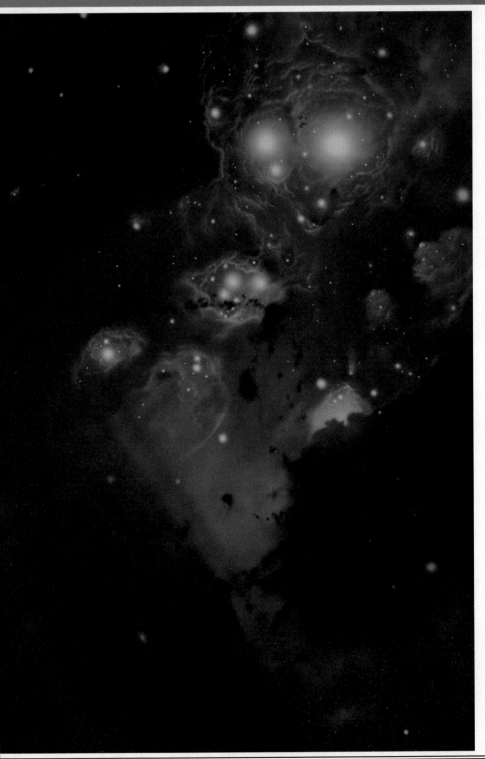

The Birth of the Main Sequence

OUTLINE

Star Formation
Dark Clouds: Sites of Star Formation
Contraction and Protostars
Observations
Star Formation Triggers
Distant Planetary Systems

The Main Sequence
Main-Sequence Lifetimes
Ages of Star Clusters

Summary

Chapter Capsule

Review Questions

For Further Reading

▬▬▬▬ASTROPROBE 15:
How to Build a Star

Inside a Cloud.
ARTIST: Adolf Schaller. Courtesy *Astronomy*
Magazine, Kalmbach Publishing Company.

THE SUN HAS USED ABOUT HALF of its available nuclear fuel and will remain on the main sequence for another five to six billion years. Because of the finite amount of fuel available to stars, such as the Sun, the main-sequence phase of a star's "life" is limited. This is particularly so for massive stars. The luminosities of stars tens of times more massive than the Sun can be millions of times greater than the Sun's. Consequently, lifetimes of massive stars are measured in millions of years. The brilliant massive stars seen in the nighttime sky must be very young indeed.

Young stars are not found alone. They belong to groups, or clusters, of stars and, presumably, the entire cluster formed at the same time. Star formation favors forming a host of stars all at once and, therefore, requires a large amount of material out of which to form the stars. Careful study of young stars shows that they form in huge, dark clouds of gas and dust that are scattered about the Galaxy. Stars slowly come together as billions of atoms, molecules, and dust grains gravitationally collapse upon themselves in these clouds. The collapse is dynamic and violent and is initiated by gigantic explosions and galactic scale disturbances.

How do stars form? Where are the stellar wombs? What triggers star formation? Once formed, how long do stars remain on the main sequence? These are the questions addressed next.

▰▰▰STAR FORMATION

Imagine a team of aliens sent to Earth to observe us for one day. Their assignment is to formulate a theory on the lives of humans. At first everyone would look more or less the same to the aliens, except for variations in size, but careful observations would reveal other differences (Figure 15.1). For instance, tall humans could be divided into "male" and "female." Closer inspection of tall people would reveal differences in the texture of the heads; faces come in a smooth variety or wrinkled, and wrinkled faces are usually associated with gray hair. The relatively few "babies" and small people compared to tall people would indicate long time scales for the tall phase. Such observations, gathered over a short length of time compared to human life expectancies, would provide data from which the aliens could formulate a reasonable theory on the lives of humans. This theory might successfully predict, for instance, which people are at the beginning of their life cycle (young) and which are near the end (old) and that humans grow from little babies to tall people.

Astronomers are faced with a similar situation. They are "aliens" observing the stellar population. With the unaided eye, stars look more or less the same except for brightness variations, but careful observations reveal many differences between stars. For example, astronomers can divide stars into spectral and luminosity classes. More detailed observations reveal signs of extreme youth and evidence of old age, quiescent phases, and unimaginable violence. As in the alien's one-day study, observations over the last few hundred years cover a short length of time compared to the life expectancies of stars. Nevertheless, astronomers

▰▰▰ FIGURE 15.1

Humans Would All Look the Same at First to an Alien

SOURCE: Science VU—ISIS/Visuals Unlimited.

have formulated a theory, called the theory of **stellar evolution,** that describes the "lives" of the stars. Because of the obvious analogy with the lives of humans, astronomers refer to the "birth" of stars, their "aging," and their "deaths." The birth of stars means their formation. The terms aging and death as applied to stars have special meaning. Aging refers to the gradual depletion of nuclear fuel, and death refers to the final state of the star after its fuel is exhausted. Stellar aging and end states are the subject of Chapter 16. This chapter concentrates mainly on the formation of stars.

Dark Clouds: Sites of Star Formation

The finite lifetimes of stars and the presence of young, massive stars indicate that star formation is probably going on now. Where were the hydrogen, helium, carbon, oxygen, and other elements before they merged into stars? What brought these billions of atoms, molecules, and dust grains together to form hot, glowing orbs of light? The answers to these questions lie in hidden, cold places between the stars.

Atoms, nuclei, and electrons are held inside the Sun by gravity. Accordingly, it is likely that atoms and molecules in space need gravity to pull them together to form stars. Atoms and molecules in the **interstellar medium,** however, are moving helter-skelter. Atomic particles inside stars are also moving randomly but they are confined gravitationally within the boundaries of the star. On the other hand, not all interstellar particles are free to roam the Galaxy. Some are observed to be limited to large, but finite, volumes called *interstellar clouds.* These clouds represent a first step toward the confinement of interstellar atomic particles and the eventual formation of stars.

The visual observations of William Herschel (1738–1822) and other astronomers in the eighteenth and nineteenth centuries and photographs in the nineteenth century revealed dark "holes in the heavens." Figure 15.2 shows such a "hole" in a part of the sky very rich in stars. By the late nineteenth century astronomers had proven that these "star voids" are clouds of dust and gas so thick that they completely block out the light from background stars. A typical interstellar cloud has a low density, about 10,000 particles per cm^3, or a millionth of a billionth times less dense than air at sea level. Because clouds are very sparse, astronomers refer to the number density of particles (number of particles/cm^3) instead of the mass density (g/cm^3). Since interstellar clouds are so large, up to 80 pc across, the cumulative effect of all the matter in a single cloud is enough to block out all light from stars behind the cloud.

The centers of these vast clouds are so cold that molecules form. Since most of the mass of these clouds is hydrogen, the predominant molecule is molecular hydrogen (H_2), but many others exist. Radio astronomers have detected over 60 different molecules in **molecular clouds.** They range from pairs of atoms, such as H_2, carbon monoxide (CO), and cyanogen (CN), to familiar molecules, such as ammonia (NH_3), formic acid (HCOOH), and formaldehyde, or embalming fluid

Stellar evolution: Changes in the physical characteristics of stars, such as luminosity, temperature, and radius, as they deplete their nuclear fuel reserves.

Interstellar medium: Diffuse matter between stars; in order of abundance, it consists of hydrogen, helium, carbon, nitrogen, and oxygen atoms and ions, dust, and molecules of many elements, such as hydrogen, carbon, nitrogen, and oxygen. Typical density is a few atoms per cm^3.

Molecular clouds: Dark, dense, cold places of interstellar material at densities thousands of times greater than that of the interstellar medium; temperatures are so low, 10–50 K, and densities are high enough, $> 10^3$ particles per cm^3, that molecules are plentiful.

A Dark Cloud

The cloud Barnard 86 near the star cluster NGC 6520 is silhouetted against the rich background of the Milky Way. No light from stars can pass through the cloud. A few stars lie between us and the dark cloud.

SOURCE: Copyright © Anglo-Australian Telescope Board 1980. Photograph by David Malin.

Dust: Solid, microscopic particles, such as silicate or iron, probably covered with a mantle of ice; interstellar dust grains are about the same size as particles of cigarette smoke.

(H_2CO), to very complex molecules, such as ethyl alcohol (C_2H_6O) and cyanopentacetylene ($HC_{11}N$). The molecules in these clouds, like atoms in stellar atmospheres, display unique spectral signatures. Carbon monoxide, for instance, emits strongly at a wavelength of 2.6 mm while water (H_2O) emits at 1.4 cm. Molecular hydrogen, on the other hand, emits ultraviolet lines that can only be detected with satellites and rockets outside the atmosphere. Consequently, molecular clouds are most readily discovered by using radio telescopes to look for long wavelength molecular lines, such as from carbon monoxide, even though molecular hydrogen is thousands of times more abundant.

About 1% of the matter in molecular clouds is **dust.** Although it is a minute fraction of the mass of a molecular cloud, dust is responsible for preventing starlight from passing through. Astronomers can detect dust in two ways. First, dust grains "redden" starlight, as dust in the atmosphere reddens sunlight, by scattering blue light more than red light. Although the effect on stars is not detectable with the eye, it changes a star's color index. An A0 star, for instance, has an intrinsic or unreddened color index of $B - V = 0.0$. If it is observed to have $B - V = 0.5$ near a molecular cloud, we infer that it is reddened. Its observed color index is redder, or larger, than its intrinsic color index. At the same time, the spectral type of a star is not affected by dust. The scattering of light does not change individual wavelengths of radiation, just the intensity of the light at different wavelengths. In fact, reddening helped prove that "holes in the heavens" were really clouds of dust and gas. Astronomers detected a greater reddening for stars closer to the centers of stellar voids than for those farther away.

Second, dust grains have the ability to absorb starlight and then to reradiate it as infrared radiation. The process is similar to the Earth's surface absorbing sunlight, heating up, and then reradiating in the infrared. Astronomers expect, therefore, to observe infrared sources near newly forming stars as the stars heat the dust in the molecular clouds. This characteristic of dust will be of prime importance as astronomers try to locate new stars.

While the atoms, molecules, and dust particles in a cloud feel the attractive gravitational force of other molecules tending to bring them together, inevitable collisions between them produce a pressure, a *thermal pressure*, that tends to disperse the cloud. Since astronomers observe what appear to be dynamically stable cosmic clouds, the gravitational attraction between molecules must be sufficient to hold the clouds together and prevent thermal pressures from scattering molecules all over space. Still, for stars to form, gravity must overwhelm the thermal pressure and cause at least part of the molecular cloud to collapse.

Sir James Jeans (1877–1946), an English mathematician and physicist, mathematically related the mass of a collapsing molecular cloud to the cloud's temperature and number density. The idea is that the greater the mass of a molecular cloud of a given size, the greater the overall gravitational forces between its constituents. This simply reflects the fact that molecules that are closer together will exert greater gravitational forces on each other. On the other hand, greater cloud temperatures result in greater thermal pressures resisting gravity. How much matter must a cloud contain before gravitational forces can overcome thermal pressure? Jeans's formulation of the answer to this question relates the critical mass, the **Jeans's mass** ($\mathfrak{M}_j$), the cloud's temperature (T), and the number density (n) required for a cloud to collapse:

$$\mathfrak{M}_j^2 \approx 10^3 \, \frac{T^3}{n} \, \mathfrak{M}_\odot^2$$

The mass required for collapse is greater for high temperatures but is less for high densities.

What are the masses, temperatures, and densities of molecular clouds? As Edward Barnard (1857–1923) photographed and mapped the sky along the Milky Way, he discovered small dark clouds with diameters of a few parsecs. Bart Bok (1906–1983) continued to study these objects, especially the small markedly round dark clouds and suggested that they were sites of star formation. Astronomers now call these small obscuring clouds **Bok globules**. The masses of Bok globules range from a few solar masses to several hundred; temperatures are about 10 K; and densities are about 10^3 to 10^4 atoms per cm^3. These small clouds were detected visually as black voids against bright stellar backgrounds, but surveys of the Galaxy, based on emissions from carbon monoxide molecules, yielded the discovery of much larger clouds. These were gigantic molecular cloud complexes with masses from thousands to millions of solar masses, diameters up to 80 pc, and temperatures and densities at their centers of 50 K and 10^5 to 10^6 molecules per cm^3, respectively (Figure 15.3). Astronomers call them **giant molecular clouds**. Both Bok globules and giant molecular clouds are characterized by dense central regions, or cores, surrounded by less dense envelopes of gas and dust.

Jeans's mass: The mass of a molecular cloud, or a fragment of one, that is great enough to ensure that gravitational forces can overcome thermal pressures and cause the cloud to collapse.

Bok globules: Small, isolated molecular clouds (diameters < 1 pc) large and dense enough to absorb starlight from stars behind them; discovered as dark "clouds" against a background of bright stars.

Giant molecular clouds: Huge regions of gas and dust of high mass, low temperature, and high particle density; discovered by radio detection of molecular emission, especially CO emission.

■■■ FIGURE 15.3

Molecular Clouds

Dark molecular clouds come in a variety of shapes. *(a)* The Horsehead nebula is part of a dark cloud silhouetted against the bright light of hot, ionized gas. A large molecular cloud complex covers the lower half of this picture where fewer stars are visible. *(b)* The Cone nebula blocks light from stars behind it; foreground stars can also be seen between the cloud and us.

SOURCE: Part (a) copyright © Anglo-Australian Telescope Board 1984. Part (b) copyright Anglo-Australian Telescope Board 1981. Photographs by David Malin.

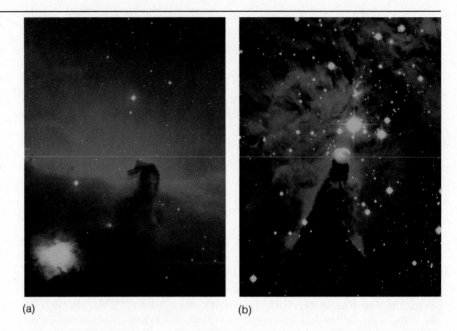

(a)   (b)

Jeans's criterion for cloud collapse can now be applied to typical Bok globules and giant molecular clouds. Table 15.1 shows that the critical mass ranges from 10 to 30 $\mathfrak{M}_\odot$ for the centers of the clouds. Molecular clouds clearly exhibit conditions ripe for the collapse of objects with masses typical of stars. In addition, the masses of the cores of the giant molecular clouds are estimated to be as high as hundreds of solar masses, many times greater than their Jeans's mass, suggesting that many stars could form. The question is how can these cold, dark, vast places transform themselves into hot, bright, compact stars?

Contraction and Protostars

Some molecular clouds look peaceful and calm in photographs. The presence of visible dark lanes and black streaks in others, however, indicates that many clouds are chaotic regions where interstellar gas and dust twist and turn in a turbulent environment (Figure 15.4). Conse-

■■■ TABLE 15.1 Jeans's Masses of Molecular Clouds

	Bok Globules		Giant Molecular Clouds	
	Envelope	*Core*	*Envelope*	*Core*
T (K)	10	10	10	50
n (particles/cm^3)	10^2–10^3	10^4	10^3	10^5–10^6
Mass (solar masses)	20	0.3–10	10^3–10^5	10^2–10^3
$\mathfrak{M}_J$ (solar masses)	30–100	10	30	10–30
Diameter (pc)	<1	0.05–0.2	<80	0.2–3

quently, the collapse of a cloud cannot be pictured as a spherical ball of gas and dust neatly falling directly toward its center. Instead, molecules and dust circulate in wisps and streamers, darting here and there throughout the stirred, collapsing mass. Amid all this turmoil, the density will increase once the collapse begins, causing gravity to tighten its grip on atoms, molecules, and dust grains. With the increasing density, the critical mass for collapse is greatly reduced so that within the collapsing cloud individual pockets of high density can collapse upon themselves. A large segment of a molecular cloud, therefore, can *fragment* into smaller condensations. Observations of multiple dense cores, density variations, and other subcondensations throughout large molecular clouds suggest that an entire giant molecular cloud does not collapse all at once. Star formation appears to occur in pockets scattered throughout giant clouds.

The possibility of star formation in molecular clouds has led astronomers to "follow" the collapse of a fragment of a molecular cloud mathematically. The details of the collapse process are known only through calculations performed on computers (see AstroProbe 15). We refer to the collapsing fragment of a molecular cloud as a **protostar.** The prefix "proto" is from the Greek meaning "going before" and is combined with other words to mean "the first stage." Thus protostar refers to the phases before the collapsing fragment becomes a main-sequence star, a star converting hydrogen into helium in its center.

The collapse process can be divided into two stages: free-fall collapse and slow contraction. Free-fall motion means that the material is free to fall under the influence of gravity. The formation of a star begins as a rapid free-fall collapse in which gas and dust grains rush inward unhindered except for collisions between themselves. Calculations show that the collapse occurs with the high-density central regions collapsing first and quickly reaching the center. Within a very short time a hot, dense core forms at the center. The outer regions trail behind, forming a temporary envelope that takes from ten thousand to a million years to reach the center, depending on the mass of the protostar.

The collapse of the central core is hindered by increasing thermal pressures. At the center where the density is increasing the fastest, collisions between particles occur more frequently than in the envelope, causing the core temperatures to rise. At the same time, the higher densities make it more difficult for photons to escape; that is, they are absorbed many times before escaping the core. Consequently, heat is trapped, core temperatures rise, and pressures increase. The pressure actually becomes high enough to stop the collapse, but only momentarily. Since heat can still escape and temperatures are too low for nuclear reactions, high pressure cannot be maintained in a protostar. No source of energy exists to keep temperatures stable. Consequently, the core will contract again. Note that the *contraction* in the core is now slow compared to the initial rapid *collapse* of the protostar and of the still infalling envelope surrounding the core. Although the contraction increases the temperature and therefore the pressure, the pressure required to stop the collapse has been raised. The protostellar core is now more

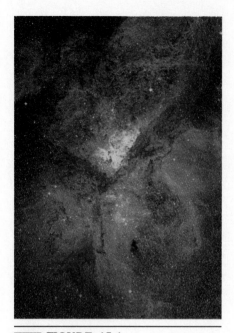

■■■ FIGURE 15.4

Molecular Clouds Near the Eta Carinae Nebula

Large and small clouds and dark streamers are silhouetted by the bright nebulosity in the background. Part of a large molecular cloud makes a V-shape from the upper right, down to the center, and up to the middle left.

SOURCE: Copyright © Royal Observatory Edinburgh/Anglo-Australian Telescope Board 1982. Photograph by David Malin.

Protostar: A collapsing fragment of a molecular cloud that forms a single or multiple star; the term refers to all phases of the collapse process before nuclear burning on the main sequence.

tightly bound because the gravitational forces between the atoms and molecules are greater. An even greater pressure is now required to support the protostar. Since no energy source is yet available to maintain temperatures, the protostar once again contracts and the cycle of contraction, momentary balance, and contraction repeats.

The protostar is now characterized by a dense core surrounded by a gas and dust envelope, which is falling onto the core. The accretion of envelope gas by the core generates heat through the collisions between the infalling envelope matter and the core. In fact, the luminosity of the protostar is due almost entirely to these collisions. Surprisingly, this radiation is not visible. It is totally obscured at visible wavelengths because the surrounding envelope of dust and gas absorbs the energy. Although the core's surface reaches temperatures of thousands of Kelvins, the dust in the envelope heats to only a few hundred Kelvins. Consequently, the infrared radiation from the outer part of the envelope is the only directly observable evidence of the existence of a protostar.

Figure 15.5 shows the results for the calculated collapse of a 1-solar-mass protostar plotted on an HR diagram. The two sets of lines, or *evolutionary tracks*, show the changes in the luminosity and temperature of the infalling envelope (right side) and the surface of the core (left side). The evolution of the protostar from point 1 to point 2 in Figure 15.5 is characterized by the core accreting matter from the envelope. During this time the core grows from about 0.01 $\mathfrak{M}_\odot$ to 1 $\mathfrak{M}_\odot$. The heat generated by the collisions increases the luminosity of the core. Once all the envelope has fallen onto the core, the outer layers of the protostar cool to a temperature of about 4000 K within a few days. Figure

■■ FIGURE 15.5

Evolutionary Tracks of a 1-Solar-Mass Protostar

During the accretion of the dust and gas envelope, the hot core of the protostar is concealed from outside observations. Shown here is the heating of both the core and envelope during the accretion of the envelope between points 1 and 2. Once the envelope has fallen onto the core and collisions cease, the core's outer layers rapidly cool (from point 2 to point 3). The protostar then slowly contracts as its luminosity decreases. (After S. W. Stahler, F. H. Shu, and R. E. Taam, 1980, *The Astrophysical Journal*, 241:637.)

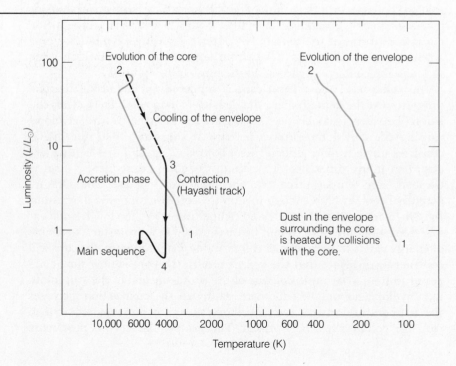

15.5 shows this as a straight dashed line from point 2 to point 3. The protostar becomes visible near point 3.

The protostar now dims as it slowly contracts; this is the second stage of star formation. Although the increasing temperatures caused by the contraction produce a greater luminosity, the surface area of the protostar decreases. Recall that luminosity is proportional to the radius squared and the temperature raised to the fourth power: $L \propto R^2 T^4$. Model calculations indicate that the surface area of the protostar decreases faster than its temperature increases. As a result, the evolutionary track of a protostar on an HR diagram is nearly a vertical line from high to low luminosity, from point 3 to point 4 in Figure 15.5. We call this vertical line on the HR diagram the *Hayashi track* after the Japanese astrophysicist, C. Hayashi, who studied this phase in detail.

The entire star transports the energy from the center to the surface by convective transport during the Hayashi phase. Recall that only the outer 15% of the Sun transports energy by convection. Somehow, the large convective region in the protostar must be transformed into a radiative region, as we find now in the Sun. The rising temperatures inside the protostar cause the convection zone to shrink. The high temperatures disassociate the molecules and ionize the atoms, making the interior more transparent to radiation and more able to transport energy by radiative transport. These changes begin at the center of the protostar where temperatures are highest and work outward. At the same time, temperatures in the protostar are ever increasing, and the resulting greater pressures slow the contraction even further. The increased energy reaching the surface and the slower contraction cause the surface temperature to rise and even the luminosity to increase slightly (Figure 15.6). The evolutionary track begins to follow an approximately horizontal path toward the main sequence. This phase of the contraction is called the *pre–main-sequence phase*.

All during the contraction of the protostar, the central temperatures continue to rise, eventually reaching tens of millions of Kelvins—high enough for hydrogen nuclear reactions. Nuclear reactions provide a

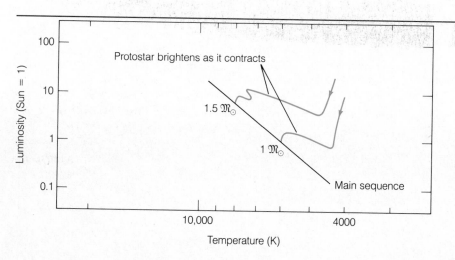

■ FIGURE 15.6

Hayashi Track and Pre–Main-Sequence Phases

As the protostar slowly contracts along its Hayashi track, its surface temperature increases only slightly as its luminosity decreases steadily. The contraction slows as interior temperatures rise and the protostar "moves" toward the left, reaching the main sequence once nuclear burning commences in its hot core.

steady source of energy that can maintain the high pressures needed to balance the gravitational forces. The energy liberated by nuclear reactions is in the form of kinetic energy, or energy of motion (see Chapter 12 for details on nuclear reactions). The product nuclei of the reactions have a greater energy than those that fused and transfer their energy to surrounding nuclei through collisions. These collisions generate the pressure necessary to support the overlying mass. At this point, the protostar has achieved a state called **hydrostatic equilibrium.** The contraction of the protostar stops. The protostar is now a star, a main-sequence star.

The picture of a star can now be extended beyond the definition of "a luminous sphere of gas." A star is indeed luminous, and its luminosity derives from the nuclear reactions deep in its core. A star's luminosity is visual evidence of the central nuclear turmoil. Throughout a star the gravitational forces are exactly balanced by thermal pressure, and the collisions between nuclei are sustained by the agitation caused by the nuclear reactions.

The resulting structure of the star (the distribution of temperature, pressure, and density with radius) is not arbitrary. Stars differ in structure because they differ in mass. Figure 15.7 shows the evolutionary tracks for protostars of different masses. The high-mass protostars in Figure 15.7 begin their pre–main-sequence tracks at higher luminosities, reach the main sequence faster, and end up as hotter main-sequence stars than low-mass protostars. As a general rule, increasing mass always speeds up processes in stars. It does so by placing greater demands on stellar energy sources. More mass in a protostar means greater gravitational forces. The resulting higher inward accelerations cause the initial collapse to be faster and the collisions to be more violent and more frequent. This heats the protostar faster, generates more

Hydrostatic equilibrium: The balance between the inward gravitational forces and the outward thermal pressures in a star; no overall expansion or contraction of the star occurs.

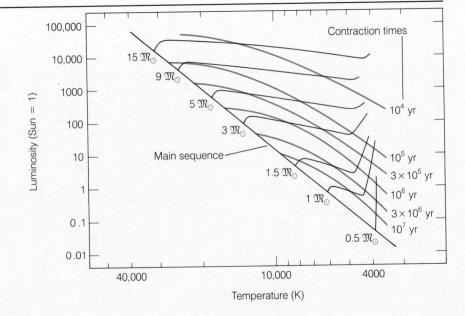

FIGURE 15.7

Contraction Times and Evolutionary Tracks

The evolutionary tracks for protostars of different masses are indicated by the solid black lines. The intersections of the magenta lines with the evolutionary tracts indicate the positions of the protostars at different times during their contraction.

energy, and results in brighter protostellar evolution. Because more mass must be supported in high-mass stars, their internal temperatures must be correspondingly higher than in low-mass stars before they attain an interior structure capable of supporting themselves. Higher central temperatures, in turn, result in greater nuclear energy generation and, therefore, in greater stellar luminosities.

Figure 15.7 also suggests that we might expect to observe protostars in the giant and supergiant regions of the HR diagram, but this is not the case. The difference between protostars and the giants and supergiants is that the latter are stars and derive their energy from nuclear reactions (see Chapter 16) while protostars are too cool to ignite their own nuclear fires. Collapse calculations indicate, however, that for stars above a few solar masses (luminosities above a few hundred solar luminosities), the envelope of infalling gas and dust shields the protostar from the time of its initial free-fall collapse to its "arrival" on the main sequence. Consequently, no visible protostars are expected in the giant and supergiant regions of the HR diagram.

Any modeling of complex processes, such as the collapse of a fragment of a molecular cloud, has its pitfalls and limitations. In the end, all the calculations must be compared to observations of real stars and protostars before astronomers have confidence in the results. If the calculations reproduce the observational characteristics of a main-sequence star, such as the Sun, we can infer that the calculated internal structure of the model is similar to the internal structure of the real star. In that case, the model has provided valuable insights into the physical properties of stars.

An obvious first test is to compare the models to the end result of the calculations—main-sequence stars. The line in Figure 15.7 connecting the main-sequence positions of the models is also the location of observed main-sequence stars. The models clearly predict that higher mass stars will be located at higher luminosities along the main sequence. Thus, the dependence of central temperatures on mass explains the trends observed in the mass-luminosity relation introduced in the last chapter.

How does the broad description of the collapse of a protostar compare with observations of objects that astronomers believe to be protostars? The predictions of protostellar collapse models appear to be quantitatively correct guides for interpreting the observations. At the same time, observers have discovered new processes not predicted by current protostellar models.

Observations

Models of collapsing protostars give a detailed account of what happens beneath the murky canopy of the infalling gas and dust. A major difficulty in comparing the model calculations with observations is that observers cannot "see" the surface of the core of a protostar. It is surrounded by the infalling dust and gas belonging to the collapsing fragment. The cloaked protostar is also embedded within a light-absorbing molecular cloud. Consequently, we cannot expect to see or view

■■■■ FIGURE 15.8

The Orion Nebula

(a) An infrared picture of the Orion constellation taken by the Infrared Astronomical Satellite. The reds, yellows, and whites indicate intense infrared emission. Two prominent sites of star formation are seen: the Rosetta nebula at the left and the Orion nebula in the lower half of the picture. *(b)* Optical view of the Orion nebula.

SOURCES: Part (a), NASA. Part (b), National Optical Astronomy Observatories.

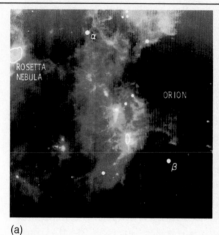

(a)   (b)

a bright, but cool star in visible light. Astronomers must use infrared detectors and radio telescopes to inspect these stellar "wombs" much as doctors use ultrasound techniques to probe an expectant mother's womb.

The vast amount of energy generated during the collapse of a protostar heats the dust-rich envelope surrounding the core. The dust reradiates the absorbed light in the infrared, and the molecules emit emission lines at long wavelengths; thus the protostar is an infrared and radio emission source. A particularly good place to look for evidence of star formation is near the Orion nebula in the constellation Orion (Figure 15.8). The Orion nebula is the middle "star" of Orion's sword. A small telescope reveals a luminous cloud; a larger telescope shows a complex distribution of gas and dust. The bright region actually lies in front of a giant molecular cloud about 50 times larger than the optically bright nebula. In fact, the whole area of the sky toward Orion is teeming with telltale signs of star birth.

Radio observations of large-scale CO and OH molecular emission radically changed our perception of star formation. Models of collapsing protostars implied mainly inflow of material around the protostar. Surprisingly, radio observations revealed large-scale molecular flows *away* from embedded infrared sources. These *molecular outflows* can extend to distances of several parsecs moving at speeds of 30 to 50 km/s (67,000–110,000 MPH). Furthermore, they are bipolar; that is, two flows extend in nearly opposite directions away from the infrared source (Figure 15.9). Bipolar flows also exist on a smaller scale as narrow, jetlike radio-emitting regions closer to the core of the protostar. These "radio jets" are elongated in the direction of the molecular outflows. Similar "optical jets" can be seen in Hα emission, indicating that the material in these supersonic jets is hot.

Why bipolar outflows? What could push or focus material in just two directions? Given the recognized turbulence in molecular clouds, the collapsing fragments will surely be rotating, even if just slightly. The studies of the formation of the solar system discussed in Chapter 11

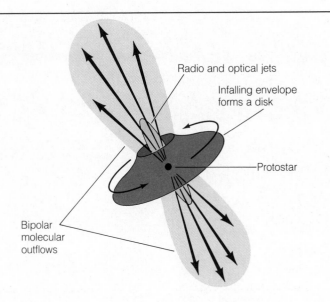

■■■■ FIGURE 15.9

Bipolar Stellar Winds

The protostar is shown at the center of a collapsing, disk-shaped, dusty envelope that exhibits strong molecular outflows. Closer to the protostar, jets are seen with radio and optical observations. The bipolar character of the outflows is detected through the Doppler shifts of emission lines; one side of the embedded infrared source shows a blueshift while the other side shows a redshift.

suggest that a collapsing rotating cloud will preferentially settle into a disk shape with most of the mass at the center. This means that more dust and gas will be distributed in the equatorial plane of the protostar than at the poles. Such a disk provides a natural barrier to radial outflows, deflecting them in two directions. Magnetic fields may also play an important role in focusing stellar outflows. We know, for example, that the Sun's solar wind is influenced by the Sun's own magnetic field.

Astronomers do not know the nature of the energy source of the outflows and jets. It could be located at the surface of the core or in the surrounding disk. If the infalling envelope or the material in the disk can be heated to very high temperatures, for instance, it can escape back into the molecular cloud. The idea is that the higher the temperature, the greater the speeds of the atoms, and therefore the greater their chances of overcoming gravity. Although the infalling matter experiences violent collisions during the collapse of a protostar and heating during the collapse does provide a source of heat, astronomers have not been able to demonstrate conclusively that the energy so generated is sufficient to power the outflows.

The above descriptions have been qualitative because we do not have observations that isolate the regions close to the protostar core-envelope interface. The task now is to observe at smaller and smaller scales to try to detect emission lines produced at the surface of the protostar's core. One point that should be kept in mind is that these outflows and jets are not phenomena associated only with protostars; they are also observed at the centers of galaxies (Chapters 17 and 18). That is, jets and outflows may be a natural consequence of gas from disks accreting onto stellar or stellarlike objects.

The dissipative tendencies exhibited by some infrared objects also occur in objects astronomers identify as being further along in their development. These are *T Tauri stars*, which are found at or below the

■■■ FIGURE 15.10

T Tauri Stars in the Orion Complex

Low-mass stars are seen to cluster near and below the stellar birthline. (After S. W. Stahler, "The Birthline for Low-Mass Stars," 1983, *The Astrophysical Journal*, 274: 822.)

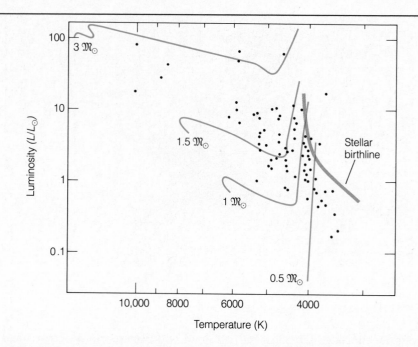

luminosities and temperatures predicted for visible protostars. Figure 15.10 compares observations of T Tauri stars in the Orion cloud complex with protostellar model predictions. The thick line in Figure 15.10 represents the stellar "birthline" for low-mass stars. It represents the luminosities and temperatures at which protostars have accreted all of the envelope and become visible as cool, luminous stellar objects. Most stars in Figure 15.10 fall on or below the stellar birthline, giving strong support to the prediction that T Tauri stars are contracting along their Hayashi tracks.

T Tauri stars were named after the first and brightest of their kind to be observed—a star identified with the letter **T** in the constellation Taurus. They are stellar in appearance with normal **G, K,** and **M** type spectra but with some spectral features, such as certain emission lines, not expected for these late spectral classes. Some of these emission lines resemble those seen in the solar chromosphere and indicate temperatures of hundreds of thousands of Kelvins, and measured Doppler shifts indicate the presence of extended regions of gas and dust in which most of the mass flows outward. It appears that T Tauri stars are protostars that have recently stopped accreting and have just become visible. Protostars that appear suddenly are not unusual. Figure 15.11 shows a dark cloud in the southern Milky Way where a protostar appeared between 1976 and 1980. Panels a and b give before and after pictures of a portion of this region showing the new star.

Once the core of a protostar accretes all of its envelope and dissipates any remaining gas and dust, astronomers can view it as a normal star. T Tauri stars have almost reached this state. Although T Tauri stars have not yet become main-sequence stars and are sometimes called "pre–main-sequence" stars, astronomers generally reserve the term *pre–*

(a)

(b)

main-sequence stars for those stars that have completely dissipated any surrounding gas and dust and are evolving approximately horizontally on the HR diagram with nearly constant luminosity and with increasing temperatures. Pre–main-sequence stars are difficult to identify because they do not have any unusual characteristics. They are best observed in young groups of stars in which some have developed beyond the T Tauri stage.

Figure 15.12 shows the HR diagram of a group of stars that have formed from the same molecular cloud at the same time. The solid straight line is the location of the main sequence as drawn in the last chapter. Many of the stars at the lower right have not arrived at their main-sequence locations and lie below the stellar birthline. Since most of the pre–main-sequence stars lie above the 10-million-year contraction time line, this cluster is approximately 10 million years old. The stars near the main sequence below the 3 $\mathfrak{M}_\odot$ track are pre–main-sequence stars; stars below the stellar birthline are T Tauri stars.

Observations of compact infrared objects, T Tauri stars, and pre–main-sequence stars indicate that the theoretical models of protostellar collapse appear to be on the right track. The models predict bright protostars with very low surface temperatures; these correspond to protostars in the free-fall collapse phase that astronomers observe as infrared sources. Models predict the appearance of protostars at luminosities and temperatures near the stellar birthline; T Tauri stars appear to be protostars that have recently appeared on their predicted Hayashi tracks. The models then predict mainly horizontal development across the HR diagram toward the main sequence; pre–main-sequence stars in clusters of stars appear to confirm this prediction (Figure 15.13). Finally, the models predict a mass-luminosity relation for main-sequence stars; the observed main-sequence mass-luminosity relation fits this prediction. The observations tell even more. They indicate that the gas and dust envelope shields the protostar from our view at visible wavelengths. Protostars are capable of dissipating any leftover gas and

■■■■■ **FIGURE 15.11**

A New Star

(a) A photograph of a dark molecular cloud in the southern Milky Way taken in 1964 before the new star appeared. *(b)* A photograph taken in 1983 showing the new star. Pictures a and b were taken with different telescopes so the star images look slightly different.

SOURCE: John R. Graham, Carnegie Institution of Washington.

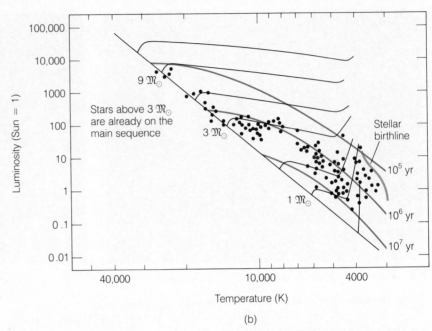

(a)

(b)

The Young Cluster NGC 2264

(a) This photograph of NGC 2264 shows it
to be spread from the tip of the Cone nebula (bottom of the picture) to the bright
star, S Monocerotis, near the top. Pre–
main-sequence stars were first discovered
in this cluster. *(b)* Luminosities and temperatures for stars in NGC 2264. The
tracks are for the same masses shown in
Figure 15.7. Stars with masses above
3 $\mathfrak{M}_\odot$ have already reached the main sequence. Those below 3 $\mathfrak{M}_\odot$ have not yet
reached their main-sequence positions.

SOURCE: Part (a) copyright © Anglo-Australian
Telescope Board 1981. Photograph by David
Malin.

H II region: A sphere of ionized hydrogen surrounding young, hot stars; also
called an emission nebula.

---

dust by generating very powerful outflows. In the late accretion phase
and T Tauri phase, protostars appear to push away surrounding dust
and gas for hundreds of thousands of astronomical units around them.
This dissipation may significantly limit the growth in mass of the protostars and may eventually help stop star formation in a molecular
cloud. On a smaller scale, a T Tauri wind can clear a newly formed
solar system of lighter gases (see Chapter 11). Observations reveal the
dynamic and violent events associated with the labor of star birth.

The dynamical nature of star formation can persist after stars reach
the main sequence. The hottest new main-sequence stars are very bright
and emit a tremendous amount of electromagnetic radiation, especially
in the ultraviolet. Ultraviolet photons from bright O and early B stars
are energetic enough to ionize surrounding hydrogen atoms to distances
of more than a parsec. The ionization forms gigantic "bubbles" of ionized hydrogen around the stars. We call these ionized spheres **H II regions.** The "II" stands for a singly ionized element, in this case hydrogen, whereas a "I," as in H I, refers to neutral hydrogen. The
recapturing of the freed electrons by hydrogen ions in H II regions produces emission lines, especially the red H_α emission at 6563 Å. Consequently, H II regions glow with a faint pinkish hue. The Orion nebula,
for instance, is illuminated by a cluster of several hundred hot, recently
formed massive stars. With a small telescope you can see four of these
new stars, called the Trapezium (Panel a in Figure 15.14). H II regions,
therefore, are telltale signs of recent star formation.

Astronomers have also detected bright nebulae that are not H II regions. The picture of the young Pleiades star cluster in Panel b in Figure
15.14 shows a nebulosity caused by reflected starlight. The bright B
stars in the Pleiades are not hot enough to produce a significant H II

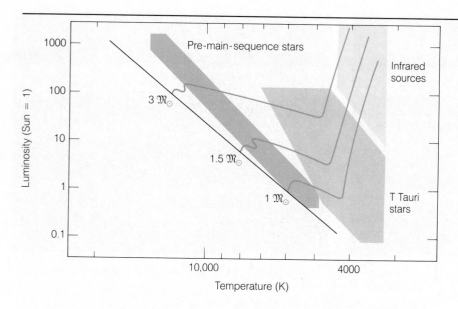

■ FIGURE 15.13

Observations and Models of Protostars

The calculated tracks for collapsing protostars and the approximate locations of objects observed.

region but can illuminate the surrounding dust, possibly left over from their formation. Such a region of dust illuminated by starlight is called a **reflection nebula**; light is reflected off the dust. The dust has a very high albedo, more like ice or snow than dark, gray dust, indicating that it may consist of small, ice-covered grains. The spectrum of a reflection nebula is the same as that of the stars generating the light. Since young stars bright enough to illuminate dust are blue, reflection nebulae are also blue and easily distinguished from the red H II regions.

The observations described in this section and model calculations establish that the Sun was not the last star formed in the Galaxy. If so, how does star formation start?

Reflection nebulae: Bright regions of dust reflecting light from nearby hot stars.

Star Formation Triggers

Star formation is occurring right now in many parts of the Galaxy. Is this not peculiar? Why didn't molecular clouds all form stars at once? Why do molecular clouds still exist today? The formation process itself is effective in preventing all of the material in a molecular cloud from being used to form stars. In particular, the ultraviolet radiation from massive stars and stellar outflows can clear out large volumes of space within which no more stars can form. Indeed, star formation is not 100% efficient; we expect some leftover material.

Instead of focusing on individual protostars as in the last section, consider the giant molecular cloud. Within the cloud, as the atoms, molecules, and dust grains twist and swirl, condensations of a slightly higher density than the average density of the cloud will form by chance or through collisions. Some will break apart again while other condensations will maintain their identity. These can grow by gravitationally attracting the matter around them, by sweeping up molecules and dust as they wander through the cloud, or through collisions with other con-

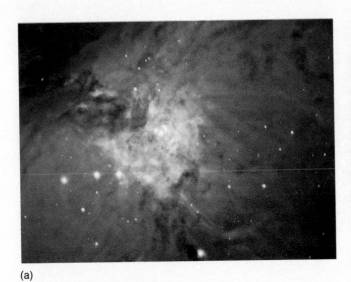

(a)

(b)

■ FIGURE 15.14

Young Stars

(a) The quartet of stars at the center of this picture is called the Trapezium and is part of a star cluster of several hundred new stars that are illuminating the Orion nebula. *(b)* A reflection nebula. Shown here is the relatively young star cluster, the Pleiades, also known as the "seven sisters."

SOURCES: Part (a) copyright © Anglo-Australian Telescope Board 1981. Photograph by David Malin. Part (b) copyright © Royal Observatory Edinburgh/Anglo-Australian Telescope Board 1985. Photograph by David Malin.

densations. It is reasonable, therefore, to expect a gradual buildup of individual fragments to masses over their Jeans's mass. Although this description is very qualitative, it is supported by observations of condensations and multiple cores in molecular clouds, of individual clusters of infrared objects in the same cloud, and of some individual T Tauri stars, which must have formed out of separate condensations within the cloud. Astronomers also have detected compact H II regions deep inside the giant molecular clouds. Since H II regions expand outward and since compact H II regions are small, these regions must be young and driven by very recently formed massive stars. Thus the quiescent buildup of condensations appears to be a reasonable working hypothesis for star formation within a molecular cloud.

Quiescent star formation, however, does not appear to explain the formation of high-mass O and B stars seen near the edges of giant molecular clouds, such as those in the Orion nebula. The existence of many young, massive stars near the boundaries of molecular clouds is puzzling. It suggests that the birth of these outlying massive stars requires an external event to "trigger" the start of the formation process.

When astronomers study H II regions and their association with large molecular clouds in greater detail, the relationship between the two becomes more complex. It appears that the formation of massive stars near the periphery of a molecular cloud generates more star formation deeper inside the cloud. Between a large H II region, such as the Orion nebula, and a nearby molecular cloud, we observe condensations in the form of infrared sources, bright CO emission regions, and compact H II regions (Figure 15.15). The edge of the H II region in Figure 15.15 is shown colliding with the edge of a molecular cloud as the H II region expands away from the cluster of O and B stars. The expansion is fueled by the intense ultraviolet radiation and outflows from the recently formed O and B stars. The edge of the H II region compresses the gas at the rim of the cloud as a snowplow compresses snow. This compression, of course, increases the probability of star formation by virtue of

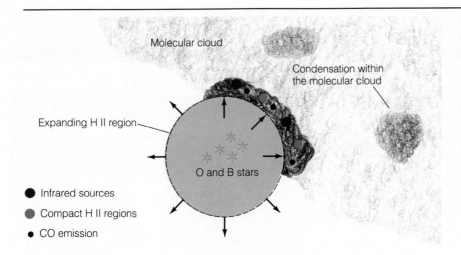

Star Formation at the Boundary of a Molecular Cloud

The expanding H II region supersonically crashes into the molecular cloud, compressing the dust and gas. The compression initiates star formation. We view infrared sources, compact H II regions, and strong molecular emission line sources near the H II region.

the increased density. Although the cumulative effect of the H II regions is to stop star formation near the site of the young stars, it initiates star formation farther away. In fact, star formation may propagate through an entire molecular cloud in a succession of expanding H II regions.

What initiates this propagating star formation? What is the trigger that produces the first H II region? Two processes appear feasible and both probably operate in the Galaxy today. First are the supernovae. A

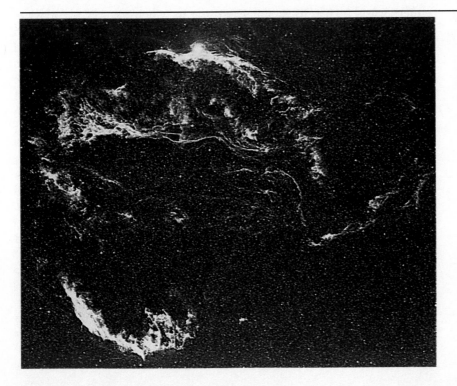

Expanding Supernova Remnant

This nebula, called the Cygnus Loop, is the remains of a supernova that occurred about 20,000 years ago. The envelope of the star has been expanding outward in a shock wave during this time and now has a radius of about 40 pc.

SOURCE: Hale Observatories.

■ FIGURE 15.17

Supernova-Triggered Star Formation

The sequence from a to d shows the relative locations of a supernova, nearby molecular clouds, and the expansion of the supernova debris into these clouds. The collision of the debris with the clouds will compress the boundary of the molecular cloud and initiate star formation. The subsequent expansion of an H II region initiates even more star formation deeper inside the cloud.

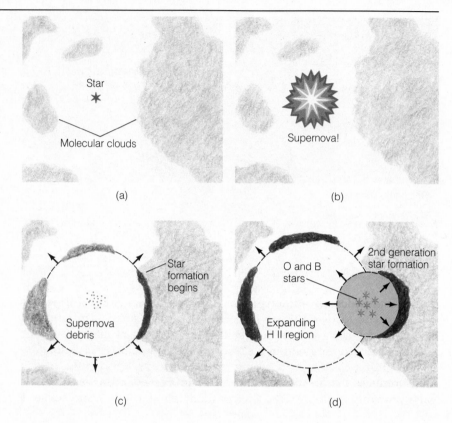

supernova is a gigantic stellar explosion in which most of the mass of the star is blasted into space (see Chapter 16 for details). The ejected material becomes an expanding shell in which the density is several times greater than the medium in which it travels (Figure 15.16). When the supernova shell intercepts a molecular cloud, it can cause the edge of the cloud to implode and initiate star formation (Figure 15.17). A second triggering mechanism is galactic in scale. Photographs of certain types of galaxies called *spirals* show beautiful spiral "arms" of bright stars, usually two arms per galaxy (Figure 15.18). Studies of these arms show that the brightest components of the arms are new O and B stars and H II regions—spiral arms are sites of star formation. Astronomers interpret these arms as being the result of a "wave," called a *density wave*, propagating around the galaxy like water waves across a lake. Whenever a density wave crosses a molecular cloud, it strongly compresses it. Because compression reduces the Jeans's mass, this can lead to star formation in molecular clouds.

Two styles of star formation seem to operate in giant molecular clouds: the quiescent coalescence of condensations within clouds and the propagating star formation starting at the boundaries of the clouds. Quiescent coalescence appears to be a natural by-product of turbulence within a molecular cloud while, at cloud borders, propagating star formation appears to require density waves and supernovae as triggers. Since star formation is not very efficient, material is left over after a cloud or a fragment of a cloud collapses. The material left over after an episode of star formation is not always returned to the interstellar medium. If it were, we would not be here.

Distant Planetary Systems

What do our models and observations say about the existence or formation of planets around other stars? Are planetary systems a natural by-product of the formation of stars? Chapter 11 suggested that this was the case. The details are sparse, but we know that at least one planetary system exists in the Galaxy, and astronomers have hints that others exist.

When astronomers model the dynamical collapse of a protostar, they find support for the idea that planetary formation is a natural by-product of star formation. The calculations imply that if a fragment of a molecular cloud has a mass equal to its Jeans's mass, its collapse can result in a single object with that mass. If the mass of the fragment is twice the Jeans's mass, then two objects may form—a binary system. Each will orbit the other, and they will therefore be unable to coalesce again into one object. It is reasonable to expect that the mass of the second object could range from stellar masses to planetary masses. In other words, if the fragment contained very little material beyond the Jeans's mass, a planetary system could form instead of a second star.

These results, of course, do not prove that planetary systems other than our own exist. What do the observations say? First, some infrared sources that were thought to be single protostars are now known to be multiple systems. Companion infrared sources within 1000 AU of each other exist, and T Tauri itself appears to have a small companion (planet?) about 100 AU distant. Second, observers have discovered disks of dust around single stars. Since a newly formed star is a very strong infrared emitter, a planet orbiting very near the new star would be hard to detect in the infrared. Like planets, dust emits infrared radiation, but the greater surface area of billions of dust particles makes a disk much brighter in the infrared than any planet. Infrared surveys have detected disks around stars, such as Vega (A0 IV–V), Fomalhaut (A3 V), and Beta Pictoris (A5 V).

Figure 15.19 shows the disk around the star Beta Pictoris. The glare of Beta Pictoris itself was blocked by covering the image of the star with a circular mask in the telescope, as the Moon covers the Sun during a solar eclipse. The disk is seen on edge and extends from 200 to 400 AU from the star. This is approximately the distance from our Sun to the inner edge of the Oort cloud (Chapter 10). The calculations in the next section show that A-type stars are less than a few hundred million years old. Consequently, although no planets have been detected, they could have recently formed. These observations clearly show that disks of solid particles do form around stars.

Another way to discover distant planets involves astrometry. Recall that astrometric binaries are detected from variations in their proper motion; they are seen to wiggle across the sky. This motion is due to faint, unseen stellar companions. A star will also exhibit wiggles in its

■ FIGURE 15.18

A Spiral Galaxy

The spiral arm pattern is clearly visible in this picture of the distant galaxy M51. The largest features seen in the arms are H II regions, indicating that spiral arms are regions of star formation. The "arms" are thought to be formed by density waves (see Chapter 17 for a more detailed discussion).

SOURCE: Official U. S. Naval Observatory photograph.

■ FIGURE 15.19

Beta Pictoris

A disk of dust is seen on edge in the CCD image of this early type star. The bright light from the star is blocked out by a small disk placed in front of the star's image when the photograph was taken.

SOURCE: NASA.

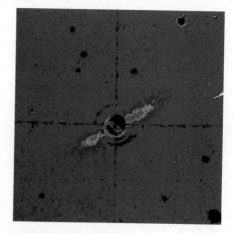

TABLE 15.2 Evidence for Distant Planetary Systems

1. Our solar system: Indicates there is at least one in the Galaxy.
2. Disks:
   a. Collapse models indicate disks are a natural result of collapse.
   b. Disks are observed around other stars.
   c. Infrared sources with bipolar outflows suggest disks exist around protostars.
3. Proper motion studies: Uncertain results so far.
4. Radial velocity studies: Best positive results to date.
5. Binary star statistics:
   a. Binaries are common.
   b. Some infrared sources also are binary.

proper motion if large planets orbit the star. Of course, the wiggles will be much smaller, but if the star is close enough astronomers can expect to detect the wiggles. The results to date, however, have been frustratingly unclear. For instance, two studies of the nearby M5 main-sequence star called Barnard's star give conflicting results: one study finds evidence for two large planets while the other does not find evidence for even one planet of any size. The conflicting results simply indicate the extreme difficulties in detecting celestial wiggles and wobbles.

Nevertheless, a recently modified conventional technique for detecting stellar motions caused by unseen planets has produced intriguing results. Instead of following wiggles in a star's proper motion, the technique measures the oscillations in the radial velocity of a star. An unseen companion will cause periodical radial velocity variations as well as proper motion wiggles. Of 15 solar type stars observed over the last decade, 7 show signs of planet-sized companions. Studies such as these, like proper motion studies, require a long history of observations, and as many as 20–30 years of observations may yet be required to "confirm" the presence of planets in these star systems. But the preliminary results are indeed encouraging.

To sum up, we clearly have circumstantial evidence of planets orbiting other stars, and models suggest that a disk of dust and gas is a natural result of star birth (Table 15.2). Astronomers hope to make substantial gains in the detection of extrasolar planets with the launching of the Hubble Space Telescope, which will be able to detect planets the size of Uranus in nearby systems. By the next century astronomers hope to have a definitive answer to the question, Do planets orbit other stars?

THE MAIN SEQUENCE

The next logical phase in the study of stars is the main sequence itself. Stars on the main sequence are in hydrostatic equilibrium in which the internal pressures that balance the gravitational forces are maintained by the heat generated from nuclear reactions. We know (see Chapter 12) that nuclear reactions in the Sun can supply energy for another 5–6 billion years. The Sun's *main-sequence lifetime*, the time it is able to convert hydrogen into helium in its core, is about 10 billion years. How long do stars of different masses last as main-sequence stars?

Main-Sequence Lifetimes

Astronomers estimate the Sun's main-sequence lifetime by determining the total amount of fuel available and measuring how fast the Sun is using up that fuel. For instance, a small car that gets 30 miles per gallon of gas uses fuel at a rate of 2 gallons per hour traveling at 60 MPH. If it has a 10-gallon gas tank, a driver could drive for 5 hours before refueling:

$$\text{Drive time} = \frac{10 \text{ gallons}}{2 \text{ gallons/hr}} = 5 \text{ hours}$$

A similar calculation can be done for stars by estimating the total amount of energy that can be generated through the conversion of hydrogen into helium and dividing this by the rate at which the star generates that energy, its luminosity. The energy generated is given by Einstein's equation $E = mc^2$. The mass of hydrogen in a star is the total mass times the percentage that is hydrogen, 75%. But only about 20% of this hydrogen ever attains temperatures high enough for nuclear reactions. Furthermore, only 0.7% of the hydrogen taking part in the proton-proton chain is converted into energy. Putting all of this together gives the energy generated by a star of $\mathfrak{M}$ solar masses (if $\mathfrak{M} = 5$, then the star's mass is 5 $\mathfrak{M}_\odot$) while on the main sequence as $E \sim 2 \times 10^{44}\,\mathfrak{M}$ watts. Let L represent the star's luminosity in solar units, then the *main-sequence lifetime*, t_{MS}, is

$$t_{MS} \sim \frac{\text{total energy generated}}{\text{luminosity}} \sim \frac{2 \times 10^{44}}{3.8 \times 10^{26}} \frac{\mathfrak{M}}{L} \text{ seconds}$$

$$= 5 \times 10^{17} \frac{\mathfrak{M}}{L} \text{ seconds}$$

Converting seconds into years gives

$$t_{MS} \sim 10^{10} \frac{\mathfrak{M}}{L} \text{ years}$$

The mass-luminosity relation from Chapter 14 (see Table 14.6) can be used to estimate main-sequence lifetimes for stars of different masses. Table 15.3 shows a dramatic range in main-sequence lifetimes, from millions to trillions of years. High-mass stars are main-sequence stars for only a short length of time compared to the Sun while low-mass stars will still be main-sequence stars long after the Sun runs out of hydrogen fuel. Despite their extra mass, the short lifetimes for massive stars tell us that they are "gas hogs"; they use up their fuel very rapidly. They do so because the requirement of higher central temperatures to maintain hydrostatic equilibrium produces an enormous generation of energy that consumes the available fuel in a very short time. Low-mass stars are "fuel efficient" and burn their fuel much more slowly; thus they have long main-sequence lifetimes despite having less fuel.

Just how luminous can a main-sequence star be? Since a star's luminosity depends on its mass, this question is really asking what is the maximum mass for a main-sequence star? The largest determined mass of a component of a binary system is 27 $\mathfrak{M}_\odot$ for the O7 V star V382 Cygni. A few members of spectroscopic binaries have minimum masses greater than 30 $\mathfrak{M}_\odot$. HR diagrams of the brightest stars in our Galaxy suggest that stars of about 60 $\mathfrak{M}_\odot$ are prevalent and a few stars with masses of about 100 $\mathfrak{M}_\odot$ probably exist. Why should a limit exist for stellar mass? During the collapse of a protostar, tremendous stellar outflows develop that eventually prevent all the surrounding nebula from falling onto the protostar. These stellar winds also operate while a star is on the main sequence; the solar wind, for example, is a weak stellar wind. Stellar winds and powerful outflows of massive stars may blow off tens of solar masses every million years. It may also be that the collapse of very massive stars is so violent and rapid that the ignition

■ TABLE 15.3
Main-Sequence Lifetimes

Spectral Type	Mass ($\mathfrak{M}_\odot$)	Luminosity ($L_\odot$)	t_{MS} (yr)
O5	40	5×10^5	8×10^5
B0	18	2×10^4	9×10^6
A0	3	100	2×10^8
F0	2	7	3×10^9
G0	1.1	1.2	9×10^9
K0	0.8	0.4	2×10^{10}
M0	0.5	0.06	9×10^{10}
M5	0.2	0.01	2×10^{12}

■■■ FIGURE 15.20

The "Jewel Box" Open Cluster (NGC 4755)

The brightest stars in this cluster are blue main-sequence stars and one red giant.

SOURCE: Copyright © Anglo-Australian Telescope Board 1977. Photograph by David Malin.

Star cluster: A group of stars formed at the same time and place and held together by their mutual gravitation.

of nuclear reactions is catastrophic—the star explodes. Furthermore, the fragmentation of collapsing segments of molecular clouds tends to make the formation of massive stars unlikely. So qualitatively, we have reasons to expect an upper mass limit.

When theoreticians try to compute models of massive stars, they find that models with masses of between 100 and 130 $\mathfrak{M}_\odot$ represent an upper limit. The reasons for the limit are complex and independent of stellar winds and protostar fragmentation. The models indicate that due to the extremely high interior temperatures, the nuclear reactions are burning so violently that the nuclear-powered cores are unstable. In qualitative terms, this results in the star pulsating—its radius grows and shrinks periodically. The amplitudes of these pulsations grow in time and become so large that shells of the outer atmospheric layers can be ejected from the star, thereby reducing its mass. At the same time, the atmospheric temperatures in stars with masses greater than 100 $\mathfrak{M}_\odot$ are so high that atmospheric gases experience a pressure from the radiation that can accelerate the atmosphere away from the star—another way for mass to escape from a massive star. Thus the models and observations agree: no stars over about 100 $\mathfrak{M}_\odot$ to 130 $\mathfrak{M}_\odot$ on the main sequence appear possible.

What about the lower end of the main sequence? Do stars have a lower mass limit? A lower limit is reasonable to expect simply because large planets such as Jupiter exist. Jupiter is about 1000 times less massive than the Sun. Although Jupiter does appear to have its own heat source, it is not a nuclear heat source because temperatures are not high enough. This is the point. If temperatures do not rise in the center of a protostar to the level necessary for nuclear reactions, a main-sequence star cannot form. Protostars with masses less than about 0.1 $\mathfrak{M}_\odot$ never reach high enough temperatures.

To sum up, mass determines the location of a star on the main sequence and limits the range of the main sequence. Mass also controls the main-sequence lifetimes of stars by its influence on their internal structure, specifically on the central temperatures. The fact that the location of main-sequence stars depends on mass has one very important consequence—it provides a means for estimating the age of the universe.

Ages of Star Clusters

Through the controlling influence of mass, massive protostars become main-sequence stars before low-mass protostars, but they spend less time on the main sequence. This has important consequences on the observed HR diagrams of **star clusters** (Figure 15.20). Since it is not possible to observe the formation of a star cluster and the subsequent changes of its main-sequence stars in our lifetimes, astronomers rely on models of protostars and main-sequence stars. Consider how the HR diagram of a hypothetical star cluster changes as protostars develop and main-sequence stars age. Let's call the cluster M2010 after the well-known science fiction movie.

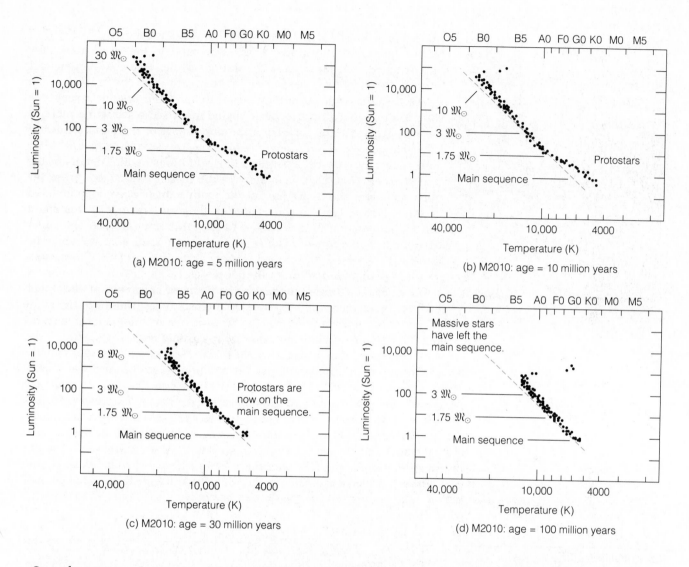

(a) M2010: age = 5 million years

(b) M2010: age = 10 million years

(c) M2010: age = 30 million years

(d) M2010: age = 100 million years

FIGURE 15.21

HR Diagrams of M2010

Star clusters are the product of the collapse of a large segment of a molecular cloud in which the segment fragments into hundreds of protostars with masses covering the entire range of the main sequence. As a result, the HR diagrams of clusters generally exhibit long main sequences populated by stars of different masses. Panel a in Figure 15.21 shows the HR diagram of M2010 at an age of 5 million years. At this age, the more massive protostars have already become main-sequence stars while the lower mass stars are still in their pre–main-sequence contraction (refer to Figure 15.7 for time scales). As the stars age and the pre–main-sequence stars become main-sequence stars, the most massive main-sequence stars will have used all of their hydrogen fuel—they will "leave" the main sequence. The brightest stars in M2010 have already evolved away from their main-sequence positions. The detailed description of "life after the main sequence" is postponed until the next chapter; for now it is enough to know that stars become giants and supergiants. Panel b in Figure 15.21 shows how the HR diagram of M2010 looks after 10 million years. A few more of the lower mass stars have reached their main-sequence stations while somewhat fainter stars are now the brightest ones left on the main sequence. In Panel c, which shows the cluster at 30 million years, most of the pre–main-sequence stars are now burning hydrogen on the main sequence while more of the massive stars are gone from the upper part of the main sequence. What happens to them after they become giants or supergiants? They blow themselves up in gigantic stellar explosions; again, details in the next chapter. Note that with more of the massive stars gone from the main sequence, the upper part of the main sequence is now populated by fainter stars. Panel d shows the HR diagram when M2010 is about 100 million years old. It continues to show the same trends. The upper part of the main sequence continues to decrease in luminosity while the low-mass stars have all reached the main sequence and are quietly converting hydrogen into helium in their cores.

These HR diagrams emphasize the changes occurring at the upper end, or tip, of the main sequence. As a cluster ages, the tip of the main sequence becomes fainter. This is the basis of a technique for determining the ages of star clusters; that is, if astronomers can determine the spectral type of the cluster's brightest main-sequence stars, they can use the model calculations that give the maximum age of a star of any spectral type. Consequently, the brightest main-sequence stars in a cluster give us enough information to determine the age of the cluster. For example, if the brightest main-sequence star is a B0 star, then the cluster cannot be older than 9 million years, the main-sequence lifetime of a B0 star. If the cluster were older than this, B0 stars would not be on the main sequence. The HR diagram in Figure 15.22 is for the Pleiades star cluster, a naked eye cluster in the winter sky. The Pleiades is old enough

FIGURE 15.22

HR Diagram of the Pleiades Star Cluster

The spectral type of the brightest main-sequence star is B6; its mass is ~5 $\mathfrak{M}_\odot$ and its luminosity is ~1000 $L_\odot$. These values correspond to a main-sequence lifetime of ~60 million years. Stars more massive than ~5 $\mathfrak{M}_\odot$ have already left the main sequence. All the faint stars have reached the main sequence.

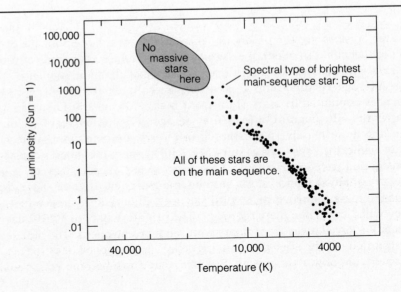

to have all of its faint stars on the main sequence. From the spectral type of its brightest main-sequence star, astronomers estimate the age of the Pleiades to be 60 million years. This is a young cluster compared to the Sun's age of 4.6 billion years.

Determining the ages of star clusters, such as the Pleiades, serves two important functions. First, a lower limit to the age of the Galaxy can be established if we locate the oldest star clusters in the Galaxy. Astronomers find that the brightest main-sequence stars of these old star clusters are slightly less massive than the Sun. The HR diagrams of these clusters imply ages of approximately *15 billion years*, three times the age of the Sun. We usually assume, of course, that the universe existed before the Galaxy; therefore, the universe must be at least this old.

A second use of star cluster dating is in the reconstruction of the history of star formation of a galaxy. For instance, if astronomers could date every star cluster in a galaxy, they would know all the occurrences of star formation in the past. This is similar to reconstructing the history of life on Earth by dating fossils; scientists can determine when different species of animals, plants, birds, and mammals lived. When star formation histories are investigated in more detail in Chapters 16 and 17, ages of stars will play a key role in these studies.

▰▰SUMMARY

Star formation occurs in cold, dark molecular clouds of gas and dust. In the densest regions of molecular clouds, gravity is able to pull gas and dust together into stable condensations. These grow by gravitational attraction or collision until they reach the critical Jeans's mass, after which they collapse. Star formation appears to be able to start quietly deep inside molecular clouds by such quiescent coalescence and fragment growth. Near the boundaries of molecular clouds, stellar explosions and the passage of galactic density waves appear to initiate star formation. The formation of massive stars near the edge of a molecular cloud can propagate star formation throughout the cloud by successive expanding H II regions.

The modeling of the collapse of individual protostars indicates that initially the collapse is an unhindered free-fall with the immediate formation of a core. As the temperatures in the core increase, the collapse slows. The heat generated by collisions raises temperatures and causes the protostar to brighten. Surface temperatures reach several thousand Kelvins, and the protostar is expected to be a compact infrared source. Observations indicate that massive molecular outflows and jets develop as the envelope collapses into a disk (Figure 15.23). Since the protostar does not have a source of energy to maintain the pressures required to support itself, it slowly continues to contract. Once the central temperature reaches millions of Kelvins, nuclear reactions begin, supplying the energy necessary to support the main-sequence star in hydrostatic equilibrium.

Observations support this picture of star formation. Infrared observations show compact infrared sources thought to be collapsing protostars cloaked by a dust-rich envelope. T Tauri stars exhibit characteristics of protostars ejecting dust and gas from part of the envelope that has not yet fallen onto the core. Young star clusters exhibit pre–main-sequence stars that have accreted all of their envelopes but have not yet reached nuclear ignition temperatures in their cores. Outflows do not stop once a protostar becomes a main-sequence star. Surrounding massive, recently formed stars are spherical regions of ionized hydrogen, called H II regions, caused by the tremendous outpouring of ultraviolet radiation from these stars.

Mass determines nearly all stellar characteristics and time scales. High-mass protostars collapse and reach the main sequence faster than low-mass pro-

FIGURE 15.23

Development of a Protostar

As the protostar collapses, it forms a dense core that contracts more slowly than the infalling envelope. Further collapse produces a disk around the core. An as yet unknown mechanism generates violent outflows from the protostar. Once the envelope and disk are mostly dissipated, the protostar becomes visible as a T Tauri star.

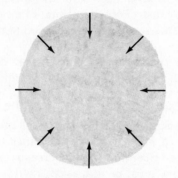

Slowly rotating fragment of a molecular cloud begins to collapse.

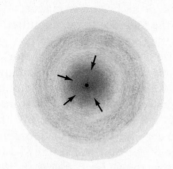

The dense core forms surrounded by a collapsing envelope.

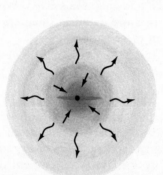

Collisions between the infalling envelope and the core generate heat causing the protostar to brighten.

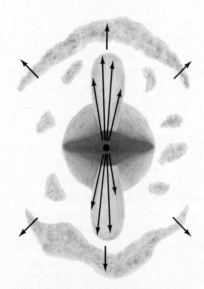

A disk forms around the protostar; bipolar outflow ejects the remaining envelope.

The protostar becomes visible as a T Tauri star when the debris expands away.

tostars. Since high-mass stars also use their fuel faster than low-mass stars, the main-sequence lifetimes of high-mass stars are very short relative to those of low-mass stars. High-mass stars are also more luminous because their high internal temperatures, necessary to maintain hydrostatic equilibrium, accelerate the rate of nuclear energy generation.

Mass also ensures that the main sequence has upper and lower limits. Stars with masses greater than about 100 $\mathfrak{M}_\odot$ to 130 $\mathfrak{M}_\odot$ generate so much radiation at their surfaces that the resulting pressure can ex-

ceed the force of gravity. They are also unstable because the nuclear reactions burn so fiercely at their centers. Stars with masses less than about 0.1 $\mathfrak{M}_\odot$ never attain temperatures high enough at their centers to start nuclear burning.

The range of main-sequence lifetimes allows astronomers to estimate the ages of star clusters by determining the spectral types of the brightest main-sequence stars. Stars give the first hint of the age of the universe. The oldest star clusters in the Galaxy are approximately 15 billion years old.

CHAPTER CAPSULE

Topics and Terms	Review and Remarks
Star formation	Sites of star formation are found in molecular clouds.
	Quiescent star formation operates within molecular clouds.
	Triggered star formation operates at boundaries of molecular clouds: triggering mechanisms are stellar explosions and density waves.
Theoretical picture	An initial rapid, free-fall collapse generates heat and warms the surrounding dust: the dust radiates in the infrared.
	A slow contraction follows after the envelope has accreted and stops when nuclear reactions have ignited in the core.
Observations	Infrared sources in molecular clouds
	T Tauri stars dissipating their remaining envelopes
	Young star clusters exhibit pre–main-sequence stars.
	Molecular outflows and jets
	H II regions are found surrounding young stars and star clusters.
Lifetimes of stars	Main-sequence lifetimes $\sim 10^{10}\ \mathfrak{M}/L$ years.
Stellar mass	Mass range along the main sequence is from about 0.1 $\mathfrak{M}\odot$ to about 100 to 130 $\mathfrak{M}\odot$.
	Mass determines most stellar characteristics and time scales.
Oldest stars	The oldest stars in the Galaxy are about 15 billion years old.

REVIEW QUESTIONS

1. How are a star's apparent magnitude and observed color index affected if it is observed through a thin dust cloud? How would its computed absolute magnitude be altered? Can you explain how astronomers might know *how much* absorption has occurred in interstellar space?

2. What are protostars and where are they likely to be found? The gravitational contraction of a protostar is not very rapid once it starts. Why?

3. During part of the formation of a star, before it reaches the main sequence, its luminosity actually decreases. What two characteristics of a star determine its luninosity and how do these change during this fading period in the star's formation?

4. During the Hayashi phase, a star's chemical composition is completely uniform. The Sun's current chemical composition is anything but uniform. What post-Hayashi conditions cause this change?

5. What is hydrostatic equilibrium and why is it a necessary condition for main-sequence stability?

6. What one physical property determines a star's temperature, size, and luminosity when it is on the main sequence?

7. What are H II regions and where are they found?

What are reflection nebulae and how do their spectra and appearance differ from those of H II regions?

8. O5 main-sequence stars have masses on the order of 200 times that of M5 main-sequence stars. Their main-sequence lifetimes, however, are *smaller* by a factor of about 2.5 million. Explain this apparent paradox.

9. An HR diagram of a single star cluster never has main-sequence stars of spectral classes O and M at the same time. Why not? What can you say about a cluster that has O main-sequence stars?

FOR FURTHER READING

Churchwell, E., and K. J. Andersen. 1985. The anatomy of a nebula. *Astronomy*, June, 66.

Malin, D. 1987. The splendor of Eta Carinae. *Sky & Telescope*, Jan., 14.

———. 1987. In the shadow of the Horsehead. *Sky & Telescope*, Sept., 253.

Mumford, G. S. 1987. The legacy of E. E. Barnard. *Sky & Telescope*, July, 30.

Shore, L. A., and S. N. Shore. 1988. The chaotic material between the stars. *Astronomy*, June, 6.

Stahler, S., and N. Comins. 1988. The difficult births of sunlike stars. *Astronomy*, Sept., 22.

544

ASTROPROBE 15

How to Build a Star

Astronomers can determine the luminosity, mass, surface temperature, chemical composition, and size of stars through the analysis of starlight. The electromagnetic radiation from stars contains all the information needed to understand stars—all astronomers have to do is put it together, like the pieces of a puzzle. Observing, however, has its limitations; we can look but not touch. Scientists cannot raise the temperature of the Sun or double the mass of Vega to see what other changes occur. Astronomers do not have the luxury of the chemist, biologist, or physicist to modify the objects being observed or the conditions under which they are studied (Figure 15A.1). Consequently, we must rely in part on variety. To see how the Sun would look if it were twice as hot, we find a star that is twice as hot as the Sun and study its properties.

Astronomers also rely on mathematical descriptions, or models, of stars. A **model** of a star is a table of numbers giving the pressure, temperature, density, mass, luminosity, and chemical composition at every point in the star (Figure 15A.2). In other words, a model defines the physical structure of a star. From these numbers we can tell, for instance, where and how much nuclear energy is being generated, how energy is transported from the center to the surface, what the hydrogen abundance is at the center, or whether the star is expand-

■ FIGURE 15A.1

A Physicist Conducts an Experiment

Scientists in many disciplines are able to work directly with the materials they are measuring. Astronomers must be satisfied with just looking at distant stars and galaxies.

SOURCE: Physics Department, Imperial College, London/Science Photo Library, Photo Researchers.

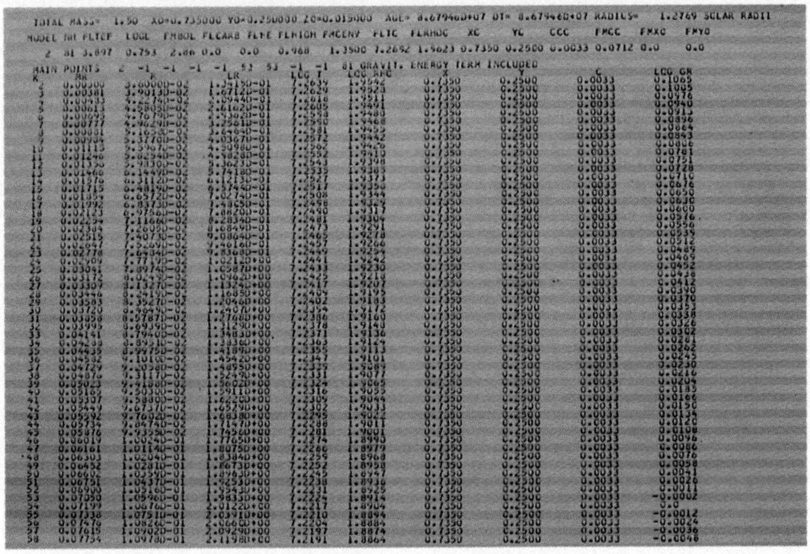

TOTAL MASS= 1.50 X0=0.735000 Y0=0.250000 Z0=0.015000 AGE= 8.67946D+07 DT= 8.67946D+07 RADIUS= 1.2769 SOLAR RADII
MODEL NO FLTEF LOGL FMBOL FLCARB FLFE FLNIGH FACENY FLTC FLRHOC XC YC CCC FMCC FMXC FMYO
2 81 3.897 0.753 2.86 0.0 0.0 0.968 1.3500 7.2692 1.9623 0.7350 0.2500 0.0033 0.0712 0.0 0.0
MAIN POINTS 2 -1 -1 -1 -1 53 53 -1 -1 81 GRAVIT. ENERGY TERM INCLUDED

K	MR	R	LR	LOG T	LOG RHO	X	Y	C	LOG GR
2	0.00300	3.60000D-02	1.34150D-01	7.2639	1.9542	0.7350	0.2500	0.0033	0.1065
3	0.00381	3.90130D-02	1.67120D-01	7.2629	1.9523	0.7350	0.2500	0.0033	0.1005
4	0.00433	4.22740D-02	2.09440D-01	7.2618	1.9511	0.7350	0.2500	0.0033	0.0976
5	0.00613	4.58050D-02	2.61620D-01	7.2605	1.9491	0.7350	0.2500	0.0033	0.0940
6	0.00695	4.76790D-02	2.93020D-01	7.2598	1.9480	0.7350	0.2500	0.0033	0.0913
7	0.00777	4.96290D-02	3.25610D-01	7.2590	1.9468	0.7350	0.2500	0.0033	0.0896
8	0.00851	5.16580D-02	3.64640D-01	7.2581	1.9455	0.7350	0.2500	0.0033	0.0864
9	0.00934	5.37700D-02	4.03670D-01	7.2572	1.9442	0.7350	0.2500	0.0033	0.0843
10	0.01113	5.59670D-02	4.50980D-01	7.2562	1.9426	0.7350	0.2500	0.0033	0.0806
11	0.01246	5.82540D-02	4.98280D-01	7.2552	1.9410	0.7350	0.2500	0.0033	0.0781
12	0.01398	5.98300D-02	5.36230D-01	7.2543	1.9398	0.7350	0.2500	0.0033	0.0751
13	0.01466	6.14490D-02	5.74180D-01	7.2535	1.9385	0.7350	0.2500	0.0033	0.0728
14	0.01576	6.31120D-02	6.12130D-01	7.2527	1.9373	0.7350	0.2500	0.0033	0.0710
15	0.01715	6.48190D-02	6.57440D-01	7.2517	1.9358	0.7350	0.2500	0.0033	0.0676
16	0.01854	6.65720D-02	7.02740D-01	7.2508	1.9344	0.7350	0.2500	0.0033	0.0650
17	0.01992	6.83730D-02	7.49650D-01	7.2498	1.9329	0.7350	0.2500	0.0033	0.0630
18	0.02123	6.97560D-02	7.88200D-01	7.2490	1.9317	0.7350	0.2500	0.0033	0.0600
19	0.02254	7.11660D-02	8.28340D-01	7.2481	1.9304	0.7350	0.2500	0.0033	0.0576
20	0.02384	7.26050D-02	8.68490D-01	7.2473	1.9291	0.7350	0.2500	0.0033	0.0556
21	0.02515	7.40730D-02	9.08640D-01	7.2465	1.9278	0.7350	0.2500	0.0033	0.0535
22	0.02647	7.52690D-02	9.46160D-01	7.2457	1.9266	0.7350	0.2500	0.0033	0.0512
23	0.02778	7.64840D-02	9.83680D-01	7.2449	1.9254	0.7350	0.2500	0.0033	0.0489
24	0.02909	7.77190D-02	1.02120D+00	7.2441	1.9242	0.7350	0.2500	0.0033	0.0469
25	0.03041	7.89740D-02	1.05870D+00	7.2433	1.9230	0.7350	0.2500	0.0033	0.0452
26	0.03172	8.02490D-02	1.09620D+00	7.2425	1.9218	0.7350	0.2500	0.0033	0.0438
27	0.03307	8.13270D-02	1.13240D+00	7.2417	1.9207	0.7350	0.2500	0.0033	0.0412
28	0.03446	8.24190D-02	1.16850D+00	7.2409	1.9195	0.7350	0.2500	0.0033	0.0390
29	0.03583	8.35270D-02	1.20460D+00	7.2402	1.9183	0.7350	0.2500	0.0033	0.0370
30	0.03720	8.46490D-02	1.24070D+00	7.2394	1.9172	0.7350	0.2500	0.0033	0.0353
31	0.03858	8.57870D-02	1.27480D+00	7.2386	1.9160	0.7350	0.2500	0.0033	0.0338
32	0.03995	8.69390D-02	1.31290D+00	7.2378	1.9148	0.7350	0.2500	0.0033	0.0326
33	0.04141	8.79400D-02	1.34830D+00	7.2371	1.9136	0.7350	0.2500	0.0033	0.0302
34	0.04288	8.89510D-02	1.38360D+00	7.2363	1.9124	0.7350	0.2500	0.0033	0.0281
35	0.04435	8.99750D-02	1.41890D+00	7.2355	1.9113	0.7350	0.2500	0.0033	0.0262
36	0.04582	9.10100D-02	1.45420D+00	7.2347	1.9101	0.7350	0.2500	0.0033	0.0245
37	0.04729	9.20580D-02	1.48950D+00	7.2339	1.9089	0.7350	0.2500	0.0033	0.0230
38	0.04876	9.31170D-02	1.52490D+00	7.2331	1.9077	0.7350	0.2500	0.0033	0.0216
39	0.05023	9.41880D-02	1.56020D+00	7.2324	1.9065	0.7350	0.2500	0.0033	0.0204
40	0.05165	9.50300D-02	1.59110D+00	7.2316	1.9055	0.7350	0.2500	0.0033	0.0185
41	0.05307	9.58800D-02	1.62200D+00	7.2309	1.9044	0.7350	0.2500	0.0033	0.0166
42	0.05449	9.67370D-02	1.65290D+00	7.2302	1.9033	0.7350	0.2500	0.0033	0.0150
43	0.05592	9.76020D-02	1.68380D+00	7.2295	1.9022	0.7350	0.2500	0.0033	0.0135
44	0.05734	9.84740D-02	1.71470D+00	7.2288	1.9011	0.7350	0.2500	0.0033	0.0120
45	0.05876	9.93550D-02	1.74560D+00	7.2281	1.9001	0.7350	0.2500	0.0033	0.0108
46	0.06019	1.00240D-01	1.77650D+00	7.2274	1.8990	0.7350	0.2500	0.0033	0.0096
47	0.06161	1.01140D-01	1.80750D+00	7.2266	1.8979	0.7350	0.2500	0.0033	0.0086
48	0.06303	1.02040D-01	1.83840D+00	7.2259	1.8968	0.7350	0.2500	0.0033	0.0076
49	0.06452	1.02810D-01	1.86730D+00	7.2252	1.8958	0.7350	0.2500	0.0033	0.0058
50	0.06602	1.03590D-01	1.89630D+00	7.2245	1.8947	0.7350	0.2500	0.0033	0.0041
51	0.06751	1.04370D-01	1.92530D+00	7.2238	1.8936	0.7350	0.2500	0.0033	0.0026
52	0.06900	1.05160D-01	1.95430D+00	7.2231	1.8925	0.7350	0.2500	0.0033	0.0011
53	0.07050	1.05960D-01	1.98330D+00	7.2224	1.8914	0.7350	0.2500	0.0033	-0.0002
54	0.07199	1.06760D-01	2.01220D+00	7.2217	1.8904	0.7350	0.2500	0.0033	0.0
55	0.07338	1.07510D-01	2.03910D+00	7.2210	1.8894	0.7350	0.2500	0.0033	-0.0012
56	0.07476	1.08260D-01	2.06600D+00	7.2204	1.8884	0.7350	0.2500	0.0033	-0.0024
57	0.07615	1.09020D-01	2.09290D+00	7.2197	1.8874	0.7350	0.2500	0.0033	-0.0036
58	0.07754	1.09780D-01	2.11980D+00	7.2191	1.8864	0.7350	0.2500	0.0033	-0.0048

FIGURE 15A.2

A Typical Computer Output of a Stellar Model

Values of mass, luminosity, temperature, density, and chemical composition are shown for different layers inside a model star.

SOURCE: Evan Flower.

ing or contracting (Figure 15A.3). The power of modeling is such that if we are able to correctly reproduce the observed temperature, luminosity, and radius of a star with a model, we can infer that the star's structure is the same as that calculated for the model. This is the only way astronomers are able to understand the difference, for instance, between main-sequence stars, giants, supergiants, and white dwarfs. In addition, stellar models are used to predict how the internal structure of a star changes over time. Models answer such questions as; What will happen to the Sun in the future? How old are the stars? Why do some stars explode? As Chapter 15 described, the analysis of models that mathematically follow the behavior of gas and dust under the dominance of gravity led to an understanding of the collapse process of protostars.

How can astronomers build a model of a star, follow changes over time, and know that the results are correct? A model of a star is a description of the physical condition at every point in a star. What is meant by "every point in a star"? First, we usually assume that the star is spherical. This is a reasonable assumption for most stars and means, among other things, that the radial distribution of temperature, is the same from the center to the equator or from the center to the poles. Consequently, we only need to describe the pressure, temperature, mass, and luminosity distributions along a single line from the center to the surface. Second, we limit ourselves to describing only a few hundred points along the star's radius. We imagine that the star is constructed in concentric shells, with each shell having

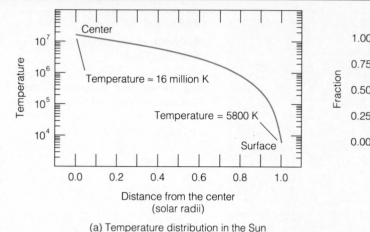

(a) Temperature distribution in the Sun

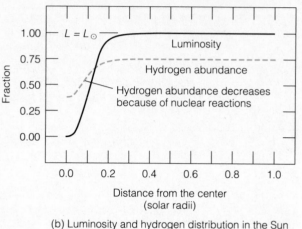

(b) Luminosity and hydrogen distribution in the Sun

■ FIGURE 15A.3

Plots of Model Data

A plot of the model parameters is usually more revealing than a table of numbers. *(a)* A plot of temperature from the center to the surface is shown for a model of the Sun. Temperature increases smoothly from the surface to the center. *(b)* Luminosity increases at the center where nuclear reactions take place; at the same time, the hydrogen abundance in the core has been lowered from its initial value because of the nuclear reactions.

specific values of pressure, temperature, mass, and luminosity. The choice of the number of shells is a trade-off between an accurate representation of a star's interior (more shells, greater accuracy) and the amount of computer time available to compute the models (more shells, more time needed).

The job of the modeler is to compute values of pressure, temperature, mass, and luminosity for each shell. This is a problem for the computer (Figure 15A.4). We must write down equations that relate pressure, mass, temperature, and luminosity to physical laws that govern the behavior of matter. These equations represent complex interrelationships between these parameters. Four equations are necessary:

■ *Hydrostatic equilibrium equation:* Describes the balance between gravity and pressure.

■ *Mass equation:* Describes how the mass changes from shell to shell.

■ *Energy transport equation:* Describes how heat is transported throughout the interior.

■ *Energy generation equation:* Describes how the luminosity changes from shell to shell due to nuclear energy generation.

These equations describe how the pressure, mass, temperature, and luminosity *change* from one shell to the next. Table 15A.1 schematically shows how we would solve these equations. Observationally, we know the luminosity, surface temperature, radius, chemical composition, and mass of a main-sequence star, for instance. Although the corona and chromosphere of a star extend above its surface, they do

(a)

(b)

■ **FIGURE 15A.4**

Two Computers Used in Modeling

(a) All model calculations are done on computers, such as this National Advanced Systems Mainframe. *(b)* Detailed analysis of the model calculations is sometimes done on smaller computers such as the VAX 3100 work station shown here.

SOURCES: Part (a), Clemson University. Part (b), Evan Flower.

not represent much mass so we can estimate that the pressure is very low. Column 2 represents the surface values of our parameters. We can now use our four equations to predict how the temperature, pressure, luminosity, and mass will change as we move inward a small distance, r_1. These *changes* are represented by t_1, p_1, and l_1, and m_1 in column 3. Once calculated, we add or subtract these changes to the surface values to obtain new values of temperature, pressure, luminosity, and mass for the next shell inward (column 4). Next we use these new values as the starting point for another step inward to the next shell. The changes are shown in column 5 and the values for the third shell are shown in column 6. We keep repeating this until we reach the center, or $R = 0$ (column 8). If we did everything right, we will know the structure of the star.

How do we know we are right? For instance, the estimate of the surface pressure may be in error. Figure 15A.5 shows what happens if we make a mistake. The dashed line represents a wrong solution; it is wrong because when the mass is calculated to be zero, the radius is still greater than zero! When the right assumptions are made, the calculations give zero mass at the center of the star, as it should be.

■ TABLE 15A.1 **Interior Model Calculations**

1	2	3	4	5	6	7	8
Radius	R	r_1	$R - r_1$	r_2	$R - r_1 - r_2$	—	0
Temperature	T	t_1	$T + t_1$	t_2	$T + t_1 + t_2$	—	$T + t_1 + t_2 + \cdots$
Pressure	P	p_1	$P + p_1$	p_2	$P + p_1 + p_2$	—	$P + p_1 + p_2 + \cdots$
Luminosity	L	l_1	$L - l_1$	l_2	$L - l_1 - l_2$	—	0
Mass	M	m_1	$M - m_1$	m_2	$M - m_1 - m_2$	—	0

Column 2: values at the surface; column 3: predicted changes moving inward a distance r_1; column 4: new values at the distance $R - r_1$ from the center (note that R and M decrease while T and P increase; L may increase or decrease); column 5: predicted changes moving inward a small distance r_2 using the new values from column 4; column 6: new values at the distance $R - r_1 - r_2$ from the center; column 8: values at the center after taking many small steps inward.

■■■■ FIGURE 15A.5

Schematic Model Calculation

The solid curve shows how the mass must vary with distance from the center to reach a value of zero at the center. The dashed line shows that the mass reaches zero "before" the center of the star is reached. Values for both the radius and the mass must be zero concurrently.

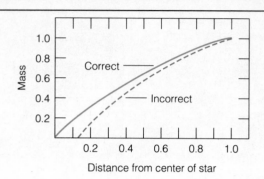

Another check is the luminosity at the center; it must also be zero (column 8 in Table 15A.1).

Although we can solve the necessary equations describing stars so that their masses and luminosities are zero at the center, are we sure that the models represent real stars? Much of the physics that enters into the calculations, such as values of the nuclear reaction rates or the behavior of gases at high temperatures and densities, may be uncertain. This, of course, is where the observations play their part. If we mathematically compute a model for a 5 $\mathfrak{M}_\odot$ main-sequence star in which the surface temperature or radius or luminosity does not agree with observational values, we must try to locate the sources of uncertainty. Nuclear physicists may redo or extend experiments on nuclear reactions, or theoretical calculations on the properties of gases may be extended as a result of discrepancies between models and observations. Only when the models and the observations agree do we have confidence in the computed models.

Although the method of constructing models of stars outlined here is certainly valid, it cannot be used to calculate the structure of an evolved star, such as the Sun, without a critical modification. The problem is that we cannot know the distribution of chemical composition inside a star from observations. Although we can assume that the star has the same chemical composition throughout and compute a model of a recently formed main-sequence star, the same procedure will not work for a red giant. The interiors of the two stars differ in that hydrogen has been depleted in the center of the red giant. The main-sequence model, however, is the starting point for the "next model." The next model is the structure of the star after a small time interval. The difference between the first and second models is that some of the hydrogen in the core has been converted into helium. But because we know the chemical composition, temperature, and density in the core, we can calculate how much hydrogen

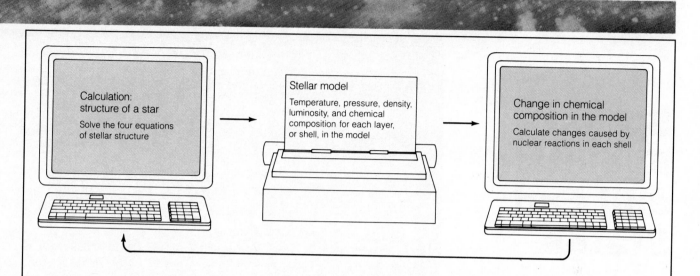

is used up in a small time interval (Figure 15A.6). We calculate the change in chemical composition for each shell in the star, and this distribution of chemical composition is then used to start another solution. In this way we can compute the changes in stars as a function of time.

Astronomers and physicists are continually refining stellar models as their understanding of physics improves and new or improved computing techniques or capabilities become available. These refinements are important because our knowledge of the "lives" of stars depends on the validity of the models. For instance, our understanding of the collapse phase of a protostar or the explosive end to stellar lives described in Chapter 16 depends on model calculations. In fact, nearly everything discussed in Chapter 16 concerning the evolution of stars is based on model calculations. Furthermore, the ages astronomers obtain for the oldest stars in our Galaxy are a very important check of the estimates of the age of the universe calculated from studies of the motions of galaxies.

FIGURE 15A.6

Changes in Time

Once a model has been calculated, we compute the changes caused by nuclear reactions at the center over a small time interval. We then recalculate the model incorporating these changes. This gives a new model that is slightly "older" than the first model.

Stellar Evolution and End States

OUTLINE

Interior Developments: The Burning of the Ashes
A 15 $\mathfrak{M}_\odot$ Star
The Iron Core

Surface Developments: The Changing Appearance of Stars
Red Giants and Supergiants
Planetary Nebulae and White Dwarfs
Supernovae
Nucleosynthesis
Neutron Stars
Black Holes

Summary

Chapter Capsule

Review Questions

For Further Reading

▬▬▬▬**ASTROPROBE 16: Relativity**

Supernova.
ARTIST: Kim Poor.

THE STUDY OF THE "LIVES" OF STARS is in part a study of the origins of the elements that make up the periodic table. Stars are capable of creating elements more massive than hydrogen and helium. Some are created during nuclear burning in stellar cores, while others are created during catastrophic stellar explosions. The heavy elements so created are dispersed throughout the Galaxy, available for use by the succeeding generations of stars. Consequently, when the Sun and planets formed, the solar nebula was already a mixture of elements produced by previous generations of stars. The common elements found on Earth, such as carbon, oxygen, silicon, and iron, were created at the centers of stars.

The heaviest nuclei are created in the death throes of massive stars. These events are extremely violent and, in some cases, the star is completely disrupted by an immense explosion. When a remnant remains, it is an exotic object in a unique state of matter and has very peculiar observational characteristics. Although the violent end of massive stars is almost instantaneous, the star methodically evolves to the point of its destruction. Gravity drives the star to the final outcome by forcing it to proceed through several nuclear-burning episodes until it runs out of fuel.

This chapter documents the changes in stars as they evolve toward their final states. The events occurring at the center of the star cause changes in luminosity, temperature, and radius at its surface. The interior events consist of a series of nuclear reactions operating at higher and higher temperatures. The changes at the surface caused by the commotion at the center lead to the formation of giants and supergiants and even more exotic objects. This study of the internal and surface developments will set the stage for the examination of the end states of stars.

INTERIOR DEVELOPMENTS: THE BURNING OF THE ASHES

"Life beyond the main sequence" is a tempestuous time for stars. They will expand, contract, and pulsate; some will even blow themselves apart. Most will leave behind a lonely cinder, bright for a while, but destined to fade from existence. The events occurring in the deep interiors of stars that drive them to their individual ends will be considered first.

A 15 $\mathfrak{M}_\odot$ Star

At the end of hydrogen burning, the core of a star is a sphere of helium "ash" left over from the main-sequence hydrogen reactions, like the ash left over from an evening campfire. Can the nuclear flame be rekindled? This question can be answered by following the results of model calculations for a 15 $\mathfrak{M}_\odot$ star. With the exhaustion of hydrogen, the nuclear reactions stop not because no more fuel is available, but because core temperatures, ~50 million Kelvins, are now too low. Helium nuclei, which consist of two protons each, need much higher speeds than hydrogen nuclei before they can overcome the repulsive electrostatic barrier between them. Helium nuclei require temperatures of 100 million Kelvins for fusion, and since core temperatures after hydrogen exhaustion are lower than this, the core begins to contract.

Core contraction has two immediate effects on the internal structure of the star. First, without the support of the core, the entire star begins to contract. The contraction raises the temperature of the hydrogen-rich gas just outside the core to values high enough to begin hydrogen burning in a shell surrounding the core. This **shell source** of nuclear energy is so powerful that it is able to support the outer layers of the star and stop their contraction (Figure 16.1). Second, temperatures in the contracting core will increase until they reach 10^8 K. At that temperature, helium ignition occurs.

Helium burning proceeds in a set of two reactions:

Shell source: A thin region of nuclear burning surrounding the core of a star; more than one shell source can be present in a star.

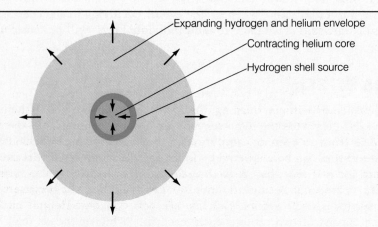

in which three helium nuclei fuse to form a carbon nucleus: $3\,^4\text{He} \rightarrow$ ^{12}C. The $\leftrightarrows$ symbol in the "helium + helium" reaction indicates that the beryllium nucleus is unstable. It will break down into two helium nuclei unless another helium nucleus quickly fuses with it. Astronomers call this set of helium-burning reactions the *triple alpha process* simply because physicists in the late nineteenth century called helium nuclei "alpha particles." The newly formed carbon nuclei can also fuse with existing helium to form oxygen, $^{12}\text{C} + {}^4\text{He} \rightarrow {}^{16}\text{O}$; small amounts of neon-20 (^{20}Ne) and magnesium-24 (^{24}Mg) are also produced. What started out as a core of hydrogen and a little helium in a main-sequence star is now being transformed into an ash composed mainly of carbon and oxygen.

■ FIGURE 16.1
Nuclear Shell Source

The continuous demands of gravity force the star to repeat these events over and over again. As the helium is depleted, the carbon-oxygen core contracts, producing a helium shell source, which operates below the still active hydrogen shell source. The contraction continues until temperatures reach $\approx 8 \times 10^8$ K, at which time carbon burning (^{12}C + ^{12}C) commences. When carbon is used up, the core again contracts and creates another shell source, a carbon shell source. The core of a 15 $\mathfrak{M}_\odot$ star contracts three more times, passing through neon burning, oxygen burning, and finally silicon burning, creating another shell source with each contraction.

The sequence of core nuclear burning (Appendix G and Table 16.1) shows ^{20}Ne being consumed before ^{16}O. This appears to contradict the rule that the nuclei with the least number of protons react first. Nuclear reactions at temperatures greater than 10^9 K take a peculiar twist. First, at these high temperatures, the energy of individual photons becomes great enough to break existing nuclei apart into lighter nuclei, a process called **photodisintegration.** Second, a careful examination of the nuclear structure of neon and oxygen nuclei reveals that an oxygen nucleus is bound together slightly more tightly than a neon nucleus. It is more difficult for energetic photons to break an oxygen nucleus apart than a neon nucleus. The photodisintegration of neon is written as a reaction of neon with a photon (γ, Greek letter gamma):

$$^{20}\text{Ne} + \gamma \rightarrow {}^{16}\text{O} + {}^4\text{He}$$

The new helium nucleus can fuse with any of the remaining neon nuclei to produce ^{24}Mg:

$$^{20}\text{Ne} + {}^4\text{He} \rightarrow {}^{24}\text{Mg} + \gamma$$

These two reactions constitute neon burning and increase the amount of oxygen and magnesium in the core.

Oxygen burning follows and its principal products are silicon and sulfur. The nuclear reactions astronomers call *silicon burning* are dominated by photodisintegrations. Although photodisintegration produces lighter nuclei, such as protons and helium nuclei, these light nuclei can fuse with silicon nuclei that have not been photodisintegrated. Such reactions produce even heavier elements. During the great profusion of photodisintegrations and fusions during silicon burning, a gradual buildup of heavy elements occurs. At the end of silicon burning, the core consists almost entirely of "iron group" nuclei: chromium, manganese, iron, cobalt, and nickel.

Figure 16.2 shows the distribution of the most abundant elements in a 15 $\mathfrak{M}_\odot$ star at the end of silicon burning. Below the still extensive hydrogen-rich envelope, the star has a layered structure. Each core contraction leads to a new episode of nuclear burning that uses the "ash," or the products, of the previous episode. At the end of each nuclear-burning sequence a shell source is created. The iron core is composed of elements and isotopes with atomic masses between about 50 and 60. Furthermore, each successive stage of core thermonuclear reactions

At temperatures of billions of degrees, the number of possible nuclear reactions increases dramatically. The main set of reactions that can occur in stars is given in Appendix G.

Photodisintegration: The destruction of atomic nuclei by collisions with high-energy photons; occurs at temperatures $\geq 10^9$ K.

■ FIGURE 16.2

Structure of a 15 $\mathfrak{M}_\odot$ Star at the End of Silicon Burning

The distribution of major elements is shown as a function of mass. Due to the variety of nuclear reactions possible at temperatures above 10^9 K, oxygen, silicon, and sulfur are mixed from about 1.5 to 2.3 $\mathfrak{M}_\odot$. Between each distinct layer a shell source burns and adds mass to the layer below it.

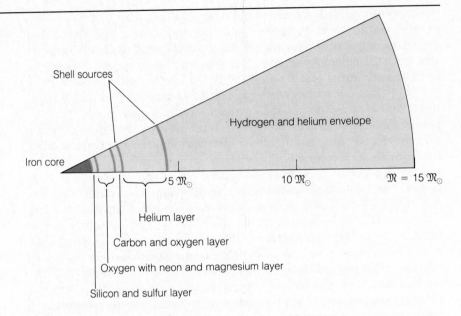

lasts a shorter length of time. Table 16.1 lists approximate time scales for a 15 $\mathfrak{M}_\odot$ star. Successive core nuclear-burning lifetimes are shorter because the higher temperatures required for the next stage of core nuclear burning also result in faster fuel consumption. The end result of the six nuclear-burning stages is a core of iron.

The Iron Core

What happens now to the iron core? Does it contract and proceed with "iron burning"? The answer to the last question is yes and no: yes, the iron core contracts, and no, iron burning does not occur. The iron-56 (^{56}Fe) nuclei are the most strongly bound of all nuclei. It takes more energy to disperse an iron nucleus than any other nucleus. This means that the fusion of two iron nuclei, or an iron nucleus with a helium nucleus, or any other combination with iron, will not produce a nucleus

■ TABLE 16.1 **Evolutionary Time Scales for a 15 $\mathfrak{M}_\odot$ Star**

Fused	Products	Nuclear Reaction	Length of Time	Temperature
H	^{4}He	Hydrogen burning	$\approx 10^7$ years	4×10^6 K
^{4}He	^{12}C	Helium burning	$\approx$ few $\times 10^6$ years	$8 \times \sim 10^8$ K
^{12}C	^{16}O, ^{20}Ne, ^{24}Mg, ^{4}He	Carbon burning	$\sim 10^3$ years	8×10^8 K
^{20}Ne $+ \gamma$	^{16}O, ^{24}Mg	Neon burning	A few years	$\sim 1 \times 10^9$ K
^{16}O	^{28}Si, ^{32}S	Oxygen burning	~ 1 year	$\sim 2 \times 10^9$ K
^{28}Si $+ \gamma$	^{56}Fe	Silicon burning	$\sim 10^{-2}$ years (days)	$\sim 3 \times 10^9$ K
^{56}Fe	Neutrons	Core collapse	< 1 second	$> 3 \times 10^9$ K

with less mass than the original nuclei. No mass is converted into energy. Consequently, when a star produces an iron core, no further energy-liberating nuclear reactions can take place in the core. It appears that the iron core must contract.

After silicon burning the density of the iron core is an incredible 10^{10} g/cm^3. At these densities electrons in the core have been squeezed so close together that no "space" exists between them. The description of this state of electrons requires quantum mechanics (only the broad outline of relevant features are given next—some other aspects of quantum mechanics are discussed in AstroProbe 4). In particular, a law called the *Pauli exclusion principle*, formulated in 1925 by the Austrian physicist Wolfgang Pauli (1900–1958), applies. It states that no two electrons, or any two identical particles, can occupy the same "quantum state." The description of a quantum state involves both position and momentum (= mass × velocity); as the density increases and the electrons become more crowded, the number of unfilled quantum states decreases. The low-momentum, or velocity, quantum states are occupied first by the electrons, as are low-energy electron orbitals in neutral atoms. The remaining electrons can only occupy high-velocity quantum states. Consequently, collisions between high-velocity electrons and other electrons or nuclei result in a very strong pressure and a very powerful resistance to further compression. We call this state **electron degeneracy** and call the pressure generated "degenerate electron gas pressure."

Electron degeneracy: A state of a gas at very high density in which all of the quantum states for electrons are filled; the pressure due to degenerate electrons is independent of temperature.

The pressure in the core of the 15 $\mathfrak{M}_\odot$ star, therefore, is the sum of the degenerate electron gas pressure and the pressure due to the nuclei of iron group elements in the core. The nuclei still behave as ideal gases; only the electrons are degenerate. In a degenerate core the pressure from the electrons greatly exceeds that due to the nuclei. In fact, degenerate electron gas pressure is capable of supporting a core without the assistance of energy generated by nuclear reactions. This pressure, however, has its limits. The Noble Prize recipient S. Chandrasekhar (1910–) showed that degenerate electron pressure can only prevent the collapse of a mass less than 1.4 $\mathfrak{M}_\odot$. This limit is called the *Chandrasekhar limit*. Cores with masses over the Chandrasekhar limit must contract, even if the electrons are degenerate. At the conclusion of core silicon burning in a 15 $\mathfrak{M}_\odot$ model, the mass of the iron core is very close to, but slightly less than, the Chandrasekhar limit.

The core cannot support itself for long by degenerate electron pressure because the silicon-burning shell surrounding the core continuously "feeds" iron into the core, increasing its mass. Once the core mass reaches the Chandrasekhar limit, it contracts. The contraction of the core accelerates the process of photodisintegration because the rate of photodisintegration increases as core temperatures increase. Photodisintegration destroys the work of previous evolutionary phases in the core by tearing apart iron group nuclei, reducing the core to protons, electrons, and neutrons. At the high densities and temperatures in the contracting core, the process of electron capture occurs:

$$\text{Electron + proton} \rightarrow \text{neutron + neutrino}$$

Since neutrinos normally do not interact with matter, they escape from the core. The loss of electrons lowers the degenerate electron gas pressure, and core collapse accelerates.

In less than a second after core collapse begins, the densities at the center of the star reach $\approx 3 \times 10^{14}$g/cm^3, and the collapse of the inner part of the core abruptly halts. The inner core has reached nuclear densities, the density of protons and neutrons inside the nuclei of atoms. Neutrons squeezed together at these densities resist further compression as did the electrons at lower densities. We call the associated pressure *degenerate neutron gas pressure*. The mass of the inner core is approximately 0.7 $\mathfrak{M}_\odot$, well below the limiting mass, 1.8 to 2 $\mathfrak{M}_\odot$, that can be supported by degenerate neutrons.

To this point we have followed the development of a 15 $\mathfrak{M}_\odot$ star from the main sequence to a state at which the inner part of a relic iron core has stopped collapsing and is supported by degenerate neutron gas pressure. The outer part of the core is still falling while at the same time several nuclear shell sources are operating outside the core. All stars with masses over 8–10 $\mathfrak{M}_\odot$ probably reach this state of affairs. Less massive stars are not expected to develop a core of neutrons or even an iron core. To understand this and what becomes of the neutron core of a massive star, astronomers follow closely the developments at the surfaces of stars.

SURFACE DEVELOPMENTS: THE CHANGING APPEARANCE OF STARS

The luminosity, radius, and surface temperature of a star respond in specific ways to the developments in the interior. Figure 16.3 shows the predicted *evolutionary tracks* for a range of masses. Hydrogen burning

■ FIGURE 16.3

Evolutionary Tracks for Stars with the Same Composition as the Sun

The dashed line above the main sequence marks the luminosities and temperatures of stars at hydrogen exhaustion in their cores. The yellow strip labeled "instability strip" represents a region in which stars are expected to pulsate.

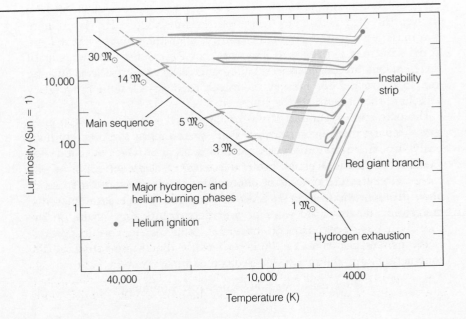

occurs between the main-sequence line and the dashed line, which represents hydrogen exhaustion in the core. During a star's main-sequence lifetime, the hydrogen abundance is slowly decreasing in the core. Whereas complete exhaustion of hydrogen leads to a rapid contraction of the core, gradual depletion of hydrogen leads to gradual core contraction. The slow contraction increases the temperature of the core, raising nuclear energy generation and causing the luminosity of the star to increase. At hydrogen exhaustion, a hydrogen shell source ignites. The energy generated by the hydrogen-burning shell source heats the inner part of the overlying envelope and pushes it outward. This begins an expansion of the layers above the hydrogen-burning shell source and a cooling of the star's atmosphere. The star expands into a supergiant or giant.

Red Giants and Supergiants

The transition from a main-sequence star to a red giant or supergiant after hydrogen exhaustion is very rapid for massive stars. It takes ~1% of the main-sequence lifetime of a 15 $\mathfrak{M}_\odot$ star and ~13% of the main-sequence lifetime of a 2.5 $\mathfrak{M}_\odot$ star. The transition is much slower for lower mass stars; for instance, it takes a third of the main-sequence lifetime of a 1 $\mathfrak{M}_\odot$ star. The part of the evolutionary track that rises steeply in luminosity is called the *red giant branch*. The rapid transition time from a main-sequence star to a supergiant for massive stars means that when we look at the HR diagram of a young star cluster, we will not see many stars between the main sequence and the red giant branch. On the other hand, the HR diagram of an older cluster should show many stars evolving off the main sequence. Figure 16.4 shows two HR diagrams, one of a young cluster and one of an old cluster. The different distributions of stars reflect the different evolutionary time scales for stars of different masses.

The expansion of the envelope on the red giant branch causes the rise in luminosity. The expansion and rise in luminosity stop when helium is ignited in the core. Most of the energy released during helium ignition is used to expand the helium-rich core while the behavior of the envelope is still controlled by the energy produced by the shell source. The expansion of the core, however, pushes the surrounding hydrogen shell source to regions of lower temperature and density, weakening the shell source. Since less energy is now available to support the envelope, it contracts; since less energy is being generated by the shell source, luminosity decreases. Accordingly, helium burning in the core is characterized by core expansion and envelope contraction.

The thick lines in the giant and supergiant regions in Figure 16.3 mark the core helium-burning phase for different masses. Since the stars have a nuclear energy source in their cores, they can maintain the luminosities and temperatures shown for a long time, as long as it takes to use their helium fuel. Consequently, the HR diagrams of stars exhibit concentrations of stars in these regions of the HR diagram (Figure 16.4).

Although the core helium-burning phase can last a long time, stars may behave erratically at times. Core helium-burning models with

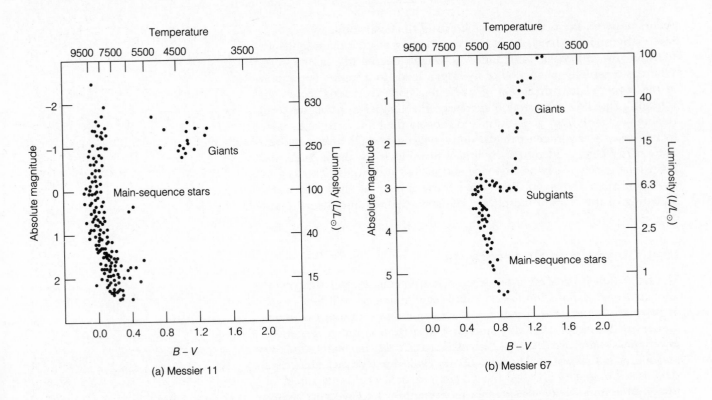

(a) Messier 11　　　　　　　　　　**(b) Messier 67**

■ FIGURE 16.4

HR Diagrams of Two Clusters

(a) Messier 11 is a young cluster, a few hundred million years old. It shows a distinct main sequence and a group of giants. A gap lies between the main sequence and the giants because it takes stars very little time to become giants after hydrogen exhaustion. Consequently, we are not likely to see stars in this part of the HR diagram. *(b)* Messier 67 is a much older cluster with an age of 6–8 billion years. The segment of the evolutionary track between the main-sequence stars and the giants is more populated than for Messier 11 because stars take a longer time to evolve through these phases.

Cepheid variables: An important group of yellow supergiants that pulsate with periods from about 1 to 50 days; the correlation between their pulsation periods and their brightnesses is very important for estimating the distances to star clusters in the Galaxy and to nearby galaxies.

masses greater than about 4 $\mathfrak{M}_\odot$ enter a short-lived stage in which they pulsate, expanding and shrinking repeatedly. In the region labeled the "instability strip" in Figure 16.3, conditions of temperature and ionization in a model's atmosphere are just right to cause its radius to increase and decrease periodically. Real stars also pulsate. Astronomers find a class of stars called **Cepheid variables,** named after the first one to be discovered (Delta Cephei), that occupy the instability strip. We infer that the masses of Cepheids are between about 4 $\mathfrak{M}_\odot$ and 15 $\mathfrak{M}_\odot$ because the instability strip is where we expect to find core helium-burning stars with those masses (Figure 16.3).

The spectra of Cepheids reveal the in-and-out motions of their atmospheres. When a Cepheid is expanding and its atmosphere is moving toward us, we record blueshifted spectral lines. When it is contracting and its atmosphere is moving away from us, the same lines are redshifted. During these motions Cepheid radii can change by as much as 25%. The resulting changes in the surface areas of Cepheids cause their brightness to change drastically. The light variations have periods ranging from about 1 day to 50 days. Delta Cephei, a bright Cepheid variable in the constellation Cepheus, changes its brightness by about a magnitude every 5.4 days. The light variations vary with the same period as the spectral changes.

Cepheid variables are very bright and large, ranging in absolute magnitude from $M \approx -2$ to $M \approx -7$ and in radius from $\approx 20\ R_\odot$ to $\approx 200\ R_\odot$. The brightest Cepheids are the largest. Since it takes more time for a large star to pulsate than a small star, we expect a correla-

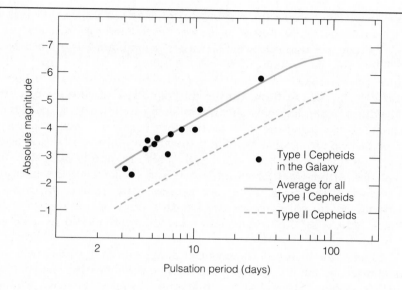

**Period-Luminosity Relations
for Cepheids**

Shown here are the period-luminosity relations for Type I Cepheids, which are similar in chemical composition to the Sun, and Type II Cepheids, which are about 1.5 magnitudes fainter and have metallicities much lower than the Sun's. Because Cepheids show a range in period and luminosity values, astronomers use an average relation for all Cepheids of a given type.

tion between luminosity and pulsation period: brighter stars should have larger periods. Cepheid variables show just this correlation. Figure 16.5 shows the **period-luminosity relation** for Cepheids in the Galaxy. As Chapters 17 and 18 will show, astronomers can use the period-luminosity relation as a powerful distance indicator to nearby galaxies.

The evolutionary tracks for masses below about 2 $\mathfrak{M}_\odot$ are slightly different from higher mass tracks in that they reach very high luminosities before helium ignition. Since low-mass stars have low central temperatures while on the main sequence, their cores must contract more than high-mass stellar cores before temperatures can reach the needed 10^8 K for helium ignition. During this contraction the star has time to reach very high luminosities. The extended contraction also results in core densities reaching values of 10^6 g/cm^3, high enough for the core to become degenerate. This leads to an explosion of galactic proportions. To understand how this leads to an explosion, let's consider the behavior of ordinary, nondegenerate gases.

In a main-sequence star, the gas is nondegenerate and behaves as an ideal gas; that is, it heats when compressed and cools when expanded. This behavior prevents a star from exploding or imploding. For example, when a protostar ignites nuclear reactions at its center, the heat generated causes the core to expand. The expansion cools the core, thereby reducing the heat produced by the nuclear reactions. Less heating reduces the expansion, and the core eventually reaches an equilibrium in which the energy derived from nuclear reactions results in just the right amount of pressure to balance the star.

Degenerate electron gas pressure, on the other hand, depends only on the density of the gas; it is independent of temperature. Increasing temperatures cause only a very slight expansion of a degenerate core because only part of the pressure, that supplied by nuclei, is due to a perfect gas. This means that a degenerate core cannot cool itself enough to regulate the triple alpha process. Therefore, core temperatures must

Period-luminosity relation: Observed correlation between pulsation period and luminosity for Cepheid variables; brighter stars take longer to pulsate than fainter stars.

Helium flash: The violent ignition of helium burning in the core of stars with main-sequence masses less than 2 $\mathfrak{M}_\odot$; uncontrolled nuclear reactions are brought about by electron degeneracy in the core.

RR Lyrae variables: A group of small, hot pulsating stars with periods less than 1 day; like Cepheid variables, RR Lyrae are also used as distance indicators.

rise. Increasing temperatures promote more nuclear reactions, which in turn raise the temperatures in the core even more. A "thermal runaway" occurs. Within hours temperatures reach hundreds of millions of Kelvins, and the amount of energy generated in the core reaches 100 times the luminosity of an entire galaxy! This burst of nuclear energy is called the **helium flash.** During this rapid rise of core temperature, the core is expanding only slightly, reducing core densities, and slowly removing the degeneracy. Once the core becomes nondegenerate, it must behave as an ideal gas. Since the temperature is now "too high" for an ideal gas at the core pressure, the pressure rapidly rises—the core explodes. Although the helium flash is very violent, all the energy is absorbed by the gases in the core, causing it to expand. Surprisingly, astronomers do not detect any associated events on the surface of the star experiencing the helium flash other than the normal reduction in luminosity.

Although the helium flash is violent, it appears that after the star has readjusted, it simply proceeds through core helium burning without further violence. Evidence for this comes from a class of variables, called **RR Lyrae variables,** that inhabit the faint end of the instability strip. They are about 100 times brighter than the Sun, have radii of 4–10 $R_\odot$, and pulsate with periods of 0.3 to 0.7 days. RR Lyrae variables are found in the oldest clusters in the Galaxy, called *globular clusters.* Figure 16.6 shows the HR diagram of the stars in a globular cluster and marks the location of the RR Lyrae variables. It shows a main sequence of faint stars, the brightest of which have luminosities of stars with masses less than 1 $\mathfrak{M}_\odot$, implying ages over 10 billion years. The distribution of stars along the giant branch is as predicted by stellar models. The horizontal distribution of stars, called the *horizontal branch,* however, indicates that stars do indeed survive the helium flash.

Observations alone of Cepheid and RR Lyrae variables will not tell astronomers why these stars pulsate. Although the pulsation mechanism is too complex to describe in detail here, our understanding of pulsations derives from the interplay between observations of real stars and analysis of model stars. Observations tell us that stars pulsate when they reach surface conditions that place them in the instability strip. Theoreticians constructed stellar models (see AstroProbe 15) with similar surface conditions and studied the interior structure of these models. The assumption was that since the real stars and the models had the same surface characteristics of luminosity, temperature, and radius, the interior structure of the stars was the same as the models. Analyses of the distribution of temperature, mass, pressure, and chemical composition in these models revealed that, indeed, the atmospheres of these stars were unstable. In fact, the models could be made to pulsate, mathematically, of course, in the same manner as the real stars.

After stars pass through the instability strip and exhaust the helium in their cores, they repeat their behavior after hydrogen exhaustion and again become red supergiants. In these stars the carbon and oxygen cores are contracting, and two thin nuclear shell sources provide energy to expand the envelope to enormous dimensions. Such expanded envelopes feel only a weak gravitational attraction to the star and are ca-

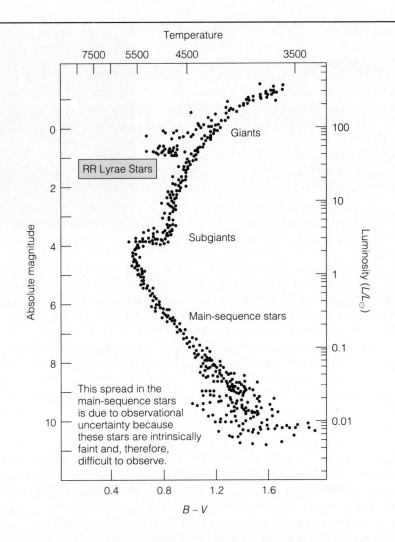

FIGURE 16.6

**HR Diagram of the Old Star Cluster
47 Tucanae in the Galaxy**

The brightest main-sequence stars have
masses $\approx 0.8 \, \mathfrak{M}_\odot$, indicating an age of
about 15 billion years. These low-mass
stars evolve so slowly between the main
sequence and the red giant branch that
the HR diagram shows a continuous sequence of stars. RR Lyrae stars in clusters this old are located in the boxed-in
region. (Adapted from J. Hesser et al.,
1987, *Publications of the Astronomical Society of the Pacific*, 99:739.)

pable of escaping from the supergiant altogether. In fact, nuclear burning by the shell sources in stars with masses less than 6–8 $\mathfrak{M}_\odot$ leads to
instabilities that work with strong stellar winds to eject the entire envelope from the star.

Planetary Nebulae and White Dwarfs

The huge, extended atmospheres and high luminosities of very evolved
stars cause tremendous stellar winds. These winds are so strong that
the amount of mass ejected can be as high as 1 $\mathfrak{M}_\odot$ every 100,000 years.
At the same time supergiants are losing mass from winds, the hydrogen
and helium shell sources add to the mass loss. The hydrogen shell
source produces helium faster than a thin helium shell source can burn
it. As a result, the helium shell source tends to "flash," or burn explosively, whenever the helium supplied by the hydrogen shell source
reaches a critical mass. Each flash can eject part of the overlying enve-

■■ FIGURE 16.7

The Ring Nebula

(a) View of the Ring nebula. As the diagram shows, we look through a thicker portion of the emission nebula when our line of sight is slightly away from the center. Consequently, the light emitted from the thick layers appears brighter.
(b) Photograph of the Ring nebula.

SOURCE: Part (b), National Optical Astronomy Observatories.

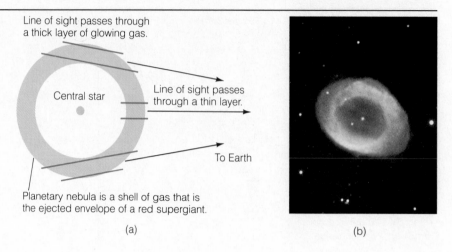

Line of sight passes through a thick layer of glowing gas.

Central star

Line of sight passes through a thin layer.

To Earth

Planetary nebula is a shell of gas that is the ejected envelope of a red supergiant.

(a)

(b)

Planetary nebula: The glowing, ejected envelope and atmosphere of a red supergiant; the core of the supergiant appears as a star at the center of the nebula.

lope. Over hundreds of thousands of years, the combination of steady mass loss by winds and pulsed ejection by thin shell sources can drive off the entire envelope of the giant star.

The ejection of the star's envelope exposes the hot inner core of the supergiant, and the intense ultraviolet radiation from the core ionizes the expanding envelope. The envelope gases then shine by emission. The ring-shaped object in Figure 16.7 represents an advanced stage of the ejection of a star's envelope. The ring, of course, is the glowing gas of the ejected envelope and is actually part of a more or less spherical shell of ionized material. Near the edges of the shell, our line of sight passes through a thicker section of the emitting material than near the center. The edge of the shell, therefore, appears brighter. We call these shells of glowing gas **planetary nebulae;** over 1000 have been cataloged. Their name originated in the eighteenth century because their green-blue color (due to oxygen emission) and disk shape resembled the appearance of the giant outer planets, Uranus and Neptune. The star in the middle of the ring, called the *planetary nebula nucleus*, is the exposed interior of the red supergiant star.

Planetary nebulae are among amateur astronomers' favorite objects to observe. Their great variety in appearance provides many delightful hours of observing (Figure 16.8). Besides rings, observers see doughnuts, double and triple shells, dumbbells, hourglasses, interlocking rings, and even faces! Sometimes the ejection from the supergiant is spherically symmetric, and we see the shell as a ring nebula. In other planetary nebulae, the envelope ejection is preferential, such as bipolar, and we see nonspherical planetary nebulae.

Planetary nebulae are a few hundredths to a few tenths of a parsec across. Their expansion velocities, measured from red and blue shifts of spectral lines, range from 20 km/s to 50 km/s, implying that the nebulae will become too thin to see in visible light in about 25,000 years or less after ejection. As the ejected gases dissipate in time, we see deeper into

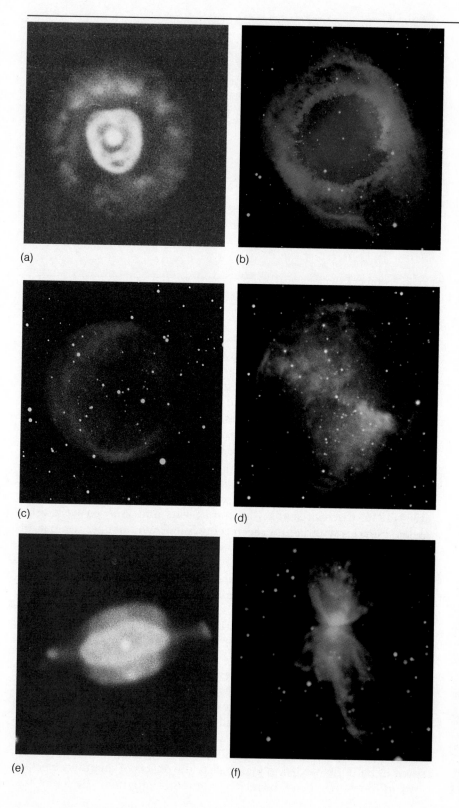

(a)

(b)

(c)

(d)

(e)

(f)

■■■ FIGURE 16.8

Planetary Nebulae

(a) The Eskimo nebula is an example of a double shell planetary in which we see the remains of two episodes of envelope ejection. *(b)* The Helix nebula is one of the largest planetaries visible; it is as large as half the diameter of the Moon. *(c)* NGC 6781 exhibits a spherical shell but more matter appears to have been ejected to one side than the other. *(d)* The Dumbbell nebula is a bipolar nebula and looks like an hourglass. *(e)* The Saturn nebula shows evidence of several ejections. The first of the visible ejections now appears as a disk, or ring. *(f)* NGC 6302, the "Bug" nebula, is an irregularly shaped planetary; velocities of 400 km/s have been measured for the expanding shell, indicating a violent explosion.

SOURCES: Part (a), Lick Observatory, University of California, Santa Cruz. Part (b), copyright © Anglo-Australian Telescope Board 1979. Photograph by David Malin. Part (c), Hale Observatories. Part (d), Lick Observatory, University of California, Santa Cruz. Part (e), National Optical Astronomy Observatories. Part (f), copyright © Anglo-Australian Telescope Board 1977. Photography by David Malin.

■ FIGURE 16.9

Evolutionary Tracks of the Cores of Planetary Nebulae

Initially, the ejected envelopes are too small to see; consequently, the region outlined in the HR diagram as marking the location of planetary nebulae starts away from the red giant branch. The slow expansion of the ejected envelopes eventually thins the nebulae until we cannot see them.

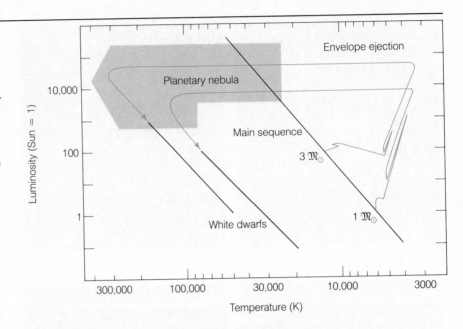

White dwarf: The exposed carbon-oxygen core of a red supergiant; its mass is below the Chandrasekhar limit, and it is supported by degenerate electron gas pressure.

■ FIGURE 16.10

Sirius B

The small dot next to the large image of Sirius A is the white dwarf Sirius B. The brilliance of Sirius A makes it very difficult to see or photograph Sirius B.

SOURCE: Lick Observatory, University of California, Santa Cruz.

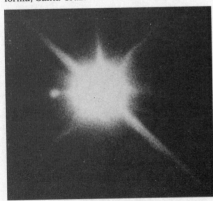

the interior of the supergiant. As a result, when we plot the luminosity and temperature of the central stars on the HR diagram, they mark a track from right to left, starting from the high luminosities and low temperatures of the red supergiants (Figure 16.9). Temperatures reach as high as 300,000 K for the hottest planetary nebula nuclei. Near the high temperature bend in the evolutionary track, the last vestiges of the ejected envelope disappear. We are left with just the central star, which we call a **white dwarf.**

White dwarfs were discovered long before astronomers calculated their structure. In 1844 the German astronomer Friedrich W. Bessel (1784–1846) discovered that the stars Sirius and Procyon were astrometric binaries with faint, unseen companions with masses comparable to their own masses. In 1862 the American telescope maker Alvan G. Clark (1804–1887), using an 18½-inch refractor, was the first person to see a white dwarf, Sirius B (Figure 16.10). White dwarfs are so faint that none can be seen with the unaided eye. Spectra of Sirius B and the white dwarf companion to 40 Eridani showed that their temperatures are high. High temperatures and low luminosities imply small radii; white dwarfs are about the size of the Earth. A "typical" white dwarf has a mass of 0.6 $\mathfrak{M}_\odot$ and a radius slightly less than that of the Earth. White dwarfs range in temperature from $\approx$150,000 K to $\approx$4000 K. Moreover, the small sizes and large masses of white dwarfs imply densities of $\approx 10^6$ g/cm^3; a ton of white dwarf material would easily fit into a small matchbox. In 1930 S. Chandrasekhar worked out the equations governing the structure of white dwarfs. Because their electrons are in a compact state with velocities equal to an appreciable fraction of the speed of light, he needed to incorporate the effects of quantum mechanics and Einstein's theory of relativity into his equations. He found that white dwarfs must all be less massive than 1.4 $\mathfrak{M}_\odot$, the maximum mass degenerate electron gas pressure can support.

Stars with main-sequence masses below 6–8 $\mathfrak{M}_\odot$ are expected to become white dwarfs following the planetary nebula phase. We find, for example, young star clusters, whose brightest main-sequence stars have masses from 3 $\mathfrak{M}_\odot$ to 6 $\mathfrak{M}_\odot$, with white dwarfs as cluster members. White dwarfs in these clusters must have resulted from the evolution of more massive stars that have evolved off the main sequence and gone through core helium burning. Furthermore, stellar models indicate that supergiants with these masses will lose mass faster than the shell sources can add carbon and oxygen ash to the core. The carbon-oxygen core, therefore, will never increase above the Chandrasekhar limit, and no more nuclear reactions can take place in the core. Because the exposed carbon-oxygen core is supported by a degenerate electron gas, its future is one of cooling at a constant radius.

During the cooling of a white dwarf, it can accrete a substantial amount of hydrogen, especially if it is a member of a binary system. In binary systems of different masses, a white dwarf represents the star that was initially more massive and has evolved faster than its companion. As the companion later evolves into a giant or supergiant, it can dump material onto the white dwarf (Figure 16.11). As the hydrogen piles up on the white dwarf, it becomes hot and dense enough to ignite. Depending on how fast the hydrogen is being accreted, hydrogen fusion can ignite every 10,000 to 100,000 years. The explosive ignition causes the white dwarf to become 10,000 times brighter (10 magnitudes) within a few days. During the explosion, the unburned hydrogen is blown off the white dwarf at speeds of up to 1000 km/s. In the seventeenth and eighteenth centuries, the sudden increase of 10 magnitudes usually meant that the star was visible for the first time. Consequently, astronomers called these stars **novae**, Latin for "new stars," not realizing that a star too faint to see existed at the site of the nova. Astronomers still use this term to describe nuclear explosions on white dwarfs.

Stars with masses less than about 6–8 $\mathfrak{M}_\odot$ eject most of their mass into interstellar space. The remaining core then finishes its existence as a cooling white dwarf. What happens to more massive stars? A nova is a hint to the end states of these stars. However, whereas a nova does not disrupt the white dwarf, the explosions characterizing the ends of more massive stars can destroy all or most of the star.

Supernovae

Let's bring together two concepts encountered in the evolution of low-mass stars: accretion of mass by a white dwarf from a companion star and the thermal runaway in a degenerate core. Consider a carbon-oxygen white dwarf in a binary system accreting material from its evolving companion. If the accretion brings the mass of the degenerate carbon-oxygen core above the Chandrasekhar limit, the subsequent collapse will raise core temperatures to carbon-burning values. This is similar to the conditions of the helium flash except now carbon instead of he-

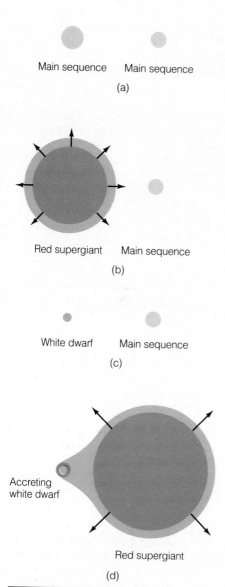

FIGURE 16.11

Stellar Evolution in a Binary System

The primary star evolves through helium burning and becomes a white dwarf after passing through the planetary nebula phase. The star that was the secondary is now the primary by virtue of its brightness, and it also expands after hydrogen exhaustion. As its expanding envelope extends near or beyond the orbit of the white dwarf, some gas is dumped onto the white dwarf. If conditions are right, the accreted hydrogen can explode.

lium will ignite under degenerate conditions. A thermal runaway occurs in which core temperatures keep increasing until electron degeneracy is removed. At that moment the white dwarf explodes. Since a white dwarf does not have an overlying envelope to hinder the explosion, it is completely disrupted and most of its mass is transmuted into iron group nuclei through explosive nuclear burning. This catastrophic disruption of a white dwarf is responsible for Type I **supernovae.**

In the early 1930s astronomers began organized searches for supernovae. A discovery of a "new" star in a galaxy sent astronomers scrambling to obtain photographs and spectra. By the 1940s astronomers recognized two types of supernovae based on spectra. Type I supernovae did not show any hydrogen lines in their spectra while the other class, called *Type II supernovae*, exhibited emission lines due to hydrogen.

The origin of Type II supernovae can be understood by returning to the study of evolutionary models of massive stars. Soon after the collapse of the iron core, which occurs after silicon burning, the inner part of the core is brought to an abrupt halt when densities reach nuclear densities, 3×10^{14} g/cm^3. Within seconds, the core transforms all of the iron and protons into neutrons and emits a flood of neutrinos, which eventually pass through the star untouched. The neutrinos are produced from electron capture and by collisions between electrons and positrons:

$$p + e^- \rightarrow n + \nu$$
$$e^- + e^+ \rightarrow \nu + \bar{\nu}$$

Here $\bar{\nu}$ represents an antineutrino. Degenerate neutron gas pressure now prevents the inner core from collapsing farther, but the rest of the star still falls onto the neutron core. In fact, the incoming matter collides with incredible speeds of 70,000 km/s (¼ the speed of light!). The collisions generate a supersonic shock that violently propagates outward through the star and blasts its way through the overlying layers, reaches the surface in a few days, and erupts in the gigantic explosion of a Type II supernova. Only the core remains intact.

The explosive incineration of a white dwarf and the disruption of a supergiant are observed as rapid increases in brightness (up to several billion solar luminosities) followed by a slow fading. This is an enormous amount of energy. It is over 100 times the total energy the Sun will emit over its 10-billion-year lifetime. A supernova generates this amount of energy in less than a second! Figure 16.12 shows the *light curves* of typical Type I and II supernovae. The rise to maximum brightness is due to emission from the hot, expanding cloud of debris. As the debris cools, however, the brightness might be expected to decrease as fast as it increased, on the order of a couple of weeks. What then produces the steady decay in brightness lasting months and even years? What is the source of light? Current modeling suggests that the decay of radioactive nickel-56 (^{56}Ni) and cobalt-56 (^{56}Co) provides the light. Nickel has a half-life of about 6 days, and its daughter ^{56}Co has a half-life of 79 days. The photons (gamma rays) liberated from the de-

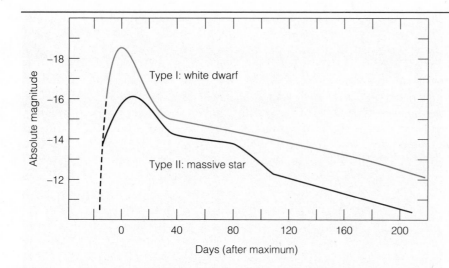

FIGURE 16.12

FIGURE 16.12

Supernovae Light Curves

The dashed part of the rise in luminosity is usually not observed. The gradual decrease in brightness after maximum is due to the decay of radioactive elements in the expanding envelope.

cays excite the expanding gases. Once most of the radioactive ^{56}Ni and ^{56}Co decays, the light from the supernova fades.

Type II supernovae can leave two remains: an expanding shell of matter and a neutron-rich core. The expanding shell moves away from the site of the supernova with velocities of 10,000 km/s and interacts with the interstellar medium. The interaction produces *supernovae remnants*. The ejected material of the supernova forms a shock front, like that of a sonic boom, that compresses and, therefore, heats any gas it plows though. The collision with the interstellar medium excites the atoms and causes visible emission. The Veil nebula in the constellation Cygnus (Panel a in Figure 16.13), for instance, is the remnant of a star that exploded about 10,000–20,000 years ago; it is still visible long after the

FIGURE 16.13

Supernovae Remnants

(a) The Veil nebula exhibits bright filaments in a circular pattern as if they were blown out from a central point. *(b)* The Crab nebula is a remnant of a supernova seen by the Chinese in A.D. 1054.

SOURCES: Part (a), Hale Observatories. Part (b), Lick Observatory, University of California, Santa Cruz.

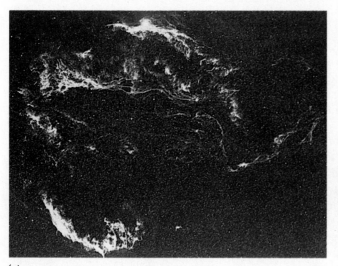

(a)

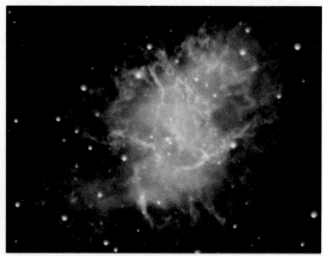

(b)

568

FIGURE 16.14

X-Ray Images of Supernova Remnants

Ringlike structures are visible for all of the remnants. The colors indicate surface brightness, the faintest regions being blue and brightest white. These images were taken with the *Einstein* X-ray (HEAO 2) satellite.

SOURCE: Fred Seward, Harvard-Smithsonian Center for Astrophysics.

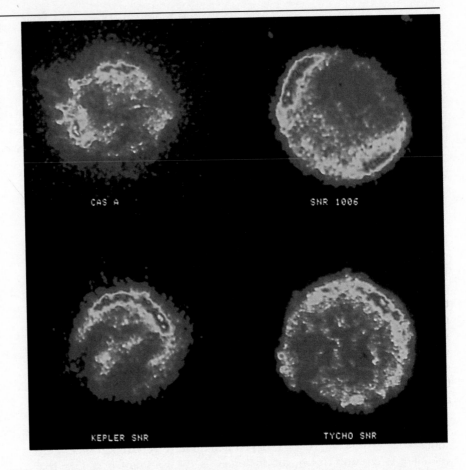

exploded star has faded from sight. Approximate dates of supernovae can be estimated from the observed expansion velocities of the visible remnants. Thus, for the remnant of the Crab nebula (Panel b in Figure 16.13) to reach its present size, it had to have started its expansion about 900 years ago. This time scale coincides with a supernova observed by Chinese astronomers and Native American Indians in A.D. 1054. It was as bright as a quarter moon and was visible for several weeks in broad daylight. It is said that one could read by its light at night. Chinese astronomers observed this supernova for nearly two years before it faded from sight. The Crab nebula even looks like an exploded star.

Supernova remnants are visible in X-rays; in fact, they are easier to find with X-ray telescopes than with optical telescopes. The X-rays are the result of million degree temperatures caused by collisions between the expanding supernova remnant and the interstellar medium. Figure 16.14 shows X-ray images of four supernovae remnants in the Galaxy. The supernovae of A.D. 1006, 1572 (seen by Tycho), and 1604 (seen by Kepler) were observed by humans. Cas A was an unseen supernova that exploded around A.D. 1700. The white, yellow, and red colors represent high X-ray intensity, which is greatest around the edges of the expanding remnant. The variation in intensity around the perimeter gives astronomers an indication of the structure of the interstellar material through which the debris is passing.

Although the Galaxy could produce as many as five Type II supernovae every 200 years, we have seen only a handful of supernovae originating there because gas and dust block our view of most of the Galaxy (see Chapter 17). Consequently, most of the 630 supernovae astronomers have observed have occurred in very distant galaxies—until recently. Orbiting the Galaxy, like planets around the Sun, are two small galaxies called the Large and Small Magellanic Clouds. Although they are about 55,000 pc away, they are the closest galaxies to our own. On February 23, 1987, Ian Shelton, a Canadian astronomer observing at the Las Campanas Observatory in Chile, discovered a supernova in the Large Magellanic Cloud while he was photographing that galaxy (Figure 16.15). The supernova is called SN 1987A, indicating that it was the first discovered in 1987. By the next evening all of the major radio and optical telescopes in the Southern Hemisphere were observing SN 1987A. Within 14 hours of the discovery astronomical satellites were obtaining ultraviolet spectra. For several years following the discovery, telescopes in Chile, Australia, New Zealand, and South Africa have monitored the supernova almost nightly. American, Japanese, and Soviet satellites and space stations have observed the supernova in ultraviolet, X-ray, and gamma ray light. Airplanes have obtained infrared spectra and balloon flights have obtained gamma ray spectra. For the first time in history astronomers have been able to study a supernova at all wavelengths on a regular basis.

Although the spectra of SN 1987A show hydrogen lines, suggesting a Type II supernova, its greatest luminosity is lower than other Type II supernovae (Figure 16.16). Astronomers have identified the precursor star, which was not a red supergiant or even a white dwarf, but a hot B3 supergiant—that star is now gone! This is the only supernova for which astronomers have identified the progenitor. The prediction is that the remnant of the explosion will be a neutron star, and observations in 1989 suggest just this (see the next section for a description of neutron stars). Theoreticians have more confidence now in their predictions associated with supernovae because another very critical prediction of the models has been verified.

One of the most remarkable observations of SN 1987A was the detection of neutrinos from the exploding star, which verified the prediction that a neutrino burst signals the collapse of the iron core of a supergiant. Two recently built underground neutrino detectors, one in Japan and one in Ohio, detected 19 neutrinos three hours before the optical sighting. Nineteen neutrinos is not very many considering that about 50 billion neutrinos from SN 1987A passed through each square centimeter of the Earth's surface. It is estimated that about one million humans each stopped one neutrino from SN 1987A on February 23, 1987. Clearly, neutrinos do not interact strongly with matter! The scientific importance of these neutrinos is that their measured energies reflect the temperature at which they were created and give us a look at the outer part of the neutron core at the time of the explosion. Analysis of the available data suggests that the neutrinos were generated at incredible

■ FIGURE 16.15

Before and After Pictures of Supernova 1987A

The arrow points to the hot supergiant before it exploded. The large image of the supernova reflects the tremendous energy output of the star as it exploded.

SOURCE: Copyright © Anglo-Australian Telescope Board 1987. Photograph by David Malin.

570

■■ FIGURE 16.16

The Light Curve of Supernova 1987A

Since hydrogen is observed in its spectrum, SN 1987A is classified as Type II. The difference between the Type II curve and that of SN 1987A is probably due to SN 1987A's unusual progenitor, a B3 supergiant. Only a few of the thousands of observations are shown.

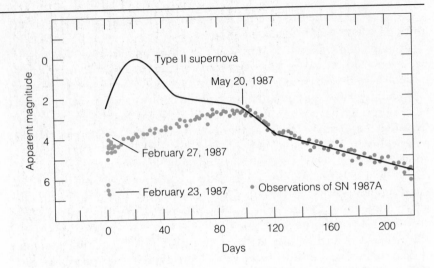

temperatures of 30–40 billion Kelvins, implying that the temperatures at the center of the supernova may have reached several hundred billion Kelvins! This again supports current models of the origin of supernovae.

The decrease in brightness of SN 1987A corresponds to what is expected if the optical light is powered by radioactivity. According to current theory, the explosion created 0.07 $\mathfrak{M}_\odot$ of ^{56}Ni (radioactive nickel) that decayed first into ^{56}Co (radioactive cobalt) and then to ^{56}Fe (iron-56). Indeed, infrared spectra showed lines due to all three elements, as well as to silicon and sulfur, within nine months of the explosion. Each time a ^{56}Co nucleus decays into a ^{56}Fe nucleus, it emits a high-energy photon, a gamma ray. During late 1987 and early 1988, several experiments detected gamma rays from SN 1987A, giving further support for radioactivity in the supernova.

Astronomers believe that this supernova was fainter than normal because the progenitor star was about ten times smaller than red supergiants, which are believed to produce most of the Type II supernovae. The small radius meant that the blue supergiant had to expand by a greater factor and, therefore, used more energy for the expansion than a larger red supergiant would. Consequently, less energy was left to provide visible light. The HR diagram in Figure 16.17 shows the approximate evolutionary track of the progenitor star of about 20 $\mathfrak{M}_\odot$. The star remained near the main sequence as an O-star burning hydrogen in its core for about ten million years. It then expanded toward the cool end of the HR diagram where it burned helium in its core for about a million years. Further nuclear reactions in the core lasted about another thousand years. Just before it exploded, the star was a blue supergiant with a radius of about 50 $R_\odot$ and a 1.4 $\mathfrak{M}_\odot$ iron core at a density of about 10^{10} g/cm^3 and a temperature of 10^{10} K.

Astronomers will be observing the light from the debris of SN 1987A for many years to come. They will try to learn what elements in what quantities were made in the explosion; whether the remnant is spheri-

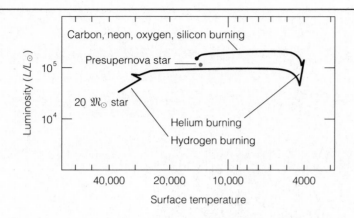

■■ ■ FIGURE 16.17

**The Evolutionary Track of
a 20 $\mathfrak{M}_\odot$ Star**

The final model (black dot) has the right
luminosity and temperature to be the observed progenitor of SN 1987A, shown by
the magenta dot.

cally symmetric or distorted; and how much material was ejected by
the star. Most interesting is the collapsed object at the center. Theory
says it is a small sphere of neutrons. Our ability to see it depends on
when the supernova becomes transparent, and this could occur just a
few years after the explosion.

Supernova 1987A also accomplished one other feat; it ejected into interstellar space another dose of very heavy elements. It created new
elements with atomic masses much greater than that of iron.

Nucleosynthesis

As Figure 16.18 shows, hydrogen and helium are by far the most abundant elements in the universe. The abundant elements with atomic
numbers greater than helium up to iron are produced in the centers of
stars and in supernovae. The peak near iron is expected since iron group
elements are the heaviest elements that can be produced in stars
through their normal cycle of nuclear reactions. What about elements
heavier than iron, such as silver-108, tin-119, tungsten-184, and ura-
nium-238? Where do they originate?

Current models of the first moments of the universe (see Chapter 19)
and observations related to the early universe suggest that hydrogen
and helium with a small amount of other light elements, such as lithium and beryllium, were the only elements in the universe before stars
formed. Thus the first stars were nearly pure hydrogen and helium. As
massive stars evolved, they built up elements as heavy as iron at their
centers and lighter elements in shells surrounding the core. Although
fusion reactions cannot produce elements more massive than the iron
group of elements, nuclei are able to capture neutrons. It is very easy
for a nucleus to capture a neutron because neutrons have no electrical
charge. A capture of a neutron produces a heavier isotope of the element; the atomic mass is changed but not the number of protons. Some
isotopes of an element are unstable, or radioactive, and will decay, in
which case a neutron in the nucleus transforms into a proton, electron,
and neutrino. The electron and neutrino escape the nucleus, but the
added proton remains and its presence changes the nucleus into an-

**Abundance of the Elements
in the Universe**

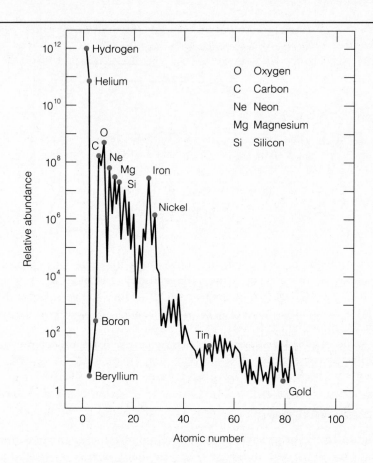

other element. In principle, successive neutron captures can fill in the periodic table in a star beyond the iron group. To do so, a large number of neutrons is required.

Neutrons are created in prodigious numbers during the collapse of the iron core of a supergiant and are ejected into the envelope during the ensuing explosion. For about a quarter of an hour, a burst of neutrons is captured by heavy and light elements alike, creating the heaviest elements known. Since this proliferation of neutrons occurs over a very short time, heavy nuclei never become as abundant as those up to the iron group.

These recently created heavy elements are thrown into interstellar space during the supernova. Every time a supernova occurs, more heavy elements are ejected into the interstellar medium. Over the history of the Galaxy, the abundance of heavy elements increased in the interstellar medium. Some were mixed with the solar nebula, giving the Sun its observed abundance and all of the heavy elements found on Earth. Gold in rings, silver in coins, titanium in aircraft, and uranium that powers nuclear reactors were all created by neutron capture during the violent explosion marking the end of a star's life.

While the envelope of the star in a Type II supernova expands outward and the neutrinos rush away, the neutron-rich matter in the core remains. The neutron core represents a second type of end state for stars.

Neutron Stars

For stars with main-sequence masses less than 25 $\mathfrak{M}_\odot$ (but greater than 6–8 $\mathfrak{M}_\odot$), the mass of the neutron core is predicted to be less than the supporting limit of degenerate neutrons. Consequently, the core does not collapse. Astronomers call the neutron core of the exploded star a **neutron star.** Because of the extremely compact state of the neutrons ($\approx 10^{14}$ g/cm^3), neutron stars must be very tiny. We expect their radii to range from 10 to 20 km, about the size of a large city (Figure 16.19). Objects this small are very difficult to detect.

Neutron stars were proposed long before supernovae models were calculated. In the 1930s, two astronomers at the Hale Observatory in California, Walter Baade (1893–1960) and Fritz Zwicky (1898–1974), suggested that supernovae were transitions from ordinary stars to neutron stars. Although no one took their suggestion seriously at the time, astronomers considered the Crab nebula to be a remnant of an explosion and studied it extensively. Astronomers could not see an obvious central star in the Crab nebula, but they did see a "star" that, unknown to them, was far from a normal star. Its identity was revealed by chance.

In 1967 radio astronomers in Cambridge, England, began to survey distant objects called quasars (see Chapter 18). In particular, they wanted to study rapid fluctuations, called scintillation, of sources of radio emission caused by the interplanetary medium and built a new kind of radio telescope just for that purpose. A graduate student, Jocelyn Bell, while analyzing the 96 feet of chart recordings that the observations produced every day, noticed a series of regular pulses buried in the data. The pulses came every 1.3373011 seconds, unsettlingly steady, like the ticking of a very well-made clock. What in nature could produce such precise pulses? Astronomers first eliminated manmade sources of radio "noise," such as radio waves generated by sparks from car or lawn mower spark plugs. Signals from extraterrestrial civilizations were also considered briefly until three more radio sources were discovered; we would not expect four separate civilizations to be trying to communicate with us at once. The name adopted for these pulsed radio sources was **pulsar.** The mystery of the source of pulsars was solved with the discovery of a pulsed radio signal coming from the Crab nebula.

By the late 1960s the Crab nebula had already been associated with a supernova that occurred in A.D 1054. Its radio source emitted pulses 30 times a second. This meant that the pulsar must be caused by an object much smaller than a white dwarf because a white dwarf could not physically vibrate more than once a second and would break up if it rotated as fast as 30 times a second. The next smallest stable objects in the universe were the hypothetical neutron stars of Baade and

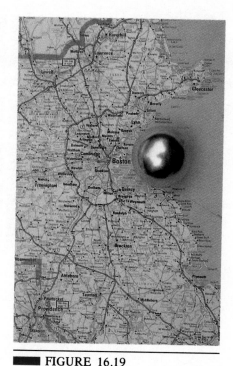

■ FIGURE 16.19

Size of Neutron Stars

Neutron stars have about the same diameter as a large city, such as Boston.

SOURCE: Evan Flower.

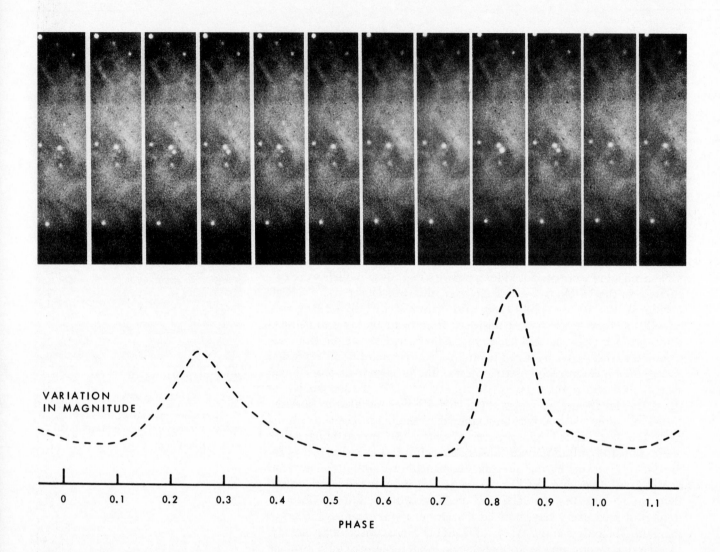

VARIATION
IN MAGNITUDE

PHASE

0   0.1   0.2   0.3   0.4   0.5   0.6   0.7   0.8   0.9   1.0   1.1

■■ FIGURE 16.20

The Crab Pulsar in Visible Light

High-speed photographs of the Crab nebula reveal the variable light output from
the pulsar. The graph shows the changes
in the brightness of the pulsar as a function of time.

SOURCE: National Optical Astronomy Observatories.

Zwicky. Continued observations showed that the Crab pulsar was slowing down; that is, its period was slowly becoming longer. Theoretical
calculations showed that rotation could easily produce pulses with a
lengthening period; therefore astronomers concluded that *pulsars were
rotating neutron stars.*

A closer examination of the stars in the Crab nebula located the pulsar. The pulsar looked like a normal star to astronomers because its
"blinking" at 30 times a second could not be detected with the eye or
on a photograph. Astronomers could see the pulsar blink only if they
used stroboscopic techniques in which a series of pictures is taken of a
pulsar at different phases (Figure 16.20). This is done by placing a rotating disk with widely spaced openings cut in it in front of a camera.
The disk is rotated so that the openings fly past the camera lens only
when the pulsar is at a certain brightness—say maximum brightness,
as in Frame 9 of Figure 16.20. The film only records light when the
pulsar is brightest. Changing the rotational rate of the disks allows the

film to record the pulsar at another brightness—say minimum light, as in Frame 7.

The radio and optical observations raised the question, "How can a rotating neutron star send us bursts of electromagnetic radiation 30 times a second? First, the collapse of the iron core will naturally increase the rotation rate of the core for the same reasons the collapse of an interstellar cloud increased its rotation rate. The greater the contraction, the faster the rotation. Since neutron stars are so tiny, very high rotational rates are expected.

Second, a neutron star is a source of extremely strong magnetic fields, a thousand billion times the Sun's average field. This is also expected from the collapse of a core because whatever magnetic field was present in the core will be compressed during the collapse. When magnetic field lines are squeezed close together, the magnetic field they represent becomes stronger. Although all the details of pulsed light emission are not completely understood, the method employed in the models of pulsars is similar to a lighthouse beacon. The general idea is that the strong magnetic and electric fields generated by the rotating neutron star rip charged particles off the surface of the star. At the surface, pressures are too low for the electrons and protons to be crushed to nuclear densities, hence a supply of charged particles. Since the greatest concentration of magnetic energy will be at the magnetic poles of the neutron star where the magnetic field lines are most compact, a stream of charged particles, mostly electrons, will concentrate along the polar magnetic field lines. "Lighthouse" models predict that the motions of charged particles produce a beaming effect along the polar axis. Furthermore, since the magnetic axes do not normally align exactly with the rotational axes, the magnetic poles will spin around the rotational axes, sending beams of radiation sweeping around the sky (Figure 16.21). Whenever the magnetic poles are pointing toward the Earth, we

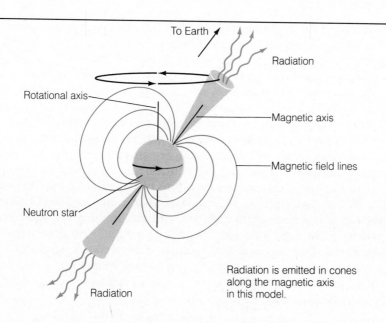

To Earth

Radiation

Rotational axis

Magnetic axis

Magnetic field lines

Neutron star

Radiation

Radiation is emitted in cones along the magnetic axis in this model.

■ **FIGURE 16.21**

Simplified Pulsar Lighthouse Model

Charged particles are accelerated by the intense magnetic fields near the magnetic poles of a rotating neutron star. We see a flash of radiation whenever the magnetic axis is pointing toward the Earth. Models of pulsar emission are based on many assumptions that are not completely understood.

■■■ TABLE 16.2 **Pulsars Identified with Supernovae Remnants**

Pulsar	Rotational Period	Approximate Age (yr)
Crab	0.033	900
PSR 0540-69	0.050	2000
Vela	0.089	10,000
PSR 1509-58	0.150	20,000
CTB 109	6.98	?

see a brief flash of radiation, like a cosmic lighthouse signaling its location.

Approximately 300 pulsars have been discovered. Their periods are as short as 0.001 second (1000 rotations per second!), and only those with the shortest periods are optically visible. The fastest spinning pulsars are also slowing down the fastest. Because pulsar rotational rates decrease over time, we associate short periods with young pulsars. The Crab nebula is one of the fastest pulsars and is only 900 years old. Several extremely fast pulsars, however, with periods of a few milliseconds (0.001 second) are not young but instead are old pulsars that have been "revived." Accreting matter from a companion star can speed up the rotation of an old pulsar just as water falling on a turbine makes it turn faster.

Astronomers have been able to identify four other pulsars associated with supernovae remnants. Table 16.2 lists these pulsars with their approximate ages. We do not expect to find pulsars with all supernovae remnants because Type I supernovae are presumably caused by the complete disruption of a white dwarf with little chance of leaving behind a neutron star. Furthermore, if the beams of radiation never point toward the Earth, we will never detect the pulsar. Finally, old pulsars are too faint to observe. On the whole, the association of pulsars with supernovae remnants and the explanation of pulsars as rotating neutron stars give astronomers much confidence in the predictions that the collapse of the iron core of a massive star creates a neutron star.

What about the stars with main-sequence masses greater than 25 $\mathfrak{M}_\odot$? Current model calculations indicate that the iron cores of these massive stars are greater than 2 $\mathfrak{M}_\odot$ and, therefore, cannot be supported by degenerate neutrons. In that case, of course, the core must collapse. In fact, it continues to collapse forever.

Black Holes

The effects of the continual collapse of a neutron core can be understood in terms of *surface gravity* and its relationship to escape velocity. Although this approach uses Newton's theory of gravity for a problem that requires general relativity, it is conceptionally easier to understand. The surface gravity for a star of mass $\mathfrak{M}$ and radius R is proportional to $\mathfrak{M}/R^2$. If a star collapses without losing mass, its surface gravity increases; it becomes more difficult to escape from the star. For small, compact stellar objects, such as white dwarfs and neutron stars, the effect can be severe (Table 16.3). For instance, the escape velocity from the surface of a tiny 1.5 $\mathfrak{M}_\odot$ neutron star is two-thirds the speed of light. If it could shrink from its radius of 10 km to 4.5 km, the escape velocity becomes equal to the speed of light. Since nothing in the universe can travel faster than the speed of light, nothing can escape from its surface, not even light itself. Although a 1.5 $\mathfrak{M}_\odot$ neutron star could never shrink that much, a 2 $\mathfrak{M}_\odot$ neutron core could. A neutron core of this mass cannot support itself by degenerate neutron pressure. Moreover, physicists do not know of any force that could stop the collapse. The neutron core must collapse forever.

■ TABLE 16.3 **Escape Velocities**

Object	Mass ($\mathfrak{M}_\odot$)	Radius (km)	Escape Velocity (km/s)
Sun	1	700,000	619
White dwarf	1	6400	6500
Neutron star	1.5	10	200,050

Speed of light = 299,793 km/s

What are the consequences of collapsing forever? Let's start at the point when the neutron core reaches the radius at which the escape velocity equals the speed of light. We call this the **Schwarzschild radius** after Karl Schwarzschild (1873–1917), a German astronomer who first calculated its magnitude. The Schwarzschild radius has another meaning that can only be appreciated with a little knowledge of Einstein's theory of general relativity (Einstein's theories are outlined in Astro-Probe 16). Einstein replaced Newton's concept of force with the geometry of space and time. Since time must be included as a coordinate in relativity we describe the three spatial coordinates and time with a single term—*spacetime*. Instead of describing gravity as exerting a force on a falling rock, Einstein described the path of the rock as following the "curvature" of spacetime. In Einstein's view, the coordinate system we use to describe spacetime is curved near the surface of the Earth. Figure 16.22 shows a representation of this geometry near a massive object, such as the Earth or the Sun. Far away from the object, spacetime is "flat," but close to the object, spacetime is very curved. Furthermore, in this geometry the path of any particle is independent of mass; both a rock and a photon will be deflected if they pass near the Sun.

Imagine a beam of light passing closer and closer to a collapsed object; its path will be deflected more and more. In fact, if the light beam passed close enough, its path would be a circle inside the gravitational "funnel" of curved spacetime. A slight deflection upward and the beam will shoot out; a slight deflection inward and it will spiral down the funnel. The distance from the collapsed object at which photons circle defines a sphere in space called the *photon sphere*.

Now let's change our perspective from outside to inside by imagining ourselves on the surface of a 3 $\mathfrak{M}_\odot$ collapsing core of a star that has just exploded. As it shrinks and its surface gravity increases, the geometry of spacetime around it becomes greatly distorted. We are equipped with flashlights, and when we reach the radius of the photon sphere, a ray of light from a flashlight will orbit the collapsing core if it is pointed exactly horizontal. But at smaller and smaller radii we will have to point the flashlight at steeper and steeper angles upward for a ray of light not to strike the surface of the core. That is, the curvature of spacetime is now so large that only light beams pointed upward have a chance of escaping from the surface (Figure 16.23). When the size of the collapsing neutron core reaches the Schwarzschild radius, even pointing the flashlight straight up does not allow the light to escape. In the terminology

■ FIGURE 16.22

The Geometric Coordinates near a Massive Object, Such as the Sun

General relativity allows us to describe the acceleration of gravity as paths in a curved coordinate system.

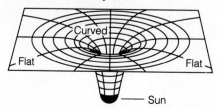

■■■ FIGURE 16.23

Light Beams from a Collapsing Neutron Core

The smaller the neutron core becomes, the steeper the angle of a flashlight must be to allow its light to escape.

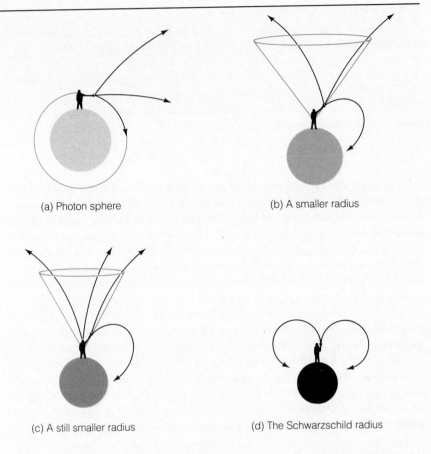

(a) Photon sphere

(b) A smaller radius

(c) A still smaller radius

(d) The Schwarzschild radius

Black hole: The volume of space surrounding the core of a massive star that has collapsed through its Schwarzschild radius and from which no electromagnetic radiation can escape.

of general relativity, the curvature of spacetime is so severe that the paths of photons curve back on themselves.

The Schwarzschild radius is the radius at which no light, or for that matter any electromagnetic radiation, can escape from the surface. Any object that reaches its Schwarzschild radius creates a **black hole.** If neutron stars shrink to radii of tens of kilometers, how small are black holes? We can easily calculate the value of the Schwarzschild radius for any mass by equating the mathematical formula for escape velocity to the speed of light; we find that the Schwarzschild radius is given by

$$\text{Schwarzschild radius} = 3 \times \frac{\mathfrak{M}}{\mathfrak{M}_\odot} \text{ km}$$

where $\mathfrak{M}$ is the mass of the object in solar masses. For example, a 3 $\mathfrak{M}_\odot$ collapsing neutron core has a Schwarzschild radius of 3 × 3 km, or 9 km; similarly a 10 $\mathfrak{M}_\odot$ neutron core has a Schwarzschild radius of 30 km. Moreover, when the neutron core reaches its Schwarzschild radius, it is still collapsing. The Schwarzschild radius defines the surface of a sphere from which no radiation or matter can escape. We call this surface the *event horizon* since we cannot observe any events occurring within it. Black holes, therefore, are expected to be very small objects with relatively large masses.

The difficulty with studying black holes is that we cannot observe them directly since they are black. Even if astronomers of the future could travel to a black hole, they would still have great difficulty exploring it. The problem, of course, is that nothing can come back once it passes beyond the event horizon. Even if a space probe is sent inside the black hole, no signals from it could get out—a form of cosmic censorship. Consequently, astronomers must rely on theoretical models of black holes to describe their interiors just as they rely on stellar models to describe the interiors of stars. Inside the event horizon the core of the supergiant is collapsing; that is, a space probe would not crash into the event horizon—it is just empty space! The space probe would feel the tremendous gravitational attraction of the collapsing core, however, and would be accelerated to an eventual collision at the center. In principle, the probe could fire rockets and travel around inside the event horizon, but eventually it would run out of fuel and fall inward.

Models describing black holes can be the source of some fanciful speculations about very strange phenomena. Recent suggestions include using black holes to travel through the universe and even to construct a time machine! A mathematical result of Einstein's equations suggests the existence of *wormholes*, or tunnels through spacetime. Under certain circumstances the collapse of a supergiant core into a black hole could result in the black hole emerging in another part of the universe, creating a "tunnel." If the tunnel could be kept open, it could be used for travel and communication. Furthermore, if an advanced civilization could find a way to move one opening of the tunnel, it could cause that opening to age differently from the other one and use it as a time machine, possibly violating causality in the process. Admittedly, these ideas are very speculative, but they are based on our knowledge of the laws of physics. In this respect, speculations provide a way for scientists to explore their understanding of the physical universe. Consequently, ideas that invalidate the whole concept of wormholes, if indeed it is invalid, will also be of interest.

Although astronomers cannot see a black hole, it occupies a place in space inside its event horizon, it moves through space, and it has a mass. The mass of the black hole is just the mass of the collapsed neutron core of a massive star. Since it has mass, it attracts objects just like any other object with the same mass. From a distance of 1 AU, for instance, a 3 $\mathfrak{M}_\odot$ black hole has the same gravitational influence as a 3 $\mathfrak{M}_\odot$ main-sequence star. Both can be members of binary systems or even have planets orbit them. The unique feature of a black hole in this regard is that regions near the black hole can be reached in which the gravitational attraction is tremendous. It is at these close regions, less than a few million kilometers from the black hole, that the bizarre effects of gravity can be felt. An object can be trapped forever *only* if it gets too close to a black hole.

So far we have presented the theoretical picture of the results of the collapse of a neutron core with a mass over 2 $\mathfrak{M}_\odot$, a product of the evolution of stars with main-sequence masses greater than 25 $\mathfrak{M}_\odot$. Do black holes really exist? How can we verify by observation the existence of objects that are invisible? Although the object creating the black hole

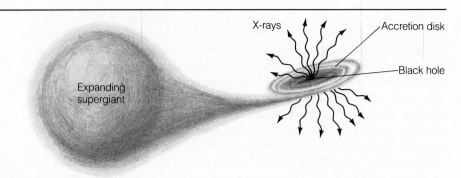

FIGURE 16.24

X-Ray Emission from a Black Hole

Some material from an expanding supergiant orbits and spirals onto the black hole in the binary system. Since the acceleration of gravity near the surface of the black hole is so high, the gas falls inward very rapidly and collisions between the atoms generate tremendous heat, resulting in high-energy X-ray photons.

is invisible to the rest of the universe, we can detect some of its effects on radiation and nearby matter. Astronomers must look for evidence of a small, stellar object with a mass greater than 2 $\mathfrak{M}_{\odot}$. If we wish to estimate the mass of the invisible object, we will need to find one in a binary system. High-energy photons, for instance, are a natural consequence of material being dumped onto a compact object such as a neutron star or a black hole (Figure 16.24). As the gas spirals toward the surface of the compact object, the atoms accelerate faster and faster and violent collisions between them raise temperatures to millions of degrees, resulting in X-rays and gamma rays. Consequently, a telltale sign of a compact object is the detection of these radiations. Furthermore, we expect such high-velocity accretion of matter to occur in binary systems in which one member is a neutron star or a black hole; a white dwarf is too large to generate such high-velocity accretion. Our observational requirements then are to find binary systems that are also X-ray sources.

Three such systems exist with well-determined masses: Cygnus X-1, A0620-00, and LMC X-3. Cygnus X-1 is an X-ray source in the constellation Cygnus in the Galaxy; A0620-00 is in the constellation Monoceros; and LMC X-3 is in the nearby galaxy the Large Magellanic Cloud. As Table 16.4 shows, all these systems have invisible companions with masses above the lower limit of stable neutron stars. Another system, LMC X-4, has a faint companion with a mass of ≈ 2.6 $\mathfrak{M}_{\odot}$ and is therefore another viable candidate. Several other X-ray systems are also being studied, but their masses are too ill determined to establish with certainty whether the compact source is a neutron star or a black hole.

TABLE 16.4 Possible Black Holes

| System | Distance (pc) | Orbital Period (days) | Black Hole Mass ($\mathfrak{M}_{\odot}$) | Companion | |
				Type	Mass ($\mathfrak{M}_{\odot}$)
Cygnus X-1	2500	5.6 days	>16	O9 I	33
LMC X-3	55,000	1.7 days	> 9	B3 V	6
A0620-00	1000	0.3 days	> 3	K5 V	0.5

To sum up, the theoretical picture of the evolution of massive stars predicts the collapse of neutron cores with masses above the limiting mass that can be supported by the pressure of a degenerate neutron gas. No known force in nature is capable of supporting such a neutron core—it must collapse. The collapse produces surface gravities so high that not even light can escape, and the object, called a black hole, essentially disappears from the visible universe. Nevertheless, it still exerts a gravitational influence by virtue of its mass. It is through this gravitational influence that we can detect objects that appear to have the properties of black holes.

▰▰SUMMARY

The "aging" and "deaths" of stars have been examined in this chapter from two points of view: interior changes and surface changes. Interior changes result from gravity's "command" that the star contract. Contraction increases central temperatures until nuclear fires ignite. Because of these nuclear transformations, the chemical composition at the centers of stars changes. Hydrogen and helium are transformed into silicon and sulfur through a series of five nuclear-burning phases: hydrogen, helium, carbon, neon, and oxygen burning. Silicon and sulfur are subsequently transformed into iron group elements through the capture of protons and helium nuclei produced by photodisintegrations during silicon burning. Finally, the heaviest elements in the universe are created through neutron capture during supernovae explosions.

The most abundant element in the core after silicon burning is iron. Because fusion with iron cannot liberate energy, the iron core collapses. During the rapid collapse, which takes less than a second, all of the iron is converted into neutrons and neutrinos, and in the process, the star explodes. A Type II supernova leaves either a neutron star or a black hole as a remnant. A less violent end to stellar evolution occurs for stars with masses less than 6–8 $\mathfrak{M}_\odot$. They only pass through hydrogen and helium burning and lose their envelopes before carbon can be ignited in their cores. The ejection of the envelope exposes the carbon-oxygen core, which we call a white dwarf. In some cases the white dwarf can accrete mass and explode as a nova or more violently as a Type I supernova.

Stars, or more correctly the cores of stars, can support themselves without nuclear reactions if they become degenerate. Degeneracy occurs at extremely high densities. Electrons become degenerate at densities of $\approx 10^6$ g/cm^3 and can support a maximum of 1.4 $\mathfrak{M}_\odot$. Degenerate neutrons can support about 2 $\mathfrak{M}_\odot$ at densities of $\approx 10^{14}$ g/cm^3.

Figure 16.25 outlines the various sequences of objects and events characterizing the visible evidence of stellar evolution. Surface changes occur in a star's luminosity, radius, and surface temperature in response to the events at the interior and, as such, are clues to what is happening at the center. All stars, of course, begin as main-sequence stars, but when hydrogen is exhausted, they become red giants and supergiants. Stars remain as giants and supergiants during the nuclear-burning episodes after hydrogen burning. During helium burning, stars pass through an unstable phase in which they pulsate. Cepheid and RR Lyrae variables are such unstable stars. Subsequent evolution beyond helium burning is characterized by either nonviolent ejection of the stellar envelope, leading to planetary nebulae, or violent ejection in the form of a supernova. Planetary nebulae are visible as distinct rings of glowing gas centered on the remnant core of the supergiant. The dissipating envelope eventually leaves only an exposed core, a white dwarf. Supernovae are briefly visible due to dramatic increases in the luminosity of the exploding stars and leave remnant nebulae visible for thousands of years. Supernovae are produced by the accretion of gas by a white dwarf (Type I) or by the catastrophic explosion following the collapse of the iron core of a massive star (Type II).

White dwarf remnants finish off their "lives" by cooling. Their temperatures decrease until they emit so little radiation that they become invisible. Neu-

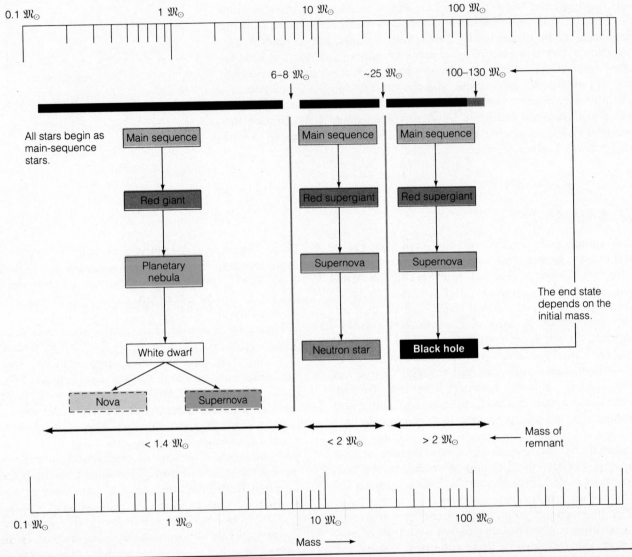

■■■ FIGURE 16.25
A Summary of Stellar Evolution

Stars less massive than 6–8 $\mathfrak{M}_\odot$ probably become planetary nebulae and a few of those erupt into novae. Between 6–8 $\mathfrak{M}_\odot$ and ~25 $\mathfrak{M}_\odot$, stars erupt into supernovae and the remnants are most likely neutron stars. Stars more massive than ~25 $\mathfrak{M}_\odot$ end up as black holes after becoming supernovae.

tron star remnants will also cool. Rapidly rotating neutron stars produce the pulsed radio signals of the pulsars. In their final state, stars with masses greater than about 25 $\mathfrak{M}_\odot$ become black holes. Black holes are stellar cores that have collapsed "beyond the visible universe." These cores are so massive that degener-ate neutron pressure is unable to support them. They collapse forever. We can identify black holes by the effects they have on the environment near them. Accreting material around black holes can emit X-rays if the black hole is part of a binary system. Currently, we have three strong candidates for black holes.

CHAPTER CAPSULE

Topics and Terms	Review and Remarks
Nucleosynthesis	Nuclear reactions can transform hydrogen and helium into iron group elements. Heavier elements are created in supernovae by neutron capture.
Supernovae	The two types of supernovae: Type I—a white dwarf explodes after accreting matter from a nearby companion; the white dwarf is completely destroyed. Type II—the rapid collapse of the iron core of a massive star initiates an explosion; only a remnant neutron star or black hole remains.
Degeneracy	Electrons are degenerate at densities of about 10^6 g/cm^3 and can support 1.4 $\mathfrak{M}_\odot$. Neutrons are degenerate at densities of about 10^{14} g/cm^3 and can support 2 $\mathfrak{M}_\odot$.
Surface evolution of stars	Changes in the interior cause changes in a star's L, R, and T. Planetary nebulae and supernovae are the final visible phase before stars attain their end states.
Stellar end states	White dwarf: the carbon-oxygen core of a star supported by electron degeneracy. Neutron star: the neutron core of an exploded star supported by neutron degeneracy. Black hole: the region of space from which no electromagnetic radiation can escape surrounding the collapsed neutron core of a massive star.
Evolutionary sequences	For stars less than about 8 $\mathfrak{M}_\odot$: Main sequence → red giant → planetary nebula → white dwarf → (supernova) For stars with masses between about 8 and 25 $\mathfrak{M}_\odot$: Main sequence → red supergiant → supernova → neutron star For stars greater than about 25 $\mathfrak{M}_\odot$: Main sequence → red supergiant → supernova → black hole

REVIEW QUESTIONS

1. As a star gets to the main sequence, the temperatures and pressures necessary for the proton-proton chain exist only in a small region of the core of the star. What happens as the core hydrogen is depleted? Does the star "burn out" as its core hydrogen is depleted and finally exhausted? Explain your answer.

2. Fusion of nuclei up to iron results in a loss of mass and a corresponding release of nuclear energy. Why can an individual star like the Sun never fuse to elements beyond carbon? What physical property of the star determines how far it can go in producing heavy elements by fusion? Where do elements heavier than iron come from?

3. The terms degenerate and degeneracy are often used in referring to conditions in the cores of certain stars. What do these terms mean and what does the condition imply about the core of the star? How is electron degeneracy connected with the Chandrasekhar limit?

4. What is photodisintegration and how does it "undo" all of the changes in the chemical composition brought about by nuclear fusion in the core of the star?

5. By what mechanism or mechanisms does the core of a star become a degenerate neutron gas?

6. During the post–main-sequence phase of a star, while it is still producing energy by nuclear fusion, the star is a red giant or red supergiant. In general, however, the core has been contracting. Can you reconcile these two apparently contradictory conditions in the same star?

7. Young cluster giants and supergiants are completely disconnected on an HR diagram from the cluster's main sequence. Older clusters, however, have a continuous stream of stars from main sequence to the giant and supergiant regions of the HR diagram. Why the difference?

8. What combination of physical characteristics causes Cepheid and RR Lyrae variables to pulse in brightness? Other than filling in parts of the story of evolution, of what other use are these variables to astronomers?

9. At what stage in the evolution of a low-mass star does the helium flash occur? What happens to the star's surface temperature and luminosity at the time of the helium flash?

10. Which stars produce planetary nebulae? By what mechanism are the planetaries produced?

11. Describe the characteristics of neutron stars and while dwarfs. For stars that are not members of binary systems, which are likely to become white dwarfs? Which are likely to become neutron stars? Which will the Sun likely become?

12. What different mechanisms produce Type I and Type II supernovae? What kinds of stars are likely to result from supernovae explosions? In what way is the progenitor of SN 1987A different from what astronomers expected?

13. How is the Schwarzschild radius defined? What is the Schwarzschild radius for the Earth? Will the Sun (or the Earth) ever become a black hole? Why or why not?

▰FOR FURTHER READING

Balick, B. 1987. The shaping of planetary nebulae. *Sky & Telescope*, Feb., 125.

Bennett, G. 1988. Cosmic origins of the elements. *Astronomy*, Aug., 18.

Darling, D. 1985. Breezes, bangs, and blowouts: Stellar evolution through mass loss—Part I. *Astronomy*, Sept., 78.

———. 1985. Breezes, bangs, and blowouts: Stellar evolution through mass loss—Part II. *Astronomy*, Nov., 94.

Kaler, J. B. 1988. Journeys on the H-R diagram. *Sky & Telescope*, May, 482.

Kawaler, S. D., and D. E. Winget. 1987. White dwarfs: Fossil stars. *Sky & Telescope*, Aug., 132.

McClintock, J. 1988. Do black holes exist? *Sky & Telescope*, Jan., 28.

Seward, F. D. 1986. Neutron stars in supernova remnants. *Sky & Telescope*, Jan., 6.

Talcott, R. 1988. Insights into star death. *Astronomy*, Feb., 6.

Turner, E. L. 1988. Gravitational lenses. *Scientific American*, July, 54.

Woosley, S., and T. Weaver. 1989. The great supernova of 1987. *Scientific American*, Aug., 32.

Relativity

The history of our attempt to understand reality has been punctuated by periods marked by extraordinary empirical achievement or theoretical ideas. At the beginning of this century, two fundamental theories—quantum theory and relativity—emerged. They extend classical physics, which started with the empirical and theoretical methods developed by Galileo and Newton through their study of mechanics. The quantum theory dates from 1900 when Max Planck (1858–1947) announced his revolutionary concept of quanta. Albert Einstein (1879–1955) is the author of relativity. He produced two relativity theories, his special theory of relativity (1905) and his general theory of relativity (1916). The special theory of relativity deals with the effects of relative motion on observations of the universe while the general theory of relativity includes the effects of gravitational fields on the observations. Relativity introduced revolutionary notions of space and time that opened up new ways to view natural phenomena.

SPECIAL THEORY OF RELATIVITY

Einstein's special theory of relativity considers the effects of motion on measurements of time, distance, and mass. It begins with two assumptions, or principles. First, *all laws of nature are the same for observers traveling at uniform velocity with respect to each other.* For example, if you throw a ball straight up, it will fall straight down whether you are standing, say, on a train station platform or inside a train moving at a constant velocity. In fact, any experiments done on the train would result in the same laws of physics found by experiments done on the platform. This seems reasonable; forces in nature operate on moving trains as well as on the ground. Observers at the station, however, notice differences between the experiments made on the moving train and on the platform. For instance, the path of a ball that is thrown straight up in the train will not be straight up and down as viewed from the platform. From the platform, the path of a ball thrown on the train would be an arc through the air (Figure 16A.1) because the ball has the same horizontal velocity as the train. You could calculate the path of the ball using the laws of physics after including the velocity of the train in your equations. Such mathematical comparisons between observers moving at constant velocity relative to each other are called *Galilean transformations.* Their exact mathematical form is not important for the following discussions, but they include subtractions and additions of velocities and coordinates.

The second principle of special relativity is that *the velocity of light is the same for all observers moving uniformly relative to each other.*

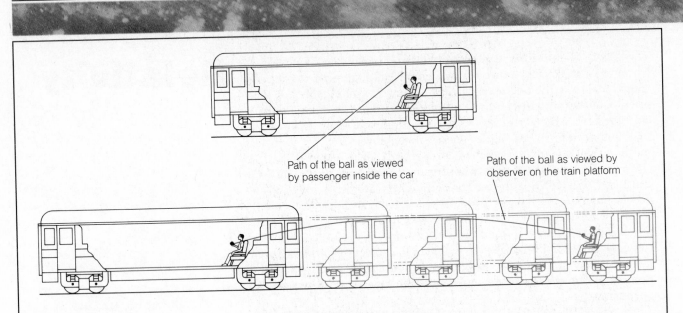

Path of the ball as viewed
by passenger inside the car

Path of the ball as viewed by
observer on the train platform

■■■■ FIGURE 16A.1

Path of a Ball on a Train

To the passenger on the train, the ball
simply moves up and comes straight
down. An observer watching the train
move by would track the ball in a
curve through the air. From the viewpoint of the observer on the platform,
the ball has a horizontal velocity equal
to that of the train. Inside the train,
both the ball and passenger are moving horizontally with the same speed.

Whereas the velocity of the ball in the train as measured relative to
the platform depends on the velocity of the train, the measured velocity of light does *not* depend on the motion of the source of light.
The constancy of the speed of light was discovered by Albert Michelson (1852–1931) and Edward Morley (1838–1923) in an experiment
now called the Michelson–Morley experiment. They used the orbital
speed of the Earth, 30 km/s, to measure the speed of light in the forward and reverse directions of the Earth's orbital movement. In both
cases the speed of light was the same.

Many of the results of special relativity, such as the constancy of
the speed of light, are not intuitive and are therefore difficult to
grasp. Generally, discussions on relativity involve many examples
and analogies to help fathom the consequences of the two principles.
Since this AstroProbe is too short to go into much detail, only the
highlights of special relativity will be given.

The constancy of the speed of light to all observers has incredible
consequences. For instance, observers moving relative to each other
discover the same laws of physics; that is, they obtain the same *relations* between speed, mass, force, time, and distance, but they measure different values for these parameters. Einstein's interpretation
of these results is that the clocks of observers moving relative to each
other show different time intervals and that measuring rods are different lengths. That is, if the speed of light is constant to all observers and if all observers discover the same laws of physics, then clocks
are found to change their rates and sticks their length when measured by observers in relative motion.

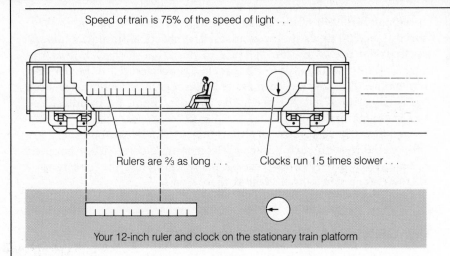

Speed of train is 75% of the speed of light . . .

Rulers are ⅔ as long . . .   Clocks run 1.5 times slower . . .

Your 12-inch ruler and clock on the stationary train platform

■■■ ■ FIGURE 16A.2

Clocks and Rulers

Clocks slow down and rulers shrink in the direction of motion for moving observers. Clocks run 1.5 times slower and rulers are ⅔ shorter traveling at 75% of the speed of light.

The relative differences in rhythm and length can be calculated by a set of equations called the *Lorentz transformations*. These changes, however, are significant only at very high speeds. For instance, if a train is traveling at 75% of the speed of light, clocks run 1.5 times slower and rulers are ⅔ times shorter relative to clocks and rulers on a platform (Figure 16A.2). At 99% of the speed of light, clocks run 7 times slower and 12-inch rulers appear slightly less than 2 inches long relative to platform measurements.

You can get a feeling for the slowing down of time with speed by imagining traveling at the speed of light. (As noted below, this is not really possible.) As you leave the Earth moving at the speed of light, you look back with a powerful telescope and view a clock that indicates it is noon. After traveling 300,000 km, which takes you one second, you look at the clock again; it still indicates noon! The light from the clock is also traveling at the speed of light, and during one second it travels as far as you did. As far as you are concerned, time on Earth has stopped. Since at slow speeds you cannot detect any time differences and at the speed of light time "stops," time must slow down as speed increases to light speed.

High speeds also affect masses. The masses of material bodies on Earth are called *rest masses;* when an object moves, it becomes more massive. The Lorentz transformations apply so that at 75% of the speed of light mass increases by a factor of 1.5, and at 99% of the speed of light the mass is 7 times its rest mass (Table 16A.1) This increase in mass has been measured at the Fermi National Accelerator Laboratory near Chicago where protons were accelerated to

TABLE 16A.1 Lorentz Transformation Predictions

Time: $T = \dfrac{T_0}{\sqrt{1 - \dfrac{v^2}{c^2}}}$

Length: $L = L_0 \sqrt{1 - \dfrac{v^2}{c^2}}$

Mass: $M = \dfrac{M_0}{\sqrt{1 - \dfrac{v^2}{c^2}}}$

T_0 = stationary time
L_0 = rest length
M_0 = rest mass

speeds of 99.9998% of the speed of light, and their masses were measured to be 500 times their rest mass. The practical limitation placed on material bodies by the increase in mass is that traveling at the speed of light is impossible. As a rocket is accelerated to higher and higher speeds, its increased mass requires a greater and greater force to increase its speed. To reach the speed of light, an infinite force would be required.

So far we have discussed situations in which two observers are moving relative to each other at a constant velocity. What happens when gravity enters the picture? Einstein answered this question by introducing a new way to look at the universe.

GENERAL THEORY OF RELATIVITY

Einstein realized that it is impossible to distinguish between the downward pull of gravity and an upward acceleration. Imagine some friends deep in space in an enclosed spaceship that is accelerating with an acceleration equal to what they would feel standing on Earth. If the spaceship were completely enclosed so that they could not see outside, your friends would conclude that they were on Earth. How could they be fooled? The acceleration provided by the spaceship's rockets approximates the Earth's gravitational field. Standing on a scale, your friends would weigh the same as they would on Earth; if they dropped a ball, it would fall to the floor as it would on Earth. This approximate equivalence between gravity and acceleration is called the *principle of equivalence*. The fact that your friends could not easily distinguish between being on the Earth's surface and in an accelerating rocket suggests that the laws of physics are the same for observers whether they are accelerating or moving uniformly with respect to each other. The problem Einstein encountered was finding a suitable way in which to express the laws of physics so that different observers obtain the same relations between mass, time, distance, speed, and force independent of their state of motion. The special theory of relativity required the Lorentz transformations between observers moving uniformly relative to each other. Another kind of "transformation," or more precisely another kind of geometry, is required for observers accelerating with respect to each other.

In the description of the Lorentz transformations, some observations seemed to defy common sense. The same occurs for accelerating observers. Let's help your friends check the laws of physics with a certain experiment that involves shining a beam of light through a window in their spaceship. Observers outside the spaceship would describe the path of the light beam as a straight line; the light would enter the window and strike the opposite wall slightly below the point directly opposite the window. The outside observers would say that while the light traveled the length of the room, the spaceship moved upward slightly, causing the light to strike a point slightly lower. Now ask your friends in the spaceship to predict where the light would strike. Remember that they do not realize they are in a moving spaceship. Your friends would say that since light travels in a straight line, the beam should strike the wall directly opposite the window through which it entered. What do they make of the observation that the beam strikes lower than they predicted? They must conclude that a beam of light bends—in a gravitational field! How can the principle of equivalence apply in this case?

If the paths of light beams are bent in an accelerated rocket and since gravity acts like an acceleration, a light beam on Earth should also follow a curved path. Although the gravitational field of the Earth is too weak for scientists to detect the bending of light beams, experiments done during solar eclipses verify the prediction. In this case, the light is supplied by distant stars and passes close to the Sun's limb. Since the Sun's gravitational field is strong, light from the stars is deflected. When we photograph the sky near the Sun during a solar eclipse, the positions of the stars are slightly different from that in pictures taken of the same part of the sky when the Sun was in another position on the ecliptic (Figure 16A.3). The theory of general relativity also predicts that gravity affects the ticking of clocks and the lengths of rulers. For example, tests with radioactive clocks, which keep time by counting the number of radioactive de-

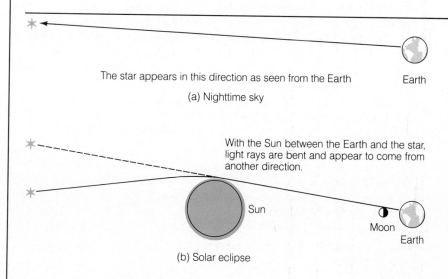

The star appears in this direction as seen from the Earth

Earth

(a) Nighttime sky

With the Sun between the Earth and the star, light rays are bent and appear to come from another direction.

Sun

Moon

Earth

(b) Solar eclipse

■■■ **FIGURE 16A.3**

Bending of Light Rays

During a solar eclipse light from distant stars is deflected. Comparison of positions of stars during an eclipse and their positions in the nighttime sky confirms Einstein's prediction that light rays will bend near a massive object.

cays, at different locations in the Earth's gravitational field have verified the different time intervals kept by clocks in gravitational fields. Gravity does bend the paths of photons, shortens the lengths of rulers, and changes the time intervals of clocks. How then are we to describe measurements in different accelerated systems so that the laws of physics are the same to all observers? What kind of "transformation" is required? Einstein's response was to concentrate on the paths of particles rather than on forces acting on them.

To satisfy the principle of equivalence we describe paths in both space and *time*. Consequently, the position of a particle in *spacetime* is designated by three space coordinates and time. Far from a massive object, we can describe spacetime by a Euclidian geometry. (Euclidian geometry was the kind introduced in high school.) Here gravity is weak and neither rulers nor clocks change appreciably. This means that we can draw a flat, square grid and locate objects by their coordinates on the grid. Near a massive object we must employ a grid that is curved because near a source of gravity rulers distort and clocks slow down. The difference between "flat" and "curved" is the same as the difference between the surfaces of a globe and a map. The map is only accurate if it represents a small area on the Earth's surface. We realize that for regions near the poles a map distorts landforms. Compare, for instance, the shape of Greenland on a globe and on a world map. Consequently, if we consider large distances on Earth, we need to take into account the curvature of the Earth. The shortest distance between two locations now becomes a curved path. Similarly, we can apply special relativity to small areas in spacetime, but over great distances we must take into account the curvature of our "map" of spacetime.

Although using the curved grid is a little more complicated, it correctly describes reality. Figure 16A.4 shows the geometry repre-

■■■ FIGURE 16A.4

Solar Eclipse Spacetime Geometry

This geometry illustrates why starlight bends near the Sun. Photons must follow the curved geometry near an object such as the Sun.

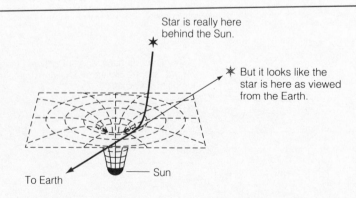

Star is really here behind the Sun.

But it looks like the star is here as viewed from the Earth.

To Earth

Sun

senting spacetime near the Sun and illustrates why a light beam from a star bends. Far from the source of gravity, spacetime can be described as flat, and the path of a photon or a particle is similar to a golf ball rolling over a level green. Near the source of gravity, a photon's path is deflected like that of a golf ball on a green with dips in it. Near massive objects, such as black holes, the curvature can be so severe that if a beam of light gets too close, it will never climb back out.

In Einstein's view of the universe, we no longer have to think about gravity as a force. Instead, we can describe the motions of objects accelerating under gravity as moving along a curve in spacetime. The curvature is determined by the strength of the local gravitational field. Furthermore, the theory of relativity predicts phenomena that Newton's theory of gravity does not. We have already mentioned the slowing of clocks and the bending of light rays. A particularly famous prediction of general relativity theory is the *precession* of the orbit of Mercury (Figure 16A.5). Since Mercury is close to the Sun, effects of general relativity become appreciable and cause the orientation of Mercury's orbit to change continuously. Newtonian theory cannot predict the total gravitational effect on Mercury's orbit whereas relativity predicts the correct value for the effects. Another example of the influence of curved spacetime is a gravitational lens. Very distant galaxies, called quasars, sometimes lie almost directly behind a massive galaxy. As the light rays from the quasar pass near the galaxy, the light is bent by the large curvature in spacetime due to the gravitational field of the galaxy. The result as shown in Figure 16A.6 is that we see what appear to be two identical quasars instead of just one. As with the effects of special relativity, which are more easily detectable under conditions of very high velocities, the effects of general relativity are more easily detectable in strong gravitational fields.

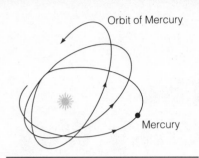

■ **FIGURE 16A.5**

Precession of Mercury's Orbit

Mercury's orbit precesses about the Sun due to gravitational interactions between Mercury, the Sun, and other planets. Because of Mercury's close proximity to the Sun, the geometry of spacetime is curved, and the correct value for the precession can only be calculated with Einstein's theory of general relativity.

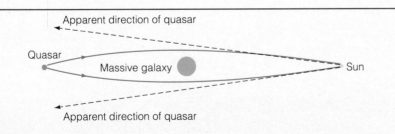

■ **FIGURE 16A.6**

Gravitational Lens

Light from a distant galaxy we call a quasar is deflected by the massive galaxy. The light from the quasar appears to be coming from the direction indicated by the dashed lines. Consequently, we see what appear to be two quasars.

The Milky Way Galaxy

OUTLINE

Galactic Dimensions

The Rotating Disk
Stellar Populations
Rotation and Structure of the Disk
The Nature of Spiral Arms
Mass of the Milky Way Galaxy

The Distribution and Evolution of Stellar Populations

The Galactic Center

Summary

Chapter Capsule

Review Questions

For Further Reading

ASTROPROBE 17:
$N \geq 1$: **Extraterrestrial Civilizations**

Rise of the Milky Way.
ARTIST: Kurt C. Burmann.

T IS TIME TO CHANGE PERSPECTIVES and view stars, not as individual orbs of gas that evolve from quiet main-sequence stars to planetary nebulae or explosive supernovae, but as a collection of tiny "bees" making up a swarm called the Milky Way Galaxy. This swarm consists of hundreds of billions of stars and is isolated from other similar swarms by hundreds of thousands of parsecs of nearly empty space.

The Galaxy is characterized by a rapidly rotating disk of young stars, gas, and dust embedded in a sphere of ancient stars. The structure, or pattern of stars, gas, and dust, of the Milky Way Galaxy eluded astronomers for centuries. The problem was that astronomers must look through thousands of parsecs of interstellar dust and gas, which block their view of the center and far side of the Galaxy. A comprehensive picture has emerged only since astronomers have been able to analyze data obtained over the entire electromagnetic spectrum, from X-rays to radio waves.

While a naked eye survey of the night sky suggests that the Sun is at the center of a flat disk of stars, analysis of old star clusters reveals that the Sun is actually located tens of thousands of light-years from the center of the disk. The Sun is so far from the center of the Milky Way Galaxy that it takes over 200 million years to orbit once. Although we are far from the Galaxy's center, astronomers can detect the presence of a mysterious object at the very center, or nucleus, of the Galaxy.

A sphere of old stars and the younger disk stars provide very important clues to the evolutionary history of the Milky Way Galaxy during the last 15 billion years. They allow astronomers to piece together a description of the earliest epochs of galactic formation.

GALACTIC DIMENSIONS

Thirty or forty years ago an author would introduce the chapter on the Galaxy by referring to the luminous band, called the *Milky Way*, that could be seen arching across the sky on a winter's evening. Today the light pollution caused by urban and suburban development prevents most people from seeing the Milky Way at all. Nevertheless, on a clear, moonless night in the quiet darkness of the countryside, the Milky Way can be seen in all its luminous glory. The name for this starry vapor of the night derives from the Greek *galaxias* and the Latin *Via Lactea* meaning milky road or way. The Milky Way can be seen crossing Sagittarius and Scorpius low in the summer sky and engulfing Cassiopeia high overhead at Christmas time (see the Observer's Handbook and the front and back inside covers of this book for constellation maps). Binoculars reveal innumerable stars along the Milky Way, yet this band of stars represents only a part of one structural component of the Milky Way Galaxy. Can we see the rest of the Milky Way Galaxy? Where is the Sun situated within the Galaxy? These are the questions that astronomers tried to answer in the eighteenth and nineteenth centuries as they critically examined the luminous band of the Milky Way.

Watching the sky all night gives one the impression that the Milky Way wraps around the celestial sphere as if the Earth were at its center.

■ FIGURE 17.1

View of the Milky Way from the Sun

Since the Sun is not in the center of the Galaxy, more stars are visible in one direction than another. When we look away from the disk of the Galaxy, we see fewer stars than when we look along the disk.

The view toward the near edge of the Galaxy will reveal only a few stars.

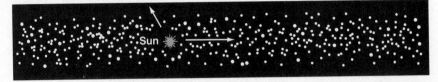

The view toward the distant edge of the Galaxy will reveal many stars.

Astronomers have been intrigued with the Sun's location within the Milky Way since at least the eighteenth century when the Englishman Thomas Wright (1711–1786) concluded that the Milky Way represented a flattened disk of stars. During the 1780s William Herschel (1738–1822) and his sister Caroline (1750–1844) tried to measure the extent of the Milky Way Galaxy in a quantitative way by counting stars. Even a small telescope will resolve the cloudlike Milky Way into thousands of individual stars. The Herschels assumed that stars were scattered evenly throughout the Galaxy and that they were equally luminous (we know today that this is far from true). They could assume, therefore, that *apparent* magnitude indicated distance and could use the inverse square law to estimate relative distances from observed magnitudes. Consequently, if the Sun was near the edge of the Galaxy in a particular direction, they expected to see only a few stars through their telescope in that direction (Figure 17.1). If the edge of the Galaxy was far away, then they expected to count many stars. From the distribution of stars in their star counts of nearly 700 regions of the sky, the Herschels believed the Galaxy was a flat, lens-shaped disk with the Sun at the center. Although they found that the disk was five times longer than it was thick, they could not determine its absolute size because distances to even the nearest stars had not yet been measured.

Henrietta Levitt (1868–1921) took an important step in developing a technique for estimating distances to stars clear across the Galaxy. In 1912, at the Harvard College Observatory, she discovered a period-luminosity relation for *Type I Cepheids* in the nearby galaxy, the Small Magellanic Cloud. But she knew the periods only as a function of apparent magnitude. A year later Ejnar Hertzsprung (1873–1967) estimated the absolute magnitudes of Cepheids thereby calibrating Levitt's period-luminosity relation. The use of the period-luminosity relation for determining distances to variables is straight forward. First, the variable star is located by taking many photographs of the same region of the sky and then searching the photographs for stars that change their brightness. The photographs will show the variable at different brightnesses. The period of the variable follows from its light curve derived from many photographs (Figure 17.2). The calibrated period-luminosity relation, which gives the period as a function of *absolute magnitude*, is then used to estimate the luminosity of the variable. Note that since the star varies its light output by as much as several magnitudes, average

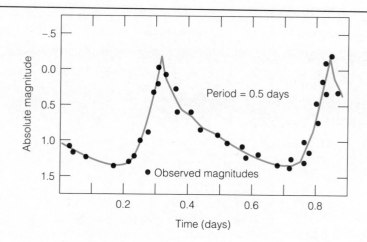

■ FIGURE 17.2

Light Curve of a Variable in a Globular Cluster

This star varies by about 1.3 magnitudes over a period of 0.5 days (= 12 hours).

magnitudes are used when determining the distance modulus, $m - M$. If the variable is a member of a star cluster, such as a globular cluster, we obtain the distance to the cluster as well.

At about the same time Levitt and Hertzsprung were working on Cepheids, Solon I. Baily, also of the Harvard College Observatory, completed an important study of variable stars found in globular clusters. Globular clusters are huge, spherical systems of tens of thousands to millions of stars (Figure 17.3). All globular clusters are old; in fact, they are the oldest systems of stars known in the Galaxy. As noted in the last chapter, the HR diagrams of globular clusters indicate that they are composed of stars with masses less than 1 $\mathfrak{M}_\odot$ and ages of about 15 billion years. These clusters proved to be fundamental in establishing the size of the Milky Way Galaxy.

Baily studied, in particular, the variable stars astronomers now refer to as *RR Lyrae* variables. These are low-mass giants in the instability strip of the HR diagram that are burning helium in their cores. They are in essence "short-period Cepheids" with pulsation periods of less than a day. Many globular clusters also contain *Type II Cepheids*, which are low-mass giants that have exhausted helium in their cores and will soon eject their envelopes to become planetary nebulae. Recall that Type I Cepheids, discussed in the last chapter, are high-mass, core helium-burning supergiants. In 1916 Harlow Shapley (1885–1972) constructed a period-luminosity relation using the Type I Cepheids in the Small Magellanic Cloud, the Type II Cepheids in globular clusters, and the RR Lyrae variables. He then applied this period-luminosity relation to estimating the distances to globular clusters. In doing so, he completely changed our idea of the Milky Way Galaxy.

Shapley determined the distances to 93 globular clusters in the Galaxy. He also knew the direction from the Sun of each cluster. Globular clusters exhibit a remarkable distribution in the sky; almost all of them are in one hemisphere. About one-third of the globular clusters known in Shapley's time are concentrated in the constellations Sagittarius, Ophiuchus, and Scorpius. From these directions and distances, Shapley derived the three-dimensional distribution of the globular clusters in

■ FIGURE 17.3

The Globular Cluster 47 Tucanae

This photograph was taken with the 4-meter telescope at the Cerro Tololo Inter-American Observatory in Chile.

SOURCE: National Optical Astronomy Observatories.

■■■■ **FIGURE** 17.4

Distribution of Globular Clusters

The vertical axis represents the height in thousands of parsecs above or below the plane of the Galaxy. The Sun lies far from the center of this distribution (marked with a "+"). Shapley estimated the distance of the Sun from the center to be 10,000 pc; the modern value of 8500 pc is used in the plots. (Data from W. E. Harris, 1976, *Astronomical Journal*, 81:1095.)

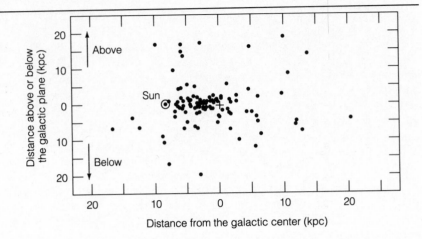

The prefix *kilo* means 1000; 8500 pc is the same as 8.5 kpc.

space (Figure 17.4). As Figure 17.4 shows, the Sun is far from the center of this distribution. In fact, Shapley determined that the center of the nearly spherical distribution of globular clusters was about 10,000 pc away from the Sun in the direction of the constellation Sagittarius. Furthermore, Shapley argued that, since a large mass is required to keep the globular clusters orbiting the Galaxy, the center of the Galaxy must lie at the center of the globular cluster distribution. Shapley's labors replaced an early twentieth-century view of the Milky Way Galaxy that placed the Sun near the center with one in which the Sun lies far from the Galaxy's center.

Two refinements to Shapley's work were necessary to obtain the modern value of 8500 pc (8.5 kpc) for the distance to the galactic center. First, in 1928 Robert Trumpler (1886–1956) of the Lick Observatory discovered that the dust in the Galaxy causes an extinction of light by about 1–2 magnitudes, on the average, every 1000 pc. In fact, this interstellar "fog" is so great toward Sagittarius that the center of the Galaxy cannot be seen in visible light. Consequently, globular cluster stars, and in particular the variables, appear fainter than they really are, just as car lights appear farther away in a fog than they really are. As a result, Shapley, who was unaware of interstellar extinction, overestimated the distance to the globular clusters. Second, in the 1940s and 1950s astronomers realized that Type II Cepheids are fainter than Type I Cepheids of the same period. In particular, the period-luminosity relation for Levitt's Small Magellanic Cloud Type I Cepheids was 1.5 magnitudes brighter than that for the Type II Cepheids in the globular clusters used by Shapley. Since Shapley was unaware of this difference, his period-luminosity relation was ≈1.5 magnitudes in error. At today's value for the distance to the center of the Galaxy, 8.5 kpc, the Sun lies in the outskirts of the galactic system.

The earliest support for Shapley's model of the Galaxy came from detailed studies of stellar motions. In 1925, Jan Oort (1900–) proved from such studies that the Galaxy was rotating and that the center of the rotation was in the same direction as the center of the distribution of globular clusters.

THE ROTATING DISK

The Milky Way and the distribution of globular clusters are two important hints to the overall structure of the Milky Way Galaxy. The globular clusters define a roughly spherical volume of stars called the **halo.** Included in the halo are old red stars and individual RR Lyrae variables. All halo stars appear to be approximately 15 billion years old. No recently formed O and B stars or molecular clouds exist in the halo. In addition, the appearance of the Milky Way suggests a flat **disk** structure. Looking along the length of the disk reveals many stars, but looking away reveals relatively few stars. Accordingly, the Galaxy can be pictured as a flat disk of stars, gas, and dust within a sphere of old stars and globular clusters.

Stellar Populations

The star clusters in the disk differ from the halo globular clusters in several important ways. First, the disk clusters contain fewer stars, on the average, than globular clusters. A typical disk cluster contains hundreds of stars instead of the hundreds of thousands of stars in globular clusters. With so few stars, disk clusters appear as loose, or open, structures instead of huge stellar spheroids so dense that we cannot see through them (Figure 17.5). Hence, star clusters in the disk are called *open clusters.* Second, open clusters are younger than globular clusters (see the **color-magnitude diagram** in Figure 17.6). Young open clusters are only a few million years old, and the oldest are about 10 billion years old, two-thirds the age of globular clusters. Finally, open cluster stars have a higher metal abundance than globular cluster stars. Metal-

Color-magnitude diagram: A plot of the observed stellar parameters, absolute or apparent magnitude, and $B - V$ color index (usually for a cluster of stars).

▬ FIGURE 17.5

A Pair of Open Clusters in Perseus

Compare the openness of these clusters to that of the globular cluster shown in Figure 17.3.

SOURCE: National Optical Astronomy Observatories.

■■■ FIGURE 17.6

Color-Magnitude Diagram Showing Main-Sequence Turnoffs

The ages from the main-sequence turnoffs of open clusters are all less than that of any globular cluster. The globular cluster main sequence is shifted slightly from the the open cluster main sequence due to its different composition; metal-poor main-sequence stars are both hotter and more luminous than their metal-rich counterparts.

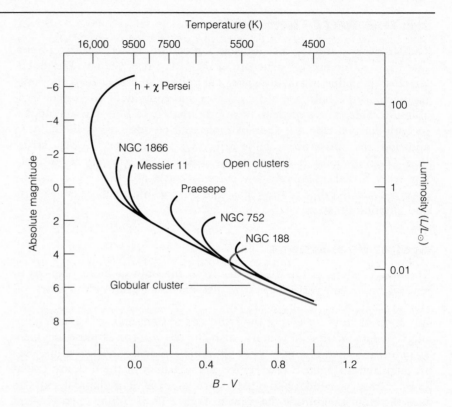

licities in the disk range from about one-fourth solar to about twice solar. Spectroscopic observations reveal that stars in globular clusters are metal poor relative to the Sun; their metallicities are as low as one-hundredth of the Sun's. Thus globular clusters are characterized by old, metal-poor stars. Open clusters are representative of the kind of stars found in the disk just as globular clusters are representative of halo stars.

The differences in structure, age, and chemical composition between globular and open clusters are indicative of two broad but distinct groups, or *populations*, of stars in the Galaxy. Walter Baade (1893–1960) first recognized two stellar populations in 1944 during his studies of nearby galaxies. Baade found himself in an opportunistic position at the Mount Wilson Observatory near Los Angeles during World War II. Since he was born in Germany, his activities during the war were restricted by the government of the United States to his job at Mount Wilson. His work with the 2.5-meter (100-inch) telescope was very productive because the Los Angeles valley was completely blacked out under wartime conditions. The subsequent dark skies allowed Baade to see extremely faint stars in the nearby Andromeda galaxy. He discovered that the visually brightest stars representing one population were red while those of the other population were blue. This same difference exists between globular clusters and young open clusters; the brightest globular cluster stars are red while those of young open clusters are blue. Furthermore, the metallicities of open clusters generally corre-

599

lated with their ages in the sense that the youngest clusters usually have the highest metal abundances. Globular clusters are both older and more metal poor than open clusters. Clusters and individual stars with characteristics similar to open cluster stars, such as Type I Cepheids and the Sun, are called **Population I**. The oldest open clusters are often referred to as *intermediate-age* clusters. Globular clusters and old stars, such as RR Lyrae variables and Type II Cepheids, are called **Population II** (Table 17.1).

Figure 17.7 illustrates the differences in the two populations for the nearby galaxy the Large Magellanic Cloud. An orange bar receives its color from G, K, and M giants of an old population while the blues and whites are from young stars and clusters. The pink clouds are H II regions, sites of very recent star formation. You can see that the whole region above the bar is an extensive area of star formation. This is the site of SN 1987A, which was produced by a massive, young star.

The preceding discussion implies that Population I stars are concentrated in the disk. What exactly is meant by the "disk" of the Galaxy? Certainly, it is a "flat" distribution of stars rather than a spherical one. The degree of flatness actually depends on the age of the group of stars being considered. For instance, O and B stars and very young open clusters are concentrated within a hundred parsecs of the plane of the disk whereas G and K stars are found several hundred parsecs above and below the plane. All stars thin out rapidly above and below the galactic plane. Very few Population I stars of any kind exist over a thousand parsecs above or below the plane. Not only are Population I stars confined to a disk that is thin compared to the Galaxy's diameter, motions of Population I stars within the disk are very organized.

Rotation and Structure of the Disk

Disk structures, such as the solar nebula (Chapter 11) or dust around protostars (Chapter 15), appear to have developed rotational characteristics as a result of a collapse. Consequently, we expect that the Sun and nearby stars are revolving about the center of the Galaxy and represent part of a tremendous rotating disk of stars. This is verified by exhaustive radial velocity and proper motion observations of nearby stars. All disk stars near the Sun are moving in nearly circular orbits around the Galaxy.

Not all nearby stars, however, are moving exactly as the Sun is. Stars in the disk a little closer to the galactic center are moving slightly faster than the Sun while those a little farther away from the center are moving slower than the Sun. The disk, therefore, exhibits *differential rotation*. The motions of nearby stars are relative motions; astronomers cannot measure the Sun's absolute speed around the Galaxy from observations of these nearby stars—they are moving almost as the Sun is! Instead, astronomers must use objects that do not share in the rotation of the disk as references; their observed velocities would mainly be reflections of the Sun's motion in the disk.

The disk is completely inside the Population II halo so that Population II stars can be inside the disk. Radial velocities of these Population

TABLE 17.1
Stellar Populations

Characteristic	I	II
Age	$<10^{10}$ yr	$>10^{10}$ yr
Metallicity	$\approx 1/4$–2 $Z_\odot$	$<1/4$ $Z_\odot$
Location	Disk	Halo
Distribution	Flat	Spherical

FIGURE 17.7

Stellar Populations in a Nearby Galaxy

SOURCE: National Optical Astronomy Observatories.

II stars indicate that they are moving very rapidly *relative* to the Sun. In fact, these *high-velocity stars* do not partake in the rotation of the disk. Imagine yourself driving along the freeway. The cars in the next lane do not appear to be moving very fast relative to you: you and they are traveling along the highway at nearly the same speed. If you observe a car entering or leaving the freeway, however, it would appear to be moving fast *relative* to you. It is not partaking in the high-speed driving that you and the other cars on the freeway are. Similarly, high-velocity stars are not rotating as other disk stars. They are stars that pass near the Sun as their orbits plunge through the disk. Since they do not share in the rotation of the disk, they can be used to estimate the Sun's velocity around the center of the Galaxy.

Since globular clusters are also members of the halo, astronomers can analyze their radial velocities to determine the motion of the Sun within the Galaxy. In both the study of high-velocity stars and globular clusters, we obtain a lower limit for the speed of the Sun because there may be a net rotation of the halo around the galactic center. At the same time, astronomers can analyze the radial velocities of nearby galaxies. They certainly do not share the disk's motion! Studies of all these objects show that most of the high velocities observed for high-velocity stars, globular clusters, and nearby galaxies are reflections of the Sun's orbital motion around the center of our Galaxy. These measurements reveal that the Sun is traveling in the disk at ≈250 km/s (560,000 MPH) in the direction of the constellation Cygnus. The direction to Cygnus is 90° away from the galactic center and toward the Milky Way, indicating that the Sun is in a nearly circular orbit.

Based on observations of disks in other galaxies, astronomers have looked for structure in the rotating disk of the Milky Way Galaxy by concentrating on the locations of certain Population I objects and using them as tracers. Imagine flying over a city at night. You cannot see the roads but streetlights trace them out. An analysis of H II regions and young star clusters, similar to that done by Shapley for globular clusters, reveals concentrations of these objects in at least three distinct bands near the Sun (Figure 17.8). These bands hint at the existence of

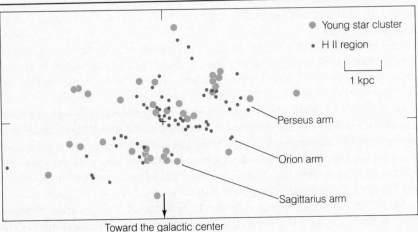

■■ FIGURE 17.8

Nearby Spiral Structure

H II regions and very young star clusters (less than a few million years old) appear to group in three elongated regions, as viewed from above the galactic plane. These are interpreted as segments of spiral arms near the Sun. The Sun's position in the Orion arm is marked with a +. The names of the "arms" are the names of the constellation in the same direction in the sky.

• Young star cluster

• H II region

1 kpc

Perseus arm

Orion arm

Sagittarius arm

Toward the galactic center

FIGURE 17.9

Spiral Arms

This nearby galaxy (NGC 2997) exhibits two spiral arms emanating from its center.

SOURCE: Copyright Anglo-Australian Telescope Board 1980. Photograph by David Malin.

spiral arms in the disk of the Galaxy like those in other galaxies (Figure 17.9). Unfortunately, from the Sun's position *in* the disk, interstellar extinction of starlight prevents views far along the disk that could locate long, distinct segments of spiral arms. In addition, when older stars are added to the map, the distinct bands blend into a smooth background of stars; that is, older disk stars and intermediate-age clusters are more uniformly distributed in the galactic plane than are younger Population I objects.

The view of the galactic disk at visible wavelengths is limited to about 10% of the Galaxy and implies that the disk is filled with obscuring dust. A more extensive view of the Galaxy is possible with radio and infrared telescope observations because long wavelength radiation is capable of penetrating interstellar dust. This is true, for instance, for molecular emissions deep within giant dust-filled clouds (Chapter 15) and holds for the galactic disk as well. Most of the matter in the interstellar medium is concentrated in *interstellar clouds* of mainly neutral hydrogen gas. Temperatures of these clouds are about 100 K, densities range from a few atoms to a thousand atoms per cubic centimeter, and diameters are typically tens of parsecs. The strongest emission from interstellar clouds is due to hydrogen atoms and is at 21.1061 cm, the *21-cm line.*

Since the 21-cm line is very important for studies of the structure of the disk, the atomic transition leading to the emission of these photons will be described. Temperatures are so low in large hydrogen clouds that hydrogen atoms are in their ground states. The ground state of hydrogen consists of two energy levels very close together, a result of electrons and protons having a quantum mechanical attribute called "spin." The only aspect of spin you need to know for this discussion is that the spin "axis" of the electron and proton in a hydrogen atom can

Spiral arm: A pattern of dust, gas, and visible stars that winds, or spirals, outward from near the center of a galaxy; spiral arms are located in the disk of a galaxy.

be either parallel or antiparallel to each other. When the spins are antiparallel, the atom is in its lowest ground state. Hydrogen atoms in interstellar clouds are moving fast enough that collisions between atoms can flip the spin of an electron from antiparallel to parallel. The subsequent return to the lowest state results in the emission of a photon. Since the energy difference between the two states is small, the energy of the photon emitted is correspondingly low, and therefore its wavelength is long, 21 cm.

In 1944 the Dutch astronomer Hendrik van de Hulst predicted that the ground state of hydrogen emits 21-cm radiation and that enough interstellar hydrogen existed in the Galaxy to radiate a detectable amount of this long wavelength radiation. Radio astronomy was a young discipline at that time, and it was not until 1951 that astronomers were able to build a radio telescope sensitive enough to detect interstellar 21-cm radiation. This detection was a major breakthrough for galactic astronomy because the long wavelength 21-cm radiation could travel the length of the Galaxy without being absorbed by interstellar dust as visual radiation is. Consequently, 21-cm radiation emitted by interstellar hydrogen clouds could be used to probe the width and depth of the Galaxy.

The overall distribution of hydrogen clouds in the disk of the Galaxy derived from 21-cm observations is shown in Figure 17.10. To construct this picture astronomers needed to know the distance to each cloud detected. Suppose a radio telescope is pointed in some direction along the disk as shown in Figure 17.11. Each hydrogen cloud, A, B, and C, along the line of sight will contribute to the 21-cm emission detected. If a hydrogen cloud is moving away from the Sun, its 21-cm line will be red shifted; if it is moving toward the Sun, the observed 21-cm line will be blue shifted. The clouds shown in Figure 17.11 all have radial velocity components away from the Sun. If the hydrogen clouds are moving in circular orbits about the galactic center, it can be shown (in a more advanced astronomy text) that the gas cloud closest to the center of the Galaxy will have the greatest observed *radial* velocity. In Figure 17.10, this will be cloud B. The geometrical relationship between the Sun, the

FIGURE 17.10

Neutral Hydrogen Distribution in the Galaxy as Revealed by 21-cm Radio Observations

(a) The blank area at the bottom of the drawing represents the far side of the Galaxy where the radial velocity component of the hydrogen clouds is negligible because they are moving across our line of sight. The Sun's position is indicated by the +. *(b)* An artist's conception of what the Milky Way Galaxy might look like viewed from above.

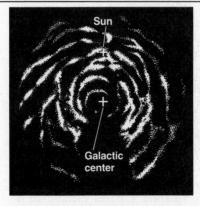

(a) Hydrogen distribution

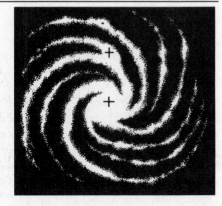

(b) Milky Way Galaxy

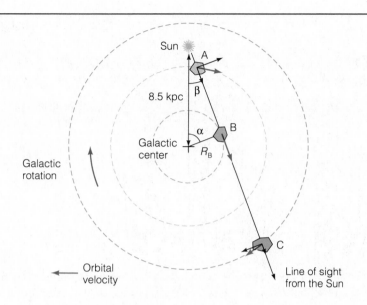

Observations at 21 cm of Three Neutral Hydrogen Clouds, A, B, and C

If radio telescopes are pointed at an angle β away from the galactic center, they may detect 21-cm radiation from several hydrogen clouds along the line of sight. The 21-cm observations are used to determine the distance to cloud B.

galactic center, and cloud B allows astronomers to determine the distance to the cloud. The geometry is identical to that of the Sun, Earth, and Venus at the greatest elongation of Venus (see Figure 3.7 in Chapter 3). In the planetary case, the distance between the Earth and the Sun, 1 AU, and all of the angles were known. In the galactic case, the distance between the Sun and the galactic center, 8.5 kpc, and all of the angles also are known. Angle β is just the angular distance on the sky away from the galactic center. Angle α is obtained by assuming that the angle at cloud B is 90°: $\alpha = 180° - 90° - \beta$. Thus all the information needed to calculate the distance to cloud B is at hand.

What about clouds A and C in Figure 17.11? Since the angles between the Sun, the clouds, and the galactic center are not right angles, their distances cannot be determined from only this geometry. Note that the distance to cloud B and its radial velocity are known. If interstellar clouds have circular orbits in the disk, then the observed radial velocity of cloud B minus the component of the Sun's galactic rotational velocity toward the cloud is its orbital velocity. These observations for cloud B gives the orbital velocity of the disk at the distance to cloud B. The same analysis can be done for other interstellar clouds by recording 21-cm radiation in different directions from the galactic center. That is, a cloud along each line of sight would exhibit the highest radial velocity, which would equal the cloud's orbital velocity after subtracting the Sun's velocity. Analyses of many clouds in many directions result in the orbital velocity of the disk as a function of distance from the galactic center. The plot of orbital velocities and distances from the galactic center gives the **rotation curve** of the Galaxy (Figure 17.12). The rotation curve shows how the orbital velocity of gas and stars changes in the disk of the Galaxy.

The measured radial velocities of clouds A and C depend on their true orbital velocities and the angle along the line of sight from the galactic

Rotation curve: A plot of orbital velocities versus distance from the galactic center for any galaxy.

■ FIGURE 17.12

The Rotation Curve for the Milky Way Galaxy

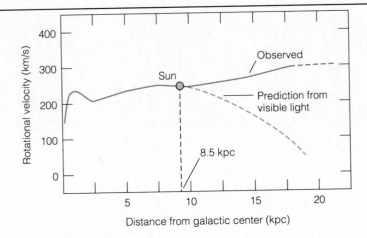

■ FIGURE 17.13

Differential Galactic Rotation

Stars and gas in the inner regions of the Galaxy travel farther in their orbits than stars and gas in the outer regions in the same length of time.

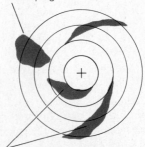

New region of star formation developing

Fragments of a spiral pattern caused by differential rotation

center. The rotation curve of the Galaxy allows us to calculate the expected radial velocity of an interstellar cloud at any position in any circular orbit in the disk. Matching this with observed velocities gives the distance of any interstellar cloud large enough to emit detectable 21-cm radiation. The intensity of the observed 21-cm lines is also a distance indicator and helps separate near clouds and far clouds with similar radial velocities. The combination of distance and direction of individual hydrogen clouds gives a map of the positions of interstellar clouds as shown in Panel a of Figure 17.10.

The Nature of Spiral Arms

Most astronomers interpret the distribution of interstellar clouds shown in Figure 17.10 as being due to spiral arms. The kinds of objects that make spiral arms visible are H II regions, O and B stars, and young star clusters. These are the most luminous objects in a galaxy and readily make the spiral patterns prominent. Since all of these objects are young and last only a few million years, an obvious question is, What happens to the spiral arms once these young, bright objects evolve and fade in brightness? Can spiral arms be permanent features of a galaxy? Since many galaxies exhibit spiral arms, spiral arms must either be long-lived or be capable of regeneration. Currently, two models address the question of how a galaxy can produce a spiral pattern that persists in time.

One model is based on observations of star formation in molecular clouds. As described in Chapter 15, star formation can begin at the border of a large cloud and propagate through the cloud. Expanding H II regions and supernovae outbursts of massive stars can initiate successive episodes of star formation and can cause a portion of a galaxy to burst into stars, as in a Fourth-of-July fireworks finale. If large regions in a galaxy were subjected to such *self-propagating star formation*, differential rotation would spread the regions into an arc of bright stars, H II regions, and young star clusters (Figure 17.13). The outer edges of the region would lag behind the inner edges because the interior gas

t = 0.4 billion years　　　t = 3.0 billion years　　　t = 7.5 billion years

(a)

(b)

clouds require less time to orbit the galaxy than the more distant gas clouds. Each region of star formation would grow into a spiral segment.

Once the star-forming material is consumed and the massive, bright stars reach their end states, the arcs will fade from prominence. If star-forming regions emerged at random, many arcs would be distributed over the disk of a galaxy at any one time, forming a collage of spiral pattern fragments. As these fade from view, new ones emerge at different locations and form a new pattern. Such segmented spiral patterns generated by computer models resemble the spiral patterns seen in many galaxies (Figure 17.14). Thus self-propagating star formation is a possible generator of spiral patterns in galaxies.

Randomly generated, self-propagating star formation models, however, cannot produce the beautiful double-armed spirals seen in some galaxies (Figure 17.15). These arms generally start near the central regions of the galaxy and spiral outward through the disk. Another current model explains these double spiral arms in terms of a gravitational wave that rotates around the galaxy. The wave is a *density wave* in that it represents an enhancement in the density of matter in the disk. The density enhancements are thought to be produced by slight changes, or perturbations, in the circular orbits of stars and gas in the disk. These perturbations are due to the gravitational influence of the Galaxy as a whole, of nearby stars and gas, and of the spiral arms themselves. The distortions can cause matter in the disk to linger slightly longer in certain parts of their orbits than in other parts. Figure 17.16 illustrates the results of a perturbation that produces oval orbits. The spiral pattern is created by a bunching of the orbits. This is where the density of matter in the disk will be greater than average.

The density wave in the form of a spiral pattern rotates around the galaxy at a slower rate than the disk itself. The spiral arm rotates in the same direction as the disk so that the tip of the arm at the rim of the disk is trailing. As a result, stars, dust, and gas in the disk overtake the density wave. Detailed calculations show that conditions conducive to star formation are created when the interstellar medium encounters the abrupt increase in density as it crosses the trailing edge of the slower moving density wave. The subsequent compression of gas and dust can cause the formation of giant cloud complexes and initiate star formation. Star formation will produce bright stellar objects that

■ **FIGURE 17.14**

Self-Propagating Star Formation

(a) Star formation is simulated in the disk of a galaxy with an imposed rotation curve. Differential rotation stretches the star formation regions into spiral-like segments. These three "snapshots" cover about 15 revolutions of the outside rim of the model galaxy. (From H. Gerola and P. E. Seiden, 1978, *The Astrophysical Journal*, 223:129.) *(b)* NGC 6744, a spiral galaxy exhibiting spiral features reminiscent of random star formation.

SOURCE: Part (b) copyright Anglo-Australian Telescope Board 1975.

■ **FIGURE 17.15**

The Spiral Galaxy NGC 628

Many galaxies display two distinct spiral arms emanating from their central regions.

SOURCE: National Optical Astronomy Observatories.

■■■ FIGURE 17.16

Density Waves and Two-Arm Spiral Patterns

These drawings illustrate how a galactic gravitational field can modify circular orbits to produce oval orbits and a spiral pattern. Panel b shows an orientation that produces a spiral pattern. The pattern defines regions where stars, dust, and gas will linger longer than in other locations in the disk.

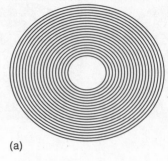

Gravitational perturbation on orbits in the disk is assumed to distort orbits into ellipses.

(a)

Gravitational effects can perturb each orbit in a slightly different manner and generate a spiral pattern: stars and gas will bunch together where their orbits are close together.

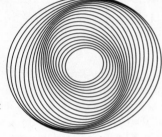

(b)

clearly outline the density wave. The O and B stars, for instance, have such short lifetimes that they will reach their end states long before they have time to move away from the density wave. Their rapid evolution is the underlying reason why they delineate spiral structure in galaxies. Many features of spiral arms, such as the distribution of H II regions, young stars, and open clusters, can be successfully explained using the density wave theory.

Although density waves may be responsible for star formation in some galaxies and appear to explain many observations, the mechanism that generates density waves is not understood. The basic driving force is probably gravity. The material in a galaxy feels the gravitational force of all the matter in the galaxy. As events occurring at the centers of stars influence their surfaces, events at the inner regions of a galaxy affect the outer regions. The linking is more subtle in galaxies than in stars and involves the transfer of rotational energy to the outer parts of the disk. The violent activity observed in the center of the Galaxy, described later in this chapter, may help initiate gravitational waves.

In both mechanisms, self-propagating star formation and density waves, the material in a spiral arm or spiral segment changes continuously. If spiral arms were composed of material that always remained part of the arm, strong differential galactic rotation would wind them up into spirals with hundreds of turns. Figure 17.17 shows the spiral pattern of a material arm after only a little more than one revolution of the innermost region. In the self-propagating star formation theory, spiral arms are *temporary* segments made up of regions of intense star formation; in the density wave theory, spiral arms are waves in which matter in the disk *temporarily* resides as it passes through.

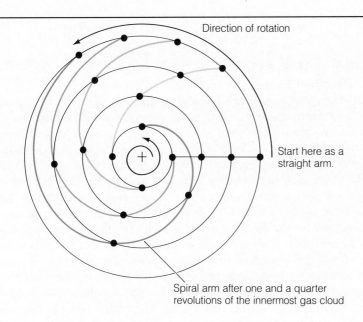

Direction of rotation

Start here as a straight arm.

Spiral arm after one and a quarter revolutions of the innermost gas cloud

■■■ FIGURE 17.17

Winding Dilemma

This diagram shows a material arm at five different times as it revolves about the center of a galaxy. The inner part of the arm takes less time to revolve around the center than the outer part. In this diagram, the inner part revolves one and a quarter times around the center while the outermost part revolves only one-third of the way around. The result is a spiral arm.

The reason astronomers have two mechanisms for spiral arm formation is that both appear to work. We find evidence of random star formation moderated by differential rotation, giving the appearance of many spiral arms. On the other hand, many galaxies exhibit beautiful twin arms emanating from the central regions. Even in the galaxies showing two major spiral arms, self-propagating star formation appears evident in the many spiral segments seen in the disk. Although spiral arms attract much attention because they are so evident, it is important to remember that most of the mass in the disk of a galaxy is composed of the older stars that lie in and between the prominent spiral arms. On top of this, it appears that most of the mass of the Milky Way Galaxy and other galaxies may be too faint to see.

Mass of the Milky Way Galaxy

Since the Sun orbits about the center of the Galaxy, we can estimate the mass of the Galaxy from the Sun's orbital motion just as we estimated the mass of the Sun from the Earth's orbital motion. Kepler's third law of planetary motion as applied to the Galaxy is

$$\mathfrak{M}_{\text{gal}} = \frac{a^3}{P^2}$$

Here a is the distance to the center of the Galaxy, 8.5 kpc or 1.75 billion AU. The orbital period of the Sun around the Galaxy is just the circumference of its orbit, $2\pi a$, divided by its orbital speed of 250 km/s (560,000 MPH). Although the orbital speed is enormous, it still takes the Sun 210 million years to orbit the Galaxy once. Kepler's law gives

$$\mathfrak{M}_{\text{gal}} = \frac{(1.75 \times 10^9)^3}{(2.1 \times 10^8)^2} \, \mathfrak{M}_\odot = 1.2 \times 10^{11} \, \mathfrak{M}_\odot$$

According to this estimate, the Galaxy contains the equivalent of at least 120 billion Suns.

Used in this way, Kepler's law only estimates the mass of the Galaxy interior to the Sun's orbit. How much mass lies beyond the orbit of the Sun? The rotation curve of the Galaxy (see Figure 17.12) shows that rotational velocities in the disk reach ≈300 km/s beyond the Sun and may stay that high at least out to about 30 kpc (≈100,000 light-years). This behavior of disk velocities is significant. Recall that the more distant planets in the solar system orbit more slowly than those close to the Sun due to the effects of the Sun's gravity. Because the gravitational force exerted by the Sun is greater for closer planets, they must move faster to maintain their orbits than more distant planets. At large distances from the center of the Galaxy, however, velocities do not decrease with increasing distance from the center—they increase. One explanation for these peculiar motions is that a substantial amount of matter must lie beyond the Sun's orbit. The additional amount of mass necessary to account for these rapid orbital speeds, however, is enormous—at least 1–2 × 10^{12} $\mathfrak{M}_\odot$. In fact, studies of the Galaxy and other galaxies have led to the suggestion that the disk and halo of the Milky Way Galaxy are embedded in a large component, called the **corona** (Figure 17.18). The corona's radius may be greater than 100 kpc, and it may have a mass of 10^{12} $\mathfrak{M}_\odot$. While most of the visible light from the Galaxy is emitted from within the Sun's orbit, most of the mass of the Galaxy may lie beyond the Sun and perhaps outside the disk itself. The most remarkable aspect of the possibility of additional mass in and beyond the halo is not so much the amount, but the fact that we cannot see it!

Astronomers have made exhaustive lists of objects that have mass but would emit so little light that they would be very difficult to detect in the outer reaches of the Galaxy. For example, faint red main-sequence stars are about 1000 times fainter than the Sun, making them difficult to detect. Planets, of course, would be impossible to see in the halo. Searches for faint main-sequence stars have been unsuccessful, however, and it is unlikely that planets would form without stars. On the other hand, objects that are not quite massive enough to ignite nuclear reactions at their centers would also be very difficult to detect. Hidden mass, of course, reminds us of black holes; perhaps, a huge halo of black holes surrounds the Galaxy. If so, black holes or other dark remnants, such as neutron stars, would have been formed preferentially in the outer parts of the Galaxy in the earliest epochs of the Galaxy's existence. They may be the remains of a very old stellar population (sometimes referred to as Population III), older than the halo globular clusters. Furthermore, studies of the very early universe (Chapter 19) hint that the dark mass may consist of elementary atomic particles produced during the first few moments of creation. Hidden mass has cosmological consequences that will be discussed in more detail in Chapter 19. At present, astronomers are completely baffled by the apparent pres-

■■■ FIGURE 17.18

The Disk, Halo, and Corona

The galactic corona may contain as much mass as the halo and disk together but may be much larger.

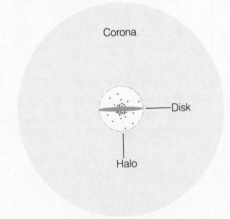

608

ence of a vast amount of dark matter surrounding the Galaxy. An intriguing implication of this is that most of the mass in the universe may be invisible to us.

THE DISTRIBUTION AND EVOLUTION OF STELLAR POPULATIONS

Optical observations of globular clusters and young stars and radio observations of hydrogen clouds suggest that the Galaxy is a rotating disk of stars, gas, and dust within a huge sphere of old stars and globular clusters. The disk and halo appear to be embedded in a very massive and extended corona of hidden, or dark, matter. The concept of two populations, Populations I and II, actually gives a simplified picture of the stellar components in the Galaxy. A more useful categorization of the Milky Way Galaxy, which also provides a framework that can be applied to other galaxies, divides the Galaxy into two major structural components. Globular clusters and Population II stars are part of a *spheroidal component*. These old stars are distributed throughout a spheroidal volume centered on the nucleus of the Galaxy. Open clusters and Population I stars are part of a flat *disk component* also centered on the nucleus.

The motions of the spheroidal and disk components provide very important clues to the evolutionary history of the Milky Way Galaxy. The term "evolutionary history" refers to the changes over time in the appearance and structure of the Galaxy and in the motions within the Galaxy. This history reflects chemical and dynamical changes occurring to the stars, gas, and dust. Let's first study the chemical history of the Milky Way Galaxy.

The dust and gas out of which stars formed in each component became enriched in heavy elements over time. The enrichment of the interstellar medium was accomplished by supernovae and planetary nebulae and was therefore the natural result of the evolution of individual stars. Accordingly, globular clusters are composed of stars with very low metallicity because they were among the first stars formed in the Galaxy. The more massive stars of this first generation exploded and ejected material enriched with heavy elements into the interstellar medium, which later formed a second generation of stars. Successive generations of massive stars continued to add to the enrichment of the interstellar medium so that each new generation of stars was slightly more enriched in heavy elements than the previous generation. This process is still occurring today. A plot of the ages of star clusters versus the metallicity of cluster members reveals the "metal enrichment history" of the Galaxy (Figure 17.19). Star clusters play the role of "fossils" in galactic evolution research as animal and plant fossils do in the study of the evolution of life on Earth. Astronomers know the age of each cluster plotted and, through spectroscopy, the chemical composition of its member stars. These two characteristics indicate the chemical composition of the interstellar medium at the time the stars in the

■■■■ FIGURE 17.19

Galactic Metal Enrichment History

Globular clusters are the oldest and most metal-poor star clusters in the Galaxy. The magenta area centered on 15 billion years represents the rapid metal enrichment of the spheroidal component. The cyan area around the Sun shows a more gradual enrichment in metals of the disk component during the last 10 billion years. No clusters are seen in the Galaxy with ages between the oldest open clusters and the globular clusters.

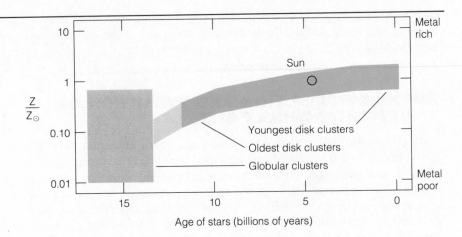

cluster were formed. For example, a star cluster with an age of 8 billion years and a metallicity of $Z = 0.01$ indicates that 8 billion years ago 1% of the interstellar medium consisted of metals. Thus the chemical compositions of stars record the aging of the Galaxy.

The metal enrichment history in Figure 17.19 does not include a very important part of the spheroidal component. Observations of other spiral galaxies reveal that each has a bright, glowing stellar aggregate, called the **nuclear bulge,** at its center (Figure 17.20). These nuclear bulges are the brightest regions in spiral galaxies, indicating that many billions of stars are present. Studies of the distribution of globular clusters and RR Lyrae stars in our Galaxy show that their space densities (number of clusters or stars per cubic parsec) increase toward the center, indicating a concentration of stars there. The center of the Galaxy,

■■■■ FIGURE 17.20

The Nuclear Bulge

This galaxy (NGC 4565), which shows a prominent nuclear bulge, is probably how our Galaxy would look if seen on edge from a great distance.

SOURCE: Official U.S. Naval Observatory photograph.

however, is very difficult to observe because the center is so obscured by dust. Astronomers can only study it at X-ray, infrared, and radio wavelengths. A few gaps in the obscuring dust do exist toward the center that allow astronomers to sample the outermost bulge population. The most remarkable observation of stars in the nuclear bulge is that a large fraction are metal rich! In fact, their metal abundances are greater than the Sun's. Furthermore, the stars in the bulge all appear to be red K and M giants and, therefore, old. No indication of a young population is seen even though the metal abundance of some bulge stars is high.

The spheroidal component (nuclear bulge and halo) of the Galaxy has experienced a chemical evolution as evidenced by the metal richness near the center of the Galaxy and the metal poorness of the most distant globular clusters. Furthermore, the globular clusters found closer to the center of the Galaxy are more metal rich than the more distant globular clusters. Consequently, the spheroidal component consists of a low concentration of old, metal-poor stars at its periphery and a high concentration of old, metal-rich stars toward its center. The range of chemical composition and its correlation with distance from the galactic center strongly suggests that the Galaxy formed by a collapse of an immense cloud of dust and gas.

The stars and clusters in the spheroidal component have very eccentric orbits (Figure 17.21). This suggests that the motion of the dust and gas at the time of star formation was directed mainly inward. Globular clusters, for instance, appear to have formed when the Galaxy was just beginning to collapse. At that time the motion of the interstellar material was directed mainly inward toward the galactic center. The most distant globular clusters, therefore, roughly outline the shape of the Galaxy very early in its collapse, which was approximately spherical (Figure 17.22). During the collapse, the density at the center would naturally be higher than elsewhere because the collapse was directed toward the center. Consequently, star formation at the center would have been intense from the earliest epoches. The bulge of the Milky Way Galaxy must be the evolved remains of this period of intensive star formation. Also during the collapse, stellar evolution of the massive stars enriched the interstellar medium, and newly formed stars close to the center of the collapsing sphere condensed out of highly enriched interstellar material. The early evolution of the Galaxy, therefore, was characterized by a radial collapse and intense star formation at the center.

Population I objects, such as the Sun and open clusters, move around the galactic center in nearly circular orbits. This suggests that the motion of the dust and gas at the time the disk component formed was mainly circular. The ages of stars and open clusters in the disk component further suggest that the disk formed well after the spheroidal component collapsed. Thus the disk was formed out of an interstellar medium that was already enriched with metals. Star formation in the disk apparently was delayed until the motion of the collapsing matter was circular.

In summary, the current description of the evolution of the Galaxy starts with the collapse of a slowly rotating cloud of dust and gas. As

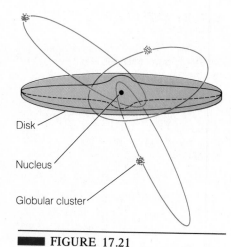

■■■■ FIGURE 17.21

Orbits of Globular Clusters and Population II Stars

The orbits are very elliptical with an average eccentricity of 0.6; consequently, globular clusters spend millions of years far away from the galactic disk and center but periodically plunge through the disk.

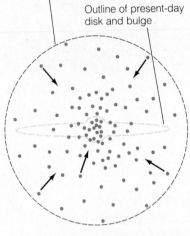

Extent of original gas and dust of the protogalaxy

Outline of present-day disk and bulge

The initial collapse is directed toward the center.

(a) 15 billion years ago

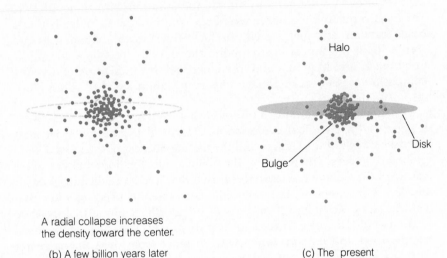

A radial collapse increases the density toward the center.

(b) A few billion years later

Halo

Disk

Bulge

(c) The present

■ **FIGURE 17.22**

Collapse of the Spheroidal Component

The galaxy starts out as a sphere of gas and dust. During its radial collapse, stars and globular clusters form. Since the density of gas and dust increases fastest at the center, more stars and clusters are formed there than in the outer regions.

the cloud collapses, its rotational motion increases, as does that of ice skaters who pull in their arms as they spin. The increased spinning of the dust and gas resists the inward motion of the collapse and transforms an essentially direct collapse into a circular motion. This dynamical transformation only applies to the dust and gas because the gas atoms and dust interact with each other. Their trajectories will evolve from *mainly directed inward toward* the center to *circular motion around* the center, that is, from spherical to flat. On the other hand, once a star forms, it no longer strongly interacts with the gas and dust or even other stars. Consequently the stars will acquire whatever orbits the gas and dust had at the time they formed.

During the more or less radial collapse, the stars and star clusters of the spheroidal component formed. These have their highest concentrations toward the center of the Galaxy. Stellar evolution during the collapse continuously enriched the interstellar medium so that the most metal-rich stars are those of the nuclear bulge. A few billion years after the spheroidal component formed, the dust and gas settled into a disk from which the Population I stars have since formed. The Galaxy in its simplest form can be visualized as a disk of gas, dust, and stars embedded inside a sphere of ancient stars (Figure 17.23).

Representatives of the major components of the Galaxy are readily seen in other spiral galaxies. Spiral arms are both beautiful and prevalent in spirals seen face on. Spiral arms appear to emanate from bright and sometimes large nuclear bulges. These bright nuclear regions have prompted astronomers to take a very careful and detailed look at the nucleus of our Galaxy—in the direction of the star clouds of Sagittarius.

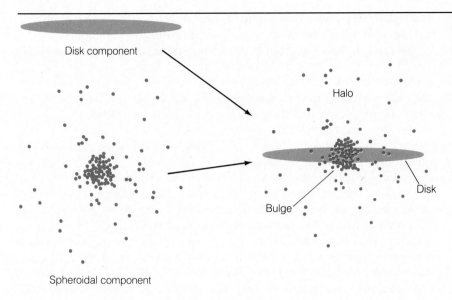

■■■■ FIGURE 17.23
Disk and Spheroidal Components
The Milky Way Galaxy is composed of two structural components, the flat disk and the spheroidal component.

■■■THE GALACTIC CENTER

Although the nuclear bulge in the Galaxy is not as obvious to us as those in other galaxies, many lines of evidence indicate its presence and, therefore, the direction toward the center of the Galaxy. Shapley demonstrated that a massive galactic nucleus exists in the direction of the constellation Sagittarius (Figure 17.24). The greatest number of stars along the Milky Way are seen in the Sagittarius sector, and the width of the Milky Way is greatest in that region of the sky (Figure 17.25). It is surprising that this obvious concentration of stars in the Sagittarius star clouds was ignored for so long as a clue to the location of the galactic center. More recently, infrared observations toward the galactic center have revealed a narrow band of dust in the plane of the Galaxy and a very strong infrared source in Sagittarius.

As noted in the last section, the stars that inhabit the nuclear bulge are difficult to detect, but certain kinds of stars appear to be concentrated toward the direction of the galactic center. All stars that have Population II characteristics show high concentrations toward the center of the Galaxy. These are old stars, such as RR Lyrae variables, late K and M giants, and planetary nebulae. Furthermore, Walter Baade discovered a small "window" in the sky very near the galactic center in which very little extinction between us and the center obstructs our view. He found the greatest number of RR Lyrae variables at a distance of 8–10 kpc from us—very close to the center of the Galaxy and certainly inside the nuclear bulge. The number density of stars near the center of the Galaxy is estimated to be about 1000 stars per cubic parsec, or a million times that near the Sun. An observer on a planet orbiting a sun near the galactic center would see hundreds of thousands of

■■■■ FIGURE 17.24
Location of the Galactic Center Near the Constellation Sagittarius

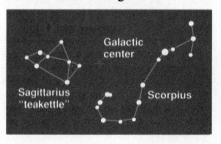

(a)

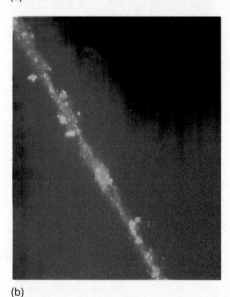

(b)

■■■■ FIGURE 17.25

The Milky Way toward Sagittarius in Visible Light and the Infrared

(a) A wide-angle view toward the center of the Milky Way Galaxy. The "teapot" shape of Sagittarius and the tail of Scorpius can be seen (compare with Figure 17.24). *(b)* Infrared wide-angle view of the center of the Galaxy. Black represents the dimmest regions of infrared emission; next is blue, then yellow, red, and white. Bright yellow and green globs represent clouds of dust heated by young stars. The large yellow-white region is the center of the Galaxy.

SOURCES: Part (a), National Optical Astronomy Observatories. Part (b), NASA.

luminous red giants in the nighttime sky. From Earth, however, observers can only view the center at radio and infrared wavelengths.

The nuclear bulge is about 6 kpc across. Near its outermost boundary are giant rings of huge H II regions, similar to the Orion nebula, and molecular clouds. Just inside these rings, however, the density of gas in the disk suddenly drops to nearly zero. Radio observations at 21 cm show an unusual "expanding spiral arm" about 3 kpc from the galactic center. It is not clear if this feature is an arm or a ring, but it is moving away from the center at speeds of 50 km/s toward us on the near side and 135 km/s away from us on the far side of the galactic center. Astronomers interpret this as an ejection of material from the nucleus of the Galaxy that occurred from 10 to 100 million years ago—a hint of violent events at the center. In fact, another expanding "smoke ring" is observed at about 300 pc from the center of the Galaxy. This ring includes giant molecular clouds and clusters of recently formed O and B stars (perhaps totaling a billion solar masses!), as if some ejection mechanism initiated star formation.

Astronomers have known since the 1930's that a very strong radio source lies within a few hundred parsecs of the galactic center. The strongest radio emission originates in a source called Sagittarius A; this source is considered to be the center of the Galaxy. Although several radio sources near Sagittarius A appear to be large H II regions, Sagittarius A itself shows signs of tremendous magnetically induced motion. Its radio emission is not that from a hot gas but from atomic particles moving at very high speeds. Electrons and ions can radiate electromagnetic energy if they are accelerated in a magnetic field. On Earth this occurs in particle accelerators, called synchrotrons, in which the speeds of atomic particles are increased to near the speed of light. In a synchrotron, powerful magnets force electrons to move in a circle at relativistic speeds (near the speed of light). During experiments in the late 1940s involving high-energy nuclear collisions, scientists noticed an eerie light emitted by electrons moving at these high speeds. Further study of this radiation, called *synchrotron radiation*, revealed that relativistic electrons emit a great deal of radio radiation as well as some visible light. In fact, the shape of the spectrum of synchrotron radiation is unlike that of a Planck curve of a hot gas. The synchrotron curve peaks in the radio part of the spectrum and decreases at shorter wavelengths. Scientists call radiation from a hot gas *thermal* radiation and radiation that does not follow a Planck curve such as synchrotron radiation, *nonthermal* radiation. Nonthermal radiation from the center of the Galaxy implies that charged particles, probably electrons, must be moving near the speed of light. One interpretation of these observations that is consistent with the expanding rings is that powerful explosive events are ejecting matter at high speeds from the center of the Galaxy.

Infrared studies have discovered many strong infrared sources near the galactic center; the strongest infrared source is also the strongest radio source, Sagittarius A. Figure 17.26 shows high-resolution radio pictures of Sagittarius A that reveal a pinwheel-like structure just tens of parsecs across. Infrared luminosities of Sagittarius A indicate millions of solar masses packed within a one-parsec radius! Most of this

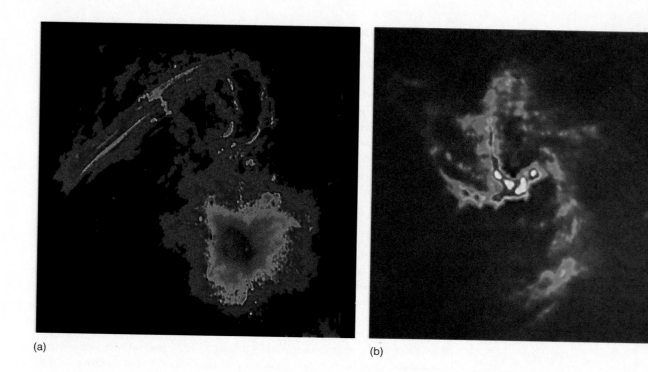

(a)

(b)

mass appears to be concentrated within the inner few tenths of a parsec.

More evidence of an immense but compact concentration of mass at the center of the Galaxy comes from the observed high speeds of matter near the center that many astronomers consider to be the result of rotation. The central few hundred parsecs of the Galaxy appear to be a disk of hydrogen that is rotating very rapidly, 200–250 km/s (450,000–560,000 MPH), making one complete rotation in tens of thousands of years. Mixed in this nuclear disk appear to be ultradense star clusters of hundreds of thousands of stars also rapidly rotating around a compact concentration of mass. This central concentration, or object, must be very massive indeed to explain the high rotational speeds of the clusters, gas, and hydrogen near the center; that is, the greater the central mass, the greater the orbital velocity needed to balance the gravitational force. The radio and infrared observations are taken as evidence for a supermassive central object of at least a million solar masses. Since it is so small, many astronomers conclude that a supermassive black hole sits at the center of the Galaxy.

Black holes result from exploding stars that leave behind neutron cores larger than ~2 $\mathfrak{M}_\odot$. The masses of such black holes are at most a few solar masses. How can a black hole of a million solar masses exist? Since nature does not appear to create stars with masses of a million Suns (see Chapter 15), a supermassive black hole may be a product of coalescence, the result of a merger of many black holes, neutron stars, or other stars. Like any other star, black holes can capture mass. If an ordinary star collides with a black hole, for instance, part or all of the star's mass will merge with the black hole, allowing the black hole to

■■■ FIGURE 17.26

Infrared Observations of Sagittarius A

(a) Filamentary structure is detected at a wavelength of 20 cm in a region of the galactic center about 75 pc (250 light-years) across. *(b)* Observations at 6 cm show the ionized gas within the central 3 pc (10 light-years).

SOURCE: NRAO/AUI.

grow; that is, its Schwarzschild radius and mass will increase. In the sparse galactic disk and halo, collisions between black holes and stars are very improbable. But at the center of the Galaxy where star formation has been intense and the number density of stars is great, collisions are much more likely. In fact, the dominant constituent of the center of a galaxy early in its evolution may have been neutron stars. Recent calculations with supercomputers show that a spherical swarm of neutron stars at the center would collapse and coalesce into a giant black hole. Initially, only a few percent of the neutron stars would form the black hole, but the remaining neutron stars would orbit the black hole and would gradually be consumed as they spiraled into the central black hole. Thus this process would provide a supermassive black hole at a galaxy's center and a source for the observed radio emissions. The radio emission does not come from the black hole itself, but from the spiraling matter as it is heated to millions of Kelvins in the swirling accretion disk before reaching the event horizon. The nucleus of the Milky Way Galaxy may be an ancient stellar graveyard.

A supermassive black hole, the result of numerous collisions over millennia, is consistent with many observations and is the most promising candidate for the energy source at the center of the Galaxy. A supermassive central object also makes sense in that the largest concentration of matter should be at the center of the Galaxy, at the center of the spheroidal component. Furthermore, astronomers find intense activity in terms of electromagnetic radiation and nonthermal emission in the nuclei of other galaxies. While some of the extragalactic observations suggest that supermassive black holes may be a common feature of the central regions of galaxies, they also reinforce the impression of dramatic and violent events occurring in the Galaxy's core.

▄▄SUMMARY

The Galaxy is huge. The Sun itself is 8500 pc from the center—it takes light 25,000 years to travel this distance. The Sun orbits the Galaxy at a speed of 250 km/s (560,000 MPH), taking 210 million years to complete an orbit. The Sun is part of a large, flat disk of stars, with a high concentration of gas and dust, that rotates around the center of the Galaxy. The second major structural component of the Milky Way Galaxy is a sphere of globular clusters and old stars symmetric about the galactic center. The highest concentration of this spheroidal component is at the center where the high density of stars and clusters produces a bulge about 6000 pc across. The sparse, outer regions of the spheroidal component form a halo of old, metal-poor globular clusters and old stars extending about 50,000 pc in all directions. Both the spheroidal and disk components of the Galaxy may be embedded in a gigantic corona of dark matter, which may be made up of remnants of a very early population of stars. From analysis of the rotation of the Galaxy, the mass of the halo and disk is estimated to be about a trillion solar masses; the corona may be equally massive.

Although dust prevents us from seeing far into the disk of the Galaxy, optical studies of nearby H II regions and young star clusters and radio studies of hydrogen clouds reveal a spiral structure within the disk. Spiral arms are thought to be generated by density waves that sweep through the disk and by self-propagating star formation in the differentially rotating disk. Spiral arms and spiral segments are so optically visible because they are the sites of recent star formation where bright massive stars and H II regions are created. Most of the mass of the disk, however, consists of faint, old stars.

The spherical halo and the flat disk are the probable result of the collapse of a giant roughly spherical cloud of dust and gas. The spheroidal component of the Galaxy may have been formed by a rapid radial collapse of the cloud. The collapse was accompanied by intense star formation, especially at the center, and a metal enrichment of the collapsing dust and gas. The intensive star formation and enrichment at the center of the collapsing cloud gave birth to what we now see as an old but metal-rich population of stars. The dust and gas that were left over after this initial burst of star formation eventually settled into a rotating disk. Star formation in this enriched disk during the last 10 billion years produced the Population I stars, of which the Sun is one.

The center of the Galaxy is invisible to optical telescopes because of interstellar extinction by dust in the disk. Infrared and radio studies of the galactic center reveal a dynamic and possibly violent region of explosions and star formation. A supermassive black hole may reside at the center of the Galaxy. Its mass is estimated to be over a million solar masses.

CHAPTER CAPSULE

Topics and Terms	Review and Remarks
Sun's place in the Galaxy	It is 8.5 kpc from the center. It orbits the center at a speed of 250 km/s. It takes 210 million years to orbit the Galaxy.
Structure of the Galaxy	A disk component is composed of stars, dust, and gas. A spheroidal component is composed of old stars. Both may be surrounded by a massive corona of invisible matter.
The disk component	The disk is composed of young and moderately old metal-rich stars Young stars and H II regions appear to group in spiral arm segments. Spiral arms are due to density waves and self-propagating star formation.
The spheroidal component	The halo is a sphere of old stars and star clusters surrounding the disk. The highest concentration of stars are the old, but metal-rich, stars in the bulge.
Stellar populations	Population I consists of young, metal-rich stars in the disk—they represent the more recent generations of stars less than 10 billion years old. Population II consists of old stars in the halo and the bulge—they represent the first generations of stars in the Galaxy.
Galactic evolution	The Galaxy is the result of a collapse of a huge, slowly rotating cloud of dust and gas. The spheroidal component may be the result of a rapid radial collapse of the cloud. Intensive star formation at the center produced the concentration of old, metal-rich stars in the bulge. The remaining dust and gas formed a disk as the collapse increased the rotation.
The galactic center	It is invisible to optical telescopes but detectable with infrared and radio telescopes. The center is a dynamic and violent region of great explosions and star formation. A supermassive black hole of millions of solar masses may reside there.

REVIEW QUESTIONS

1. Describe the apparent shape, size, and stellar composition of the Milky Way Galaxy.

2. How do the stellar populations (Population I and Population II) differ? To which of the populations do the Sun, globular clusters, and open clusters belong?

3. In our Galaxy, the open clusters are always younger than the globular clusters. Can their metallicities help to explain the differences in age? Does this mean that no open clusters were formed early in the development of the Galaxy? Explain.

4. How did RR Lyrae variable stars aid in the determining of the structure of the Milky Way Galaxy?

618

5. We can observe only about 10% of the disk of the Galaxy but we can observe a much greater percentage of the galactic halo. Why?

6. The 21-cm line originates with neutral hydrogen. How does this allow us to infer the spiral structure of parts of the galactic disk that are not directly observable with the usually visible objects?

7. Describe the position of the Sun in the Galaxy and its motion around the galactic center.

8. It is believed that the galactic halo and disk have many old, faint (and therefore unobservable) stars. What particular objects do we use to observe the nearby spiral structure? Would you think this structure is representative of the general distribution of stars in the galactic disk?

9. What is a density wave and how is it related to the spiral structure of the Galaxy? How does the density-wave concept help with the winding dilemma?

10. Is the existence of a supermassive black hole at the center of the Milky Way Galaxy consistent with our overall view of the Galaxy? How is the galactic core observed?

FOR FURTHER READING

Clark, G. O. 1986. Stellar populations: Key to the clusters. *Astronomy*, Oct., 106.

Dane, T. M. 1988. The molecular milky way. *Sky & Telescope*, July, 22.

Darling, D. 1987. Star trek part one: The adventure begins. *Astronomy*, Mar., 94.

———. 1987. Star trek part two: The distant shores. *Astronomy*, Apr., 94.

Gingerich, O., and B. Welther. 1985. Harlow Shapley and the Cepheids. *Sky & Telescope*, Dec., 540.

Goldsmith, D. 1988. SETI: The search heats up. *Sky & Telescope*, Feb., 141.

Kaufman, M. 1987. Tracing M81's spiral arms. *Sky & Telescope*, Feb., 135.

Olsen, E. 1985. Intelligent life in space. *Astronomy*, July, 6.

Verschuur, G. L. 1988. Is the Milky Way an interacting galaxy? *Astronomy*, Jan., 26.

N ≥ 1: Extraterrestrial Civilizations

Where would the science fiction movie industry be without Klingons, Romulans, and Jedi Knights? Television series and movies from "Star Trek" to *Star Wars* clearly assume that life is to be found everywhere in the Galaxy. UFO enthusiasts try to give this idea reality by interpreting common and uncommon events and phenomena in terms of alien visits to the Earth. On the other hand, some of us believe we are so special that humans are the only inhabitants of the whole universe. Consider the following quotations from two astrophysicists:

. . . no technological society which has advanced more than a century beyond us exists now, or has ever existed, in the Galaxy.

> Frank J. Tipler (1982, *Mercury*, 11:10)

. . . during the past 5 to 10 billion years of galactic history our Galaxy must have housed close to one billion independent civilizations.

> Michael Papagiannis (1982, *Mercury*, 11:14)

What a range for estimates of the number of civilizations, N, in the Galaxy! Clearly, such estimates must be uncertain. Are we dealing with opinion or fact, guesswork or scientific analysis? Let's go through a version of the standard estimate step by step to illustrate how such extreme values are possible.

The estimate for N involves the disciplines of astronomy, biology, and sociology. Astronomers try to estimate the number of stars in the Galaxy that can have Earth-like planets orbiting them. Biologists try to estimate the chances of life evolving on these planets if conditions are right. Finally, once a civilization becomes a technological society, how long will it last? A technological civilization is defined as one that is capable of communicating with other extraterrestrial civilizations. The sociological aspects deal with such questions as, Do all technological civilizations blow themselves up once they learn how to build an atomic bomb, or do they survive to explore the Galaxy? Let's begin by counting stars.

$N \geq 1.$

NUMBER OF STARS

A reasonable estimate for the number of Population I stars in the disk of our Galaxy is about 400 billion. Only Population I stars are considered because life as we know it requires heavy elements, which are lacking in Population II stars. Of these 400 billion stars, how many are likely to have Earth-like planets around them? The Sun has at least nine planets with only one Earth-like planet. It could be argued that Mars and, to a lesser extent, Venus are nearly Earth-like. Under slightly different conditions, these two planets could have produced conditions hospitable to life. In fact, Mars did have running water

Number of Population I stars in the Galaxy = 400,000,000,000.

■ **FIGURE 17A.1**

Ecospheres

The ecospheres shown here are regions around the stars in which water can be liquid and presumably life can emerge.

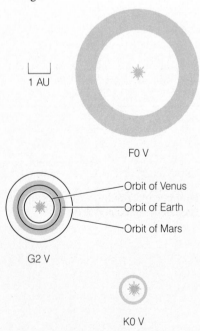

1 AU

F0 V

Orbit of Venus
Orbit of Earth
Orbit of Mars

G2 V

K0 V

and warmer temperatures during its first billion years of planetary history. Most astronomers and biologists believe that an abundant supply of water is a necessary condition for life. This restricts the "search for life" to only those locations in a solar system where water is liquid. Water will evaporate on a planet too near a star, and water will freeze on a planet too far from a star. We call this region around a star in which temperatures are conducive to liquid water the **ecosphere.**

The ecosphere around the Sun lies between ≈0.7 AU and ≈2 AU. Ecospheres around more massive stars will be larger because these stars emit a greater amount of radiation while ecospheres around less massive stars will be smaller (Figure 17A.1). In fact, ecospheres around mid to late K and all M stars are probably too narrow for us to expect to find planets within them. This limits the search to stars between spectral classes O and early K. This group comprises only about 10% of all Population I stars, giving 40 billion stars in the Galaxy with large ecospheres. If evolution of life on Earth is typical for the Galaxy, then a planet requires 4–5 billion years for life with our level of intelligence to evolve. Consequently, those stars with main sequence lifetimes less than 4–5 billion years are unsuitable. This includes all stars with spectral classes earlier than about F8 and eliminates 10 billion stars from the total, leaving 30 billion stars with large enough ecospheres and long enough main-sequence lifetimes for life to evolve.

How many of these 30 billion stars will have orbiting planets? This is unknown. Only recently have astronomers had reliable hints of even large planets orbiting other stars. Models of collapsing protostars and observations of young stars, however, strongly suggest that disks of dust and gas are common results of the star formation process. Furthermore, even though half of these stars are binary systems, recent studies of planetary orbits around binaries suggest that stable orbits within the ecospheres around members of binary systems are still likely. Let's assume that all 30 billion stars form planetary systems. How many of these planetary systems will have habitable Earth-like planets within the ecosphere? This is also unknown. Some crude models of possible solar systems can help answer this question. These models tend to produce terrestrial planets in the inner part of the solar system and gaseous planets farther away (see Figure 11.6). Taken at face value, these models suggest that about two-thirds of all planetary systems will have an Earth-like planet within their ecospheres. Recent work modeling the evolution of a planet's atmosphere, however, suggests that habitable zones around stars may be as much as ten times smaller than their ecospheres. These models include phenomena such as a runaway greenhouse effect and glaciation that may affect a planet's environment. Let's choose a reduction factor of ¹/₁₀, realizing that it could be larger or smaller. This results in about 3 billion Earth-like planets in the Galaxy on which conditions could be right for life to develop.

Number of Earth-like planets = 3,000,000,000.

This is as far as star counting can help in the estimate of N. The choices yet to be made fall into two categories: those by pessimists and those by optimists.

▰▰▰EVOLUTION OF EXTRATERRESTRIALS

Of these 3 billion Earth-like planets, how many will actually develop life? Some biologists believe that, given the right conditions on a planet, life is inevitable. This is clearly an optimistic viewpoint; a pessimist may rightfully say that life actually emerges only 1%, or even less, of the time. Which value is right, 1 or ¹/₁₀₀? Scientists do not have any data that allow them to choose one over the other. Now personal preferences begin to enter the estimate. Let's choose ¹/₁₀, a middle-of-the-road value, which gives about 300 million stars in the Galaxy that have developed life in the last 4–5 billion years.

Number of planets on which life develops = 300,000,000.

If life does emerge on these planets, will it evolve into one or more intelligent species? If it does, will that species develop a technological civilization capable of communicating with other technological civilizations in the Galaxy? Again, the answers are unknown. Earth has produced at least one intelligent species, and some species of whales and dolphins appear to be very intelligent. Let's again be moderate and assume that only 10% of the planets on which life emerges evolve at least one intelligent species. This gives 30 million planets in the Galaxy on which intelligent life evolves. Will these 30 million species actually develop the technology capable of communicating with other civilizations on other planets? If, for instance, the intelligent life on a planet is mainly sea life, it does not appear that they could develop a means of interstellar communications. Let's again use ¹/₁₀ as an estimate of the fraction of intelligent species that develop into technological civilizations, giving 3 million technological civilizations in the Galaxy.

Number of planets on which intelligent life develops = 30,000,000.

We have derived two interesting numbers (of unknown reliability). One is the number of planets on which intelligent life has developed, 30 million. The other, 3 million, represents an estimate of the number of technological civilizations produced in the Galaxy around Population I stars during the last 4–5 billion years. These are really just guesses. A pessimist could easily end up with a number like 3000 for the number of technological civilizations by choosing the factor of ¹/₁₀₀ for all of the biological factors. On the other hand, an optimist could just as easily end up with 3 billion technological civilizations

Number of planets on which technological civilizations develop = 3,000,000.

by choosing factors of 1 instead. The number of 3 million, however, is not the number of civilizations estimated to exist in the Galaxy right now; this depends on how long a civilization lasts.

▰ LONGEVITY OF A GALACTIC TECHNOLOGICAL CIVILIZATION

If all the technological civilizations emerged at the same time as ours, then we would expect to find 3 million technological civilizations in the Galaxy now. Of course, some galactic civilizations could have developed earlier than ours. Let's assume that alien beings evolved on the same time scale as Earth mammals and that like Earth mammals, they emerged about 250–300 million years ago on all of the 3 million planets. Let's further assume that intelligent life could have developed anytime within the last 300 million years. For instance, humans might have evolved earlier if the dinosaurs had not lasted as long as they did. The number 300 million years is just convenient for our estimate, but perhaps 400 million or a billion years is more appropriate—we just do not know. Suppose further that the emergence of life in the Galaxy was spread uniformly over the last 300 million years. That is, just as many technological civilizations formed between 150 and 200 million years ago as formed between now and 50 million years ago. This means that, over the last 300 million years, a civilization would form in the Galaxy approximately every hundred years:

$$\frac{300 \times 10^6}{3 \times 10^6} = 100 \text{ years}$$

The number of technological civilizations present today depends on their longevity. If each technological civilization lasted 300 million years, then 3 million technological civilizations should exist in the Galaxy today. Mathematically, this can be written as

$$N = \frac{3 \times 10^6}{300 \times 10^6} L = 10^{-2} L$$

where the factor 10^{-2} is just the number of civilizations produced each year and L is the average *longevity* of a technological civilization. For instance, if L is small, then a civilization that emerged 200 million years ago would not exist today. One more guess must be made: how long does a technological civilization survive? How long will our civilization survive? Although we hope that it will last a long time, we cannot answer this question. History, however, gives clues in the recorded lifetimes of ancient human civilizations.

■ FIGURE 17A.2

The Ancient River Flows from the Land to Reach the Sea: Midday by Jesse Allen

Shown is the middle panel of this triptych.

SOURCE: Reproduction rights arranged courtesy of Vorpal Gallery, San Francisco and New York City.

The ancient Egyptian, Hellenic, Chinese, and Indic civilizations did not destroy the Earth as we are capable of doing today, but they were nevertheless destroyed. These civilizations lasted 2000 to 3000 years (Table 17A.1). Adopting this number as a reasonable estimate for L gives $N = 20$ to 30 civilizations. What a low number! Twenty or thirty technological civilizations spread throughout the 6×10^{11} cubic parsecs of the Galaxy means that humans are essentially alone. We would likely be tens of thousands of parsecs away from the nearest technological civilization. Clearly, if the lifetime of a civilization is short, we are not likely to communicate with or be visited by another technological civilization.

$$N = 20\text{–}30 \text{ (?)}.$$

On the other hand, a technological civilization could last much longer. Some astronomers suggest that if a technological civilization survives such catastrophic events as the nuclear destruction of its world or excessive population growth, it could exist for times on the order of geological time scales. L could be a million years. In that case, we would expect several thousand technological civilizations to be in existence now, and our civilization would, on the average, be less than a few hundred parsecs away from one. With so many civilizations present in the Galaxy at once, the prospects of communicat-

$$N = 10,000 \text{ (?)}.$$

■ TABLE 17A.1
Approximate Longevities of Ancient Earth Civilizations

Egyptian	≈4000 B.C. to ≈30 B.C.
Hellenic	≈1000 B.C. to ≈A.D. 600
Chinese	≈1500 B.C. to ≈A.D. 1900
Indic	≈1500 B.C. to ≈A.D. 500

■ TABLE 17A.2 **An Estimate of** N		
Number		**Factor***
Number of Population I stars in the Galaxy:	400,000,000,000	$1/12.5$
Number of stars around which life could evolve:	30,000,000,000	1
Number of stars that support stable planetary orbits:	30,000,000,000	$1/10$
Number of stars with Earth-like planets:	3,000,000,000	$1/10$
Number of planets on which life develops:	300,000,000	$1/10$
Number of planets on which intelligent life emerges:	30,000,000	$1/10$
Number of planets on which a technological civilization emerges:	3,000,000	—
Number of technological civilizations in the Galaxy now:	20 to 30	$L = 10^3$ years**
	~10,000	$L = 10^6$ years

*Multiply by this factor to obtain next number in the estimate.
**L is the longevity of a civilization.

ing with other civilizations and, perhaps, being visited by one are greatly improved. How can we choose between $N = 20$–30 and $N = 10,000$ or between any other estimates? We cannot, of course. Individual astronomers have their own biases and, therefore, their own estimates of N; Table 17A.2 summarizes the estimates made in this AstroProbe. Some astronomers, however, ignore this kind of calculation in favor of a much narrower approach.

■ $N = 1$?

Two lines of thought allow some people to reach the conclusion that the human race is alone in the Galaxy. The first concerns the probability of life; the second deals with the fact that humans have not seen alien spacecraft in the solar system. Some biologists and astronomers claim that the probability of life developing on a planet is infinitesimally small. They base this conclusion on the assumption that the formation of the complex molecules necessary for life to develop is a random process. For instance, they assume that the formation of the amino acid glycine (NH_2CH_2COOH) is just the chance meeting of the 10 hydrogen, nitrogen, carbon, and oxygen atoms. Scientists, however, have no indication that the emergence of life is a random process. The distinction between random and nonrandom processes is very important to the $N = 1$ argument. The following example illustrates the difference. In an experiment involving 100 of each of two objects A and B, they can come to rest in one of two positions, position 1 or 2. If the position A or B takes is random, then the probability that all the A's will end up in position 1 and all the B's in position 2 is 2^{-2n}, or in a more familiar notation 10^{-60}, where $n = 100$. Indeed, this result is not likely. Consider, however, the following experiment (Figure 17A.3). Let objects A be corks and objects

B be lead balls, and the experiment is to throw them into a tub of water. All of the A's would float to the surface (position 1), and all of the B's would sink to the bottom (position 2). This result is explained using physics. Light objects float and heavy ones sink. Throwing corks and lead balls into a tub of water is not a random process.

Similarly, the formation of organic molecules is not a random process if conditions are right. For instance, complex organic molecules exist in giant molecular clouds. Yet, conditions in these clouds are far less ideal than in the primitive oceans of Earth. Any argument for $N = 1$ based on the emergence of life being a random event cannot be taken too seriously.

The second argument for $N = 1$ involves the idea that an advanced civilization could manufacture space probes that would reproduce themselves. That is, a probe, after traveling to a nearby planet, would land on the planet and use the planet's resources to clone itself. Both ships would then launch themselves and continue the exploration of the Galaxy, doubling their numbers with each planetfall. It is assumed further that if such a probe landed on the Earth, instead of Mars or an asteroid, it left a sign of its visit. The argument is that since such space probes could visit every solar system in the Galaxy in "just" millions of years and since none have been found yet, no other civilization exists in the Galaxy: $N = 1$.

It is possible to conceive of a technological civilization several hundred or thousands of years more advanced than ours that is able to construct space probes that are controlled by on-board computers. This would be necessary for any deep space exploration because such probes would travel many parsecs away from their home world and would have to be able to make decisions on a short time scale, such as how to avoid an asteroid in an alien solar system. Further, these space probes would probably have to make self-repairs. It is easy to imagine a space probe carrying replacement mechanical parts or electronic components with the ability to replace them in case of malfunction. Complete self-repair requires at least the capability to replace all the parts of the space probe. The probe must also be able to diagnose problems and determine the correct repair. This may not seem impossible for an advanced civilization. But the $N = 1$ proponents state that a space probe that is capable of a high degree of self-repair can be made to reproduce itself.

Consider a self-replicating *Saturn V* rocket. It must be able to manufacture itself from the raw material it finds on its voyages. It must contain the equivalent of all the hundreds of factories needed to build its individual components as well as all the mining facilities needed to obtain the raw material required to manufacture these components. It must also be able to put all of this together into a

The probability that the balls will sink and the corks will float is 1.

■ **FIGURE 17A.3**
Cork–Lead Ball Experiment

working copy of itself. This is certainly an imaginative space probe. Can it be built? Will the space probe and its clones mechanically last the millions of years that will be required to explore the Galaxy? No one can say for sure. We can only guess that a civilization thousands of years more advanced than ours may be capable of building such a superprobe. Of course, if a disaster befalls the first probe, then all has failed.

If such a vehicle is possible, would a civilization actually build it? Some astronomers try to answer this question. How much would such a space probe cost? Would a civilization build it knowing that they would derive no benefit from it? Could a wealthy individual, intoxicated with the thought of his or her ship exploring the entire Galaxy, afford to build it? These lines of argument and questions are indeed interesting, but they are not a strong foundation for believing that $N = 1$.

WHERE ARE THEY?

If we dismiss arguments for $N = 1$ based on the assumed randomness of life or on the speculative building of superprobes and if we are convinced that thousands of technological civilizations exist today, then where are they? Why has contact not been made with at least one of these civilizations? Of course, some humans believe that aliens have visited the Earth; the aliens are the imagined pilots of UFOs and the kidnappers of humans. This is fanciful thinking—although many UFO sightings involve trained people, such as airline flight crews, scientists, and law enforcement officers, those cases that have been analyzed objectively and scientifically have been *explained* without invoking aliens. No solid evidence exists to support alien fly-bys and abductions.

The lack of evidence of alien visits to Earth may indicate that colonization of the Galaxy is very difficult. One major roadblock, of course, is the vast distances between stars. Although physically possible, space travel to the nearest stars would take decades (Figure 17A.4). Consequently, if someone traveled to another star system it would be to stay there, not to peer at its inhabitants. An exploring civilization may also find that the existing biologies on newly discovered planets are so different from their own that they could not metabolize the existing organisms. If they find sterile planets, they may be able to "terraform" them, but that would probably take tens of thousands of years (see AstroProbe 7). The time consuming aspects of space exploration on a galactic scale and the finite population resources of any civilization seem to indicate that the expansion rate of any spacefaring civilization would be very slow. In fact, estimates

■ FIGURE 17A.4

Starship Daedalus

A nuclear-propelled starship designed by the British Interplanetary Society to travel to Barnard's star 5.9 light-years away. This ship would attain a speed of 13% of the speed of light and take 50 years to reach Barnard's star.

SOURCE: Illustration by Gavin Roberts from *Man and the Planets: The Resources of the Solar System* by Duncan Lunan (Bath, Avon: Ashgrove Press Ltd., 1983). Copyright © Duncan Lunan 1983.

indicate that this expansion rate could be so slow that it is reasonable to assume that the existing civilizations in the Galaxy simply have not reached us yet.

Arguments for $N = 1$ based on random chemical reactions, speculative superprobes, or even religious traditions are clearly very weak arguments. On the other hand, estimates leading to values of N greater than 1 are very uncertain. Indeed, N could be very low by any estimate and humans would essentially be alone in the Galaxy. If N is large, it may be that space travel beyond the solar system is a difficult task. But the existence of a large number of technological civilizations in the Galaxy may result in communications with extraterrestrials some day.

CHAPTER 18

Galaxies

OUTLINE

Island Universes

Appearances of Galaxies
Content and Classification of
    Galaxies
Beyond the Hubble Classification

Distances to Galaxies

Quasars

Clusters of Galaxies
The Local Group
Larger Clusters of Galaxies
Superclusters

Summary

Chapter Capsule

Review Questions

For Further Reading

ASTROPROBE 18:
    Quasars: Far or Near?

Spiral Galaxy.
ARTIST: Pamela Lee.

EFORE THE EARLY 1920s, no one knew if a "realm of galaxies" existed. No one knew if other swarms of stars, like the Milky Way Galaxy, existed beyond the borders of our Galaxy. At first scientists believed that the Galaxy was the center of the universe as Greek philosophers believed that the Earth was the centerpiece of the universe. Discoveries in this century forced scientists to recognize that the Galaxy is not unique and is not at the center of the universe just as Copernicus forced sixteenth-century scientists to recognize that the Earth is not the center of the solar system. Today, in every direction from the Earth, astronomers see faint patches of light representing island universes of tens of billions of stars.

The distances between these islands are immense. The radiation we observe from the nearest galaxy was emitted long before humans became curious about the nature of the universe around them. The most distant known galaxies are so far away that the light we see today left the galaxies billions of years ago when they were much younger and the Earth did not yet exist. We are witnessing "ancient history" when we observe galaxies!

The appearance of galaxies reflects the environment in which they formed, the history of star formation and evolution over their lifetimes, and in some cases, collisions with other galaxies. Despite these diverse influences, the myriad galaxies can be divided, or classified, into only three or four distinct groups.

The Milky Way Galaxy is a member of a small cluster of galaxies that itself is part of a much larger group, numbering in the thousands of galaxies. Clusters of galaxies can include a few galaxies or many thousands of galaxies. At the centers of the largest clusters lie huge, giant galaxies that grow by consuming smaller galaxies. The largest clusters of galaxies tend to string themselves together in long filaments, creating the largest structures in the universe. Galaxies trace out the vast volume of the universe. Their distribution within its structure gives scientists important clues to events in the early universe, which are unobservable by us today.

▰ISLAND UNIVERSES

Although the invention of the telescope opened the door to the wonders of the night sky, early observers could not always identify the objects they were seeing. Some objects were distinct but fuzzy patches of light, and many were just barely visible, tantalizing yet unidentifiable. Charles Messier (1730–1817), a noted comet hunter, cataloged over 100 fuzzy celestial objects that could easily be confused with comets that had not yet developed tails. A century later, J. L. E. Dreyer (1852–1926) cataloged nearly 8000 objects in his New General Catalog, referred to as the "NGC." Most of the Messier objects, designated M1 to M110, and Dreyer's NGC objects were emission nebulae, planetary nebulae, and star clusters, which clearly were members of the Milky Way Galaxy. These catalogs also contained other objects, however, that, unknown to Messier, Dreyer, and their contemporaries, were *extragalactic* objects. These extragalactic objects, which appeared only as dim patches of

Galaxy: An organized system of hundreds of millions to thousands of billions of stars, sometimes mixed with interstellar gas and dust.

Nebula: Any diffuse cloudlike object nonstellar in appearance; since many objects looked fuzzy through early telescopes, the term referred to H II regions, supernovae remnants (Crab nebula), and galaxies (Andromeda nebula).

■ FIGURE 18.1

The Spiral Galaxy M51

(a) A drawing of M51 by William Parsons (1800–1867), an Irish astronomer who built a 1.8-m (72-inch) telescope that for many years was the largest in the world. *(b)* A modern photograph of M51 shows the similarity to Parsons's drawing.

SOURCES: Part (a) from page 76 of *A Handbook of Descriptive and Practical Astronomy* by George F. Chambers (Oxford: The Clarendon Press, 1890). Part (b), National Optical Astronomy Observatories.

light to early observers, are known today as **galaxies**. Since eighteenth- and nineteenth-century astronomers could not see individual stars in the nebulosities, their nature was the subject of much speculation.

In the eighteenth century, the German philosopher Immanuel Kant (1724–1804) developed the idea of "island universes." Simply stated, Kant believed the observed nebulosities were vast systems of stars, like the Milky Way Galaxy, but at immense distances from us. Kant, however, did not know the distances to the nebulosities and, therefore, could not prove his hypothesis. As more powerful telescopes with finer optics became available in the nineteenth century, astronomers could separate the fuzzy patches of light into star clusters and **nebulae.** The nebulae were soon divided into two groups. One group consisted of clouds of hot gas within the Milky Way Galaxy; they were H II regions and planetary nebulae. The second group consisted of small symmetrical objects, many of which exhibited spiral structures (Figure 18.1); they were called *spiral nebulae.* It was not until 1924, however, that astronomers were able to ascertain the true nature of the spiral nebulae.

How far away were the fuzzy patches of light called spiral nebulae? Were they members of the Milky Way Galaxy like the H II regions, or were they farther away, beyond the boundaries of the Galaxy? Distances would reveal their true nature, but here astronomers encountered a technological problem. They had collected much data on spiral

(a)

(b)

■■■■ FIGURE 18.2

The 2.5 meter (100-inch) Hooker Reflector of the Hale Observatories on Mt. Wilson in California

SOURCE: Hale Observatories.

nebulae, such as their relative sizes, distribution in space, and classification, but the data simply accumulated. They could not provide an understanding of the spiral nebulae until their distances were known. For this astronomers needed bigger instruments and improved techniques to penetrate the depths of intergalactic space. The building of the 100-inch Hooker reflector on Mt. Wilson in California filled this need (Figure 18.2). This telescope, which remained the largest in the world for nearly 30 years was used by Edwin Hubble (1889–1953) in the early 1920s to resolve a few of the nearest spiral nebulae into individual stars. These stars were so faint that Hubble reasoned that the spiral nebulae had to be very distant. But how distant?

The Cepheid variables discovered by Hubble in 1924 in the nearby Andromeda nebula provided the means for the necessary distance estimates. Once they were identified and their periods obtained, Cepheid absolute magnitudes followed from the Cepheid period-luminosity relation previously established by Hertzsprung and Shapley. With the measured apparent magnitudes, the distance moduli, $m - M$, for the Cepheids were easily obtained. For instance, a typical Cepheid in M31 has an apparent magnitude of $m = 18$ and a period of 30 days. Today's period-luminosity relation gives an absolute magnitude of $M \approx -6$ for this period so that $m - M \approx 18 - (-6) = 18 + 6 = 24$ magnitudes. Recall the table in Chapter 14 (shown here in Table 18.1) giving the relation between distance modulus and distance. A distance modulus of 24 magnitudes places M31 at a distance of nearly a million parsecs (about 2.2 million light-years) from the Sun, far beyond the boundaries of the Milky Way Galaxy.

Once absolute magnitudes were established for the Cepheids, other images were identified as bright O and B stars, H II regions, and star clusters. Soon the similarity between the Milky Way Galaxy and the

■■■■ TABLE 18.1
The Distance Modulus

$m - M$	Distance (pc)
−5	1
0	10
5	100
10	10^3
15	10^4
20	10^5
25	10^6
30	10^7

spiral nebulae was complete—Kant's island universes were galaxies, many of them like the Milky Way Galaxy.

Not all extragalactic nebulae have spiral features. Some are huge, spherical stellar swarms while others are chaotic jumbles of stars, dust, and gas. Once astronomers were able to see individual stars in the various types of galaxies, they proceeded to the first step to gaining a deeper understanding of galaxies—classifying them.

▰▰APPEARANCES OF GALAXIES

The first step in the scientific study of galaxies, of course, was to collect data. The data were photographs of individual galaxies as well as their distributions in space, apparent sizes, and spectra. Since no two of the thousands of galaxies looked exactly alike, astronomers needed to classify them into similar groups. The idea, as with all classifications, is that the properties of a few galaxies of a particular type will characterize other galaxies that resemble them. This eliminates the impossible task of studying every galaxy in the sky to understand the nature of galaxies. Edwin Hubble pioneered the classification of galaxies in the 1920s, and astronomers still use his basic classification scheme today.

Content and Classification of Galaxies

The majority of galaxies fall into one of two types: *spirals*, which are characterized by flat, prominent disks similar to that of the Milky Way Galaxy, and *ellipticals*, which are ellipsoidal-shaped swarms of stars. About 30% of all galaxies are spirals and 60% are ellipticals; most of the remaining 10% are irregularly shaped systems.

Spiral galaxies have a nuclear bulge, a flat disk, a halo of old stars, and spiral arms. A rarer type of spiral galaxy shows a bar-shaped concentration of stars centered on the nucleus. In the barred spirals the arms emerge from the ends of the bar instead of directly from the nuclear bulge. Although the disks of many spiral galaxies are prominent due to the brilliance of H II regions and young stars in the arms, an older population of stars and clusters is present throughout the disk. In edge-on photographs of spirals, the dust in the disk is readily visible as dark lanes against a bright nucleus (Figure 18.3). The nuclear bulges and halos of spiral galaxies represent a spheroidal stellar component and consist of Population II stars and globular clusters. Globular clusters can be seen surrounding nearby spirals like bees around a hive. Although distance prevents us from observing individual stars in the nuclear bulges, the bulges of spirals appear yellow in color photographs in contrast to the blue of the spiral arms. The yellow is caused by the many old stars in the bulge.

Hubble divided spiral galaxies into subclasses according to (1) the degree of winding of their arms, (2) the relative size of the nuclear bulge compared to the rest of the galaxy, and (3) the patchiness of the stars, clusters, and H II regions in the disk (Figure 18.4). He designated spirals

▰▰ FIGURE 18.3

NGC 253

This is a spiral galaxy seen nearly on edge. The dark filaments are dust in the disk of the galaxy silhouetted against the bright nuclear bulge and the bright blue stars in the disk.

SOURCE: Copyright © 1980 Anglo-Australian Telescope Board. Photograph by Freeman and Malin.

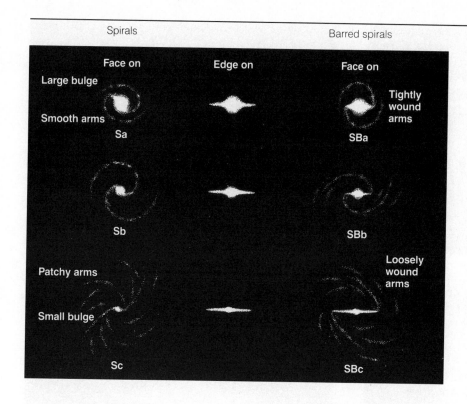

■■■■ FIGURE 18.4
Subclasses of Spiral Galaxies

(and barred spirals) as Sa, Sb, and Sc (SBa, SBb, and SBc), respectively. The sequence Sa → Sb → Sc, or SBa → SBb → SBc, follows a pattern:

■ Spiral arms change from tightly wound (closed) to loosely wound (open).

■ The size of the nuclear bulge decreases.

■ Spiral arms change from a smooth distribution of gas and stars along the arms to clumpy and loose spiral structures.

Figure 18.5 shows several examples of spiral galaxies. The Sa and SBa galaxies show tightly wound arms, large nuclear bulges, and smooth bright arms. Large nuclear bulges are evident in NGC 4594, seen edge on, and NGC 4622 in Figure 18.5. The disks of Sa and SBa galaxies show no prominent H II regions or young star clusters; it is as if star formation has stopped. On the other extreme, Sc and SBc galaxies show very open arms, small or nonexistent nuclear bulges, and highly resolved disks. The openness of the arms in an Sc galaxy is visible in NGC 5457 (M101) in Figure 18.5. Here H II regions, young O and B stars, and clusters are visible throughout the loose spiral structures in the disk. The Sb and SBb galaxies show intermediate characteristics. The Milky Way Galaxy and the nearby Andromeda nebula (M31) appear to be Sb spirals.

The three classification criteria for spiral galaxies reflect the concentration of stars, gas, and dust toward the centers of the galaxies. The

(a)

(b)

(c)

(d)

(e)

(f)

large nuclear bulges of Sa and SBa galaxies, for instance, indicate a strong concentration of spheroidal stars toward the center of the galaxy. The lack of nuclear bulges in Sc and SBc galaxies indicate a weak concentration toward the center.

Spiral galaxies tend to be large, bright, and massive (see Table 18.2). Astronomers use the orbital motion of stars and gas in the disks to obtain the masses of spiral galaxies, as is done for the Milky Way Galaxy. Recall that the Sun's speed around the Galaxy is related to the mass of the Galaxy in the same way that the Earth's orbital speed about the Sun is related to the Sun's mass. If the Sun were more massive, the Earth would need to move faster around the Sun to maintain its orbit and not spiral into the Sun; if the Sun were less massive, the Earth would have to move slower or else it could escape the solar system. The Sun's speed of 250 km/s (560,000 MPH) around the Galaxy is just right to maintain its orbit about a mass of 120 billion $\mathfrak{M}_\odot$. A more refined method of estimating masses of galaxies is to use the motions of the entire disk. These motions are reflected in the rotation curves of galaxies. The way the stars, gas, and dust are distributed in a galaxy determines the orbital velocities at each location in the galaxy. For instance, the very high velocities found far from the center of our Galaxy indicate the presence of substantial mass beyond the Sun's galactic orbit. Similar analyses of rotation curves of other spiral galaxies can be done to estimate how the mass in these galaxies is distributed and to determine their total masses.

Elliptical galaxies are spheroidal in shape; that is, they look like the three-dimensional figure generated by rotating an ellipse around its longest axis. Ellipticals show a much wider range in mass than spirals because many ellipticals are small, or *dwarf ellipticals* (Figure 18.6). In fact, dwarf ellipticals are probably the most common type of galaxy in the universe. Ellipticals lack prominent internal structure. The concentration of stars simply decreases away from the center, making it very difficult to identify the boundaries of an elliptical galaxy. Beyond these ambiguous stellar boundaries astronomers have detected halos of globular clusters surrounding large, nearby elliptical galaxies. The overwhelming majority of the stars in elliptical galaxies are old, Population II stars. These galaxies appear to have converted nearly all of their gas and dust into stars. Very little evidence of recent star formation is seen, and only a few ellipticals exhibit even small dark lanes of dust.

Elliptical galaxies are swarms of stars moving within a gravitational field that they themselves create. The stars do not collapse to a central

■ FIGURE 18.5 (preceding page)
Spiral Galaxies

(a) NGC 4622, an Sa galaxy. *(b)* NGC 3031 (M81), an Sb galaxy. *(c)* NGC 5457 (M101), an Sc galaxy. *(d)* NGC 4594, an Sa galaxy. *(e)* NGC 4565, an Sb galaxy. *(f)* NGC 1300, an SBb galaxy.

SOURCES: Parts (a), (b), (d), and (e), National Optical Astronomy Observatories. Part (c), Lick Observatory, University of California, Santa Cruz. Part (f), Hale Observatories.

■ TABLE 18.2 **Properties of Galaxies**

	Spirals	**Ellipticals**	**Irregulars**
Diameter (kpc)	5 to >100	1 to >200	2–10
Luminosity ($L_\odot$)	10^8–10^{11}	10^6–10^{11}	10^7–10^9
Mass ($\mathfrak{M}_\odot$)	10^9 to >10^{12}	10^6 to >10^{13}	10^8–10^{11}
Population	I and II	II	I and II

■■■ FIGURE 18.6

Two Dwarf Elliptical Galaxies

(a) Leo I. *(b)* Fornax. Both galaxies are extremely inconspicuous and contain very faint stars.

SOURCE: Part (a) copyright © Anglo-Australian Telescope Board 1987. Photograph by David Malin. Part (b) copyright © Anglo-Australian Telescope Board 1982.

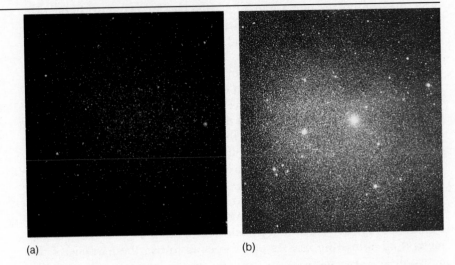

(a)   (b)

mass because they are moving more or less randomly with respect to each other. Most stellar orbits of stars in elliptical galaxies are probably very eccentric, similar to orbits of the spheroidal component of our Galaxy. Since elliptical galaxies rotate very slowly, the observed flattened shapes of ellipticals cannot be due to rotational flattening as with the disks in spiral galaxies. The observed flattening of elliptical galaxies is due to the random velocities of individual stars not being equal in all three directions. That is, if we let v_x, v_y, and v_z represent the average velocities in the three possible directions (left or right, toward or away from you, and up or down), then in a flattened elliptical galaxy, one of these average velocities is greater than the other two. If all three were equal, the galaxy would look like a sphere. How the random motions came to be unequal is not yet known. Although elliptical galaxies appear to be the simplest kind of galaxies structurally, astronomers do not completely understand the internal motions or shapes of most of these spheroidal systems.

Since ellipticals do not have rotating disks, astronomers had to develop a new method for estimating their masses. The orbits of stars can be in any direction in the three-dimensional space within the galaxy; consequently, at any moment some stars in the galaxy will be moving toward us and others away from us, and all will be moving at different speeds. When astronomers record the spectrum of an elliptical galaxy, each star adds its own Doppler shift to the observed spectral lines. The resulting *spread* in the lines is called the *velocity dispersion*. Since orbital velocities of stars will be greater for a greater galaxy mass, as with stars in circular orbits in a spiral galaxy, the velocity dispersion is a measure of the mass of the galaxy. The greater the velocity dispersion, the greater the mass of the galaxy. As in spiral galaxies the distribution of the mass in an elliptical galaxy determines orbital velocities. Consequently, observed velocity dispersion can be compared with mathematical models of mass distributions of elliptical galaxies to determine their total masses.

Hubble labeled elliptical galaxies with the letter E followed by a number representing their degree of flattening (Figure 18.7); the formula for calculating the degree of flatness is

$$10 \times \frac{\text{longest diameter} - \text{shortest diameter}}{\text{longest diameter}}$$

Ellipticals that are spherical (no flattening) are classified as E0; the most flattened elliptical galaxies are classified as E7 (Figure 18.8). For comparison, a basketball's shape would be classified E0 while that of a football would be E4.

Hubble discovered other galaxies that were flatter than E7 and had disks but showed no spiral arms, young stars, or H II regions. He classified these "transitional" galaxies as S0 and SB0 and called them **lenticular galaxies** (Figure 18.9). Lenticular galaxies have characteristics of both ellipticals and spirals. They have a spherical, dominating bulge with the same structure as an elliptical galaxy; star formation appears to have stopped in the bulge. Apparently, only a small amount of dust and gas were left to form a disk after the collapse of the galaxy, and it was used up very quickly to form an old disk population.

About 10% of the known galaxies do not show the obvious disklike structure of spirals or the spheroidal symmetry of ellipticals. They have a chaotic, irregular appearance. Hubble simply classified them as **irregulars,** abbreviated Irr (Figure 18.10). Irregulars show much evidence of active star formation in the form of patches of young stars, star clusters, and H II regions. Most of the light from irregulars comes from their young stars and luminous gas clouds, all signs of the youthfulness of the stellar population in these galaxies. At the same time, irregulars have an old population of stars made up of globular clusters, old red stars, planetary nebulae, and RR Lyrae variables. Some irregulars have barlike structures but no obvious emerging spiral arms, and most do not have identifiable nuclei. Irregular galaxies look like Sc galaxies in which spiral arms never developed. A few irregulars have a chaotic, yet amorphous appearance, which gives the impression of great, explosive activity at their centers.

Why do we see only three or four types of galaxies? Can any understanding of galaxies be gleaned from their classification? Astronomers

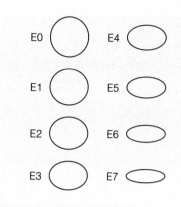

■ **FIGURE 18.7**

Classification of Elliptical Galaxies

■ **FIGURE 18.8**

Elliptical Galaxies

(a) NGC 4486 (M87), an E0 galaxy.
(b) NGC 221 (M32), an E2 galaxy.
(c) NGC 3115, an E6 galaxy.

SOURCE: National Optical Astronomy Observatories.

(a)

(b)

(c)

(a)

(b)

(c)

■■■ FIGURE 18.9

Lenticular Galaxies

(a) NGC 2685 is an S0 galaxy surrounded by a "cone" of dust. Extinction by the dust is apparent in the cone. *(b)* NGC 5586 is an S0 galaxy with a dust lane slightly inclined to its long axis. *(c)* NGC 4762 is an S0 galaxy seen edge on and is the flattest form of any known galaxy.

SOURCES: Part (a), Hale Observatories. Part (b), Lick Observatory, University of California, Santa Cruz. Part (c), National Optical Astronomy Observatories.

know, for instance, that the spectral classification of main-sequence stars is really a temperature indicator and that temperatures are controlled by mass. Do we have a similar situation for galaxy classification? It should be clear from these brief descriptions of spiral, elliptical, and irregular galaxies that all galaxies have an old, Population II component of globular clusters. Elliptical galaxies are pure Population II. Although spiral galaxies have a young disk Population I stellar component, they also have an old Population II component of old stars and globular clusters. Because each type contains old globular clusters, all galaxies are thought to be the same age. Based on age estimates of globular clusters in the Milky Way Galaxy, all galaxies are about 15 billion years old. Therefore, astronomers must treat the classification of galaxies as they would the spectral classification of main-sequence stars of a star cluster in which all of the stars were formed at the same time. They must ask, what "hidden" parameters determine a particular galaxy type?

Since we have not yet found any young galaxies that can be studied in detail, we must look for clues to the past from the present state of old galaxies. The conventional view of the formation of the Milky Way Galaxy is that it formed from the collapse of a slowly rotating cloud of gas and dust (Figure 18.11). During the collapse, rotation became more and more important until it prevented gas and dust from settling at the center. The gas and dust that did not condense into stars during the collapse spread out into a flat, rotating disk. Two competing processes can be recognized in this scenario: rotation and star formation. In this view, the competition between these processes decides the type of galaxy that will form.

In all collapsing galaxies, less gas and dust will be concentrated toward the center if rotation is rapid. We would expect, therefore, that the collapse of a rapidly rotating cloud would generate a substantial disk. In this case the galaxy reaches a *rotation limit;* that is, it reaches a point during the collapse in which rotation balances gravity, allowing dust and gas to circle in a disk instead of falling toward the center. Keep in mind that the collapse and the generation of a disk occur at the same time as the formation of stars. If stars form rapidly, using all of the dust and gas, then none will be left to form a disk. In this case, the galaxy reaches a *formation limit;* that is, all the dust and gas form stars

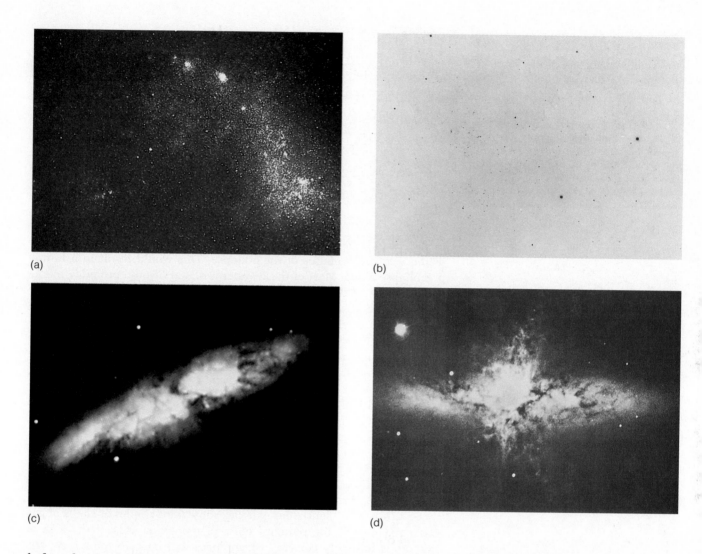

(a)

(b)

(c)

(d)

before the rotation limit is reached. Therefore, the final structure of the galaxy depends on which limit is reached first: rotation or formation.

Let's apply these ideas to real galaxies. Spirals and irregulars are galaxies that reached the rotation limit before the formation limit; they had enough remaining material in the disk to form stars. The sequences Sa → Sb → Sc and SBa → SBb → SBc reflect an increase in the dominance of rotation over star formation. The Sc and SBc galaxies formed their disks before much concentration toward their centers developed and, therefore, formed small nuclear bulges. This is even more true for irregular galaxies, which never developed nuclear bulges. Significant star formation and concentration toward the center occurred in Sa and SBa galaxies before the disk formed. Elliptical galaxies appear to have reached the formation limit long before the rotation limit. All of their dust and gas formed stars before a disk developed.

In the conventional view just described astronomers do not rule out the possibility that at least part of the dust and gas could have frag-

■ FIGURE 18.10

Irregular Galaxies

The Small Magellanic Cloud, a satellite galaxy to the Milky Way Galaxy. *(b)* A negative photograph of the faint nearby galaxy IC 1613. *(c)* NGC 3034 (M82) in visible light. *(d)* M82 in H_α shows long filaments extending outward on each side of the center of the galaxy.

SOURCES: Parts (a) and (c), National Optical Astronomy Observatories. Part (b), Paul Hodge, University of Washington. Part (d), Hale Observatories.

■■■■ FIGURE 18.11

Conventional Picture of the Formation of the Milky Way Galaxy

All during the collapse of the galaxy, stars and star clusters formed. Stars and star clusters that formed very early in the collapse filled a spherical volume with nearly the same dimensions as the original cloud. Those formed later were more concentrated toward the center of the cloud. The gas and dust that settled into the disk were used to form more stars.

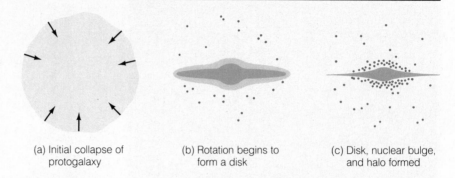

(a) Initial collapse of protogalaxy

(b) Rotation begins to form a disk

(c) Disk, nuclear bulge, and halo formed

mented into larger concentrations prior to the collapse of the galaxy or in the very early phases of the collapse. This would result in a lumpy precollapse cloud. Most of these systems of stars would probably merge with the rest of the stars, gas, and dust during the collapse, but some could survive as satellite galaxies. The Milky Way Galaxy, for instance, has two such satellite galaxies.

One of the most recent developments in the understanding of galaxy types is the mounting evidence suggesting that elliptical galaxies may not be the product of a collapse of a large cloud of gas and dust. Instead, elliptical galaxies may be the result of the merger of spiral galaxies. The natural results of such a collision would be a spherical nucleus and a burst of star formation that could consume much of the colliding gas. The collision need not be a direct head-on collision, but one in which the orbits of two galaxies bring them close to each other. Another signature of a collision, which is revealed in both numerical calculations and observations, is the presence of long "tails" like those shown in Figure 18.12. Furthermore, about half of all elliptical galaxies and about a third of all lenticular galaxies show faint ripples or shells of gas that appear to be the remnant disks of merged spirals. If the idea of mergers is basically correct, astronomers will have to reinterpret the Hubble sequence of galaxies. Mergers imply that the position of a galaxy along the sequence, E → S0 → Sa (SBa) → Sb (SBb) → Sc (SBc) → Irr, may simply depend on how many mergers it has experienced over its lifetime. Ellipticals would have had many collisions while irregulars would not have had any.

Although astronomers can readily classify nearly all galaxies as spiral, elliptical, and irregular based on their visual appearance, galaxies show many surprises and much individuality when observed at other wavelengths.

Beyond the Hubble Classification

Much has happened in extragalactic research in the decades since Hubble's work. In particular, radio astronomers have discovered that a small percentage of galaxies are strong sources of radio radiation. The radio radiation is nonthermal *synchrotron radiation*, described in the last chapter. Recall that synchrotron radiation is caused by fast moving

Colliding Galaxies

NGC 4038 and NGC 4039 are shown here during a collision that can last for a million years. Note the long tails of matter caused by the gravitational interactions between the two galaxies. Current simulations of galaxy collisions predict that the two nuclei will merge into a single nucleus.

SOURCE: Hale Observatories.

electrons passing through a strong magnetic field. The electrons emit long wavelength photons as they are forced to move in spirals by the magnetic field. Because the radio sources are so far away, astronomers realize that they must be very powerful emitters. The observed radio emissions have a characteristic pattern: **jets** of high-velocity material shoot out in opposite directions from the nucleus of the galaxy and end in large blobs, or *lobes*, far from the galaxy (Panel a in Figure 18.13). Sometimes the jets are bright enough and the galaxy is close enough that we see, at radio wavelengths, the jets emerging right from the center of the galaxy. Neither the jets nor lobes, however, are visible at optical wavelengths. Radio-emitting galaxies are called *radio* or *active galaxies*, but they include normal spirals, ellipticals, and irregulars as well as a few exotic systems (Panel b in Figure 18.13). High-resolution observations show that small, but powerful, sources of radio emission are located at the centers of active galaxies.

Several characteristics of active galaxies mentioned above are already familiar from our studies of stars and the Milky Way Galaxy and provide important clues to the nature of the source of radiation. The location and size of the radio sources in radio galaxies are similar to the source at the center of the Galaxy. The bipolar flow resembles the molecular outflows and jets of protostars, which are attributed to a disk of material expected to circle a newly forming star. As the discussion of black holes in Chapter 16 explained, the material in an accretion disk surrounding a black hole generates a tremendous amount of radiation as dust and gas spiral into the black hole. Finally, the source at the center of our Galaxy has an apparent mass of millions of solar masses. Thus the emitters of radio radiation at the centers of active galaxies

Jets: Narrow, collimated streams of ionized gas from the center of a galaxy. Lobes are formed when the jets collide with intergalactic gas.

(a)

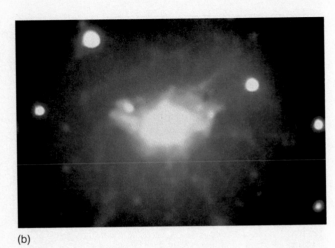

(b)

■ FIGURE 18.13

Radio Galaxies

(a) The radio image (red) taken at 20 cm with the Very Large Array radio telescope is superpositioned onto the optical image of the galaxy NGC 1316 (blue-white). The radio emission shows two large lobes on opposite sides of the galaxy. *(b)* NGC 1275 is a very strong radio and X-ray source and shows an extensive system of long filaments moving outward at speeds of 2500 km/s (90,000 MPH).

SOURCES: Part (a), NRAO/AUI. Part (b), National Optical Astronomy Observatories.

have the characteristics of a supermassive black hole surrounded by an accretion disk.

How does matter interact with a supermassive black hole to generate bipolar jets? While the consensus among astronomers is that a supermassive black hole is responsible for the jets, the exact mechanism is incompletely understood. Current models attempt to explain the jets as matter escaping along magnetic field lines that are rotating with the black hole. As the black hole rotates, the magnetic field lines twist together in a spinning spiral pattern, and particles are flung outward away from the black hole. Figure 18.14 shows the envisioned pattern from two different orientations and the orientation of the jets relative to the accretion disk. The observed jets are streams of particles exploding from the nucleus of the galaxy.

The observed patterns of radio emission result from the interaction of the jets with the interstellar gas and dust within the galaxy and intergalactic gas outside the galaxy. In spiral galaxies, for instance, the jets can pick up dust and gas, which can form new stars along the jet. The new stars and associated supernovae and stellar black holes can generate small lobes of intense radio emission along the jets. Once out of the galaxy, the jets eventually collide with intergalactic gas. The collisions slow the jets, forming large concentrations of radio emission far from the galaxy. Often the jets and lobes are swept back, as in Figure 18.15, by intergalactic gas passing rapidly by the galaxy.

Although much evidence points to huge black holes as the central sources of galaxies, what is the source of the accretion disk? It is important to realize that the electrons producing synchrotron radiation slow down as they radiate; this implies that a continuous source of energy is needed to maintain the synchrotron radiation. The amount of material converted into energy that is required to generate the strength of the radiation observed is at least a few solar masses per year. But stars near the center of a galaxy are rotating around the central black hole rather than colliding into it. Although it is possible that the atmospheres of these stars are slowly stripped away to provide the fuel, radio galaxies would seem to need an outside source of "food" for the super-

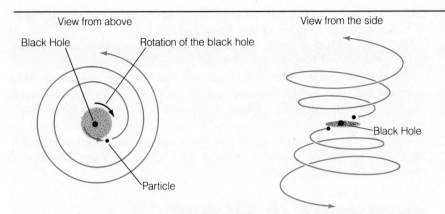

View from above

Black Hole   Rotation of the black hole

Particle

View from the side

Black Hole

A particle tries to rotate with the black hole, but the magnetic field lines lag behind the direction of rotation. The subsequent spinning action whips the particle along the spiraling magnetic field lines and away from the black hole.

(a) Motion near a supermassive black hole

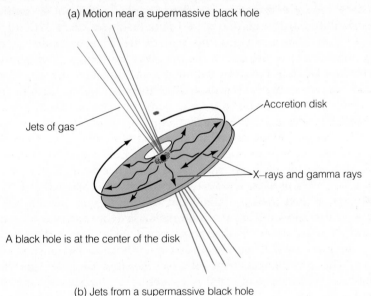

Jets of gas

Accretion disk

X–rays and gamma rays

A black hole is at the center of the disk

(b) Jets from a supermassive black hole

■■■ **FIGURE 18.14**

Jets from a Supermassive Black Hole

Matter in an accretion disk surrounding a supermassive black hole may be forced to shoot out in the direction of the rotational axis of the accretion disk by sliding along a rotating and twisting magnetic field. The accretion disk may appear more like a puffed up doughnut than a flat circular disk.

massive black holes huddled hungrily at their centers. Astronomers know, for instance, that some galaxies are "cannibals." That is, if a small galaxy travels too close to a larger one, the gravitational interaction between the two will result in the smaller galaxy being completely dissociated and merged with the larger. The nucleus of the smaller galaxy reaches the center of the larger galaxy, possibly providing the food for the central black hole. In fact, at the centers of large clusters of galaxies lie huge, fat cannibals called *cD galaxies*. Although cD galaxies resemble lenticular, or S0 galaxies, they are much more diffuse and more luminous. Hubble did not include them in his classification system because they are so rare. The cD galaxies often show more than one nucleus, perhaps the remains of recent meals. They are also strong radio sources, indicating that their "stomaches" have recently been fed.

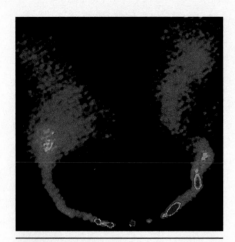

Galactic cannibalism will be examined in more detail later in this chapter when clusters of galaxies are described.

One special kind of active galaxy, discovered since Hubble's classification, has played a very controversial role in extragalactic astronomy. These are the *quasars*. They are closely related to active galaxies in that they are radio sources, but radio sources that can be much more powerful. A more detailed description of quasars will be given later in the chapter, and some of the controversy over quasars is described in AstroProbe 18. Before the significance of quasars can be understood, it is important to know how astronomers determined the distances to these remote systems of stars.

DISTANCES TO GALAXIES

Shapley used the period-luminosity relation of Cepheids to estimate the size of the Milky Way Galaxy, and Hubble used it to prove that spiral nebulae were extragalactic. Before Shapley and Hubble could use the period-luminosity relation to estimate distances, the relation had to be *calibrated*. That is, the absolute magnitudes of some Cepheids had to be measured. Unfortunately, no Cepheid in the Galaxy is close enough to the Sun to determine its distance from direct geometric techniques, such as trigonometric parallax. How then can we measure the absolute magnitudes of Cepheids? Astronomers start by measuring the distance between the Sun and the Earth.

The period-luminosity relation is part of an elaborate framework astronomers have constructed to span the vast voids between galaxies. The foundation of this framework is the astronomical unit, 149,597,871 km. Radar is used to measure, or calibrate, the astronomical unit. Geometry is then used to extend the volume of space within which distances are known, from the inner solar system to the outer boundaries of the Sun's domain. At that point astronomers must search for another technique that will serve as a distance indicator beyond the solar system. One technique is trigonometric parallax (Chapter 13), which can be used to distances of ≈100 pc (≈300 light-years), extending the range of known distances by a factor of about 400,000. Since Cepheids lie beyond this 100-pc limit, astronomers must search for yet another distance indicator. They discovered that cluster main sequences provide the bridge to the Cepheids.

Comparisons between color-magnitude diagrams of different star clusters are used to obtain distances to the clusters. One nearby star cluster, the Hyades cluster in the constellation Taurus, is close enough for astronomers to measure its distance by geometric means, such as trigonometric parallax. This allows them to calculate the absolute magnitudes of the main-sequence stars in the Hyades cluster. A color-magnitude diagram of a more distant cluster gives only the apparent magnitudes of its main-sequence stars. If the stars in both clusters have the same chemical composition, then their main-sequence stars are assumed to have the same absolute magnitudes. That is, a G0 star in the more distant Pleiades cluster, for instance, probably has the same absolute magnitude as a G0 star in the Hyades cluster because their chem-

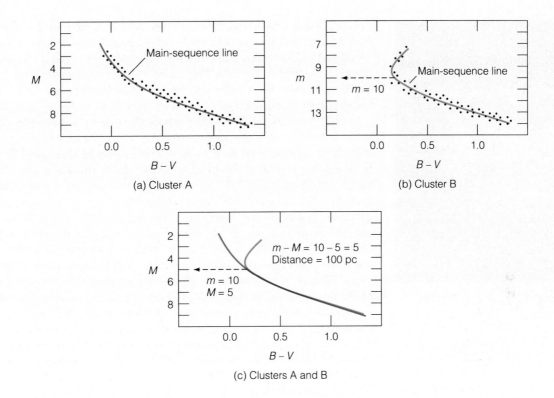

(a) Cluster A

(b) Cluster B

(c) Clusters A and B

ical compositions are similar. Consequently, if the main sequence of the Hyades cluster, which is calibrated in absolute magnitudes, is compared with that of the Pleiades cluster, which is measured in apparent magnitudes, then the distance modulus of the Pleiades and, therefore, its distance are easily determined (Figure 18.16). The absolute magnitude of a Cepheid follows if the Cepheid is a member of the cluster. This technique of comparing color-magnitude diagrams is called **main-sequence fitting.** Small corrections are required with this technique if the clusters being compared have different chemical compositions and if they are reddened by intervening interstellar dust.

The main-sequence fitting technique can be used to calibrate the period-luminosity relation by determining distances to star clusters in the Milky Way Galaxy that contain Cepheid variables. Once their absolute magnitudes are known, the period-luminosity relation is constructed with the observed pulsational periods of the same Cepheids. With a calibrated period-luminosity relation astronomers can extend the volume of known distances to beyond the Milky Way Galaxy. In fact, Cepheids are so bright that they can be detected in galaxies within about 4 million pc (Mpc), or about 13 million light-years.

Let's review this technique. We first use a distance indicator to extend the volume of space within which we can determine distances; main-sequence fitting is a distance indicator that works within the Milky Way Galaxy. Next we search for another distance indicator within this volume of space that can be used to extend the volume of measurable distances even farther; Cepheids in our Galaxy fill this bill. Once a new

■■■ **FIGURE 18.16**

Main-Sequence Fitting Technique

This technique involves superimposing the main sequences of two star clusters, one of which is at a known distance. The $B - V$ colors are matched, and the color-magnitude diagrams are moved up and down relative to each other until the main sequences overlap. *(a)* Cluster A with the known distance is plotted with the absolute magnitudes, M, of the individual stars. *(b)* Cluster B with an unknown distance is plotted with apparent magnitudes, m. *(c)* The main sequences are compared after shifting cluster B's main sequence until it lies on top of cluster A's main sequence.

(a)

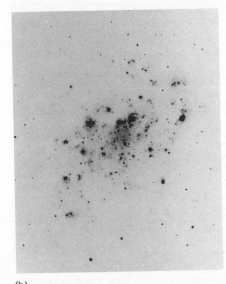

(b)

■ **FIGURE 18.17**

H II Regions in NGC 2403

(a) Visual photograph of NGC 2403, an Sc galaxy, showing its spiral structure.
(b) This photograph of NGC 2403 was taken with an H_α filter allowing us to see H II regions, the large nonstellar features that trace out the spiral arms.

SOURCES: Part (a), Hale Observatories. Part (b), Paul Hodge, University of Washington.

potential distance indicator is discovered, it is calibrated; the period-luminosity relation is calibrated with Cepheids whose distances are determined by main-sequence fitting. Now we can expand the volume of measurable distances to 4 Mpc. The cycle is *calibrate* a potential distance indicator; *extend* the volume of known distances; and *search* for another distance indicator.

Within a volume measured by the 4-Mpc radius, astronomers find two more potential distance indicators: the largest H II regions in a galaxy and the brightest stars in a galaxy. The largest H II regions all seem to be the same size and the brightest stars have the same absolute magnitudes (Figure 18.17). H II regions and the brightest stars can be detected to distances of ≈50 Mpc (160 million light-years). Beyond these distances galaxies are unresolved patches of light, but it is possible to use the total luminosity of individual galaxies as distance indicators. Galaxies with small images can be treated more or less like stars, and their apparent and absolute magnitudes can be measured. Astronomers can calibrate luminosities, or absolute magnitudes, with those galaxies of known distance within 50 Mpc. Furthermore, astronomers can assign luminosity classes to galaxies as is done for stars. For instance, the absolute magnitude, M_g, of a distant Sc galaxy follows from its luminosity class, and its apparent magnitude, m_g, can readily be measured. Since the light from an entire galaxy will diminish exactly the same as the light from an individual star, the galaxy's distance modulus, $m_g - M_g$, can be converted into a distance. Once calibrated, luminosities of galaxies extend the volume of space of measurable distances to ≈500 Mpc.

How far away is 500 Mpc? Can such a distance be comprehended? A better understanding of vast distances is possible by relating distances to travel times. Let's convert this distance to light-years, the distance light travels in one *year:* 500 million parsecs is equivalent to 1600 million light-years. The light from these distant galaxies, therefore, has taken 1.6 billion years to reach the Earth! We are looking at galaxies as they appeared 1.6 billion years ago. Astronomers refer to this time as the *look-back time,* because they are really looking back in time when viewing these distant galaxies. The look-back time is related to the age of the universe. That we see galaxies at distances of 500 Mpc implies that the universe is at least 1.6 billion years old. One way to determine the age of the universe is to determine the distances of the most distant galaxies. Although discussion of the age of the universe will be left for the next chapter, this section provides the foundation for that determination.

The step-by-step extension of the volume of space with known distances was Hubble's plan for determining the distances to the faintest galaxies visible. While Hubble and his collaborators were carrying out this program, other astronomers collected spectra of galaxies. It soon became apparent that nearly all galaxies showed a remarkable relationship between their distances and their measured radial velocities.

In 1912 at the Lowell Observatory in Arizona, Vesto M. Slipher (1875–1969) measured the first radial velocity of a galaxy. Spectra of galaxies were more difficult to obtain than spectra of stars because a galaxy is a diffuse source of light while a star is a concentrated point of light. As a result, exposure times for faint galaxy spectra were measured in hours. Sometimes exposures had to be continued from night to night to record the spectra of very distant galaxies. Slipher's spectra of the Andromeda galaxy, M31, showed stellar absorption lines from which he could measure Doppler shifts. The radial velocity of M31 measured about 300 km/s toward us. By 1929 astronomers had measured radial velocities for 45 galaxies and found that many measured over 1000 km/s, much larger than any stellar radial velocity. Furthermore, only a few galaxies, the nearest, were moving toward us—the majority of galaxies were moving away from us. At that time Hubble had reliable distances to about half of those galaxies and had found that radial velocities increased with distance from us (Figure 18.18). By 1935, about 150 galaxies had measured radial velocities, some as high as 40,000 km/s (90 million MPH)! Hubble's relationship between velocity and distance was confirmed and extended: distance is proportional to velocity. This is known today as **Hubble's law.**

Hubble's law appears to be the last span of the "bridge" across the voids of space (Figure 18.19). This law is normally written in equation form with D representing distance, V representing the measured radial velocity, and H_0 representing the constant of proportionality:

$$V = H_0 \times D$$

The constant of proportionality, H_0 is called the *Hubble constant* and must be calibrated from galaxies with known distances. Once H_0 is known, the measurement of the radial velocity of a faint galaxy gives its distance.

The conceptual and physical consequences of Hubble's law will be explored in the next chapter. Let's now consider objects that have the largest measured radial velocities in the nighttime sky.

QUASARS

During the 1960s astronomers discovered surprisingly bright radio sources from very faint starlike images. Astronomers were puzzled because until that time radio emission had always been from objects such

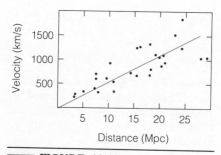

FIGURE 18.18

Hubbles's Relationship

The observations become more scattered as distance increases because velocities and distances for the most distant galaxies are the most uncertain. (Data from A. Sandage and G. A. Tammann, 1975, *Astrophysical Journal*, 196:313.)

MathTools 2: Proportions a/b

FIGURE 18.19

The Distance Indicators

The various techniques act as bridges expanding the volume of space with known distances. The objects to be calibrated include magnitudes of the brightest stars in galaxies, diameters of H II regions [D(H II)], and luminosities of galaxies ($L_{galaxies}$). The box below the bridges gives the maximum distances attainable with each technique.

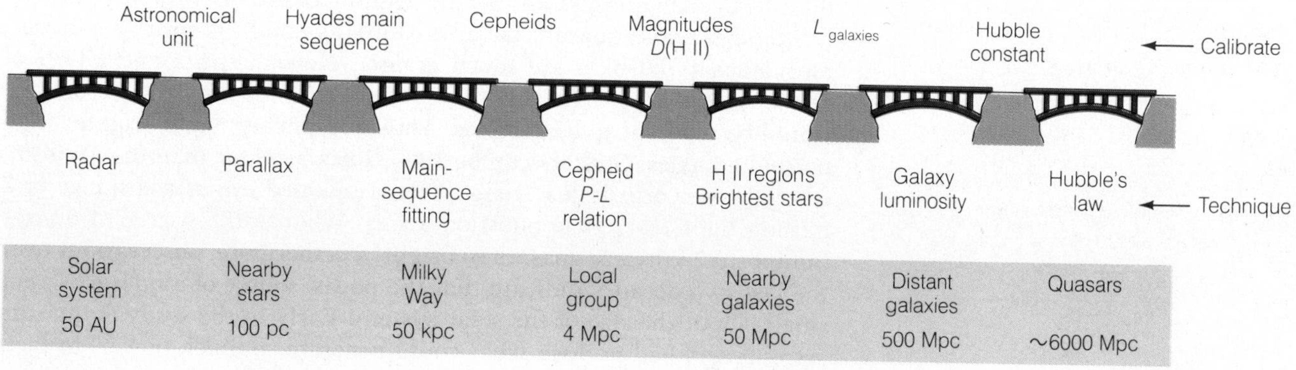

Astronomical unit	Hyades main sequence	Cepheids	Magnitudes D(H II)	$L_{galaxies}$	Hubble constant	← Calibrate
Radar	Parallax	Main-sequence fitting	Cepheid *P-L* relation	H II regions Brightest stars	Galaxy luminosity	Hubble's law ← Technique
Solar system	Nearby stars	Milky Way	Local group	Nearby galaxies	Distant galaxies	Quasars
50 AU	100 pc	50 kpc	4 Mpc	50 Mpc	500 Mpc	~6000 Mpc

648

as stellar jets, ionized hydrogen, supernovae remnants, and active galaxies—not stars. Furthermore, spectra of these faint radio sources did not show the standard absorption lines, but only emission lines *that could not be identified.* These sources became known as quasi-stellar radio sources, or QSO's, and later as **quasars.** Within a year of the discovery of quasars, the *pattern* of emission lines from the brightest quasars was identified as being due to excited hydrogen gas, but it was *redshifted* far from its normal location even for the fastest moving stars in the Galaxy. Some of the early redshifts implied speeds of 150,000 km/s, half the speed of light! Clearly, such objects could not belong to the Milky Way Galaxy. Astronomers concluded that quasars must be extragalactic.

Recall from the study of stars in Chapter 13 that a radial velocity away from the observer results in spectral lines that are shifted to the red end of the spectrum. Because all distant galaxies and quasars show radial velocities indicating motions away from us, astronomers call the velocities *redshifts.* Redshifts of galaxies and quasars are usually designated by the letter z:

$$\text{Redshift} = z = \frac{\Delta\lambda}{\lambda}$$

where $\Delta\lambda$ is the shift in wavelength of a spectral line as described in Chapter 13. At the relatively low velocities observed for stars and most galaxies, the redshift is related to the star's radial velocity, V, and the speed of light, c, by

$$z = \frac{V}{c}$$

For quasars, however, the observed redshifts are so high, $z > 4$, that relativistic effects must be included when calculating velocities. That is, it is impossible for radial velocities to be 4 times the speed of light! The relativistic form for redshift is shown in the equations in the margin. If quasars are assumed to be galaxies and if V represents the velocity of the quasar, then from Hubble's law, the redshift indicates the distance to the quasar. Since the value of H_0 is known only to within a factor of two (see Chapter 19), the distance to quasars with $z = 4$ is between 2.8 and 5.5 billion parsecs (9 to 18 billion light-years). The light from such quasars has been traveling for 9 to 18 billion years!

Although some quasars have redshifts as small as nearby galaxies, most quasar redshifts are much greater. Normal spiral and elliptical galaxies, seen at the distances of quasars as implied by their redshifts, would be too faint to be detected. Thus quasars are much brighter than normal galaxies. Quasars can be 1000 times brighter than the Andromeda galaxy, which is just visible to the unaided eye at a distance of 2 million light-years. The question arises, What is the source of quasar luminosity? Why are quasars so bright? Furthermore, observations over the last two decades indicate that the power source of a quasar is very small, about the size of the solar system! Early in the study of quasars astronomers had no idea what could generate so much power. In fact, astronomers doubted the large distances implied by the observed red-

Relativistic redshift relationship:

$$z = \sqrt{\frac{c+V}{c-V}} - 1 \quad \text{or}$$

$$\frac{V}{c} = \frac{(z+1)^2 - 1}{(z+1)^2 + 1}$$

shifts. The estimated high luminosities and small sizes of quasar power sources result *only* if it is assumed that the redshifts of quasars reflect their distances just as redshifts do for normal galaxies. Although some astronomers have suggested that the abnormally high redshifts may be due to something other than distance, they have been unable to find other phenomena that neatly explain quasar redshifts; consequently, it is difficult to show that quasars are not far away. Nevertheless, some observations appear to show that at least some quasar redshifts do not indicate distances as calculated with Hubble's law (see AstroProbe 18 for more details of this controversial topic). Observations in the 1980s, however, gave reassuring support for, but not total confirmation of, the mainstream view that quasar redshifts are true indications of their distances. Observations with sensitive CCD cameras (AstroProbe 14) showed what appear to be disks surrounding the bright nuclei of some quasars with low redshifts—the disks had the same redshifts as the recognized quasars. Furthermore, some low z quasars have companion galaxies with similar redshifts. Thus some quasars appear to be spiral galaxies with *extremely* active galactic nuclei.

Astronomers do not yet completely understand the source of quasar luminosity. Most theoretical models of quasars assume that the tremendous energies are generated by supermassive objects at their centers. The small size points to a black hole, but one with a mass of 100 million Suns. The observed radio emission is synchrotron radiation as in radio galaxies. Apparently, whatever mechanism operates in the cores of quasars ejects particles very energetically, probably in only two directions as in radio galaxies. In fact, the same mechanism could be operating in both quasars and radio galaxies but at much different scales. In short, an energetic black hole is the only source that astronomers can think of at present that can explain the tremendous energy generated by quasars.

A remarkable property of quasars was discovered in the late 1960s when astronomers had accumulated data on hundreds of quasars: many more quasars are found at great distances (high redshift) from us than near to us. Quasars with redshifts greater than 2 are a thousand times more numerous than those with smaller redshifts. Recall the relationship between distance and time; the light from these distant quasars tells us how quasars looked billions of years ago. That is, the distance information on quasars implies that quasars were more plentiful in the universe when the universe was much younger, when it was about 20–30% of its present age. Astronomers conclude, therefore, that in the earliest epochs of galaxy formation conditions favored the formation of energetic galactic nuclei.

Unfortunately, the nature of those conditions is unknown. Perhaps they are related to an initial burst of star formation during the collapse of a galaxy. At that time, the greatest concentration of dust and gas would be at the center of the collapsing galaxy where massive star formation could create supermassive black holes and provide plenty of fuel to generate X-ray and radio emission. The remains of that active period would then be the radio "quiet" supermassive objects we suspect reside in normal galaxies. Evidence of a supermassive object in the nucleus of the Milky Way Galaxy was described in the last chapter, and recent observations of the giant elliptical galaxy M87, for instance, support the presence of a supermassive object in its nucleus. Perhaps the order "quasars → active galaxies → normal galaxies" is a natural evolutionary sequence of activity in the nuclei of galaxies. Most galaxies today appear to have relatively inactive nuclei, perhaps due to scarcity of fuel to feed the supermassive object at their centers.

Quasars also represent a kind of galactic probe into the early history of the universe in that their large redshifts provide a view of the universe when it was very young. By 1990 observers found quasars with $z = 4.73$, implying that the light viewed from those quasars was from galaxies that had formed only a billion years after the big bang.

More evidence of conditions in the very early universe is found in the arrangement of galaxies in the sky. Astronomers look for patterns that may tell them about the distribution of matter *before* galaxies were born.

CLUSTERS OF GALAXIES

The ability to estimate distances to galaxies allows astronomers to study their three-dimensional distribution in the universe. Galaxies are not uniformly distributed in space; they tend to cluster. Probably most galaxies in the visible universe occur in clusters. Clusters of galaxies range from loosely structured aggregates of a few galaxies of mixed type to enormous, compact assemblages of thousands of mainly elliptical and lenticular galaxies. The Milky Way Galaxy itself is a member of a small group of at least 20 galaxies called the **Local Group.** The nearest clusters to the Local Group are 3 to 5 Mpc (10–16 Mly; Mly abbreviates a million light-years) away.

The Local Group

Two large spirals, the Andromeda nebula (M31) and the Milky Way Galaxy, dominate the Local Group. They have satellites of small irregular and elliptical galaxies. One other small spiral, the Triangulum nebula (M33), is also a member of the Local Group as is a scattering of dwarf galaxies. All Local Group galaxies are within a radius of about 1 Mpc (3 Mly) of each other. Table 18.3 lists the known members of the Local Group along with their sizes and distances from the Sun, and Figure 18.20 shows a map of the Local Group as seen from above. The giant elliptical or lenticular galaxy, Maffei I, was discovered in 1971, but since it is difficult to study because it must be viewed through obscuring dust in the Milky Way Galaxy, its membership is uncertain. Astronomers have used a variety of distance indicators to establish distances within the Local Group. In the spirals M31 and M33, the small dwarf irregular galaxies NGC 6822 and IC1613, and the Large and Small Magellanic Clouds, Cepheid variables are easily detected. The elliptical galaxies, all of which are dwarf ellipticals, have no Cepheids, but they do have color-magnitude diagrams similar to globular clusters in our Galaxy. This similarity allows astronomers to assume that the brightest

■ TABLE 18.3 **The Local Group Galaxies**

Galaxies near the Milky Way				Galaxies near Andromeda			
	Type	Distance (kpc)	Diameter (kpc)		Type	Distance (kpc)	Diameter (kpc)
Milky Way	Sb	—	30	Adromeda nebula	Sb	680	40
Large Magellanic Cloud	Irr	50	10	M32	E2	680	2.5
Small Magellanic Cloud	Irr	60	8	NGC 205	E5	680	5
Ursa Minor	E5	70	1	NGC 147	E5	600	3
Draco	E3	70	1.5	NGC 185	E3	600	2.5
Sculptor	E3	80	2	Andromeda I	E3	≈680	0.5
Carina	E4	150	1.5	Andromeda II	E2	≈680	1
Fornax	E3	200	5	Andromeda III	E5	≈680	1
Leo I	E3	220	1.5	M33	Sc	720	18
Leo II	E0	220	1.5				
Galaxies far from the Milky Way and the Andromeda Nebula							
NGC 6822	Irr	500	3	Maffei I	S0(?)	1000	30
NGC 1613	Irr	700	5				

stars in these ellipticals are nearly identical to those in galactic globular clusters. Some also have RR Lyrae variables, which is expected from their similarity to globular clusters.

The importance of the Local Group galaxies is that their proximity allows astronomers to study their contents in detail. The Andromeda nebula, for instance, contains all the features of the Milky Way Galaxy: a luminous bulge, H II regions and neutral hydrogen gas clouds, spiral arms speckled with bright blue stars and young clusters, molecular clouds, great dust bands, planetary nebulae, open clusters, and a halo of old globular clusters. Certainly, the study of M31 and M33 has helped

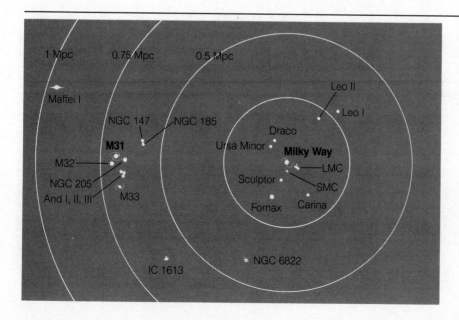

■ FIGURE 18.20

Map of the Local Group

This is a view looking down on the Local Group of galaxies. LMC and SMC stand for the Large and Small Magellanic Clouds.

astronomers better understand the Milky Way Galaxy and other spirals. Furthermore, many Local Group galaxies are the small, faint variety, impossible to detect in distant clusters of galaxies.

Viewed with the naked eye, the Andromeda nebula is only a fuzzy nebulosity, but it is the most distant object we can see without binoculars or a telescope (Panel a in Figure 18.21). The light from M31 travels for over 2 million years before reaching us. The study of M31 over the decades has revealed another distance indicator besides Cepheid variables. Hubble discovered over 60 novae in M31. Astronomers have since found that the light curves of these novae are similar in shape to those in our Galaxy and that the shape is related to the brightnesses of the novae; the brightest novae dim the fastest. Consequently, the shape of the light curve of a nova indicates its brightness at maximum light and, therefore, allows it to be used as a distance indicator within the Local Group. Hundreds of planetary nebulae and star clusters also have been identified in M31. H II regions, although plentiful, are all very indistinct. This appears to be typical for Sb and Sa galaxies and means that we cannot rely on H II regions as distance indicators for these galaxies.

Although the spiral arms in M31 are difficult to follow because the galaxy is tilted about 12° to our line of sight, the spiral arms in the Triangulum nebula are clearly visible because the galaxy is seen almost directly face on (Panel b in Figure 18.21). The Triangulum nebula is an excellent example of an Sc galaxy. Large diffuse H II regions are unmistakable in the arms of M33. In fact, H II regions are large and distinct enough for distance indicators in only Sc and Irr galaxies. Two spiral arms in M33 are readily visible emerging from the nucleus, but they disintegrate into a dozen spiral fragments. Open star clusters are plentiful whereas only a few globular clusters are seen. This must indicate a slightly different history of star formation for M33 compared to M31 or our Galaxy. It is probably related to the fact that Sc spirals did

■■■ **FIGURE** 18.21

Nearby Spirals

(a) The Andromeda Nebula, M31, is an Sb galaxy with two small elliptical companions, NGC 205 and NGC 221 (M32).
(b) The Triangulum Nebula, M33, is an Sc galaxy in the Local Group. See Figure 1.4 for a black-and-white photograph of M33.
SOURCE: Hale Observatories.

(a)

(b)

not use up their gas and dust efficiently to form stars early in their history and, consequently, have plenty for the formation of new stars and star clusters.

Two dwarf irregular galaxies, NGC 6822 and IC 1613 (Figure 18.10), lie within the Local Group but are very distant from both M31 and the Milky Way Galaxy (Figure 18.22). Both have prominent H II regions, many Cepheid variables, open clusters, and perhaps one or two globular clusters. Both are also metal poor relative to the Milky Way Galaxy. This is more or less expected since irregular galaxies, like Sc galaxies, do not appear to have used their gas and dust very efficiently for star formation. With less overall star formation, these irregular galaxies have gone through fewer generations of stars and, therefore, have not been enriched in heavy elements as have M31 and our Galaxy.

Two small irregular galaxies, the Large Magellanic Cloud and Small Magellanic Cloud, orbit the Milky Way Galaxy (Figure 18.23). They are visible to the unaided eye but only from the Southern Hemisphere where they are seen as ghostly clouds on a clear night. In fact, Portuguese sailors called them the "Cape Clouds." The historian Pigafetta described the clouds during Magellan's around-the-world trip between 1518 and 1520, and they have since been called the Magellanic Clouds. These are our closest galactic companions and are rich in celestial delights. Recall that astronomers discovered the period-luminosity relation from Cepheids in the Small Magellanic Cloud and that Supernova 1987A in the Large Magellanic Cloud was the closest observable supernova in centuries and the most thoroughly observed supernova in history. Both galaxies contain many visible star clusters, from very young open clusters to ancient globular clusters. These star clusters have proven to be very useful tools for the understanding of stellar evolution because they contain a much greater variety and number of stars in all stages of stellar evolution than clusters in the Milky Way Galaxy.

At the same time, the Magellanic Clouds have provided astronomers with types of clusters not seen before. Hodge 11, for instance, looks similar to a globular cluster in the halo of the Milky Way Galaxy (Panel b in Figure 18.23). Notice the blue and white stars in this cluster and recall that globular clusters in our Galaxy contain mainly bright red stars. The Large and Small Magellanic Clouds contain a class of massive, globular-like star clusters that are much younger than the 15 billion-year-old globulars in the Milky Way Galaxy but look physically similar. Clearly, the Magellanic Clouds have had a different history of star formation than the Milky Way Galaxy; somehow they were able to form massive star clusters relatively recently whereas our Galaxy could not.

The Andromeda nebula also has two satellite galaxies, NGC 205 and M32. Both are dwarf elliptical galaxies, and their closeness to the disk of M31 produces visible distortions in the spiral arms. Both dwarf galaxies have predominantly old Population II stars, but NGC 205 has visible dust lanes and a small, but prominent, population of young stars. Probably a few young stars are present in most elliptical galaxies and formed out of a small amount of dust and gas left over from the formation of Population II stars.

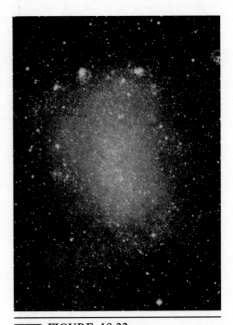

■ FIGURE 18.22

NGC 6822, a Nearby Dwarf Irregular Galaxy in the Local Group

SOURCE: Copyright Anglo-Australian Telescope Board 1981. Photograph by David Malin.

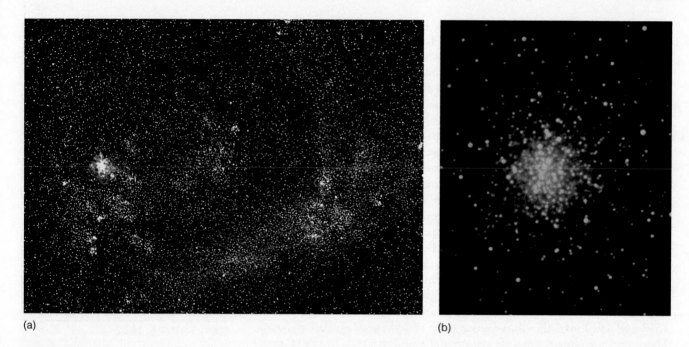

(a)   (b)

■■■■ ■ FIGURE 18.23

**The Large Magellanic Cloud (LMC)
and Hodge II**

(a) The LMC is an irregular galaxy in the
Local Group. *(b)* Hodge II is a globular
cluster in the LMC.

SOURCES: Part (a), National Optical Astronomy
Observatories. Part (b), copyright Anglo-Austra-
lian Telescope Board 1984. Photograph by
David Malin.

Both M31 and the Milky Way galaxies are surrounded by distant
dwarf irregular and elliptical galaxies. A few recently discovered dwarf
galaxies are possible members of the Local Group but their distances
have not yet been reliably established (Figure 18.24).

Larger Clusters of Galaxies

Large-scale groupings of galaxies give us clues to how matter was distributed in the early universe because not enough time has elapsed for
these galaxies to group together on their own. Early studies of galaxy
clusters recognized two distinct forms, *regular* and *irregular,* which can
contain a few galaxies or many. The Local Group is a small cluster, but
many other clusters are large, containing thousands of galaxies. Of
course, the more distant the cluster, the more difficult it is to identify
the small galaxies, such as the dwarf galaxies found within the Local
Group. Consequently, when astronomers try to compare the numbers of
galaxies in different clusters, they usually limit the counting to galaxies
not more than two or three magnitudes fainter than the brightest galaxy. Even so, the numbers reach the thousands in large clusters.

The Virgo cluster of galaxies is a large but irregularly shaped cluster
(Panel a in Figure 18.25). Irregular clusters generally contain mainly
spiral and irregular galaxies. The Virgo cluster is spread out so much
that only detailed counts of galaxies can locate its center. It is about 15
Mpc (50 Mly) from the Milky Way Galaxy and several times larger in
diameter than the Local Group. Some of its many large spiral members,
such as M100 and M61, were cataloged by Messier.

An example of a large but regular cluster is the Coma cluster of galaxies (Panel b in Figure 18.25). It is at a distance of about 100 Mpc (330
Mly) and is very compact. About 85% of the visible galaxies are ellipti-

cal and lenticular galaxies; the few spirals are found near the boundary of the cluster. The Coma cluster is also a radio emitter, probably from a few strong radio galaxies near the center. In such concentrated clusters of galaxies, collisions between galaxies are inevitable.

Past collisions between galaxies in compact clusters provide numerous examples of distorted pairs of galaxies (Figure 18.26). The distortions are due to the gravitational interaction between the stars, dust, and gas in the individual galaxies. The stars themselves, however, do not collide; the average distance between stars is so great that a direct collision between two stars is very unlikely. Close encounters between two galaxies, however, can pull off stars, gas, and dust from each galaxy, producing long tails streaming from each galaxy. In addition, the effect of a small galaxy plowing through a large one is to cause the stars of the large galaxy to bunch up behind the path of the small galaxy, forming a sort of "wake." At the same time, the gravitational force of the stars in the wake slows down the small galaxy, causing it to spiral toward the center of the larger galaxy. We call this slowing process *dynamical friction*.

In the centers of large, compact clusters of galaxies, frequent collisions between galaxies must occur because the density of galaxies is so high. At the center of the Coma cluster, for example, astronomers find two giant elliptical galaxies, NGC 4874 and NGC 4889, classified as cD galaxies (Panel b in Figure 18.25). If galaxies collide at relatively low velocities, one will slow and spiral into the center of the other because of dynamical friction. As it does so, the gravitational interaction will slowly strip the outer stars from the spiraling galaxy until nothing is left. The larger galaxy acts as a "cannibal," becoming larger and brighter as it swallows up the smaller galaxy. If the "eaten" galaxy had a compact nucleus, it may survive, lodged at the center of the cannibal galaxy. We do find, in fact, many examples of cD galaxies with multiple cores. After swallowing a number of victims, the cannibal galaxy swells

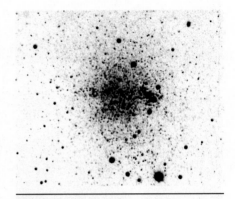

FIGURE 18.24

Phoenix—A Recently Discovered Galaxy in the Local Group
SOURCE: Phillip Flower.

FIGURE 18.25

Clusters of Galaxies

(a) This is only one section of the Virgo cluster; thousands of galaxies form this populous, irregular cluster. *(b)* The Coma Berenices cluster is a populous, regular cluster with a high concentration of elliptical and lenticular galaxies at its center. The two large elliptical galaxies near the center are often classified as cD galaxies. Except for the bright star, nearly all of the images in this photograph are distant galaxies.

SOURCE: National Optical Astronomy Observatories.

(a)

(b)

■ FIGURE 18.26

Interacting Galaxies

NGC 2992 and NGC 2993 show severe distortion due to their encounter.

SOURCE: Copyright Anglo-Australian Telescope Board 1979.

Supercluster: A cluster of clusters of galaxies; usually in long (hundreds of millions of parsecs) strings of galaxies and clusters of galaxies.

to great proportions, dominating the centers of rich, compact clusters of galaxies.

Collisions between galaxies also produce X-ray emission. Whereas the stars in two spiral galaxies would streak right past each other during a galactic collision, the gas and dust in the two galaxies would collide. As the stars in the spirals move on, a cloud of gas and dust is left at the site of the collision. The spirals now would resemble elliptical or S0 galaxies. Perhaps frequent collisions between galaxies in compact clusters are responsible for the lack of spirals seen in these clusters. The collisions between the gas and dust, moreover, produce high temperatures, 10^8 K, generating X-rays. X-ray emission is detected in about a third of all clusters observed.

The largest clusters of galaxies are classified according to how galaxies are distributed within the cluster (Figure 18.27). The most concentrated clusters are dominated by either a single giant galaxy, such as a cD galaxy, or by a pair of large galaxies. These *cD* and *binary clusters* contain mainly elliptical and lenticular galaxies. A less concentrated group of clusters is usually dominated by several bright galaxies, of any type, at the center. The central galaxies are surrounded by many fainter galaxies that form an extended halo. Some of these clusters are very linear in shape with the dominant galaxies spread along a line instead of at a center. We call these clusters *core-halo* and *linear clusters*. The most irregularly shaped clusters do not show a strong concentration toward a center. Some of these clusters appear flattened or elongated on the sky. These *irregular* and *flattened clusters* contain all types of galaxies.

This classification scheme illustrates the dynamical nature of galaxy clusters. The cD and binary clusters were initially the most concentrated of the cluster types. That is, they represented the densest clumps of matter in the universe at the time of galaxy formation (see Chapter 19 for when galaxy formation took place). Their high concentration meant that many collisions occurred as individual galaxies orbited about the cluster centers. These collisions produced the giant elliptical galaxies that now dominate the clusters. These clusters probably started out as irregularly shaped clusters but *dynamically evolved* through many collisions to their present concentrated state. The least dense clumps of matter in the early universe have dynamically evolved into the irregular and flattened clusters. The galaxies in these clusters formed at greater distances from each other and, therefore, have not yet suffered enough collisions to form giant galaxies at their centers.

Although clusters of galaxies can contain hundreds to thousands of galaxies, they are not the largest structures in the universe. The Virgo cluster of galaxies, for instance, is massive enough and close enough to the Local Group to pull us toward it. But the motion is not directly toward the Virgo cluster. The Virgo cluster lies about 50° away from the direction of our motion (Figure 18.28). Furthermore, the Virgo cluster also appears to be moving in a similar direction. A vast concentration of galaxies is pulling the Local Group and the giant Virgo cluster toward it. This concentration of mass is in the form of galaxies, but it is much larger than a "mere" cluster of galaxies.

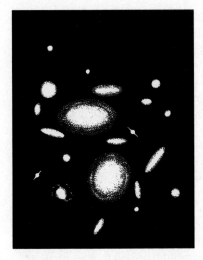
(a) Binary — mainly E, S0, and cD galaxies

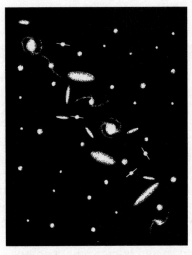
(b) Linear — all types except cD galaxies

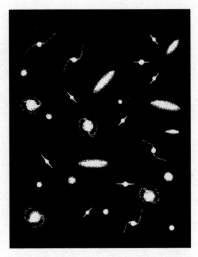
(c) Irregular — all types except cD galaxies

Superclusters

The Local Group appears to be a member of a group of clusters of galaxies called the local **supercluster.** The local supercluster is made up of at least 11 large clusters of galaxies, including the Virgo cluster. These clusters form a relatively flat structure with its center about 20 Mpc away in the direction of the Virgo cluster. Some 50 other smaller clusters and thousands of individual galaxies form a halo with a diameter of about 30 Mpc around this group.

■■■■ FIGURE 18.27

Classification of Galaxy Clusters

The progression from concentrated (binary) clusters to loose, or irregularly shaped, clusters reflects differences in their dynamical histories. The most compact clusters have had more collisions between member galaxies, leading to the giant cD galaxies that dominate their centers.

■■■■ FIGURE 18.28

Motion of the Local Group and the Virgo Cluster

A great mass, called the Great Attractor, is dragging the Local Group and the Virgo cluster toward it. The Local Group's motion is partly toward the Virgo cluster and partly toward the "great mass."

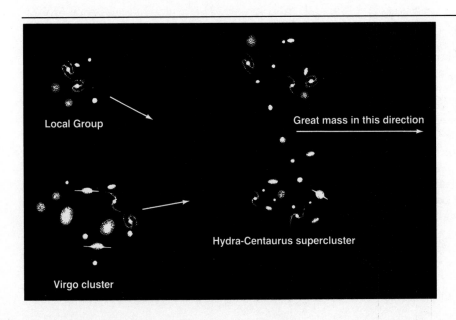

Local Group

Great mass in this direction

Hydra-Centaurus supercluster

Virgo cluster

FIGURE 18.29

Superclusters

A small section of the sky showing the filamentary structure of superclusters.

SOURCE: M. Seldner, B. Siebers, E. J. Groth, and P. J. E. Peebles, 1977, *Astronomical Journal*, 82:249.

Superclusters are the largest structures found in nature. They are generally long filaments composed of clusters of galaxies. Superclusters appear to be linked with other superclusters by thin chains of galaxies. Although over a dozen superclusters have been studied in detail, preliminary studies of the distribution of galaxies indicate that hundreds probably exist (Figure 18.29). The largest supercluster known today is called the "Great Wall." It is over 350 Mpc long, 120 Mpc wide, and 10 Mpc thick; about 100 Mpc away; and contains thousands of galaxies. Between the long filaments of clusters of galaxies are immense *voids*. Even in the local supercluster, galaxies only represent about 5% of its volume. The pattern of galaxies in the universe can be likened to Swiss cheese. Most of the matter in the universe corresponds to the cheese while the voids correspond to the holes.

How did such large, filamentary structures come into existence? Which came first, the galaxies or the filaments? That is, did galaxies form and later group themselves into filaments, or did matter form into filaments first and later condense into galaxies? Given the size of these structures and an age of the universe of 10–20 billion years, some astronomers conclude that the galaxies have not had enough time since their formation to form into filaments. Consequently, superclusters may represent remnants of structures of matter that formed very early in the history of the universe. The origin of these primeval structures is left to the next chapter because it requires a study of the creation of the universe.

The study of the Galaxy and the classification of galaxies allow astronomers to understand the events after primordial clouds of gas and dust began to collapse. The large scale filamentary structure of the universe can only be understood by studying the beginnings of the universe.

SUMMARY

The visible galaxies can be grouped into three broad classes: spirals, ellipticals, and irregulars. Spirals are similar to the Milky Way Galaxy and feature flat disks, prominent spiral arms, and a central nuclear bulge. Ellipticals are spheroidal-shaped without any striking features; they contain almost no gas or dust.

Since all galaxies that astronomers have extensively studied appear to have old Population II components, they are all probably the same age. Conditions and events in the galactic cloud during its collapse may determine the type of galaxy formed. A collapse in which star formation is so rapid that all of the gas and dust is used to form stars before a disk develops results in an elliptical galaxy. On the other hand, when rotation dominates and a disk develops before star formation can deplete the interstellar gas

and dust, spirals and irregulars result. Star formation during the collapse was more important for Sa and Sb galaxies than for Sc and Irr galaxies.

Large telescopes allow present-day astronomers to look inside galaxies to itemize their contents. They see open and globular clusters, H II regions and giant molecular clouds, Cepheid and RR Lyrae variables, planetary nebulae and novae, and Type I and II supernovae. Not every galaxy, however, has everything on this list. Elliptical galaxies are predominantly composed of Population II objects such as globular clusters, RR Lyrae variables, planetary nebulae, and Type I supernovae. Not surprisingly, elliptical galaxies have very little gas and even less dust; nearly all has been converted into stars. Spirals and irregulars, on the other hand, have everything on the list; Population I and II objects as well as gas and dust. Irregulars have the greatest fraction of gas and dust;

Sa galaxies, the least. The gas and dust are spread over the entire galaxy in irregulars and Sc galaxies, but are concentrated mainly in the disks of Sa and Sb galaxies.

Distances to galaxies are required before astronomers can determine their intrinsic properties, such as luminosity and size, and the characteristics of their member stars and gas clouds. Several distance indicators, each with a limited range, are employed to extend our ability to determine the distances of the most remote galaxies visible in our telescopes. Each distance indicator that is used to expand the volume of space with known distances must be calibrated. Once the indicator is calibrated and the volume of space with known distances is expanded, astronomers search for new distance indicators to extend this volume even farther. The pattern "calibrate-extend-search" is repeated for each new distance indicator. For the most distant galaxies a very simple relationship between the radial velocity, or redshift, of the galaxy and its distance is valid: $V = H_0 \times D$; this is known as Hubble's law.

Some galaxies are strong emitters of radio radiation. The Galaxy even has a radio source at its center, albeit a weak one. The Milky Way Galaxy and radio galaxies have the characteristics associated with supermassive black holes located at their centers. High rotation and strong magnetic fields in a surrounding accretion disk appear able to generate strongly focused winds that blast out of the galaxy. The most powerful radio sources are the quasars, which are among the most distant objects known in the universe. Quasars were also more abundant in the early universe than now, suggesting that galactic nuclei may evolve from powerful quasar sources to the radio quiet sources in galaxies such as the Milky Way Galaxy. Some controversy exists over the relationship between redshift and distance for quasars as discussed in AstroProbe 18.

Galaxies tend to group into clusters, from small clusters of only a few galaxies to giant clusters of thousands of galaxies. The form of a cluster of galaxies reflects the history of collisions between individual galaxies in the cluster. Giant elliptical and cD galaxies are found at the centers of the most concentrated clusters and are probably the result of galactic cannibalism caused by many collisions. The most irregularly shaped clusters show little concentration and are composed of galaxies of all types. The Local Group is an irregular cluster with about 20 members.

Clusters of galaxies group into long strings called superclusters. These are the largest known structures in the universe; some are hundreds of millions of parsecs across. The Local Group lies near the outer edge of the local supercluster, a group of at least 11 giant clusters of galaxies and many thousands of other galaxies in small clusters. The filaments of superclusters are strung across the universe like a million tangled fishing nets. Between the strings are large voids almost completely lacking in galaxies. The stringy structure of the universe is probably the result of the distribution of matter in the early universe before the time of galaxies and stars.

▰CHAPTER CAPSULE

Topics and Terms	Review and Remarks
Classification of galaxies	Spiral, elliptical, irregular, and lenticular

Formation and galaxy type	The type of galaxy formed depends on conditions and events at the time of collapse:
	  Elliptical galaxies used up all the dust and gas before a disk could form.
	  Rotation became important in spiral galaxies before star formation could deplete the dust and gas.

Ages of galaxies	Since all galaxies appear to have Population II stars, they are assumed to be the same age—15 billion years.
Contents of galaxies	Spirals and irregulars contain Population I and II stars and much dust and gas. Ellipticals predominantly contain Population II stars with very little dust and gas.

(continued)

CHAPTER CAPSULE (continued)

Topics and Terms	Review and Remarks

Extragalactic distance scale	Each distance indicator must be calibrated; this is the first step in a pattern that is repeated over and over:
	    Calibrate a new distance indicator.
	    Extend the volume of space with known distances.
	    Search for new distance indicators.
	The final distance indicator is Hubble's law: velocity = H_0 × distance.

Radio sources	Sources may be supermassive black holes at their centers.
Quasars	The most powerful radio sources and the most distant objects known in the universe Controversy exists over the relationship between redshift and distance for quasars.
Clusters of galaxies	Clusters range from a few galaxies to many thousands of members. Cluster types range from very compact and concentrated to irregular and loose. The most compact clusters of galaxies exhibit huge cannibal galaxies. Clusters of galaxies group into long strings called superclusters.

REVIEW QUESTIONS

1. Describe the three broad classes of galaxies with particular emphasis on their differences.

2. Regular spirals are classified as Sa, Sb, and Sc. What distinguishes the subclasses? Ellipticals are classified as E0, E1, . . . E7. What distinguishes these subclasses? Who originated this classification scheme for galaxies?

3. What role did rotation apparently play in determining the type of galaxy that would result for a particular system?

4. Describe the constitution of the local cluster of galaxies. Is it a comparatively large cluster? Which type of galaxy dominates in numbers? What type dominates in size? What is the closest galaxy to the Milky Way Galaxy?

5. What are *transitional* or *lenticular* galaxies? How are they related to the other galaxy classifications?

6. What are the observed characteristics of quasars? Why do some astronomers think they are very young galaxies?

7. Many older texts refer to some galaxies as nebulae, for example, the Great Andromeda nebula. Expain why they used this term.

8. How are the distances to nearby galaxies determined? Why can't these same methods be used with more distant galaxies?

9. What is Hubble's law? How is it used to determine the distances of the most distant objects?

FOR FURTHER READING

Burbidge, Geoffrey. 1988. Quasars in the balance. *Mercury* volume XVII, number 5, September/October, 136.

Burns, J. 1986. Very large structures in the universe. *Scientific American*, July, 38.

Comins, N., and L. Marschall. 1987. How do spiral galaxies spiral? *Astronomy*, Dec., 6.

Gregory, S. 1988. Our cosmic horizons part three: The structure of the visible universe. *Astronomy*, Apr., 42.

Hartley, K. 1989. Elliptical galaxies forged by collisions. *Astronomy*, May, 42.

Hodge, P. 1988. How far are the Hyades? *Sky & Telescope*, Feb., 138.

Kanipe, J. 1988. Quest for the most distant objects in the universe. *Astronomy*, June, 20.

Keel, W. C. 1989. Crashing galaxies, cosmic fireworks. *Sky & Telescope*, Jan., 18.

Kiernan, V. 1989. How Far to the Galaxies? *Astronomy*, June, 48.

Mathewson, D. 1985. The clouds of Magellan, *Scientific American*, Apr., 106.

Melott, A. L. 1988. Our cosmic horizons part four: Recreating the universe. *Astronomy*, May, 18.

Smith, Harding E. 1978. Quasi-stellar objects. *Mercury* volume VII, number 2, March/April, 27.

Trimble, V. 1988. Our cosmic horizons part two: The search for dark matter. *Astronomy*, Mar., 18.

Quasars: Far or Near?

Quasars exhibit the largest observed redshifts, and Hubble's law predicts that they are the most distant objects in the universe. The largest measured quasar redshifts, $z \approx 5$, correspond to radial velocities of 95% of the speed of light and to distances of 3 to 6 billion parsecs (10 to 20 billion light-years). Since quasars are so far away, the time it takes the light from quasars to reach us is enormous—10 to 20 billion years! Since the universe must have been very young when the light from quasars started its long journey toward Earth, astronomers believe that the light from distant quasars represents radiation emitted by newly formed galaxies. The great distances to quasars appear to be a very well-founded assumption since the measured velocities and distances of low-redshift ($z << 1$) galaxies clearly show a linear relation between distance and velocity.

Astronomers never seriously questioned the assumption that the observed radial velocities of distant galaxies correspond to distances until quasars were discovered. Figure 18A.1 illustrates the problem quasars present. It shows redshifts and magnitudes of normal galaxies together with those of quasars. Magnitudes are used instead of distance estimates from Hubble's law in this figure so our interpretation will not be biased by assuming that redshifts imply distances. Two interpretations of these data are possible. One assumes that redshifts do represent distances. This is the interpretation adopted in Chapter 18 and requires that the luminosities of quasars must be abnormally high, as indicated in Figure 18A.1. These high luminosities are attributed to the presence of supermassive black holes at the centers of the quasars. Admittedly, quasar models incorporating super-

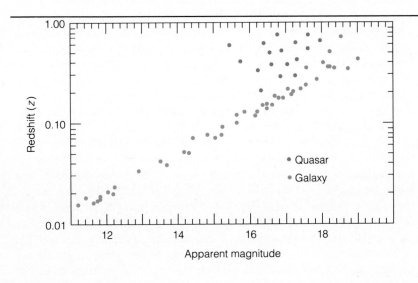

FIGURE 18A.1

Redshifts and Magnitudes for Normal Galaxies and Quasars

Quasars are brighter than galaxies with the same redshift.

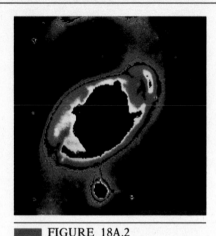

■ FIGURE 18A.2

The Quasar Markarian 205 and the Galaxy NGC 4319

This enhanced false-color picture shows a luminous red bridge connecting the quasar (small image) and the galaxy. Colors are used to better emphasize the subtle differences in brightness.

SOURCE: Halton Arp, Max Planck Institute of Astrophysics.

massive black holes are incomplete and do not describe the exact mechanism responsible for the high luminosities.

The second interpretation of the quasar data shown in Figure 18A.1 is that redshifts do not reflect distances; that is, quasars are local to, or nearby, the galaxy they are seen near. Why should astronomers consider this alternate view? Does this not strike at the very foundations of our current view of galaxies in the universe? Yes it does, and the reason for considering it is *observational.* Several kinds of observations appear to indicate that at least some quasars and perhaps galaxies have redshifts that do not indicate distance. The evidence includes (1) apparent physical connections between quasars and galaxies; (2) signs of mutual interaction; and (3) statistical studies that indicate there are too many associations to just be attributed to chance.

Physical associations observed between pairs of galaxies with very different redshifts clearly indicate that at least one of the redshifts is not directly related to distance. That is, if one of the galaxies is much farther away, how can it be connected to the other? These associations, or apparent connections, between galaxies and quasars are observed as luminous bridges. Figure 18A.2 shows the low-redshift quasar Markarian 205 near the spiral galaxy NGC 4319. NGC 4319 has an observed radial velocity of 1700 km/s while the quasar has one of 21,000 km/s. If the radial velocities represent distances, then they imply a distance of ≈30 Mpc for NGC 4319 and ≈400 Mpc for Markarian 205. Careful studies of these two galaxies indicate that the bridge between them is physical and not an artifact of the photographic process. Furthermore, a filament not only extends to the quasar from the nucleus of NGC 4319 but another one extends in the opposite direction from the nucleus, possibly indicating ejection from the nucleus. The apparent physical connection makes it difficult to accept the relatively high velocity of Markarian 205 as an indication that it is a distant galaxy behind NGC 4319. Observations exist of dozens of galaxy-quasar pairs that exhibit widely different redshifts but appear to be physically connected or interacting.

Why accept the high radial velocity of Markarian 205 as an indication of distance in the first place? It is important to realize that if astronomers did not know the redshift of Markarian 205, they would conclude on the basis of its proximity to NGC 4319 and the apparent bridge between the two that both were at the same distance. The analyses of this system and others like it get muddled because astronomers *assume* that Markarian 205 *must* be at a distance much different from that of NGC 4319 due to the observed differences in their redshifts. The underlying problem with accepting the concept of local quasars is that astronomers do not have a convincing theory to explain juxtapositions such as that shown between Markarian 205

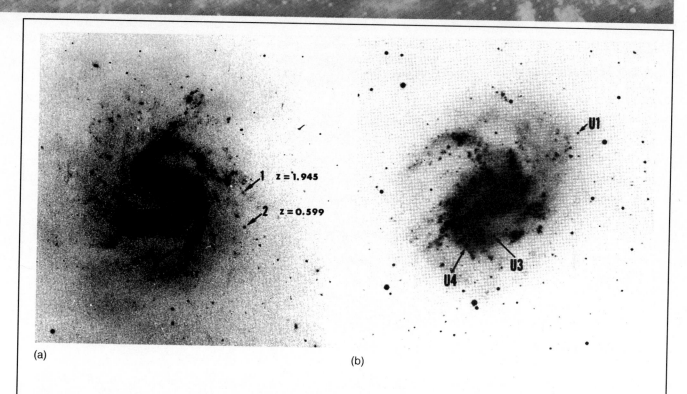

(a)

(b)

and NGC 4319. A similar situation surfaced in the discussion about possible Sun-Earth connections in AstroProbe 12. In that case, scientists did not feel comfortable with possible connections between solar activity and weather on Earth without a theory to explain them. Scientists are always very skeptical of observations that cannot be understood.

Statistical evidence also exists that suggests quasars and galaxies of very different redshifts are associated. Panel a in Figure 18A.3 shows the barred spiral galaxy NGC 1073 with three quasars, each with a much higher redshift than NGC 1073, apparently located in the disk of the galaxy. Although no bridges of matter are seen, the probability of finding three high-redshift quasars so close to a low-redshift galaxy is extremely low; some astronomers estimate this probability at 1 in 50,000. Panel b shows another group of quasars with large redshifts that appear to lie within a galaxy. Figure 18A.4 shows a pair of quasars within 10 arc seconds of each other that have very different redshifts: $z = 0.44$ and $z = 1.90$. The low-redshift quasar has the same redshift as a nearby small group of galaxies. Some astronomers argue that such a close pair is so unlikely that another explanation for their redshifts is needed. Furthermore, statistical studies of bright quasars suggest that they are found more frequently around bright, or nearby, galaxies than can be explained by chance.

■ FIGURE 18A.3

Pairs of Galaxies with Very Different Redshifts

(a) Three quasars with similar redshifts are seen "in" the spiral arms of the barred spiral NGC 1073, which has a very different redshift from the quasars. *(b)* The galaxy NGC 4593 with three quasars lying near and apparently in the galaxy.

SOURCES: Part (a), The Astronomical Society of the Pacific. Part (b), Halton Arp, Max Planck Institue of Astrophysics.

FIGURE 18A.4

A Pair of Quasars Named 1548 + 114a and b with Very Different Redshifts

SOURCE: The Astronomical Society of the Pacific.

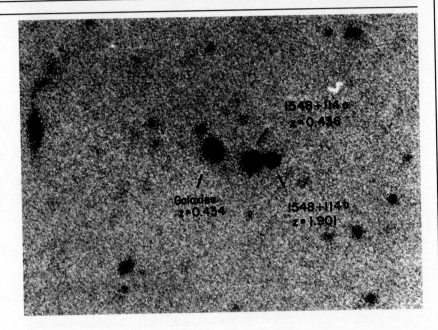

These kinds of observations suggest not only that not all redshifts are related to distance but also that alternate explanations for the nature of quasars themselves are needed. The models suggested so far are not entirely satisfactory. Many models, for instance, suggest that quasars are violently ejected from the center of galaxies. In these models, it is difficult to explain why no quasars with blueshifts have been observed. One interesting idea is that quasars direct radiation in a narrow cone in the opposite direction of their motion. Although this would explain why we do not see quasars with blueshifts, no one has any idea why quasars should emit in this way. Again astronomers are at a point where they have no reasonable theory to explain quasars.

Perhaps our view of the structure and evolution of the universe, not just quasars, is wrong. During the last two decades astronomers have obtained observations that suggest a remarkable pattern in the observed redshifts of galaxies that cannot be explained by conventional models. When individual radial velocities of galaxies in a cluster of galaxies are compared, they appear to differ by amounts equal to simple fractions of 72 km/s. For instance, velocities of several galaxies in a cluster may be 5000 km/s, 5035 km/s, 5072 km/s, 5109 km/s, and 5144 km/s; the average differences are simple multiples of ½ × 72 km/s, or 36 km/s. Radial velocity observations of pairs of galaxies also suggest this "quantization." Redshift quantization has been suspected only recently because its detection requires very accurate velocity measurement for large groups of galaxies, which has been possible only in the last decade. Astronomers are extending their observations to determine if redshift quantization is a real phenomenon shared by galaxies across the universe.

Redshift quantization may prove to be an even more severe test of conventional wisdom than quasars. The term "quantized" is used analogously to quantized energy states in atoms where electrons can only be in certain discrete energy states, or orbitals. Quantization of redshifts may imply that the observed redshifts of galaxies are not Doppler shifts but are fundamental properties of the galaxies. Perhaps quantization rules apply to the redshifts of galaxies in clusters of galaxies in which only certain redshifts (multiples of 72 km/s) are allowed. Hubble's law then could be explained by galaxies somehow evolving from high to low redshifts as the universe ages, as an electron moves from high to low energy as an atom de-excites. These are clearly speculations, but they give an indication of the possible drastic changes to the conventional view of the universe and to the views of large-scale gravitation that could result from new observations.

The astronomical community has not wholeheartedly endorsed either the idea that redshifts do not indicate distances or that they are quantized. In fact, many astronomers dismiss evidence for local quasars as a few accidental configurations or are simply unconvinced of the existence of quantized redshifts. Caution, of course, is necessary in science, but sometimes investigators in a science or a specialized field within that science, who have invested a great deal of effort into formalizing a coherent model, are reluctant to throw away their model. If local quasars or quantized redshifts are real phenomena in the universe, then the conventional views of the universe would have to be completely revised. For instance, what if redshifts did not always correlate with distance? The degree of "not always" is unknown at present so that astronomers do not know which redshifts can be used as distance indicators. As mentioned in Chapter 18, mainstream scientists have good scientific arguments for redshifts as indicators of distances: (1) Hubble's law for individual galaxies and galaxies in clusters strongly indicates that redshifts represent distances; (2) "fuzz" around quasars suggests that they are galaxies rather than small objects ejected out of galactic nuclei, for instance; and (3) low-redshift quasars have companion galaxies with the same redshifts.

The controversy between redshifts as distance indicators and local quasars will eventually be settled—at the telescope by the observer and with pencil, paper, and computer by the theorist. Observations and the theories that fit the observations are the arbitrators of science.

CHAPTER 19

The Expanding Universe

OUTLINE

The Big Bang

Expansion of the Universe

3 K Microwave Background Radiation

Age of the Universe

Future of the Universe

Summary

Chapter Capsule

Review Questions

For Further Reading

ASTROPROBE 19: Origins

Looking Back from the Large Magellanic Cloud.

ARTIST: Mark Paternostro. Courtesy *Astronomy* Magazine, Kalmbach Publishing Company.

THE PRECEDING CHAPTERS have described the present state and the past history of the universe from times as early as a few billion years after the beginning of the universe to the present—a span of about 10 to 15 billion years. The light from the most distant quasars, for instance, may be from galaxies forming when the universe was only a few billion years old or even younger. How did the universe begin? What is the fate of the universe? Models of the early universe try to answer the first question and are based on three observations: Hubble's law of galaxy recession; the observed temperature of the universe today; and the present abundances of hydrogen and helium. These three observations lead to certain predictions about the early universe.

The first moments of the universe were characterized by a hot, explosive expansion out of which all the matter in the universe was created. During the first few minutes of the universe, nuclear reactions produced nearly all of the hydrogen and helium observed in the universe today. As the universe expanded, it cooled, leaving a faint background of low-energy microwave photons as a relic of its violent beginnings.

The answer to the second question—the fate of the universe—requires the most exacting observations. From the present conditions of the universe, scientists predict that its future will be cold and dark.

THE BIG BANG

Through a host of myths and religious traditions, humans have tried to explain the origin of the universe. To the inquiring and skeptical mind, however, deities dreaming the universe and its contents as in the Hindu myth of Vishnu or ordering the universe into existence as in Judeo-Christian writings are not very satisfying explanations of the creation of the universe. Yet serious scientific study of the early history of the universe has been regarded as a respectable field of scientific inquiry only in the last few decades. The reason for the past reluctance to study origins was simply a lack of strong observational evidence with which to work. Today, scientists have both the observational material and the theoretical background to recount the events of the early universe.

The study of the evolution and organization of the universe is called **cosmology.** It is based on three crucial observations. First, Hubble's law implies that galaxies are receding from each other; this indicates that galaxies were closer together in the past. Second, astronomers observe a cosmic microwave radiation coming from all directions with a black body spectrum of 3 degrees above absolute zero; this, together with Hubble's law, indicates that the universe was hotter in the past than it is now. Finally, the chemical composition of the oldest stellar objects is almost totally hydrogen and helium; this indicates that nucleosynthesis in the early universe produced mainly hydrogen and helium. These three observations present severe limits to any cosmological model describing the evolution of the universe.

This section will describe the events that took place in the early universe as scientists currently understand them. Although the early universe may at first seem to be a complicated set of unconnected events, the model presented here will prepare the way for understanding how the observations, described in the following two sections, compel scientists to construct this particular history of the early universe.

The universe "exploded" into existence. This explosion sent matter "flying," as evidenced by the galaxies now viewed rushing away like shrapnel from an exploding bomb. This first explosive event traditionally has been called the *big bang*. The current understanding of physics does not allow scientists to describe exactly how the "bomb" detonated. Therefore theorists can only begin to describe the universe after the first 10^{-43} seconds of its existence. At earlier times, the universe was so dense that not even the general theory of relativity can describe it. It is impossible to describe, for instance, the center of a black hole because the collapsing core of a supergiant is thought to shrink to a point of infinite density and zero radius. In contrast, the universe appears to begin in a state of infinite density, which scientists cannot describe, and then to expand explosively. The following description of the early universe begins at a time when physics can describe the state of matter and radiation and predict their interaction.

As the universe expanded, it cooled. The incredibly high temperatures in the early universe dropped rapidly, from $\sim 10^{32}$ K to $\sim 10^{10}$ K between 10^{-43} seconds and 1 second after the big bang! After 4 seconds the temperature of the universe had fallen to $\sim 5 \times 10^9$ K, slightly higher than that reached in the centers of massive stars (Figure 19.1). The temperature dropped below a billion Kelvins only after the universe was about 3 minutes old. The temperature continued to decrease with time, reaching 3000 K nearly a million years after the big bang and only 3 K some 15 billion years later.

The very earliest moments of the universe can be described only with the most sophisticated theories of particle physics. These theories, called grand unified theories (GUTs), propose that under the extreme temperatures and densities found in the early universe the four forces of nature—gravitation, electromagnetic, weak nuclear, and strong nuclear (see AstroProbe 4)—were but one "superforce" with its own unique characteristics. Grand unified theories predict that as the universe expanded and cooled, the superforce separated into the four forces

■ FIGURE 19.1

Temperatures in the Early Universe

Temperatures in the early universe decreased as the universe aged.

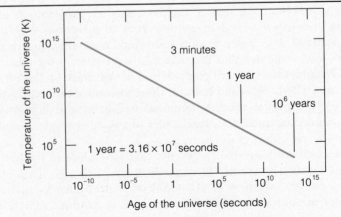

observed in the universe today (Figure 19.2). Cosmologists have applied GUTs to the earliest moments of creation to describe the hot, chaotic inferno of the big bang.

Let's follow the physical changes in the universe as it expanded and cooled. During its initial expansion, the currently observable universe was small enough that all its parts were causally connected. That is, light from one part of the universe had enough time to travel to another part before significant expansion occurred. This means, for instance, that all parts of the universe were at the same temperature. To understand this, consider the following analogy involving a room with two air conditioners on opposite walls. If the room is small, the air conditioners will quickly cool the room to a comfortable, uniform temperature, mixing cool air with the warm air in the room. If the room is too large, the air conditioners will not be able to circulate enough cool air across the room to keep the temperature comfortable and uniform. The early universe was like the small room in that the interaction of radiation and particles produced a uniform temperature. The observed cosmic microwave background radiation today also appears to be at a uniform temperature. That is, stars and galaxies are surrounded by a low-energy radiation field with a 3 K black body spectrum. The uniformity of the early and the present universe led researchers to discover a remarkable event that took place very early in the history of the universe.

As the universe cooled, the unified superforce separated. Grand unified theories predict that this separation released a tremendous amount of energy that fueled a rapid expansion of the universe. This rapid and sudden expansion, called *inflation*, caused the universe to grow by about 30 orders of magnitude in less than 10^{-30} seconds. Written in powers of 10, this means an increase by a factor of about 10^{30}. If the observable universe was the size of an atom, then it grew instantly to the size of a galaxy!

The consequences of the period of rapid inflation are visible in the universe today. As noted in the last chapter, the universe possesses a

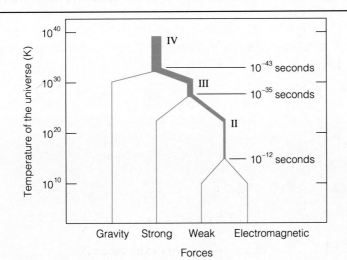

■■■ FIGURE 19.2

The Separation of the Four Forces

The times, since the big bang, when the separations are predicted to have occurred are shown on the right.

hierarchical structure, progressing from individual stars, to star clusters, to star clusters, to galaxies, to clusters of galaxies, up to huge superclusters. On a small scale, therefore, the universe looks lumpy with galaxies and clusters of galaxies clumped here and there. But on a scale as large as the distances between clusters of galaxies, the universe looks more or less the same in all directions. Wherever astronomers look, they see nearly the same number of galaxies, and galaxies at the same distance from us are receding at the same velocity no matter where they are located in the sky. This uniformity of the universe is readily observed in the microwave background radiation. Observed at any wavelength, it has the same intensity to within 1 part in 10,000 even when observed from opposite directions in the sky; that is, different parts of the universe seem to be bathed in radiation at the same temperature. Two points in opposite directions on the sky, however, are so far apart today that radiation could not possibly have traveled between them over the age of the universe. Consider two galaxies 10 billion light-years away from us in opposite directions on the sky. They are so widely separated from each other, 20 billion light-years, that they have no connection with each other. That is, the universe is not old enough for radiation from the two galaxies to have reached each other. The same applies to the microwave radiation coming from the same regions of the universe as the two galaxies. The only way both parts of the universe could have the same temperature today is if they were causally connected *in the past* and, therefore, had a common origin. The observed uniformity of the universe is a natural consequence of inflation occurring during the first moments of time.

When the universe was only $\frac{1}{100}$ of a second old, its temperature was high enough, $\sim 10^{11}$ K, for many collisions, or nuclear reactions, to occur between particles and antiparticles in the universe (Figure 19.3). Included in the reactions are the processes of *pair production* and *annihilation* (Panel a). Pair production represents the complete conversion of the energy of colliding photons into an amount of matter dictated by Einstein's relation, $m = E/c^2$. Annihilation is the reverse process. Pair production is commonly observed in high-energy nuclear physics exper-

■■■ FIGURE 19.3

Nuclear Reactions in the Early Universe for Times Greater than 0.01 Seconds

The symbol "↔" means that the reactions occur in both directions with equal frequency.

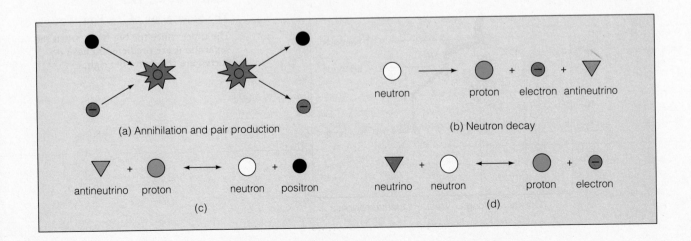

(a) Annihilation and pair production

neutron → proton + electron + antineutrino

(b) Neutron decay

antineutrino + proton ↔ neutron + positron

(c)

neutrino + neutron ↔ proton + electron

(d)

iments in which energetic photons (gamma rays) collide. The reaction in Panel b in Figure 19.3 is the decay of the neutron into a proton, electron, and antineutrino. The decay of neutrons is responsible for the present chemical composition of the universe because it reduced the number of neutrons relative to protons as the universe cooled.

Once the universe reached temperatures of about 10^{10} K, after about 1 second, neutrinos no longer interacted with matter. The universe was then transparent to neutrinos, which were free to roam the universe and still do so. After about 4 seconds, temperatures were too low for pair production. At this time the universe was composed of neutrons, protons, electrons, and photons that could no longer create particles and neutrinos that no longer interacted with the other particles. Although no more neutrons were created, they still decayed into protons and electrons. This led to even more protons relative to neutrons. Temperatures were still too high for protons and neutrons to bond into nuclei and, of course, too high for electrons to be permanently captured by protons to form atoms. The free electrons, however, did interact with the photons. The interaction is called *scattering* because only the direction of the photon is changed during the interaction. Since photons could not travel very far before scattering off an electron, the universe was opaque.

As the hot, opaque universe cooled further, more protons were created at the expense of neutrons. Only about 3 minutes after the big bang, when temperatures dropped below a billion Kelvins, could protons and neutrons assemble together into deuterium nuclei. Almost immediately, all of the neutrons in the universe were used up in forming deuterium. Further captures led to helium as shown in Figure 19.4. The remaining protons, about 12 for every helium nucleus, remained free as hydrogen nuclei. Since a helium nucleus is about four times more massive than a proton, the total mass of 1 helium nucleus and 12 protons is 16 atomic mass units, where one atomic mass unit is about equal to the mass of a proton. Therefore, the mass fraction of helium in the universe after about 3 minutes was $^4/_{16} = 0.25$ and that of hydrogen was $^{12}/_{16} = 0.75$. After a few minutes of expansion the chemical composition of the early universe was fixed at approximately 75% hydrogen and 25% helium by mass. The big bang model also predicts the production of a very small amount of the light elements, deuterium, lithium, and boron. As temperatures continued to decrease, nuclear reactions between the components of the universe stopped. *No buildup of massive elements was possible in the early universe.*

The conception of the big bang theory resulted from attempts in the late 1940s to explain the abundances of all elements. At that time, George Gamow (1904–1968) and his colleagues assumed that the universe started in a very compressed state at a very high temperature. Their calculations traced the nuclear reactions as the big bang fireball expanded and cooled. Although they were actually trying to account for the origin of all the elements, Gamow and his associates succeeded in accounting for only hydrogen and helium. The process of element buildup in the early universe was blocked at atomic masses of 5 and 8; the universe does not contain stable elements with these atomic masses.

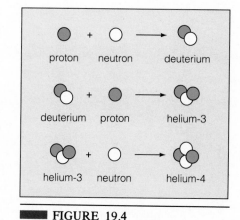

■ FIGURE 19.4

Nucleosynthesis in a Hot Universe

Since the capture of a proton by ^{4}He results in an unstable nucleus, which immediately decays, significant nucleosynthesis of heavier elements is prevented.

Decoupling: The epoch in the early universe when the radiation field was too cool to ionize atoms, thus allowing atoms to form; this occurred about 600,000 years after the big bang.

Consequently, it was nearly impossible for a helium nucleus to capture a proton and then remain in this unstable state long enough to capture yet another proton. Recall that conditions inside red giants are somewhat different from the early universe. In stars, the density is high enough so that a helium nucleus can capture another helium nucleus and then does not have to wait long before another nucleus collides with it. Although Gamow considered his attempt at explaining the elements a failure, the results represented an important new direction for studies of the creation of the universe.

Although temperatures cooled to a point where nuclear reactions stopped after a few minutes, the universe stayed too hot for atoms to form for about 300,000 years. Then after about 600,000 years of cooling, photons were no longer energetic enough to ionize any atoms. Photons and atoms then roamed freely through the universe without interacting; the universe became transparent. We call this event **decoupling.** The photons freed at decoupling have been traveling uninhibited through the universe ever since. Astronomers now observe them coming from all directions as the microwave background radiation. Because the universe was opaque prior to decoupling, we will not be able to see any farther back in time no matter how much our telescopes improve. The opaqueness of the early universe prevents us from ever observing the big bang in visible light.

Decoupling was a significant event—it allowed galaxies to form. Before decoupling, radiation kept the matter in the universe hot enough to generate high thermal pressures and to resist gravitational collapse. Soon after decoupling, the Jeans's mass (see Chapter 15) was about that of a galaxy. Nothing as small as individual stars, for instance, could form then. When did galaxy formation occur? To answer this question astronomers must look back in time for light originating from the era of galaxy formation; that is, they must look for the most distant galaxies. These appear to be the quasars. The largest redshift observed for a quasar is just under 5. A later section in this chapter will show that this redshift corresponds to a time of 1 to 2 billion years after the big bang. This is when galaxies appeared.

The formation of galaxies and superclusters is intimately associated with the formation of particles in the early universe. They are connected not because the particles eventually become constituents of galaxies, but because small variations in the distribution of these particles grew into galaxies and superclusters. For example, if part of the early universe was denser than another part, its higher density relative to the surrounding matter would persist as the universe expanded. Once the universe cooled sufficiently for atoms to form, these concentrations of matter would then attract more matter, become larger, and eventually collapse into galaxies. Studies of the masses of galaxies discussed in Chapter 18 suggest that "dark" matter may make up as much as 80% of the mass of the universe. Cosmologists do not know what this dark matter is, but since the largest structures in the universe today probably reflect the distribution of particles in the early universe, an understanding of the nature of the dark matter may come from particle physics. Current theories suggest that atomic particles, more massive than pro-

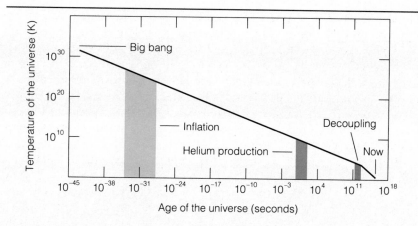

■■■ FIGURE 19.5

**Thermal History of the
Early Universe**

The temperature of the universe is shown
at different times after the big bang. Specific events discussed in the text are indicated. Note that this graph exaggerates
early times.

tons and neutrons, were produced in the early universe and could have
generated substantial irregularities in the distribution of particles
through gravitational interactions. Later in the expansion, protons, neutrons, and electrons would then group around these irregularities, forming the seeds of future galaxies. It is possible that the early massive
particles may still exist in the universe today and may, in fact, be the
dark matter. Scientists are currently devising experiments that may detect these hypothetical particles.

To sum up, the modern big bang cosmology begins with an explosive
event that initiated the expansion of the universe (Figure 19.5). An extremely rapid phase of inflation followed immediately. During the subsequent expansion, the universe cooled. One important result of all the
nuclear reactions, pair productions, and annihilations was an excess of
protons over neutrons. When the universe cooled to several thousand
Kelvins, most of the matter was in the form of hydrogen and helium.
Because the distribution of particles in the early universe was not completely smooth, subsequent cooling allowed density fluctuations to collapse into galaxies, clusters of galaxies, and superclusters.

This picture of the early universe is one of intense heat, high density,
and continued expansion. Two fundamental observations allow astronomers to work their way back from the present to the earliest times. We
turn to them in the next section.

■■■EXPANSION OF THE UNIVERSE

Let's take a closer look at Hubble's law, $V = H_0 \times D$. The observed
redshifts of galaxies indicate that all distant galaxies are moving away
from us. It is as if we were at the center of an exploding Fourth-of-July
fireworks rocket watching all the incandescent fragments fly away. The
first impression, therefore, might be that the Milky Way Galaxy is near
the center of an expanding universe of galaxies. Figure 19.6 illustrates
the observed Hubble's law and helps interpret the observed recessional
velocities of galaxies. Arrows indicate the direction and magnitude of

■ **FIGURE 19.6**

Hubble's Law

Shown here are observed radial velocities as viewed from two different galaxies. Arrows indicate the magnitude and direction of the velocities. Panel b shows how to add the velocity of galaxy C, as observed from galaxy B, to obtain the observed velocities from C. Observers from either galaxy B or C derive the same relation between distance and velocity; all galaxies would appear to move away from the observers.

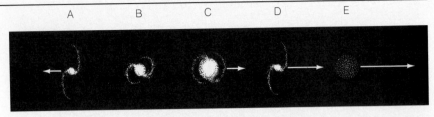

(a) Velocities observed from galaxy B

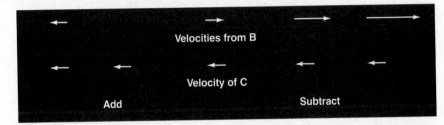

(b) Adding the velocity of galaxy C

(c) Velocities observed from galaxy C

the radial velocities of several galaxies shown in a line. The most distant galaxies observed from galaxy B in Panel a have the largest velocities—this is Hubble's law. Panel c shows how the radial velocities would look for the same set of galaxies but viewed from galaxy C. Correcting for that galaxy's own motion, which observers could not detect if they were in that galaxy, would result in the same Hubble's law. Even though all distant galaxies astronomers observe are receding from us, the Galaxy is not at the center of the universe.

Where then is the center of the universe? Hubble's law implies that the universe is expanding uniformly. This can be illustrated by comparing a uniformly expanding universe to rising raisin bread dough. The individual raisins represent galaxies. Before any yeast bread is baked, it is left out at room temperature to rise. Figure 19.7 shows the bread before and after it rises for one hour during which time the bread doubled in size. Consequently, the distances between the raisins doubled, representing the uniform expansion of the dough. Notice, however, that the raisin nearest to raisin 1, raisin 2, moved only 1 cm in an hour while the most distant raisin, raisin 4, moved 3 cm in the hour (Table 19.1). This is as predicted by Hubble's law—the most distant raisins move away the fastest. Clearly, the raisins spread apart because they are embedded in the expanding dough, not because they are speeding away from each other in a stationary dough. Raisin "radial velocities" are

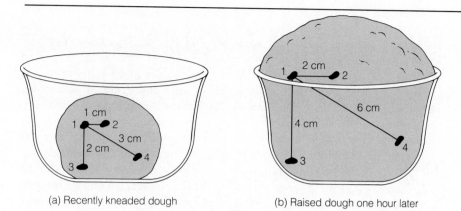

■ FIGURE 19.7

Rising Raisin Bread Dough

After the dough rises for one hour all raisins are twice as distant from each other.

(a) Recently kneaded dough

(b) Raised dough one hour later

■ TABLE 19.1 **Raisin Velocities**

Raisin	Distance from Raisin 1 at $t = 0$ (cm)	Distance from Raisin 1 at $t = 1$ hr (cm)	Velocity (cm/hr)
2	1	2	1
3	2	4	2
4	3	6	3

Hubble's law for raisins: $V = \dfrac{1}{2 \text{ hr/cm/cm}} \times D.$

caused by the expansion of the dough. In the same way, the radial velocities of galaxies are caused by the *expansion* of the universe in which the very "fabric" of space is stretched.

The Hubble's law of raisins would be observed from any of the raisins in the raisin bread dough, and every raisin would seem to be the center of the doughy universe. This analogy, however, breaks down near the edges of the dough. The universe as we know it has no edge that is detectable in three dimensions. Another analogy illustrates this. If a balloon, on which many dots have been painted, is blown up, the dots would "move" away from each other just as the raisins "moved" away from each other in the dough. A Hubble's law is obtained by anyone observing the dots on the surface of the balloon. Whereas the dots are part of the two-dimensional surface of the three-dimensional balloon, scientists view galaxies as part of a three-dimensional surface of a four-dimensional universe. Of course, as three-dimensional beings, humans cannot detect the extra dimension. By analogy, in the same way that the two-dimensional surface of a sphere has no edge, three-dimensional space has no edge. But the *surface* of a sphere does not have a center either. Which one of the dots on the balloon is at the center of the surface of the balloon? Similarly, it makes no sense to speak of the center of the universe. The three-dimensional universe has no observable edge or center.

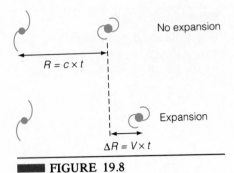

No expansion

$R = c \times t$

Expansion

$\Delta R = V \times t$

FIGURE 19.8

Expansion versus No Expansion

Although the universe is expanding uniformly, galaxies are not. The gravitational force between stars in a galaxy and between galaxies in a cluster of galaxies holds the galaxies and clusters together. Furthermore, the presence of large masses in the universe causes motions that are not tied to the expansion. Within the Local Group, for instance, the Milky Way and the Andromeda galaxies are converging at about 300 km/s. At the same time, the entire Local Group is moving toward a very large mass in the direction of the Hydra-Centaurus supercluster of galaxies. In other words, superimposed on the uniform expansion of the universe are individual motions of galaxies and clusters of galaxies.

The expansion of space causes the observed redshifts of galaxies so astronomers call them *cosmological* redshifts. In fact, we can go further and say that the wavelengths of photons traveling through the universe are increased as the universe expands. Consider a photon of light with wavelength λ traveling between two galaxies at *rest* with respect to each other as shown in Figure 19.8. The separation between the galaxies, R, is simply the time it takes for light to travel the space between the galaxies multiplied by the speed of light: $R = t \times c$. Now let the galaxies move away from each other at a velocity V caused by the expansion of the universe. During the time t, the galaxies separate by a distance $\Delta R = t \times V$. Remember that the symbol Δ denotes change, here a change in separation. Notice that

$$\frac{\Delta R}{R} = \frac{t \times V}{t \times c} = \frac{V}{c}$$

That is, the greater the relative velocity of the galaxies, the greater the separation attained in the time interval. From the Doppler shift, $\Delta\lambda/\lambda$ also equals V/c, so that

$$\frac{\Delta R}{R} = \frac{\Delta\lambda}{\lambda}$$

In other words, as the universe expands (ΔR increases), the wavelengths of light lengthen ($\Delta\lambda$ increases). The expansion of the universe is the expansion of space itself. The longer a photon spends traveling in an expanding universe, the more its wavelength increases. Distant galaxies show large radial velocities because photons from those galaxies have traveled a long way.

The importance of Hubble's law is that it implies that galaxies were closer together in the past than they are now. On the other hand, astronomers have no way of knowing the absolute size of the universe. If light from a very distant galaxy needs more time than the age of the universe to reach us, astronomers could not detect the light from that galaxy. Consequently, when scientists refer to the size of the universe, they are really referring to the separation between galaxies. In other words, billions of years ago, when the universe was 1000 times smaller than it is now, galaxies were 1000 times closer together.

The separation between galaxies, R, is related to the observed redshift, z, in a simple way. A distant galaxy will show a large cosmological redshift since the light from that galaxy has been traveling a long time. The light was emitted when the separation between galaxies was smaller. Let $R(t)$ represent the separation between two galaxies at the time, t, of the emission of the light compared to the separation between the same two galaxies now. The parenthesis around *"t"* in $R(t)$ is short-hand for the value of R at the time t. Without going through the mathematical derivation, the separation between a galaxy with redshift z and our Galaxy at the time of emission is

$$R(t) = \frac{1}{z + 1}$$

For example, the light from a quasar with a measured redshift of $z = 4$ originated from the quasar when that galaxy and our Galaxy were five times closer together than they are today.

Hubble's law implies that all matter in the universe was more compressed in the past than it is now. We can imagine viewing the universe at a time when galaxies were very close together; at an earlier time when the matter that formed the galaxies was closer together; and at an even earlier time when this matter was so compressed and heated that only nuclei and electrons could exist. How can we know the temperature of the universe or the compressed gas at these various times? Radio observations of a diffuse microwave radiation hold the clue.

■■■3 K MICROWAVE BACKGROUND RADIATION

In 1964 two radio astronomers, Arno Penzias (b. 1933) and Robert Wilson (b. 1936), working at the Bell Telephone Laboratory in Holmdel, New Jersey, set about to detect radio emission from outside the plane of the Milky Way Galaxy. Their 20-foot radio telescope (Figure 19.9) and others like it were used in the early 1960s for television and telephone links with England via satellites such as Bell Telephone's Telstar series.

■■ FIGURE 19.9

Bell Laboratory Horn-Radio Telescope at Holmdel, New Jersey

SOURCE: Courtesy of AT&T Archives.

The horn funneled microwaves to the focus of the telescope located in a square building at the end of the horn. The reflecting surface of the horn was a fine mesh needed to reflect the 7.35-cm wavelength microwave photons Penzias and Wilson were trying to detect. As they meticulously scanned the sky they discovered a radio static, or noise, that was always present. The intensity of this noise appeared to be independent of direction in the sky, time of day, and season of the year. And the intensity of this *isotropic* radio emission was that of a source with a temperature of about 3 degrees above absolute zero. Since the noise seemed like an interference caused by a faulty electronic component or an imperfection in the horn's surface, Penzias and Wilson checked every component of the telescope thoroughly and then carefully calibrated the horn. The noise persisted; it puzzled and frustrated them. Their only explanation was that it was radiation coming from space, but they knew, or thought that they knew, that nothing was out there emitting at 7.35 cm.

Although Penzias and Wilson did not know it at the time of their observations, other astronomers expected to find a low-temperature microwave noise. In fact, Soviet astronomers realized that this background noise would be observable with the Holmdel horn! The expectation of radio noise resulted from the work of Gamow and others in the 1940s in which it was realized that the high helium abundance, $Y = 0.25$, observed in stars today had to be the result of nuclear reactions in a hot universe rather than in stars. The nuclear reactions in stars have not added significantly to the helium content in the universe. The helium produced by hydrogen burning in main-sequence stars, for instance, is converted to carbon and oxygen before the planetary nebula or supernova phase can disperse it into the interstellar medium. Astronomers predicted present-day cosmic temperatures in the range of 5 to 10 K would result from the cooling expansion of the universe. Penzias and Wilson unknowingly discovered a background radiation of 3 K. Since the observed radio emission is in the microwave region of the spectrum, astronomers refer to it as the *3 K microwave background radiation*.

More thorough investigations of this radiation in the last few decades have shown that it is uniform to within 1 part in 10,000. That is, the temperature is about 0.0035 K hotter in one certain direction and about 0.0035 K cooler in the exact opposite direction. This anisotropy is caused by the motion of the Local Group toward the Virgo cluster; the microwave radiation is slightly blueshifted in the direction of the Virgo cluster and redshifted in the opposite direction.

Observations at shorter wavelengths using telescopes, rockets, and satellites show that the background radiation is distributed in a Planck curve corresponding to a temperature of about 2.9 K (Figure 19.10). This means that the wavelengths of photons have been stretched to these long wavelengths as the universe expanded. Since this nearly isotropic radio emission appears to be Planckian, the wavelength of its maximum intensity follows Wien's law: $\lambda_{max} = 0.29/T$. As the universe expanded and the wavelengths of photons increased, λ_{max} increased. Therefore, the corresponding temperature of the universe decreased. For example, if $z = 1000$, then the universe was 1001 times smaller

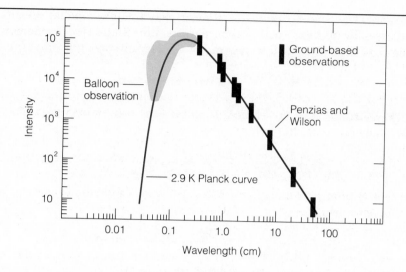

Observed Planck Curve for the 3 K Microwave Background Radiation

The data follow the general shape of a Planck curve for a temperature of about 2.9 K. Observations near the peak of the Planck curve must be made above the atmosphere, either with balloons or rockets.

than it is now. But λ_{max} was also 1001 times shorter; therefore, the temperature of the universe must have been 1001 times greater than it is now, or about 3000 K. This is the temperature of the universe when it was about a million years old and radiation and matter decoupled. The photons detected at microwave wavelengths today are those same photons emitted at decoupling but redshifted by the expansion of the universe.

The significance of the observed background radiation is that it allows astronomers to calculate the past temperature of the universe. When galaxies were closer together, the background radiation was hotter. We are compelled, therefore, by our observations to prescribe high temperatures for the early universe.

In this chapter, times have been assigned to certain phases of the universe, such as when matter and radiation decoupled about a million years after the big bang. How can astronomers know the times of various events in the early universe? How can they say that the universe was 10^{10} K when it was 1 second old? To answer these questions we must take a careful look at Hubble's law.

Relation between z and T after decoupling:

$$T = 3 \times (z + 1) \text{ K}$$

■■■AGE OF THE UNIVERSE

Hubble's law can be used to estimate the age of the universe. The expansion of the universe implies that galaxies were once closer together. In fact, the distances to galaxies represent how far our Galaxy has separated from them during the expansion of the universe. The distance traveled by a car, for instance, is related to its velocity: distance = velocity × travel time. Writing Hubble's law as $D = V/H_0$ shows that $1/H_0$ represents time. This is called the *Hubble time* and corresponds to the *maximum* age of the universe. Since Hubble's goal was to determine the distances to the faintest visible galaxies, he had to determine the value of H_0. Astronomers have followed Hubble's recipe for the last few decades and have determined a value of 50 km/s/Mpc for the Hubble

680

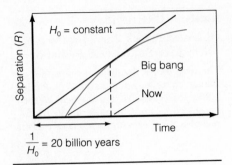

■ FIGURE 19.11

Hubble Time

The separation of galaxies, R, is plotted against the age of the universe. If gravity were not slowing the expansion, then the point where the straight line crosses the time axis would indicate the age of the universe, 20 billion years. Since matter in the universe does slow the expansion, the separation has changed as indicated schematically by the curved line. The age of the universe is less than the Hubble time because the expansion was faster in the past than it is now.

constant. The peculiar units for H_0 mean that a galaxy's radial velocity increases by 50 km/s each million parsecs, or 3.3 Mly. For instance, a galaxy 10 Mpc away will have a radial velocity of

$$50 \frac{km}{s \, Mpc} \times 10 \, Mpc = 500 \, km/s$$

The calculation of the Hubble time involves converting "km/s/Mpc" into units of time. That is,

$$\frac{km}{s \, Mpc} = \frac{km}{s \times 3.1 \times 10^{19} \, km} = \frac{1}{3.1 \times 10^{19} \, s}$$

since a million parsecs contain 3.1×10^{19} km. The Hubble time, t_H, is the inverse of H_0:

$$t_H = \frac{1}{H_0} = \frac{1}{50 \, km/s/Mpc} = \frac{3.1 \times 10^{19} \, s}{50} = 20 \text{ billion years}$$

since one year contains about 3.16×10^7 seconds.

The Hubble time represents the maximum age of the universe because the galaxies themselves are slowing the expansion of the universe. Even though galaxies are moving farther apart, they still exert a gravitational force on each other. Their mutual gravity continuously acts to pull galaxies together. This means that the universe was expanding faster in the past than it is now. Figure 19.11 shows how the separation of galaxies changes with time, or the age of the universe. The curved line schematically shows the actual expansion, rapid at first then slowing because of the mutual gravitational attraction of the galaxies. The straight line is what we would expect if the universe expanded at a steady rate; this corresponds to a universe without mass. The Hubble time is simply where this straight line crosses the time axis. Since the curved line, which schematically represents a universe with galaxies, crosses the time axis at zero separation before the straight line, the age of the universe must be less than the Hubble time of 20 billion years.

Since the expansion rate of the universe varies with time, so will the Hubble constant. The Hubble constant can be written as $H(t)$; H_0 refers to the value of $H(t)$ now. To calculate how $H(t)$ varies with time, the effects of gravity between the matter in the universe must be taken into account using Einstein's theory of general relativity. Applying this to the universe gives the age of the universe as $\frac{2}{3}(1/H_0)$. Using a value of $H_0 = 50$ km/s/Mpc, the age of the universe is ≈ 13 billion years. This is close to the ages of globular clusters, ≈ 15 billion years, in the Milky Way Galaxy. This age seems satisfactory, but a few years ago astronomers developed a new technique to measure H_0 and obtained a much different age for the universe.

The new technique uses 21-cm observations of galaxies to determine their masses and infrared observations to estimate their luminosities. This technique allows astronomers to skip the distance calibrations of H II regions and of the brightest stars in a galaxy. The surprising result is that the new technique gives values for the Hubble constant of ≈ 100 km/s/Mpc, a Hubble time of only 10 billion years, and an age of the universe of only 7 billion years. Although these numbers are at odds with ages of the oldest stars, the technique appears to be sound. Astronomers are now studying both methods of determining H_0 with the hope of resolving these age differences. We may, in fact, have to look closer at age estimates of stars based on nuclear reactions inside low-mass main-sequence stars or at the cosmological models that give the age of the universe as ⅔ the Hubble time. Perhaps H_0 means something very different from what astronomers think it means. Clearly, we do not understand something. The resolution of this kind of conflict, which occurs often in science, will lead to a better understanding of the universe.

In addition to determining the age of the universe, astronomers are interested in the relation between time and the size and temperature of the universe. Ultimately, they want to be able to state the size and temperature of the universe at any time since the big bang. The temperature and size of the universe are related to the observed redshift, z, by the relations introduced in the last two sections:

$$T = 3 \times (z + 1) \, \text{K}$$

and

$$R = \frac{1}{z + 1}$$

At the present time $z = 0$, so that the temperature of the universe is 3 K and $R = 1$. The value of R is arbitrary because we have no way of knowing the absolute size of the universe; all we can measure are separations. The relation for the temperature simply reflects the value of the temperature now, 3 K, and the lengthening of wavelengths due to the expansion of the universe.

The analysis of Hubble's law reveals a relation between the age and size of the universe. Both are related through the dependence of the Hubble constant on time. That is, when astronomers consider times earlier or later than the present, the Hubble constant cannot be assumed to be a constant and is usually written as $H(t)$. When galaxies were closer together, for instance, the universe was expanding faster because the gravitational forces between galaxies had not reduced the expansion rate to its present low value. Consequently, $H(t)$ is closely related to the separation between galaxies. When theorists analyze the dynamics of the expanding universe, they find that $H(t)$ is proportional to $\sqrt{1/R^3}$. For example, when the universe expands to four times ($R = 4$) its present size, the Hubble constant will be eight times smaller ($\sqrt{1/4^3} = \sqrt{1/64} = 1/8$). The Hubble constant would then be about 6 km/s/Mpc and the age of the universe ($= ⅔ \times t_H$) would be about 110 billion years.

When theoreticians combine all of these relations, letting t represent the time since the big bang and using a Hubble constant of 50 km/s/Mpc at present, they obtain the set of equations shown in the margin. These can be used to estimate the age and temperature of the universe for any redshift. Let's take $z = 5$, about the largest redshift observed. The universe was six times smaller then, $R(t) = 1/(z + 1) = 1/6$; the light from a galaxy with this redshift originated when the universe was only 1.4 billion years old; and the temperature at that time was 18 K.

Matter-dominated universe:

$$R = \sqrt[3]{\left(\frac{t}{2 \times 10^{10}} \right)^2}$$

$$t = 2 \times 10^{10} \times \sqrt{R^3} \text{ years}$$

$$T = 3 \times (z + 1) \, \text{K}$$

What value of a redshift corresponds to the time of decoupling, about 600,000 years after the big bang? At that time the universe was about 1000 times smaller than it is now and the temperature was about 3000 K. Light coming from this epoch would have a redshift of about 1000! The largest redshift observed is almost 5; astronomers have a long way to go to observe decoupling.

The above relation between age and size of the universe is only applicable back to decoupling. From decoupling until now, matter has dominated the expansion of the universe. Before decoupling, however, radiation interacted strongly with matter. In fact, radiation was so dominant that it slowed the expansion of the universe faster than matter did. The dominance of radiation in the early universe is shown by the ability of photons to ionize atoms, destroy nuclei, and create matter through pair production. Another way to measure the importance of radiation is to calculate its mass equivalent from Einstein's equation $E = mc^2$. The Stefan-Boltzmann equation says that the total energy in the radiation field is proportional to T^4. Dividing this energy by c^2 gives the mass equivalent of the radiation field. Scientists call this the *energy density* of the radiation. Currently, the energy density of the 3 K microwave background radiation is about a thousand times less than the density of matter. Radiation density and mass density, however, were equal at decoupling. At times earlier than that the radiation density was greater, and we say that the universe was a *radiation-dominated universe*. The present universe is a *matter-dominated universe* in which matter determines the expansion rate.

When the Hubble equation is evaluated for the radiation-dominated era as it was for the matter-dominated era, a slightly different set of equations is found. This set, shown in the margin, can be used for times less than about 600,000 years after the big bang. Figure 19.12 shows how the separation between galaxies changes as a function of time throughout both the radiation-dominated and the matter-dominated eras.

Hubble's law and the observation of the 3 K microwave background radiation allow astronomers to calculate the size and temperature of the universe as a function of time. Once the temperature of the early universe is known at all times, theoreticians can calculate what nuclear reactions took place and when pair production occurred. Theories of particle physics then fill in the details. These calculations form the basis of the big bang model described in the first section of this chapter.

As we have seen, the universe has had a rich and complicated history that we can describe. What about the future of the universe? What will become of all the matter? What will become of all the galaxies, stars, planets, and moons?

Radiation-dominated universe:

$$R = \sqrt{\frac{t}{6.3 \times 10^{11}}}$$

$$t = 6.3 \times 10^{11} \times R^2 \text{ years}$$

$$T = \frac{2.5 \times 10^6}{\sqrt{t}} \text{K}$$

FUTURE OF THE UNIVERSE

Cosmologists have been successful in reconstructing a plausible history of the universe from its very earliest moments to the present. Can they now predict the future of the universe? Since Hubble's law shows that

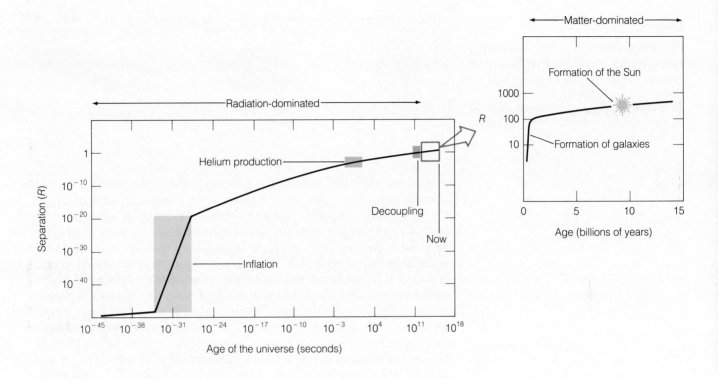

FIGURE 19.12

History of the Universe

The separation, R, is plotted as a function of time. Inflation causes a sudden increase in R by ≈ 30 orders of magnitude. The small graph in the upper right shows the change in R in the matter-dominated universe (the time axis is in billions of years). Gravitational forces between matter slow the increase of R after inflation.

the universe is expanding, it is natural to ask if the expansion will continue forever. For any prediction concerning the future, we need to identify starting points. One starting point is the present temperature and age of the universe, which can be used to predict temperatures as the universe ages. This is not enough, however. We must also know how the universe will expand.

The universe can change or evolve in one of three ways: (1) it can continue to expand forever; (2) it can expand for a while, reach a maximum size, and then collapse upon itself; or (3) it can expand and stop at an infinite size. The fate of the universe depends on how successful galaxies are at slowing the expansion. If the force of gravity between galaxies is strong enough, it can slow the expansion until it stops and then reverse it, causing the galaxies to merge in the distant future. We call such a universe a **closed universe.** If, on the other hand, the gravitational force between galaxies is not strong enough to halt the expansion, then the galaxies will continue to separate, moving farther and farther away from each other. We call this an **open universe.** If a balance exists between the gravitational tendency to collapse and the expansion, then the universe will stop expanding yet not collapse. For reasons given below, we call this a **flat universe.**

Consider an analogy of the expansion of the universe in an open, closed, or flat universe to the flight path of a rocket. A rocket launched with a velocity less than the escape velocity will fall back to the Earth; this is analogous to a closed universe that eventually collapses upon itself. If the rocket is launched with exactly the escape velocity, then it will just manage to escape the Earth; this is analogous to the flat uni-

■ FIGURE 19.13

Possible Geometries of the Universe: Spherical, Flat, and Hyperbolic

One test (impractical for us) of different geometries is whether parallel lines remain parallel after great distances. Parallel lines will converge or diverge in closed or open universes, respectively.

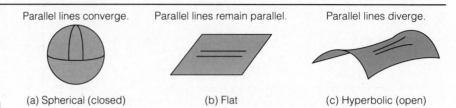

Parallel lines converge.   Parallel lines remain parallel.   Parallel lines diverge.

(a) Spherical (closed)   (b) Flat   (c) Hyperbolic (open)

verse. If the rocket is launched at a velocity much greater than the escape velocity, then it not only will escape the Earth but perhaps escape the solar system as well; this is analogous to the open universe. Furthermore, just as a rocket with a launch velocity less than or greater than the escape velocity can have a range of velocities, the open and closed universes can have a range in the strength or weakness of the mutual gravitational interaction between the matter in the universe.

We have just described the universe in terms of matter and the gravitational force between matter. The general theory of relativity, which is the modern theory of gravity, allows scientists to describe the universe in another way—in terms of geometry (see AstroProbe 16). Within the context of general relativity we can ask, What is the shape, or geometry, of the universe? Open, closed, and flat universes have special geometries caused by the gravity of all matter in the universe. First, if the universe is closed, then the geometry of space is *spherical* like a globe (Figure 19.13). Second, if the universe is open, then the geometry is *hyperbolic* like a saddle. In both the open and closed universes, the **curvature,** or degree of curving of a surface, can vary. For instance, the curvature of a baseball is greater than that of a basketball. The geometry of a flat universe is that of a flat surface, one with zero curvature. In terms of expansion, a flat universe will just barely expand forever. It represents a balance between expansion and contraction, between open and closed. In a flat universe the gravitational force between galaxies is not quite strong enough to halt the expansion completely.

In the last section, the age of the universe was calculated by multiplying the Hubble constant by a factor of $2/3$. This strictly applies to a flat universe. As will be pointed out below, the universe may indeed be flat. Figure 19.14 schematically shows how the separation between galaxies changes with time in expanding universes. The flat universe is represented by curve 2, and the time since the big bang is $2/3 \times t_H$, where $t_H = 1/H_0$ is the Hubble time. Curve 1 represents a closed universe. Notice that the age of the closed universe is less than $2/3 \times t_H$. This is because the stronger gravitational attraction of the galaxies slowed the expansion faster relative to that in the flat universe. Therefore, less time would be needed to reach the present rate of expansion. Curve 1 represents only one possible closed universe. Any number are possible depending on the effects of gravity, and they would all be drawn so that the big bang starts to the right of $2/3 \times t_H$. Curve 3 represents an open universe. Since the gravitational attraction in an open universe is weaker than that in either a flat or a closed universe, more time is

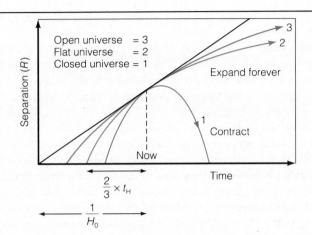

Relationship between the Age of the Universe and Its Geometry

Closed universes have ages less than that for a flat universe, $\frac{2}{3} \times t_H$, while open universes can be older than this.

needed since the big bang for the universe to reach its present rate of expansion. Consequently, the age of an open universe must be greater than $\frac{2}{3} \times t_H$. In all possible universes, the age is always less than t_H (Table 19.2).

A critical parameter in deciding the universe's future is the average density of matter in the universe. The force of gravity between closely packed matter is, of course, greater than that between dispersed matter. If the average density were high enough, then gravity would slow and eventually stop the expansion. The universe would be a closed universe. The critical density needed now to produce a closed universe is ≈5–20 × 10^{-30} g/cm^3. The obvious question is, what is the present average density of the universe? Astronomers can certainly locate matter contained in such visible objects as galaxies, stars, and planets. Their total mass is found by simply adding the masses of all the galaxies in a large volume of space. The density of *luminous* matter in the universe follows by dividing the mass by that volume. The average density found in this way is ≈3 × 10^{-31} g/cm^3, about 20 to 60 times too low to close the universe. Unfortunately, astronomers are not very good at locating matter in the universe. Recall that we suspect that most of the matter in the universe is dark, or invisible, and we do not know exactly how much is present or what it is. When astronomers attempt to estimate the amount of dark matter, for instance, from rotational curves of galaxies, they cannot account for more than ~20% of the mass needed to close

■■■ TABLE 19.2 **Age of the Universe**

Universe	Curve (Figure 19.14)	Geometry	Age (billions of years)		
			$H_0 = 50 \ km/s/Mpc$	$H_0 = 75 \ km/s/Mpc$	$H_0 = 100 \ km/s/Mpc$
Closed	1	Spherical	<13	<9	<7
Flat	2	Flat	13	9	7
Open	3	Hyperbolic	13 <age <20*	9 <age <13	7 <age <10

*"13 <age <20" means less than 20 billion years but greater than 13 billion years.

the universe. Still, we are not very secure in concluding from this data that the universe is open or flat.

Astronomers can take another approach to try to decide whether the universe is open, flat, or closed. The data used to derive Hubble's law show a linear relation between the velocities and distances of galaxies. Hubble, of course, only observed relatively nearby galaxies. Suppose astronomers were able to observe very distant galaxies, whose light has been traveling for a large fraction of the age of the universe. In the distant past, the expansion rate would have been faster, resulting in a different Hubble constant. Consequently, if we plotted velocities and distances of these galaxies, they would deviate from the straight line of the nearby galaxies. We can predict, moreover, how Hubble's law should change depending on whether the universe is open or closed. These changes are shown in Figure 19.15; also shown are the data available today for nearby and distant galaxies. Notice that the magnitudes of galaxies are used instead of their distances in such an analysis. If Hubble's law were used to obtain distances, we would be assuming that the Hubble constant is unchanged—but we are looking for changes in the Hubble constant! Although the data appear to favor a closed universe, careful analyses of the data do not allow a clear choice between open or closed. Too much scatter and uncertainty exist in the data for faint and presumably distant galaxies. Part of the uncertainty is due to the difficulty associated with observing such faint objects. Part is due to the evolution of stars. The total luminosity of a galaxy will change with age as it proceeds through generation after generation of stars. Unfortunately, astronomers do not know exactly how this occurs with time. Thus these observations do not allow us to know the fate of the universe.

Since astronomers cannot decide if the universe is open or closed from observations of the average density of matter or from the recessional velocities of galaxies, perhaps the universe is flat. The universe

FIGURE 19.15

The Velocity-Magnitude Relation for Open and Closed Universes

The most distant galaxies are very difficult to measure, making the interpretation of these data uncertain. (Data from J. Kristian, A. Sandage, and J. A. Westphal, 1978, *Astrophysical Journal*, 221:383.)

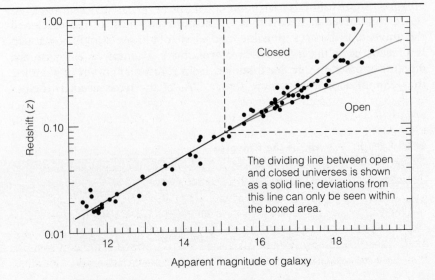

may be so balanced between being open and closed that we cannot make a choice. Normally this would be an unusual statement for scientists to make because it implies a very special set of circumstances. Our models of the early universe, however, indicate that the fate of the universe is sensitive to the amount of matter in the universe in the first moments of creation. If the average density of the universe was just slightly more than the critical density at that time, then the universe would be closed and remain closed. The effect of the slight enhancement would be greatly magnified during the inflationary epoch, and we should have no difficulty in recognizing the universe as a closed universe. On the other hand, if the average density was just slightly less than the critical density, then we would also have no trouble recognizing the universe as an open universe. As used here, "slightly" means that the difference between the average and critical densities are more than one part in a million million (10^{12}). This is sensitive indeed to initial conditions! The point is that for the universe to appear as balanced between open and closed as it does now, the average density of the universe before inflation had to be almost exactly the critical density. Why this should be is still an unanswered question.

A flat universe is exactly what is predicted by inflationary big bang models. Inflation leaves the universe expanding at just the velocity necessary to prevent the collapse of the universe. Inflation also explains the isotropy of the 3 K microwave background radiation as well as the large-scale smooth distribution of matter in the universe. It is also responsible for making the universe appear flat. During the inflationary epoch the universe rapidly expanded by about 30 orders of magnitude. Just as a small region on the surface of a balloon becomes less curved as the balloon is blown larger and larger, the small portion of the universe visible to us appears flat. We simply cannot detect any curvature. This is the same for small distances on the Earth. A baseball field appears flat on the curved Earth because we cannot detect the Earth's curvature over small distances. For all practical purposes, *the universe is flat*.

Well then, what is the future of a flat universe? Galaxies will continue to separate from each other; they will do this forever. The galaxies will evolve as the rate of expansion continuously slows. Elliptical galaxies will continue to age as their main-sequence stars, one by one, burn all of their hydrogen and helium fuel (Figure 19.16). They will shine brightly as red giants for a short while, fading to white dwarfs and then to dark, cold cinders. If we could see into the future, we could watch elliptical galaxies change from their bright splendor of today into dull red embers of old, dying stars.

Spiral and irregular galaxies, on the other hand, have a little life in them yet (Figure 19.17). They still have dust and gas from which to form massive stars. These stars will shine brilliantly for a short time, explode, and disappear as black holes or neutron stars. The black holes will emit X-rays and gamma rays as long as residual dust and gas feeds them. Neutron stars will flash their signals across the universe as long as they keep spinning. Eventually, their steady pulse will become feeble and fade away. But these stars will have long faded while low-mass

■ FIGURE 19.16

An Elliptical Galaxy

The future of this galaxy is one of gradual fading as all of its stars use up their hydrogen and helium fuel.

SOURCE: National Optical Astronomy Observatories.

■■■ FIGURE 19.17

A Spiral Galaxy

Spiral and irregular galaxies have much gas and dust to convert into stars but eventually all will be used up, leaving billions of cold, dark dying stars.

SOURCE: Hale Observatories.

■■■ FIGURE 19.18

A Cluster of Galaxies

The large elliptical galaxy will grow through collisions with all of the other members of the cluster, forming massive, galaxy-sized black holes.

SOURCE: Hale Observatories.

main-sequence stars steadily burn their hydrogen fuel. The lowest mass stars will take 100 billion years to use their hydrogen. They will briefly brighten as red giants but eventually fade away as cooling white dwarfs. These low-mass stars will be the last specks of starlight in the expanding universe.

As the expansion slows, the universe will fade into darkness. Dead planets will orbit dead suns; dead suns will orbit in dead galaxies. The remnant stars will be dull embers in a dying universe that began in a glorious explosion of energy creating radiation and matter.

This seemingly static state of the universe is only a dormant phase. Recent grand unified theories predict that the proton is not stable; it may have a half-life of $\sim 10^{32}$ years. This means that after about 10^{32} years protons that make up matter will begin to decay in significant numbers. As protons decay into positrons and gamma rays, the remaining neutrons will also decay. The disintegration of matter may take on the order of 10^{70} years! The future of matter in the universe is to eventually decay into electrons, positrons, and photons. Of course, positrons and electrons near to each other will annihilate themselves, producing even more photons.

During the decay of matter, dead galaxies will merge (Figure 19.18). Although collisions in the universe are probably rare today, given enough time, billions upon billions of years, nearly all galaxies will merge into gigantic black holes. During the collisions some stars will be flung out across space, becoming derelict bodies floating in an ocean of emptiness. These galactic collisions will add only brief flares of light to the dark void, but they set the stage for the final explosions in the universe.

Black holes are also not stable; they evaporate. This remarkable result was discovered by Stephen Hawking (b. 1942) of Cambridge University. Quantum mechanics allows a black hole to slowly radiate particles and radiation. The particles and radiation carry away mass and increase the rate of emission. Eventually, the black hole will disappear in a burst of gamma rays and particles. The evaporation of black holes, however, takes a long time. A 10 $\mathfrak{M}_\odot$ black hole will evaporate in ~10^{70} years; one the size of a galaxy takes ~10^{97} years; and a black hole the size of a supercluster would take ~10^{110} years.

Thus the universe comes to an end in gigantic bursts of energy, spread over 10^{40} years, from black holes, scattered thinly throughout the universe, that were once stars, galaxies, clusters of galaxies, and superclusters. Imagine an utterly dark universe lit up by occasional bursts of light from an exploding supermassive black hole. After all of the black holes have evaporated, the universe will once again be dark, but forever dark.

▰▰ SUMMARY

Modern cosmological theories are rooted in three observations: (1) the recession of galaxies as described by Hubble's law; (2) the existing 3 K microwave background radiation; and (3) the observed hydrogen and helium abundances in stars.

Hubble's law of galaxy recession implies that the universe is expanding and that galaxies were once closer together in the past, suggesting a primordial universe of very small dimensions and very high density. The explosive event that marks the beginning of space and time and caused the expansion is called the big bang. Since the big bang, radiation and matter in the universe have acted to slow the expansion. Hubble's law reflects the present rate of expansion, and the Hubble constant, H_0, is a measure of the maximum age of the universe. The Hubble constant is known only to within a factor of two, and current measurements suggest values between 50 km/s/Mpc and 100 km/s/Mpc. These values correspond to maximum ages of the universe of 20 billion years and 10 billion years, respectively.

The radial velocities measured for distant galaxies are the result of the expansion of the universe; photons of light are redshifted as they travel through the expanding universe. The 3 K microwave background radiation is composed of photons that originated in an earlier time. Because the microwave background radiation has a black body distribution, astronomers can use Wien's law together with Hubble's law to calculate a temperature for each epoch in the history of the universe.

As the universe expanded, it cooled. Initially, the temperature of the universe was thousands of billions of Kelvins. The density of matter and of radiation was so high at times less than 10^{-43} seconds that no present theory of physics can describe the behavior of radiation and matter under such intense conditions. At that time the four forces of nature were unified into a single superforce, but during the expansion the superforce separated. This separation fueled an epoch of rapid inflation of the universe in which it grew by ~30 orders of magnitude. In the high-temperature environment of the early universe, reactions between photons and nuclear particles characterized the interactions. After the first few minutes of the expansion, the universe cooled to a temperature at which no more nuclear reactions were possible. During these first few minutes, hydrogen and helium nuclei were created with mass fractions of about 0.75 and 0.25, respectively. This initial mix of elements in the universe is reflected in the chemical compositions of the firstborn stars in the Milky Way Galaxy. When the universe reached a temperature of ≈3000 K, radiation no longer interacted with matter, allowing atoms to form. The formation of galaxies followed, occurring about 1–2 billion years after the big bang.

The future of the universe depends on its geometry, which in turn depends on the distribution of matter in the universe. A closed universe will eventually reverse the expansion and contract to its initial state while an open universe will expand forever. Observations designed to determine whether the universe is open or closed are inconclusive. These observations may indicate that the universe is so balanced between open and closed that it is flat. Indeed, theories of the early universe based on grand unifying theories predict a flat universe after it passes through an inflationary epoch.

The age of the universe also depends on its geometry. If the universe is flat, for a Hubble constant of 50 km/s/Mpc (or 100 km/s/Mpc), the age of the universe is $\frac{2}{3}(1/H_0) = 13$ (or 7) billion years. A closed uni-

verse would be younger than this limit while an open universe would be more than this limit but less than 20 (or 10) billion years old.

CHAPTER CAPSULE

Topics and Terms	Review and Remarks
Observational cosmology	Three observations form the basis of modern cosmological models: The observed recession of galaxies The existence of the 3 K microwave background radiation The observed hydrogen and helium abundances in the universe
Expanding universe	Hubble's law suggests an explosive beginning (the big bang) to the universe. Matter has been gravitationally slowing the expansion since the big bang.
Microwave background	Observed photons in the universe exhibit a Planck curve of a 3 K black body. About a million years after the big bang, photons decoupled from matter. Photon wavelengths increase over time because the universe is expanding— wavelengths of light expand with the universe.
Nucleosynthesis	The universe was initially extremely hot but cooled as it expanded. Nuclear reactions created hydrogen and helium during the first few minutes of expansion—temperatures cooled before heavier elements could be created. Current models predict $X = .75$ and $Y = .25$.
Inflation	The universe expanded by 30 orders of magnitude during the earliest moments. This was fueled by the separation of a superforce into the four known forces.
The future of the universe	An open universe will expand forever. A closed universe will expand to a maximum and then collapse upon itself. A flat universe represents a balance between open and closed. Current observations are inconclusive; current theory predicts a flat universe.
The age of the universe	It depends on whether it is open, flat, or closed and on the value of H_0. The measured Hubble constant, H_0, lies between 50 and 100 km/s/Mpc. The corresponding ages of the universe lie between about 7 and 20 billion years.

REVIEW QUESTIONS

1. What is the *big bang* theory? Review the scientific evidence that seems to support this theory. Do you know of any scientific evidence that seems to contradict it?

2. What is the Hubble constant? How does its value imply an upper limit to the age of the universe? What is the approximate value of this upper limit?

3. All galaxies outside the Local Group seem to be moving away from us at speeds that increase with distance according to Hubble's law. Does this imply that we are at the center of the universe? Explain.

4. How might the Hubble Space Telescope help astronomers decide what the fate of the universe is to be?

5. What is meant by the terms *closed universe, flat universe,* and *open universe?*

6. What is the significance of the 3 K microwave background radiation?

7. What is meant by the term *decoupling?*

8. The Doppler effect is used to mathematically describe "redshifts" of spectra when the distance between a radiation source and its observer is increasing. What do we mean when we say that redshifts are cosmological?

9. What do the terms *radiation-dominated universe* and *matter-dominated universe* mean?

FOR FURTHER READING

Corwin, M., and D. Wachowiak. 1985. Discovering the expanding universe. *Astronomy*, Feb., 18.

Darling, D. 1986. Deep time: The fate of the universe. *Astronomy*, Jan., 6.

Davies, D. 1985. New physics and the big bang. *Sky & Telescope*, Nov., 406.

———. 1986. The arrow of time. *Sky & Telescope*, Sept., 239.

———. 1988. Does the universe rotate? *Sky & Telescope*, June, 599.

LoPresto, J. C. 1987. The geometry of space and time. *Astronomy*, Oct., 6.

Mallove, E. F. 1988. The self-reproducing universe. *Sky & Telescope*, Sept., 253.

Odenwald, S. 1987. To the big bang and beyond. *Astronomy*, May, 90.

Parker, B. 1986. Discovery of the expanding universe. *Sky & Telescope*, Sept., 227.

Rothman, T., and G. Ellis. 1987. Has cosmology become metaphysical? *Astronomy*, Feb., 6.

Scherrer, R. 1988. Our cosmic horizons part one: From the cradle of creation. *Astronomy*, Feb., 40.

ASTROPROBE 19

Origins

Nineteen chapters in this book have described the scientific investigation of the universe. The important word in that sentence is *scientific*. Science was defined in Chapter 3 as a consistent body of knowledge, strongly tied to experiment, and expressed in as few laws as possible. The scientific approach is basically a three-step process in which scientists perform experiments or make observation to obtain facts of nature, summarize their observational facts as laws, and then deduce consequences and test the laws. The models, theories, and laws presented throughout this text are the products of this scientific approach to understanding the universe. This is why this book contains no chapters on the "types of aliens who are piloting unidentified flying objects" or on the "influence of your zodiac sign on your life." These subjects have no scientific basis; they are not founded on experiments or observations. UFOlogy and astrology together with other subjects such as psychokinesis or clairvoyance are collectively called **pseudosciences.**

Only one pseudoscience will be discussed in this book. In recent years, Christian fundamentalists have been placing more and more pressure on schoolteachers to present a pseudoscientific theory of the origin of the universe, called "biblical creationism," *as a science.* The origin model of biblical creationism, sometimes referred to as young-Earth creationism or scientific creationism, is outlined in Table 19A.1. The outline was prepared by Dr. Frank Awbery of San Diego State University and published in *Creation/Evolution.* Several features of the model stand out. First, all time scales have been compressed. Where astronomical and geological observations indicate millions and billions of years for a process, the biblical creation model reduces them to hundreds and thousands of years. Second, geological formations were produced by the "Flood." Plate tectonics and long-term erosion did not occur before the flood. Finally, the evolution of life on Earth did not take place; all life was created essentially as we find it today. The similarity of this model to biblical traditions is why it is called biblical creationism. It is a literal fundamentalist interpretation of the Book of Genesis.

Proponents of biblical creationism, usually referred to as creationists, try to convince the public that their hypothesis of creation and subsequent history of the world is a valid scientific model. Recall from Chapter 3 the criteria for a good scientific model: (1) it must account for all data; (2) it must be testable; and (3) it must explain other experiments or observations. Biblical creationism is an attempt to account for what is written in Genesis; Genesis is the source of data. This is certainly not scientific data but "belief" data. The model is not based on a set of observations and experimental data; it begins with a belief that Genesis is a true description of the world

▬▬ TABLE 19A.1 **Model of Biblical Creationism**

I. The Creation
   A. Accomplished by a supernatural being.
   B. Everything was created from nothing relatively recently.
   C. The Earth was perfectly designed for life:
      1. Protected by a vapor layer:
         a. Uniform warm climate from pole to equator.
         b. Cosmic radiation could not penetrate.
      2. No wind or rain.
      3. The land was irrigated by water from underground.
   D. All "kinds" of plants and animals were created separately:
      1. Each kind is unique and fixed.
      2. Each kind is genetically highly variable.
   E. Humans were uniquely created.
   F. No decay occurred.
II. The Fall
   A. The second law of thermodynamics is invoked:
      1. Perfect order began to degenerate.
      2. Death, decay, and disorder began.
   B. People began to populate the Earth. All humans are descended from the original couple.
   C. The vapor barrier enabled great longevity.

III. The Flood
   A. Simultaneous, worldwide cataclysm.
   B. All land was covered within 40 days.
   C. Flood water had two sources:
      1. The vapor barrier.
      2. Undergound reservoirs.
   D. The Flood began 1656 years after creation.
   E. The Flood formed and deposited the geological columns (strata).
   F. The Flood split the landmass into the present continents.
   G. The only survivors were aboard one boat.
      1. Eight humans.
      2. One pair of most kinds of animals.
      3. All were aboard the boat for 371 days.
IV. The Post-Flood Period
   A. Leftover flood energy caused the ice ages.
   B. Flood survivors repopulated the Earth.
   C. All living species are descendants of the flood survivors:
      1. They were modified by horizontal change to fill the Earth.
      2. The animals had original genetic variability.
   D. The vapor barrier was destroyed—longevity decreased.
   E. All species degenerate since disorder *must* increase.
   F. Present geological processes are different from those before the Flood.

Adapted from F. Awbery, *Creation/Evolution*, 1980, 1:1.

in early times. With this belief firmly established, the model is checked by searching for evidence that supports the belief.

▬▬INTRICACIES OF THE BIBLICAL CREATION MODEL

In using Genesis as their source of data, creationists must introduce events and describe phenomena that violate much of what is known about the universe. Let's describe a few of these events. What is the source of water for the assumed 40-day flood in which Noah set sail? The biblical creation model places the source of water, not in clouds in the atmosphere, but in a vapor barrier, or canopy. This canopy is thought to have been composed of large water "globules" about 2 km above the equatorial plane and large ice fragments above the polar regions. The flood was caused by the bursting of the water globules.

The ice canopy fell later, burying the mammoths, changing the polar climate, and generating the ice ages (see AstroProbe 5). Note that prior to the flood and the collapse of the ice canopy, the biblical creation model claims that the Earth did not have polar caps. Furthermore, the dinosaurs were destroyed soon after the collapse of the ice canopy because the temperature on the Earth was lowered by the presence of all that ice. Dinosaurs are believed to have lived together with humans in a "Flinstonian Epoch."

Although scientists know that ice ages did occur, what about the flood, the vapor barrier, the water globules and ice fragments, and the coexistence of humans and dinosaurs? The idea of a flood comes from Genesis. In fact, biblical creationists try to interpret all geological formations in terms of a flood. The vapor barrier and its constitution are introduced simply to explain a few statements in Genesis. Nothing in nature resembles the vapor barrier nor does any theory based on observations of the universe predict any such structure. At any rate, if so much water were surrounding the Earth, it would generate a greenhouse effect that would produce an Earth as hot as Venus! What about the Sun? Could humans see it clearly through the water and ice? The physical difficulties associated with globs of water and icebergs in the sky, of course, require a miracle. Creationists do not hesitate to incorporate miracles into their theories. Finally, no evidence exists showing that humans and dinosaurs walked the Earth together. The strongest evidence for this was a set of dinosaur tracks found in a limestone bed of the Paluxy River, near Glen Rose, Texas. Creationists have now admitted that the smaller tracks next to the large dinosaur tracks are, in fact, small dinosaur tracks.

The biblical creation model accounts for the formation of comets, asteroids, meteorites, and other planetary moons in the following way. These are made up of small rocks broken away from the Earth as the water and ice from the vapor barrier crashed onto the Earth. They struck with such violence that this debris was flung throughout the solar system, coalescing into icy bodies. Readers must try to distinguish between a story, or idea, and a valid model. Is this account of the origin of comets a valid model? Do the orbital characteristics of any of these objects suggest an Earth origin? Is the chemical composition of these bodies similar to the crust of the Earth? How much of the Earth was chipped away to produce the mass of all these objects? Do we see any evidence on the Earth's surface reflecting the violence occurring several thousand years ago when the vapor barrier collapsed? What evidence do we have of tons and tons of ice falling from the sky?

Modern biblical creationism contains many subtle chapters. For instance, the creation model claims that it did not rain before the flood because the Bible does not contain any references to pre-flood rain. But then, if the vapor layer kept all of its moisture at the 2-km level, how did plants and animals obtain water? The creationists' answer is that a Creator constructed a vast network of "pipes" running from a deep reservoir located under the ground. Since the water did not need to run continuously, the Creator must have used shutoff valves. Creationists do not yet fully understand the construction and operation of these valves, but they believe they were operated by heat.

All of these ideas are clearly contrived in the sense that no observations or experiments provided data from which such hypotheses were constructed. Moreover, the biblical creation model contradicts observations of the real world.

CONFLICTS WITH NATURE

Various parts of the biblical creation model given in Table 19A.1 deal with different fields of science. Parts I and II, the creation and the fall, concern various aspects of astronomy and physics; Part III, the flood, deals with geology; and Part IV, the post-flood period, relates mainly to biology. Let's now compare the biblical creation model with some scientific data.

The last few chapters in this book dealt with the scale of the universe. As we have seen, astronomers have discovered that galaxies are millions of light-years away. The Andromeda nebula, for instance, is at a distance of 2 million light-years. Astronomers interpret this distance to mean that light from the Andromeda nebula has been traveling for 2 million years. How can this be if the universe is a few thousand years old as the biblical creation model holds? Creationists have an answer to this question, several answers, in fact. The simplest is that when the universe was created, the light from stars and galaxies was created already on its way to us. A more sophisticated answer is that light traveled faster in the past than it does now; somehow light "tires" on its journey. Finally, creationists invoke the theory of general relativity, proposing that light travels "paths" that are independent of time and distance. These answers are not based on the results of observations or experiments; they are not the result of the accumulation of new data. The motivation for these hypotheses is the *belief* that the Earth is only a few thousand years old. Thus the biblical creation model asks astronomers to throw away all their distance estimates because they are being fooled. The universe is not what it looks to be; it is something that we cannot fathom.

Most of the conflict in schools and the courts centers around the question of evolution. The biblical creation model does not allow for evolutionary branching nor for the formation of new species. Biblical creationism states that every animal or plant represents a certain "kind" that can evolve only within its kind; that is, no crossing of kinds is allowed. Humans represent a kind as do chimpanzees, dogs, cats, and horses. In biblical creationism, individual kinds were created with the ability to vary, or evolve (a kind of "microevolution"), thus accounting for the diversity of life-forms found on Earth. The fossil record clearly shows that the biblical creation model predictions are wrong. The fossil record of the horse is a complete record of its evolution during the last 40 million years. It evolved from a tiny four-toed animal, which gradually increased its size over time and developed a hoof. We do not have to delve into a detailed analysis of the fossil record to test this hypothesis. At the same time, the fossil record recorded the extinction of nearly all life forms that have existed on Earth and the emergence of new life forms (see AstroProbe 10).

Biblical creationism must also be consistent with Genesis; recall that all living kinds must have been on Noah's ark. Simply stated, Noah's ark was not big enough for all kinds. We can work out the dimensions of Noah's ark from biblical references as well as the food requirements for all kinds. It seems that a miracle is required.

The biblical creation model also ignores all evidence of an ancient Earth. For instance, the Green River rock formation in Wyoming consists of 6 million layers of *varved clay*. Varved clay is sediment that forms in lakes that freeze over in the winter. Each layer represents a grading of clay from coarse grains on the bottom deposited in the summer to fine grains at the top deposited in the winter. Geologists know from observing sediments forming today that each layer represents a settling of microscopic particles over one year. Consequently, the lowest layer of the Green River formation settled 6 million years ago. The biblical creation model must explain this layering by the Noachian Flood: for the flood to have produced such layering, deposits would have to had been put down at a rate of about one layer per second! Even in still water, the settling of the clay takes several days. No observations made in the last few hundred years can support such an idea. Thus the biblical creation model requires that we ignore laws of nature, such as universal gravitation. Furthermore, the Green River formation is just a thin layer on top of even more rock formations.

The dating of rocks from radioactive elements is a crucial difficulty for the biblical creation model. The radiometric dating of Earth rocks, described in Chapters 4 and 5, gives an age of nearly 4 billion years for the oldest rock formations on Earth. Neither scientists nor proponents of biblical creationism can find any indication that ages of radioactive dating are in error by a factor of a million. Furthermore, scientists know of about 50 radioactive elements with half-lives of 1000 years to 50 million years that should still be on the Earth if the Earth is as young as the biblical creation model assumes. Only 7 of these are found on Earth today, and these are either produced by the decay of long-lived isotopes or by cosmic rays. In addition, when scientists combine the varved-clay-layering dating technique with ages from radioactive decay rates, they find that the ages correspond very well. For instance, comparisons of varved clay and radioactive ages for a rock formation called the Newark Basin in New Jersey give a consistent age of 40 million years. On top of this, when geologists study the variation in thickness of the varved-clay layers, they find that it changes cyclically with periodicities that match the Milankovitch cycles (see AstroProbe 5). Since the amount of solar radiation reaching the Earth varies during the Milankovitch cycles, so does the amount of rainfall and the rates of sediment deposition. These observations clearly indicate that the Earth is ancient, and they are simply ignored in the biblical creation model.

Fossils discovered in the Earth involve both geology and biology and, in particular, the subject of evolution. The first hypothesis considered by *scientists* concerning geological strata and fossils was, in fact, a global flood as described in Genesis. The eighteenth-century scientists who first considered a flood geology soon discovered that a flood could not explain the fossils of increasingly unfamiliar animals found at greater and greater depths in the ground. The current biblical creation model is just a revival of the old flood theory thrown away long ago by geologists after sifting through their observations. The modern biblical creation model must invent explanations to explain the stratification of fossils. These explanations involve different animals living at different elevations, resistance to gravitational settling in the flood waters, and the ability of some animals to flee the flood waters. These explanations fail to account for all of the observed series of fossils. That is, flood geology cannot account for all of the data.

Most of the readers of this text are using it in a course and have been tested on the material presented here and in lectures. If the biblical creation model were to be accepted by the educational community as a scientific model, our children would have to answer a whole new set of questions. For instance, what did Noah do with the manure? How did saltwater marine life survive the 40 days during the (freshwater) flood? Creationist beliefs also spill into other subjects, such as astronomy. Students might be asked to calculate the length of the day on which Joshua commanded the Sun and Moon to stand still in the sky (Joshua 10:12). They would also be required to recall when the planets were created. Current research in biblical creationism places this on Wednesday, March 22, 4001 B.C. at about 6:00 P.M. Jerusalem time.

Science is founded on experimental and observational data, not on biblical reading or simply contemplating the universe. Those who study the biblical creation model try to convince us that they are gathering data to support the model. Are these workers really scientists looking *objectively* at the universe and simply offering another interpretation of the data scientists have already gathered? Many of these researchers belong to one of the following organizations: Creation Research Society, Institute for Creation Research, and the Bible-Science Association. As members of these organizations, they *must* endorse the organizations' position statements. These statements include the following:

- The Bible should be interpreted literally; that is, Genesis is factual presentation of historical fact.

- The Flood did occur and crustal rock and the fossil record record the effects of the Flood.

- The basic kinds of living things were individually created; that is, no evolution from another kind of organism occurred.

- The laws of nature were created and are now maintained by the Creator who can miraculously intervene at will.

These statements represent beliefs with which creationists start; that is, before they begin to study the universe, they already know the answers. Some of the results of this approach have been presented in this AstroProbe. It is clear that biblical creationism is an attempt to account for what is written in Genesis. It is not science. It should not be taught as science to an adult or to a child.

MODULE 1

MathTools 2

This is the second compartment to your "toolbox" of mathematics. Some of the topics may be new to you, while others will be just a review from high school mathematics. You may find it useful to read through this section before reading the book so that you are familiar with these topics and can refer to them quickly when you need to refresh your memory.

■ PROPORTIONS $^a/_b$

The concept of proportionality involves common sense. Two quantities, or variables, are **proportional** if they increase by the same ratio. For example, in MathTools 1 we studied the dinner needs (number of hot dogs) of children at summer camp and found the following

■ For 10 children we needed 20 hot dogs.

■ For 20 children we needed 40 hot dogs.

■ For 40 children we needed 80 hot dogs.

The number of hot dogs increased proportionally with the number of children. When the number of children doubled, the number of hot dogs needed also doubled. This relationship between hot dogs and children can be described in several ways:

■ The number of hot dogs is *proportional to* the number of children.

■ The number of hot dogs *varies directly* with the number of children.

■ The number of hot dogs $\propto$ the number of children.

The symbol "$\propto$" is shorthand for "is proportional to." These are all ways of saying that as one increases, the other increases also.

Direct proportionality can also be described as

Number of hot dogs = *constant* × number of children

The term "constant" is called the *proportionality constant* and tells us by how much the need for hot dogs increases as the number of children increases. For the camp we found in MathTools 1 that

Number of hot dogs = 2 × number of children

The value of the proportionality constant is "2." Consider a summer camp for older children, say, for Explorer Scouts. Older children are likely to eat more hot dogs than younger children so we might find a relationship between hot dogs and children as shown in Figure 1. Here we see that the number of hot dogs increases three times faster than the number of Explorer Scouts:

OUTLINE

Proportions

Percentages and Fractions

Error and Uncertainty

Units

Powers and Roots

Angular Measurement
Angles
Triangles

Cubes, Circles, and Spheres

Temperature

Summer Camp Food Needs

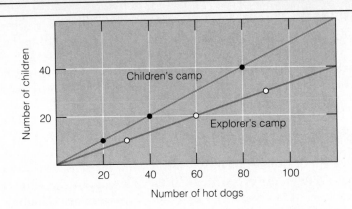

Number of hot dogs = 3 × number of Explorer Scouts

The proportionality constant is "3" for this camp. You can determine the proportionality constant by dividing one variable by the other as shown in Table 1.

Sometimes a quantity will decrease as another quantity increases. For instance, the average speed for a trip to an airport 50 miles away decreases the longer it takes to get there. We write this as

$$\text{Average speed} \propto \frac{1}{\text{travel time}}$$

and say that the average speed is *inversely proportional* to the travel time. Note that the line representing the inverse proportionality

■■■ TABLE 1 **Determining the Proportionality Constant**

Camp	Hot Dogs	Children	Ratio: Hot Dogs to Children
Children's camp	20	10	$\frac{20}{10}$ = 2 hot dogs per child
	40	20	$\frac{40}{20}$ = 2 hot dogs per child
	80	40	$\frac{80}{40}$ = 2 hot dogs per child
Explorer camp	30	10	$\frac{30}{10}$ = 3 hog dogs per child
	60	20	$\frac{60}{20}$ = 3 hot dogs per child
	90	30	$\frac{90}{30}$ = 3 hot dogs per child

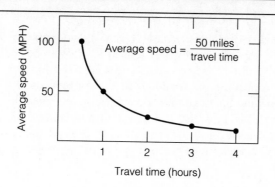

Average Speed for Trips to an Airport 50 Miles Away

The average speed is inversely proportional to the travel time.

starts at the upper left of the graph in Figure 2 and ends at the lower right; a line showing direct proportionality would start at the lower left and end at the upper right. The proportionality constant in this case is 50 miles:

$$\text{Average speed} = \frac{50 \text{ miles}}{\text{travel time}}$$

When we represent quantities, such as the number of hot dogs or the number of children, with symbols such as X and Y, we can represent relationships between the quantities in a shorthand notation. For example, if "Y" represents the number of hot dogs and "X" the number of children, the proportionality for the children's camp is written as $Y \propto X$ or $Y = 2 \times X$. This is generalized by using another symbol, such as "b," to represent the proportionality constant: $Y = b \times X$. This is an **equation** with X and Y as variables and "b" as a constant. It tells us that if X increases, so must Y because both sides of the equation must stay equal. Using this equation we can make a table of X and Y values by choosing a value for X and multiplying it by b. In our example, the proportionality constant for the children's camp is $b = 2$ while for the Explorers camp $b = 3$.

An advantage of using equations is that we can manipulate them. When we used our camp data to find the proportionality constants, we divided the number of hot dogs, Y, by the number of children, X: $b = X/Y$. We say that we *solved* the equation $Y = b \times X$ for b, and it represents the ratio of X to Y. We did this by dividing both sides of the equal sign by X; that is:

$$\frac{Y}{X} = b \times \frac{X}{X} = b \times 1$$

A number divided by itself is always equal to unity. We can use the same procedure to solve the equation $Y = b \times X$ for X: $X = Y/b$.

Equations may have more than two variables. If *"V"* represents our average speed to the airport and *"T"* the travel time to the airport, we can write an equation for our trip to an airport 50 miles away: $V = 50$ miles$/T$. This equation can be generalized for any airport by letting *"D"* represent the distance to the airport, or $V = D/T$. This equation can now be solved for any of the other variables: $D = V \times T$ or $T = D/V$. The equation we use will simply depend on the data we have. For instance, in MathTools 1 we plotted the equation $D = V \times T$ where V was 50 MPH. In this case, D is proportional to both V and T.

PERCENTAGES AND FRACTIONS %

The earliest mathematical treatise on fractions was written by an Egyptian priest named Ahmar between 1700 and 1100 B.C. Fractions were used in dividing land into smaller parcels or dividing a farmer's grain production among his creditors. Fractions are also very much a part of our lives. Certain fractions of our salaries go to national, state, and city governments and to Social Security; baseball batting averages are expressed as fractions; salary raises are a certain fraction of our present salaries; and gasoline taxes are a certain fraction of the price per gallon. In astronomy, we use fractions to represent the amount of hydrogen gas in the Sun, the speeds of distant galaxies in units of the speed of light; and the relative sizes of planetary orbits.

Sometimes fractions are expressed in another form, as a *percent*. You have probably heard of car loans of 10%, sales taxes of 6%, and sale items marked down by 50% of their normal price. When fractions are represented as a ratio of two numbers, such as $0.75 = ¾$ or $0.5 = ½$, they are expressing 3 as a fraction of 4 and 1 as a fraction of 2, respectively. To express 3 as a percentage of 4, we multiply the decimal 0.75 by 100; 3 is 75% of 4. The percent symbol *"%"* simply means "divide by 100." That is, 2% means $2/100 = 0.02$, 5.8% means $5.8/100 = 0.058$, and 0.02% means $0.02/100 = 0.0002$. The percent symbol represents a part out of 100. When astronomers say, for instance, that 90% of the Sun is hydrogen gas, they mean that 90 out of every 100 atoms in the Sun are hydrogen atoms.

ERROR AND UNCERTAINTY Δ

The term "error" in science does not mean a mistake or blunder. It refers to the inevitable uncertainty in any measurement. Experimenters cannot eliminate errors; the best they can hope for is to reduce errors as much as possible.

To illustrate the inevitable uncertainty in any measurement, consider measuring the width of a bookcase for which you need to replace a shelf. Just from looking at the bookcase, you might estimate that it was 73 cm (about 29 inches) wide. This estimate, of course, is subject to uncertainty. You might, if pressed, estimate that the shelf you need must be between 71 and 75 cm long. Before you cut any wood, of course, you would want a better measurement and probably would use a tape measure or a yardstick. Let's say that you use a tape measure and measure a length of 72.9 cm. Even this measurement is uncertain, that is, you cannot say that the length you measured is 72.900 cm rather than 72.901 cm.

Several sources of uncertainty exist in your measurement. For instance, you may make the measurement in poor lighting, or you may not hold the tape measure exactly horizontal, or the edge of the bookcase may line up between two marks on the tape measure. Some of these sources of error can be corrected or minimized. Better lighting, for instance, or using a level will improve your measurement. On the other hand, some uncertainty is intrinsic to the measurement. You probably will have to estimate the fractional distance between marks on the tape measure. You could reduce this uncertainty by buying a tape measure with closer and finer markings. But even then, each marking has a thickness, and you would have to estimate the position of the edge of the bookcase within the mark. Although you would not need to go to such extremes to measure the length of a bookcase, the point is that no physical quantity can be measured with complete certainty.

Suppose you wish to know how precise your measurement of the length of the bookcase is. One measurement would not tell you, but repeated measurements would. Let's say that you carefully measure the length of the bookcase four times and you obtain the following values in cm: 72.9, 72.8, 72.9, and 73.0. You make sure before each measurement that the lighting is right and that the tape measure is level. The *average value* (add all the values and divide by the number of values) of these measurements is 72.9 cm; therefore you can reasonably conclude that the length of the bookcase lies between 72.8 and 73.0 cm:

Average value = 72.9 cm

Probable range = 72.8 to 73.0 cm

The average value lies at the midpoint of the measurements which is usually the case for almost all measurements. This allows us to express the results of a measurement in a very compact form. We can write the above result as

Measured bookcase length = 72.9 ± 0.1 cm

This gives the best estimate of the measurement and states that you are confident that the result lies within 0.1 cm of 72.9 cm. This form can be used to express the result of any measurement of a quantity x:

Measured value of $x = x_{\text{average}} \pm \Delta x$

The term Δx is called the error, or uncertainty, in the measurement of x. The highest possible value of x is $x_{\text{average}} + \Delta x$, while the lowest value is $x_{\text{average}} - \Delta x$.

All of the values of physical and astronomical constants given in Appendix B, for instance, are uncertain. Often the uncertainties are quite small. For instance, the equatorial radius of the Earth and the speed of light are

Equatorial radius of the Earth = 6378.164 ± 0.002 km

Speed of light = 299,792,458 ± 1 m/s

The equatorial radius of the Earth is known to within 2 meters, and the speed of light is known to within 1 meter per second. These uncertainties are small because of repeated and careful measurements.

UNITS

Most of us have been taught the English system of measurement in which the fundamental units of length, mass, and time are the foot, pound, and second respectively. In science, we use the metric system in which the fundamental units are the meter, kilogram, and second. Since we are more familiar with the English system, distances such as miles and inches can be visualized more easily than kilometers and meters. Consequently, conversions between the metric and English systems are given in Table 2 for the most commonly used quantities.

POWERS AND ROOTS $\sqrt{}$

We discussed the term "power" when we introduced the "power of ten" in MathTools 1. We said that the "2" in 10^2 is the power of ten and means that 10 is multiplied by itself 2 times. Another way to read 10^2 is "ten raised to the second power." Raising to a **power** is not limited to the number 10; any number can be raised to a power. For instance, 3 raised to the 4th power is $3^4 = 3 \times 3 \times 3 \times 3 = 81$ and 5 raised to the 2d power is $5^2 = 5 \times 5 = 25$. We use the terms "squared" and "cubed" when the powers are 2 and 3, respectively.

■ TABLE 2 **Metric and English Equivalencies**

Length
1 km = 1 kilometer = 1000 meters = 0.621 miles
1m = 1 meter = 100 centimeters = 39.37 inches
1 cm = 1 centimeter = 0.01 meter = 0.394 inches
1 mile = 5280 feet = 1.609 kilometers
1 inch = 2.54 cm

Mass
1 kg = 1 kilogram = 1000 grams = 2.205 pounds
1 lb = 1 pound = 453.6 grams

Velocity
1 m/s = 100 cm/s = 3.28 ft/s = 2.24 MPH
1 km/s = 2240 MPH
1 km/h = 0.621 MPH

Time
1 d = 1 day = 86,400 seconds
1 yr = 1 year = 3.16 × 10^7 seconds

That is, "2 squared" is $2^2 = 2 \times 2 = 4$ and "5 cubed" is $5^3 = 5 \times 5 \times 5 = 125$.

Taking the **root** of a number is just the opposite of raising it to a power. The symbol for taking a root is the *square root* sign, "$\sqrt{}$" which represents the power of ½. That is, the square root of 100 can be written as

$$\sqrt{100} = \sqrt{10^2} = (10^2)^{1/2}.$$

The "½" signifies the square root and it operates as an exponent. To complete the above operation, multiply the power of 2 by ½, so that

$$\sqrt{100} = 10^{2 \times 1/2} = 10^1 = 10$$

The square root of 100 is 10; the square of 10 is 100. The cube root is similar and is designated as $\sqrt[3]{}$. The cube root of 27 is

$$\sqrt[3]{27} = (27)^{1/3} = 3$$

Similarly 3 cubed is 27. In the same line, the cube root of 1000 is

$$\sqrt[3]{1000} = (10^3)^{1/3} = 10^{3 \times 1/3} = 10^1 = 10$$

Again the cube root symbol $\sqrt[3]{}$ is represented by a fraction "⅓" in power of ten notation, and we simply treat it as any other power of ten.

ANGULAR MEASUREMENT

What are the fundamental measurements astronomers have been making for thousands of years? They are measurements of time and measurements of angles. For instance, astronomers can arrange a telescope so that it pivots on an axis that points east and west; the telescope then can point only north and south but at any elevation. With such a telescope, called a transit instrument, we can measure the times stars are seen due south. One star may pass due south at 10:15 P.M. and another star at the same altitude may pass due south at 11:15 P.M. the same evening. These time measurements are also *angular* measurements in that, since the Earth spins 360° in one day, any time measurement between passages of stars can be expressed as an angle through which the Earth has turned. Before we explore this further, we must first define what we mean by an angle.

Angles

A line along which all points are at the same distance from its center is called a *circle*. Angles have to do with dividing circles into segments. We are all familiar with dividing straight lines into segments. Rulers, for example, are divided into inch-long segments. Similarly, circles can be divided into segments, but instead of using inches, we use degrees (the symbol is °) and divide the circle into 360 degrees. Furthermore, just as inches are subdivided into small segments, such as 8ths or 16ths, degrees are subdivided into smaller segments. Each degree is divided into 60 segments called *minutes of arc* (the symbol is ′). Each minute of arc is further divided into 60 *seconds of arc* (the symbol is ″). Clearly, a second of arc is a small segment (1/3600 of a degree), but many important measurements in astronomy require divisions this small (Figure 3).

FIGURE 3

Degrees, Minutes, and Seconds

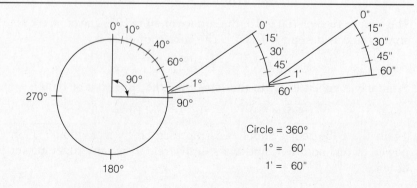

Circle = 360°

1° = 60′

1′ = 60″

The divisions or segments of a circle are called **angles.** An important property of angles is that they represent the same fraction of a circle no matter how large or how small the circle is. The circumferences of the two circles pictured in Figure 4 differ only in proportion to their radii. If the radius of the outer circle is twice that of the inner circle, then the circumference (distance around the circle) of the outer circle is twice that of the inner one. One way mathematicians designate angles is by placing a letter, usually a Greek letter, near the point where the lines making the angle meet. The Greek letter "alpha" (α) is used to designate the angle in Figure 4. Another way to designate angles is to label the ends of the two lines making the angle and the point where they meet with letters. The angle α is the same as the angle *AOB;* the middle letter is the point at which the two lines meet. Furthermore, the angle α is equal to angle *aOb* although the circles are different sizes.

Another measure of angle α is the *arc length AB* divided by the radius *OB* or *OA.* If, for instance, the radius *OB* is twice *Ob,* then the arc length *AB* is twice *ab;* therefore, the ratio *AB/OB* is the same as *ab/ob.* This also shows that an angle is independent of the size of the circle. The representation of an angle as the arc divided by the radius leads to another natural segment of a circle. Suppose the arc length *AB* equaled the radius *OB.* The fraction *AB/OB* then equals 1. This angle is given a special name, one *radian,* it is the angle subtended by a length of arc along the circumference of a circle equal to the radius of the circle (Figure 5). One radian = $57.2958° = 3437.75' = 206,265''$.

If we draw a line that just touches the outer radius of a circle, we say that the line is *tangent* to the circle (Figure 6). An important property of such a line is that the radius line drawn to it makes a *right angle,* or a 90° angle. The two lines are exactly perpendicular to each other.

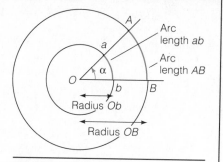

█ FIGURE 4

Two Circles

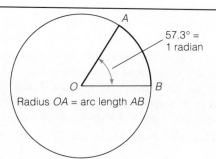

█ FIGURE 5

A Radian

A radian is the angle subtended by an arc length along the circumference of a circle that is the same length as the radius of the circle.

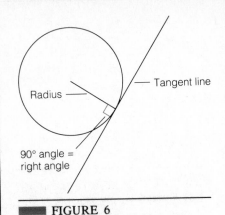

■ FIGURE 6

A Tangent Line

A line tangent to a circle makes a 90°
angle with the radius of the circle.

We began this section with the observation of two stars, which crossed the meridian an hour apart. In one hour, the Earth turns ¹/₂₄ of 360°, or 15°; the two stars, therefore, are 15° apart on the sky. The terms "minute of arc" and "seconds of arc" are used to differentiate them from minutes and seconds of time, which also derive from a circle, the clock. In time measurements, a circle is represented by 24 hours (abbreviated 24^h); each hour is divided into 60 minutes (60^m); each minute is divided into 60 seconds (60^s). A "second" of time means a 3600th part of an hour, just as a "second of arc" means a 3600th of a degree. The relationship between time measurements and angular measurements is given in Table 3.

Triangles

The prefix "tri" is Greek for three. Triangles, therefore, are geometric shapes with three angles. The branch of mathematics called trigonometry is the study of triangles. It was probably invented by the Greek astronomer Hipparchus in the second century B.C. Trigonometry was invented because astronomers needed it for their research. We will use only a few fundamental trigonometric ideas in this text. A fundamental proposition in geometry is that the sum of the angles of a triangle is always 180°. For the triangle in Figure 7 we have α + β + γ = 180° or BAC + ABC + BCA = 180°. The special triangle, the right triangle, is one in which one of the angles is a right angle. Often the 90° angle is represented by a square, □, at the corner of the triangle. Although the two triangles, Abc and ABC, in Figure 7 are obviously different in size, all of the angles are identical. This means that angle Abc = angle ABC, and angle bcA = angle BCA, and angle cAb = angle CAB. This property of similarity of triangles makes them fundamental figures in trigonometry. For instance, surveyors measure distances by using triangles in a fundamental technique called triangulation in which they measure one side of a triangle and two angles. These three measurements allow them to calculate the length of the other two sides.

Triangulation is based on the principle that, if all three angles of a triangle are known, then the "shape" of the triangle is also known. Here shape is distinguished from size. Moreover, if we can measure the length of one of the sides of the triangle, then, with as few as two of the angles, we can determine the lengths of the other sides. Figure 8 shows a circle with a right triangle inside it. Recall that the angle α is defined as the arc length AB divided by the radius OB. For the right triangle BOa, the same angle can also be represented by the

■ TABLE 3 Angles and Time

Time	Angle
24^h	360°
1^h	15°
4^m	1°
1^m	15'
4^s	1'
1^s	15"

ratio aB/OB. This ratio is called the *sine* of angle α (abbreviated as sin α); from Figure 8 we have

$$\sin \alpha = \frac{aB}{OB} = \frac{y}{h}$$

Mathematicians have made extensive tables relating angles to this ratio. For instance, the ratio is 0.0872 for 5°, 0.7071 for 45°, and 1.00 for 90°. Consequently, if we know the length aB and the angle α, we can determine the length OB from such tables. Say the angle α is 45° and the length aB is 10 feet. Since the ratio aB/OB for 45° is 0.7071, OB must equal $aB/0.7071$, or 14 feet.

Similarly, mathematicians have a name for the ratio of the length aO divided by OB; this is called the *cosine* of α (abbreviated as cos α):

$$\cos \alpha = \frac{aO}{OB} = \frac{x}{h}$$

Although we will not make use of sines and cosines in this text, we will use the concepts of angles and triangles repeatedly.

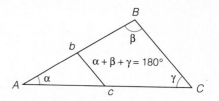

FIGURE 7

Two Triangles

Triangles *ABC* and *Abc* are similar triangles because all of their three angles are identical.

CUBES, CIRCLES, AND SPHERES

The concepts of circumference, area, and volume can be illustrated most readily with the geometric figures, squares and cubes. Consider a parcel of land with sides *(S)* of 100 meters. The *circumference* of the square, or the distance around the square, is the sum of the four sides: $S + S + S + S$, or 400 meters. When we buy land, we generally are more interested in the total amount of land, or *area*, enclosed by the circumference. For a square, the area is calculated by multiplying the length of two sides together:

Area of a square $= S \times S = 100 \text{ m} \times 100 \text{ m} = 10{,}000 \text{ m}^2$

If the parcel of land is not a square but a rectangle, the area is calculated by multiplying the length by the width.

Suppose you build a house on this square parcel of land. If you needed to paint a square room in your house, you would need to calculate the *surface area* of the walls and ceiling to buy the correct amount of paint. The surface area is simply the sum of the surface areas of each wall and the ceiling. If the length of the room is L meters, then the surface area of each wall is $L \times L = L^2$ and that for the walls and ceiling is $5 \times L^2$. Furthermore, the six surfaces of this room enclose a *volume*. Mathematically, the volume of a cube is the height × width × length, or $L \times L \times L = L^3$. In astronomy, how-

FIGURE 8

Trigonometric Definitions of Sines and Cosines

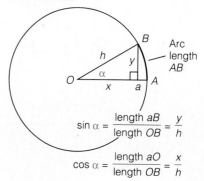

ever, most geometric shapes, such as orbits, planets, and stars, are more similar to circles and spheres, than to squares and cubes.

In the "Angular Measurement" section, we noted that the circumference of a circle is proportional to its radius *(R)* or diameter *(D = 2 × R)*. Mathematicians express the proportionality between circumference and diameter with the Greek letter π ("pi"):

$$\text{Circumference} = \pi D = 2\pi R$$

Pi is a constant and is always the same regardless of the size of the circle. Although we can evaluate π to nearly any degree of accuracy (for instance, π has been evaluated to over a billion digits following the decimal), for most calculations $\pi = 3.14159$ is sufficient.

The circumference of a circle encloses an area as did the sides of the square parcel of land. For a circle this area is

$$\text{Area} = \pi R^2$$

The three-dimensional form of the circle is a sphere. The surface area of a sphere of radius *R* is

$$\text{Surface area} = 4\pi R^2$$

This is the total area of the outer surface of the sphere. And this surface encloses a volume given by

$$\text{Volume} = \frac{4}{3}\pi R^3$$

For instance, the Earth has a radius of 6371 kilometers. Its surface area is $4\pi \times (6371 \text{ km})^2$ or $5.1 \times 10^8 \text{ km}^2$. The volume of the Earth is $(4/3)\pi(6371 \text{ km})^3$ or $1.08 \times 10^{12} \text{ km}^3$. Table 4 summarizes the calculations of areas and volumes.

▰▰▰TEMPERATURE

Three temperature scales are in use today. Most of us are familiar with the Fahrenheit (°F) scale in which the freezing point of water is 32°F and its boiling point is 212°F. In science we use two other scales. In the Celsius (°C), or centigrade, scale, the freezing temperature of water is 0°C and its boiling temperature is 100°C; that is, only 100 degrees separate the freezing and boiling temperatures. The Kelvin (K), or absolute, temperature scale also separates the freezing and boiling points of water by 100 degrees, but the difference is between 273 K and 373 K. The degree symbol is not used with K because degrees in the absolute temperature scale are called Kelvins; that is, 373 K is 373 Kelvins while 200°C is 200 degrees Celsius. The lowest

TABLE 4 Areas and Volumes

Figure	Circumference	Area	Volume
Square (length of side = S)	$4 \times S$	$S \times S$	—
Cube (height = L)	$4 \times L$	$6 \times L \times L$	L^3
Circle (radius = R)	$2\pi R$	πR^2	—
Sphere (radius = R)	$2\pi R$	$4\pi R^2$	$(4/3)\pi R^3$

possible temperature, absolute zero, in which molecular motions cease differs in the different temperature scales:

$$\text{Absolute zero} = 0 \text{ K} = -273°\text{C} = -459°\text{F}$$

Astronomers usually express temperatures with the absolute temperature scale. When the planets are discussed, however, we encounter temperatures within a few hundred degrees of what we are used to on Earth. Consequently, conversion between the absolute and Fahrenheit scales is useful in obtaining a better feeling for these temperatures. The conversion requires multiplying degrees centigrade or Kelvins by a factor of $180/100 = 9/5$. This factor comes from the fact that the difference between the freezing and boiling points of water is 180 degrees in the Fahrenheit scale and only 100 degrees in the absolute and centigrade scales. To convert centigrade temperatures (C) to Fahrenheit temperatures (F) multiply by $9/5$ and add 32: $F = 9/5 \times C + 32$. For example, the average temperature on Mars is about 220 K. In centigrade this is $C = K - 273 = 220 - 273 = -53°C$. To convert to Fahrenheit:

$$F = \frac{9}{5} \times (-53) + 32 = -95 + 32 = -63°\text{F}$$

Table 5 gives temperatures in the three scales for the range of temperatures typical of the solar system.

TABLE 5 Temperature Equivalencies

K	°C	°F	K	°C	°F
0	−273	−459.0	300	27	80.6
50	−220	−364.0	325	52	125.6
100	−173	−279.4	350	77	170.6
150	−123	−189.4	400	127	260.6
200	−73	−99.4	450	177	350.6
225	−48	−54.4	500	227	440.6
250	−23	−9.4	600	327	620.6
275	+2	35.6	700	427	800.6

MODULE 2

Astronomical Instruments and Telescopes

Although the first great problem of astronomy, the working out of the celestial motions of the Sun, Moon, and planets, was solved with observations made with the naked eye, the invention of the telescope about 400 years ago opened up the visual universe to astronomers. Astronomers progressed from using small "spy glasses" to giant mirrors more than 5 m (16 feet) in diameter in less than 350 years. Today, telescopes with mirrors as large as 10 m (33 feet) in diameter and novel configurations equivalent to mirrors 16 m (52 feet) in diameter are being built. This new generation of "monster" telescopes will expand our horizon to the visible edge of the universe. Observations at radio wavelengths became possible after World War II and revealed structures and phenomena only guessed at or not even imagined. The "nonvisible" universe of the infrared, the ultraviolet, X-rays, and gamma rays has been viewed only in the last two decades with orbiting observatories. Astronomers are now able to observe astronomical objects at nearly all wavelengths, detecting the emissions from most of the electromagnetic spectrum.

BEFORE THE TELESCOPE

No one can say who first recognized that the apparent motions of certain celestial objects, which we now call planets, were different from stars. The Sumerians, who inhabited the lower valley of the Euphrates around 4000 B.C., appear to have been the first to make systematic naked eye studies of the planets. The Sumerians devised the angular measure in degrees still used today, which helped them produce star maps and enabled them to tabulate the positions of the planets relative to stars. Neither the Sumerians nor their successors in the Near East, the Babylonians, tried to explain planetary motions except to say that they were divine functions of the gods. The Greeks, who came later, wished to deduce the structure of the universe and felt reasoning power was superior to observations. Nevertheless, they still made many observations. Summarized by Ptolemy in the *Almagest*, these observations provided the basis for the Greek geocentric view of the universe (see Chapter 3).

Naked eye observations of the stars and planets continued throughout the Middle Ages and reached a climax with the exacting observations of Tycho Brahe (1546–1601) and their interpretation by Johannes Kepler (1571–1630). By the beginning of the seventeenth century naked eye observations had resulted in several discoveries:

■ The correct description of our planetary system with the planets orbiting the Sun at known relative distances.

■ The circumference of the Earth.

OUTLINE

Before the Telescope

Optical Telescopes
The First Telescopes
The Long Telescopes
Shorter Telescopes
Large Reflectors
The Great Refractors and
    Reflectors
New Technology Optical
    Reflectors

Radio Telescopes

Space Astronomy

Astronomical Detectors
Imaging
Spectroscopy
Photometry

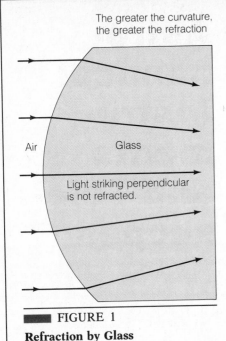

The greater the curvature, the greater the refraction

Air

Glass

Light striking perpendicular is not refracted.

FIGURE 1

Refraction by Glass

Refraction: The change in direction of any electromagnetic radiation, such as light, as it passes obliquely from one transparent medium to another of different density (see also Chapter 4).

Main functions of a telescope:

- Magnification
- Resolving power
- Light-gathering ability

- The relative distances of the Moon and Sun.
- The fact that comets were celestial, but of unknown nature.

Thus the first great problem of astronomy—understanding the celestial motions of the Sun, Moon, and planets—was solved with naked eye observations. Many other problems, most not even imagined in the sixteenth century, could only be solved with optical aid to the eye.

OPTICAL TELESCOPES

The light detected by early astronomers traveled in a nearly straight line from the star or planet to the astronomer's eye. Light travels in straight lines if the properties, such as density and temperature, of the medium through which it travels are constant. If the properties change abruptly, light can change its direction of travel. This change in the direction, or "bending," of light is called **refraction.** Glass lenses can cause refraction because the interface of air and glass produces an abrupt change in the medium through which light is traveling. Furthermore, glass of different chemical compositions produces different amounts of refraction. The amount of bending also depends on the angle at which the beam of light strikes the glass surface. If a beam strikes a lens perpendicular to its surface, no change in the direction occurs. Light striking the lens obliquely, however, is bent, and the farther from the center of the lens the light strikes, the greater the refraction (Figure 1). The first telescopes used the phenomenon of refraction to give the first magnified views of the celestial universe.

Magnification is the first of three main functions, or advantages, of a telescope. The other two are light-gathering ability and resolving power. Light-gathering ability refers to the capability of a telescope to produce brighter images, allowing fainter objects to be seen. Resolving power measures how well a telescope can distinguish between two objects close together or how much detail it can show of extended objects such as planets, nebulae, and galaxies. Refinements in these characteristics have been developed over the last four centuries and still continue today.

The First Telescopes

Although eyeglasses were common by about A.D. 1250, it was not until about 350 years later that someone held up two lenses and noticed that they magnified. In 1604 Hans Lippershey (1570–1619), a spectacles maker in Holland, enclosed two lenses in a metal tube, making

the first telescope. Galileo Galilei (1564–1642) heard of the invention and built his own telescopes. Galileo's first telescope used a lens with a diameter of 4 cm (1.6 inches), which magnified three times (Figure 2). Sizes of telescopes are described by the diameter, or aperture, of the lens (or mirror). Galileo's first telescope is referred to as a 4-cm (1.6-inch) telescope. His largest telescope was 4.5 cm (1.75 inches) in diameter, magnified 33 times, and was 1.2 m (4 feet) long. Galileo's observations of the Moon and planets between 1609 and 1612 with these telescopes changed our view of the universe (see Chapter 3 for details).

Johannes Kepler was not an observational astronomer because he had poor eyesight. He satisfied himself with studying the theory of lenses. Galileo, for instance, did not understand how a lens formed an image. Kepler correctly described how light passes through a lens, is refracted, and meets at a point. This point is the **focus** of the lens. Most of us have played with lenses and perhaps started small fires by focusing the light from a lens onto paper or a pile of leaves. The distance between the lens and the point where the image of the Sun is smallest, and therefore most concentrated, is called the **focal length** and is denoted by f (Figure 3). Opticians combine the lens diameter, D, and the focal length into a quantity called the focal, or f, ratio, n:

$$\text{Focal ratio} = n = \frac{f}{D}$$

The focal ratio of a lens is usually written as f/n. For instance, since Galileo's largest telescope had a focal ratio of 27, it would be described as a 4.5-cm $f/27$ telescope. The focal length of Galileo's telescope would be

Focus of a Lens

Lenses refract light so that it converges to a common point at a distance f, called the focal length, from the lens.

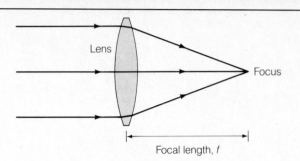

Focal length, f

$$f = n \times D = 27 \times 4.5\ \text{cm} = 120\ \text{cm} = 1.2\ \text{m}$$

Thus the eyepiece needed to be about 1.2 m from the main, or *objective*, lens at the front of the telescope.

The degree that a telescope magnifies the object viewed is also a property of focal length. Magnification depends on the focal lengths of both the objective and the eyepiece and is simply the ratio formed by dividing the focal length of the objective by the focal length of the eyepiece:

$$\text{Magnification} = \frac{\text{focal length of objective}}{\text{focal length of eyepiece}}$$

For instance, a 7.6-cm f/11 refractor has an objective focal length of $n \times D = 11 \times 7.6\ \text{cm} = 84\ \text{cm}$. If an eyepiece with a focal length of 2.8 cm is used, the magnification of the telescope is

$$\frac{84\ \text{cm}}{2.8\ \text{cm}} = 30\,X$$

The "X" means times; this telescope magnifies 30 times. Another eyepiece with a 1.4 cm focal length would give a magnification of

$$\frac{84\ \text{cm}}{1.4\ \text{cm}} = 60\,X$$

The smaller the eyepiece focal length, the greater the magnification. Manufacturers of small telescopes usually give the magnification when advertising their instruments. If a different magnification is needed, these examples can be used to determine the focal length of the eyepiece needed to achieve the desired magnification.

Using his knowledge of the theory of lenses, Kepler built his own refractor, which improved upon Galileo's telescopes. In the Keplerian telescope (Figure 4), an image is brought to a focus at a distance f_1 from the objective. An eyepiece with a focal length of f_2 then views the focused image. Although all images were upside down in Kepler's telescope,

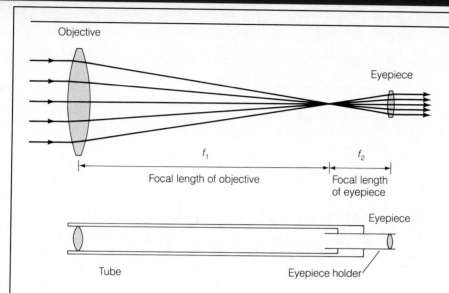

Objective

Eyepiece

f_1
Focal length of objective

f_2
Focal length of eyepiece

Eyepiece

Tube

Eyepiece holder

■ FIGURE 4

The Keplerian Telescope

The Keplerian telescope uses two glass lenses. The eyepiece is inserted in a movable holder or tube so that the observer can move it to the proper position for focusing.

this was not a serious disadvantage; a star just looks like a point of light either way, and it does not matter if the north pole of a planet is at the top of the image or the bottom. More important were the advantages of Kepler's telescope: it allowed wide fields of view, and cross hairs could be placed at the focus of the objective, which allowed astronomers to measure positions of stars and planets accurately. A device with cross hairs used to measure relative positions of stars viewed through a telescope is called a *micrometer*.

Kepler was the first to notice that images of stars and planets viewed through telescopes were fuzzy even with meticulous focusing. Astronomers call this fuzziness **aberration**, and Kepler realized that it was due to the light rays from an image not meeting, or coming to a focus, at the same distance from the lens. Kepler was aware of two types of aberrations:

1. *Chromatic aberration* in which a ring of color surrounded each image

2. *Spherical aberration* in which lenses did not bring light to a sharp focus (Figure 5)

Although the cause of chromatic aberration was unknown in Kepler's time, he suspected that the fuzzy images were caused by the spherical surfaces of the lenses. That is, if the lenses were ground in some other shape, spherical aberration would disappear. It took another hundred years however, before opticians could grind nonspherical lenses. Seventeenth-century astronomers did find a way of reducing spherical aberration, but it required building telescopes as long as a house!

Spherical Aberration

The location of the focus of light passing through a spherical lens depends on where the light enters the lens. A spherical lens is not capable of bringing all the light passing through it to a common focus.

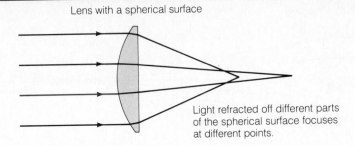

Lens with a spherical surface

Light refracted off different parts of the spherical surface focuses at different points.

The Long Telescopes

Kepler was correct in suspecting the spherical curvature of lenses was the cause of spherical aberration. Simply put, the greater the curvature of the surface of a lens, the greater the spherical aberration. Astronomers found by trial and error that they could reduce the effects of spherical aberration and, therefore, produce sharper images by grinding lenses with less curvature. Figure 6 shows the effect of a smaller curvature on the focal length—the focal length increases. The result of "flat" lenses with long focal lengths was the construction of long telescopes, but with less spherical aberration.

In fact, these new telescopes could be called long, skinny, flimsy telescopes. Figure 7 shows two examples of long telescopes. In 1659

Focal Length and Lens Curvature

The less the curvature of the lens, the greater the focal length.

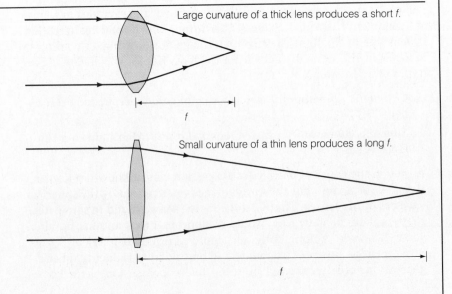

Large curvature of a thick lens produces a short *f*.

f

Small curvature of a thin lens produces a long *f*.

f

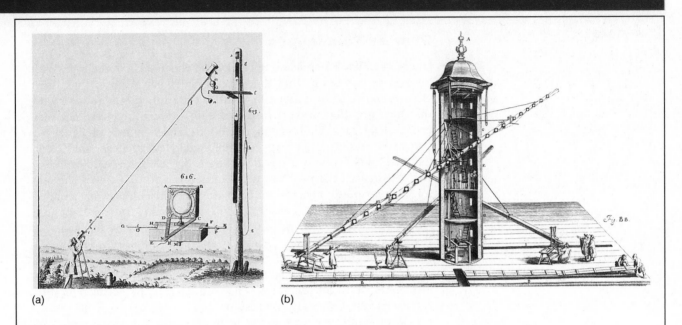

(a)   (b)

Christian Huygens (1629–1695) built a telescope 37.5 m (123 feet) long. The objective was placed on a tall pole and "connected" to the eyepiece through a long, stiff wire. Needless to say, it was very difficult to line up the eyepiece and objective to make an observation. A few years later in 1673, the Polish astronomer Johannes Hevelius (1611–1687) built a telescope 45.7 m (150 feet) long. It was basically a wooden tube suspended from a 90-foot pole. It was lowered and raised by ropes controlled by assistants. These long telescopes presented many problems to the observer. The telescopes would sway in the wind; it was difficult to align lenses that were over a hundred feet apart; stray light easily entered the optical path, making it difficult to view faint objects; and the wood would warp and the ropes change length with changes in humidity during the night. Astronomers had nothing better. It was not technologically possible to manufacture good lenses with short focal lengths. Even as late as 1722, a telescope 65 m (212 feet) long was in use.

Despite these practical difficulties with long telescopes, astronomers made many important observations and discoveries. Hevelius (1647) and Riccioli (1651) produced very accurate maps of the Moon. Huygens discovered a moon of Saturn in 1655 and determined the 14¼-year period of the tilt of Saturn's rings in 1659. Cassini discovered the Great Red Spot of Jupiter in 1664, moons of Jupiter in 1671, 1672, and 1684, and the gap in Saturn's ring in 1675. In the eighteenth century, however, astronomers found one solution to the long telescopes—they used mirrors.

■ FIGURE 7

Aerial Telescopes

(*a*) The objective lens was 37.5 m (123 feet) from the eyepiece of Huygens's telescope. The lens was so far away that it could only be located by looking for the reflection of a lantern on the lens. (*b*) A band of assistants was required to raise and lower the long tubes of Hevelius's telescopes. Then they had to maneuver the tubes so that the observer could follow and observe objects at high magnification. The slightest breeze would cause the whole framework to vibrate. Consequently, this kind of telescope was used only for occasional observing.

Shorter Telescopes

One suggestion for shortening telescopes was to reflect the light with a series of mirrors so that the light bounces back and forth instead of traveling straight down a long tube. The immediate problem with that idea was that mirrors in the seventeenth century were not very good reflectors of light. Each reflection caused a loss of light; too many reflections caused a loss of the image! Nevertheless, Isaac Newton (1642–1727) pursued the idea of building telescopes with mirrors. He investigated the problem with refractors and discovered the reason for chromatic aberration: light of different colors was refracted by different amounts. Lenses act like prisms and spread light into individual colors. This meant that red light would be focused at a slightly different distance behind a lens than blue light (Figure 8). Newton convinced himself that chromatic aberration could not be corrected and that mirrors were the only solution to the long, awkward telescopes. Since light was not refracted by reflecting off a mirror, no chromatic aberration resulted.

Newton's mirrors were made of mixtures of copper, tin, and arsenic in the ratio 6:2:1. The tin and arsenic were whiteners. Since mirrors reflected light, these telescopes were called **reflectors.** New-

■ FIGURE 8

Chromatic Aberration

A lens tends to refract light like a prism, spreading the incoming light into its constituent wavelengths. Since different colors are refracted different amounts, each color has its own focus.

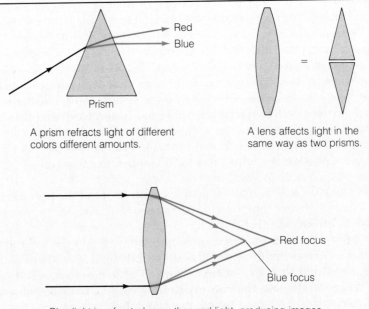

Red
Blue

Prism

A prism refracts light of different colors different amounts.

=

A lens affects light in the same way as two prisms.

Red focus

Blue focus

Blue light is refracted more than red light, producing images that are in focus in one color but not in the other.

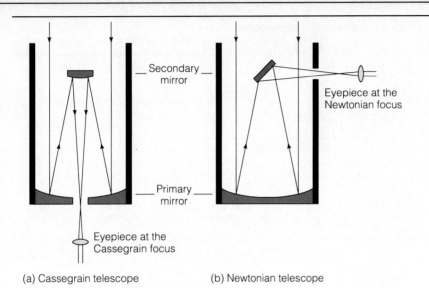

(a) Cassegrain telescope   (b) Newtonian telescope

■ FIGURE 9

Cassegrain and Newtonian Reflectors

(a) A hole drilled in the mirror allows light reflected from a secondary mirror to pass through the primary mirror at the rear of the telescope; this focus is called the Cassegrain or Cass focus. *(b)* A Newtonian reflector brings the focus to the side of the telescope tube; this focus is called the Newtonian focus.

ton made his first successful reflector in 1668. It had a diameter of 2.5 cm (1 inch), a focal length of 15 cm (6 inches), and a magnification of 40 *X*. Refractors with 2.5-cm objectives at that time were 1 to 2 m (3 to 6 feet) long! Newton's design (Panel b in Figure 9) in which the focus of the mirror is brought out to the side of the telescope tube is called a *Newtonian* reflector. A slightly different design for a reflector was invented by a Frenchman by the name of Sieur Cassegrain in 1672 (Panel a in Figure 9). The *Cassegrain* reflector brings the focus of the mirror to the rear of the telescope by reflecting light with a secondary mirror back through a hole made in the primary mirror. This design is slightly more convenient for observers and is very useful for placing heavy equipment on a telescope. Several problems, however, made the first reflectors unusable for research. They reflected less than 20% of the incident light; the mirrors tarnished easily and had to be repolished often; and it was difficult to position a micrometer. Furthermore, since no one knew how to grind appropriately shaped nonspherical mirrors, reflecting telescopes suffered from spherical aberration.

By 1721 astronomers and opticians had improved upon mirrors, and John Hadley (1682–1744) built the first usable reflector (Figure 10). He solved the spherical aberration problem by grinding a *parabolic* mirror (Figure 11). A parabolic mirror is deeper in the center than a spherical mirror and brings the light striking anyplace on the mirror to a common focus. His telescope had a 15-cm (6-inch) diam-

■ FIGURE 10

The First Usable Reflecting Telescope

John Hadley built this 15-cm reflector, which could be easily maneuvered.

SOURCE: Reproduced by permission of the Trustees of the Science Museum.

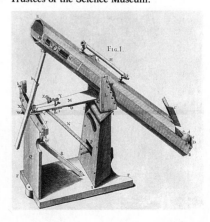

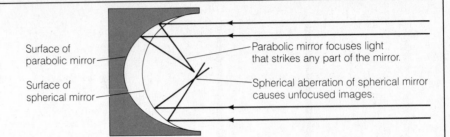

■ FIGURE 11

Parabolic Mirrors

The curvature of a parabolic mirror brings the light reflected off any part of the mirror to a common focus, thus eliminating spherical aberration.

eter mirror with a focal length of 1.8 m (6 feet), was easy to maneuver, and allowed no scattered light to reflect off the mirror. Thus, reflectors in the eighteenth century were free of both spherical and chromatic aberration. In that century, both aberrations were solved for lenses as well.

In 1733 Chester Moore Hall (1703–1771) discovered that dense flint glass refracted light more than the less dense crown glass. He built an *achromatic* lens by cementing a convex lens of crown glass to a concave lens of flint glass. The individual deviations for each lens for different colors balanced each other, thereby eliminating chromatic aberration. Hall was neither an optician nor an astronomer so he did not publish the fact that he had built a 2.5-cm (1-inch) refractor with a focal length of only 12 cm (4.5 inches)! John Dolland (1706–1761) began manufacturing achromatic lenses in 1757. He noticed that the achromatic lens also corrected spherical aberration. Again, the aberration of the concave lens compensates for the aberration of the convex lens.

Large Reflectors

Although achromatic refractors with short focal lengths began to replace the long telescopes, opticians had difficulty casting large pieces of flint glass without defects. By the end of the eighteenth century, the largest achromatic lenses were only 10 cm in diameter. It was natural, therefore, for astronomers to think in terms of large reflectors, and it was William Herschel (1738–1822) who started the "age of the large reflector."

Herschel discovered the planet Uranus with a 15-cm (6-inch) reflector that had a focal length of 2.1 m. Whereas other observers saw Uranus only as a point of light, Herschel saw it as a disk; that is, his telescope was able to *resolve* the image of Uranus. Even today telescopes cannot magnify the image of a star enough to see stellar disks.

When viewed in a telescope stars are not exact point images, they are blurred. Blurring has two causes: one is due to the telescope itself and the other is due to the Earth's atmosphere. Light that passes through a small hole produces an image, called a diffraction pattern, that looks like a bright circle with rings around it (Figure 12). A telescope acts as a hole and causes star images to have this diffraction pattern. With very good optics, about 80% of the light from the star is concentrated in the central circle.

The diffraction pattern of a star is visible through the eyepiece of a telescope or detected in photographic images only if the Earth's atmosphere is very "calm." Astronomers refer to the effects of atmospheric turbulence as "seeing" and a calm atmosphere is one of good seeing. Turbulence is a measure of the vertical motions of air pockets of different temperatures and densities in the atmosphere. The varying densities of air cause light from celestial objects to be refracted many times in slightly different directions along the optical path through the atmosphere to the observer. The many different paths taken by the light from a star will cause the image of a star seen through a telescope to blur. On nights of poor seeing, star images dance about, appear bloated, and expand and contract, showing much activity! Without a telescope, seeing is indicated by the degree of "twinkling" of stars. On nights of poor seeing, stars appear to sparkle like jewels; on nights of good seeing, they appear to shine with an almost steady glow.

The resolving ability of a telescope is defined as the distance between two images for which there is a clear separation of the images. For instance, a pair of stars can be so close together that the central disks of their diffraction patterns blend together so much that the observer cannot distinguish two individual stars (Figure 13). The unit of measurement of resolving ability, or angular resolution, is the "arc second," which is calculated with the following equation:

$$\text{Angular resolution} \propto \frac{\text{wavelength}}{\text{diameter}}$$

and for visual wavelengths

$$\text{Angular resolution} = \frac{11.4}{\text{diameter in centimeters}} = \frac{4.5}{\text{diameter in inches}}$$

A telescope with an 11.4-cm or 4.5 inch lens or mirror is able to resolve images 1 arc second apart. Closer than that, the stars look like one object. Atmospheric turbulence limits the resolving power of any Earth-based optical telescope to about 1 arc second except at the premier observing sites in the world where resolutions of 0.5 arc seconds have been reported in extremely good seeing.

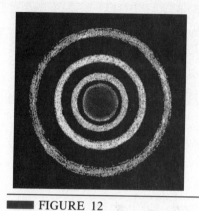

FIGURE 12

Diffraction Pattern of a Star

Under high magnification and calm conditions in a very steady atmosphere, star images appear as a bright central disk surrounded by fainter rings.

See MathTools 2: Angular Measurement and Proportions a/b

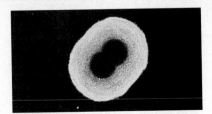

Images of two stars that are not resolved. Atmospheric conditions cause the images to be blurred.

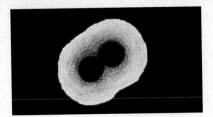

Images of two stars are almost resolved. The observer knows that two or more stars are there, but the telescope cannot resolve them.

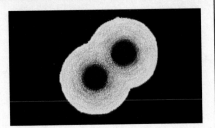

Images are resolved.

■■■ **FIGURE 13**

Resolving Two Stars

The farther apart the stars or the better the telescope optics or the calmer the atmosphere, the easier it is to separate the images of two stars.

■■■ **FIGURE 14**

William Herschel's 1.2-m (48-inch) Reflector

The triangular latticework of poles and ladders was over 15 m (50 feet) high. The whole structure turned on rollers along brick circles.

SOURCE: Yerkes Observatory.

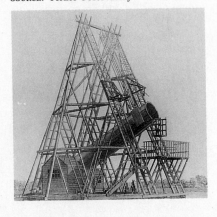

Herschel's discovery of Uranus spurred him on to make larger reflectors. In 1789 he constructed the largest telescope in the world: a 1.2-m (48-inch) reflector 12 m (40 feet) long (Figure 14). This was large in both the diameter of the mirror and in the structure needed to house and support it. Telescopes of this size suffered from problems similar to those of the "long" telescopes of the seventeenth century. They were clumsy! They had to be maneuvered by pulleys and muscle power, and much of the time was spent getting ready to observe.

While astronomers using reflectors were struggling with huge telescopes, two new developments at the beginning of the nineteenth century made refractors competitive with reflectors. First, a new method of casting lenses by stirring was developed, enabling large, defect-free lenses to be manufactured. Second, mounting for the telescope improved with the *equatorial* mount shown in Figure 15. Equatorial mounts are designed to let the telescope swing east or west around an axis that points toward the north celestial pole and to move north and south, allowing easy viewing of the whole visible celestial hemisphere. Aligning the telescope's "polar axis" with the Earth's polar axis allows a simple, slow motion of the telescope to compensate for the rotation of the Earth and permits a celestial object to be viewed in the eyepiece for extended periods of time. The compensating motion today is provided by electric motors; in the past, it was provided by clock drives or simply by cranking a gear. Equatorial mounted refractors were so well balanced that they could be moved with a gentle push of the fingertip. Thus these developments allowed refractors to become larger and easier to use.

Despite the improvements of refractors, reflectors were still "growing." In 1845 a rich, Irish astronomer, William Parsons, the third earl of Rosse (1800–1867), built a giant 1.8-m (72-inch) reflector dubbed the "Leviathan" (Figure 16). With the Leviathan, Parsons could see fainter objects than had ever been visible before, and the brightness

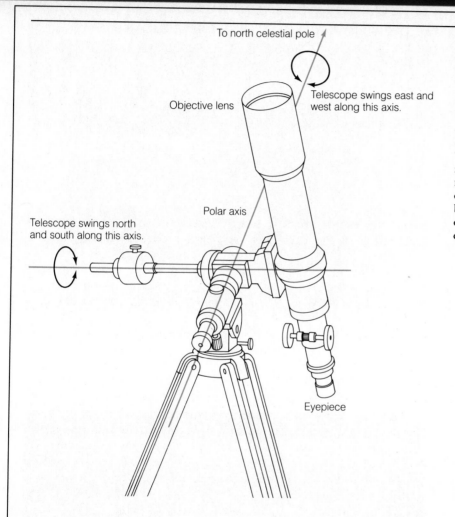

To north celestial pole

Telescope swings east and west along this axis.

Objective lens

Polar axis

Telescope swings north and south along this axis.

Eyepiece

**Equatorial Mounting
for a Small Refractor**

The "polar" axis points toward the north celestial pole near Polaris. The telescope can move east and west along this axis and mimics the motion of the stars on the celestial sphere. The second axis, shown here as horizontal, permits the telescope to swing north and south. The object at the end of this axis is a counterweight that balances the telescope, allowing the observer to move the telescope very easily.

of objects surpassed everyone's expectations. A bright planet such as Jupiter would momentarily blind the observer. The view of the Moon with the Leviathan revealed a profusion of small craters, rilles, and mountains. Parsons was the first astronomer to see details of the spiral structure in galaxies (Figure 17). Although the Leviathan was awkward to use, it produced three important results that greatly influenced further development of observational astronomy. First, it proved that building large telescopes was practical. Second, because Ireland was a poor site for observing (poor weather made the telescope useless most of the time), it showed that the selection of an observing site was important. Finally, one reason that the Leviathan was awkward to use was that it mainly moved up and down and not

■ FIGURE 16

The Leviathan

This was the largest telescope in the
world in the nineteenth century. It
was built in 1845 in Ireland by the
third earl of Rosse, William Parsons. It
could move north and south but only a
short distance east and west.

SOURCE: Reproduced by permission of the
Trustees of the Science Museum.

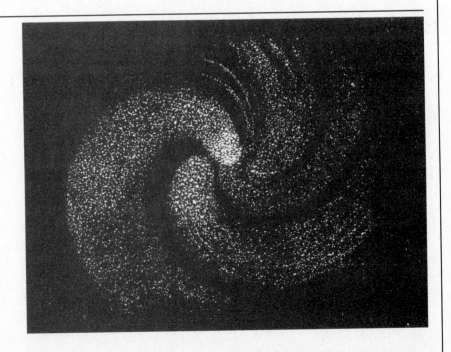

■ FIGURE 17

**M99, a Spiral Nebula in
Coma Berenices**

This was one of the first drawings of a
spiral nebula and indicated the power
of large telescopes to discern detail
unattainable with smaller instruments
(see also Figure 18.1a for another of
Parson's drawings).

SOURCE: From page 77 of *A Handbook of
Descriptive and Practical Astronomy* by
George F. Chambers (Oxford: The Claren-
don Press, 1890).

left and right relative to the horizon. Hence, astronomers realized they had to devise methods to maneuver large telescopes so that they could point anywhere in the sky.

In 1861 William Lassell (1799–1880) built the first large (1.2-m) Newtonian reflector that could be easily maneuvered (Figure 18). The observer in the tower at the Newtonian focus turned a crank that slowly moved the telescope to keep it pointed at the object being observed; this permitted the observer to view the object in the eyepiece for a long time. This was important because astronomers often drew pictures or made positional measurements of what they were observing. At the same time, an assistant could move the tower when the telescope moved too far from the observer. Parsons proved that large telescopes could be built; Lassell proved that they could be used.

Why build larger and larger telescopes? Larger telescopes allow the observer to see fainter objects. The mirror or lens of a telescope is a light collector. A star emits light radially away from itself in all directions in space. Figure 19 illustrates that a large mirror is able to collect more of the light from a star than a small mirror. The mir-

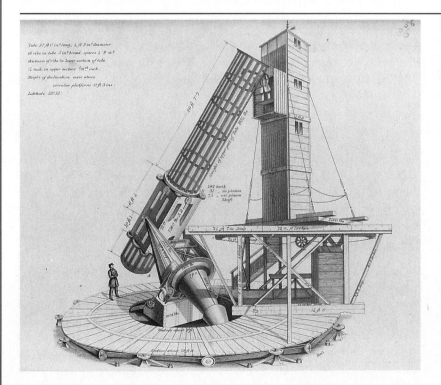

■■■ FIGURE 18

Lassell's 1.2-m (48-inch) Reflector

This was one of the first large Newtonian reflectors that was easy to maneuver.

SOURCE: Royal Astronomical Society.

■ FIGURE 19

**Light-Gathering Power of
Mirrors or Lenses**

A larger mirror or lens is able to intercept (reflect or refract) more light than
a smaller one. Telescopes are often referred to as light buckets.

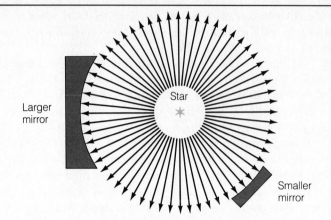

The larger mirror intercepts more light from a star;
therefore, the star appears brighter.

ror then brings all of this light to a focus. The larger the mirror, the
more light that is brought to a focus, and the brighter the star appears. That is why objects appeared so bright when seen through the
Leviathan. Since the area of the mirror or lens is proportional to the
square of its radius, the comparison of the *light gathering power* of
two telescopes is simply the ratio of their radii or diameters squared.
For instance, the light-gathering power of the Leviathan compared to
the 24-cm Dorpat refractor at the Pulkowa Observatory, for many
years the largest refractor in the world, is

$$\frac{(180 \text{ cm})^2}{(24 \text{ cm})^2} = 56$$

The Leviathan collected nearly 60 times more light than the Dorpat
refractor and, therefore, could see much fainter celestial objects. Table 1 summarizes these and later events in the history of the telescope.

The Great Refractors and Reflectors

In the late 1800s and early 1900s major telescope advances took
place in the United States. Alvan Clark (1804–1887) learned how to
make excellent lenses by grinding and polishing glass blanks himself.
At that time astronomers, including American astronomers, would
not buy American-made lenses. To sell his lenses, Clark had to prove
that they were top quality. He began making observations of close
double stars, which required excellent lenses to resolve the pairs, and

■■■■ TABLE 1 **Major Events in the History of the Telescope**

Year	Event
1250	Lenses used for spectacles.
1604	Telescope invented.
1609–1612	Galileo's observations: four moons of Jupiter discovered.
1655–1757	"Age of long refractors."
1655	Huygens discovers Titan, a moon of Saturn.
1659	Huygens announces Saturn has a ring.
1664	Cassini discovers Jupiter's Great Red Spot.
1668	Newton makes first reflector.
1671–1684	Cassini discovers Iapetus, Rhea, Tethys, and Dione, all moons of Saturn.
1721	Hadley makes first "usable" reflector.
1733	Hall invents achromatic lens.
1781	Herschel discovers Uranus with a 15-cm (6-inch) reflector.
1789	Herschel discovers Mimas (Saturn) and Oberon (Uranus) with the 1.2-m (48-inch) reflector.
1807	First equatorial mounting for refractors.
1845	Leviathan built.
1846	Neptune discovered.
1846–1851	Lassell discovers Triton (Neptune), Hyperion (Saturn), Ariel and Umbriel (Uranus) with a 0.6-m (24-inch) reflector.
1856	Metal-coated glass mirrors developed.
1888/1897	Lick 0.9-m and Yerkes 1-m refractors built—largest in the world.
1918	100-inch Hooker telescope built.
1932	Jansky detects radio signal coming from the Milky Way Galaxy.
1939	Reber produces first radio map of the Milky Way.
1946	First radar signals bounced off the Moon.
1948	200-inch Hale reflector built.
1951	Detection of 21-cm radiation from interstellar hydrogen gas.
1965	Penzias and Wilson discover 3 K radiation at 7.35 cm.
1976	Soviet 6-m reflector built.
1978	*International Ultraviolet Explorer (IUE)* launched.
1981	Very Large Array operational.
1983	*Infrared Astronomical Telescope (IRAS)* launched.
1990s	*Hubble Space Telescope* launched; Very Long–Baseline Arrays operational; age of the "new technology telescopes."

reported some of his results to the English astronomer W. R. Dawes, who spread the word in Europe of Clark's excellent lenses and even purchased several himself. Clark's lens was reported to resolve pairs of stars as close together as 0.7 arc seconds, enabling him to discover several double stars that were so close together that no other existing telescope could resolve them. Clark's observations proved that his lenses were by far the best made in the world. In fact, Alvan Clark's son, Alvan George Clark, using a 0.45-m (18½-inch) Clark lens was the first person to see the faint white dwarf companion of the bright star Sirius. This lens is still in use at the Dearborn Observatory of Northwestern University in Evanston, Illinois. Alvan Clark and his

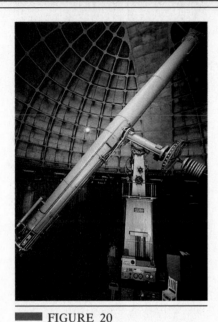

■ FIGURE 20

The Lick 0.9-m (36-inch) Refractor

SOURCE: Lick Observatory, University of California, Santa Cruz.

sons figured the lenses for the two largest refractors operating today. In 1888 they made the objective for the Lick Observatory (California) 0.9-m (36-inch) refractor, and in 1897 they made one for the Yerkes Observatory (Wisconsin) 1-m (40-inch) refractor, the largest astronomical lens in the world (Figure 20).

The person behind the building of the giant Yerkes 1-m refractor was the astronomer George Ellery Hale (1868–1938). The lens for the 1-m telescope originally was to be purchased by the University of Southern California, but the university's plans to raise the money failed. Hale was able to raise the money for the telescope by locating a wealthy donor, Charles T. Yerkes, a Chicago trolley-car magnate. Hale dreamed of building even larger telescopes but realized that the largest possible lens could not be much larger than 1 meter in diameter. Indeed, larger refractors were never built. It is not easy to cast a perfect blank of flint glass necessary for shaping and figuring into an astronomical lens. The 0.9-m lens for the Lick telescope was cast 19 times before a perfect blank resulted! Moreover, lenses can only be supported around their edges. Since they are so heavy (the Yerkes 1-m lens weighs 500 pounds), larger lenses tend to sag and deform, resulting in a poor focusing ability. Hale's dreams became reality as he became the moving force behind the largest reflectors built in the first half of this century.

These were made possible, in part, because a process had been invented in 1856 that allowed a thin layer of metal to be applied to the surface of a polished mirror. The first of these mirrors were silver coated with a layer thin enough not to be expensive. Later mirrors used aluminum coatings because aluminum is less expensive and reflects more of the incident light. Today's aluminum mirrors reflect more than 90% of incident visible light. The advantage of silvering or aluminizing a mirror is that the mirror can be made of glass, which is easier to shape and lighter than metal. The shaping is done by slowly grinding the glass with a series of finer and finer powders that scratch the glass. After the glass blank has the correct shape, a high polish is obtained with jeweler's rouge made of microscopic particles of iron oxide. The test to see if the mirror is actually parabolic is called the *Foucault test*. It is conducted by looking through a pinhole at the focus of the mirror. If the mirror is correctly shaped without lumps or bumps, the image of the mirror seen in the eyepiece will be uniformly bright. The new coating and grinding processes made metal mirrors obsolete.

Hale was largely responsible for the building of the 1.5-m (60-inch) and the 2.5-m (100-inch) telescopes at Mt. Wilson in California and the 5-m (200-inch) telescope on Palomar Mountain also in California (Figure 21). The 1.5-m telescope was the largest in the world from

(a)

(b)

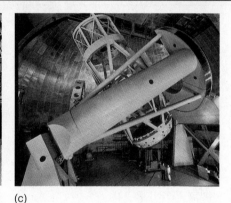
(c)

1908 until 1917 when the 2.5-m Hooker telescope was completed. This 2.5-m reflector was the largest until 1948 when the 5-m reflector, now called the Hale telescope, was completed. The 2.5-m telescope contributed much to the revolution in our outlook on the universe. The Hooker telescope enabled astronomers to gauge the size and nature of the Milky Way Galaxy; it allowed astronomers to determine the nature of other galaxies; and it was used to gather the data supporting the concept of an expanding universe. In 1976 the Soviet 6-m (236-inch) reflector on Mt. Pastukhov in the southern USSR began operation. Like the Yerkes 1-m refractor, the 5-m Hale and 6-m Soviet reflectors seemed to herald the end of the growth of a particular type of telescope—those with large, thick glass mirrors. Before the 1970s it was not possible to build significantly larger telescopes than the 5-m Hale telescope, but key technical breakthroughs in the last decade have made larger apertures possible.

New Technology Optical Reflectors

Several factors made the building of telescopes larger than the 5-m Palomar and the 6-m Soviet reflectors prohibitive. The dominant cost factors are the weight of the supporting structure for the mirror and the size of the building to house the telescope. These in turn are determined by the exact shape of the mirror and its weight. The larger the telescope, of course, the larger the building needed to house the instrument. Building costs can be kept to a minimum if the telescope has a short focal ratio, such as $f/3$. The greater the weight of the mirror, the greater the mass of the supporting structures. The 5-m Palomar mirror weighs 29,000 pounds and requires a supporting structure of 140 tons. Why were heavy mirrors needed in the first place? Mirrors bend, or flex, under stress from gravity. The degree of stress varies as the telescope is moved to different positions during the

■■■ FIGURE 21

Telescopes at the Mt. Wilson and Palomar Observatories

(a) The 1.5-m telescope; *(b)* the 2.5-m telescope; *(c)* the 5-m telescope.

SOURCE: Hale Observatories.

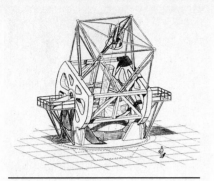

■ FIGURE 22

Design of the NOAO 8-m Telescopes

Two single-mirror 8-m telescopes are planned for the National Optical Astronomy Observatories (NOAO) on Mauna Kea in Hawaii and a site in Chile.

SOURCE: National Optical Astronomy Observatories.

night. These distortions of the mirror cause its focal length to change slightly, and therefore, to produce out of focus images. Making the mirror thick and, therefore, as rigid as possible was one method used to minimize flexing. Thick mirrors cause another problem, however. Mirrors change their shape while expanding when heated or contracting while cooled, causing the focal length to change also. A mirror requires time to adjust from daytime temperatures to nighttime temperatures. This is why telescope domes at observatories are opened before dark. The ventilation helps the mirror reach the same temperature as the outside air. The thicker the mirror, the longer the time it needs to reach the temperature of its surroundings.

The key technological breakthrough was the development of the ability to make thinner mirrors and to support them. The 5-m Palomar mirror is 0.6 m (2 feet) thick. The largest single mirror we are able to build today is about 8 meters in diameter, but it can be cast so that it is only 10 cm (4 inches) thick! Supporting such thin mirrors is tricky. Thin mirrors must be adjusted constantly to maintain their proper shape. This is done by a system of actuators that can push or pull the mirror to make up for flexure. Several 7- to 8-m telescopes are being built jointly by consortia of universities, including Arizona, Ohio State, and Johns Hopkins, and by the Carnegie Foundation, Japan, and the National Optical Astronomy Observatories (Figure 22). These will begin operating in the 1990s.

Another solution to the problems of increasing aperture is to use a multiple-mirror approach. The idea is to place several mirrors on a common structure and bring the images from each mirror to a common focus. An example of this configuration is the MMT (Multiple-Mirror Telescope) of the Smithsonian Institution and the University of Arizona. It uses six 1.8-m (72-inch) mirrors (Panel a in Figure 23). The total area of the six mirrors is equivalent to that of a 4.5-m (177-inch) mirror. The University of Texas and Pennsylvania State University are building an 8-m telescope employing 73 1-m mirrors (Panel b in Figure 23). Each mirror is only 4.5 cm thick and together they form an 8-m spherical mirror. Spherical aberration is corrected by secondary and tertiary mirrors at the prime focus. Instruments are housed in an elevated control tower and the focused light enters by a fiber-optics cable.

The largest planned telescope in the world is the European Southern Observatory (ESO) 16-m Very Large Telescope (Panel a in Figure 24). The design calls for four 8-m reflectors individually mounted and placed in a straight line. Each telescope is enclosed by a collapsible dome and each can be operated individually or in tandem with any of the others. Working together, the four telescopes will have the collecting area of a 16-m single mirror. Panel b in Figure 24 shows an-

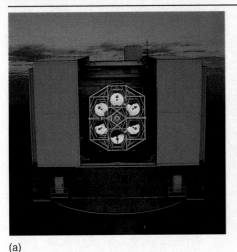

(a)

(b)

FIGURE 23

Multiple-Mirror Telescopes

(a) The Multiple-Mirror Telescope on Mt. Hopkins, Arizona uses six 1.8-m (72-inch) mirrors. *(b)* The 8-m Spectroscopic Survey Telescope will use 73 mirrors, each 1-m in diameter. The instrumentation is located in the elevated building connected to the telescope with a fiber-optic cable.

SOURCES: Part (a), MMT Observatory. The Multiple-Mirror Telescope is a joint research facility of the Smithsonian Institution and the University of Arizona. Part (b), courtesy of The University of Texas McDonald Observatory.

other telescope that uses the multiple-mirror concept. The University of California and the California Institute of Technology have built a 10-m telescope that uses 36 1.8-m hexagonal mirror segments to form a honeycombed pattern 10 meters across (Figure 25). A computer control system is needed to align the mirrors to an accuracy of a millionth of an inch, a thousand times thinner than a human hair. The mirror segments are made of a special glass-ceramic hybrid material that is very stable under changing temperatures.

These monster telescopes are expensive projects. The California 10-m cost almost $90 million and the European Very Large Telescope is expected to cost $130 million. Why spend so much money for larger and larger telescopes? What is the advantage of 10- and 15-meter telescopes?

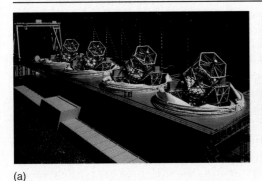

(a)

(b)

FIGURE 24

The Next Generation of Telescopes

(a) The European Very Large Telescope combines four 8-m mirrors to give the collecting area of a 16-m telescope. *(b)* The Keck 10-m telescope of the University of California and the California Institute of Technology uses thirty-six 1.8-m mirrors.

SOURCE: Part (a), European Southern Observatory. Part (b), California Association for Research in Astronomy.

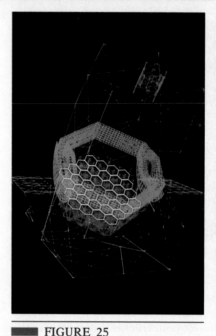

■ FIGURE 25

**Honeycombed Pattern of the 10-m
Keck Telescope**

SOURCE: California Association for Research
in Astronomy.

■ FIGURE 26

**The Cerro Tololo Inter-American
Observatory 4-m Telescope**

This is one of the largest telescopes in
the Southern Hemisphere.

SOURCE: National Optical Astronomy Observatories.

Observations that will help us understand the formation and evolution of galaxies, the origin of the elements, the large-scale structure
of the universe, and the mechanism of star formation are just beyond
the reach of existing telescopes (Figure 26). The study of galaxy evolution and formation requires locating and studying the faintest galaxies possible so that astronomers can see galaxies forming and
changing over time. By observing very distant galaxies, we are looking back in time to the early days of the universe. Observations of
faint galaxies will also indicate how matter was distributed in the
very early universe and help us understand how the universe evolved
from a sea of atoms and molecules to large structures of galaxies.
These are very central problems in astronomy today. We are also on
the verge of understanding the process of star formation, but we need
to observe the details of the formation process itself. This requires
observation of very dynamic events occurring on small scales deep
inside huge clouds of atoms, molecules, and dust. Large telescopes

operating in the infrared will also allow astronomers to image planets orbiting distant stars, if indeed other planets exist. If astronomers are to determine distances, chemical compositions, and motions of celestial objects and understand the range of violent processes occurring in nature, they need greater apertures.

Larger telescopes help in basically two ways. As we have seen, larger telescopes increase our light-gathering ability and resolving power. Therefore, fainter objects can be studied. In the last two decades astronomers have developed detectors that can record three out of four photons collected by the telescope. With little improvement possible in the future development of detectors, the only way to extend the present observational limits is to build larger telescopes.

Yet optical telescopes are only sensitive to a small portion of the electromagnetic spectrum. Since World War II, we have developed detectors capable of recording radiation at almost all wavelengths.

RADIO TELESCOPES

Radio astronomy began in 1932 when Karl Jansky of the Bell Telephone Laboratories detected radio signals with wavelengths of 15 m coming from the Milky Way Galaxy (Figure 27). Although astronomers did not recognize the importance of Jansky's discovery immediately, an amateur named Grote Reber (1911–) built a telescope designed to detect celestial radio radiation. Reber was able to map the

FIGURE 27

Karl Jansky's Radio Telescope

Karl Jansky is shown adjusting his rotating antenna he used to discover radio waves from space. His observations gave the world a new science—radio astronomy.

SOURCE: Courtesy of AT&T Archives.

radiation from the entire Milky Way at a wavelength of 1.87 m. For nearly a decade, Reber was the only radio astronomer in the world. Today, the largest astronomical observing instruments are radio telescopes.

Radio telescopes range from stationary arrays of antennas to fully steerable parabolic reflectors (Panel a in Figure 28). A straight wire, or dipole, antenna detects radio waves by electronically measuring electrical currents. The electrons in the antenna are excited into periodic vibrations by oscillating electric fields in the radio wavelength electromagnetic waves (see Chapter 4). As the electromagnetic waves pass through the antenna, they induce an alternating current that is measured by electronic receivers. A strong source of radio radiation will induce strong currents. The problem with a simple dipole antenna is that it detects radiation from all angles, and, therefore, cannot tell the direction to the source of the emission. This can be partially overcome by using a grid of antennas in which each dipole is suitably spaced so that interference effects between the dipoles limit the detection in certain directions.

Another way to determine the direction to a source is to use dish antennas. Dish antennas are large parabolic reflecting surfaces made of a conducting material with a dipole antenna at the focus. The parabolic dish focuses the radio waves from the source it is pointing toward onto the dipole. The antenna at the focus produces electric currents, which are then amplified and recorded. The reflecting surface does not have to be a smooth mirror because radio wavelengths are so long that a wire mesh "appears" as a solid surface to the radio

▬▬ FIGURE 28

Radio Telescopes

(a) A multiple-dipole radio telescope (foreground) and a disk antenna (background) at NASA's Johannesburg acquisition station. (b) The 64-m (210-foot) parabolic dish radio telescope at Parkes, Australia. Notice that you can see through the wire dish. Radio wavelengths are so long that this disk looks like a solid mirror to them.

SOURCES: Part (a), NASA. Part (b), photograph by J. Masterson, Division of Radiophysics CSIRO.

(a)

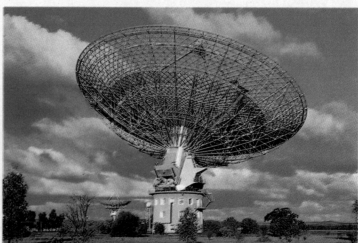

(b)

waves (Panel b in Figure 28). Even chicken wire can make a suitable surface for detecting long radio wavelengths. In fact, the largest radio telescope in the world, the 300-m (1000-foot) Arecibo telescope in Puerto Rico, was originally constructed with chicken wire. It has since been resurfaced with metal plates. The smoother the reflecting surface, the shorter the wavelengths that can be focused. Although a smooth parabola curved to within a millimeter accuracy makes a good radio telescope, it still makes a very poor optical telescope.

The major disadvantage of radio telescopes is their poor resolving ability. Recall that the ability to separate two images, or angular resolution, depends on the observed wavelength and the diameter of the telescope. For radio telescopes the angular resolution in degrees is approximately equal to

$$\text{Angular resolution} = 57 \times \frac{\text{wavelength}}{\text{diameter}}$$

FIGURE 29

The 100-m Radio Telescope near Bonn, West Germany

SOURCE: Max-Planck-Institut für Radioastronomie. Photo by G. Hutschenreiter.

where the units of wavelength and diameter are the same. The angular resolution of a 25-m radio telescope observing at 1-m wavelengths would be

$$\text{Angular resolution} = 57 \times \frac{1 \text{ meter}}{25 \text{ meters}} = 2.3 \text{ degrees}$$

To this radio telescope a strong radio source would look like a fuzzy image on the sky about *five* times the angular size of the Moon. The poor resolution of radio telescopes results from radio wavelengths being hundreds of thousands times longer than optical wavelengths. Consequently, astronomers try to build radio telescopes as large as possible. Fiscal limits, however, dampen astronomers' enthusiasm for large telescopes. To achieve an angular resolution equal to that of even a moderately sized optical telescope, a radio telescope observing at 1 cm would have to be 12 km (7 miles) across (Figure 29). Such an antenna would collapse under its own weight. The best possible angular resolution of a single-dish radio telescope is only about 10 arc seconds, 10 times poorer than optical telescopes. Nevertheless, even at these poor resolutions, a great deal of information is being discovered about the universe from operating radio telescopes.

Astronomers can greatly improve the resolving power of radio telescopes by using two or more telescopes in tandem. The technique is called *aperture synthesis*. The idea is to synthesize a large radio telescope electronically by using several smaller ones. Basically, two telescopes separated by a distance *D* means that their effective diameter is *D*! Because the telescopes are at different distances from the source, a radio signal arrives at one antenna slightly ahead of, or out of phase with, the other one. The key is to merge the signals electron-

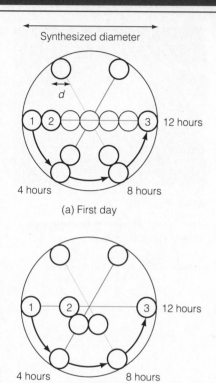

Synthesized diameter

d

1 2   3   12 hours

4 hours   8 hours

(a) First day

1   2   3   12 hours

4 hours   8 hours

(b) Second day

■■■ FIGURE 30

Aperture Synthesis

Three radio telescopes each with diameter, *d*, can synthesize a telescope of diameter $D = 7 \times d$. The Earth's rotation rotates the telescopes through 360° each day. The next day one or more of the telescopes are moved to sample a different part of the larger area.

ically so that the combined signals are in phase. The two telescopes represent only part of a large dish. Imagine this single large radio telescope as having a diameter *D*. The two smaller dishes collect radio waves striking only two spots on the imaginary larger dish. To "fill in," or finish, the synthesis of the larger telescope, observations must be made at all the points between the two dishes (Figure 30). This can be done with a movable radio telescope that can be placed at varying distances between the two. In practice, a radio source is observed one day with the telescopes in one configuration. The next day a different configuration is used to observe the same object. If observations are taken as the Earth rotates 360°, telescopes arranged in a straight line can mimic the effect of a large mirror. By adding all of the signals from observations of different configurations of the telescopes, a computer can make a picture of the source as if it were observed by a single large dish. Since the radio telescopes can be miles apart, the effective diameters synthesized produce angular resolutions 10 times *better* than the largest optical telescopes.

This is possible because, in working with radio waves that are so much longer than light waves, modern electronic devices enable us to measure the time from crest to crest of radio waves arriving at the telescope. This allows astronomers to coordinate the radio waves that are arriving at each of the telescopes in an array. In the future, we may be able to measure the very short time intervals between the wave crests of light waves. We can then use aperture synthesis with optical telescopes and synthesize really large optical telescopes kilometers in diameter!

The world's largest array of telescopes used for aperture synthesis is the 36-km Very Large Array (VLA) located near Socorro, New Mexico (Figure 31). It consists of 27 movable radio dishes, each 25 m in diameter. The dishes are arranged in a Y-shaped pattern and move along railroad tracks. The signals from each of the 27 telescopes travel in underground waveguides about 6 cm in diameter to a common point. Each signal from a telescope is delayed by the proper amount depending on the telescope's position in the pattern being used at the time. All of the signals are in phase to within a few billionths of a second and are sent to a computer that organizes them so that radio maps and other information can be extracted for the particular research project for which the data were collected.

Several other large arrays are located throughout the world. The Australian Telescope consists of several sites across the Australian continent. A group of six 22-m dishes compose the 6-km Compact Array (Figure 32). One dish is stationary while the other five can move along a 6-km-long rail track. Near Cambridge, England, an array called the Five-Kilometer Telescope uses 8 dishes while the 3-km

■ FIGURE 31

The Very Large Array

Several of the 25-m dishes of the Very Large Array near Socorro, New Mexico.
SOURCE: NASA.

Westerbock Synthesis Radio Telescope in Holland uses 14 dishes. At Jodrell Bank, England, six antennas make up the Multi Element Radio Linked Interferometer Network (MERLIN), 133 km long.

■ FIGURE 32

The 6-km Compact Array of the Australian Radio Telescope

Six 22-m dishes compose this array; five are shown here.
SOURCE: Photograph by J. Masterson, Division of Radiophysics CSIRO.

Even larger telescopes can be simulated by using telescopes thousands of kilometers apart. Hundreds of kilometers apart is not far enough; two radio telescopes 130 km apart give the same angular resolution as only a 1-m optical telescope! The technique of using telescopes across continents or oceans simultaneously is called *very long–baseline interferometry*. Telescopes far apart can synthesize a telescope with a diameter equal to the Earth's diameter. The data from each telescope must be recorded simultaneously on magnetic tapes. To ensure simultaneity, the tapes require time marks from clocks that must be accurate to within a billionth of a second per day. Once the observations are collected, the tapes are played back into a computer that combines the signals as if they were from a single telescope. It is not possible to synthesize a single dish with that large a diameter, because the telescopes are stationary and cannot "fill in" the gaps between them. Nevertheless, the resolution is superb! The resolutions attainable with very long baselines are 0.001 arc seconds. Yet some radio sources observed are actually smaller than this!

Astronomers in the United States are constructing the Very Long–Baseline Array (VLBA) to span the country. It will consist of 10 telescopes with 25-meter diameters spread from Hawaii to the Virgin Islands, producing a baseline of 8000 km (Figure 33). The Australian

■■■■ FIGURE 33

The Very Long–Baseline Array

Ten telescopes are planned to be spread over 8000 miles.

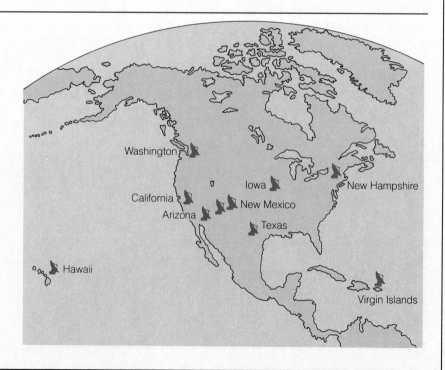

6-km Compact Array is part of the Australian VLBA consisting of 13 telescopes to create a telescope 3000 km across. Canada is building the Canadian Long–Baseline Array with eight 32-m dishes across Canada.

Radio astronomers synthesize apertures to observe radio sources in as much detail as possible. They are looking for phenomena operating at very small scales at sites of star formation and in the active centers of galaxies. Radio astronomy has provided a new look at the universe hitherto unavailable through optical observations. A similar new look at different wavelengths is being provided by satellite observations above the atmosphere of the Earth.

SPACE ASTRONOMY

While most visual and radio wavelengths penetrate the Earth's atmosphere, most infrared, ultraviolet, X-ray, and gamma-ray radiation does not (Figure 34). These are only accessible through observations made with telescopes in orbit or with instrument packages lofted briefly into space with rockets. The first space observations were made from instruments launched with German-made V2 rockets after World War II. After the *Sputnik* launches in 1957, the United States and other nations began launching scientific satellites into orbit.

Several problematical properties of the Earth and its environs make space astronomy attractive, even for optical observations with small orbiting telescopes. The Earth's atmosphere distorts optical images. The twinkling of stars is due to the bending of light rays from stars by pockets of warm air in the atmosphere. This limits the ability of telescopes to resolve stars. Furthermore, the Earth's atmosphere is never completely transparent even to visible wavelengths.

FIGURE 34

Transparency of the Earth's Atmosphere

The transparency of the atmosphere is shown as the percentage of the radiation that reaches the surface. Visible and radio radiation reach the surface of the Earth as does some infrared radiation. Several "windows" exist in the infrared through which infrared radiation can be detected. Most infrared radiation penetrates to high elevations. The major contributors to the absorption of the radiation are indicated.

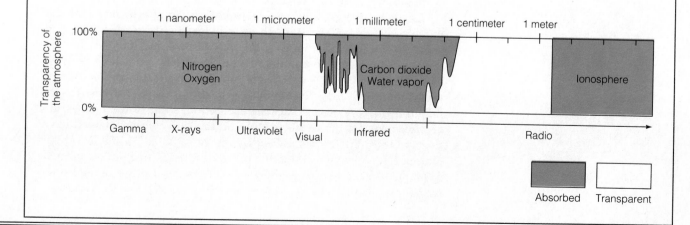

■■■ FIGURE 35

**A Satellite Photograph of the
United States Taken at Night**

Populated areas are clearly visible as
are some interstate highways.

SOURCE: Science VU/Visuals Unlimited.

Dust, clouds, and humidity diminish the intensity of observable light. At some wavelengths, molecules in the atmosphere emit radiation that mixes with that from the object being observed, causing confusion in the recorded signal. Radiation from streetlights, neon lights, and radio broadcasts also interferes with observations (Figure 35). At the same time, the Earth's gravitational field limits the precision with which instruments can be pointed and moved and also distorts optical mirrors and lenses. Finally, the Earth's daily rotation and orbital motion around the Sun limit when observations can be carried out. Objects have to be above the observer's horizon to be observed. This in turn depends on the time of year and the location of the observer on Earth.

Although infrared and visible radiation can be detected at the Earth's surface, eliminating these problems is very attractive and useful to astronomers. Some problems can be reduced by placing observatories on high mountains. High elevations are a help because water vapor is the major source of infrared absorption and is concentrated mainly at lower elevations in the atmosphere. The best Earth-based infrared telescope sites are located on some of the highest accessible peaks in the world. NASA and the University of Hawaii have the 3-m Infrared Telescope Facility on the 4200 m (13,800 feet) high Mauna Kea volcano in Hawaii, and the United Kingdom has located a 3.8-m infrared telescope there as well. Several other optical telescopes are also located on Mauna Kea (Figure 36). The University of

■■■■ FIGURE 36

Mauna Kea Observatory

Several large telescopes have been
built on this extinct volcano in Hawaii: the 3.8-m United Kingdom Infrared Telescope, the 3.6-m Canada-
France-Hawaii Telescope, the 3-m
NASA–University of Hawaii Telescope,
and the Hawaii 2.24-m telescope.

SOURCE: Canada-France-Hawaii Telescope
Corporation.

Wyoming's 2.3-m (92-inch) infrared telescope is located at an elevation of about 3000 m in the mountains of Wyoming.

Infrared observations are needed to solve several important astronomical problems associated with the birth and death of stars and
with the huge energy sources at the center of galaxies. The first major
infrared satellite was the *Infrared Astronomical Satellite (IRAS)*
launched in 1983. It used a 0.6-m (22.5-inch) mirror, small by Earth-
based telescope standards, and viewed the universe at wavelengths
that never penetrate the Earth's atmosphere. *IRAS* was a joint venture of the United States, the Netherlands, and the United Kingdom.
Infrared instruments need to be cooled to very low temperatures because they are trying to detect heat. Cooling is usually done with
liquid helium. *IRAS*'s detectors were cooled to 10 K, and the satellite
lasted 10 months before the liquid helium coolant was depleted. During its 10 months of operation, *IRAS* was able to complete a survey
of the entire sky. Astronomers are still analyzing these data and preparing for the next generation of infrared satellite observatories.

The largest and most complex astronomical satellite ever built, the
Hubble Space Telescope (Figure 37) is designed to observe from the
mid-ultraviolet (1200 Å) to near-infrared wavelengths (12,000 Å). It is
a 2.4-m (94.5-inch) reflecting telescope with several scientific instruments attached, including a wide-field and planetary camera, a faint-
object camera, a high-speed photometer, a faint-object spectrograph,
and a high-resolution spectrograph (these instruments will be dis-

■■■■ FIGURE 37

The *Hubble Space Telescope*
SOURCE: NASA.

cussed later in this module). The resolution of the mirror is 0.05 arc seconds, 20 times that of optical telescopes on the ground. The *Hubble Space Telescope* will be able to observe objects 10 to 100 times fainter than is possible with current Earth-based telescopes, allowing astronomers to see the most remote objects in the universe.

Ultraviolet space observations began in 1946 with instruments launched by V2 rockets. Between 1962 and 1972 a series of eight orbiting solar observatories carried out ultraviolet observations of the Sun. The *Solar Maximum* satellite, launched in 1980, operated until 1989 after being repaired by shuttle astronauts. Still operational is the successful *International Ultraviolet Explorer (IUE)*, which uses a 0.4-m (18-inch) mirror and is in a stationary (geosynchronous) orbit (Figure 38). Ultraviolet observations are important for studying celestial objects and interstellar matter because constituent atoms and molecules emit ultraviolet radiation undetectable by Earth-based telescopes.

Ultraviolet, visible, and infrared observations in space are accomplished with telescopes with parabolic mirrors. High-energy astronomical observations of X-rays and gamma rays require a different kind of telescope. The energies of X-ray and gamma-ray photons (see Chapter 4) are so great that they penetrate mirrored surfaces. The high energies of X-rays and gamma rays indicate that they originate in material that is extremely hot, millions to thousands of millions of Kelvins.

The first high-energy instruments in space carried electronic detectors similar to Geiger counters to detect the presence and intensity of X-rays and gamma rays. Rocket-launched instruments identified about 30 discrete X-ray sources in the 1960s. The successful X-ray

■■■ FIGURE 38

The *International Ultraviolet Explorer, IUE*

This satellite has been operating since its launch in 1978.

SOURCE: NASA.

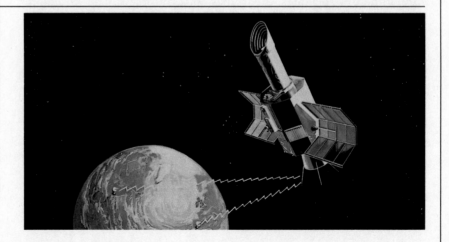

satellite, *Uhuru* (Swahili for "freedom") surveyed the sky and located over 200 sources of X-rays. These instruments were able to tell the intensity and the direction of the X-rays but did not have imaging capability. In the late 1970s, the *Einstein X-Ray Telescope* provided the first images of X-ray sources. It accomplished this with a series of concentric mirrors, which were able to focus X-rays that struck at a grazing angle. If an X-ray strikes a mirror head on, it would just penetrate; if it strikes at a grazing angle, it could be reflected, as a stone skips over water. The *Einstein* satellite discovered thousands of X-ray sources, revealing the hot environments associated with high-density neutron stars and black holes and with events on the surface of the Sun.

Gamma rays are associated with the decay of radioactive elements. The first extraterrestrial gamma rays were accidentally observed by military surveillance satellites designed to detect gamma rays from nuclear explosions. The study of extragalactic gamma rays is in its infancy. The United States' *Gamma Ray Observatory (GRO)*, launched in 1990, is designed to survey the entire sky for gamma-ray sources and to study in detail some of those sources at several wave-lengths (Figure 39). Like the X-ray observatories, gamma-ray observ-

■■■■ FIGURE 39
NASA's *Gamma Ray Observatory*
SOURCE: NASA.

atories have and will open views never before seen of energetic events occurring in the universe.

ASTRONOMICAL DETECTORS

The main purpose of a telescope, whether optical, radio, or X-ray, is to gather electromagnetic radiation and bring it to a focus. Astronomers use a variety of instruments to measure and record the focused radiation. The first detector ever used, of course, was the human eye. The eye is useful for identifying the object to be studied in the field of view of the telescope and for making some measurements at the eyepiece, such as those with a micrometer or requiring a drawing. The eye's major disadvantage is its inability to make a permanent record of what it sees. Consequently, early astronomers had to rely on drawings until the photograph gave them the means to store images seen through the telescope. Today, astronomers have an array of techniques available to record and analyze light from the cosmos.

Imaging

Imaging refers to reproducing the view seen through the eyepiece, whether it is from visual light in an optical telescope or from X-rays detected by an orbiting X-ray observatory. Pictures can be obtained through *photography* or through *electronic imaging*. Both techniques are described in detail in Astroprobe 14. The heart of the photographic process is a chemical reaction between light and silver bromide atoms in the film. The reaction separates the silver and bromine, and developing makes the separation permanent by removing the separated bromine atoms and the remaining silver bromide molecules. Wherever photons of light produce a reaction, a dark spot appears, and the other parts of the film untouched by light remain transparent. After developing, the dark and transparent regions constitute a photographic negative where bright stars appear as dark spots and the dark sky as a transparent background. Although prints can be made from the negative, astronomers usually do their analysis with the negatives (Figure 40).

The disadvantage of the photographic process is its low efficiency. Only a few percent of all photons falling onto the silver bromide produce a chemical reaction that results in a dark image. During the last few decades, astronomers have searched intensely for a means of increasing the efficiency of imaging. The most impressive gains have been with electronic imaging, in particular with charge coupled devices (CCDs). A CCD is an array of thousands of silicon detectors arranged in a square or rectangle. A picture can be envisioned as com-

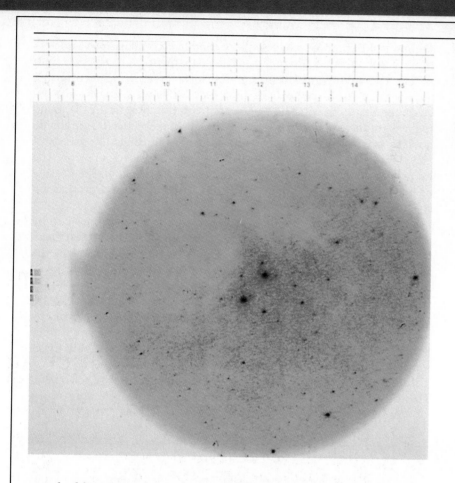

FIGURE 40

A Photographic Plate

Most astronomical photography is done with glass plates instead of film. Shown here is a negative of a star field in a nearby galaxy. Each speck is an individual star and the larger spots are star clusters. One of the major advantages of photographic plates is their ability to make a permanent record of a large area of the sky.

SOURCE: Evan Flower.

posed of hundreds of thousands of small elements, or pixels, much like the picture on a television screen. Each element is sensitive to light and builds up an electric charge when photons strike it. The electric charge can be measured and converted into an intensity. A picture then is a grid of elements all with different intensities. The most important characteristic of CCDs is that they are more than 60% efficient; that is, more than 6 out of 10 photons register on a CCD compared to a few out of 100 on a photographic film. This means that images can be created with CCDs in just a fraction of the time needed with the photographic process.

Spectroscopy

The maximum amount of information is attained from electromagnetic radiation by spreading it into its wavelength components. The process is called *spectroscopy* and is fully explained in Chapter 4 and the information obtainable, such as chemical compositions and motions, is described in Chapter 13. The instrument that disperses light is called a *spectrograph*. In its simplest form, an optical spectrograph uses a prism to disperse light into individual wavelengths and focuses the resulting spectrum onto photographic film or a CCD, making a permanent record called a *spectrum*. Modern spectrographs do not use prisms but use diffraction gratings. Gratings are pieces of glass onto which thousands of closely spaced grooves are cut. The grooves can be designed so that light can either reflect off the grating or pass through it. In either case, light is dispersed and produces a spectrum.

Spectrographs can be bulky instruments. The smaller ones can be placed at the Cassegrain focus of a large telescope. The largest spectrographs are so heavy that they cannot be mounted, even on the largest telescopes. In this case, they are placed at the Coudé focus (Figure 41), which is usually in the basement of the observatory where the spectrograph rests on the floor in an environmentally controlled room. Small telescopes can also use large spectrographs by feeding the light from the telescope to the instrument through fiber optical wire. The spectrograph can rest on the floor of the observatory and not interfere with the operation of the telescope.

Radio telescopes can also obtain the radio spectrum of an object. The radio telescope's receiver is tuned to different wavelengths much

FIGURE 41

The Coudé Focus

Light is reflected away from the telescope tube, usually along the polar axis, to the observatory's floor or a room below the floor. The advantage of the Coudé focus is that large, heavy instruments can be used to analyze the incoming light.

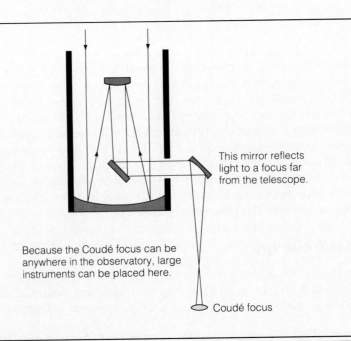

This mirror reflects light to a focus far from the telescope.

Because the Coudé focus can be anywhere in the observatory, large instruments can be placed here.

Coudé focus

the same way a radio receiver is used to locate different stations. Whenever the receiver is set at a wavelength that corresponds to the emission of an atom or molecules of radiation of the same wavelength, the radio telescope records a large signal.

Photometry

Another electronic means of measuring the intensity of light from stars is to use a *photomultiplier*. This is an electronic tube that operates on the photoelectric effect. Certain metals, such as cesium, were found to emit electrons when struck with light. A photomultiplier tube electronically multiplies the number of electrons knocked off the metal and generates a current that is easily measurable. The tube has a negatively charged "cathode" made of photoelectric material and a series of "anodes," each at a slightly different voltage. When light strikes the cathode, it releases an electron that is attracted to the first anode. When it hits the anode, it knocks off a few more electrons, which in turn are attracted to the next anode. Each time this happens, more electrons are produced. In the end a single photon can generate a flood of millions of electrons, which can easily be measured as an electric current. The brighter the star, the more light that strikes the cathode, and the greater the resultant current. The brightness of a star is proportional to the electric current it produces. Such photoelectric detectors are called *photometers* (Figure 42).

Intensity measurements with photometers are very accurate. The major disadvantage of photoelectric measurements is that only one star can be measured at a time. No image is produced, just an electric current. The telescope must be accurately lined up on the star to be studied and its light passed through a small hole just big enough to let the light fall onto the cathode. CCDs combine the accuracy of photometers and the imaging properties of photographs. The price to be paid for this combination is a wealth data. These data can only be effectively analyzed with computers with methods called image processing. Some of the techniques associated in these analyses are described in AstroProbe 14.

The combination of detectors with monster telescopes and spaceborne observatories has opened up the universe to astronomers. We are now able to view the cosmos at virtually all wavelengths. Some of the first glimpses have been described in the chapters in this book, but much more will come in the next few decades as larger orbiting telescopes are launched and large Earth-based telescopes are built. Astronomers will be able to see the edge of the universe, and therefore the depths of time, and view the processes deep in giant dust and gas clouds that give rise to stars.

■■■■■ FIGURE 42

A Typical Photometer

The photomultiplier tube is enclosed in a light-tight box. Eyepieces allow the observer to look through the telescope to make sure that the proper star is being measured.

SOURCE: Phillip Flower.

Asteroids and Comets

ASTEROIDS AND COMETS ARE SMALL BODIES belonging to the solar system. Asteroids reside mainly in the asteroid belt between 2 and 3 AU from the Sun, but a few have orbits that take them within the Earth's orbit. Jupiter has "captured" two groups of asteroids, called the Trojan asteroids, at the Lagrangian points in its orbit. A significant population of asteroids may lie beyond the orbit of Saturn.

TABLE A.1 **Representative Asteroids**

Number	Name	Semimajor Axis AU	Perihelion[1] AU	Aphelion[2] AU	Inclination	Diameter km	Classification[3]
Apollo Asteroids[4]							
1566	Icarus	1.1	0.2	2.0	23°	0.7	Unknown
1862	Apollo	1.5	0.7	2.3	6°	0.5	Unknown
1864	Daedalus	1.5	0.6	2.4	22°	≈3	Silicate
Belt Asteroids							
3	Juno	2.7	2.0	3.4	13°	250	Silicate
1	Ceres	2.8	2.6	3.0	11°	1000	Carbonaceous
2	Pallas	2.8	2.1	3.4	35°	540	Silicate
10	Hygiea	3.2	2.8	3.5	4°	450	Carbonaceous
153	Hilda		3.4	4.6	8°	225	Metallic
279	Thule	4.3	4.1	4.4	2°	≈100	Carbonaceous
Trojan Asteroids							
624	Hektor	5.1	5.0	5.2	19°	150 × 300	Carbonaceous
911	Agamemnon	5.2	4.8	5.5	22°	150	Carbonaceous
588	Achilles	5.2	4.4	6.0	10°	120	Carbonaceous
1208	Troilus	5.2	4.7	5.6	34°	100	Carbonaceous
Outer Solar System							
944	Hildalgo	5.9	2.0	9.6	42°	30–40	Carbonaceous
2060	Chiron	13.7	8.5	18.9	7°	350	Carbonaceous

[1]Perihelion distance is the closest the asteroid gets to the Sun.
[2]Aphelion distance is the farthest the asteroid gets from the Sun.
[3]Asteroids are classified as carbon rich, silicon rich, or metallic.
[4]Apollo asteroids are found near the Earth's orbit.

TABLE A.2 **Selected Comets**

Name	Discovered	Period yr	Semimajor Axis AU	Perihelion AU	Eccentricity	Inclination	Date of Next or Last Perhileion
			Short-Period Comets				
Encke	1786	3.28	2.2	0.33	0.85	12°	1990
Giacobini-Zinner	1900	6.61	3.5	1.03	0.71	32°	1992
Tuttle	1790	13.5	5.6	1.00	0.82	55°	1994
Tempel-Tuttle	1866	33.2	10.3	0.98	0.91	162°	1998
Halley	240 B.C.	76	17.9	0.59	0.97	162°	2062
			Long-Period Comets				
Swift-Tuttle	1862	≈120	≈24	0.96	0.96	114°	Has not returned
Thatcher	1861	415	≈56	0.92	≈.98	—	2276
Brooks	1911	2100	164	0.49	—	—	
Mrkos	1957	13,200	560	0.35	—	—	
West	1976	558,300	6780	0.20	—	—	Split

Comets are so small that they are extremely difficult to detect unless they are near the Sun. They are first seen as they approach within about 4 AU of the Sun; at this time, their comas have developed sufficiently to reflect enough sunlight to make them bright. The debris of some comets can intercept the orbit of the Earth. When the Earth passes through this debris, spectacular meteor showers can result. Table A.3 lists the major meteor showers during the year; the dates of the showers are the same from year to year.

TABLE A.3 **Major Meteor Showers**

Shower Name	Date	Meteors per Hour	Constellation of Radiant	Source
Quadrantids	Jan. 3	40–150	Boötes, Hercules, Drako	Unknown
Lyrids	Apr. 22	20; sometimes more	Hercules-Lyra border	Comet Thatcher
Eta Aquarids	May 4	10–40	Aquarius	Comet Halley
Delta Aquarids	Jul. 30	10–35	Aquarius	Unknown
Perseids	Aug. 12	50–100	Perseus	Comet Swift-Tuttle
Draconids	Oct. 10	varies	Draco	Comet Giacobini-Zinner
Orionids	Oct. 20	10–70	Orion	Comet Halley
Taurids	Nov. 5	15	Taurus	Comet Encke
Andromedids	Nov. 14	5–15	Andromeda	Comet Biela
Leonids	Nov. 17	15; can be very high	Leo	Comet Tempel-Tuttle
Geminids	Dec. 13	50–80	Gemini	1566 Icarus*
Ursids	Dec. 22	10–15	Little Dipper	Comet Tuttle

*Although 1566 Icarus is called an asteroid, it may actually be an inactive comet.

Astronomical and Physical Constants

TABLE B.1 **Astronomical Constants**

TABLE B.1 **Astronomical Constants**

Quantity	Symbol	Value and Units (cgs)*
Astronomical unit	AU	149,597,870.7 km
Parsec	pc	3.085678×10^{18} cm
Light-year	ly	9.460536×10^{17} cm
Solar mass	$\mathfrak{M}_\odot$	1.9891×10^{33} g
Solar radius	$R_\odot$	696,265 km
Solar luminosity	$L_\odot$	3.83×10^{33} erg/s
Solar constant		1.37×10^6 erg/cm^2/s
Earth mass	$\mathfrak{M}_\oplus$	5.974×10^{27} g
Earth radius	Equatorial	6378.140 km
	Polar	6356.755 km
	Mean	6371.004 km
Mass ratio	Sun to Earth	332,946
	Earth to Moon	81.3
Tropical year (equinox to equinox)		365.2422
Julian year		365.2500
Gregorian year		365.2425
Sidereal year (fixed star to fixed star)		365.2564

*cgs units are centimeters (cm), grams (g), and seconds (s).

TABLE B.2 **Physical and Atomic Constants**

Quantity	Symbol	Value and Units (cgs)*
Speed of light in a vacuum	c	$2.99792458 \times 10^{10}$ cm/s
Newton's constant of gravitation	G	6.67259×10^{-8} cm^3/g/s^2
Planck constant	h	6.626075×10^{-27} erg/s
Boltzmann constant	k	1.380658×10^{-16} erg/K
Stefan-Boltzmann constant	σ	5.67051×10^{-5} erg/cm^2/K^4/s
Wien's law constant	$\lambda_{max}T =$	0.2897756 cm K
Standard acceleration of gravity	g	980.665 cm/s^2
Atomic mass unit	u (amu)	$1.6605402 \times 10^{-30}$ g
Mass of proton	m_p	$1.6726231 \times 10^{-24}$ g
Mass of neutron	m_n	$1.6749286 \times 10^{-24}$ g
Mass of electron	m_e	$9.1093897 \times 10^{-28}$ g
Radius of first Bohr orbital	a_o	$0.529177249 \times 10^{-8}$ cm
Electron volt	eV	$1.60217733 \times 10^{-12}$ erg

*cgs units are centimeters (cm), grams (g), and seconds (s).

Abundances of the Major Elements

HYDROGEN AND HELIUM, the most abundant elements in the universe, were created during the big bang. Hydrogen burning inside stars also produces helium, but this is destroyed during helium burning when carbon and, through alpha capture, oxygen are created. Carbon, oxygen, and neon burning and alpha capture produce elements as massive as sulfur in stars more massive than about 10 $\mathfrak{M}_\odot$. Silicon burning creates elements with atomic weights of up to 60. More massive elements are created by neutron capture during supernovae.

Table C.1 gives the abundances of elements relative to hydrogen. The last column of abundances does not use powers of 10 to emphasize the great abundance of hydrogen and helium in the universe.

TABLE C.1 **Abundances of the Major Elements**

Name	Symbol	Atomic Number	Atomic Weight	Number of Atoms per	
				10^{12} Hydrogen Atoms	100 Hydrogen Atoms
Hydrogen	H	1	1.008	1×10^{12}	100
Helium	He	2	4.003	9×10^{10}	9
Lithium	Li	3	6.940	5	0.0000000005
Beryllium	Be	4	9.013	14	0.000000001
Boron	B	5	10.82	$<1 \times 10^{3}$	0.0000001
Carbon	C	6	12.01	4×10^{8}	0.04
Nitrogen	N	7	14.01	8×10^{7}	0.008
Oxygen	O	8	16.00	7×10^{8}	0.07
Fluorine	F	9	19.00	4×10^{4}	0.000004
Neon	Ne	10	20.18	1×10^{8}	0.0001
Sodium	Na	11	22.99	2×10^{6}	0.0002
Magnesium	Mg	12	24.32	3×10^{7}	0.003
Aluminum	Al	13	26.98	3×10^{6}	0.0003
Silicon	Si	14	28.09	4×10^{7}	0.007
Phosphorus	P	15	30.98	3×10^{5}	0.00003
Sulfur	S	16	32.07	2×10^{7}	0.007
Chlorine	Cl	17	35.46	3×10^{5}	0.00003
Argon	Ar	18	39.94	1×10^{6}	0.0001
Potassium	K	19	39.10	1×10^{5}	0.00001
Calcium	Ca	20	40.08	2×10^{6}	0.0002
Scandium	Sc	21	44.96	1×10^{3}	0.0000001
Titanium	Ti	22	47.90	1×10^{5}	0.00001
Vanadium	V	23	50.95	1×10^{4}	0.000001
Chromium	Cr	24	52.01	5×10^{5}	0.00005
Manganese	Mn	25	54.94	3×10^{5}	0.00003
Iron	Fe	26	55.85	3×10^{7}	0.003
Cobalt	Co	27	58.94	3×10^{4}	0.000003
Nickel	Ni	28	58.71	2×10^{6}	0.0002
Copper	Cu	29	63.54	1×10^{4}	0.000001
Zinc	Zn	30	65.38	3×10^{4}	0.000003
Gallium	Ga	31	69.72	630	0.000000063
Germanium	Ge	32	72.60	3×10^{3}	0.0000003
Arsenic	As	33	74.91	250	0.000000025
Selenium	Se	34	78.96	2×10^{3}	0.0000002
Bromine	Br	35	79.92	500	0.00000005
Krypton	Kr	36	83.80	2×10^{3}	0.0000002
Rubidium	Rb	37	85.48	400	0.00000004
Strontium	Sr	38	87.63	790	0.000000079
Yttrium	Y	39	88.92	130	0.000000013
Zirconium	Zr	40	91.22	560	0.000000056
Molybdenum	Mo	42	95.95	140	0.000000014
Silver	Ag	47	107.88	4	0.0000000004
Tin	Sn	50	118.7	100	0.00000001
Tellurium	Te	52	127.61	250	0.000000025
Xenon	Xe	54	131.30	210	0.000000021
Barium	Ba	56	137.36	120	0.000000012

Eclipses

TABLE D.1 **Solar Eclipses**

Date	Duration (minutes)	Type of Eclipse	Location*
1990 Jan. 26	2.1	Annular	Antarctic
1990 July 22	2.6	Total	Finland, Arctic regions
1991 Jan. 15	7.9	Annular	South Pacific, Tasmania, Australia
1991 July 11	7.1	Total	Hawaii, Central America, Brazil
1992 Jan. 4	11.7	Annular	Central Pacific Ocean
1992 June 30	5.4	Total	South Atlantic
1992 Dec. 24	—	Partial	
1993 May 21	—	Partial	
1993 Nov. 13	—	Partial	
1994 May 10	6.2	Annular	Mexico, United States, Atlantic Ocean, Africa
1994 Nov. 3	4.6	Total	South America
1995 Apr. 29	6.6	Annular	South Pacific, South America
1995 Oct. 24	2.4	Total	South Asia
1996 Apr. 17	—	Partial	
1996 Oct. 12	—	Partial	
1997 Mar. 9	2.8	Total	Siberia, Arctic regions
1997 Sept. 2	—	Partial	
1998 Feb. 26	4.4	Total	Central America
1998 Aug. 22	3.2	Annular	Indonesia, South Pacific
1999 Feb. 16	1.3	Annular	South Atlantic, Australia
1999 Aug. 11	2.6	Total	Central Europe, Central Asia
2000 Feb. 5	—	Partial	
2000 July 1	—	Partial	
2000 July 31	—	Partial	
2000 Dec. 25	—	Partial	
2001 June 21	4.9	Total	Southern Africa
2001 Dec. 14	3.9	Annular	Pacific Ocean, Central America
2002 June 10	1.2	Annular	Southern Mexico, Pacific Ocean
2002 Dec. 4	2.1	Total	South Africa, Australia
2003 May 31	3.6	Annular	North Atlantic, Iceland
2003 Nov. 23	2.0	Total	Antarctic
2004 Apr. 19	—	Partial	
2004 Oct. 14	—	Partial	
2005 Apr. 8	0.7	Total	South Pacific
2005 Oct. 3	4.5	Annular	Indian Ocean, Northern Africa, Spain
2006 Mar. 29	4.1	Total	Africa, Asia Minor, USSR
2006 Sept. 22	4.1	Annular	South America, South Atlantic
2007 Mar. 19	—	Partial	
2007 Sept. 11	—	Partial	
2008 Feb. 7	2.2	Annular	Antarctic, South Pacific
2008 Aug. 1	2.4	Total	Arctic Ocean, Siberia, China
2009 Jan. 26	7.9	Annular	Indonesia, Indian Ocean, South Atlantic
2009 July 22	6.6	Total	India, China, South Pacific
2010 Jan. 15	11.2	Annular	Africa, Indian Ocean, China
2010 July 11	5.3	Total	South Pacific

*Partial eclipses are seen over a large area of the Earth; a solar eclipse is seen as a partial eclipse outside the path of totality.

TABLE D.2 **Lunar Eclipses**

Year	Date	Duration (minutes)[1]	
		Partial[2]	Total[3]
1990	Feb. 26	204	42
	Aug. 6	176	*
1991	Jan. 30	*	*
	June 27	*	*
	July 26	*	*
	Dec. 21	64	*
1992	June 15	180	*
	Dec. 9	208	74
1993	June 4	218	96
	Nov. 29	210	46
1994	May 25	104	*
	Nov. 18	*	*
1995	Apr. 15	72	*
	Oct. 8	*	*
1996	Apr. 4	216	86
	Sept. 27	202	70
1997	Mar. 24	202	*
	Sept. 16	196	62
1998	Mar. 13	*	*
	Aug. 8	*	*
	Sept. 6	*	*
1999	Jan. 31	*	*
	July 28	142	*
2000	Jan. 21	202	76
	July 16	236	106
2001	Jan. 9	196	60
	July 5	158	*
	Dec. 30	*	*
2002	May 26	*	*
	June 24	*	*
	Nov. 20	*	*
2003	May 16	194	52
	Nov. 9	210	22
2004	May 4	202	76
	Oct. 28	218	80
2005	Apr. 24	*	*
	Oct. 17	56	*
2006	Mar. 14	*	*
	Sept. 7	90	*
2007	Mar. 3	220	74
	Aug. 28	212	90
2008	Feb. 21	204	50
	Aug. 16	188	*
2009	Feb. 9	*	*
	July 7	*	*
	Aug. 6	*	*
	Dec. 31	60	*
2010	June 26	162	*
	Dec. 21	208	72

[1]An * means that the eclipse is either a partial eclipse where only part of the Moon enters the umbral shadow of the Earth or a penumbral eclipse where the Moon does not enter the Earth's umbral shadow.
[2]Total time before and after total eclipse that part of the Moon is eclipsed.
[3]Length of time the Moon is completely in the umbral shadow of the Earth.

APPENDIX E

The Greek Alphabet

THE ANCIENT GREEKS played an important role in the early history of astronomy, and the Greek alphabet continues to be used in astronomy today. For example, the ancient Greeks classified stars according to the order of brightness within a constellation. Thus, α Orionis was the brightest star in the constellation Orion. Although other names have since been assigned to these stars, the Greek names incorporating the letters of the alphabet are used for the brightest stars in a constellation.

TABLE E.1 **The Greek Alphabet**

Name of Letter	Capital	Lowercase	Name of Letter	Capital	Lowercase	Name of Letter	Capital	Lowercase
Alpha	A	α	Iota	I	ι	Rho	P	ρ
Beta	B	β	Kappa	K	κ	Sigma	Σ	σ
Gamma	Γ	γ	Lambda	Λ	λ	Tau	T	τ
Delta	Δ	δ	Mu	M	μ	Upsilon	Υ	υ
Epsilon	E	ε	Nu	N	ν	Phi	Φ	φ
Zeta	Z	ζ	Xi	Ξ	ξ	Chi	X	χ
Eta	H	η	Omicron	O	o	Psi	Ψ	ψ
Theta	Θ	θ	Pi	Π	π	Omega	Ω	ω

The Brightest and Nearest Stars

TABLE F.1 LISTS the 24 brightest stars seen in the sky. They are arranged according to apparent magnitude, *V*. The last column gives their estimated absolute visual magnitudes. The distances for stars farther than about 100 pc are very uncertain.

TABLE F.1 **Stars Brighter than 1.5 Magnitudes**

Name		Distance		Spectral Type	V	$B - V$	M_v
		pc	*ly*				
Sun	Sirus	—	—	G2 V	−26.72	0.63	4.8
α Canis Majoris	Canopus	2.7	9	A1 V	−1.46	0.00	1.4
α Carinae	Arcturus	23	74	A9 II	−.72	0.15	−2.5
α Boötis	Rigil Kentaurus	10.3	34	K2 III	−.04	1.23	0.2
α Centauri A	Vega	1.3	4.3	G2 V	−.01	0.71	4.4
α Lyrae	Capella	7.5	25	A0 V	0.03	0.00	0.6
α Aurigae AB	Rigel	12.5	41	G6 III	0.08	0.80	0.4
β Orionis A	Procyon	430	1400	B8 Ia	0.12	−.03	−8.1
α Canis Minoris	Achernar	3.4	11	F5 IV–V	0.38	0.42	2.7
α Eridani	Betelgeuse	21	69	B3 V	0.46	−.16	−1.3
α Orionis	Hadar	430	1400	M2 Iab	0.5	1.85	−7.2
β Centauri	Altair	98	320	B1 III	0.6	−.23	−4.4
α Aquilae	Aldebaran	5.0	16	A7 V	0.77	0.22	2.3
α Tauri	Antares	18.5	60	K5 III	0.85	1.54	−0.3
α Scorpii	Spica	160	522	M2 Iab	0.9	1.83	−5.2
α Virginis	Pollux	67	220	B1 V	1.0	−.23	−3.2
β Geminorum	Fromalhaut	10.6	35	K0 III	1.14	1.00	0.7
α Piscis Austrini	Becrux	6.7	22	A3 V	1.16	0.09	2.0
β Crucis	Deneb	141	460	B1 III	1.2	−.23	−4.7
α Cygni	Acrux	460	1500	A2 Ia	1.25	0.09	−7.2
α Crucis		156	510	B1 IV	1.33	−.24	−4.2
α Centauri B		1.3	4.3	K1 V	1.33	0.88	5.7
α Leo A	Regulus	21	69	B7 V	1.35	−.11	−0.3
ε Canis Majoris A	Adara	175	570	B2 II	1.5	−.21	−4.8

After R. F. Garrison in the *Observer's Handbook 1989*, The Royal Astronomical Society of Canada.

Table F.2 lists all known stars within 5 parsecs (16 light-years) of the Sun. Nearly half, 28 of 61 stars, are members of multiple star systems. Most of these stars are intrinsically faint and are main-sequence stars, while those in Table F.1 are intrinsically bright stars and are giants or supergiants.

TABLE F.2 Stars within 5 Parsecs of the Sun

Name[1]	Distance		Spectral Type[2]	V	M_v
	pc	ly			
Sun	—	—	G2 V	−26.72	4.85
Proxima Centauri	1.30	4.2	M6 V	11.05	15.49
α Centauri A	1.33	4.3	G2 V	−0.01	4.37
B			K1 V	1.33	5.71
Barnard's Star	1.83	6.0	M4 V	9.54	13.22
Wolf 359	2.28	7.7	M6 V	13.53	16.65
BD+36°2147	2.52	8.2	M2 V	7.50	10.50
L-726-8 A	2.58	8.4	M6 V	12.52	15.46
B			M6 V	13.02	15.96
Sirius A	2.65	8.6	A1 V	−1.46	1.42
B			WD	8.3	11.2
Ross 154	2.90	9.4	M4 V	10.45	13.14
Ross 248	3.18	10.4	M5 V	12.29	14.78
ε Eridani	3.30	10.8	K2 V	3.73	6.14
Ross 128	3.36	10.9	M4 V	11.10	13.47
61 Cygni A	3.40	11.1	K4 V	5.22	7.56
B			K5 V	6.03	8.37
ε Indi	3.44	11.2	K3 V	4.68	7.00
BD+43°44 A	3.45	11.2	M1 V	8.08	10.39
B			M4 V	11.06	13.37
L786-6	3.45	11.2		12.18	14.49
Procyon A	3.51	11.4	F5 V–IV	0.37	2.64
B			WD	10.7	13.0
BD+59°1915 A	3.55	11.6	M3 V	8.9	11.15
B			M4 V	9.69	11.94
CD−36°15693	3.58	11.7	M1 V	7.35	9.58

[1]Components of binary systems are labeled A and B.
[2]WD refers to white dwarfs; no luminosity class indicates uncertainty.
After A. H. Batten in the *Observer's Handbook 1989*, The Royal Astronomical Society of Canada.

TABLE F.2 **Stars within 5 Parsecs of the Sun (continued)**

Name[1]	Distance		Spectral Type[2]	V	M_v
	pc	ly			
G51-15	3.60	11.7	M7 V	14.81	17.03
τ Ceti	3.61	11.8	G8 V	3.50	5.72
BD+5°1668	3.76	12.3	M4 V	9.82	11.94
L725-32	3.83	12.5	M4 V	12.04	14.12
CD−39°14192	3.85	12.5	M6 V	6.66	8.74
Kapteyn's star	3.91	12.7	M0 V	8.84	10.88
Krüger 60 A	3.95	12.9	M3 V	9.85	11.87
B				11.3	13.3
BD−12°4253	4.05	13.2	M4 V	10.11	12.07
Ross 614 A	4.06	13.3	M4 V	11.10	13.12
B				14.	16.
van Maanen's star	4.31	14.1	WD	12.37	14.20
Wolf 424 A	4.35	14.2	M5 V	13.16	14.97
B				13.4	15.2
CD−37°15492	4.44	14.5	M2 V	8.56	10.32
L1159-16	4.46	14.6	M4 V	12.26	14.01
BD+50°1725	4.50	14.7	K5 V	6.59	8.32
L143-23	4.52	14.8		13.92	15.64
LP731-58	4.57	14.9		15.60	17.30
CD−46°11540	4.63	15.1	M3 V	9.37	11.04
G158-27	4.67	15.2	M5	13.74	15.39
CD−49°13515	4.67	15.2	M2 V	8.67	10.32
CD−44°11909	4.69	15.2	M4 V	10.96	12.60
BD+68°946	4.69	15.3	M3 V	9.15	10.79
G208-44 A	4.74	15.3		13.41	15.03
B		15.5	M5	13.99	15.61
BD−15°6290	4.78	15.6	M4 V	10.17	11.77
o² Eridani A	4.83	15.7	K1 V	4.43	6.01
B			WD	9.52	11.10
C			M4 V	11.17	12.75
BD+20°2465	4.85	15.8	M3 V	9.43	11.00
L145-141	4.85	15.8	WD	11.50	13.07
70 Ophiuchi A	4.93	16.1	K0 V	4.22	5.76
B			K4 V	6.00	7.54
BD+43°4305	5.00	16.3	M5	10.2	11.7

[1]Components of binary systems are labeled A and B.
[2]WD refers to white dwarfs; no luminosity class indicates uncertainty.
After A. H. Batten in the *Observer's Handbook 1989*, The Royal Astronomical Society of Canada.

Nuclear Reactions in Stars

NUCLEAR REACTIONS IN STARS are fusion reactions in which two nuclei fuse and release energy, gamma rays (γ), neutrinos (ν), and positrons (e^+). The fusion of an element with a helium nucleus or with a neutron is called alpha capture and neutron capture, respectively. Photodisintegrations destroy nuclei through bombardment by high-energy photons. This occurs for temperatures above a few billion Kelvins. For massive stars, nuclear reactions create elements with atomic weights near 60, such as iron and nickel.

HYDROGEN BURNING

Proton-Proton Chain

Stars less massive than about 1.5 $\mathfrak{M}_\odot$ generate most of their energy through the proton-proton chain. The proton-proton chain has three branches, all of which operate at the same time after helium-4 (^{4}He) and beryllium-7 (^{7}Be) are created.

$$^1\text{H} + {}^1\text{H} \rightarrow {}^2\text{D} + e^+ + \nu + \text{energy}$$

$$^2\text{D} + {}^1\text{H} \rightarrow {}^3\text{He} + \gamma + \text{energy}$$

$$^3\text{He} + {}^3\text{He} \rightarrow {}^4\text{He} + {}^1\text{H} + {}^1\text{H} + \text{energy}$$

$$^3\text{He} + {}^4\text{He} \rightarrow {}^7\text{Be} + \gamma + \text{energy}$$

$$^7\text{Be} + e^- \rightarrow {}^7\text{Li} + \nu + \text{energy}$$

$$^7\text{Li} + {}^1\text{H} \rightarrow {}^4\text{He} + {}^4\text{He} + \text{energy}$$

$$^7\text{Be} + {}^1\text{H} \rightarrow {}^8\text{B} + \gamma + \text{energy}$$

$$^8\text{B} \rightarrow {}^8\text{Be} + e^+ + \nu + \text{energy}$$

$$^8\text{Be} \rightarrow {}^4\text{He} + {}^4\text{He} + \text{energy}$$

The Carbon-Nitrogen-Oxygen Cycle

Stars with masses greater than 1.5 $\mathfrak{M}_\odot$ generate energy by a more complex set of nuclear reactions. These reactions use carbon-12(^{12}C) as a catalyst; that is, carbon-12 begins the reaction sequence and is an end product.

$$^{12}C + {}^1H \rightarrow {}^{13}N + \gamma + \text{energy}$$

$$^{13}N \rightarrow {}^{13}C + e^+ + \nu + \text{energy}$$

$$^{13}C + {}^1H \rightarrow {}^{14}N + \gamma + \text{energy}$$

$$^{14}H + {}^1H \rightarrow {}^{15}O + \gamma + \text{energy}$$

$$^{15}O \rightarrow {}^{15}N + e^+ + \nu + \text{energy}$$

$$^{15}N + {}^1H \rightarrow {}^{12}C + {}^4He + \text{energy}$$

▬HELIUM BURNING

Triple-Alpha Process

In the triple-alpha process, three alpha particles (helium nuclei) fuse to produce a carbon nucleus. The ^{8}Be is an unstable nucleus, but it exists long enough to fuse with a helium nucleus.

$$^4He + {}^4He \rightarrow {}^8Be$$

$$^8Be + {}^4He \rightarrow {}^{12}C + \gamma + \text{energy}$$

Alpha Capture

Once carbon-12 is created, several alpha captures are possible, resulting in the creation of several more elements.

$$^{12}C + {}^4He \rightarrow {}^{16}O + \gamma + \text{energy}$$

$$^{16}O + {}^4He \rightarrow {}^{20}Ne + \gamma + \text{energy}$$

$$^{20}Ne + {}^4He \rightarrow {}^{24}Mg + \gamma + \text{energy}$$

$$^{24}Mg + {}^4He \rightarrow {}^{28}Si + \gamma + \text{energy}$$

$$^{28}Si + {}^4He \rightarrow {}^{32}S + \gamma + \text{energy}$$

$$^{32}S + {}^4He \rightarrow {}^{36}Ar + \gamma + \text{energy}$$

▬CARBON, NEON, AND OXYGEN BURNING

Carbon Burning

When temperatures greater than 8×10^9 K are reached, carbon will react with itself in several ways. Note that some of these reactions require energy rather than supply energy.

$$^{12}C + {}^{12}C \rightarrow {}^{24}Mg + \gamma + \text{energy}$$
$$\rightarrow {}^{23}Na + {}^{1}H + \text{energy}$$
$$\rightarrow {}^{20}Ne + {}^{4}He + \text{energy}$$
$$\rightarrow {}^{23}Mg + n - \text{energy}$$
$$\rightarrow {}^{16}O + 2{}^{4}He - \text{energy}$$

Neon Burning

This is a photodisintegration of neon-20 followed by an alpha capture.

$$^{20}Ne + \gamma \rightarrow {}^{16}O + {}^{4}He$$
$$^{20}Ne + {}^{4}He \rightarrow {}^{24}Mg + \gamma + \text{energy}$$

Oxygen Burning

At temperatures of 2×10^9 K, oxygen reacts with itself in several ways.

$$^{16}O + {}^{16}O \rightarrow {}^{32}S + \gamma + \text{energy}$$
$$\rightarrow {}^{31}P + {}^{1}H + \text{energy}$$
$$\rightarrow {}^{31}S + n + \text{energy}$$
$$\rightarrow {}^{28}Si + {}^{4}He + \text{energy}$$
$$\rightarrow {}^{24}Mg + {}^{4}He + {}^{4}He - \text{energy}$$

SILICON BURNING

At the end of oxygen burning, the most abundant nuclei will be silicon-28 (^{28}Si) and sulfur-32 (^{32}S) with significant amounts of magnesium-24 (^{24}Mg). Above temperatures of 3×10^9 K, the photodisintegration of silicon proceeds rapidly, releasing protons, neutrons, and alpha particles. Here are some examples of the photodisintegrations:

$$^{28}Si + \gamma \rightarrow {}^{27}Al + {}^{1}H - \text{energy}$$
$$^{18}Si + \gamma \rightarrow {}^{24}Mg + {}^{4}He - \text{energy}$$
$$^{24}Mg + \gamma \rightarrow {}^{20}Ne + {}^{4}He - \text{energy}$$
$$^{20}Ne + \gamma \rightarrow {}^{16}O + {}^{4}He - \text{energy}$$

The concentration of heavier elements builds up in an equilibrium process in which helium nuclei are captured faster than photodisintegration can destroy all of the light elements; for example

$$^{28}Si + {}^{4}He \rightarrow {}^{32}S + \gamma$$
$$^{32}S + {}^{4}He \rightarrow {}^{36}Ar + \gamma$$

Eventually iron and nickel will be synthesized as in

$$^{52}Fe + {}^{4}He \rightarrow {}^{56}Ni + \gamma$$

Planets and Satellites

THE TABLES IN THIS APPENDIX list the orbital and physical characteristics of both the planets and their satellites. The values given in columns with units of 10^6 km and 10^3 km are in millions and thousands of kilometers; that is, multiply the number in the table by 10^6 or 10^3.

TABLE H.1 Orbital Characteristics of the Planets

Planet	Semimajor Axis		Sidereal Period		Orbital Speed	Eccentricity	Orbital Inclination	Satellites*
	AU	10^6 km	Years	Days	km/s			
Mercury	0.387	57.9	0.24	87.97	47.9	0.206	7°	0
Venus	0.723	108.2	0.62	224.70	35.0	0.007	3.4°	0
Earth	1.000	149.6	1.00	365.26	29.8	0.017	0.0°	1
Mars	1.524	227.9	1.88	686.98	24.1	0.093	1.8°	2
Jupiter	5.203	778.3	11.86		13.1	0.048	1.3°	16+
Saturn	9.539	1427.0	29.46		9.6	0.056	2.5°	17+
Uranus	19.191	2869.6	84.01		6.8	0.047	0.8°	15+
Neptune	30.058	4496.6	164.79		5.4	0.009	1.8°	8+
Pluto	39.43	5913	248.6		4.7	0.248	17.2°	1

*A plus sign (+) indicates that more small moons probably orbit the planet.

TABLE H.2 Physical Characteristics of the Planets

Planet	Diameter			Mass	Density	Surface Gravity	Escape Speed	Rotational Period		Inclination[1]	Temperature[2]
	km	Earth = 1		Earth = 1	g/cm³	Earth = 1	km/s	Hours	Days		K
Mercury	4878	0.38		0.0553	5.43	0.38	4.3		58.646	0.0°	620
Venus	12,104	0.95		0.8150	5.24	0.91	10.4		234.017	177.3°	750
Earth	12,756	1.00		1.0000	5.52	1.00	11.2	23.93	0.997	23.3°	293
Mars	6787	0.53		0.1074	3.94	0.38	5.0	24.45	1.026	25.2°	220
Jupiter	142,796	11.23		317.833	1.33	2.53	59.6	9.81	0.410	3.1°	163
Saturn	120,000	9.41		95.159	0.70	1.07	35.6	10.63	0.444	26.7°	133
Uranus	51,200	4.01		14.500	1.20	0.92	21.3	17.18	0.718	97.9°	78
Neptune	48,600	3.81		17.204	1.76	1.18	23.8	16.05	0.671	29.6°	80
Pluto	≈2,300	≈0.18		≈.002	≈2	≈.1	≈1		6.387	94°	50

[1]Inclination of the equator to the orbital plane.
[2]Mean surface temperature.

■ TABLE H.3 **Orbital and Physical Characteristics of the Satellites of the Solar System**

Planet	Satellite	Semimajor Axis		Orbital Period*	Eccentricity	Diameter	Density
		Planet Radii	10^3 *km*			*km*	*g/cm³*
Earth	Moon	30.1	384.5	27.322 d	0.0549	3476	3.34
Mars	Phobos	2.8	9.4	7.65 hr	0.015	21 × 20 × 18	≈2
	Deimos	6.9	23.5	1.263 d	0.0005	25 × 12 × 10	≈2
Jupiter	Metis	1.79	128	7.08 hr	0.0	40	—
	Adrastea	1.81	129	7.08 hr	0.0	20	
	Amalthea	2.55	180	11.73 hr	0.003	270 × 170 × 150	—
	Thebe	3.11	222	16.08 hr	0.013	90	—
	Io	5.95	422	1.77 d	0.004	3632	3.55
	Europa	9.47	671	3.55 d	0.010	3126	3.04
	Ganymede	15.1	1070	7.16 d	0.001	5276	1.93
	Callisto	26.6	1885	16.69 d	0.007	4820	1.83
	Leda	156	11,110	240 d	0.147	≈10	—
	Himalia	161	11,470	251 d	0.158	180	—
	Lysithea	164	11,710	260 d	0.107	≈20	—
	Elara	165	11,740	260 d	0.207	80	—
	Ananke	297	21,200	1.67 yr R	0.17	≈30	—
	Carme	317	22,600	1.89 yr R	0.21	44	—
	Pasiphae	329	23,500	2.01 yr R	0.38	70	—
	Sinope	332	23,700	2.08 yr R	0.28	40	—
Saturn	Atlas	2.30	137	14.45 hr	0.002	40 × 30	—
	Prometheus	2.32	139	14.72 hr	0.002	140 × 100 × 74	—
	Pandora	2.4	142	15.10 hr	0.004	110 × 90 × 66	—
	Janus	2.5	151	16.57 hr	0.009	220 × 190 × 160	—
	Epimetheus	2.5	151	16.57 hr	0.007	140 × 116 × 100	—
	Mimas	3.1	187	22.57 hr	0.020	394	1.4
	Enceladus	3.9	234	1.37 d	0.004	502	1.2
	Tethys	4.9	295	1.89 d	0.000	1048	1.2
	Telesto	4.9	295	1.89 d	0.0	30 × 20 × 16	—
	Calypso	4.9	295	1.89 d	0.0	24 × 22 × 22	—
	Dione	6.3	378	2.74 d	0.002	1120	1.4
	Helene	6.3	378	2.74 d	0.005	34 × 32 × 30	—
	Rhea	8.7	526	4.52 d	0.001	1530	1.3
	Titan	20.3	1221	15.95 d	0.029	5150	1.9
	Hyperion	24.6	1481	21.28 d	0.104	410 × 260 × 110	—
	Iapetus	59.0	3561	79.3 d	0.028	1436	1.2
	Phoebe	215.7	12,960	1.51 yr R	0.163	230 × 210	—

*Abbreviations: hr = hour; d = day; yr = year; R = retrograde.

TABLE H.3 **Orbital and Physical Characteristics of the Satellites of the Solar System (continued)**

Planet	Satellite	Semimajor Axis		Orbital Period*	Eccentricity	Diameter	Density
		Planet Radii	10^3 *km*			*km*	*g/cm^3*
Uranus	Cordelia	1.9	49.8	8.07 hr	0.0	≈40	—
	Ophelia	2.1	53.8	9.07 hr	0.0	≈50	—
	Bianca	2.3	59.2	10.47 hr	0.0	≈50	—
	Cressida	2.4	61.8	11.15 hr	0.0	≈60	—
	Desdemona	2.4	62.6	11.37 hr	0.0	≈60	—
	Juliet	2.5	64.4	12.0 hr	0.0	≈80	—
	Portia	2.6	66.1	12.35 hr	0.0	≈80	—
	Rosalind	2.7	70.0	13.45 hr	0.0	≈60	—
	Belinda	2.9	75.3	15.03 hr	0.0	≈60	—
	Puck	3.4	86.0	18.28 hr	0.0	170	—
	Miranda	5.1	129.9	1.41 d	0.017	484	1.3
	Ariel	7.5	190.9	2.52 d	0.003	1160	1.6
	Umbriel	10.4	266.0	4.14 d	0.004	1190	1.4
	Titania	17.0	436.3	8.71 d	0.002	1610	1.5
	Oberon	22.7	583.4	13.46 d	0.001	1550	1.5
Neptune	1989 N6	1.98	48.1	7.10 hr	—	≈50	—
	1989 N5	2.06	50.1	7.5 hr	—	≈90	—
	1989 N3	2.16	52.5	8.0 hr	—	≈140	—
	1989 N4	2.55	62.0	9.5 hr	—	≈160	—
	1989 N2	3.03	73.6	13.3 hr	—	≈200	—
	1989 N1	4.84	117.6	1.12d	—	≈420	—
	Triton	14.1	354	5.87 d R	0.005	2720	≈3
	Nereid	230	5600	1.00 yr	0.75	340	—
Pluto	Charon	≈9	≈20	6.39 d R	0.0	≈1000	—

*Abbreviations: hr = hour; d = day; yr = year; R = retrograde.

Glossary

Absolute age: Definite or certain age in the sense of assigning numbers to the age of an object.

Absolute magnitude: The apparent magnitude a star would have if it were placed at a distance of 10 pc from the Earth; designated with an *M*.

Absolute orbit: The orbits of double stars about their common center of mass.

Absorption line: A radiative feature in a spectrum of a star or planet representing a deficiency of radiation.

Absorption spectrum: The spectrum of a luminous object, the light of which is passed through a gas, showing vertical dark lines representing the absence of light.

Acceleration: A change of a body's speed, direction of motion, or both.

Accretion: Gradual growth in size by accumulating matter.

Achromatic: Free from chromatic aberration.

Albedo: The fraction of incident sunlight a planet, moon, asteroid, or comet reflects.

Alignment: An arrangement in a straight line between an observer, a marker or markers, and a celestial object.

Alpha particle: The nucleus of a helium atom; contains two protons and two neutrons.

Altitude: The angular distance of a star, a planet, the Moon, or the Sun above the horizon.

Angular diameter: The angle made by the diameter of an object.

Annihilation: The complete conversion of an amount of matter into energy dictated by Einstein's relation, $m = E/c^2$.

Annular eclipse: A solar eclipse in which the Moon covers all but a ring of sunlight when it is directly in front of the Sun.

Annulus: Ring of sunlight visible during an annular eclipse.

Anorthosite: A highland lunar rock composed of low-density calcium-rich aluminum silicate.

Antarctic Circle: The region of the Earth with latitudes of 66½° south of the equator.

Antiparticle: A subatomic particle with the same mass and spin of a normal particle but with all other attributes, such as electric charge, being opposite.

Aphelion: The point in a planet's elliptical orbit at which it is farthest from the Sun.

Apogee: The location in the orbit of a satellite around the Earth at which it is farthest from the Earth.

Apollo asteroids: About 30 asteroids whose orbits cross the Earth's orbit.

Apparent magnitude: The magnitude assigned to a star based on its appearance and is designated by the letter *m*.

Archaeoastronomy: The study of the astronomy of ancient people; involves study of ancient astronomical observatories and written records.

Arctic Circle: The region of the Earth with latitudes of 66½° north of the equator.

Asteroid: Any of the numerous small rocky bodies orbiting the Sun; most lie between the orbits of Mars and Jupiter; sometimes referred to as "minor planets."

Asteroid belt: A region in the solar system between the orbits of Mars and Jupiter containing most of the known asteroids.

Asthenosphere: The region between the lithosphere and the outer core; it is semifluid, or plastic.

Astrometric binary: A double star in which one companion is "invisible"; the binary nature of the star is detected by periodic changes in the position of the primary component as it moves through space and around the center of mass of the system.

Astrometry: A branch of astronomy that deals with the measurement of the positions of stars.

Astronomical unit: The mean distance from Earth to Sun; it equals 149,597,870 km, or about 92,956,000 miles.

Astronomy: The science that deals with the material universe beyond the Earth's atmosphere.

Atom: The smallest atomic particle that retains the properties of an element.

Atomic number: The number of protons in the nucleus of an element.

Atomic weight: The number of protons plus the number of neutrons in the nucleus of an atom.

Aurorae australis: Glowing lights visible in the skies at high southern latitudes and caused by trapped solar wind particles spiraling around the Earth's magnetic field lines.

Aurorae borealis: Glowing lights visible in the skies at high northern latitudes and caused by trapped solar wind particles spiraling around the Earth's magnetic field lines.

Autumnal equinox: The point on the celestial sphere where the Sun crosses the celestial equator moving from north to south; occurs on September 22 or 23.

Barred spiral galaxy: A spiral galaxy in which the spiral arms emerge from the ends of a "bar" running through the nucleus.

Basaltic lavas: Fluid lavas.

Basins: Impact craters with diameters of more than 300 km.

Belts: Dark colored bands of low pressure seen running parallel to the equator of the Jovian planets; belts are believed to be regions of descending gas.

Beta particle: An electron.

Big bang: The primeval explosive event in the universe, responsible for the observed expansion of the universe.

Binary star: Two stars revolving around each other and orbiting a common center of mass; also called double star.

Bit: A single digit, either 0 or 1, in a binary number system; the numbers we use, such as 6 and 8, can be represented by a series of bits.

Black body: A hypothetical perfect radiator that absorbs and re-emits all radiation incident upon it; the distribution of radiation from it depends only on its temperature.

Black body radiation: The radiation from a black body.

Black hole: The volume of space surrounding the core of a massive star that has collapsed through its Schwarzschild radius and from which no electromagnetic radiation can escape.

Blueshift: A Doppler shift toward the blue part of the spectrum; means motion toward the observer.

Bok globules: Small isolated molecular clouds (diameters of about 1 pc) large and dense enough to absorb starlight from stars behind them; discovered as dark "clouds" against a background of bright stars.

Bolide: A very bright fireball that breaks up during atmospheric entry.

Bow shock: The discontinuity in the flow of solar wind particles on the sunward side of Earth's or another planet's magnetic field.

Brecciated rock: A rock made from fragments cemented together by heat created during an impact.

Butterfly diagram: A graph of the location of sunspot formation over time, so called because it looks like a collection of butterflies.

Caldera: A craterlike depression near the top of a volcano; caused by an explosion or collapse of the center of the volcano.

Carbon-nitrogen-oxygen cycle: A series of thermonuclear reactions converting hydrogen into helium using carbon as a catalyst.

Carbonaceous chondrite: A stony meteorite rich in carbon and other elements with low melting temperatures; believed to be very old, virtually unaltered remains of the early history of the solar system.

cD galaxy: A supergiant elliptical galaxy frequently found at the centers of clusters of galaxies.

Celestial equator: The projection of the Earth's equator onto the celestial sphere; a circle on the celestial sphere 90° from the celestial poles.

Celestial horizon: The dividing line 90° from the zenith cutting the celestial sphere in half.

Celestial north pole: The projection of the Earth's north pole onto the celestial sphere; the point in the northern sky about which the celestial sphere appears to rotate.

Celestial south pole: The projection of the Earth's south pole onto the celestial sphere; the point in the southern sky about which the celestial sphere appears to rotate.

Celestial sphere: An imaginary sphere of the heavens upon which celestial objects like the Sun, Moon, and stars are considered to be attached.

Center of mass: The point around which two objects appear to rotate.

Central peak: Mountains near the centers of large craters caused by the radial modification of the floor and walls after impact; the inward flow meets near the center causing a central upheaval.

Cepheid variables: An important group of yellow supergiants that pulsate with periods from about 1 to 50 days; the correlation between their pulsation periods and their brightnesses is very important for estimating the distances to star clusters in the Galaxy and to nearby galaxies.

Chandrasekhar limit: The largest mass, about 1.4 solar masses, that can be supported by degenerate electron pressure.

Charge coupled device (CCD): An array of electronic light-sensitive (silicon) elements of very high sensitivity.

Chondrites: The most common type of stone meteorite; contains small, glasslike spheres of melted rock called chondrules.

Chromatic aberration: A defect of a lens or a mirror whereby light of different colors is focused at different places.

Chromosphere: A transition region between the relatively cool photosphere and the hot corona of the Sun.

Circumpolar stars: Stars that are always visible at night or stars that are never visible from a given latitude on Earth.

Closed universe: A universe that will expand for a while, reach a maximum size, and then collapse upon itself under the force of gravity.

Co-orbital satellites: Small moons that share orbits in the sense that they switch orbits periodically.

Color index: The difference between the B and V magnitudes of a star.

Color-magnitude diagram: A plot of the observed parameters, absolute or apparent magnitude, and $B - V$ color index.

Coma (of a comet): The diffuse envelope of dust and gas surrounding the nucleus; the gas and dust are liberated from the nucleus when the nucleus is near the Sun.

Comet: A small body of ice and dust in orbit about the Sun; if they pass too close to the Sun, their vaporized ices can develop long extensions, called tails, and a large cloud of dust and gas, called a coma, that surrounds the comet.

Comparison spectrum: An emission spectrum of an element, such as iron, placed above a spectrum of a star to provide spectral lines of known wavelengths.

Compressional seismic waves: Waves in which the particles move back and forth along the direction of travel; also called P waves.

Condensation sequence: The sequence of elements, minerals, and ices that condensed out of the solar nebula as it cooled.

Condensation: The process by which substances change from a gaseous or vapor phase to their liquid or solid phases; above a certain temperature, called the condensation temperature, the substance is a vapor.

Conjunction: The position in the orbit of a superior planet when it is on the opposite side of the Sun from the Earth and is at its farthest distance from the Earth; also the term used when the apparent positions of two or more planets bring them in close proximity to each other on the celestial sphere.

Continuous spectrum: The spectrum emitted by a luminous solid and is a continuous sequence of wavelengths, not interrupted by dark or bright spectral lines.

Convection: Movement of a fluid or gas because of differences in density caused by localized heating.

Coplanar: Existing in the same plane.

Core (of a planet): The highest density, innermost portion of the Earth or any planetary body.

Core (of a star): The central most high density region in which nuclear reactions can occur.

Coriolis effect: The apparent motion of projectiles or air relative to Earth's surface caused by Earth's rotation; the motion is a deflection, toward the right in the Northern Hemisphere and toward the left in the Southern Hemisphere, of the direction of motion.

Corona (of the Galaxy): A region surrounding the disk and halo of the Galaxy; the corona's radius may be greater than 100 kpc and it may have a mass of 10^{12} solar masses.

Corona (of the Sun): The faintly luminous outermost region of the solar atmosphere consisting of ionized gas at temperatures of several million Kelvins.

Coronagraph: A device that uses a man-made disk inside a telescope to block out the light from the photosphere.

Coronal hole: A region in the corona of the Sun where magnetic field lines do not close back onto the surface but open outward into space.

Cosmic rays: Energetic solar wind particles and particles originating in supernovae; mainly protons and electrons.

Cosmological redshifts: The observed redshifts of galaxies, caused by the expansion of space.

Cosmology: The study of the evolution and organization of the universe.

Crater: A bowl-shaped cavity resulting from an interplanetary collision between a planet or satellite and a rock from space.

Crust: The outermost solid layer of the Earth or another planetary body.

Curie temperature: The temperature beyond which a magnetic material loses its magnetic properties.

Curvature: The degree of curving of a surface; examples are flat, spherical surface, or hyperbolic or saddle shape.

Daughter nucleus: The nucleus of the new element produced by spontaneous radioactive decay; the daughter nucleus also may be radioactive.

Decoupling: The epoch in the early universe when the radiation field was too cool to ionize atoms, allowing atoms to form; this occurred about 600,000 years after the big bang.

Deferent: A circle centered on the Earth, used to describe the retrograde motions of planets in the geocentric model.

Degenerate electron gas pressure: The pressure caused by degenerate electrons in a state of very high density in which all of the quantum states for electrons are filled; the pressure due to degenerate electrons is independent of temperature.

Degenerate neutron gas pressure: The pressure caused by degenerate neutrons in a state of very high density in which all of the quantum states for neutrons are filled; the pressure due to degenerate neutrons is independent of temperature.

Density: A measure of compactness of matter; the ratio of the mass of an object to its volume.

Density wave: An enhancement in the density of gas and dust in the disk of a galaxy; the density wave rotates at a speed different from that of the stars and gas in the disk.

Differential gravitational force (tidal force): A gravitational force acting across a body such that the side closer to the source of gravity feels a stronger gravitational force than the opposite side.

Differential rotation: The rotation of a nonrigid object in which parts adjacent to each other move at different speeds and, therefore, do not stay close together.

Differentiation: The process by which heavy minerals separate from lighter minerals in cooling molten rock.

Digitizing: The process of converting a picture into numbers that can be analyzed by computers.

Disk (of the Galaxy): The flat circular component of our Galaxy composed of gas and dust, relatively young stars, and spiral arms.

Distance modulus: The difference between the apparent magnitude of a star and its absolute magnitude (m − M).

Diurnal circle: The apparent path of a star, planet, or the Sun on the sky during a complete rotation of the Earth.

Doppler shift: The apparent change in the wavelength of radiation from a source due to the relative radial motion of the observer and source.

Dust grains (dust): Solid microscopic particles composed of silicates, carbon, or metals such as nickel and iron, probably covered with a mantle of ice; interstellar dust grains are about the same size as particles of cigarette smoke.

Dwarf elliptical galaxy: Small elliptical galaxy; probably the most common type of galaxy in the universe.

Dwarfs: Main sequence stars; stars like the Sun, converting hydrogen into helium through thermonuclear reactions in their cores.

Dynamical friction: The gravitational deceleration of a star cluster or a small galaxy as it moves through a galaxy.

Dynamics: The study of the motions of material bodies under the action of forces, such as the study of the motions of the bodies in the solar nebula.

Dynamo models: Mathematical models that try to explain Earth's magnetic field as the motion of metallic iron producing electric currents that generate magnetic fields.

Eccentricity: The property of an ellipse that describes its shape; the ratio of the distance between foci to the major axis.

Eclipse seasons: The period of time during which the line of nodes aligns with the Sun; lunar and solar eclipses can occur only during these periods.

Eclipsing binary: A double star in which the orbital plane is viewed nearly edge on from the Earth so that the stars eclipse each other.

Ecliptic: The apparent annual path of the Sun projected onto the celestial sphere; it defines the orbital plane of the Earth.

Ejecta blanket: The area surrounding a crater covered by the material that was thrown radially outward during an impact; most of the material is deposited close to the crater rim.

Electromagnetic radiation: Propagating waves of changing electric and magnetic fields; these include radio, infrared, visible light, ultraviolet, X-rays, and gamma rays.

Electromagnetic spectrum: The whole set of electromagnetic waves.

Electron: A subatomic particle possessing a negative electrical charge; an elementary particle.

Electron degeneracy: A state of a gas at very high density in which all of the quantum states for electrons are filled; the pressure due to degenerate electrons is independent of temperature.

Element: A substance that cannot be separated into a combination of other substances by normal chemical methods.

Ellipse: The closed curve representing the shape of planetary orbits; the shape of a circle when viewed at an angle.

Elliptical galaxy: A galaxy that is spheroidal in shape and lacking in prominent internal structure.

Elongation: The angular distance on the celestial sphere between a planet and the Sun.

Emission line: A radiative feature in a spectrum of a star or planet representing an excess of radiation.

Emission nebula: A cloud of hot gas emitting radiation; heating is due to the ultraviolet emissions of nearby hot stars.

Emission spectrum: The spectrum of a rarified heated gas and is characterized by a series of bright, colored lines in an otherwise dark spectrum.

Energy level diagram: A diagram of the various possible electron transitions of an atom.

Energy: The capacity to do work; forms of energy are elastic (spring), chemical, heat, kinetic (energy of motion), gravitational, and nuclear.

Epicycle: A circle whose center moves along the circumference of a circle centered on the Earth; it is used to describe the retrograde motions of planets in the geocentric model.

Equation of state: An equation, such as the perfect gas law, relating pressure, temperature, and density of a substance.

Equator: A circle on the Earth or another planetary or stellar body 90° from the poles.

Erg: A small unit of energy equal to one ten-millionth of a joule.

Escape velocity: The minimum speed needed to move away from a body and never to return.

Event horizon: The surface of a sphere whose radius is equal to the Schwarzschild radius; so called because we cannot observe any events occurring within it.

Evolutionary tracks: Lines on an HR diagram that show the changes in a star's luminosity and temperature as a function of time.

Excited state (of an atom): The state of an atom in which an electron has been moved to an orbital farther away from the nucleus.

Extragalactic: Beyond the Galaxy.

Fall: A meteorite that is seen descending through the atmosphere.

Find: A meteorite that is found on or in the soil but was not seen descending through the atmosphere.

Fireball: A very bright meteor with a train that persists for as long as half an hour.

First-quarter moon: The phase of the Moon, between new moon and full moon, in which half of the side facing the Earth is sunlit.

Flash spectrum: The spectrum of the chromosphere obtained just before and after totality during a solar eclipse.

Flat universe: A universe in which a balance exists between the gravitational tendency to collapse and expansion; a flat universe will stop expanding yet not collapse.

Flow front: A cliff formed where fluid lavas stopped flowing.

Flux tube: The concentration of magnetic field lines into rope-like strands of strong magnetic fields.

Focal length: The distance between a lens or mirror and the point where an image is in focus.

Focus (of a telescope): The point at which rays (of light) appear to come to a point after being reflected or refracted.

Force: An influence on a body producing or tending to produce a change in movement; force equals mass multiplied by acceleration.

Formation limit: A point during the formation of a galaxy at which all the dust and gas form stars before the rotation limit is reached.

Fossils: Mineralized remains (impressions, outlines, tracks, or body parts) of plants and animals of some previous geological period preserved in a rock formation on the Earth's crust after the original organic material is transformed or removed; the original bone, shell, stem, etc., is seldom preserved having been dissolved by ground water.

Frequency: The number of waves passing any given point in a second.

Full moon: The phase of the Moon in which the entire lighted hemisphere of the Moon faces Earth.

Fusion: A thermonuclear reaction in which nuclei fuse together to form a more massive nucleus; energy is released because the product nucleus is less massive than the reacting nuclei.

Galaxy: An organized system of hundreds of millions to thousands of billions of stars, sometimes mixed with interstellar gas and dust.

Galilean satellites: The four largest moons of Jupiter; discovered by Galileo.

Gamma rays: The most energetic form of electromagnetic radiation.

Geocentric model: The model that asserts that the Earth is the center of the universe with the Sun, Moon, planets, and stars moving around it.

Geomagnetism: The description of Earth's magnetic field as that of a bar magnet with north and south poles.

Giant molecular cloud: A huge region of gas and dust of high mass, low temperature, and high particle density; discovered by radio detection of molecular emission, especially CO emission.

Giants: Stars that are above the main sequence in the Hertzsprung-Russell diagram.

Globular clusters: The oldest clusters of stars in the Galaxy; they form a more or less spherical system centered on the center of the Galaxy.

Granulation: The cellular pattern of convective cells seen in the Sun's photosphere; bright areas are sites of rising gas and dark areas are regions of sinking gas.

Granules: Bright regions of rising gas in the photosphere of the Sun.

Gravitational constant, G: The constant of proportionality in Newton's law of universal gravitation.

Greatest eastern elongation: The largest angular separation on the celestial sphere an inferior planet can have to the east of the Sun.

Greatest western elongation: The largest angular separation on the celestial sphere an inferior planet can have to the west of the Sun.

Greenhouse effect: The increase in temperature at and near a planet's surface due to the absorption and emission of infrared radiation by water vapor, carbon dioxide, and other gases in the atmosphere.

Gregorian calendar: A 365-day calendar with an extra day, called a leap day, added every four years except in certain century years; the calendar used today by most nations; introduced by Pope Gregory XIII in 1582.

H II region: A sphere of ionized hydrogen surrounding young, hot stars; also called an emission nebula.

Half-life: The time after which half of a quantity of a radioactive element has transformed itself into another element.

Halo (of a galaxy): A roughly spherical volume of old stars and globular clusters.

Heavy elements: Those elements more massive than helium.

Heisenberg uncertainty principle: The statement that we cannot know exactly where a particle is and at the same time know how fast and in what direction it is moving.

Heliocentric model: The model that places the Sun at the center of the solar system with the Earth and planets in motion around it.

Helium flash: The violent ignition of helium burning in the cores of stars with main sequence masses less than 2 solar masses; uncontrolled nuclear reactions are brought about by electron degeneracy in the core.

Hertz: A unit of frequency equal to one cycle per second.

Hertzsprung-Russell (HR) diagram: A graph of the absolute magnitudes versus spectral types of individual stars; named after the astronomers who promoted its use, Ejnar Hertzsprung and Henry Russell.

High velocity stars: Stars that belong to the halo of the Galaxy, but are passing through the disk and are moving very rapidly relative to the Sun.

Highland regions: The heavily cratered areas on the Moon.

Hohmann orbits: Interplanetary orbits between planets.

Horizontal branch: A horizontal part of the evolutionary track of a low-mass star during core helium burning; RR Lyrae variables are located in the horizontal branch.

Hubble time: The maximum age of the universe, derived from Hubble's law, and found to be between 10 and 20 billion years.

Hubble's constant, H_0: The constant of proportionality between distance and the velocities of remote galaxies.

Hubble's law: Mathematical relationship which states that the distance to a galaxy is proportional to its radial velocity.

Hydrogen cloud (of a comet): Immense sphere of hydrogen gas surrounding the nucleus and coma of a comet; it is visible in the ultraviolet.

Hydrostatic equilibrium: The balance between the inward gravitational forces and the outward thermal pressures in a star; no overall expansion or contraction of the star occurs.

Hypothesis: The statement or mathematical relation that unifies a collection of experimental data, observations, measurements or collections of life forms or rocks.

Ice age: Any period of geological time when large parts of the Earth are covered with glaciers.

Icy-conglomerate model: The model of comets in which they are composed of ice and dust packed together into a single mass.

Igneous rocks: Rocks that formed from the cooling and solidification of a hot, molten rock, called "magma" when it is underground and "lava" when it reaches the surface.

Inclination (of an orbit): The angle between the orbital plane of a planet or a moon and the ecliptic.

Inertia: The property of a body that resists changes in motion and requires a force to act on the body to change its state of motion; momentum (mass × velocity) is a measure of inertia.

Inferior conjunction: The place in the orbit of an inferior planet where it lines up between the Earth and the Sun.

Inferior planet: The planets with orbits closer to the Sun than the Earth: Mercury and Venus.

Inflation: The sudden and rapid expansion of the universe predicted to have occurred when the unified superforce separated.

Insolation: The amount of solar energy falling on the Earth's surface.

Intercalary months: Months periodically inserted into lunar calendars to keep them in phase with the seasons.

Interferometer: An instrument, usually consisting of two or more detectors, that is used for improving the resolving ability of a telescope.

International Date Line: An imaginary line on the Earth's surface near longitude 180° across which the date changes by one day.

Interstellar clouds: Large volumes of relatively high density in the interstellar medium.

Interstellar medium: Diffuse matter between stars; in order of abundance: hydrogen, helium, carbon, nitrogen, and oxygen atoms and ions, dust, and molecules of many elements such as hydrogen, carbon, nitrogen, and oxygen. Typical density is a few atoms per cubic centimeter.

Inverse square law: A mathematical relationship in which a property decreases with the square of the distance; astronomers use the term "inverse square law" to describe the decrease in light intensity with distance.

Ion: An atom or molecule with one or more electrons missing.

Ion tail: The straight tail of a comet made up of ions in which one or more electrons have been removed by solar ultraviolet radiation.

Ionized state (of an atom): The state of an atom in which an electron has been lost.

Iron: A type of meteorite composed of iron and nickel.

Irregular galaxy: A galaxy with a chaotic, irregular appearance; it lacks both the obvious disklike structure of spirals and the spheroidal symmetry of ellipticals.

Isotope: An atom of an element that has a different number of neutrons.

Isotropic: Independent of direction; in cosmology it refers to an assumed property of the universe in which the universe looks the same in all directions to a typical observer.

Jeans's mass: The mass of a molecular cloud, or a fragment of one, that is great enough to ensure that gravitational forces can overcome thermal pressures and cause the cloud to collapse.

Jet stream: Strong winds concentrated within a narrow band high in the atmosphere.

Jets: Narrow, collimated streams of ionized gas from the center of galaxy; lobes are formed when the jets collide with intergalactic gas.

Joule: Unit of energy roughly equivalent to the energy expended placing a pound of beans in a grocery cart.

Jovian planets: The Jupiter-like planets: Jupiter, Saturn, Uranus, and Neptune.

Julian calendar: A 365-day calendar with an extra day, called a leap day, added every four years; introduced by Julius Caesar in 45 B.C.

Kepler's laws: Three laws of planetary motion that give us a precise description of planetary movement.

Kinetic energy: Energy in the form of motion.

Kirkwood gaps: Gaps in the distribution of asteroids in the asteroid belt due to gravitational resonances between the orbital periods of the asteroids and that of Jupiter.

Lagrangian points: Five stable locations in the orbital plane of two bodies revolving around each other in which a third body of negligible mass can remain in the same relative position to the two larger bodies; two stable locations, L_4 and L_5, form an equilateral triangle with the two larger bodies.

Latitude: An angle measured from the center of the Earth either north or south of the equator along the meridian on Earth passing through a place.

Leap day: An extra day added every four years to 365-day calendars designed to make the average length of the year equal to the tropical year.

Lenticular galaxy: A galaxy with characteristics of both ellipticals and spirals; it has a spherical, dominating bulge with the same structure as an elliptical galaxy and a flat disk in which star formation appears to have stopped.

Light curve: A graph of brightness, usually in magnitudes, versus time for a binary system.

Light year: The distance that light travels in one year; 1 ly = 9.5×10^{17} cm.

Line of nodes: The line connecting the nodes of the Moon's orbit that passes through the Earth.

Liquid metallic hydrogen: A very highly compressed state of hydrogen in which the hydrogen electrons are no longer bound to an individual proton but are free to migrate throughout the liquid; the ability of the electrons to move gives this state of hydrogen the electrical properties of a metal.

Liquid molecular hydrogen: A highly compressed state of hydrogen in which molecules of hydrogen still show random movement but are partially restricted (as with molecules of a liquid); this occurs for hydrogen only under high pressures.

Lithosphere: The solid upper 100 km of the Earth that includes the crust and the upper mantle; the solid part of the mantle of a solid body.

Local Group: A small group of at least 20 galaxies of which the Milky Way Galaxy is a member.

Longitude: An angle measured east or west along the equator from Greenwich, England to a place on the Earth.

Luminosity: The total amount of energy emitted every second by a star.

Luminosity classes: The classification of a star based on its intrinsic brightness; ranges from luminosity class I to V.

Lunar eclipse: When the Moon passes through the Earth's shadow.

Magnetosheath: The turbulent region of disordered magnetic fields and variable particle densities inside of the bow shock.

Magnetosphere: The region of space surrounding the Earth in which the Earth's magnetic field controls the motion of charged particles.

Magnitude: A numerical scale for measuring stellar brightness; the larger the magnitude, the fainter the star. Abbreviated "mag."

Main sequence: A band in a graph of absolute magnitude (luminosity) versus spectral type (temperature) extending from the lower right to the upper left in which the majority of stars are found; like the Sun, the stars comprising the main sequence are converting hydrogen into helium in their cores.

Main-sequence fitting: A technique that involves superimposing the main sequences of two star clusters, one of which is at a known distance; the technique is used to determine the distance to the other star cluster.

Main-sequence lifetime: The time it takes for a star to convert hydrogen into helium in its core.

Main-sequence star: A star, like the Sun, converting hydrogen into helium through thermonuclear reactions in its core.

Mantle: A thick layer of rock extending 2900 km below the crust of the Earth; a region of intermediate density surrounding the core of a planetary body.

Mantle plume: Isolated column of upwelling magma originating deep in the mantle.

Maria: The large dark gray patches on the lunar surface, once thought to be seas but now known to be vast solidified lava beds whose dark color is due to a black oxide of iron and titanium (singular: mare).

Mass: A measure of the quantity of matter in a body.

Mass extinction: The disappearance of a large fraction of life on Earth all at the same time.

Mass-luminosity relation: The empirically determined trend for main-sequence stars: the more massive a star is, the brighter it is.

Mechanics: The study of the motions of material bodies.

Megaregolith: A 1–2 km thick region of rock fragments and fracturing on the Moon.

Meridian: An imaginary arc on the celestial sphere passing through the poles and zenith and crossing the horizon due south at a right angle.

Metallicity: The abundance of elements other than hydrogen and helium; these are referred to as the "metals." Astronomers call elements such as carbon, iron, nitrogen, and oxygen "metals," and designate them collectively by the letter Z.

Metamorphic rock: Any igneous or sedimentary rock that has been transformed by being subjected to high temperatures, high pressures, impact, or all three.

Meteor: A brief trail of light that marks the destruction of a small particle heated to incandescence by friction with air molecules as it plunges through our atmosphere; a "shooting star."

Meteor shower: Many meteors over a period of several nights that seem to radiate from a common point in the sky; showers are caused by the Earth passing through the debris of a comet.

Meteorite: A part of a small, solid rock that survived the passage through Earth's atmosphere and crashed into the surface; when in space it is called a meteoroid.

Meteoroid: A small, solid rock in space.

Midnight sun: A time when the Sun is visible for 24 hours.

Milky Way Galaxy: The galaxy in which the Sun is located.

Milky Way: The luminous band visible in the night sky representing a part of one structural component of our Galaxy.

Mineral: A chemical compound in the form of solid crystals that make up rocks.

Molecular clouds: Dark, dense, cold places of interstellar molecules at densities thousands of times greater than that of the interstellar medium.

Molecular outflows: High-velocity outflows of gas in two directions from newly formed stars.

Morphology: The form and structure of an object.

Neap tides: The tides that occur when the Moon is at first or third quarter; the tidal effects of the Moon and Sun partially cancel at neap tides producing the smallest difference between high and low tides.

Nebula: Any diffuse cloudlike, nonstellar-looking object; since many objects looked fuzzy through early telescopes, the term refers to H II regions, supernovae remnants (Crab nebula), and galaxies (Andromeda nebula).

Neutrino: A fundamental particle without mass or electrical charge.

Neutron: An electrically neutral subatomic particle.

Neutron star: The neutron core of an exploded star.

New moon: The phase of the Moon in which the sunlit half faces away from the Earth.

Newton's laws: Three laws of motion and one of gravitation formulated by Isaac Newton.

Node: The intersection of an orbit with a fundamental plane, such as the Moon's orbit with the ecliptic.

Nonthermal radiation: Radiation, such as synchrotron radiation, that does not follow a Planck curve.

Northern Hemisphere: The area on the Earth north of the equator.

Nova: A nuclear explosion on a white dwarf, causing a rapid increase in brightness of many magnitudes.

Nuclear bulge: The large, bright, glowing stellar aggregation at the center of a galaxy.

Nuclear energy: Energy derived from the annihilation of matter.

Nucleosynthesis: The creation of heavy elements from light elements through thermonuclear reactions at the centers of stars and during supernovae.

Nucleus (of a comet): The solid part of a comet composed of a loose, porous conglomerate of dust grains embedded in ices.

Nucleus (of a galaxy): The central concentration of matter in a galaxy; the center of the nuclear bulge.

Objective: The main lens or mirror of a telescope; the size of a telescope is given as the diameter of the objective.

Occultation: An eclipse of a planet or star by the Moon or a planet.

Oort cloud: A reservoir of cometary nuclei orbiting the Sun at distances of up to 100,000 AU.

Open cluster: A cluster of stars found in the disk of the Milky Way Galaxy characterized by its openness, allowing the observer to see through the cluster; also called galactic cluster.

Open universe: A universe that will continue to expand forever because the gravitational force between galaxies is not strong enough to halt the expansion.

Opposition: The position in the orbit of a superior planet when it is directly opposite the Sun on the celestial sphere and is closest to the Earth.

Optical binary: Stars that appear to be a double star system but which are not gravitationally bound to each other; they just happen to lie in nearly the same direction from Earth.

Orbital: The "orbit" of an electron about the nucleus of an atom.

Outgassing: The process by which gases inside a planet or moon are expelled through the crust.

P waves: Waves in which the particles move back and forth along the direction of travel.

Pair production: The complete conversion of the energy of colliding photons into an amount of matter dictated by Einstein's relation, $m = E/c^2$.

Paleomagnetism: Remnant magnetization in ancient rocks; also the study of such "fossil" magnetism.

Parent body: A body from which meteorites formed as sections of it broke off through collisions.

Parent nucleus: The nucleus of the original radioactive element in spontaneous radioactive decay.

Parsec: A unit of distance used in astronomy; the distance (3.26 light-years) to a star that has a parallax of 1 second of arc.

Partial eclipse: An eclipse viewed from the penumbra.

Path of totality: The path of the lunar umbral shadow across the surface of the Earth.

Pauli exclusion principle: States that no two electrons, or any two identical subatomic particles, can occupy the same "quantum state."

Penumbra: The partially lighted area of a shadow surrounding the umbra.

Perfect gas law: The relationship between temperature, density, and pressure of an ideal gas.

Perigee: The location in the orbit of a satellite around the Earth at which it is nearest to the Earth.

Perihelion: The point in a planet's elliptical orbit at which it is closest to the Sun.

Period-luminosity relation: Observed correlation between pulsation period and luminosity for Cepheid variables; brighter stars take longer to pulsate than fainter stars.

Periodic comets: Comets whose elliptical orbits are well determined and have periods less than 200 years; also called "short period" comets.

Phases of the Moon: Changes in the fraction of the sunlit side of the Moon visible to observers on Earth.

Photodisintegration: The destruction of atomic nuclei by the collision with a high-energy photon; occurs at temperatures greater than 10^9 K.

Photographic plate: Glass that has a light-sensitive coating, called an emulsion, cemented onto it; when the emulsion is exposed to light and then developed, it produces a permanent record of an image, called a negative.

Photon: A discrete unit of electromagnetic energy having both particle and wave behavior; the energy of a photon is inversely proportional to its wavelength.

Photon sphere: The distance from a collapsed object at which photons circle.

Photosphere: The bright, thin, lowermost layer of the Sun's atmosphere from which we receive most sunlight.

Photosynthesis: The production of organic molecules, mainly carbohydrates, and atmospheric oxygen from carbon dioxide and water in the presence of sunlight by green, or chlorophyll-bearing, plants.

Pixel: Abbreviation of the term *picture element;* an individual component of a digital image.

Planck curve: A graph of intensity versus wavelength for a black body.

Plane: Any flat, level, or even surface.

Planet: Any of the nine large bodies that orbit the Sun; any large solid body orbiting a star.

Planetary nebula nucleus: The exposed interior of a supergiant star found at the center of a planetary nebula.

Planetary nebula: The glowing, ejected envelope and atmosphere of a supergiant; the core of the supergiant appears as a hot star at the center of the nebula.

Planetesimal: A small (centimeters to hundreds of kilometers) body that condensed out of and grew in the solar nebula; eventually accreted to form the planets, moons, asteroids, and comets found in the solar system today.

Plate tectonics: The theory and study of plate formation, movement, interaction, and destruction; the attempt to explain the formation and deformation of large-scale structural features on Earth in terms of plate motions.

Plates: Rigid segments of the lithosphere that move independently of each other.

Polar cap: An ice cap usually located at the rotational axes of a planet or moon.

Populations: Two broad but distinct groups of stars in the Galaxy. Clusters and individual stars with characteristics similar to the open cluster stars, such as Type I Cepheids and the Sun, are called Population I. Globular clusters and old stars, such as RR Lyrae variables and Type II Cepheids, are called Population II.

Position angle: In binary stars, the angle between north and the fainter component measured toward the east.

Pre–main-sequence stars: Stars that have completely dissipated any surrounding gas and dust and are evolving approximately horizontally on the HR diagram with nearly constant luminosity but with increasing temperatures.

Precession: A slow, conical motion of the rotational axis of a spinning body.

Pressure: The force per unit area exerted by a fluid (gas or liquid) against a surface within itself or bounding it.

Proper motion: The annual motion of a star on the celestial sphere; measured in "/yr.

Proton: A positively charged subatomic particle.

Proton-proton chain: The nuclear reactions that convert hydrogen into helium.

Protostar: A collapsing fragment of a molecular cloud that forms a single or multiple star; the term refers to all phases of the collapse before nuclear burning on the main sequence.

Protosun: The hot concentration of matter at the center of the solar nebula that eventually formed the Sun.

Pulsar: A rotating neutron star.

Quantum mechanics: A mathematical theory in physics that starts with the assumption that energy is not infinitely divisible and describes subatomic particles and the interaction between themselves and with electromagnetic radiation.

Quark: A fundamental constituent of matter with a fractional electric charge.

Quarter moon: Either of two phases of the Moon (first or third quarter) where the Moon appears half full.

Quasar: A distant galaxy with emission lines of large redshifts; also referred to as a QSO.

Quiescent prominence: A luminous cloud of gas in the corona of the Sun; it represents coronal gases falling to the photosphere by following magnetic field lines toward sunspots below.

Radial velocity: The component of a star's velocity directed away from or toward the observer along the line of sight; measured from spectra using the Doppler effect on the spectral lines.

Radial velocity curve: A graph of the radial velocity of a double-star system versus time.

Radiant: Point in the sky from which meteors, due to cometary debris traveling parallel to each other, appear to diverge as they approach us.

Radiation laws: Mathematical equations that describe the relationship between the distribution of radiation at different wavelengths emitted and temperature; Wien's law, Stefan-Boltzmann law, and Planck's law.

Radiative transport: The transfer of heat from hot regions to cold regions by electromagnetic radiation.

Radio galaxy: A galaxy that emits a greater amount of radio radiation than normal; also called active galaxy.

Radioactivity: The spontaneous disintegration of unstable atomic nuclei, resulting in the ejection of a helium nucleus, an electron, or a gamma ray.

Radiometric dating: A process that derives the age of a rock from the analysis of its radioactive parent and daughter atoms.

Rays: Bright streaks emanating radially away from the primary crater, consisting of fine particles of ejecta, very small secondary craters, and local surface regolith disturbed by the falling debris.

Red giant: A large, cool star of high luminosity that has converted all of its hydrogen in its core to helium.

Red giant branch: The part of the evolutionary track that rises steeply in luminosity after hydrogen exhaustion in the core.

Redshift: A Doppler shift toward the red part of the spectrum; means motion away from observer.

Reflectance spectra: Spectra produced by reflected sunlight off a surface.

Reflecting telescope: A telescope that brings electromagnetic radiation to a focus by reflecting light off a mirror.

Reflection nebula: Bright regions of dust reflecting light from nearby hot stars.

Refracting telescope: A telescope that brings electromagnetic radiation to a focus by refracting light through a lens.

Refraction: The bending of electromagnetic radiation passing from one transparent medium to another.

Refractory element: An element or compound characterized by high melting temperature.

Regolith: Crushed rock fragments weathered by meteorite bombardment lying on the surface of the Moon and other bodies.

Regular solid: A three-dimensional figure in which (1) all edges are of equal lengths; (2) all facing sides have equal areas; and (3) all corners and angles between corners are the same.

Relative ages: Ages meaningful only in relationship in time; one object is older than another.

Relative orbit: The orbit of one double star (the fainter star) referred to the other (the brighter star).

Remote sensing: The detection of electromagnetic radiation from distant objects with instruments located far from the observer.

Resolution: The degree to which fine detail of an image can be separated or resolved.

Resonance: Gravitational tugs by one body on another that repeat; they occur with the same strength at the same relative configuration.

Retrograde motion: The westward motion of a planet relative to the stars on the celestial sphere.

Retrograde rotation: Planetary rotation in the opposite direction of the Earth's rotation.

Revolution: The motion of one body around another.

Roche limit: The outer boundary of a zone in which a satellite may break up due to tidal forces generated by the planet it orbits; Roche originally calculated this limit for a liquid satellite. Pronounced "ro sh."

Rotation curve: A plot of orbital velocities versus distance from the galactic center for any galaxy.

Rotation limit: A point during the collapse of a galaxy at which rotation balances gravity, allowing dust and gas to circle in a disk instead of falling toward the center.

Rotation: The spinning of an object about an axis running through it.

RR Lyrae variables: A group of small, hot pulsating stars with periods less than 1 day; like Cepheid variables, RR Lyrae are also used as distance indicators.

S waves: Waves in which particle motion is perpendicular to the direction of propagation.

Scarp: A rounded cliff caused by one block of rock riding over another as a result of compression.

Schwarzschild radius: The radius of a neutron core at which escape velocity equals the speed of light.

Science: A consistent body of knowledge, strongly tied to experiment, and expressed in as few laws as possible.

Scientific laws: Statements or mathematical relations formulated from facts of nature.

Scientific method: The process or sequence of steps that are followed in formulating scientific laws: (1) obtain facts of nature through observations, experiments, collecting, or cataloging; (2) summarize the facts in the form of a hypothesis; (3) deduce consequences of the hypothesis and test them.

Scientific revolution: The two hundred years of intellectual advancement following the Renaissance.

Secondary craters: Craters formed by the impact of debris thrown out of primary craters.

Sedimentary rock: Rock that is an accumulation of fragments of rocks either by mechanical means, such as the transport of fragments by wind forming sand dunes, or by hydraulic means, such as moving grains down a river to a delta or settling on the ocean floor.

Seismic waves: Vibrations produced by earthquakes and explosions that propagate through the Earth's interior and across its surface as a result of an elastic response of the Earth; they occur in other planets and moons as well.

Seismograph: An instrument that detects and records seismic waves.

Self-propagating star formation: Star formation characterized by repeated generation of stars in giant molecular clouds by successive generations of massive stars.

Semimajor axis: One-half the longest distance across an ellipse.

Shell source: A thin region of nuclear burning surrounding the core of a star; more than one shell source can be present in a star at the same time.

Shield volcano: A volcano that arises from thousands of fluid lava flows forming a large flattened dome, similar in shape to an ancient war shield lying on the ground.

Shock wave: A surface of highly compressed gas moving through a medium (air or interstellar space, for instance) at the speed of sound; shock waves are produced by an object moving at greater than the speed of sound.

Sidereal day: The time it takes for the Earth or another body to turn exactly once on its axis; for Earth it is $23^h\ 56^m\ 4^s$.

Silicate: Any of a large class of minerals containing silicon and oxygen mixed with calcium, aluminum, and other elements.

Sinuous rilles: Long, narrow lunar features that may be collapsed lava tubes.

Solar constant: The amount of energy passing through one square centimeter every second at the Earth's orbit.

Solar cycle: The 22-year period in which the global solar magnetic field returns to a given polarity.

Solar day: The interval of time between meridian crossings of the Sun; for the Earth it is 24^h.

Solar eclipse: When the Moon's shadow sweeps across parts of the surface of the Earth.

Solar flare: Localized, short-lived, explosive bursts of light, X-rays, and particles from the vicinity of sunspots.

Solar nebula: The isolated collapsed fragment of a molecular cloud out of which were formed the Sun, planets, and lesser bodies in the solar system.

Solar wind: A continuous stream of ionized gas, mostly protons and electrons, escaping from the Sun.

Southern Hemisphere: The area on the Earth south of the equator.

Space velocity: The speed and direction of a star in space relative to the Sun.

Spacetime: A single term that describes the three spatial coordinates and time.

Species: The basic category of biological classification in which related individuals resemble each other and are able to breed among themselves but not with other species.

Spectral line: A radiative feature in a spectrum of a star or planet representing an excess of radiation (emission line) or a deficiency of radiation (absorption line).

Spectrograph: An instrument designed to photographically or electronically record a spectrum.

Spectroscopic binary: Double star detected by periodic shifts of spectral lines and occasionally by overlapping of two normal spectra (double-line spectroscopic binary).

Spectrum: The array of wavelengths obtained after dispersing light.

Spicules: Spearlike projections of the chromosphere of the Sun.

Spin-orbit coupling: The ratio of the number of complete rotations to complete revolution of a planet or moon.

Spiral arm: A pattern of dust, gas, and visible stars that winds, or spirals, outward from near the center of a galaxy; spiral arms are located in the disk of a galaxy.

Spiral galaxy: A galaxy characterized by a nuclear bulge, a flat disk, a halo of old stars, and spiral arms.

Spring (vernal) equinox: The point on the celestial sphere where the Sun crosses the celestial equator moving from south to north; occurs on March 20 or 21.

Spring tides: The tides that occur when the Sun and Moon line up with the Earth at new moon and full moon; in the absence of storms spring tides produce the highest tidal differences.

Star: A self-luminous sphere of gas.

Star cluster: A group of stars formed at the same time and place held together by their mutual gravitation.

Stefan-Boltzmann law: The mathematical equation that relates the amount of energy in the radiation of a black body or a star to its temperature; the total energy emitted through each square centimeter of the surface of a black body every second is proportional to its temperature raised to the fourth power.

Stellar evolution: Changes in the physical characteristics of stars, such as luminosity, temperature, and radius, as they age and deplete their nuclear fuel reserves.

Stellar parallax: The apparent motion of stars caused by the Earth's motion around the Sun; the term parallax is also used to denote the angle subtended by 1 AU at the distance of a star.

Stone: A meteorite composed mainly of silicates with only 10–15% iron and nickel.

Stony-iron: A meteorite composed of about half iron and half silicate.

Stratification: Arranged in layers or strata.

Stratosphere: The layer of the Earth's atmosphere between approximately 10 km and 50 km above the surface.

Strength (of spectral lines): A measure of how many photons were absorbed by a certain transition; calculated by measuring the amount of light subtracted from the Planck curve at the wavelengths of the lines.

Sublimation: The process by which a solid (an ice for example), when heated, becomes a gas without passing through the liquid phase.

Summer solstice: The point on the celestial sphere where the Sun reaches its greatest distance north of the celestial equator; occurs on June 21 or 22.

Sunspot: A dark region of intense magnetic fields in the Sun's photosphere; it appears darker because it is cooler than the surrounding photosphere.

Sunspot cycle: The 11-year cycle between the minimum and the maximum number of sunspots on the surface of the Sun.

Supercluster: A cluster of clusters of galaxies; usually in long (hundreds of millions of parsecs) strings of galaxies and clusters of galaxies.

Supergiant: The brightest giant stars; they are passing through advanced nuclear burning phases.

Supergranule: A large granule about thirty times larger than a normal granule.

Superior conjunction: The place in the orbit of an inferior planet where it is on the opposite side of the Sun from the Earth.

Superior planet: The planets that are more distant from the Sun than the Earth: Mars, Jupiter, Saturn, Uranus, Neptune, and Pluto.

Supernova: A catastrophic explosion of a star during which the star becomes millions of times brighter; a Type I supernova is the disruptive explosion of a white dwarf and a Type II supernova is the explosion of a massive (more than 6–8 solar masses) star.

Supernova remnants: The expanding debris of a supernova; forms a shock wave as it moves through the interstellar medium.

Surface gravity: The acceleration produced by the gravitational attraction of an object at the surface of a body; the weight of one gram at the surface of a body.

Synchrotron radiation: Radiation emitted by electrons traveling at nearly the speed of light in a magnetic field.

Synodic period of the Moon: The period of time from new moon to new moon.

Synodic period: The length of time between successive occurrences of a planetary or lunar configuration.

3 K microwave background radiation: Present temperature of the radiation field filling the universe; this radiation has been redshifted by the expansion of the universe until its Planck spectrum is that of a 3 K black body.

21-cm line: The spectral line of neutral hydrogen at the radio wavelength of 21.11 cm.

T Tauri stars: Recently formed protostars still shedding mass and contracting toward the main sequence.

T Tauri wind: A phase in the evolution of a young star during which it ejects a tremendous amount of matter into the surrounding interstellar space.

Tail (of a comet): Gas and dust grains forced away from the coma by the solar wind and the pressure of sunlight.

Tangential velocity: The part of a star's velocity across our line of sight in the plane of the sky; determined from measured proper motions and distances.

Terraforming: Large-scale planetary engineering to produce Earth-like environments.

Terrestrial planets: The Earth-like planets: Mercury, Venus, Earth, and Mars.

Theory: A hypothesis or set of hypotheses and laws that has gathered considerable experimental support.

Thermal pressure: Pressure due to the motions of atoms and molecules; the force per unit area exerted by a fluid (gas or liquid) against a surface within itself or bounding it.

Thermal radiation: Radiation from any object with a temperature greater than absolute zero.

Thermonuclear reaction: The high-speed collision of two nuclei resulting in the fusion of the nuclei into a different element.

Third-quarter moon: The phase of the Moon occurring about three weeks after new moon, in which half of the side facing the Earth is sunlit.

Tides: The gravitational distortion of one celestial object by another; normally refers to the alternate rise and fall of the Earth's surface of oceans.

Total solar eclipse: A solar eclipse in which the shadow of the Moon reaches the Earth's surface; observers within the shadow's umbra will experience a total solar eclipse.

Transverse seismic waves: Waves in which particle motion is perpendicular to the direction of propagation; also called S waves.

Triple alpha process: The nuclear reactions that convert helium into carbon.

Tropic of Cancer: Places on the Earth with latitudes of 23½° north of the equator.

Tropic of Capricorn: Places on the Earth with latitudes of 23½° south of the equator.

Tropical year: The length of time for the Sun to travel exactly once around the celestial sphere with respect to the vernal equinox.

Troposphere: The bottommost layer of the Earth's atmosphere where temperature decreases with altitude.

Twilight: The interval of time preceding sunrise and following sunset during which the Earth's surface is partially illuminated by sky brightness; the Sun is below the horizon during twilight.

Type I supernova: The catastrophic disruption of a white dwarf; it does not exhibit hydrogen lines in its spectrum.

Type II supernova: The explosion of a massive star that leaves either a neutron star or a black hole; spectrum exhibits hydrogen emission lines.

Umbra: The inner region of a shadow where there is no illumination.

Van Allen belts: Two doughnut-shaped regions above Earth's magnetic equator where electrons and protons oscillate in a north-south direction in Earth's magnetic field.

Velocity dispersion: The spread in the Doppler shifts (radial velocities) as measured from the spectra of elliptical galaxies.

Velocity of light: The velocity of all electromagnetic radiation traveling in a vacuum and is equal to 299,792 km/s (186,282 miles per second).

Vernal (spring) equinox: The point on the celestial sphere where the Sun crosses the celestial equator moving from south to north; occurs on March 20 or 21.

Visual binary: Double star in which both components are individually visible.

Volatile element: An element or compound characterized by low melting temperature; it is loosely bound to existing mineral structure and, therefore, easily escapes upon heating.

Waning crescent: The phases of the Moon between third-quarter and new moon.

Waning: The decrease of the fraction of the illuminated side of the Moon visible from the Earth.

Waning gibbous: The phases of the Moon between full and third-quarter.

Watt: A unit of power describing how fast energy is being used; measured in joules per second.

Wavelength: The distance between successive maxima or minima of a wave; usually designated by the Greek letter lambda, λ.

Waxing crescent: The phases of the Moon between new moon and first-quarter moon.

Waxing: The increase of the fraction of the illuminated side of the Moon visible from the Earth.

Waxing gibbous: The phases of the Moon between first-quarter and full.

White dwarf: The exposed carbon-oxygen core of a red supergiant supported by degenerate electron gas pressure.

Widmanstätten patterns: Interlocking long crystal patterns in iron alloys and meteorites.

Wien's displacement law: The mathematical relationship between the wavelength of maximum intensity of a Planck curve and the temperature of the emitting black body; the temperature is inversely proportional to the maximum wavelength.

Wind: The horizontal motion of air due to horizontal differences in air pressure.

Winter solstice: The point on the celestial sphere where the Sun reaches its greatest distance south of the celestial equator; occurs on December 21 or 22.

Wormholes: Hypothetical tunnels through spacetime.

X: The hydrogen abundance in a star or planetary atmosphere expressed as the fraction of the total mass that is hydrogen.

Y: The helium abundance in a star or planetary atmosphere expressed as the fraction of the total mass that is helium.

Z: The mass fraction of all elements more massive than helium; also called metallicity.

Zeeman effect: The splitting of spectral lines by an external magnetic field.

Zenith: The point on the celestial sphere directly overhead the observer.

Zero-age main sequence: The main sequence for a cluster of stars consisting of stars that have just begun to convert hydrogen into helium in their cores.

Zones: Light colored bands of high pressure seen running parallel to the equator of the Jovian planets; zones are believed to be regions of rising gas.

Index

A

A0620-00, 580
Aberration
  chromatic, M2-5, M2-8, M2-10
  spherical, M2-5, M2-6, M2-9, M2-10, M2-20
Absolute age, 172
Absolute orbit, 491–92
Absolute magnitude, 485–87, 594–95, 631, 644, 645, 646
Absolute zero, M1-13
Absorption lines, 141, 148, 425, 454, 457
Absorption spectrum, 141
Acceleration, 110, 120
Accelerators, 151, 152
Accretion, 397–99
  disk, 580, 641, 642, 643
  planetary, 399–402
Achromatic lens, M2-10
Acid rain, 384–85, 444
Active galaxies, 641–44
Adams, John, 300, 306
Adrastea, 327, 330
Age. See specific entity, e.g., Earth, age
Ahmar, M1-4
Alcor, 493, OH-7
Aldebaran, OH-17
Alfonsine Tables, OH-1, OH-4
Alfonso X (king of Spain), OH-1
Algol, 497, 498, OH-4, OH-16
Alignment, 71–72, 81
Allende meteorite, 362
Almagest, 85, M2-1
Alpha Capricorni, OH-14
Alpha capture, 552, A-13
Alpha Centauri, 467–68, 493
Alpha decay, 144–45
Alpha Orionis. See Betelgeuse
Alpha particles, 144, 552
Alps (Moon), 212, OH-27
Altair, OH-21
Altitude, 39, 40
Alvarez, Luis, 384
Alvarez, Walter, 384
Amalthea, 327, 330
Amplitude modulation, 318–19
Analog signals, 317–18
Analytical reading, I-2, I-3 to I-6

Andromeda (constellation), OH-7, OH-12
Andromeda galaxy (M31), 598, 631, 633, 647, 650–54, 676, OH-7, OH-12
Angles, M1-8 to M1-10
Anglo-Australian Telescope, 3, 480
Ångström, 131
Ångström, Andres J., 131
Angular diameter, 54
Angular measurement, 465–66, M1-8 to M1-11
Angular resolution, M2-11, M2-25 to M2-26
Annihilation, 670–71
Annular solar eclipse, 57, 59
Anorthosite, 216, 217
Antarctic Circle, 44
Antares, OH-23, OH-24
Antimatter, 153
Antineutrinos, 153, 566, 670–71
Antiparticles, 152–53
Antlia, OH-1
Apennines (Moon), OH-27
Aperature, M2-3
  synthesis, M2-25 to M2-26
Aphelion, 99, 100, 195–96
Aphrodite Terra (Venus), 246, 248
Apian, Peter, 370
Apogee, 119
Apollo (spacecraft/missions), 185, 205, 206, 215, 216
Apollo asteroids, 365–66, 381, 416, A-1
Apparent celestial motions, 37–68
  Moon, 47–53
  planets, 62–68
  stars, 37–40
  Sun, 41–46
Apparent magnitude, 460–61, 462, 594, 631, 646
Approximation signs, 34–35
Aquarius, OH-13
Aquila, OH-1, OH-21, OH-22, OH-23
Archaeoastronomy, 3, 70–81
  ancient observatories, 73–77
  lunar calendars and eclipse prediction, 77–81
  solar calendars, 70–72
Arc length, M1-9
Arc, minutes of, 465, M1-8
Arc, seconds of, 466, M1-8, M2-11

Arctic Circle, 44
Arcturus, 456, OH-20 to OH-21
Areas, M1-11, M1-12, M1-13
Arecibo radio telescope, 242, M2-25
Ariel, 325, 335, 336
A ring, 324, 341, 343
Aristarchus of Samos, 86–87, 89
Aristotle, 103, 369, OH-15
Artificial gravity, 281
Asterisms, OH-7
Asteroids, 357–61, 365–68, 381–82. See also Apollo asteroids; Asteroid belt; Trojans
  classification by composition, 361
  discovery, 357–59
  extinction of dinosaurs and, 384–90
  list of, A-1
  meteorites and, 364–65
  orbits of, 365, 366–67
  relative ages, 401
  sizes, 359–60, 361, 367, 382
Asteroid belt, 258, 278, 291, 365–67, A-1
Asthenosphere, 166, 167
Astrobiology (exobiology), 3
Astrochemistry, 3
Astrodynamics, 3
Astrogeology, 3
Astrometric binary, 494, 535, 564
Astrometry, 494, 535–36
Astronomers, 3–4. See also individual astronomers
  amateur, role of, 357, 359, 360
  ancient, 86–89. See also Archaeoastronomy
  of scientific revolution, 89–113
Astronomical constants, A-3
Astronomical unit (AU), 90, A-3
Astronomy, 2, 3
  Day, 357
Astrophysics, 3
Atmosphere. See specific entity, e.g., Earth, atmosphere
Atmospheric pressure, 178–79
Atmospheric turbulence (seeing and), M2-11
Atomic constants, A-3
Atomic number, 138
Atomic spectra, 140–44
Atomic weight, 137

Atoms, 137, 138. *See also* Nuclear reactions
  excited state, 142
  heavy elements, 571–72
  ionized state, 143
Auriga, OH-16, OH-17
Aurora (e), 185–86, 449, 450
  on Jupiter, 298
Australian Radio Telescope, Compact Array, M2-26, M2-27, M2-28 to M2-29
Autumnal equinox, 42–43, OH-5, OH-19
Autumn constellations, OH-7, OH-12 to OH-14
Average density, 160
Average value, M1-5
Awbery, Frank, 692

B

Baade, Walter, 367, 573, 598, 613
Background extinction, 386
Baily, Solon I., 595
Bar charts, 26
Barnard, Edward E., 322, 519
Barnard's star, 471, 536
Barred spirals (galaxies), 632–33
Basins (impact)
  Mercury, 224
  Moon, 212, 215, 217
Bell, Jocelyn, 573
Belts (Jovian planets), 295–96
Bessel, Friedrich W., 494, 564
Beta Andromedae, OH-12
Beta Capricorni, OH-14
Beta Cygni, OH-22
Beta Lyrae, OH-22
Beta Persei. *See* Algol
Beta Pictoris, 535
Beta rays, 144
Beta Regio (Venus), 245, 246, 247, 248
Beta Scorpii, OH-24
Betelgeuse, 462, 463, OH-4, OH-14
Bethe, Hans, 422
Biblical creationism, 692–98
Biermann, Ludwig, 373
Big bang, 5, 667–73, 687
Big Dipper, 472, 493, OH-7
Bighorn Medicine Wheel (Wyoming), 72, 77, 78
Binary clusters (galaxies), 656, 657
Binary numbers, 318–19, 508, 509
Binary stars, 490–99, 503–4, 535, 537
  astrometric, 494, 535, 564
  black holes and, 580
  eclipsing, 497–98, 501
  spectroscopic, 495–97, 499
  visual, 493, 499
  white dwarfs and, 564, 565

Bipolar outflows, 526–27, 641–42, 643
Bit, 318, 508–9
Black body, 134
Black holes, 576–81, 582, 608, 688
  active galaxies and, 641–43
  galactic center and, 615–16
  quasars and, 649
Blink-microscope comparator, 306
Blueshift, 470, 494, 495
  Cepheid variables, 558
  planetary nebulae, 562
  21-cm line, 602
B magnitude, 462–65
Bode, Johann, 299, 357–58
Bode's law. *See* Titus-Bode law
Bok, Bart, 519
Bok globules, 519, 520
Bolide, 362
Boltzmann, Ludwig, 135
Bonner Durchmusterung (BD) catalog, OH-4
Boötes, OH-6, OH-20 to OH-21
Bow shock, 184, 185
Brahe, Tycho, 83, 93–97, 98, 99, 102, 108, 369, 568, M2-1
Brecciated rock, 208, 216, 217
B ring, 324, 341, 343
Brook's comet, 379
"Bug" nebula, 563
Bunsen, Robert, 141
Butterfly diagram, 430, 431

C

Caldera, 262
Calendars, 18–20, 70–72, 77–79
Calibration (of period-luminosity relation), 644–46
Callisto, 322, 326–28, 329
Calypso, 334
Canadian Long-Baseline Array, M2-29
Canals (Mars), 253, 256
Cancer, OH-18
Canis Major, 463, OH-15
Cannibalism (galactic), 6, 643–44, 655–56
Cannon, Annie J., 454, 456, 457
Capella, OH-17
Capricornus, OH-13, to OH-14
Caracol tower (Yucatán), 72, 75–76
Carbonaceous chondrites, 271
Carbonaceous meteorites, 364
Carbon burning, 553, 554, A-13 to A-14
Carbon-nitrogen-oxygen cycle, A-13
Cas A (supernova), 568–69
Cassegrain reflector, M2-9
Cassegrain, Sieur, M2-9

Cassini division, 323, 324, 341, 342, 343–44
Cassini, Giovanni Domenico, 323, 324, M2-7
Cassiopeia, 93, 94, 593, OH-12, OH-13
Castor, 498, 499, OH-17
cD galaxies, 643, 655, 656
Celestial equator, 37, 38, OH-4, OH-5
Celestial equatorial coordinate system, OH-4 to OH-6
Celestial horizon, 13, 39
Celestial north and south poles, 37, 38, 161, OH-4
Celestial sphere, 13
Celsius (centigrade) scale, M1-12 to M1-13
Central peak (craters), 212, 225
Cepheid variables, 558–59
  as distance indicators, 594, 631, 644–46
  short-period, 595
Cepheus, OH-12, OH-13
Ceres, 358, 359, 361, 365
Cerro Tololo Inter-American Observatory, 476, 477, M2-22
Chandrasekhar limit, 555, 565
Chandrasekhar, S., 555, 564
Charge coupled devices (CCDs), 317, 513-14, M2-34 to M2-35, M2-37
Charles E. Daniel Observatory, 478, 479
Charon, 309–10, 311, 312
Chemical elements. *See* Elements
Chinese tower, 72, 76–77
Chiron, 367, 368
Chloroflurocarbons, 176
Chrondrites, 364
Christy, James, 309
Chromatic aberration, M2-5, M2-8, M2-10
Chromosphere, 435–36
Chryse Planitia (Mars), 261, 262, 263, 264, 278
Circles, M1-8 to M1-10, M1-11 to M1-12
Circumference, M1-11, M1-12
Circumpolar stars, 40
Clark, Alvan, M2-16 to M2-18
Clark, Alvan G., 564, M2-17
Climate, 444-48, 450-51
Closed universe, 683–87
Clusters, galaxies, 650–58
  Coma cluster, 654–55
  Local Group, 650–54, 657, 676, 678
  superclusters, 5–6, 656, 657–58
  Virgo cluster, 654, 655, 656, 657, 678
Clusters, star, 538–41, 644–45
  globular, 560, 561, 595–96, 597, 598, 599, 600–601, 609, 610, 632, 635
  open, 597–99, 600–601, 606, 609, 610, 652

Co-accretion model (of satellite
    formation), 403–4, 405
Color index, 463–65, 518
Color-magnitude diagram, 597, 598,
    644–45
Coma (of a comet), 374, 375–76, 377,
    378
Coma Berenices (constellation), M2-14,
    OH-21
    cluster of galaxies at, 654–55
Comet(s), 278, 368–81, 382
    Biela, 372, 373
    Brook's, 379
    coma of, 374, 375–76, 377, 378
    early observations, 368–70
    Encke, 380
    extinction of dinosaurs and,
        384–90
    Giacobini-Zinner, 374
    Halley and, 370–71
    Halley's, 100, 369, 370–71, 374–78,
        379, 380, 381
    icy-conglomerate model, 373
    list of, A-2
    meteor showers and, 372–73
    nucleus, 374–75, 376, 378
    origin, 378, 380–81
    periodic (short-period), 373
    study of, 373–74
    tail, 376–78
    variety of forms, 378, 379
    West, 368, 373, 379
Comparison spectrum, 470
Compressional (P) waves, 163–64
Condensation, 397
    sequence, 398
Cone nebula, 520, 530, OH-15
Conjunction, 63, 64, 66
Constellations, 453, OH-1 to OH-4. See
    also specific constellations
    circumpolar, OH-7
    names, 354–55, OH-2 to OH-3
    in star charts, OH-6 to OH-24
        autumn, OH-7, OH-12 to OH-14
        polar, OH-7
        spring, OH-19 to OH-21
        summer, OH-21 to OH-24
        winter, OH-14 to OH-19
Continental drift, 168–70, 194
Continuous spectrum, 141
Contrast enhancement, 513
Convection, 168–70, 428
Co-orbitals, 330, 333–34
Copernicus, Nicolaus/Copernican model,
    85, 86, 89–93, 98, 99, 108, 113
Coplanar (characteristic of the solar
    system), 393
Cordelia, 347
Cordillera Mountains (Moon), 212
Core-halo clusters (galaxies), 656

Core helium burning, 552–53, 554, 557–
    58, 560, 565, 570
Core hydrogen burning, 422–23, 523–24,
    551, 554
Coriolis effect, 180
    Jupiter and Saturn, 296
    Mars, 267
    Venus, 252
Coriolis, G. G. de, 180
Corona
    galactic, 608
    of the Sun, 55, 436–39
Corona Borealis, OH-20
Coronal holes, 438
Coronas (Venusian plains), 246
Coronograph, 435
Cosine, M1-11
Cosmic rays, 364, 445–46
Cosmological redshift, 676–77
Cosmology, 2, 667. See also Big bang;
    Universe
Coudé focus, M2-36
Coulomb, Charles A. de, 128, 129
Crab nebula, 6, 567, 568, 573–74, 576
Craters
    Deimos, 270
    Earth, 231–39
        Deep Bay (Canada), 235
        Gosses Bluff (Australia), 238, 239
        Henbury (Australia), 238–39
        Manicouagan (Canada), 235, 236
        Meteor (Arizona), 232, 235–36, 366
        Ries (Germany), 237–38
        Steinheim (Germany), 238
        Sudbury Structure (Canada), 236–
            37, 416
    impact vs. volcanic, 232
    Jupiter's satellites, 327–28, 329
    Mars, 258–60, 264
        Yuty, 260
    Mercury, 223–25
    Moon, 207–13, 214–16, 233, OH-27
        Arago, 211
        Archimedes, OH-27
        Aristarchus, 213
        Bruno, 216
        Copernicus, 215, 217, OH-27
        Eratosthenes, OH-27
        Euler, 210
        Plato, OH-27
        South Ray, 216
        Tycho, 217
    Phobos, 270
        Stickney, 270
    Saturn's satellites, 330, 332, 333
    secondary, 210
    Triton, 341
    Uranus' satellites, 335, 338
    Venus, 246, 247
        Klenova, 247

Creationism, 692–98
Cretaceous-Tertiary (K-T) boundary,
    384–90
C ring, 324, 341, 342, 343
Cubes, M1-11 to M1-12
Curie temperature, 182
Curvature of spacetime, 577–78, 590–91,
    684
Cycloid, 87
Cygnus (constellation), 161, 567, 580,
    600, OH-21 to OH-22, OH-23
Cygnus Loop, 533
Cygnus X-1, 580

D

Data transmission (by spacecraft), 317–
    20
Daughter nucleus, 144, 145, 147
Dawes, William, 255, M2-17
Daylight saving time, 17
Dearborn Observatory, M2-17
Declination, OH-4
Decoupling, 672, 682
Deep Space Network (NASA), 314, 315,
    318, 319
Deferent, 87–89
Degenerate electron gas pressure, 555,
    559
Degenerate neutron gas pressure, 556,
    566
Deimos, 269–71, 272, 276, 360, 404
Delta Cephei, 558
Deneb, 161, OH-21
Density, 160–61, 227, 685
    of common substances, 162
    slicing, 511–12
    waves, 534, 605–6
De Revolutionibus Orbium Coelestrium,
    85, 89
Deuterium, 422–23
Differential gravitational force, 201–4
Differential rotation
    galactic disk, 599, 604–5
    Jovian planets, 288
    Sun, 429, 431–32
Differentiation, 167
Diffraction pattern, M2-11
Digital image processing, 509–13
Digital signals, 317–18
Dinosaurs, extinction of, 384–90
Dione, 331, 332, 333, 334
Dipole, 129
Direct proportionality, M1-1
Disk
    galactic, 597–609, 632
    solar nebula, 394–95, 396, 397–99
Dish antennas, M2-24 to M2-25

Distance 465–68, 644–47
  absolute, 90
  modulus, 487, 595, 631
  relative, 90, 91
  relativity and, 586–87
Diurnal circle, 40, 41
Dolland, John, M2-10
Doppler shifts, 470, 494–95, 498, 636
Dorpat refractor, M2-16
Double stars, 490, OH-7, OH-14, OH-16,
    OH-17, OH-19, OH-21, OH-22, *See*
    also Binary stars
Dresden eclipse tables, 80
Dreyer, J. L. E., 629
D ring, 342, 343
Droughts (and sunspots), 446–47
Dumbbell nebula, 563
Dust, 518–19, 601, 611. *See also*
    Interstellar dust
  grains, 394
  storms (Mars), 257, 263, 266, 267
  tail, 376–77
Dwarf elliptical galaxies, 635, 636, 650,
    653
Dwarf irregular galaxies, 650, 653
Dwarfs, 489, 503, 504–5. *See also* White
    dwarfs
Dynamical friction, 655
Dynamics, 393
Dynamo models, 183

E

Earth, 7, 158–87, 190–97, 199, 200. *See*
    also Craters; Volcanoes
  age, 171–73
  Apollo asteroids and, 365–66
  atmosphere, 158, 174–81, 192–93, 272,
    M2-29 to M2-30
  climate and the Sun, 444–48, 450–51
  core, 162, 164, 166
  crust, 161–62, 163
  data, table of, 159
  de-terraforming of, 274–75
  as habitat for life, 158–59
  ice ages, 190–97, 445–46
  interior, 163–67
  magnetic field, 181–86, 187, 389
  magnetosphere, 183–86
  mantle, 162, 164, 166
  and Moon system
    formation of, 404–5
    size, 8–9
  orbit, 11, 195–97
  plate tectonics, 167–71, 194–95, 272
  radiation belts, 185–86
  size, shape, and mass, 159–61
  stages of development, 406–7

  tides, 201–4
  weather and the Sun, 448–51
Earthquakes, 163–64, 170–71
Eccentricity, 100–101
Eclipse(s), 53–62, 68
  annular, 57, 59
  lunar, 53, 57–60, A-7
  partial, 57
  path, 57
  prediction of, by ancient astronomers,
    79–81
  seasons, 60–62
  solar, 53, 54–57, 58, 59, 589, 590–91,
    A-6
Eclipsing binary, 497–98, 499, 501
Ecliptic, 44–46, 47
Ecosphere, 620
Einstein, Albert, 140, 151, 422, 423, 564,
    577, 579, 585, 586, 588, 590, 680,
    682. *See also* Relativity
Einstein X-Ray Telescope, M2-33
Ejecta blankets
  Mars, 260
  Mercury, 224, 225
  Moon, 207–11
Electromagnetic force, 150–51
Electromagnetic radiation, 130–33, 147
  laws, 133–37
  synchrotron, 614, 640–41, 642
  thermal, 614
  3 K, 677–79
Electromagnetic spectrum, 130–33, 148
Electromagnetism, 128–30, 147
Electronic imaging, M2-34
Electron(s), 129, 137–38
  capture, 555–56, 566
  degeneracy, 555
  spin, 601–2
  transitions, 142–43, 148
Elementary particles, 151–53
Elements, 137–40
  abundances
    Sun, 392–93
    universe, 571, 572, A-4 to A-5
  age, 144–47
  heavy, 571–72
  in early universe, 671–72
  periodic table, 138–39
  radioactive, 144–47
  refractory, 217
  in the solar nebula, distributions of,
    397–99
  volatile, 217
Elliot, James L., 346
Ellipse, 100, 101
Elliptical galaxies, 632, 635–37, 638,
    639, 640, 648, 687
  dwarf, 635, 636, 650, 653
Elongation, 63–64
Elysium Rise (Mars), 259, 262, 264

Emission nebula. *See* H II region
Emission lines, 141, 148
Emulsion (film), 507
Enceladus, 331, 332, 333, 342
Encke division, 324, 341
Encke, Johann Franc, 324
Energy, 135
Energy generation equation, 546–47
Energy level diagram, 142–43
Energy transport equation, 546–47
Epicycle/epicycloid, 87–89, 90
Epimetheus, 333–34
Epoch, OH-6
Epsilon Boötes, OH-21
Epsilon Lyrae, OH-22
Epsilon ring, 347
Equations, 30, M1-3 to M1-4
Equatorial mount (telescopes), M2-12,
    M2-13
Equinoxes, 41, 42–43, 45–46, 195–96
Erg, 135
Eratosthenes, 159–60, 187
E ring, 342, 343
Error (in science), M1-4 to M1-6
Eruptive prominences, 440
Escape velocity, 120–22, 576, 577
Eskimo nebula, 563
Eta Carinae nebula, 521
Europa, 322, 326, 327, 328, 329
Event horizon, 578
Evolutionary tracks, 522, 523, 524, 528,
    530, 531, 556–57, 559, 564
Exchange particles, 155–56
Excited state (of an atom), 142
Exobiology, 3
Extinction
  interstellar, 596
  of life on Earth, 384–90
Extragalactic astronomy, 2
Extraterrestrial civilizations, possibility
    of, 619–27
Eyepiece (telescope), M2-4, M2-9

F

Facsimile camera, 316–17
Fahrenheit scale, M1-12 to M1-13
Falls (meteorite), 362
False color images, 319–20
Fan Mountain Station (Leander
    McCormick Observatory), 478
Finds (meteorite), 362
Fireballs, 362
First-quarter moon, 50
Fission model (of satellite formation),
    403, 404
Five-Kilometer Telescope (England),
    M2-26

Flares. *See* Solar flare
Flash spectrum, 435
Flat universe, 683–87
Fleming, Williamina, 456
Flow fronts, 212, 213
Flux tubes, 431–32
Focal length, M2-3, M2-4, M2-6
Focal ratio, M2-3, M2-4
Focus
  ellipse, 100–101
  lens, M2-3, M2-4
Fomalhaut, 535, OH-14
Fontana, Franciscus, 241
Force(s)
  of nature, 150–56, 668–69
  in Newtonian physics, 109–10
  in quantum mechanics, 155–56
Formation limit, 638–39
40 Eridani, 564
Fossils, 172–73, 386
Foucalt test, M2-18
Fractions, M1-4
Franklin, Benjamin, 128
Fraunhofer, Joseph von, 141
Frequency, 133
Frequency modulation, 318–19
F ring, 342–43, 347, 348
Full moon, 51
Fusion, 422

G

Galactic astronomy, 2
Galactic cannibalism. *See* Galaxies,
  cannibalism
Galactic center, 613–16
Galaxies, 5–6, 629–59
  active, 641–44
  age, 638
  appearances, 632–44
  black holes and, 641–43
  cannibalism, 6, 643–44, 655–56
  cD, 643, 655, 656
  classification, 632–40
  clusters, 650–58
  collisions, 640, 641, 655–56
  diameters, 635
  discovery, 629–32
  distances, 630–32, 644–47
  elliptical, 632, 635–37, 638, 639, 640,
    648, 650, 653, 687
  formation, 638–40, 672–73
  future of, 687–88
  irregular, 635, 637, 638, 639, 640, 650,
    653, 687
  lenticular, 637, 638, 640, 643, 650
  Local Group, 650–54, 657
  luminosities, 635, 646

  mass, 635, 636
  movements of, 676–77, 682, 683
  nucleus, 641–43, 649, 650
  quasars and, 644, 647–50
  radio, 641–44
  redshifts, 648–50, 676–77
  rotation, 635, 636, 638–40
  satellite, 640, OH-12
  specific. *See* Galaxies, specific
  spectra, 646–47
  spirals, 534, 535, 604–7, 632–35, 638,
    639, 642, 648, 649, 650, 687, 688
  stellar populations, 632, 633, 635, 637,
    638
  superclusters, 656, 657–58
Galaxies, specific
  Andromeda (M31), 598, 631, 633, 647,
    650–54, 676, OH-7, OH-12
  Fornax, 636
  IC 1613, 639, 650, 653
  Leo I, 636
  M61, 654
  M82, 639
  M87, 637, 650
  M100, 654
  Maffei I, 650
  Magellanic Clouds, 569, 580, 594, 599,
    639, 650, 653, 654
  Markarian, 205, 662
  Milky Way. *See* Milky Way Galaxy
  NGC 205, 652, 653
  NGC 221 (M32), 637, 652, 653
  NGC 253, 632
  NGC 628, 605
  NGC 1073, 663
  NGC 1265, 644
  NGC 1275, 642
  NGC 1300, 634
  NGC 1316, 642
  NGC 2403, 646
  NGC 2685, 638
  NGC 2992, 656
  NGC 2993, 656
  NGC 2997, 601
  NGC 3031 (M81), 634
  NGC 3034, (M82), 639
  NGC 3115, 637
  NGC 4038/4039, 641
  NGC 4319, 62, 663
  NGC 4486 (M87), 637, 650
  NGC 4565, 610, 634, 635, OH-21
  NGC 4593, 663
  NGC 4594, 633, 634
  NGC 4622, 633, 634
  NGC 4762, 638
  NGC 4874, 655
  NGC 4889, 655
  NGC 5457 (M101), 633, 634
  NGC 5586, 638
  NGC 6744, 605

  NGC 6822, 650, 653
  Phoenix, 655
  Sombrero, OH-20
  Triangulum (M33), 650, 651, 652,
    OH-12
  Whirlpool (M51), 535, 630
Galilean satellites, 105, 322, 326–29, 349
Galilean transformations, 585–86
Galilei, Galileo, 83, 93, 98, 102–8, 113,
  116, 204, 253, 254, 290, 300, 322,
  323, 429, 585, M2-3, OH-23
Galileo (spacecraft), 293
Galle, Johann, 300
Gamma Leonis, OH-19
Gamma rays, 144, 422, 688, 689
  black holes and, 580
  from SN 1987A, 570
  telescopes and, M2-29, M2-32, M2-33
    to M2-34
  wavelengths, 132
Gamma Ray Observatory (GRO), M2-33
Gamow, George, 671–72
Ganymede, 322, 326–27, 328, 329
Gauss, Karl Frederick, 358
Gemini, 498, OH-17 to OH-18
Gemini (missions), 205
General theory of relativity, 564, 576,
  577, 588–91, 680, 684
Geocentric model, 85, 86–89, 98, 99, 113
Geomagnetism, 181–83
George III (king of England), 299
Geosynchronous orbits, 119–20, 121
Giant molecular clouds, 519–20, 531–32,
  614
Giants, 489, 500, 503, 504–5, 525, 539,
  540, 565
  red, 556–61, 581–82, 687, 688
Giotto (spacecraft), 374, 375, 376
Globular clusters, 560, 632, 635, OH-12,
  OH-24
  ages, 560, 597, 598, 599
  distances, 595–96
  distribution of, 595–96, 597
  47 Tucanae, 595
  in galactic halo, 597
  HR diagrams, 561
  mapping, 600
  metallicities, 598, 610, 611
  orbits, 611
  radial velocities, 600
  in spheroidal component of the
    Galaxy, 609
Gluons, 155
Goldschmidt, Hermann, 359
Grand unified theories (GUTs), 668–69
Granulation, 429
Graphs and plots, 25–34
Gravitation/gravity. *See also* Surface
  gravity
  artificial, in a space settlement, 281

escape velocity of satellites and, 120–22

general theory of relativity and, 588–91

orbits of satellites and, 116–20, 121

principle of universal, 108–9, 111–13, 160, 576

Gravitational capture model (of satellite formation), 403, 404

Gravitational constant, 112, 160

Gravitational force, 150

differential, and tides, 201–4

Gravitational lens, 591

Gravitational resonance, 344, 366

Gravitons, 155

Great Attractor, 657

Great Red Spot (Jupiter), 290, 292–93, 296–97, 302

Greek alphabet, OH-1, OH-4, A-8

Greeks, ancient, 86–89, 113, M2-1

Greenhouse effect, 177–78, 192–93

Mars and, 265, 268

Venus and, 250–51

Gregorian calendar, 19–20

Gregory XIII (pope), 19

G ring, 342, 343

H

Hadley, John, M2-9 to M2-10

Hadley Rille, 214

Hale, George Ellery, M2-18

Hale telescope, M2-18, M2-19

Half-life, 145

Hall, Asaph, 269

Hall, Chester Moore, M2-10

Halley's comet, 100, 369, 370–71, 374–78, 379, 380, 381

Halley, Edmund, 370

Halo (galactic), 597, 632, 635

h and χ Persei, OH-16, OH-17

Hastings, Joel, 359

Hawking, Stephen, 688

Hayashi, C., 523

Hayashi track, 523, 528, 529

Heisenberg uncertainty principle, 154–55, 424

Helene, 334

Heliocentric model, 85, 86, 89–93, 98, 99, 106, 108, 113

Helium, 5. See also Elements, abundances

Helium burning, 552–53, 554, A-13

Helium flash, 560, 561

Helix nebula, 563

Helmholtz, Hermann von, 421

Henry Draper catalog (HD), OH-4

Hercules, 473, OH-6, OH-24

Herschel, Caroline, 594

Herschel, William, 254, 298–99, 306, 325, 357, 358, 444–45, 517, 594, M2-10, M2-12, OH-20

Hertz, 133, 318

Hertzsprung, Ejnar, 488, 594, 595, 631

Hertzsprung-Russell (HR) diagram, 488–90

ages of star clusters and, 538–40

evolutionary tracks, 522–25, 529–30, 556–57, 559, 564

instability strip, 556, 558, 560

masses of stars, 499–500

radii of stars, 504–5

young stars, 557, 558

Hevelius, Johannes, 323, M2-7

Hidalgo, 367, 368

Hidden mass, 608, 685

Highlands (Moon), 214, 215, 216, 217

High-temperature rock, 397

High-velocity stars, 600

H II region, 530–31, 532–33, 534, 599, 600, 604, 614, 630, 631, 632, 633, 637, 646

Himalaya Mountains, 171

Hipparchus, 460, 461, M1-10

Histograms, 26

Hodge II, 653, 654

Hohmann orbits, 122–26

Holmes, Arthur, 168

Hooker reflector, 631, M2-19

Horizontal branch stars, 560

Horizontal velocity, 116–18

Horn radio telescope (Bell Laboratory), 677–78

Horsehead nebula, 520, OH-15

Hot spot tectonics, 248–49, 263

Houk, Nancy, 456

HR diagram. See Hertzsprung-Russell diagram

Hubble, Edwin, 631, 632, 637, 643, 644, 646, 647, 652, 686

Hubble's constant H_0, 647, 680, 681, 686

Hubble's law, 647, 648, 649, 661, 665, 667, 673–74, 676, 677, 679, 681, 682, 686

Hubble Space Telescope, 536, M2-31 to M2-32

Hubble time, 679

Huygens, Christian, 254, 323, 324, M2-7

Hyades, 644-45, OH-16 to OH-17

Hydra, OH-18

Hydrogen, 5

abundances. See Elements, abundances

energy level diagram, 142–43

interstellar clouds, 601

liquid metallic, 285, 286

liquid molecular, 285, 286

21-cm line, 601–2

Hydrogen burning, 422–23, 551–52, 554, 556–57, A-12 to A-13

Hydrogen cloud (of a comet), 374, 378

Hydrostatic equilibrium, 524

equation, 546–47

Hyperion, 324, 331, 332–33

Hypothesis, 83–84

I

Iapetus, 324, 330, 332, 334

Ice ages, 190–97, 431, 445–46, 451

Icy-conglomerate model (for comets), 373

Igneous rock, 162

Imaging systems, 315–17, M2-34 to M2-35

stellar imaging, 507–14

Impact basins. See Basins

Impact craters. See Craters

Inertia, 108

Inferior conjunction, 63

Inferior planets, 62, 63–65

Inflation (in early universe), 669–70, 683, 687

Infrared Astronomical Satellite (IRAS), M2-31

Infrared radiation, 131, 132, 137, 175, 250

diameters of asteroids and, 360

dust and, 518–19

Earth's atmosphere and, 177–78

protostars and, 526

telescopes and, M2-29, M2-30 to M2-31, M2-32

Infrared Telescope Facility (Mauna Kea), M2-30, M2-31

Infrared thermal mapping, 319–20

Insolation, 192–97

Inspectional reading, I-2 to I-3

Instability strip, 556, 558, 560

Intercalary month, 79

Intercrater plains (Mercury), 225, 227

Interference pattern, 502–3

Interferometer, 502

International Cometary Explorer, 374

International Date Line, 17–18, 19

International Ultraviolet Explorer (IUE), M2–32

Interplanetary orbits, 122–26

Interplanetary travel, 116–26

Interstellar clouds, 601–4, See also Interstellar dust; Interstellar gas; Molecular clouds

Interstellar dust, 518–19, 531, 596, 601, 605, 609, 611–12, 616–17, 638–40, 642, 653, 655, 656

Interstellar gas, 517, 601–4, 605, 609, 611–12, 614, 616–17, 638–40, 642, 653, 655, 656
Interstellar extinction, 596
Interstellar medium, 517, 601, 609–10. *See also* Interstellar dust; Interstellar gas; Molecular clouds
Interstellar reddening, 518
Inverse proportionality, M1-2 to M1-3
Inverse square law, 485, 486
Io, 293, 322, 326, 327, 328–29, 349
Ionized state (of an atom), 143
Ions, 137
Irons (meteorites), 362–63
Irregular clusters (galaxies), 656
Irregular galaxies, 635. 637, 638, 639, 640, 650, 653, 687
    dwarf, 650, 653
Ishtar Terra (Venus), 246, 247, 248, 249
Island universes, theory of, 630
Isotopes, 137, 571
Isotropic radio emission, 678

J

Jansky, Karl, M2-23
Janus, 333–34
Jeans, Sir James, 519
Jeans's mass, 519, 520, 534, 535, 672
Jets, 519–20, 532, 641–42, 643
Jet streams, 180–81
"Jewel box" open cluster, 538
Joule, 135, 419
Jovian planets, 199–201, 284–89, 311, 395–96, 408
    chemical composition and internal structure, 285–86
    comets and, 380
    data, table of, 284
    internal energy sources, 287
    rings, 323–25, 341–49, 350
    rotations and orientations, 287–89
    satellites, 322–23, 324, 325–26, 326–41, 349–50
Julian calendar, 19
Jupiter, 290–98, 311–12
    asteroid belt and, 365, 366–67
    atmosphere, 293–94
    comets and, 380
    data, table of, 284
    exploration, 290–93
    features, 293–98
    Galilean moons, 105, 322, 326–29, 349
    Great Red Spot, 290, 292–93, 296–97, 302
    interior, 285–87
    as Jovian planet, 199–201, 284–89
    magnetic field and magnetosphere, 288–89

ring, 293, 322, 345–46
rotation and orientation, 287, 288, 289, 295–96
satellites, 293, 322–23, 326–30, 349, 403–4
zones and belts, 295–96

K

Kant, Immanuel, 421, 630
Kappa Arietis, 496
Keck telescope, M2-21, M2-22
Kelvin temperature scale, M1-12 to M1-13
Kepler, Johannes, 83, 98–102, 108, 113, 253, 269, 568, M2-1
    first law of planetary motion, 100–101, 102
    lenses and telescopes, M2-3 to M2-5
    second law of planetary motion, 100, 102, 110, 120
    third law of planetary motion, 101–2, 112, 123, 490, 607–8
Kinetic energy, 423
Kirchhoff, Gustav, 141
Kirkwood, Daniel, 366
Kirkwood gaps, 366
Kowal, Charles, 367–68
Krüger 60 A and B (binary system), 490, 493
Kuiper Airborne Observatory, 346
Kuiper, Gerard, 325

L

Lagoon nebula (M8), OH-24
Lagrangian points, 279, 334, 335, 367
Lambda Aquilae, OH-23
Laplace, Pierre Simon de, 324
Large Magellanic Cloud, 569, 580, 599, 650, 653, 654
Lassell, William, 325, M2-15
Latitude, 39, 40, 43–44, 46
Lava, 162, 212–13, 216, 217, 225–26, 245–46. *See also* Volcanoes
Leap days and years, 19
Lens(es), M2-3 to M2-5, M2-6, M2-10, M2-12, M2-16 to M2-18
Lenticular galaxies, 637, 638, 640, 643, 650
Leo, OH-19
Lepus, OH-15
Leverrier, Urbain, 300, 305, 306
Leviathan (telescope), M2-12 to M2-13, M2-14, M2-15, M2-16
Levitt, Henrietta, 594, 595, 596
Lick Observatory (California), M2-18

Light, 128–44
    absorption, 141
    emission, 141
    constancy of speed of, 585–86
    relativity and, 585–89
    wave nature of, 130, 131
    velocity of, 133
Light curve, 497–98, 594–95
Light-gathering ability (telescopes), M2-2, M2-15, to M2-16
Lighthouse model (pulsars), 575–76
Light-year, 467–68, A-3
Limitlessness (advantage of space), 413–14
Linear relationship, 31
Line of nodes, 60–61
Lippershey, Hans, M2-2 to M2-3
Liquid metallic hydrogen, 285, 286
Liquid molecular hydrogen, 285, 286
Lithosphere
    Earth, 166, 167, 407
    Moon, 218, 407
Little Dipper, OH-7
Little Ice Age, 191–92, 193
    sunspots and, 431, 445–46, 451
LMC X-3, 580
LMC X-4, 580
Lobes, 641–42
Local Group (galaxies), 650–54, 657, 676, 678
Logarithmic scale, 31, 32
Longitude, 15
Look-back time, 646
Lorentz transformations, 587–88
Lowell, Perceval, 256, 274, 304–5, 310
Low-temperature rock, 397
Luminosity(ies), 419. *See also* Hertzsprung-Russell diagram; Mass-luminosity relation; Period-luminosity relation
    classes, 489, 491
    stellar, 485–87
    Sun's, 419–20, 484–85
Luna (spacecraft), 204, 206
Lunar calendars, 77–81
Lunar eclipses, 53, 57–60, 79–80, A-7
Lunar Orbiter (spacecraft), 204–5, 206, 315
Luther, Martin, 93
Lyra, 473, OH-6, OH-21, OH-22

M

Maffei I, 650
Magellan (spacecraft), 245
Magma
    Earth, 162, 166–67
    ocean on Moon, 217
    Venus, 246

Magnetic field(s), 129
  Earth, 181–86, 187, 389
  galaxies, 642
  Jovian planets, 288–89
  Mercury, 222, 223, 228
  Moon, 219
  neutron stars, 575
  Sun, 376–77, 430–34, 436, 438, 439,
    440, 441–42
  Venus, 252
Magnetosheath, 184, 185
Magnetosphere, 181, 183–86
  Jupiter, 289
  Mercury, 222, 223
  Saturn, 289
  Venus, 252–53
Magnification
  focal length and, M2-4
  function of telescopes, M2-2
Magnitude, 460
  absolute, 485–87, 594–95, 631, 644,
    645, 646
  apparent, 460–61, 462, 594, 631, 645,
    646
  B − V, 462–65
Major axis, 100
Main sequence, 487–88, 489, 504–5,
  536–41, 560, 564, 565. See also
    Main-sequence stars
  ages of star clusters, 538–41
  color-magnitude diagrams, 598
  fitting technique, 645–46
  lifetimes, 536–38, 557, 581–82
  transition from main sequence to
    other stars, 557–82
  turnoff, 598
Main-sequence stars, 488–89, 499–500,
  524, 525, 529, 530, 541, 559, 561,
  608, 644, 688. See also Main
    sequence
Mantle
  Earth, 162, 165–66
  Mercury, 228
  Moon, 218
  plumes, 246
Maria/mare, 212–13, 214, 215, 216, 217,
  OH-25
  Crisium, 212, 215
  Imbrium, 210, 212, 213, 215, OH-27
  Nubrium, 214
  Oceanus Procellarum, 212, 213, 215
  Serenitatis, 213, 215
  Tranquilitatis, 215
Mariner (spacecraft/missions), 221–23,
  228, 243, 252, 257, 292
Markarian 205, 662
Mars, 199, 253–72, 352, 408. See also
  Craters; Polar caps; Volcanoes
  apparent celestial motions, 65–66
  asteroid belt and, 365, 366

  atmosphere, 265–67
  canals, 253, 256
  data, table of, 253
  exploration, 253–58
  geological history, 264–65
  interplanetary mission to, 123–25
  retrograde motion, 67
  rotation and orbit, 254–55
  satellites, 269–71, 404
  surface, 254–55, 258–65
  temperature, 253, 265, 267
  terraforming, 276–79
  as Terrestrial planet, 199–201
Mars (spacecraft), 257
Mass(es), 109, 110–11
  driver, 415
  equation, 546–47
  rest, 587–88
Mass extinction, 384–90
Mass-luminosity relation, 499–500, 525,
  529, 537
Mathematics, I-1 to I-2, 22–35, M1-1 to
  M1-13
  angular measurements, 465–66, M1-8
    to M1-11
    angles, M1-8 to M1-10
    triangles, M1-10 to M1-11
  approximation signs, 34–35
  cubes, circles, and spheres, M1-11 to
    M1-12
  error and uncertainty, M1-4 to M1-6
  equations, 30, M1-3 to M1-4
  fractions, M1-4
  graphs and plots, 25–34
  MathTools, how to use, 22–23
  percentages, M1-4
  powers, M1-6 to M1-7
  powers of ten, 23–25
  proportions, M1-1 to M1-4
  roots, M1-7
  temperature scales, M1-12 to M1-13
Maunder Minimum, 431, 441, 445
Maury, Antonia C., 456
Maxwell, James Clerk, 128, 130, 324
  equations, 130
Maxwell Montes (Venus), 246–47, 248
Maya, 75–76
  Dresden eclipse tables, 80
Mechanics, discipline of, 107–8
Megalith, 73
Megaregolith, 218
Mercury, 219–228, 229, 407, 408
  apparent celestial motions, 64–65
  atmosphere, 222–23
  data, table of, 220
  exploration, 221–23
  interior, 227–28
  magnetic field, 222, 223, 228
  orbit and rotation, 219–21, 591
  temperature, 222–23

  as Terrestrial planet, 199–201
  surface, 223–27
Mercury Project, 205
Meridian, 13, OH-6
Mesosphere, 176
Messier, Charles, 629, 654, OH-7, OH-27
  catalog, OH-28 to OH-30
Metallicity, 458–59
Metamorphic rock, 162
Meteor Crater, 232, 234–35, 366
Meteorites, 207, 362–65, 382, 396. See
  also Craters; Meteoroids; Meteors
  classification, 362–64
  Earth, 233, 237, 238–39, 385
  Mars, 258, 268
  Mercury, 226, 228
  Moon, 207–12, 214–15, 217
  parent bodies, 363, 364–65
  relatives ages, 401
Meteoroids, 280–81, 361–62, 364, 365.
  See also Meteorites; Meteors
Meteors, 298, 361–62. See also
  Meteorites; Meteoroids
Meteor showers, 372–73, A-2
Metis, 227, 330
Metric system, M1-6, M1-7
Michelson, Albert, 586
Michelson-Morley experiment, 586
Microdensitometer, 510
Micrometer, 467, M2-5, M2-9
Microwave background radiation (3 K),
  677–79, 682
Microwave radiation, 131, 132
Mid-Atlantic Ridge, 168–70
Milankovitch, Milutin, 195, 197
Milky Way, 593, OH-13, OH-23
Milky Way Galaxy, 6, 528, 593–617, 633,
  676
  age, 541, 638
  center, 613–16
  corona, 608, 609
  differential rotation, 599, 604–5
  dimensions, 593–97
  disk, 597–609
    component, 609, 611, 612, 613
    rotation and structure of, 599–604
    stellar populations, 597–99
  distances within, 594–96
  evolution, 609–12
  formation, 611–12, 638, 640
  halo, 597, 608, 609
  Local Group and, 650–54
  mass, 607–9
  metal enrichment history, 609–11
  nuclear bulge, 610–11, 612, 613–14
  Population I and II in, 599, 600, 601,
    609
  rotation curve, 603–4, 608
  Sagittarius A, 614–15
  satellite galaxies, 640

spheroidal component, 609–12, 613
spiral arms, 601, 604–7, 612
structural components, 609
Sun's location in, 593, 596, 599, 600, 607
Miller, Stanley, 296
Mimas, 330, 332, 333, 334, 342, 343–44

Minutes of arc, 465, M1-8
Miranda, 325, 335, 337
Mirrors (telescope), M2-8 to M2-10, M2-18, M2-19 to M2-21
Mizar, 493, OH-7
Models, 85–86, 525, 544–49
Molecular clouds, 392, 517–20, 525, 531–33. *See also* Interstellar medium
giant, 519–20, 531–32, 614
Molecules, 137–38
Monoceros, 580, OH-15
Moon, 7, 68, 104, 199, 201–19, 228–29. *See also* Basins; Craters; Highlands; Maria; Volcanoes
age, 214–16, 217, 229
atmosphere, lack of, 206–7
data, table of, 205
and Earth system
formation, 404–5
size, 8–9
eclipses of, 53, 57–60
exploration, 204–7
history, 216–17
interior, 218–19
magnetic field, 219
map, OH-24 to OH-27
mining resources on, 414–15
moonrise and moonset, 52
phases, 47–53
space settlements and, 279–82
stages of development, 407, 408
surface features, 207–16
synodic period, 53
temperature, 207
tides and, 201–4
Moonquakes, 218
Moons, planetary. *See* Satellites, planetary
Morley, Edward, 586
Morphology, 208
Mountain ranges, 171, 214
Mount Everest, 160, 247
Mount Pastukhov (USSR) reflector, M2-19
Mount St. Helens, 171
Mount Wilson telescope, 502, 631, M2-18, M2-19
Mu Cephei, OH-12
Multi Element Radio Linked Interferometer Network (MERLIN), M2-27

Multiple-Mirror Telescope (MMT), M2-20, M2-21
Mythology, and planetary names, 352–55

N

Names/naming systems
classical, for geological features, 246
constellations, OH-1, OH-2 to OH-3
lunar features, 212
Martian features, 255
Mercurian features, 223
mythology and, 352–55
planetary satellites, 322, 335, 352–54
stars, OH-1, OH-4
National Optical Astronomy Observatories (NOAO), 476, M2-20
National Radio Astronomy Observatory (NRAO), 476
Neap tides, 203
Nebula(e). *See also* Bok globules
emission, 530. *See also* H II region
planetary, 562–64, 581, 613, 637
reflection, 531, 532
specific. *See also* names of specific nebulae
M99, M2-14
NGC 6781, 563
spiral, 630–32
Negative (photography), 508
Nemesis, 390
Neon burning, 553, 554, A-14
Neptune, 302–4, 310, 311, 312
atmosphere, 285, 302–3
discovery, 299–300
data, table of, 284
exploration, 292, 293, 301, 302–4
features, 302–4
interior, 285–86, 302
as Jovian planet, 199–201, 284–89
magnetic field, 288, 289, 303–4
orbit, 306–7, 308
rings, 325, 343, 347–49
rotation and orientation, 287, 289, 303, 304
satellites, 325–26, 338–41
Nereid, 311, 326, 338, 339, 341, 348
Neutrinos, 152, 153, 422, 555–56, 566, 571, 573, 671
SN 1987A and, 569–70
Neutrons, 137, 422, 556, 571–72, 573, 670–71
Neutron capture, 571–72
Neutron stars, 573–76, 580, 582, 608, 616
New General Catalog (NGC), 629, OH-13
Newgrange (Ireland), 72, 73–75
New moon, 48–49

Newton, Isaac, 83, 84, 108–13, 116, 299–300, 358, 370, 424, 490, 576, 577, 585
first law of motion, 109, 110
second law of motion, 109, 111, 120
third law of motion, 109, 111
Newtonian reflector, M2-9, M2-15
Noctis Labyrinthus (Mars), 261
Nonthermal radiation, 614, 616
Northern lights. *See* Aurora
North star. *See* Polaris
Novae, 565, 652
Nuclear bulge (galaxy), 610–11, 613–16, 632, 633, 635, 639, 640
Nuclear forces, 150–51
Nuclear reactions, 5
in early universe, 670–71
in stars, 523–24, 537–38, 542, 551–54, 557, 559–60, 565, 566, 570, 581, 678, A-12 to A-14
in Sun, 421–25
Nuclear winter, 193, 385
Nucleosynthesis, 571–73, 667, 671
Nucleus
atom, 137, 138
comet, 374–75, 376, 378
galaxy, 610–11, 613–16, 642
planetary nebula, 562
Nu Scorpii, OH-24

O

OBAFGKM (spectral sequence), 456
Oberon, 325, 336
Objective lens, M2-4
Observatories, 476–79. *See also* Observing; Telescopes
ancient, 72–81
Observing, 479–82. *See also* Observatories; Telescopes
naked eye, M2-1 to M2-2
Occultation, 307, 346–47, 348, 359–60, 501
Oceanic ridge, 168, 169, 170, 263
Oceanic trench, 171, 263
Oceanus Procellarum (Moon), 212, 213, 215
Oersted, Hans Christian, 128, 129
Olbers, Heinrich, 358–59, 367
Olympus Mons, 262, 263
O'Meara, Stephen, 300
O'Neill, Gerard K., 279
Oort cloud, 357, 380, 390, 535
Oort, Jan, 380, 596
Open clusters, 597–99, 606, 652
ages, 538–41, 597, 598–99
chemical composition, 597–98, 610
in galactic disk, 597–99, 609
HR diagrams, 560, 561

intermediate-age, 599
    spiral arm tracers, 600–601
Open universe, 683–87
Ophelia, 347
Opposition, 65, 66
Optical doubles, 493
Orbit. *See* specific entity, e.g., Earth,
    orbit
Orbitals, 137–38
Orientale Basin (Moon), 211, 212
Orion, 462, 463, 526, OH-14, to OH-15
Orion nebula (M42), 462, 526, 530, 532,
    OH-15
Oxygen burning, 553, 554, A-14
Ozone, 175–77

P

Pair production, 670
Paleomagnetism, 182
Palitzsch, Johann, 370
Pallas, 358, 365
Palomar Mountain Observatory, 480,
    M2-18 to M2-19, M2-20
Pandora, 342, 344
Pangaea, 168, 170
Parabolic mirrors, M2-9 to M2-10, M2-
    18, M2-32
Parallax, 92, 465–66, 644
    stellar, 467–68
Parent bodies (meteorites), 363, 364–65
Parent nucleus, 144
Parsec, 468, A-3
Parsons, William, M2-12, to M2-13, M2-
    14, M2-15
Partial eclipse, 57, 59
Pauli exclusion principle, 555
Pauli, Wolfgang, 555
Pegasus, OH-1, OH-6, OH-7
Penumbra, 54
Penzias, Arno, 677, 678
Percentages, M1-4
Perfect gas law, 178
Perigee, 119
Perihelion, 99, 100, 195–96
Periodic comets, 373
Periodic table, 138, 139
Period-luminosity relation, 559, 594–96,
    631
    calibration of, 644–46
Perseus, 497, OH-15 to OH-16
Perturbation, 300, 304, 339, 380
Phases (of the Moon), 47–53
    and lunar calendars, 77–78
Phobos, 269–71, 272, 276, 360, 404
Phoebe, 324–25, 330, 331, 332
Photodisintegration, 553, 555
Photographic plate, 305, 507–8, M2-35
Photography, 507–8, M2-34, M2-35

Photometers, M2-37
Photometry, M2-37
Photomultiplier tube, 315, M2-37
Photons, 140–44, 147, 155, 156, 422,
    553, 570, 577, 602, 670–71, 672, 682,
    688
Photon sphere, 577
Photosphere, 428–35
Photosynthesis, 158, 175, 277
Physical constants, A-3
Pi (π), M1-12
Piazzi, Guiseppe, 358
Pickering, William H., 306
Pigafetta, 653
Pioneer (spacecraft/missions), 244, 245,
    247, 252, 289, 291, 293, 295, 325,
    341–42, 345
Pisces, OH-7
Pixels, 316–19, 509–13
Planck constant, 140, 154–55, A-3
Planck curves, 134–35, 136, 147, 463,
    464, 614, 678, 679
Planck, Max, 134–35, 585
Plane, 11
Planetary astronomy, 2
Planetary nebula(e), 562–63, 564, 581,
    613, 637
    nucleus, 562
Planetary standing wave, 449
Planetary systems, formation of distant,
    535–36
Planetesimals, 399–402, 405, 406–9
Planets, 68. *See also* Solar system;
    individual planets
    distances from Sun, and Titius-Bode
        law, 357–58
    eccentricities, 100
    extraterrestrial civilizations on,
        likelihood of, 620–21
    flight times to, from Earth, 126
    formation, 397–402, 408–9
    inferior, 62, 63–65
    Jovian, 199–201, 284–89, 395–96
    later development, 406–8, 409
    motion(s)
        apparent celestial, 62–68
        Kepler's laws of, 100–102
        Newton's laws of, 109–12
        retrograde, 66–67
    names, 352–53
    orbital characteristics, A-15
    overview, 199–201
    physical characteristics, A-15
    remote sensing, 314–20
    satellites. *See* Satellites, planetary
    superior, 62, 65–66
    surface gravity, 122
    temperatures, determining, 136–37
    terraforming, 275–79
    Terrestrial, 199–200, 395–96

Plates, 167–71
Plate tectonics, 167–71, 194–95, 272
    Mars, absence of, 262–63
    Moon, absence of, 214, 218
    Venus, 248–49
Plato, 103
Pleiades, 530–31, 532, 540–41, 644–45,
    OH-17
Pleistocene Glacial Cycle, 190–91, 193
Pluto, 199–201, 304–11, 312
    atmosphere, 308–9
    data, table of, 305
    discovery, 304–6
    name, 352–53
    orbit and rotation, 306–8
    origin, 310–11
    satellite, 309–10
Polar axis (telescope), M2-12, M2-13
Polar caps (Mars), 254–55, 267, 276
Polar constellations, OH-7
Polar hood (Mars), 255–56
Polaris, 37, 39, 40, 161, OH-7
Pollux, OH-17
Pope, Alexander, 335
Population I and II, 632, 635, 638
    characteristics, 599
    in Milky Way Galaxy, 599–600, 601,
        609, 612, 613, 619
    orbits, 611
Population III, 608
Position angle, 493, 494
Position measurements, 94–95
Positron, 422, 688
Powers, M1-6 to M1-7
Powers-of-ten notation, 23–25
Praesepe (M44), OH-18 to OH-19
Precession, 160, 161, 195–96, 591, OH-5
    to OH-6
Pre–main-sequence phase, 523, 524
Pre–main-sequence stars, 528–29, 530,
    539
Pressure (atmospheric), 178–79, 223, 268
Primary minimum, 497, 498, 501
Principia, 108
Principle of equivalence, 588–89
Procyon, 564
Prometheus, 342, 344
Proper motion, 471–73
Proportionality constant, M1-1 to M1-2
Proportions, M1-1 to M1-4
Proton-proton chain, 422–23, A-12
Proton(s), 137, 422–25, 571, 575, 671–72
    spin, 601–2
Protostars, 521–25, 537, 538, 541–42,
    559
    observations, 525–31
Protosun, 397
Pseudosciences, 692
Ptolemy, 85, 88, M2-1
Puck, 338

Pulsars, 573–76
Pulsating stars, 558–59, 560
P (compressional) waves, 163–64
Pyramid, Great (Egypt), 72, 75
Pysix, OH-1

Q

Quadrants, 95, 96
Quantum mechanics, 140, 154–56, 424, 555, 564
Quarks, 152, 153
Quasars, 573, 591, 644, 647–50, 661–65, 672
Quiescent prominences, 439

R

Radar, 220, 242, 244, 245, 246, 248
Radial motion, 471
Radial velocity, 470, 472, 536, 599–600, 602, 603, 604, 647, 648, 662, 664, 674–75, 676
   curve, 495–97
Radian, M1-9
Radiant, 373
Radiation, 128. See also specific types of radiation
   belts, 185–86
   black body, 134
   laws, 133–37
   solar, 175–78, 207, 250–51, 449, 450–51
Radiation-dominated universe, 682
Radiative transport, 427
Radioactivity, 144–47, 148, 425
Radio astronomy
   Milky Way and, 602–4, 614–15
   pulsars, 573–74
   telescopes. See Radio telescopes
   21-cm radiation, 602, 603, 604
Radio galaxies, 641–44
Radiometric dating, 146–47, 173, 215
Radio telescopes, M2-23 to M2-29, M2-36 to M2-37
Radio waves, 131
Ranger (spacecraft), 204–5
Rays (Moon), 210–11
Reading (a science text book), I-1 to I-6
Reber, Grote, M2-23 to M2-24
Red giant(s), 556–61, 581–82, 687, 688
   branch, 556, 557
Redshifts(s), 470, 494, 495
   Cepheid variables, 558
   cosmological, 676–77
   planetary nebula, 562
   quantization, 664–65
   quasars, 648–50, 661–65
   21-cm line, 602

Red supergiants, 556, 560, 581–82
Reflectance spectra, 361
Reflection nebula, 531, 532
Reflectors (reflecting telescopes), M2-8 to M2-9, M2-10 to M2-16
Refraction, 131, M2-2
Refractors (refracting telescopes), M2-2 to M2-5, M2-10, M2-12, M2-16
Refractory elements, 217
Regolith, 205, 218
Regular solids, 98, 99
Regulus, OH-19
Relative age, 172
Relative orbit, 491–92
Relativistic redshift relationship, 648
Relativity
   general theory of, 564, 576, 577, 588–91, 680, 684
   special theory of, 585–88
Remote sensing (of planets), 314–20
   data transmission, 317–20
   imaging systems, 315–17
Resolving ability (telescopes), M2-2, M2-11, M2-12, M2-23, M2-25 to M2-26
Resonance, 344
Rest masses, 587–88
Retrograde motion, 66–67, 68, 87–88, 90, 91
Retrograde rotation, 243
Rhea, 332, 333
Riccioli, Giovanni, 493, M2-7
Rigel, 462, OH-14
Right angles, M1-9, M1-10
Right ascension, OH-4
Rilles, 213–14
Ringlets, 325
Ring nebula, 562, OH-22
Rings, planetary, 341–49, 350
   Jupiter, 293, 322, 345–46
   Neptune, 325, 343, 347–49
   Saturn, 290, 323–25, 341–45, 349
   Uranus, 325, 343, 346–47, 349
Ritter Astrophysical Research Center, 478
Roche, Edward, 345
Roche limit, 345, 400
Rock. See specific types of rock, e.g., Brecciated rock
Rook Mountains (Moon), 212
Roots, M1-7
Rosetta nebula, 526, OH-15
Rosse, earl of. See Parsons, William
Rotation. See specific types of rotation, e.g., Differential rotation, and specific entities, e.g., Jupiter
Rotation curve, 603–4, 608
Rotation limit, 638–39
RR Lyrae variables, 560, 595, 597, 599, 610, 613, 637, 651
Russell, Henry Norris, 488

S

Sagittarius, 593, 595, 596, 613, OH-24
Sagittarius A, 614–15
San Andreas Fault, 170–71
Satellites (artificial), 116–22, 413
Satellites, planetary, 322–41, 349–50.
   See also specific planets
   co-orbitals, 330, 333–34
   discovery, 322–23, 324, 325–26
   formation, 403–5, 409
   Lagrangian, 334
   orbital characteristics, A-16 to A-17
   physical characteristics, A-16 to A-17
   shepherding, 342–43, 347
Satellite galaxies, 640, OH-12
Saturn, 105–6, 290–98, 301, 311–12, 367, 368
   atmosphere, 285, 293–94
   data, table of, 284
   exploration, 290–93
   features, 293–98
   interior, 285–87
   as Jovian planet, 199–201, 284–89
   magnetic field, 288, 289
   rings, 290, 323–25, 341–45
   orbit, 308
   rotation and orientation, 289
   satellites, 324–25, 330–34
   zones and belts, 295–96
Saturn nebula, 563
Scarps (Mercury), 226, 227, 228
Scatter diagram, 31, 33–34
Scattering (of light), 671
Schipiarelli, Giovanni, 255, 256
Schwabe, Samuel H., 430
Schwarzschild, Karl, 577
Schwarzschild radius, 577, 578, 616
Science/scientific method, 83–85, 113–14
Scientific creationism, 692
Scintillation, 573
Scorpius, 593, 595, OH-23 to OH-24
Seasons, 42–44, 45, 195, 196–97
Secchi, Angelo, 255
Secondary minimum, 497, 498
Seconds of arc, 466, M1-8, M2-11
Sedimentary rock, 162
Seeing, M2-11
Seismic waves, 163
Seismology, 163–65
Self-propagating star formation, 604–5
Semimajor axis, 100, 101, 102
Sextants, 95, 96
Seneca, 369
Shapley, Harlow, 595–96, 613, 631, 644
Shell source, 552, 560–61, 562
   shell helium burning, 552–53, 561
   shell hydrogen burning, 556–57, 561
Shelton, Ian, 569

Shepherding
  reverse effect, 399
  satellites, 342–43, 347
Shock wave, 437, 567
Sidereal day, 14–15, 20
Silicates, 139, 162
Silicon burning, 553, 554, A-14
Sine, M1-11
Sinuous rilles, 213–14
Sirius A and B, 463, 494, 495, 564, M2-17, OH-15
Skylab, 438
Slipher, Vesto M., 646–47
Slumping (craters), 211
Small Magellanic Cloud, 569, 594, 639, 650, 653
Smithsonian Astrophysical Observatory (SAO) catalog, OH-4
Solar astronomy, 2
Solar calendars, 70–72
Solar constant, 419, 420, 484–85, A-3
Solar day, 14–15
Solar eclipses, 53, 54–57, 58, 59, 589, 590–91, A-6
Solar flare, 440, 441, 449
Solar Maximum Mission, 438, M2-32
Solar nebula, 392–93, 408
  collapse and rotation of, 394–95, 396
  distribution of elements in, 397–99
  planetary accretion in, 399–402
Solar system, 90
  age, 393
  characteristics, 392–97
  orbits and rotations in, 393–94
  origin, 392–409
  resources for future in, 414–17
  size, 8–10
Solar wind, 183–85, 222, 223, 252–53, 373, 376–77, 439
Solstices, 18–19, 41, 43–44, 45, 46, 69, 70–71, 195–96
Sombrero galaxy, OH-20
Southern lights. See Aurora
Space astronomy, M2-29 to M2-34
Space exploration, 3. See also specific spacecraft/missions
  comets, 374
  industrialization of space, 412–14
  interplanetary travel, 116–26
  Jupiter and Saturn, 290–93, 345
  Mars, 254–58
  Mercury, 221–23
  Moon, 204–7
  settlements in space, 279–82
  Uranus and Neptune, 300–301, 339, 341, 346, 347
  Venus, 243–45
Spacetime, 577–78, 590–91
Space velocity, 472–73
Spatial resolution, 314

Special theory of relativity, 585–88
Species, 385
Spectral lines, 140, 141, 144
  strength, 455–56
Spectral sequence, 456–58
Spectrograph, M2-36
Spectroscopic binary, 495–97, 537
Spectroscopic Survey Telescope, M2-20, M2-21
Spectroscopy, M2-35 to M2-37
Spectrum(a), 140–44, M2-36
  absorption, 141
  comparison, 470
  electromagnetic, 130–32
  emission, 141
  flash, 435
  solar, 425–26
  stellar, 454–60
Speed
  of light, 133
  relativity and, 586–88
Spheres, M1-11 to M1-12
Spherical aberration, M2-5, M2-6, M2-9, M2-10, M2-20
Spica, OH-19
Spicules, 435–36
Spin, 601–2
Spin-orbit coupling, 221
Spiral arms, 600–601, 632, 652–53
  differential rotation and, 604–5
  mechanisms for, 604–7
  density wave, 605–6, 607
  self-propagating star formation, 604–5, 606–7
  tracers, 600–601
Spiral galaxies, 534, 535, 632–35, 638, 639, 642, 648, 649, 650, 687, 688–89
Spörer Minimum, 445
Spring constellations, OH-19 to OH-21
Spring (vernal) equinox, 42–43, OH-5
Spring tides, 203
Stars, 6–7, 453–73, 484–505, 516–42, 544–49. See also specific types of stars, e.g., Giants, and names of specific stars
  absolute magnitude, 485–87
  apparent magnitude, 460–61, 462
  binary, 490–99, 503–4
  brightest, A-9
  charts, OH-6 to OH-11
  chemical composition, 458–60
  classification, 453–60
  colors, 461–65
  data, table of, 504
  distances, 465–68
  evolution. See Stellar evolution
  HR diagrams, 487–90, 504–5
  imaging, 507–14
  luminosities, 484–87, 504
  luminosity classes, 489–90

  main sequence. See Main-sequence stars
  masses, 490–500, 504
  mass-luminosity relation, 499–500
  models, 544–49
  motions, 37–41, 468–73
  nearby, A-10 to A-11
  observing, OH-6 to OH-24
  radii, 500–503, 504–5
  spectral classes, 456–58
  temperatures, 135, 454–56, 504
Star clusters, 538–41, 557, 558, 644–45
  See also Globular clusters; Open clusters
  See also names of specific clusters
  M3, OH-21
  M4, OH-24
  M6, OH-24
  M7, OH-23 to OH-24
  M11, OH-23
  M13, OH-24
  M15, OH-12
  M21, OH-24
  M30, OH-14
  M34, OH-16
  M35, OH-18
  M36, OH-17
  M37, OH-17
  M38, OH-17
  M39, OH-22
  M41, OH-15, OH-16
  M44, OH-18 to OH-19
  M50, OH-15
  NGC 457, OH-13
  NGC 2158, OH-18
  NGC 2244, OH-15
  NGC 7789, OH-13
Stefan-Boltzmann constant, 135, 420, A-3
Stefan-Boltzmann law, 135, 147, 420, 488, 500–501, 682
Stefan, Josef, 135
Stellar astronomy, 2
Stellar evolution, 517–42
  end states, 564–81
  formation, 516–36, 541–42
    contraction and protostars, 520–42
    of planetary systems, 535–36
    sites of, 517–20
    triggers, 531–35
  future, 687–88
  interior developments, 551–56
    iron core, 554–56
    nuclear burning, 551–54
  main sequence, 536–41, 542
    lifetimes, 536–38
    models of, 538–41
  stages
    black holes, 576–81
    neutron stars, 573–76

nucleosynthesis, 571–73
planetary nebulae and white dwarfs, 561–65
red giants and supergiants, 557–61
supernovae, 565–71
summarized, 582
surface developments, 556–81
Stellar parallax, 467–68
Stellar winds, 526–27, 537, 561–62
Stonehenge (England), 72, 73, 80–81
Stones (meteorites), 364
Stony-irons (meteorites), 363–64
Stratification, 172–73
Stratosphere, 176–77
Strength (of spectral lines), 455
Stroboscopic techniques, 574–75
Sublimation, 261, 268, 375
Summer constellations, OH-21 to OH-24
Summer solstice, 43, 44, 45, 46
Sun, 11, 419–42, 444–51
    absolute magnitude, 486
    apparent celestial motions, 41–46
    apparent magnitude, 485, 486
    chemical composition, 392–93, 425–26
    chromosphere, 435–36
    convection zone, 428, 429
    corona, 55, 436–39
    data, table of, 420
    Earth's climate and weather and, 444–51
    eclipses, 53, 54–57, 58, 59, 589, 590–91
    ecosphere, 620
    interior, 426–28
    location in Galaxy, 593, 596, 599, 600, 607
    luminosity, 419–20, 484
    magnetic field, 376–77, 430–34, 436, 438, 439, 440, 441–42
    main-sequence lifetime, 536
    mass, 419, 420
    nuclear reactions, 421–25, 426–27
    photosphere, 428–35
    prominences and flares, 439–40, 449
    solar wind, 183–85, 222, 223, 252–53, 373, 376–77, 439
    sunspots, 429–35, 445–51
Sunspots, 429–35, 445–51
Superclusters (galaxies), 5–6, 656, 657–58
Supergiants, 489, 500, 503, 504–5, 525, 540, 556–61, 565, 569, 570, 581–82
Supergranules, 436
Superior conjunction, 64
Superior planets, 62, 65–66
Supernova(e), 6–7, 401, 533–34, 566–71, 572, 573, 581, 604
    remnants, 567, 568, 576
Surface area, M1-11
Surface gravity, 120–22, 576

Surge (eruptive) prominences, 440
Surveyor (spacecraft), 204–5, 206
S (transverse) waves, 163–65
Swift, Jonathan, 269
Synchronous rotation, 221
Synchroton radiation, 614, 640–41, 642
Synodic period (Moon), 53, 77–78

T

Tail (of a comet), 376–78
Tails (galactic), 640, 641
Tangent, M1-9, M1-10
Tangential motion, 471
Tangential velocity, 472
Taurus, 644, OH-15, OH-16 to OH-17
Tectonics. See Plate tectonics
Telescopes, 3, 103, 501–2. See also Observatories; Observing; specific telescopes
    early history, M2-2 to M2-10, M2-17
    gamma rays and, M2-29, M2-32, M2-33 to M2-34
    infrared radiation and, M2-29
    new technology optical reflectors, M2-19 to M2-23
    radio, M2-23 to M2-29, M2-36 to M2-37
    reflectors, M2-8 to M2-9, M2-10 to M2-16, M2-18 to M2-19
    refractors, M2-2 to M2-5, M2-10, M2-12, M2-16, M2-18
    size, advantage of, M2-21 to M2-23, M2-25
    space astronomy and, M2-29 to M2-34
    ultraviolet radiation and, M2-29, M2-31, M2-32
    X-rays and, M2-29, M2-32 to M2-33
Telescopium, OH-1
Telesto, 334
Temperature. See also specific entity, e.g., Mars, temperature
    vs. heat, 437
    and radiation, 134–37
    scales, 457, 465, M1-12 to M1-13
Terminator (Moon), 206, OH-27
Terraforming, 274–82
Terrestrial planets, 199–200, 395–96
Tethys, 331, 332, 333, 334, 367
Tharsis Rise (Mars), 259, 261, 262, 263, 264
Theory, 84
Thermal pressure, 519
Thermal radiation, 614
Thermosphere, 176, 177
Third-quarter moon, 50, 52
Thrust faults, 226
Tides, 201–4, 328–29

Time
    and angular units of a circle, 17, M1-10
    calendars, 18–20
    daylight saving, 17
    Hubble, 679–81
    relativity and, 586–87
    sidereal and solar days, 13–15
    zones, 15–18
Titan, 324, 326, 330–32, 349–50
Titania, 325, 336
Titius-Bode law, 357–58
Titius, Johann, 357
Tombaugh, Clyde, 306, 307
Transverse (S) waves, 163–65
Trapezium, 530, 532
Triangles, M1-10 to M1-11
Triangulum galaxy (M33), 650, 651, 652, OH-12
Triple alpha process, 552, 559, A-13
Triton, 311, 325, 338–41, 348
Trojans (asteroids), 365, 367
Tropic of Cancer, 43
Tropic of Capricorn, 44
Troposphere, 176, 177, 179
Trumpler, Robert, 596
T Tauri stars, 527–30, 532
T Tauri wind, 399, 530
Tunguska River (Siberia) explosion, 381
Twain, Mark, 371
21-cm line, 601
Twilight, 46
Type I and Type II Cepheid variables, 559, 594, 595, 596, 599
Type I supernovae, 566, 567, 576, 581
Type II supernovae, 566, 567, 569, 570, 573, 581

U

Uaxactún temples (Guatemala), 72, 76
Uhuru (satellite), M2-33
Ultraviolet radiation
    and ozone in Earth's atmosphere, 175–77
    telescopes and, M2-29, M2-31, M2-32
    wavelengths, 132
Umbra, 53–54
Umbriel, 325, 336
Uncertainty, M1-4 to M1-6. See also Heisenberg uncertainty principle
Universe, 5–8, 8–11, 571, 572, 667–90
    age, 5, 541, 646, 679–82, 684–85
    big bang, 5, 667–73, 687
    closed, 683–87
    density of matter in, 685–87
    expansion, 673–77
    future, 667, 682–89
    flat, 683–87

geometry of, 684–85
inflation, 669–70, 687
matter-dominated, 681, 682
nuclear reactions, 670–71
open, 683–87
radiation-dominated, 682
size, 681, 682
temperature, 668, 681, 682
3 K microwave background radiation, 677–79
Uraniborg (observatory), 97
Uranus, 301–2, 310, 312
atmosphere, 285
data, table of, 284
discovery, 298–99
exploration, 292, 293, 300–301
features, 301–2
interior, 285–87
as Jovian planet, 199–201, 284–89
magnetic field, 288, 289, 304
orbit, 306–7, 308
rings, 325, 343, 346–47, 349
rotation and orientation, 287–88
satellites, 288, 325, 335–38
Urata, Takeshi, 359
Urey, Harold, 296
Ursa Major, 472, 493, OH-7, OH-20
Ursa Minor, OH-7
U.S. Naval Observatory, 476, 477
Utopia Planitia (Mars), 263, 264

V

Valhalla Basin (Callisto), 327
Valles Marineris (Mars), 261, 262, 264
Van Allen radiation belts, 185–86
van de Hulst, Hendrik, 602
Variable(s), 27, M1-3 to M1-4
Variable stars. See Cepheid variables;
    RR Lyrae variables
Vega (spacecraft/missions), 245, 374, 375
Vega, 473, 535, OH-21
Veil nebula, 567
Velocity-magnitude relation, 686
Venera (spacecraft/missions), 243–45, 246
Venus, 199, 241–53, 271–72, 301, 407.
    See also Craters; Volcanoes
apparent celestial motions, 63–65
atmosphere, 243–44, 249–53
data, table of, 242
exploration, 243–45
interplanetary mission to, 125–26

magnetosphere, 252–53
orbit and rotation, 241–43
phases, 91–92, 104
surface, 245–49
temperature, 243, 245, 250–51
terraforming, 278
as Terrestrial planet, 199–201
Vernal (spring) equinox, 42–43, OH-5
Very Large Array (VLA), 477, M2-26, M2-27
Very Large Telescope (European Southern Observatory), M2-20, M2-21
Very Long-Baseline Array (VLBA), M2-28
Very long-baseline interferometry, M2-28
Vesta, 359, 365
Viking (spacecraft/missions), 3, 257, 263–64, 314, 316
Virgo (constellation), OH-19 to OH-20
cluster of galaxies at, 654, 655, 656, 657, 678
Visual binary, 493, 499
V magnitude, 462–65
Volatile elements, 217
Volcanoes/volcanism, 407
Earth, 165, 170, 171, 193, 194, 388–89, 446
Io, 293, 328–29
Mars, 257, 262–63, 264, 268
mass extinction and, 388–89
Moon, 213–14
shield, 248
Venus, 247–48, 251
Volume, M1-11 to M1-12, M1-13
von Weizsäcker, Carl, 422
Voyager (spacecraft/missions), 9, 10, 291–93, 294, 295, 298, 300–301, 302, 303, 322–23, 325, 326, 335, 341–42, 345, 347

W

Waning, 51
crescent, 52
gibbous, 52
Washington, George, 191–92
Watt, 419
Wavelength, 130–31, 132
Waxing, 49
crescent, 49–50
gibbous, 51
Weak nuclear force, 150–51

Weakons, 155
Weather, 444, 448–51
Wegener, Alfred, 168, 170
Westerbock Synthesis Radio Telescope (Holland), M2-27
Whipple, Fred, 373
Whirlpool Galaxy (M51), 535, 630
White dwarfs, 489, 500, 504–5, 564–65, 566, 573, 576, 580, 581–82, 687, 688
White spots (Jupiter), 293, 296–97, 302–3
Widmanstätten pattern, 362–63
Wien's displacement law, 136, 147, 678
Wien, Wilhelm, 136
Wilson, Robert, 677, 678
Wind, 179–81. See also Solar wind; Stellar wind; T Tauri wind
Jupiter and Saturn, 296–97
Mars, 266–67
Uranus, 301
Venus, 252
Winter constellations, OH-14 to OH-19
Winter solstice, 18–19, 43–44, 45, 195–96
Working Group for Planetary System Nomenclature of the International Astronomical Union, 223
Wormholes, 579

X

X-rays, 133
sources
black holes, 580
supernova remnants, 568
telescopes and, M2-29, M2-32 to M2-33

Y

Year, 18–20, 70, 197
Yerkes, Charles T., M2-18
Yerkes Observatory (Wisconsin), M2-18

Z

Zeeman effect, 430
Zeeman, Pieter, 430
Zenith, 13, OH-6
Zond (spacecraft/missions), 204, 206
Zones (on Jovian planets), 295–96
Zwicky, Fritz, 573, 574

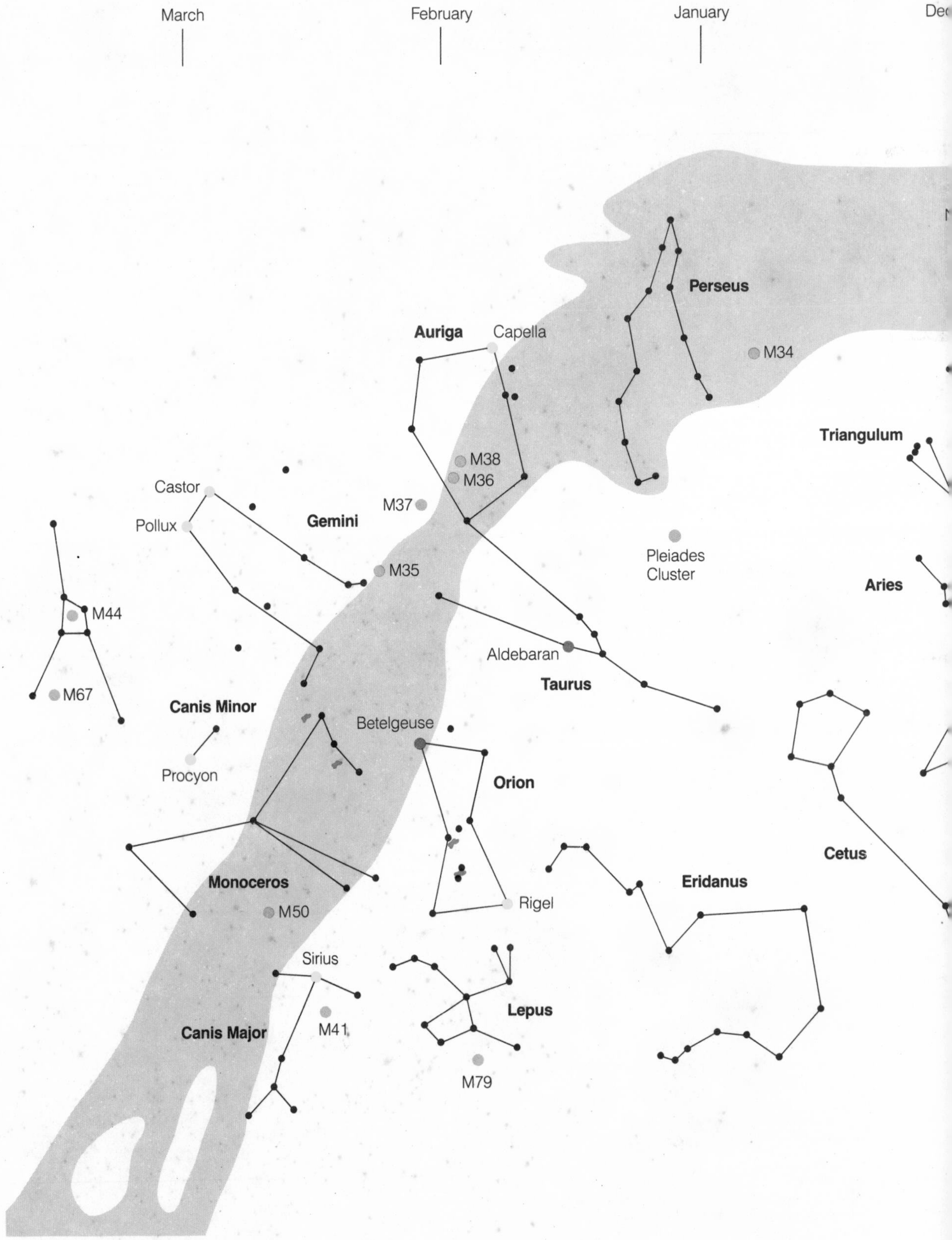

March

February

January

Dec

Perseus

Auriga   Capella

M34

Triangulum

M38

M36

M37

Castor

Pollux   Gemini

Pleiades
Cluster

Aries

M35

M44

Aldebaran

M67

Taurus

Canis Minor

Betelgeuse

Procyon

Orion

Cetus

Monoceros

Eridanus

M50

Rigel

Sirius

Lepus

Canis Major

M41

M79

Major Constellations